SO-AKG-284

DISCARDED

EDITORIAL BOARD

Chairman: HERMAN F. MARK
Polytechnic Institute of Brooklyn

JOHN J. McKETTA, JR.
The University of Texas

DONALD F. OTHMER
Polytechnic Institute of Brooklyn

EXECUTIVE EDITOR

ANTHONY STANDEN

Interscience Publishers
a division of John Wiley & Sons, Inc.
New York • London • Sydney • Toronto

Kirk-Othmer

ENCYCLOPEDIA
OF CHEMICAL
TECHNOLOGY

Second Edition

VOLUME 19

Stilbene Derivatives

to

Terpenes and Terpenoids

Kirk-Othmer

ENCYCLOPEDIA

OF CHEMICAL

TECHNOLOGY

Second completely revised edition

VOLUME 19

Stilbene Derivatives
to
Terpenes and Terpenoids

COLLEGE OF THE SEQUOIAS
LIBRARY

Copyright © 1969 by *John Wiley & Sons, Inc.*

All Rights Reserved.   This book or any part
thereof must not be reproduced in any form
without permission of the publishers in writing.
This applies specifically to photostatic and
microfilm reproduction, as well as to translations
into foreign languages.

Library of Congress Catalog Card Number:
63-14348

Printed in the United States of America

CONTENTS

EDITORIAL STAFF FOR VOLUME 19

Associate Editor: EVA PAROLLA DUKES

Estelle P. Henson   Nancy Hutto   Anna Klingsberg   Jane Maxwell

CONTRIBUTORS TO VOLUME 19

Ralph Aarons, *E. I. du Pont de Nemours & Co., Inc.,* Sulfamic acid and sulfamates

J. S. Autenrieth, *Hercules Incorporated,* Terpenes and terpenoids (Terpene resins)

Marion D. Barnes, *Covenant College,* Sulfur (Special uses)

Karl M. Beck, *Abbott Laboratories,* Sweeteners, nonnutritive

R. F. Benenati, *Polytechnic Institute of Brooklyn,* Stoichiometry, industrial

Albert B. Booth, *Hercules Incorporated,* Terpenes and terpenoids (Survey; Terpene resins)

Raymond F. Boyer, *The Dow Chemical Company,* Styrene plastics

Frederick W. Camp, *Sun Oil Company,* Tar sands

D. F. Chichester, *Chas. Pfizer & Co., Inc.,* Tartaric acid

P. T. Comiskey, *Freeport Sulphur Company,* Sulfur

K. E. Coulter, *The Dow Chemical Company,* Styrene

Raymond S. Dalter, *Carlisle Chemical Works, Inc.,* Sulfurization and sulfur-chlorination

G. S. Dominguez, *Geigy Chemical Corporation,* Stilbene derivatives (Economic aspects, under Stilbene dyes)

Leonard Doub, *Parke, Davis & Co.,* Sulfonamides

E. M. Elkin, *Canadian Copper Refiners Limited,* Tellurium and tellurium compounds

Julius Fuchs, *E. I. du Pont de Nemours & Co., Inc.,* Sulfuric and sulfurous esters

H. G. Gerstner, *Colonial Sugars Company,* Sugar (Cane sugar)

Everett E. Gilbert, *Allied Chemical Corporation,* Sulfonation and sulfation; Sulfonic acids

L. B. Gittinger, Jr., *Freeport Sulphur Company,* Sulfur

L. F. Good, *Freeport Sulphur Company,* Sulfur

William T. Gray, *Leeds & Northrup Company,* Temperature measurement

Ernest Hainsworth, *Tea Research Institute of East Africa,* Tea

T. S. Harrer, *Allied Chemical Corporation,* Sulfuric acid and sulfur trioxide

Ingenuin Hechenbleikner, *Carlisle Chemical Works, Inc.,* Sulfurization and sulfur-chlorination

J. L. Hickson, *International Sugar Research Foundation, Inc.,* Sugar (Sugar derivatives; Sugar economics; Special sugars)

B. F. Hiscock, *The Dow Chemical Company,* Styrene

F. L. Jackson, *Freeport Sulphur Company,* Sulfur

H. Kehde, *The Dow Chemical Company,* Styrene

Henno Keskkulla, *The Dow Chemical Company,* Styrene plastics

W. S. MacGregor, *Crown Zellerbach Corporation,* Sulfoxides

Emma J. McDonald, *U.S. Department of Agriculture,* Sugar (Sugar analysis)

R. A. McGinnis, *Spreckels Sugar Co.,* Sugar (Properties of sucrose; Beet sugar)

D. McNeil, *The Coal Tar Research Association,* Tar and pitch

Pat Macaluso, *Stauffer Chemical Co.,* Sulfur compounds

G. S. Morrow, *Shell Chemical Company,* Sulfolane

H. T. Mulryan, *United Sierra Division, Cyprus Mines Corporation,* Talc

L. A. Nelson, Jr., *Freeport Sulphur Company,* Sulfur

Denis G. Orton, *Southern Dyestuff Company, a division of Martin Marietta Corporation,* Sulfur dyes

D. Perlman, *University of Wisconsin,* Streptomycin and related antibiotics

L. M. Pidgeon, *University of Toronto,* Strontium

Alan E. Platt, *The Dow Chemical Company,* Styrene plastics

Louis Preisman, *Pittsburgh Plate Glass Co.,* Strontium compounds

Donald Santmyers, *E. I. du Pont de Nemours & Co., Inc.,* Sulfamic acid and sulfamates

H. R. Schwander, *J. R. Geigy AG, Basel,* Stilbene derivatives (Stilbene dyes)

Chapin E. Stevens, *Management Research Consultants,* Surfactants

Dan C. Tate, *U.S. Plywood-Champion Papers Inc.,* Tall oil

Donald F. Taylor, *Fansteel Inc.,* Tantalum and tantalum compounds

Paul Turi, *Sandoz, Inc.,* Succinic acid

T. K. Wiewiorowski, *Freeport Sulphur Company,* Sulfur

Reinhard Zweidler, *J. R. Geigy AG, Basel,* Stilbene derivatives (Optical brighteners of the stilbene series)

ABBREVIATIONS AND SYMBOLS

A	ampere(s)
A	anion (eg, HA)
Å	Angstrom unit(s)
AATCC	American Association of Textile Chemists and Colorists
abs	absolute
ac	alternating current
ac-	alicyclic (eg, *ac*-derivatives of tetrahydronaphthalene)
accel(d)	accelerated(d)
acceln	acceleration
ACS	American Chemical Society
addn	addition
AEC	Atomic Energy Commission
AGA	American Gas Association
Ah	ampere-hour(s)
AIChE	American Institute of Chemical Engineers
AIME	American Institute of Mining and Metallurgical Engineers
AIP	American Institute of Physics
AISI	American Iron and Steel Institute
alc	alcohol(ic)
alk	alkaline (not alkali)
Alk	alkyl
AMA	American Medical Association
A-min	ampere-minute(s)
amt	amount (noun)
anhyd	anhydrous
AOAC	Association of Official Analytical (formerly Agricultural) Chemists
AOCS	American Oil Chemists' Society

APHA	American Public Health Association
API	American Petroleum Institute
app	apparatus
approx	approximate(ly)
aq	aqueous
Ar	aryl
as-	asymmetric(al) (eg, *as-*trichlorobenzene)
ASA	American Standards Association. Later (1966) called USASI
ASHRAE	American Society of Heating, Refrigerating and Air-Conditioning Engineers
ASM	American Society for Metals
ASME	American Society of Mechanical Engineers
ASTM	American Society for Testing and Materials
atm	atmosphere(s), atmospheric
at. no.	atomic number
at. wt	atomic weight
av	average
b	barn(s)
b (as in b_{11})	boiling (at 11 mm Hg)
bbl	barrel(s)
bcc	body-centered cubic
Bé	Baumé
Bhn	Brinell hardness number
bp	boiling point
BP	*British Pharmacopoeia* (General Medical Council in London)
Btu	British thermal unit(s)

bu	bushel(s)	crystd	crystallized
C	Celsius (centigrade); coulomb(s)	crystn	crystallization
		cSt	centistokes
C-	denoting attachment to carbon (eg, *C*-acetyl-indoline)	cu	cubic
		d	density (conveniently, specific gravity)
ca	circa, approximately	*d*	differential operator
CA	Chemical Abstracts	*d-*	*dextro-*, dextrorotatory
cal	calorie(s)	D	Debye unit(s)
calcd	calculated	D-	denoting configurational relationship (as to *dextro*-glyceraldehyde)
cfm, ft³/min	cubic foot (feet) per minute		
cg	centigram(s)	db	dry-bulb
cgs	centimeter-gram-second	dB	decibel(s)
Ci	curie(s)	dc	direct current
CI	Colour Index (number); the CI numbers given in *ECT*, 2nd ed., are from the new *Colour Index* (1956) and Suppl. (1963), *Soc. Dyers Colourists*, Bradford, England, and *AATCC*, U.S.A.	dec, decomp	decompose(s)
		decompd	decomposed
		decompn	decomposition
		den	denier(s)
		den/fil	denier(s) per filament
		deriv	derivative
		detd	determined
		detn	determination
		diam	diameter
CIE	Commission Internationale de l'Eclairage (see also ICI)	dielec	dielectric (adj.)
		dil	dilute
cif	cost, insurance, freight	DIN	Deutsche Industrienormen
cl	carload lots	distd	distilled
cm	centimeter(s)	distn	distillation
coeff	coefficient	dl	deciliter(s)
compd, cpd	compound (noun)	*dl-*, DL	racemic
		dm	decimeter(s)
compn	composition	DOT	Department of Transportation
concd	concentrated		
concn	concentration	dp	dewpoint
cond	conductivity	dyn	dyne(s)
const	constant	*e*	electron; base of natural logarithms
cont	continued		
cor	corrected	ed.	edited, edition, editor
cp	chemically pure	elec	electric(al)
cP	centipoise(s)	emf	electromotive force
cpd, compd	compound (noun)	emu	electromagnetic unit(s)
		eng	engineering
cps	cycles per second	equil	equilibrium(s)
crit	critical	equiv	equivalent
cryst	crystalline	esp	especially

esr, ESR	electron spin resonance
est(d)	estimate(d)
estn	estimation
esu	electrostatic unit(s)
eu	entropy unit(s)
eV	electron volt(s)
expt(l)	experiment(al)
ext(d)	extract(ed)
extn	extraction
F	Fahrenheit; farad(s)
F	faraday constant
FAO	Food and Agriculture Organization of the United Nations
fcc	face-centered cubic
Fed, fedl	federal (eg, Fed Spec)
fl oz	fluid ounce(s)
fob	free on board
fp	freezing point
frz	freezing
ft	foot (feet)
ft-lb	foot-pound(s)
ft³/min, cfm	cubic foot (feet) per minute
g	gram(s)
g	gravitational acceleration
G	gauss(es)
G	Gibbs free energy
gal	gallon(s)
gal/min, gpm	gallon(s) per minute
g/den	gram(s) per denier
gem-	geminal (attached to the same atom)
g-mol	gram-molecular (as in g-mol wt)
g-mole	gram-mole(s)
G-Oe	gauss-oersted(s)
gpm, gal/min	gallon(s) per minute
gr	grain(s)
h, hr	hour(s)
hl	hectoliter(s)
hmw	high-molecular-weight(adj.)
hp	horsepower(s)
hr, h	hour(s)
hyd	hydrated, hydrous

hyg	hygroscopic
Hz	hertz(es)
i, insol	insoluble
^{i} (eg, Pr^i)	iso (eg, isopropyl)
i-	inactive (eg, i-methionine)
IACS	International Annealed Copper Standard
ibp	initial boiling point
ICC	Interstate Commerce Commission
ICI	International Commission on Illumination (see also CIE); Imperial Chemical Industries, Ltd.
ICT	International Critical Tables
ID	inner diameter
IEEE	Institute of Electrical and Electronics Engineers
in.	inch(es)
insol, i	insoluble
IPT	Institute of Petroleum Technologists
ir	infrared
ISO	International Organization for Standardization
IU	International Unit(s)
IUPAC	International Union of Pure and Applied Chemistry
J	joule(s)
K	Kelvin
K	dissociation constant
kbar	kilobar(s)
kc	kilocycle(s)
kcal	kilogram-calorie(s)
keV	kilo electron volt(s)
kg	kilogram(s)
kG	kilogauss(es)
kgf	kilogram force(s)
kJ	kilojoule(s)
kp	kilopond(s) (equals kilogram force(s)
kV	kilovolt(s)
kVa	kilovolt-ampere(s)
kW	kilowatt(s)
kWh	kilowatt-hour(s)

l	liter(s)	mm	millimeter(s)
l-	*levo-*, levorotatory	mM	millimole(s)
L-	denoting configurational relationship (as to *levo*glyceraldehyde)	m*M*	millimolar
		mo(s)	month(s)
lb	pound(s)	mol	molecule, molecular
LC$_{50}$	concentration lethal to 50% of the animals tested	mol wt	molecular weight
		mp	melting point
		mph	miles per hour
lcl	less than carload lots	MR	molar refraction
LD$_{50}$	dose lethal to 50% of the animals tested	mV	millivolt(s)
		mμ	millimicron(s) (10^{-9} m)
liq	liquid	^{n} (eg, Bu^{n}),	
lm	lumen	*n-*	normal (eg, normal butyl)
lmw	low-molecular-weight (adj.)	n (as, n_D^{20})	index of refraction (for 20°C and sodium light)
ln	logarithm (natural)		
log	logarithm (common)	*n-*, ^{n}	normal (eg, *n*-butyl, Bu^{n})
m	meter(s)	N	normal (as applied to concentration)
m	molal		
m-	meta (eg, *m*-xylene)	*N-*	denoting attachment to nitrogen (eg, *N*-methylaniline)
M	metal		
M	molar (as applied to concentration; not molal)		
		NASA	National Aeronautics and Space Administration
mA	milliampere(s)		
mAh	milliampere-hour(s)	ND	*New Drugs* (NND changed to ND in 1965)
manuf	manufacture		
manufd, mfd	manufactured	NF	*National Formulary* (American Pharmaceutical Association)
manufg, mfg	manufacturing		
max	maximum	nm	nuclear magneton; nanometer(s) (10^{-9} m)
Mc	megacycle(s)		
MCA	Manufacturing Chemists' Association	nmr, NMR	nuclear magnetic resonance
		NND	*New and Nonofficial Drugs* (AMA) (1958–1965). Later called ND
mcal	millicalorie(s)		
mech	mechanical		
meq	milliequivalent(s)	NNR	*New and Nonofficial Remedies* (1907–1958). Later called NND
MeV	million electron volt(s)		
mfd, manufd	manufactured		
		no.	number
mfg, manufg	manufacturing	NOIBN	not otherwise indexed by name (DOT specification for shipping containers)
mg	milligram(s)		
min	minimum; minute(s)	*o-*	ortho (eg, *o*-xylene)
misc	miscellaneous	*O-*	denoting attachment to oxygen (eg, *O*-acetylhydroxylamine)
mixt	mixture		
ml	milliliter(s)		
MLD	minimum lethal dose	Ω	ohm(s)

Ω-cm	ohm-centimeter(s)
OD	outer diameter
Oe	oersted(s)
o/w	oil-in-water (eg, o/w emulsion)
owf	on weight of fiber
oz	ounce(s)
p-	para (eg, *p*-xylene)
P	poise(s)
pdr	powder
PhI	*Pharmacopoeia Internationalis*, 2 vols. and Suppl., World Health Organization, Geneva, 1951, 1955, and 1959
phr	parts per hundred of rubber or resin
pos	positive (adj.)
powd	powdered
ppb	parts per billion (parts per 10^9)
ppm	parts per million
ppt(d)	precipitate(d)
pptn	precipitation
Pr. (no.)	Foreign prototype (number); dyestuff designation used in *AATCC Year Books* for dyes not listed in the old *Colour Index* (1924 ed.; 1928 Suppl.); obsolete since new *Colour Index* was published (1956 ed.; 1963 Suppl.)
prepd	prepared
prepn	preparation
psi	pound(s) per square inch
psia (psig)	pound(s) per square inch absolute (gage)
pt	point
pts	parts
qual	qualitative
quant	quantitative
qv	which see (quod vide)
R	Rankine; roentgen; univalent hydrocarbon radical (or hydrogen)

rad	radian
Rep	roentgen(s) equivalent physical
resp	respectively
rh	relative humidity
Rhe	unit of fluidity (1/P)
RI	Ring Index (number); from *The Ring Index*, Reinhold Publishing Corp., N.Y., 1940. See also RRI
rms	root mean square
rpm	revolutions per minute
rps	revolutions per second
RRI	Revised Ring Index (number); from *The Ring Index*, 2nd ed., American Chemical Society, Washington, D.C., 1960
RT	room temperature
s, sol	soluble
^{s} (eg, Bu^s), *sec*-	secondary (eg, *sec*-butyl)
s-, *sym*-	symmetrical (eg, *s*-dichloroethylene)
S-	denoting attachment to sulfur (eg, *S*-methylcysteine)
SAE	Society of Automotive Engineers
satd	saturated
satn	saturation
scf, SCF	standard cubic foot (feet) (760 mm Hg, 63°F)
scfm	standard cubic feet per minute
Sch	Schultz number (designation for dyes from *Farbstofftabellen*, 4 vols., Akademie Verlag, Leipzig, 1931–1939)
sec	second(s)
sec-, ^{s}	secondary (eg, *sec*-butyl; Bu^s)
SFs	Saybolt Furol second(s)
sl s, sl sol	slightly soluble
sol, s	soluble
soln	solution

soly	solubility		(ASA changed to USASI in 1966)
sp	specific		
sp, spp	species (sing. and pl.)	USP	(*The*) *United States*
Spec	specification		*Pharmacopeia* (Mack
sp gr	specific gravity		Publishing Co., Easton,
SPI	Society of the Plastics Industry		Pa.)
		uv	ultraviolet
sq	square	V	volt(s)
St	stokes	*v-, vic-*	vicinal (attached to
STP	standard temperature and pressure (760 mm Hg, 0°C)		adjacent atoms)
		var	variety
		vic-, v-	vicinal (attached to adjacent atoms)
subl	sublime(s), subliming		
SUs	Saybolt Universal second(s)	vol	volume(s) (not volatile)
		v s, v sol	very soluble
sym, s-	symmetrical (eg, *sym-*dichloroethylene)	vs	versus
		v/v	volume per volume
^{t} (eg, Bu^t),		W	watt(s)
t-, tert-	tertiary (eg, tertiary butyl)	Wh	watt-hour(s)
t-, tert-, ^{t}	tertiary (eg, *t*-butyl)	w/o	water-in-oil (eg, w/o emulsion)
TAPPI	Technical Association of the Pulp and Paper Industry		
		wt	weight
		w/v	weight per volume
tech	technical	w/w	weight per weight
temp	temperature		
tert-, t-, ^{t}	tertiary (eg, *tert*-butyl)	xu (ca 10^{-11}	
theoret	theoretical	cm)	x unit(s)
Twad	Twaddell	yd	yard(s)
USASI	United States of America Standards Institute	yr	year(s)

Quantities

Some standard abbreviations (prefixes) for very small and very large quantities are as follows:

deci (10^{-1})	d	deka (10^1)	dk
centi (10^{-2})	c	hecto (10^2)	h
milli (10^{-3})	m	kilo (10^3)	k
micro (10^{-6})	μ	mega (10^6)	M
nono (10^{-9})	n	giga (10^9)	G (or B)
pico (10^{-12})	p	tera (10^{12})	T
femto (10^{-15})	f		
atto (10^{-18})	a		

S continued

STILBENE DERIVATIVES

STILBENE DYES

The stilbene dyes (1) contain the residue of 2,2′-stilbenedisulfonic acid (1) together with azo, azoxy, and triazole groups as structural elements. They form a sub-

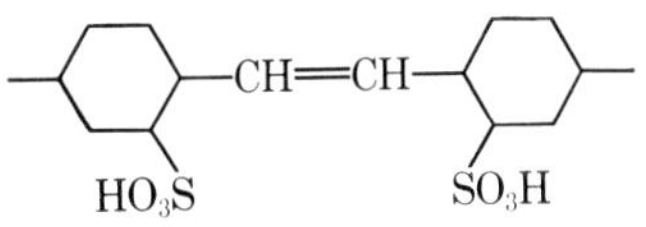

(1)

division of the azo dyes (see Vol. 2, pp. 897, 899) but, owing to these common structural features and to the fact that many of them are not prepared by the classical azo coupling reaction, they are treated as a separate class.

The stilbene dyes are mainly direct dyes used for the dyeing of natural or man-made cellulosic fibers (cotton, viscose rayon—see Cotton; Rayon). Their affinity to cellulose is due in great part to the stilbene system (see Dyes—application and evaluation, Vol. 7, pp. 534, 583). Some of these dyes are used in the dyeing of paper (qv) and leather (qv).

The hue range of stilbene dyes, originally covering only yellow and orange shades, has been extended to red, brown, khaki, green, and gray. Lightfastness, in general, is rather high. Some of these dyes are very inexpensive and have come to be classed among the most important direct dyes, especially for orange and brown shades.

A more recent development led to reactive dyes based on the stilbene nucleus as a chromophoric system (see Dyes, reactive; see also Vol. 7, pp. 563, 577).

Another very important application of the stilbene system is to be found in some optical brighteners derived from diaminostilbenedisulfonic acid or from stilbene triazoles (see p. 14; see also Brighteners, optical).

1

INTERMEDIATES

5-Nitro-*o*-toluenesulfonic acid (**2**) (*p*-nitrotoluene-*o*-sulfonic acid) is the intermediate common to all stilbene dyes (see also Dyes and dye intermediates, Vol. 7, p. 473).

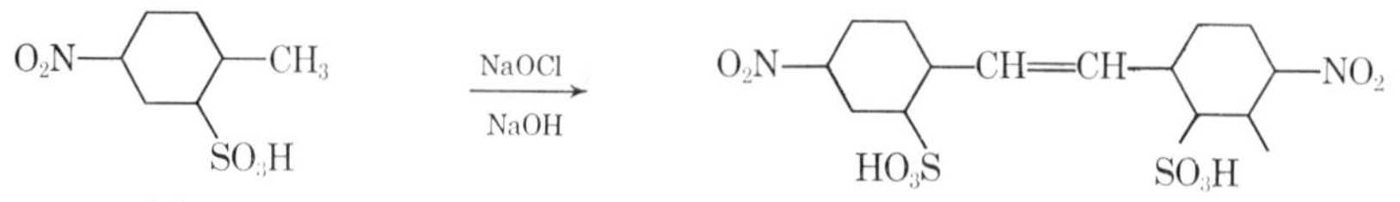

(**2**)   (**3**)

4,4′-Dinitro-2,2′-stilbenedisulfonic acid (**3**) (**2**), a key intermediate for stilbene dyes, is obtained by the alkaline oxidation of (**2**) with sodium hypochlorite or with air (oxygen).

4-Amino-4′-nitro-2,2′-stilbenedisulfonic acid (**4**) results from the reduction of one of the nitro groups of (**3**) with sodium sulfhydrate under closely controlled conditions.

(**3**)

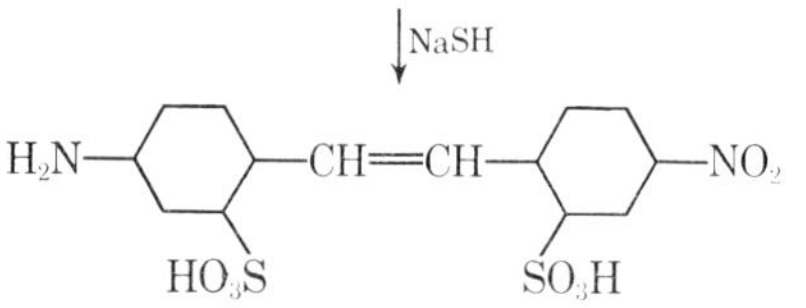

(**4**)

4,4′-Diamino-2,2′-stilbenedisulfonic acid (**5**) is obtained by the Béchamp or catalytic reduction of (**3**).

(**3**)

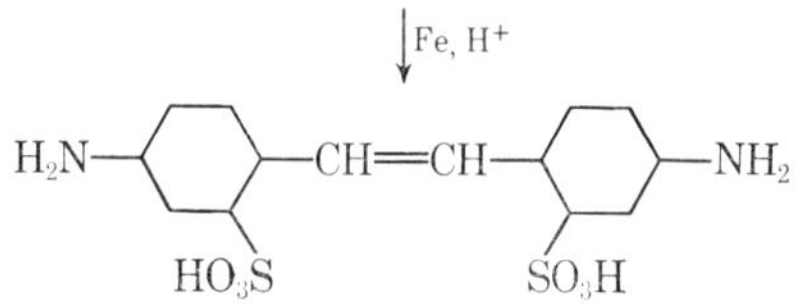

(**5**)

Aminostilbenenaphthotriazoles (**6**) are prepared by the following sequence of reactions:

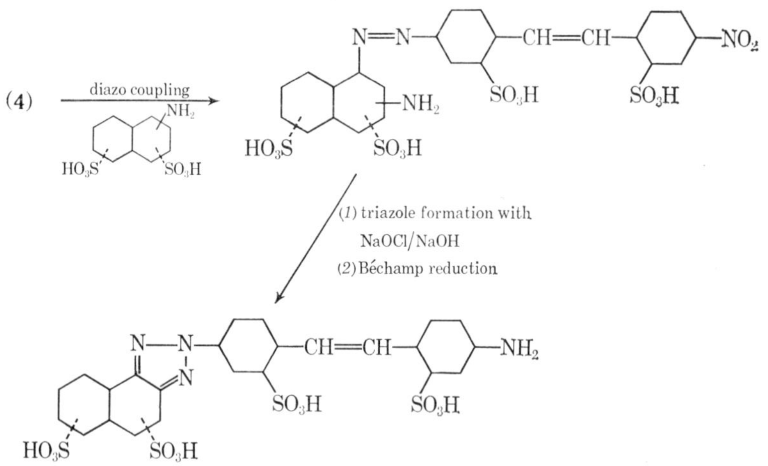

(**6**)

Miscellaneous. As a specific example, starting from 4-amino-1-naphthalenesulfonic acid, the intermediate corresponding to structure (**7**) is formed (4):

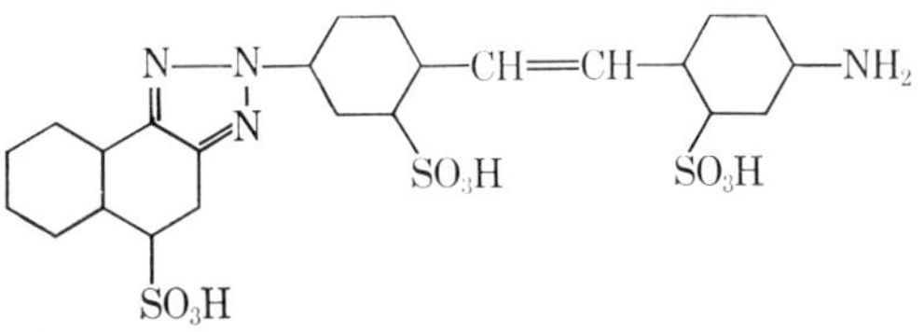

(**7**)

Dyes from 5-Nitro-*o*-toluenesulfonic Acid by Intermolecular Condensation (5)

Intermolecular condensation of (**2**) under alkaline conditions leads to yellow dyes of good substantivity, which were the earliest products among stilbene dyes (J. Walter, 1883, J. R. Geigy AG). Oxidative aftertreatment of these condensation products with hypochlorite produces greenish-yellow shades (6), whereas reductive aftertreatment under alkaline conditions (glucose, sodium sulfide) yields orange to brown-orange shades (7). Dyes subjected to reductive aftertreatments contain free amino groups which may be acylated to form dyes having more brilliant shades and better lightfastness (8).

These dyes are sold under a great number of trade names, such as *Curcumine S* (CI 40000, Direct Yellow 11), Sun Yellow G, 3G, and R, Stilbene Yellow TP, TR, and GX, Chlorazol Paper Yellow G, and Chrome Leather Yellow T; and *Diamine Fast Orange D* (CI 40002/3, Direct Orange 15), Mikado Orange 3R and 5R, Direct Fast Orange R, 2R, 3R, and 6RAS-CF, Direct Brilliant Orange RAF, Chlorantine Fast Orange TR, Pontamine Fast Orange MRL and GRN, and Stilbene Orange 4R.

All of these dyes are complex mixtures, mainly of azo and azoxy compounds. The number and exact constitutional formulas of the individual components are still unknown. The constitutional formula proposed by Green (9) for Curcumine S is considered to be incorrect (10). Later, in a publication from the I.G. laboratories, formula (**8**) was proposed for this dye (11):

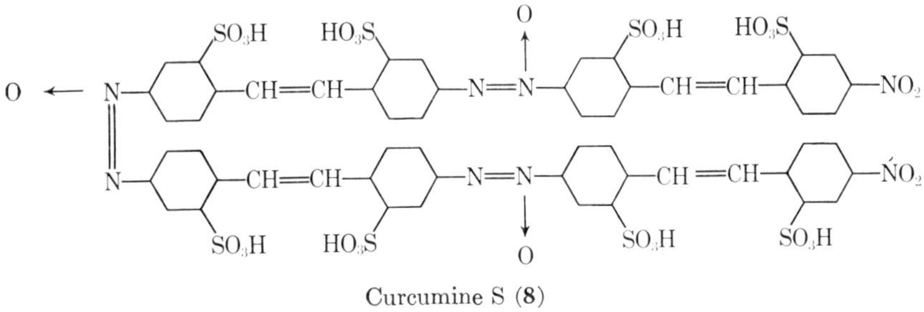

Curcumine S (**8**)

Because dyes of this type are low-priced, they are still of great commercial importance.

Dyes of similar composition and properties can also be obtained by treatment of dinitrostilbenedisulfonic acid (**3**) with reducing agents like sodium sulfide, glucose, or formaldehyde, the shades obtained depending on the reaction conditions applied. Dyes so produced give purer shades of better lightfastness, but are more expensive. One of the most important stilbene dyes on the U.S. market, *Stilbene Yellow 3GX* (CI

40001/6, Direct Yellow 6) (12), is prepared in this manner, by reduction with formaldehyde.

Condensation Dyes from 4,4′-Dinitro-2,2′-stilbenedisulfonic Acid (13)

Dinitrostilbenedisulfonic acid (3) can be condensed in aqueous alkaline solution with *aromatic amines*, producing dyes which are now to a great extent obsolete (14). Condensation with some aromatic heterocyclic sulfonated amines leads to dyes of good lightfastness. Of special importance is Chlorophenine Orange (CI 40055), obtained by condensation with *dehydrothio-p-toluidinesulfonic acid* (9) (15). Con-

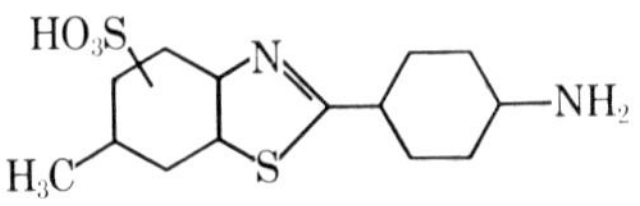

(9)

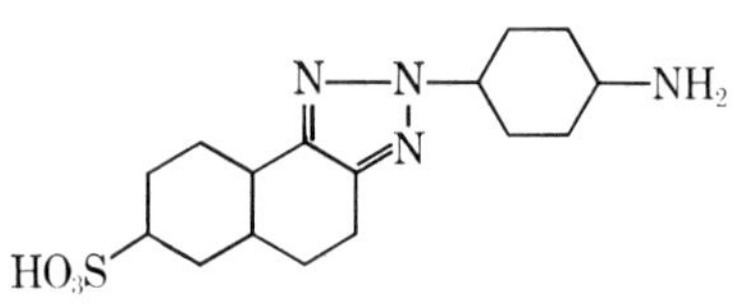

(10)

densation products of (3) with *p-aminophenylnaphthotriazolesulfonic acids*, such as (10) (16), show even better lightfastness, but are more expensive and therefore without commercial importance.

Under specific conditions diamines may be condensed to form monoazo or disazo compounds which can be used as intermediates not obtainable otherwise by the classical diazo-coupling reaction, as shown by the example below (17):

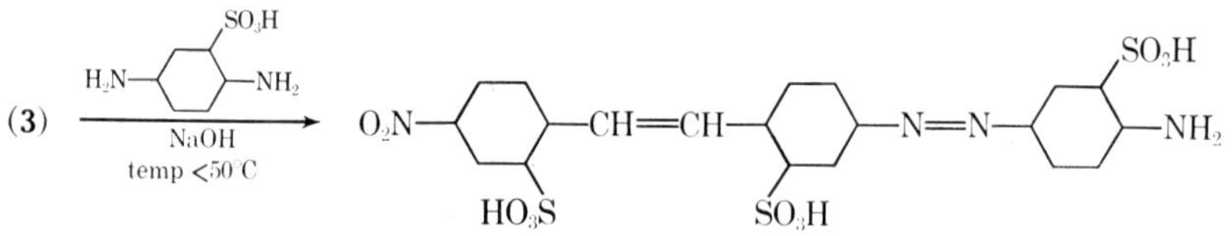

(11)

The most important class of stilbene dyes is produced by condensing (3) with *aminoazo compounds*. This reaction yields dyes that rank among the most important direct dyes for producing orange and scarlet shades (A. Gressly, 1907, Farbwerke Cassella) (18). They are of the tetrakisazo type, but no clean formation of azo compounds takes place in these condensations, azoxy and other compounds being formed as by-products and part of the aminoazo compound being consumed as reducing agent. The dyes so formed are generally purified by an aftertreatment with hypochlorite, glucose, or sodium sulfide. By stepwise reaction with two different aminoazo compounds, unsymmetrical dyes can be synthesized. Table 1 lists some commercial dyes of this kind.

Table 1. Condensation Dyes from Dinitrostilbenedisulfonic Acid and Aminoazo Compounds

Dye name	Aminoazo compound condensed	After-treatment
Sirius Supra Orange 7GL (CI 40215, Direct Orange 34 and 39)	HO₃S—⟨ ⟩—N=N—⟨ ⟩—NH₂	glucose
Sirius Supra Orange RRL (CI 40235, Direct Orange 44)	H₃CO—⟨ ⟩—N=N—⟨ ⟩—NH₂ (SO₃H; CH₃, CH₃)	glucose
Sirius Supra Orange 3R (CI 40265, Direct Orange 37)	HO₃S—⟨ ⟩—N=N—⟨ ⟩—NH₂ (CH₃, OCH₃)	Na₂S
Sirius Supra Scarlet 2G (CI 40270, Direct Red 76)	H₃CO—⟨ ⟩—N=N—⟨ ⟩—NH₂ (SO₃H; CH₃, OCH₃)	glucose
Sirius Supra Brown 3R (CI 40290, Direct Brown 78)	HO₃S—⟨ ⟩—N=N—⟨naphthyl⟩—NH₂	

Copper-Complex Condensation Dyes

Copper-complex dyes can be prepared by condensation of (**3**) with *o*-oxy-*o'*-methoxyaminoazo compounds in caustic alkaline solution (*o,o'*-dihydroxyaminoazo compounds are not sufficiently stable under the condensation conditions) either alone or in admixture with one another or with various proportions of nonmetalizable amino or aminoazo compounds. The condensation products are finally converted into the copper complex under demethylating conditions.

In particular, by using mixed condensations the range of shades can be extended to include olive, khaki, brown, and gray shades of good general fastness properties and with noticeably high lightfastness. This class of dyes represents the most important development in this field (E. Keller, 1940, J. R. Geigy AG) (19). As examples, a gray dye (**12**)

gray (**12**)

and a brown dye (**13**) may be shown.

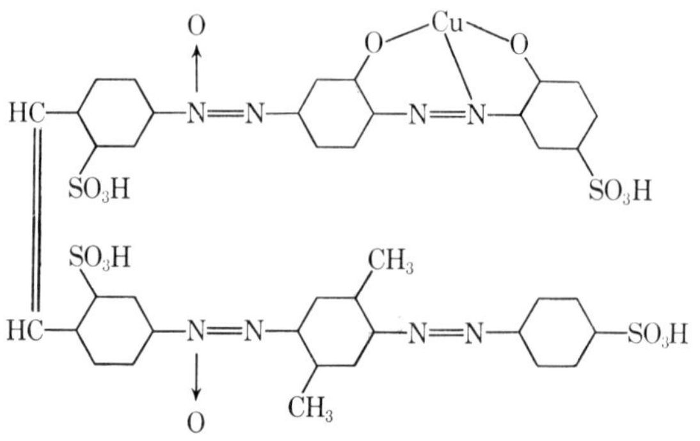

brown (**13**)

The use of naphthotriazolylnitrostilbenedisulfonic acids like (**14**) instead of (**3**)

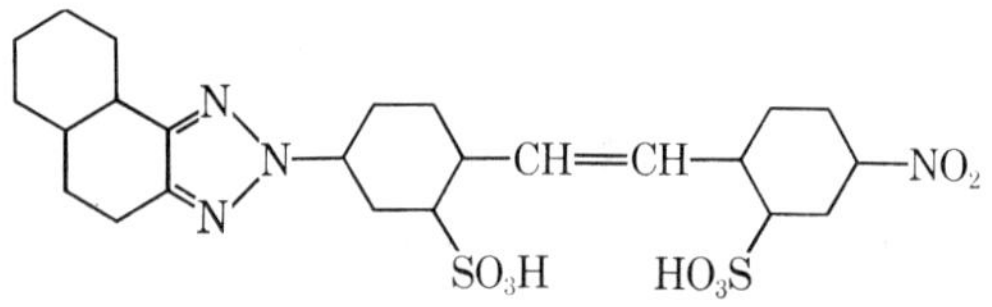

(**14**)

in these condensations (20) produces dyes having similar properties.

Dyes from 4,4′-Diamino-2,2′-stilbenedisulfonic Acid

Diaminostilbenedisulfonic acid (**5**) may be tetrazotized and coupled with the usual azo coupling components to produce disazo dyes. Of great importance is the yellow dye *Chrysophenine* (CI 24895, Direct Yellow 12) (**15**) (21), obtained by coupling with two equivalents of phenol and subsequent ethylation of the free phenolic OH groups:

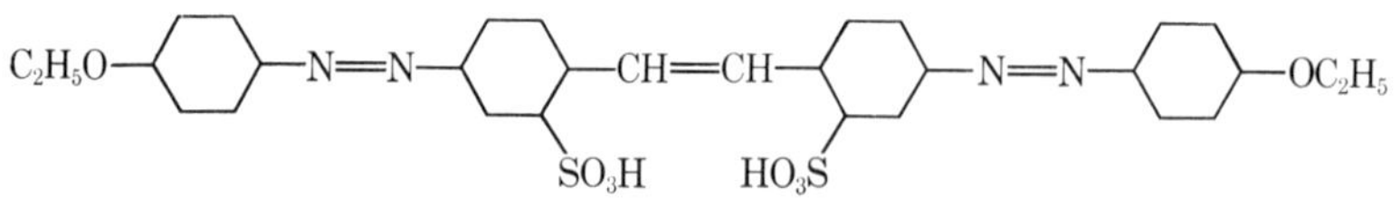

Chrysophenine (**15**)

The corresponding nonethylated, alkali-sensitive dye is the pH-indicator *Brilliant Yellow* (CI 24890, Direct Yellow 4).

By reacting the condensation product prepared from (**5**) and two equivalents of cyanuric chloride with aminoazo compounds and with amines, yellow to orange dyes like the yellow dye (**16**) (22) are obtained.

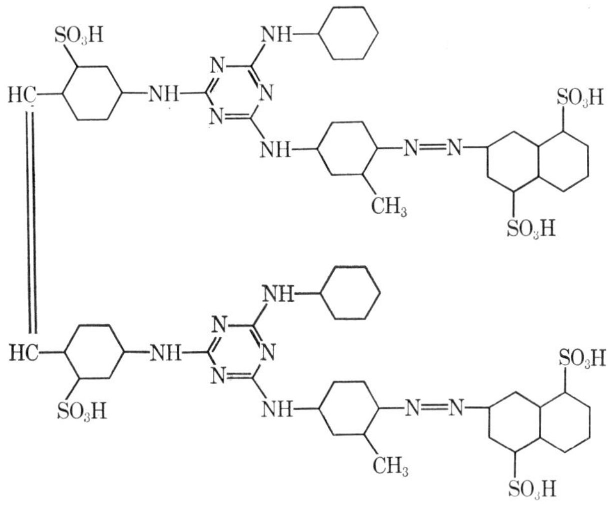

yellow (**16**)

Dyes from 4-Amino-4′-nitro-2,2′-stilbenedisulfonic Acid

If diazotized aminonitrostilbenedisulfonic acid (**4**) is coupled with phenol and the phenolic hydroxyl group is methylated, the dye *Sirius Orange I* (**17**) is produced.

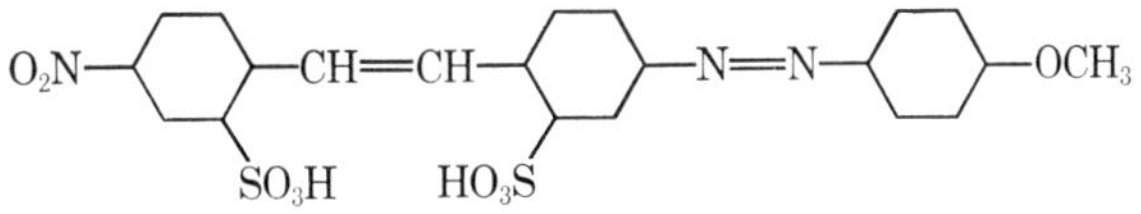

Sirius Orange I (**17**)

Reduction of Sirius Orange I with glucose produces the trisazo dye *Sirius Supra Orange F3G* (CI 25030, Direct Orange 63) (**18**) (**23**).

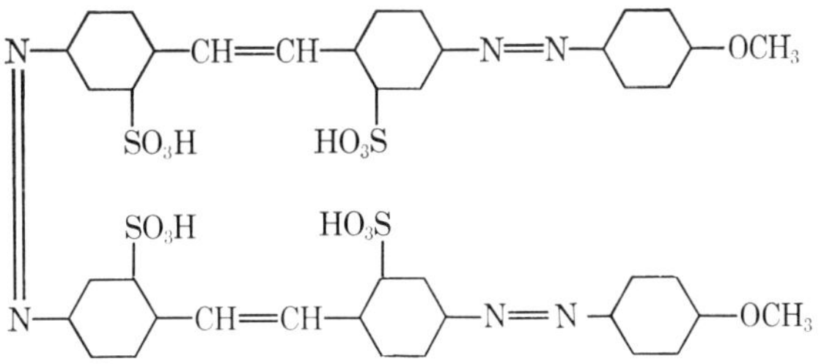

Sirius Supra Orange F3G (**18**)

Yellow to orange dyes are prepared by condensing (**4**) with cyanuric chloride, reacting this intermediate with aminoazo compounds or amines, and finally reducing with glucose to the dyestuff, as illustrated by the yellow-orange dye (**19**) (**24**).

By coupling of diazotized (**4**) with a coupling component *A*, reduction of the nitro group, diazotation of the amino compound obtained in this manner, and coupling with a coupling component *B*, azo dyes unsymmetrical with respect to the stilbene

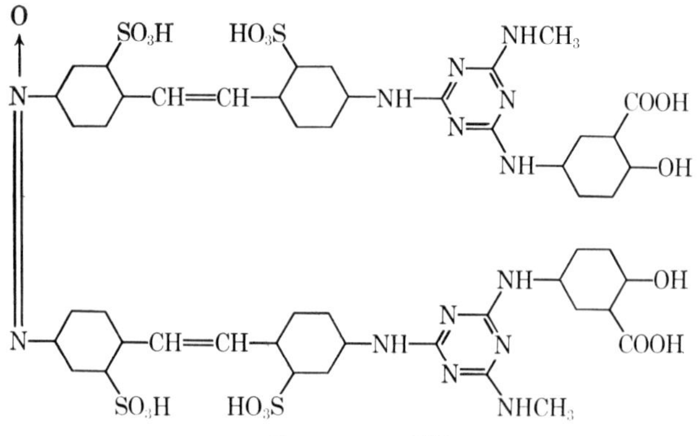

yellow-orange (**19**)

residue can be manufactured. From the great number of such dyes covered by patents, reference is made to the following examples. A yellow bistriazole dye (**20**) is obtained

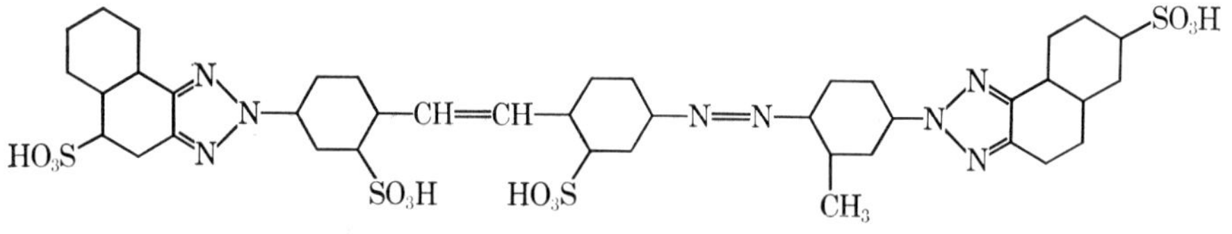

yellow (**20**)

by starting from intermediate (**6**) (25). An example of a disazo copper-complex green dye based on the same intermediate (**6**) is Sirius Supra Green BTL (CI 27970, Direct Green 34) (**21**) (H. Schindhelm, 1937, I. G. Hoechst) (26),

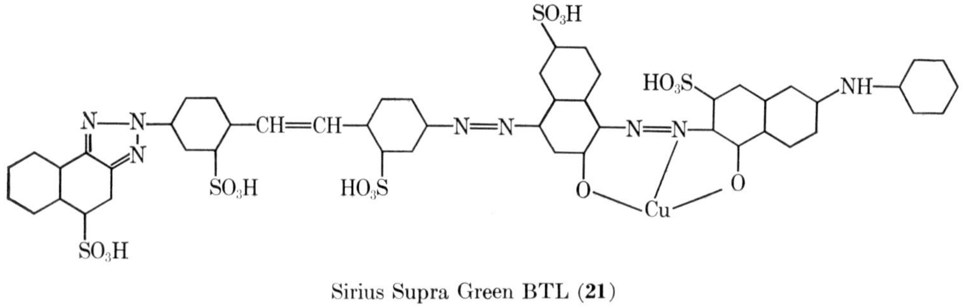

Sirius Supra Green BTL (**21**)

Sirius Orange I (**17**) serves as an intermediate in the synthesis of *Sirius Supra Olive GL* (CI 31985, Direct Green 23) (**22**) (27),

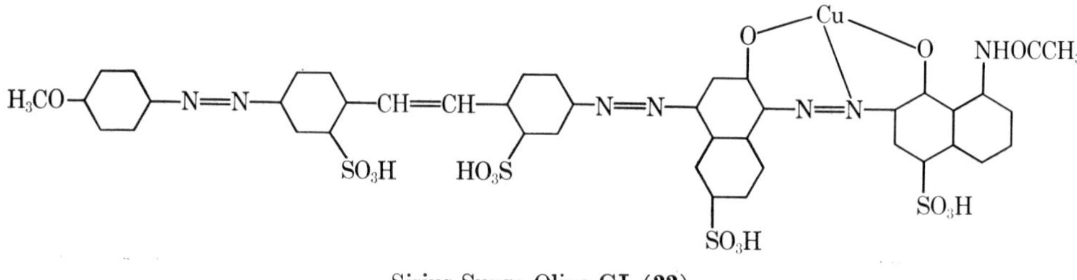

Sirius Supra Olive GL (**22**)

Stilbene Reactive Dyes

Yellow reactive dyes (see Dyes, reactive) containing the chromophoric system of stilbene dyes are a recent development. From the numerous dyes disclosed in patents, structures (**23**) to (**25**) are typical examples.

A yellow dye with good chlorine fastness is obtained starting with the intermediate (**6**) as the diazo component (**23**) (28):

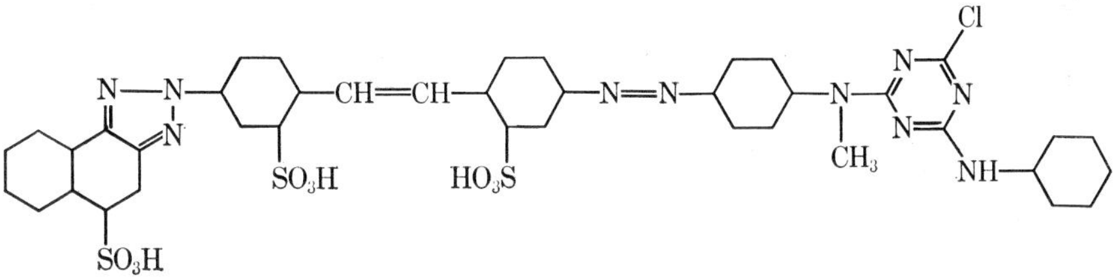

yellow (**23**)

Another example of a yellow dye (**24**) fast to chlorine is shown below (29).

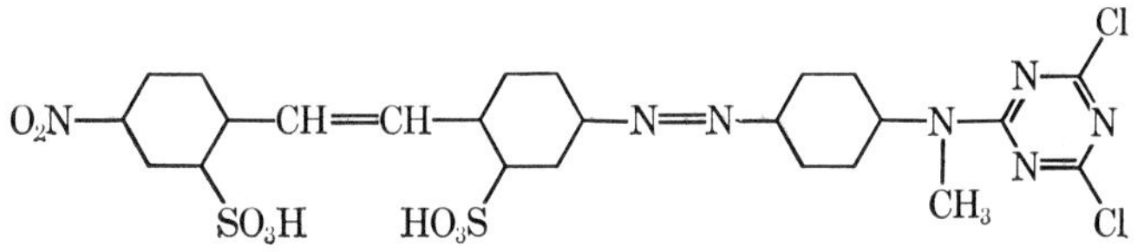

yellow (**24**)

The following compound (**25**) dyes cotton in orange-yellow shades (30).

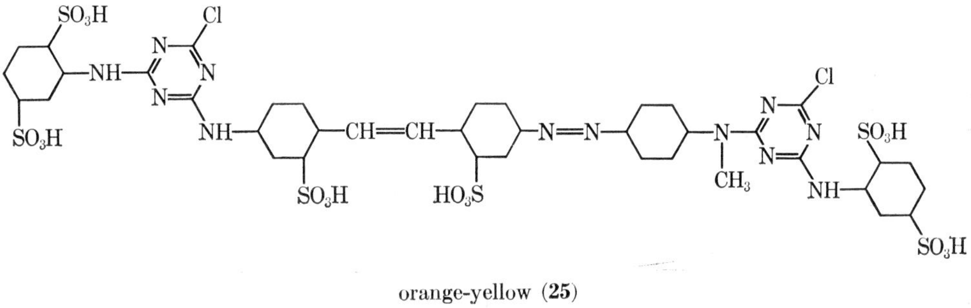

orange-yellow (**25**)

Economic Aspects

Although methods are known for the large-scale manufacture of stilbene dyes of other than the yellow or orange hue, only the yellows and oranges are of any commercial significance. Early in the development of stilbene dyes, yellows and oranges predominated and, in most instances, these same compounds are still the ones that enjoy substantial sales today (1969).

The principal advantages of these products are their combination of attractive shade, good buildup, reasonable fastness, and economy. Tables 2 and 3 summarize the production and sales position of yellow and orange stilbene dyes in the United States in recent years and also, based upon latest reports (31), reflect essentially the current market.

Table 2. U.S. Production of Stilbene Dyes,[a] 1962–1967

Dye (CI name)	In 1000 lb[b]					
	1967	1966	1965	1964	1963	1962
Direct Yellow 4	457	436	468	414	392	385
Direct Yellow 6	514	868	752	783	893	1,186
Direct Yellow 11	1,074	925	974	871	735	678
			(1,100)[c]			
Direct Yellow 12	327	415	388	368	393	330
		(1,321)[c]	(1,380)[c]	(1,980)[c]		
Direct Yellow 105	244	244	188			
Direct Yellow 106	1,137	810	191			
Direct Orange 8	142	167	164	143	149	79
Direct Orange 15	226	230	201	129	182	134
		(50)[c]				
Direct Orange 34	111	135	137	97	91	98
Direct Orange 37	48	57	63	56	57	57
Direct Orange 39	217	156	132	98	72	
Total Stilbene Yellows and Oranges	*4,497*	*4,433*	*4,158*	*2,959*	*2,964*	*2,947*
Total Direct Yellows	9,383	8,217	6,719	5,752	4,959	4,626
Total Direct Oranges	2,201	2,336	1,901	1,726	1,850	1,630
Total Yellow-Orange dyes	*11,584*	*10,553*	*8,620*	*7,748*	*6,809*	*6,256*
Total of Stilbenes/Total Yellows and Oranges, %	38.8	42.1	48.2	39.6	43.5	47.1
Total Directs (all colors)	32,264	37,343	36,080	31,490	28,399	27,425
Total Stilbenes (all colors)[d]	*13,900*	*11,900*	*11,500*	*9,400*	*10,400*	*10,700*

[a] From reports of the U.S. Tariff Commission (31).

[b] Except where percent or pounds are indicated.

[c] Imports, shown in pounds. (These figures are not included in any of the totals shown below.)

[d] In these totals only the first three figures are significant.

NOTE: Direct Yellows 19, 21, 23, 55, 99, 103, and 124 were not listed in the issues of the *U.S. Tariff Commission Report* covering the period 1962–1967. This does not necessarily mean that they were not bulk-produced.

Examination of these figures, as well as sales figures for the years 1963 and 1964 (not shown), indicates the following:

1. Stilbene oranges and yellows have accounted for approx 12–13% of the total numbers of pounds produced and the total dollar value sold of all direct dyestuffs in the period 1962–1967.

2. Stilbene oranges and yellows account for approx 35–40% of the total pounds produced and dollar value sold of all direct yellows and oranges in the period 1962–1967.

3. Total annual sales value of stilbene orange and yellow dyes in 1967 was $7,163,000, accounting for 14.6% of the dollar value of all direct dyes sold in that year.

4. The production and sales of stilbene oranges and yellows have been relatively stable throughout the 1962–1967 period, and the growth seen in 1967 can be attributed primarily to an increase in paper production where these products are used.

5. Importation of stilbene dyes is minimal and relatively insignificant.

The above statistics do not reflect the relative use distribution of stilbene dyes in the paper, leather, and textile industries. Actually some of these products find acceptance in all three (Direct Yellow 11), whereas others are used almost exclusively

Table 3. U.S. Sales of Stilbene Dyes[a,b]

Dye (CI name)	1967 Sales 1000 lb	1967 Sales $1000	1967 Value, $/lb	1966 Sales 1000 lb	1966 Sales $1000	1966 Value, $/lb	1965 Sales 1000 lb	1965 Sales $1000	1965 Value, $/lb	1962 Sales 1000 lb	1962 Sales $1000	1962 Value, $/lb
Direct Yellow 4	434	887	2.04	442	909	2.06	427	897	2.13	390	801	2.05
Direct Yellow 6	564	822	1.46	841	1,280	1.52	703	1,101	1.57	1,135	1,670	1.47
Direct Yellow 11	984	978	0.99	955	993	1.04	865	979	1.13	723	897	1.24
Direct Yellow 12	300	785	2.62	414	1,047	2.53	393	926	2.36	328	799	2.44
Direct Yellow 105	241	565	2.34	225	544	2.42	220	536	2.44			
Direct Yellow 106	1,089	1,863	1.71	877	1,482	1.69	592	1,008	1.70			
Direct Orange 8	145	225	1.55	162	239	1.48	170	228	1.34	108	156	1.44
Direct Orange 15	204	220	1.08	204	246	1.21	184	222	1.21	154	184	1.19
Direct Orange 34	105	241	2.30	128	289	2.47	124	272	2.19	83	191	2.30
Direct Orange 37	50	132	2.64	53	131	2.47	61	153	2.51	53	133	2.51
Direct Orange 39	222	445	2.00	159	319	2.01	121	250	2.07			
Total Stilbene Yellows and Oranges	*4,339*	*7,163*		*4,460*	*7,479*		*3,856*	*6,572*		*2,974*	*4,831*	
Total Direct Yellows	9,116	14,150	1.55	8,181	12,497	1.65	6,214	10,972	1.77	4,722	8,496	1.80
Total Direct Oranges	2,169	5,110	2.36	2,206	5,142	2.33	1,829	4,044	2.21	1,568	3,754	2.39
Total Yellow-Orange dyes	*11,285*	*19,260*		*10,387*	*18,639*		*8,043*	*15,016*		*6,290*	*12,250*	
Total of Stilbenes/Total Yellows and Oranges, %	38.4	37.2		42.1	40.1		47.9	43.8		47.3	39.4	
Total Directs (all colors)	32,549	49,138		36,773	56,820		33,663	50,970		26,812	40,315	
Total Stilbenes (all colors)[c]	*13,300*	*14,600*		*12,100*	*13,200*		*11,400*	*12,900*		*11,100*	*11,900*	

[a] From reports of the U.S. Tariff Commission (31).
[b] Units in pounds or dollars, as shown, except where percent are indicated.
[c] In these totals only the first three figures are significant.

in the paper industry (Direct Yellows 4, 6, 8, 11, 12, and 103), and still others are used principally on textiles (Direct Yellows 105 and 106; Direct Oranges 34, 37, and 39). It thus becomes apparent that in spite of some overlap in the market segments in which stilbene dyes are utilized, the primary areas of consumption, based upon both pounds sold and dollar value, would be in paper and textiles.

In view of the fact that this relative distribution has been in effect for several years and that there are no technological innovations foreseen at this time, the essential position now prevailing in terms of percentage of total dyes produced as well as usage would not be expected to change in the immediate future.

Bibliography

"Stilbene Dyes" in *ECT* 1st ed., Vol. 12, pp. 949–955, by A. F. Plue, General Aniline Works, a Division of General Aniline & Film Corporation.

Manufacturers' Code Names

Bayer	Farbenfabriken Bayer AG, Leverkusen, West Germany
Cassella	Cassella Farbwerke Mainkur AG, Frankfurt/Main, West Germany
Ciba	Gesellschaft für Chemische Industrie, Basel, Switzerland
Clayton	Clayton Aniline Co., Manchester, England
du Pont	E. I. du Pont de Nemours & Co., Inc.
Geigy	J. R. Geigy AG, Basel, Switzerland
ICI	Imperial Chemical Industries Ltd., Manchester, England
I.G.†	Interessengemeinschaft für Farbenindustrie AG, Frankfurt/Main, West Germany
Leonhardt†	Farbwerke Mühlheim, formerly A. Leonhardt und Co., Frankfurt/Main, West Germany

† Firm no longer in existence.

References

1. For more detailed information see the textbooks and other reference works on the chemistry of dyestuffs, as, for example, K. Venkataraman, *The Chemistry of Synthetic Dyes*, Vol. 1, Academic Press, Inc., New York, 1952, p. 628, and *Colour Index*, Vol. 3, 2nd ed., 1956, Nos. 40000–40510, and Supplement Volume, 1963.
2. *BIOS (British Intelligence Objectives Subcommittee) Doc. No. 1440/1122/H/a/39.*
3. *BIOS Final Report 1153*, p. 197.
4. *BIOS 1152*, p. 124.
5. Ger. Pat. 38,735 (1886), (to Leonhardt).
6. Ger. Pat. 42,466 (1886), (to Leonhardt).
7. Ger. Pats. 46,252 (1888), 48,528 (1888), (to Leonhardt).
8. Ger. Pat. 737,323 (1940), H. Roos (to I. G.).
9. A. Green, *J. Chem. Soc.* (*London*) **85**, 1427 (1904); **89**, 1610 (1906); **91**, 2076 (1907); **93**, 1721 (1908).
10. A. H. Knight, *J. Soc. Dyers Colourists* **66**, 410 (1950).
11. *BIOS Doc. No. 2351/2247/1.*
12. *BIOS 1548*, p. 145.
13. E. Müller, ed., *Houben-Weyl Methoden der Organischen Chemie*, Vol. X/3, 4th ed., Georg Thieme Verlag, Stuttgart, West Germany, 1965, pp. 339–344.
14. Ger. Pat. 113,514 (1897), (to Clayton); Ger. Pats. 100,613 (1897), 101,760 (1897), 105,057 (1897), 106,230 (1897), Chr. Ris (to Geigy).
15. Brit. Pat. 12,922/96 (1896), (to Clayton).
16. U.S. Pat. 2,385,862 (1940), E. Keller (to Geigy).
17. Ger. Pat. 741,469 (1940), H. Roos (to I.G.).

18. Ger. Pat. 204,212 (1907), (to Cassella); Brit. Pat. 736,619 (1952), (to Bayer); Ger. Pat. 883,024 (1951), G. Dittmar, F. Suckfüll (to Bayer).
19. Brit. Pat. 532,970 (1938), Ger. Pat. 746,555 (1938), Brit. Pat. 555,867 (1940), U.S. Pats. 2,385,862 (1940), 2,468,204 (1942), E. Keller (to Geigy); U.S. Pat. 2,467,262 (1945), A. H. Knight (to ICI).
20. U.S. Pat. 2,394,998 (1941), E. Keller (to Geigy).
21. *BIOS 1548*, p. 148.
22. U.S. Pat. 2,459,435 (1943), E. Keller, R. Zweidler (to Geigy).
23. U.S. Pat. 2,004,250 (1932), H. Schindhelm, R. Gast (to I.G.); *BIOS 1548*, pp. 120–121.
24. Fr. Pat. 902,481 (1943), E. Keller, R. Zweidler (to Geigy).
25. Brit. Pat. 1,073,220 (1965), G. Manz (to Bayer).
26. U.S. Pat. 2,175,552 (1937), H. Schindhelm, C. Th. Schultis (to I.G.).
27. U.S. Pat 2,197,350 (1935), H. Schindhelm, C. Th. Schultis (to I.G.).
28. U.S. Pat. 3,117,958 (1959), R. E. Starn, W. H. Gumprecht (to du Pont).
29. U.S. Pat. 3,084,152 (1957), H. F. Andrew (to ICI).
30. U.S. Pat. 3,394,122 (1964), K. Seitz (to Ciba).
31. U.S. Tariff Commission, *Synthetic Organic Chemicals, United States Production and Sales*, U.S. Govt. Printing Office, Washington, D.C. (Annual publication. The years covered range from 1962 to 1966, corresponding to publication dates 1963–1967.) U.S. Tariff Commission, *Synthetic Organic Chemicals, United States Production and Sales, Preliminary, 1967* (1968).

H. R. SCHWANDER
J. R. Geigy AG, Basel
G. S. DOMINGUEZ (Economic aspects)
Geigy Chemical Corporation
Ardsley, N.Y.

OPTICAL BRIGHTENERS OF THE STILBENE SERIES

The majority of optical brighteners that are commercially available are based on stilbene derivatives. Various compounds of this type have previously been described in the article Brighteners, optical. Development in that field is rapid and many of the previously mentioned compounds have again disappeared from the market either partially or entirely. On the other hand, the following types of compounds have become more important:

1. **Derivatives of 4-stilbenecarboxylic acid** having the general formula (where X = —O—, —S—, —NH—)

Compounds of this type have been proposed for brightening polyesters of terephthalic acid, and of synthetic polyamides, or of polyolefins (1,2). Compounds having the general formula

have been patented for similar uses (3).

2. **Derivatives of 4,4′-stilbenedicarboxylic acid** having the general formula,

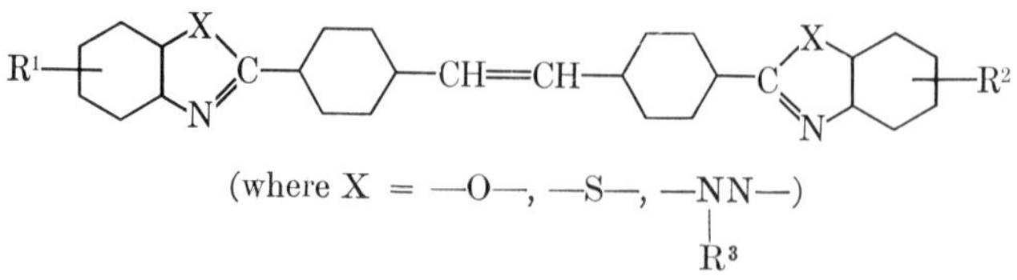

(where X = —O—, —S—, —NN—)
R³

The well-known 4,4′-bis(2-benzimidazolyl)stilbene group has been further developed for better detergent applications (4). The 4,4′-bis(2-benzoxazolyl)stilbenes (5,6), as well as the compounds with phenyl or heterocyclic group substituents (7,8), have attained considerable importance. Compounds containing an oxadiazolyl residue (9) instead of the benzoxazolyl residue, ie bis(oxadiazolyl) compounds (10) having the following structure,

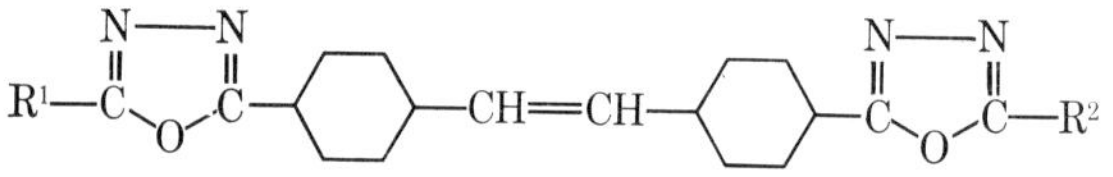

have also been mentioned.

The 4,4′-bis(6-triazinyl)stilbene series (11) furnished compounds of the type shown below (where R¹, R² = aryl)

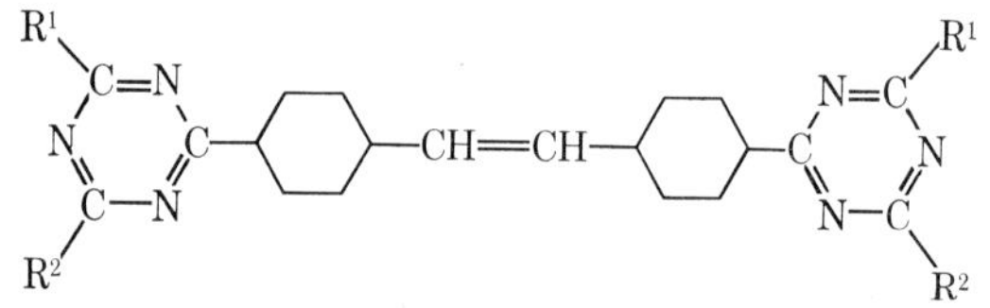

as optical brighteners. These bis(azolyl)- or bis(azinyl)stilbenes are used primarily for the brightening of spinning solutions of polyesters of terephthalic acid; of polyolefins; and of synthetic polyamides.

3. **Derivatives of 4-Aminostilbene.** The well-known system of stilbylarenotriazoles (see also Vol. 3, p. 741) has been further developed. Compounds of the general formula

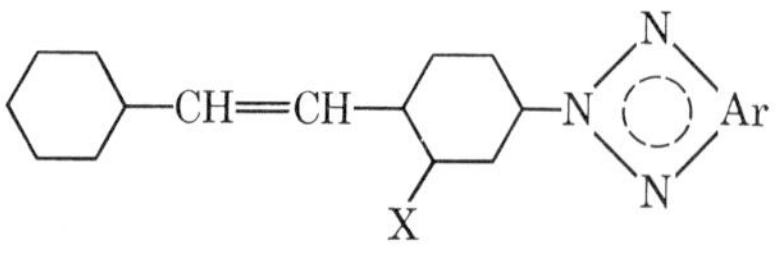

where X = H and Ar = a substituted benzene (12) or indazole (13) radical, are suitable for the brightening of polyesters, polyolefins, synthetic polyamides, etc. Compounds containing sulfonic acid groups, where X = —SO_3H and Ar = a substituted indazole (14) or triazolylbenzo group (15), have been proposed for brightening cellulosic fibers. Compounds free of sulfonic acid groups, where X = —Cl and Ar = a naphtho group (16) or where X = carboxylamide (17), reportedly may be used to brighten a wide variety of man-made fibers. The stilbylnaphthotriazoles that contain sulfonic acid groups (where X = —SO$_3$H and Ar = a naphtho group) are well known as detergent brighteners. Their properties have been improved by the use of chlorine-substituted derivatives (18–20).

4. **Derivatives of 4,4′-Diaminostilbene.** a. *Bis(2-azolyl)stilbenedisulfonic Acids.* Compounds of structure (where X = =N—, =CH—; R^1 = —H, alkyl, aryl; R^2 = alkyl, aryl)

$$\text{R}^1\text{—C}=\text{N} \quad \text{R}^2\text{—C}=\text{X} \rangle\text{N—} \bigcirc\text{(SO}_3\text{H)—CH}=\text{CH—}\bigcirc\text{(HO}_3\text{S)—N}\langle \begin{smallmatrix}\text{N}=\text{C—R}^1\\ \text{X}=\text{C—R}^2\end{smallmatrix}$$

represent a relatively new development (21–23). Compounds of this type are most frequently employed for brightening cellulosic fibers in the presence of chlorine or chlorites.

b. *Bis(triazinylamino)stilbenedisulfonic Acids.* The optical brighteners that are actually sold in the largest quantities are the reaction products of 4,4′-diamino-2,2′-stilbenedisulfonic acid with cyanuric chloride. Subsequently the mobile chlorine atoms are partially or wholly replaced by other groups. Products of this kind find application in brightening cellulosic fibers (textile or paper), synthetic polyamides, etc, either in finishing operations or as detergent brighteners.

These compounds, which have the following general structure,

$$\text{(triazinyl)—NH—}\bigcirc\text{(SO}_3\text{H)—CH}=\text{CH—}\bigcirc\text{(HO}_3\text{S)—NH—(triazinyl)}$$

were mentioned in Vol. 3, p. 740. The following information and references are supplementary: (*1*) Compounds where R^1 = —Cl, R^2 = an amino group (24,25). Other compounds are described where (*2*) R^1 = —O—alkyl and R^2 = an aliphatic (26,27) or aromatic (28–30) amino group, or where (*3*) R^1 = —O—aryl and R^2 = an aliphatic amino group (31). (*4*) Compounds where R^1 and R^2 = an aliphatic amino group were cited as, for instance, brighteners for cotton in the presence of cationic softeners (32). Many other combinations are possible (25,33), depending on the intended use. (*5*) Further work on compounds having R^1 = —NH—alkyl and R^2 = —NH—aryl led, on the one hand, to liquid commercial products (34,35) and, on the other, to various products including white forms (36) which do not produce discoloration when used as detergent additives. Other things being equal, solubility may be increased by the introduction of additional sulfonic acid groups (where R^2 = —NH—aryl—(SO$_3$H)1 − 2) or modified sulfonic acid groups (37–40). (*6*) In the case of the tetraanilino compound (where R^1 and R^2 = —NH—C$_6$H$_5$), a white (β) form was found (41), and its application in detergents was patented (42).

Research on the bis(triazinylamino)stilbenedisulfonic acids continues. At the same time persistent attempts are being made to adapt these compounds to many highly diversified consumer demands.

Patent References

The date shown in parentheses after the patent number is the priority date. For instance, reference 9 shows that U.S. Pat. 3,351,541 has a Swiss priority of September 14, 1964.

U.S. patents are cited preferentially. Where none exists the English patent or, as a third choice, the French patent is shown.

1. U.S. Pat. 3,133,196 (Swiss, June 2, 1960) Ciba AG, Basel, Switzerland.
2. Fr. Pat. 1,467,750 (Swiss, May 12, 1965) Ciba.
3. Fr. Pat. 1,479,071 (Swiss, May 10, 1965) Ciba.
4. U.S. Pat. 2,980,625 (U.S., May 11, 1959) Sterling Drug, Inc., New York.
5. U.S. Pat. 3,322,680 (Brit., Dec. 17, 1962) Eastman Kodak Company, Rochester, N.Y.
6. U.S. Pat. 3,260,715 (Brit., Dec. 17, 1962) Eastman Kodak.
7. Fr. Pat. 1,455,330 (Swiss, Sept. 1, 1964) Ciba.
8. Fr. Pat. 1,445,949 (Swiss, Sept. 1, 1964) Ciba.
9. U.S. Pat. 3,351,591 (Swiss, Sept. 14, 1964) Ciba.
10. Fr. Pat. 1,445,768 (Swiss, June 15, 1964) Ciba.
11. U.S. Pat. 3,351,592 (Swiss, Sept. 23, 1964) Ciba.
12. U.S. Pat. 3,287,358 (U.S., Oct. 22, 1963) General Aniline & Film Corp. (GAF), New York.
13. U.S. Pat. 3,062,814 (U.S., Nov. 3, 1959) American Cyanamid Co., New York.
14. U.S. Pat. 3,048,584 (Brit., Sept. 18, 1956) Hickson & Welch, Ltd., Castleford, Great Britain.
15. U.S. Pat. 3,157,644 (U.S., April 4, 1956) GAF.
16. U.S. Pat. 3,288,786 (U.S., Sept. 10, 1962) GAF.
17. U.S. Pat. 3,341,530 (U.S., May 24, 1965) GAF.
18. Brit. Pat. 1,057,294 (Swiss, July 9, 1964) J. R. Geigy AG, Basel, Switzerland.
19. Fr. Pat. 1,494,443 (Swiss, Sept. 23, 1965) Geigy.
20. Fr. Pat. 1,494,442 (Swiss, Sept. 23, 1965) Geigy.
21. Fr. Pat. 1,534,169 (Ger., Aug. 10, 1966) Farbenfabriken Bayer.
22. Fr. Pat. 1,463,324 (Ger., Jan. 9, 1965) Bayer.
23. Fr. Pat. 1,420,699 (Ger., May 20, 1965) Bayer.
24. Fr. Pat. 1,480,093 (Brit., May 5, 1965) Imperial Chemical Industries Ltd., Great Britain.
25. Brit. Pat. 1,064,618 (Swiss, Nov. 20, 1965) Geigy.
26. Brit. Pat. 1,041,530 (Ger., Aug. 14, 1964) Bayer.
27. U.S. Pat. 3,371,089 (Ger., Aug. 8, 1963) Bayer.
28. Fr. Pat. 1,298,553 (Brit., June 24, 1960) ICI.
29. Brit. Pat. 1,021,193 (Brit., Feb. 4, 1963) Hickson & Welch.
30. Jap. Appl. 15'004/67 (Jap. Feb. 24, 1964) Sumitomo Chemical Company, Japan.
31. U.S. Pat. 3,350,395 (U.S., Oct. 21, 1966) GAF.
32. U.S. Pats. 3,356,524 and 3,309,363 (U.S., May 11, 1964) American Cyanamid.
33. Brit. Pat. 1,010,759 (Ger., Sept. 17, 1963) Bayer.
34. U.S. Pat. 3,211,665 (U.S., Dec. 3, 1962) American Cyanamid.
35. Fr. Pat. 1,504,243 (Swiss, Dec. 12, 1965) Geigy.
36. Neth. Pat. 6,981,472 (Swiss, May 13, 1966) Geigy.
37. U.S. Pat. 3,360,479 (Swiss, Nov. 20, 1959) Geigy.
38. Brit. Pat. 1,042,891 (Ger., Feb. 1, 1962) Farbwerke Hoechst AG, Frankfurt/M, West Germany.
39. U.S. Pat. 3,066,055 (Ger., Feb. 2, 1958) Bayer.
40. Brit. Pats. 1,008,457 and 1,021,527 (U.S., April 12, 1963) GAF.
41. Brit. Pat. 997,044 (U.S., June 6, 1962) Geigy.
42. U.S. Pat. 3,309,319 (U.S., Sept. 23, 1965) Procter & Gamble Co., Cincinnati, Ohio.

REINHARD ZWEIDLER
J. R. Geigy AG, Basel

STILBESTROL, $HOC_6H_4C(C_2H_5):C(C_2H_5)C_6H_4OH$.   See Hydrocarbons;   Non-steroidal estrogens under Hormones.

STIMULANTS OF THE NERVOUS SYSTEM.   See Psychopharmacological agents.

STODDARD SOLVENT.   See Drycleaning;   Vol. 15, p. 81.

STOICHIOMETRY, INDUSTRIAL

Stoichiometry is the application to chemical processes of the law of conservation of matter and the chemical laws of combining weights. These laws may be applied to reactions carried out under controlled conditions in the laboratory and to the more complex processes usually occurring in the industrial plant. The techniques are the same in either case. However, the application of the techniques is usually considerably more complicated in industrial practice than in the analytical laboratory, and emphasis is therefore placed here on the stoichiometry of industrial operations. In its broadest sense, stoichiometry is a system of accounting applied to the matter and energy taking part in a process involving physical or chemical change. It is a system of calculations which permits a surprisingly large amount of information to be obtained from a seemingly small number of facts.

In processes operating continuously and in steady state, the total quantity of input items must balance the total quantity of output items. Material and energy balances may be made over the entire process or over a fractional part of the process. They may be made for the sum of all the components, for any one component, or for any element in the process. Each balance will result in one equation, and there must be as many *independent* equations as there are unknowns in the process.

Until the mid-1950s, stoichiometry used hand computation to work out material and energy balances, to predict or extrapolate physical properties, and to do other calculations called for by the physical or chemical processes under consideration. The techniques that were used are reviewed here and are well developed in Hougen and Watson's classical text (4), as well as in the many similar texts (2,3,5,6) published more recently. With the introduction of electronic computers in the 1950s, however, and with their rapid development and improvement, machine computation became an alternative to these hand methods. Since the computer increased computational speed and made it easier to handle large problems, it was inevitable that it should be used for solving problems in industrial stoichiometry. It was equally inevitable that as machine computation displaced manual computation, crude techniques would give way to highly refined techniques, and coarse approximations would be replaced by more precise solutions. Unfortunately, most of the machine systems developed for stoichiometric calculations are proprietary, making detailed discussion impossible. Nevertheless, after presenting the classical techniques, this article will touch briefly on these new methods.

Basic Principles. The law of conservation of matter states that matter can be neither created nor destroyed, but only altered in form. (The usual form of the law of conservation of matter must necessarily be modified slightly when dealing with radioactive phenomena, but even then the correction is usually slight.) The strength of this law stems from the fact that no exceptions to it have ever been found. It forms the basis for our entire system of quantitative analysis and is of fundamental importance in almost all industries. Though this fundamental law is concerned with units of mass, when applying it to processes involving chemical change it is frequently convenient to use the mole as the unit of quantity. The laboratory chemist uses the gram-mole, that is, that weight in grams numerically equal to the molecular weight; the chemist in an industrial plant often prefers the larger unit, the pound-mole, ie, that weight in pounds numerically equal to the molecular weight. Frequently one speaks of a gram-mole (or pound-mole) of aluminum or silicon or some other elemental material, meaning of course a gram-atom (or pound-atom) of the element in question.

Just as basic as the law of conservation of matter is the first law of thermodynamics —the law of conservation of energy. This law states that energy can be neither created nor destroyed, but only altered in form. This law, too, is proved by the fact that no exceptions to it have ever been found. In the light of developments which clearly establish the relationship of matter to energy, it becomes apparent that the law of conservation of matter is in reality only a special case of the first law of thermodynamics in its broadest sense.

Since these laws may be applied to innumerable industries, each industry giving rise to its own problems and requiring its own particular technique for solution, the principles of stoichiometry are herein developed through a series of examples.

Material Balances

Simple Gas Problems. Many industrial problems depend on the gas laws for their solution. In the familiar equation of state for a perfect gas:

$$PV = nRT$$

where P = pressure, V = volume, n = number of moles, R = universal gas constant, T = absolute temperature, it is convenient to remember the constants involved in both cgs and engineering units:

$$R = 0.08205 \text{ (liter)}\text{(atm)}/(°\text{K})\text{(g-mole)}$$

$$= 1546 \text{ (ft}^3\text{)}\text{(atm)}/(°\text{R})\text{(lb-mole)}$$

The absolute temperature on the Kelvin scale, °K, is obtained by adding 273 to the degrees centigrade, t. The absolute temperature on the Rankine scale, °R, is obtained by adding 460 to the degrees Fahrenheit. One g-mole of a perfect gas under standard conditions (1 atm and 0°C) occupies 22.4 l; the corresponding volume for 1 lb-mole is 359 ft³.

Illustration. When ammonia is heated to temperatures above 900°F, it dissociates into its constituents in accordance with the equation:

$$2 \text{ NH}_3 \rightarrow \text{N}_2 + 3 \text{ H}_2$$

The extent of the dissociation is a function of the temperature and the pressure.

A tank of liquid ammonia weighs initially 232 lb, and a pressure gage shows the contents to be at 114.1 psia. The tank is placed in a constant temperature bath and part of the contents is removed, the gas being first heated to a high temperature and then cooled. After 1100 ft³ of gas (measured at 68°F and atmospheric pressure) are withdrawn, the tank weighs 206.5 lb. Determine the percent dissociation of the ammonia in the gas phase.

$$\text{lb-moles NH}_3 \text{ removed from tank} = \frac{232 - 206.5}{17} = 1.5$$

If we let x = pound-moles of NH_3 dissociated, $x/2$ equals the pound-moles of N_2 formed and $3x/2$ equals the pound-moles of H_2 formed. The total pound-moles present after dissociation is therefore:

$$1.5 - x + x/2 + 3x/2 = 1.5 + x$$

This gas was contained in 1100 ft³ at 68°F and 14.7 psia. Using the pound-molar volume and correcting for temperature, we find the total number of moles to be:

$$\frac{1100}{359} \times \frac{460 + 32}{460 + 68} = 2.86$$

from which we solve for x:

$$1.5 + x = 2.86$$

$$x = 1.36$$

$$\% \text{ dissociation} = \frac{1.36}{1.5} \times 100 = 90.7\%$$

Industrial operations in which gases are brought into contact with liquids usually involve conditions of partial saturation of the gas phase. When the gas and vapor are air and water, respectively, stoichiometric problems can best be solved by using a psychrometric chart (see Vol. 1, p. 483; Vol. 7, p. 349). This chart is generally a plot of humidity, ie, amount of water vapor contained in a unit quantity of dry gas, vs temperature for various degrees of saturation. Other properties of the wet gas which are usually superimposed on this plot are: *dewpoint temperature*, the temperature at which the gas would be saturated if cooled at constant humidity; *wet-bulb temperature*, the equilibrium temperature attained by a small amount of water brought into contact with a large amount of unsaturated air; *percent humidity*, the percentage ratio of the weight of water carried by 1 lb of dry air, at any temperature and pressure, to the weight of water 1 lb of dry air could carry if saturated at that same temperature and pressure.

For systems other than air and water, psychrometric charts are not generally available. They may be constructed, however, if the volume of work can justify the time involved in their preparation.

Solutions. Industrial operations involving crystallization from solution give rise to problems which are amenable to graphical solution based on the solubility data or phase diagram, as demonstrated in the following example:

Illustration. One hundred pounds of a solution initially containing 50% naphthalene and 50% benzene are cooled to 5°C. Determine the quantity and composition of the crystals precipitated from this solution, as well as the maximum amount of naphthalene crystals which can be recovered free of benzene.

This type of problem is best solved by using the phase diagram or solubility data for the system.

Line AB (see Fig. 1) represents the solubility of naphthalene, and line BC represents the solubility of benzene. Point B at 19% naphthalene is called the eutectic point and represents the particular solution with the lowest freezing point. If the initial solution represented by point 1 is cooled to 5°C (point 2), the solid phase will contain pure naphthalene since line 1–2 crosses the naphthalene solubility curve. In other words, at about 35°C a 50% solution of naphthalene in benzene would be saturated. Cooling below this temperature must necessarily result in precipitation of naphthalene. The quantity of crystals produced by cooling to 5°C may be calculated by making a naphthalene balance between the crystals and the mother liquor, which from the phase diagram is seen to contain 23% naphthalene.

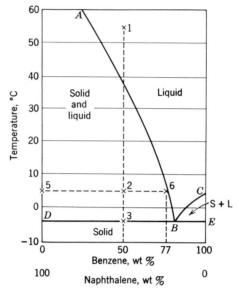

Fig. 1.

Let

$$x = \text{wt of crystals produced}$$

$$x + (100 - x)0.23 = 100(0.5)$$

$$x = \frac{100(0.5 - 0.23)}{(1 - 0.23)}$$

$$x = 35.1 \text{ lb}$$

It should be noted that the quantity $(0.5 - 0.23)$ is represented on the phase diagram by the distance 2–6, whereas the quantity $(1 - 0.23)$ is represented by the distance 5–6. Thus the same result could have been determined by taking the quotient of the appropriate line segments.

The maximum recovery of pure naphthalene from this solution is obtained when cooling is continued until the mother liquor is at the eutectic composition, point B. On the basis of line segments the weight of crystals at this new condition is found to be:

$$\text{wt} = 100 \left(\frac{\text{line } 3\text{–}B}{\text{line } D\text{–}B} \right)$$

$$= 100 \left(\frac{50 - 19}{100 - 19} \right)$$

$$= 38.3 \text{ lb}$$

This weight of pure naphthalene crystals could be recovered by cooling the solution to about $-3.5°\text{C}$.

Use of an Inert Component. Frequently in an industrial operation, one or more materials will pass through a process and be unaffected by the chemical reactions taking place. One example is the nitrogen from the air in a combustion process. The nitrogen enters the combustion zone and leaves by the stack without gain or loss, and without suffering any change. Such an inert component can be used as a key component to interrelate the inlet and exit streams. If the amount of air employed in a combustion process and the percentage of nitrogen in the flue gas are known, the total quantity of flue gas can be immediately determined.

Illustration. An iron ore of the following composition: FeO_3 76%, SiO_2 14%, MnO 1%, Al_2O_3 9%, is smelted in a blast furnace to produce pig iron of the following analysis: Fe 94.2%, C 3.5%, Si 1.5%, Mn 0.8%. Eleven hundred pounds of coke containing 88% C and 12% SiO_2 are used per ton of pig iron. Analysis of the gases shows 26% CO, 13% CO_2, and 61% N_2. It can be assumed that no iron is lost in the slag and that the slag contains 36% CaO. Determine the weight of ore and limestone (taken as pure calcium carbonate) and the volume of blast air and exit gases per ton of pig iron produced.

It is apparent that the element iron can be considered a tie substance, since it exists in known percentages in both the ore and the product, pig iron, and nowhere else. It is therefore possible to determine the amount of ore required per ton of pig iron by a balance on iron:

$$\text{iron in pig} = \text{iron in ore}$$

$$(2000)(0.942) = (\text{lb ore})(0.76)(111.7/159.7)$$

$$\text{lb ore} = 3550 \text{ lb}$$

In order to determine the amount of limestone required, it is necessary to consider the components of the slag, namely:

$$\left.\begin{matrix} \left.\begin{matrix} MnO \\ SiO_2 \\ Al_2O_3 \end{matrix}\right\} \text{from ore} \\ SiO_2 \quad \text{from coke} \end{matrix}\right\} \quad \text{These components constitute 64\% of slag.}$$

CaO   from flux   This component constitutes 36% of slag.

The following individual component balances can be made:

For MnO: $\dfrac{3550 \times 0.01}{70.9} - \dfrac{2000 \times 0.008}{54.9} = 20.8 = 1470$

           (moles in ore)   (moles in pig)   (moles in slag)   (lb in slag)

For SiO_2: $\dfrac{3550 \times 0.14}{50} - \dfrac{2000 \times 0.015}{28} + \dfrac{1100 \times 0.12}{28} = 13.56 = 675$

      (moles in ore)   (moles in pig)   (moles in coke)   (moles in slag)   (lb in slag)

For Al_2O_3: $\dfrac{3550 \times 0.04}{102} = 1.39 = 142$

         (moles in ore)   (moles in slag)   (lb in slag)

$$\text{wt of 64\% of the slag} = 1470 + 675 + 142 = 2287 \text{ lb}$$

With CaO as the tie substance, the weight of flux, $CaCO_3$, required per ton of pig iron is:

$$\text{lb flux} = \frac{(2287)(36)(56.1)}{(64)(100.1)} = 720 \text{ lb}$$

By making a carbon balance, it is now possible to determine the volume of exit gases. Since the carbon is present in several different molecular forms, and since a gas volume is desired, it is best to make this balance on a molar basis:

$$\frac{1100 \times 0.88}{12} + \frac{720}{100.1} = \frac{2000 \times 0.035}{12} \text{ moles } (CO \text{ and } CO_2) \text{ in exit gases}$$

$$\text{moles } (CO \text{ and } CO_2) \text{ in exit gases} = 73.1 + 7.2 - 5.8 = 74.5$$

from which the volume of gas is found to be:

$$\text{vol} = 359 \times 74.5 = 26{,}600 \text{ SCF}$$

Obviously the nitrogen in the air and in the exit gases is an excellent tie substance for determining the volume of the air blast since:

$$N_2 \text{ in exit gases} = N_2 \text{ in air blast}$$

$$(26{,}600)(0.61) = \text{vol of blast } (0.79)$$

$$\text{vol of blast} = 20{,}500 \text{ SCF}$$

Dilution Metering. Dilution metering is a relatively simple application of stoichiometry to the problem of measuring the flow of fluids. The technique is based on the addition of a foreign substance which is soluble in the fluid and is susceptible to easy quantitative measurement when so mixed. The foreign substance is added to the flowing fluid at a constant, accurately measured rate, and its concentration in the fluid is determined both upstream and downstream from the point of addition; from the concentration the rate of flow of the fluid can be readily calculated.

Illustration. A vacuum line carrying hydrogen chloride gas is found to contain 3% by volume of gases insoluble in water. After passing a metering section where 30 ft³/min of air is introduced into the line, the hydrogen chloride gas is found to contain 5% by volume of water-insoluble gases. What is the rate of flow of hydrogen chloride?

At the point of addition of the diluent, the flow conditions are:

$$(x + 30) \text{ ft}^3/\text{min} \begin{cases} 95\% \text{ HCl} \\ 5\% \text{ insoluble} \end{cases} \xleftarrow{\quad} \begin{array}{c} 30 \text{ ft}^3/\text{min air} \\ \downarrow \end{array} \xleftarrow{\quad} x \text{ ft}^3/\text{min HCl} \begin{cases} 97\% \text{ HCl} \\ 3\% \text{ insoluble} \end{cases}$$

A material balance on insolubles gives:

$$0.03x + 30 = 0.05(x + 30)$$

$$x = \frac{30(1 - 0.05)}{(0.05 - 0.03)} = 30 \frac{(0.95)}{(0.02)} = 1425 \text{ ft}^3/\text{min}$$

If care is taken to ensure thorough mixing before the downstream analysis station is reached, very accurate results can be obtained. The same accuracy can be achieved more conveniently by introducing a measured quantity of heat into a flowing stream. In place of chemical analysis, one merely measures the temperature both upstream and downstream from the point of addition. If the duct is well insulated between the two temperature stations, and the total temperature rise is small (so as not to alter the velocity head of the flowing fluid), a heat balance will give the desired flow rate as follows:

$$W(H_2 - H_1) = Q$$

For liquids and for perfect gases this becomes:

$$W(\text{lb moles/sec}) = \frac{Q(\text{Btu/sec})}{C_p(t_2 - t_1)}$$

Recycle Operations. It is often useful to recycle part of a process stream from the exit end of a piece of equipment back to the inlet end. In drying certain solids, for example, the drying rate is carefully controlled by regulating the humidity of the air circulated through the drying chamber. One method of controlling the humidity is to recycle a portion of the exit wet air which, when blended with the incoming dry air, results in an air stream with the desired humidity. Another example occurs in air conditioning in the wintertime. The outside air must be both heated and humidified to bring it to the proper conditions for maximum comfort. By recycling a portion of the inside air to the fresh air inlet duct, a considerable amount of heat energy can be saved. A typical example based on a drying operation is given below.

Illustration. In order to ensure a slow rate of drying and thereby prevent checking of the dried product, an inlet relative humidity of 70% at 75°F is specified. The air leaving the dryer has a relative humidity of 95%. If the outside air has a dewpoint of 40°F, what fraction of the air passing through the dryer must be mixed with the outside air to provide the desired moisture content in the air fed to the dryer?

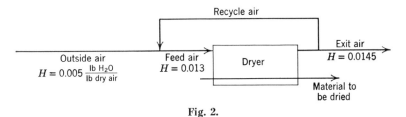

Fig. 2.

A diagram of the process flow is shown in Figure 2. The indicated humidities are read from a psychrometric chart. In the usual case, problems involving recycle or bypass streams can be solved by making a material balance around the point where the recycle stream joins the main stream:

Recycle
X lb dry air
$H = 0.0145$

$(1 - X)$ lb dry air   1 lb dry air
$H = 0.005$ $H = 0.013$

A material balance on water gives:

$$0.005(1 - X) + 0.0145X = 0.013$$

$$X = (0.013 - 0.005)/(0.0145 - 0.005) = 0.842$$

Thus 84.2% of the air passing through the dryer is recycled and reused.

Countercurrent Processing. Many extraction or washing operations are carried out stepwise with a countercurrent flow of the wash liquors and the material being washed. The countercurrent nature of these operations makes it possible to wash with a minimum amount of solvent and obtain comparatively concentrated solutions as the final extract liquors.

Calculations on countercurrent washing operations usually reduce to straight material balances when three assumptions are made. These assumptions are that (*1*) sufficient time has been allowed in each mixer-settler unit for equilibrium to be achieved; (*2*) the wash liquid has been completely and uniformly mixed with the solution adhering to the surface of the solid; and (*3*) the solid exerts no selective adsorbing action on the solute but is completely inert.

For problems which reduce to straight material balances, it is usually sufficient to establish a number of independent equations equal to the number of unknowns of composition and mass. It is important to be certain that each of the equations established is truly independent. Any material balance equation which can be derived from other material balance equations already written cannot be regarded as an additional independent equation. The use of equations that are not truly independent generally results in proving such things as that zero equals zero. Where more independent equations can be written than are required, it becomes a matter of judgment which equations should be used. In such cases the selection of the balances for calculating the unknowns should be based on those quantities which are known most precisely and will therefore introduce the minimum error. In addition, choosing the appropriate equations may result in considerable simplification of the problem. An example follows.

Illustration. Ten tons per hour of dry seashore sand containing 1% sodium chloride by weight are to be washed by 10 ton/hr of saltfree water running countercurrently to the sand through two classifiers in series. Assuming perfect mixing of the sand and wash water in each classifier and assuming that the sand is discharged from each classifier containing 50% liquid (on dry basis), determine the salt content of the sand if it is dried after leaving the second classifier.

Figure 3 (basis, 1 hr) indicates the flow streams for the washing operation employing two classifiers. The problem involves the determination of the salt concentration in the solution carried from the No.1 classifier by the sand. This is best ac-

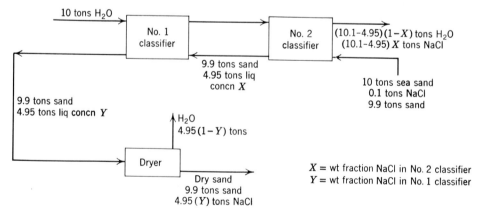

Fig. 3.

complished by making an overall salt balance as well as a salt balance on the No. 2 classifier.

Overall salt balance:

$$0.1 = 4.95Y + (10.1 - 4.95)X$$

Salt balance on No. 2 classifier:

$$0.1 + 10Y = (10.1 - 4.95)X + 4.95X$$

These equations can be simplified to:

$$0.1 = 4.95Y + 5.15X$$

$$0.1 = -10Y + 10.1X$$

which can be solved simultaneously to give $Y = 0.00488$, from which the hourly salt loss is found to be $4.95Y = (4.95)(0.00488) = 0.0242$ ton, and the salt content of the dried sand is $0.0242/9.9 = 0.24\%$ (dry basis).

Countercurrent Process with Recycle. Industrial operations are seldom simple idealized operations of the type shown here as examples. However, even the most complex processes can usually be shown to be combinations of simple operations. In the following example, the idea of recycle is combined with the principle of countercurrent contacting in a washing operation.

Illustration. One hundred thousand pounds of cotton waste containing 0.4 lb of oil per lb of dry waste are to be extracted per day in a two-cell continuous countercurrent system. Fifty thousand gallons of oilfree gasoline, sp gr = 0.72 (ie, 300,000 lb) are sent to the system per day. The waste leaving each cell contains 1.0 lb of solution per pound of dry waste. The waste leaving the last unit is centrifuged down to 0.20 lb of solution per pound of dry waste and the solution sent to the overflow from the last cell. How many pounds of oil are recovered per day?

Let

$$x = \text{lb oil/lb soln in cell 1}$$

$$y = \text{lb oil/lb soln in cell 2}$$

(See Fig. 4.)

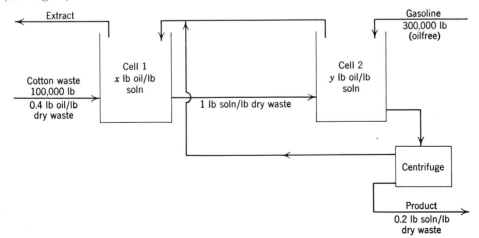

Fig. 4.

Feed contains $100,000(0.4)/(1.4) = 28,600$ lb oil (since $0.4/1.4$ is the fraction of oil in the untreated waste.

$$100,000 - 28,600 = 71,400 \text{ lb dry waste}$$

An overall oil balance gives:

$$28,600 = 71,400\,(0.2)(y) + (300,000 + 28,600 - 71,400 \times 0.2)\,(x)$$

$$28,600 = 314,320x + 14,280y \tag{1}$$

An oil balance in cell 2 gives:

oil in waste from cell 1 = oil in waste from cell 2 + oil in overflow

$$71,400x = 71,400y + 300,000y$$

$$y = 71,400x/371,400 \tag{2}$$

Substituting equation 1 in equation 2 and solving for x:

$$28,600 = 314,320x + 14,280(71,400/371,400)x$$

$$x = 0.0905$$

Weight of oil recovered per day is $314,320(0.0905) = 28,400$ lb.

Energy Balance

The material balance, although of tremendous importance, is still only one part of most problems. The other part is concerned with the energy which is absorbed or liberated in every chemical reaction. The quantity of energy may be large, as in combustion reactions, or small, as in most organic syntheses. This energy usually manifests itself as heat which must be supplied to or withdrawn from the system. This gives rise to the heat balance, that is, a balance of all the heat quantities entering, leaving, generated in, or stored in a given chemical process.

There is considerable advantage in completing the material balance before attempting the heat balance. The material balance is usually simpler to complete and is more readily checked for correctness. Then, with the material balance completed, the only additional work involved in the heat balance is the evaluation of the enthalpies of each and every item appearing in the material balance.

The heat of reaction is the difference between the enthalpies of the products and reactants of a chemical reaction. This heat of reaction is dependent on the chemical nature of each reacting material and also on their physical states. The standard heat of reaction is defined as the change in enthalpy of a system resulting from the reaction under 1 atm pressure, starting and ending with all materials in their standard states of aggregation at 18°C.

Special cases of the heat of reaction are heat of formation, heat of combustion, and heat of dilution. The first represents the enthalpy change when a compound is formed from its elements. The next represents the enthalpy change when the compound is burned in air, the combustion products being cooled to 18°C. The third represents the heat effect accompanying the solution of 1 mole of solute in a specified number of moles of solvent (integral heat of solution) or the heat effect accompanying the solution of a unit mass of solute in a solution, of specified concentration, so large in amount as to result in no appreciable change of composition (differential heat of solution). Tabled values of these standard heats of formation, combustion, or solution may be found in most handbooks. See also Thermodynamics.

Two basic laws greatly simplify problems involving the use of heats of reaction. The law of Lavoisier and Laplace teaches that as much energy is required to decompose a compound into its elements as was required to form the compound from its elements. In other words, changing the direction of a chemical reaction requires that the sign be changed on the heat of reaction. The law of Hess states that the net heat change in a chemical process is the same whether the reaction takes place in one or several steps.

Illustration. Steam at 200°C, 50° superheat, is blown through a bed of coke weighing 6000 lb and initially at 1200°C. The gases leave at an average temperature of 800°C with the following composition by volume on a dry basis: H_2 53.5%, CO 39.7%, CO_2 6.8%. Of the steam introduced, 30% passes through undecomposed. If the reaction must stop when the bed has cooled to 900°C, what fraction of the bed will have been consumed and what volume of water gas will have been produced? (Specific heat of coke = 0.35 Btu/(lb)(°F). Basis, 100 lb-moles of dry water gas.)

The equation representing the chemical reaction is:

$$46.7 \text{ C} + 76.4 \text{ H}_2\text{O} \longrightarrow 6.8 \text{ CO}_2 + 39.7 \text{ CO} + 53.5 \text{ H}_2 + 22.9 \text{ H}_2\text{O}$$

1200°C　　200°C　　　　　800°C　　800°C　　800°C　　800°C
　　　　50° superheat

It is necessary to evaluate the enthalpy of each compound relative to a common datum. The elements in their standard states of aggregation at 18°C being chosen as the datum, the enthalpy per mole is given by:

$$H = \Delta H_f + \sum \lambda + C_p(t - 18)$$

where ΔH_f = heat of formation from the elements; C_p = heat capacity per mole; t = temperature of compound; $\Sigma\lambda$ = sum of latent heat of phase changes occurring between 18°C and t°C.

For coke (NOTE: β-Graphite is usually taken as the standard state of aggregation for carbon. Thus coke has, strictly speaking, a heat of formation relative to β-graphite.):

$$H = 2600 \times 1.8 + 0.35 \times 12 \left(\frac{1800 - 18}{1.8} \right) = +8850 \text{ Btu/lb-mole}$$

For water (as reactant):

$$H = -68,320 \times 1.8 + 1435 \times 1.8 + 8.13 \left(\frac{200 - 18}{1.8} \right) = -119,580 \text{ Btu/lb-mole}$$

For carbon dioxide:

$$H = -94,030 \times 1.8 + 11.57 \left(\frac{800 - 18}{1.8} \right) = -163,970 \text{ Btu/lb-mole}$$

For carbon monoxide:

$$H = -26,620 \times 1.8 + 7.44 \left(\frac{800 - 18}{1.8} \right) = -44,760 \text{ Btu/lb-mole}$$

For hydrogen:

$$H = 7.07 \left(\frac{800 - 18}{1.8} \right) = 3080 \text{ Btu/lb-mole}$$

For water (as product):

$$H = -68,320 \times 1.8 + 1435 \times 1.8 + 8.91 \left(\frac{800 - 18}{1.8} \right) = -121,620 \text{ Btu/lb-mole}$$

The heat effect accompanying any reaction is equal to the sum of the enthalpies of all the products minus the sum of the enthalpies of all the reactants. Therefore, for the reaction written above, the heat effect is

$$\Delta H_R = \sum H_P - \sum H_R$$
$$= 6.8(-163,970) + 39.7(-44,760) + 53.5(3080) + 22.9(-121,620)$$
$$- 46.7(8850) - 76.4(-119,580)$$

$$= +3,213,000$$

The positive sign indicates that heat is absorbed in this reaction. This heat must be supplied by the unreacted coke, which cools from 1200°C to its final temperature, 900°C.

Let X = lb coke reacted. Then, by heat balance:

$$\frac{X}{(12)(46.7)} \times 3,213,000 = (6000 - X)(0.41) \left(\frac{1200 - 900}{1.8} \right)$$

$$X = 71 \text{ lb coke}$$

$$(X/6000) \times 100 = 1.185\% \text{ of original bed reacted}$$

From the original equation it is apparent that 46.7 moles of carbon produced 122.9 moles of water gas. The volume of water gas produced when 71 lb of coke are consumed is therefore:

$$V = 122.9 \times 359 \times 71/(12 \times 46.7) = 5600 \text{ ft}^3 \text{ at STP}$$

or

$$V = 5600 \times (460 + 800)/492 = 14,350 \text{ ft}^3 \text{ at exit of coke bed}$$

Stoichiometry and Computers

The introduction of computer techniques into the realm of stoichiometry has increased the value of stoichiometric calculations for both process engineers and engineers responsible for operating complex chemical plants. Computers make possible parametric studies of the effect of process variables, recycle rates, bypass flows, purge streams, etc, with relatively little effort on the engineer's part. The traditional approach was to regard each new process as a unique problem to be solved in a unique way. With the advent of modern computers, however, it became possible to build generalized programs to take over all the tedious calculations and perform them to a degree of precision impossible with the traditional approach.

Unfortunately, most of the programs of this type are proprietary, but Table 1 lists some of the better-known systems with brief indications of their functions. In general, those indicated as being in the industrial sector are larger and more sophisticated than those indicated as being in the academic sector.

Although the programs listed in Table 1 differ in detail, their internal organization is similar and is represented by the hierarchical structure shown in Figure 5. The hierarchy, based on program function, consists of four different levels which work very

Table 1. Computer-Based Stoichiometry Programs

Program name	Function	Source	Machine
Industrial sector			
CHEOPS	chemical engineering optimization system	Shell Oil Co.	
CHEVRON	generalized heat and material balance	Chevron Research Co.	IBM 7094
CHIPS-2	chemical engineering information processing system	IBM Service Bureau	IBM 360
Kellogg Flexible Flowsheet		The M. W. Kellogg Co.	IBM 7070
NETWORK 67/68		Imperial Chemical Industries Ltd.	
PECOS		Bechtel Corp.	
PEDLAN	process engineering design language	Mobil Oil Co.	
University sector			
CHESS	chemical engineering systems simulator	University of Houston	IBM 360, CDC
FLIPS	flowsheet information processing system	Polytechnic Institute of Brooklyn	IBM 360
GEMCS		McMaster University	GE 625
MAEBE	material and energy balance execution	University of Tennessee	IBM 1620
PACER	process and case evaluation routines	Dartmouth College	GE 265
SLED	simplified language for engineering design	University of Michigan	IBM 360
SPEED–UP	simulation program for economic design of unsteady-state processes	Imperial College (England)	

closely together. The executive, or monitor, program handles all data inputs, performs error checking, calls in convergence and optimization schemes, and calls up programs to perform routine calculations involving individual pieces of equipment, such as heat exchangers and distillation columns. This is also the level at which chemical-reaction calculations are made. Routines for individual unit operations or unit processes will in all probability require the services of other programs designed to handle fundamental thermodynamic calculations. For example, a routine to perform a dewpoint calculation may be required at one point by a distillation-column calculation, at another point by a dryer calculation, and at yet another point by a heat-exchanger calculation. With proper design, a single dewpoint program could serve

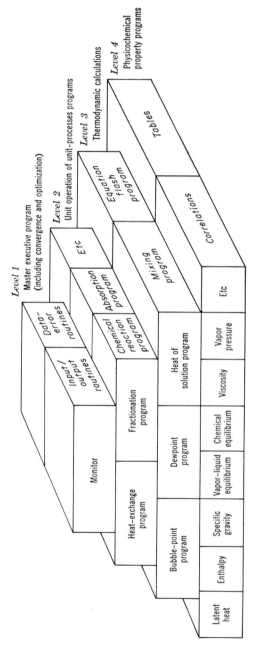

Fig. 5. Hierarchical structure showing internal organization of programs used for stoichiometric calculations.

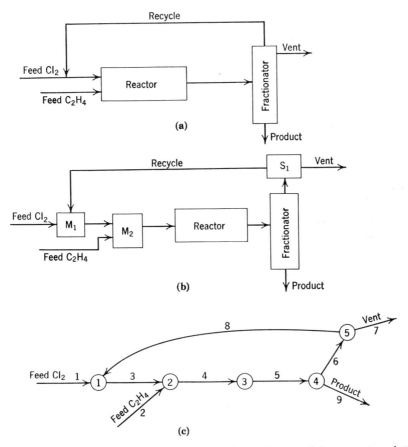

Fig. 6. (**a**) Simple process flowsheet; (**b**) process flowsheet reformatted for computer solution; (**c**) topological graph of reformatted flowsheet.

all of these needs. The thermodynamic programs in their turn have the capability of calling up even more fundamental programs that deal with the physical and chemical properties of the various substances involved in the process. These basic programs may in some instances involve tables of data which are stored in the computer's memory and in other instances involve equations and correlations from which the individual properties can be calculated.

For such a system to function successfully, considerable thought must be given to the structure of the internal data files. The input programs which are indicated as being part of the monitor serve the purpose of sorting the input data, checking them for consistency, completeness, etc, and storing them in the files. The output programs pick the appropriate results from these files and format the results into an easily read report.

Another function of the monitor is to permit concise description of a process by a topological graph in which nodes represent items of equipment (or, in certain instances, equipment functions) and arrows represent process streams. Figure 6 shows a simple process flowsheet and the topological graph which is its equivalent. In reformatting the flowsheet shown in 6a to the form shown in 6b, it has been assumed that the program which handles the function of mixing permits only two input streams to be joined at a time; hence, two mixer functions, M_1 and M_2, are indicated (even though the actual process does not have these as separate pieces of equipment). The degree to which this type of reformatting must be carried out is dependent on the level of sophistication built into each specific computer system.

If the flowsheet contains no recycle streams, the solution can usually be carried out by direct techniques which are both efficient and fast. When recycle streams are involved, however, some form of iterative solution is usually called for. Conceptually, at least, the recycle is broken and treated as a feed stream where it enters the process and as a product stream where it leaves. One can then assign values to the recycle stream where it enters the process and compare these values with those computed for the recycle stream where it leaves the process, making a suitable correction to the assigned values before repeating the computation. This process is repeated until some predetermined agreement between the assigned and computed values is achieved.

The techniques for reassigning values for each succeeding iteration have been reviewed by Naphtali (9). The simplest procedure is to use the calculated recycle from one iteration as the input to the next iteration. While this technique usually guarantees convergence to the correct solution, the procedure is often very slow and therefore costly in computer time. More sophisticated convergence techniques usually achieve convergence much more rapidly, or not at all, depending on the structure of the problem. Available computer programs differ markedly from one another in this area.

Stoichiometry is a means to an end; the end usually involves minimizing a cost, maximizing a product rate, stepping up a time schedule, or, in general, finding that set of process conditions which best satisfies some useful objective function. With computerized stoichiometric calculations, it is usually possible to include in the programming system the details of the objective function and the techniques for optimization. This usually results in solutions which more closely approach the optimum case than when using hand-calculation techniques.

Bibliography

"Stoichiometry" in *ECT* 1st ed., Vol. 13, pp. 45–56, by R. F. Benenati, Polytechnic Institute of Brooklyn.

1. L. Clarke, *Manual for Process Engineering Calculations*, McGraw-Hill Book Co., Inc., New York, 1947.
2. D. M. Himmelblau, *Basic Principles and Calculations in Chemical Engineering*, Prentice-Hall Inc., Englewood Cliffs, N. J., 1962.
3. E. J. Henley and H. Bieber, *Chemical Engineering Calculations*, McGraw-Hill Book Co., Inc., New York, 1959.
4. O. A. Hougen and K. Watson, *Industrial Chemical Calculations*, Vol. 1, John Wiley & Sons, Inc., New York, 1943.
5. O. A. Hougen, K. Watson, and R. Ragatz, *Chemical Process Principles*, John Wiley & Sons, Inc., New York, 1954.
6. K. Kammermeyer and J. Osburn, *Process Calculations*, Prentice-Hall, Inc., Englewood Cliffs, N. J., 1956.
7. C. G. Kuhbride, *Chemical Engineering Fundamentals*, McGraw-Hill Book Co., Inc., New York, 1947.
8. W. K. Lewis and A. H. Radasch, *Industrial Stoichiometry*, McGraw-Hill Book Co., Inc., New York, 1926.
9. L. Naphtali, *Chem. Eng. Progr.* **60**, 70–74 (1964).
10. M. Tyner, *Process Engineering Calculations*, The Ronald Press Co., New York, 1960.

R. F. Benenati
Polytechnic Institute of Brooklyn

STONEWARE. See Ceramics, chemical stoneware.

STORAX. See Resins, natural, Vol. 17, p. 390.

STOUT. See Beer and brewing, Vol. 3, p. 299.

STREPTOMYCIN AND RELATED ANTIBIOTICS

This group of clinically important aminoglycoside antibacterial antibiotics includes the streptomycins, neomycins, paromomycins, kanamycins, gentamicins, hygromycins, and kasugamycin. These compounds have many chemical and antimicrobial features in common. They are all mixtures of water-soluble, basic carbohydrates that are chemically closely related, and most of them form crystalline sulfates and hydrochlorides; they inhibit the growth of Gram-positive and Gram-negative bacteria, and are also effective against mycobacteria; they are biosynthetically formed from carbohydrate components of the fermentation medium.

The streptomycins contain streptidine, a diguanidinyl derivative of the 1,3-diaminocyclitol streptamine, while each of the other members of the group listed in Table 1 contains 2-deoxystreptamine or a related unit. Except for the gentamicins (antibiotics from species of *Micromonospora*) all are derived from various species of *Streptomyces*. For a discussion of other Streptomyces-derived antibiotics see the articles Chloramphenicol; Macrolide antibiotics; Polyene antibiotics; Polypeptide antibiotics; Tetracyclines. See also the general articles Antibiotics; Fermentation; Microorganisms.

None of the aminoglycoside antibiotics is absorbed effectively from the alimentary tract, and neomycin has thus been widely used in the treatment of intestinal infections and in the "chemosterilization" of the bowel prior to surgery of that organ. The aminoglycoside antibiotics are often used in combination with other antibiotics and other chemotherapeutic agents. Some of these combinations are listed in Table 2.

The Streptomycins

Preliminary investigations by Schatz, Waksman, and Bugie (21,22) of the antibacterial properties of the metabolites from two strains of *Streptomyces griseus* showed marked activity in vitro against Gram-positive and Gram-negative bacteria, as well as particular effectiveness against *Mycobacterium tuberculosis* (see Table 3). Further study established the utility of streptomycin in the treatment of human tuberculosis and, in combination with penicillin, in the treatment of enterococcal endocarditis.

Manufacture. Streptomycin is prepared by fermentation processes in a number of countries (in addition to the ones indicated by the list of manufacturers in Table 4) and at one time was one of the most widely used antibiotics. The fermentation processes vary somewhat from one manufacturer to another, but most utilize media containing soybean meal, glucose, and some form of pH control, eg direct addition of alkali or acid to the growing culture, or addition of calcium carbonate. Addition of cornsteep liquor, distillers' solubles, and/or other crude nitrogenous materials has been reported as advantageous under some circumstances. The large cylindrical tanks provided with aeration and agitation devices and the other types of equipment in which the fermentations are carried out are all very similar to those used in the preparation of penicillin and other antibiotics. The antibiotic activity is found partly associated with the *Streptomyces griseus* cells at the end of the fermentation cycle and

Table 1. Relationships Among the Aminoglycoside Antibacterial Antibiotics

Name	Synonyms or closely related substances	Microbial source	Clinical use	Chemical features		Reference
				base	amino sugar	
aminosidine	catenulin; hydroxymycin; paromomycin; chrestomycin; zygomycin A	Streptomyces chrestomyceticus	yes	deoxystreptamine	D-glucosamine, neosamine B	1
bluensomycin	U-12898; glebomycin	S. bluensis var. bluensis	no	bluensidine	N-methyl-L-glucosamine	2
gentamicin A		Micromonospora purpurea; M. echinospora	yes	deoxystreptamine	2-amino-2-deoxy-D-glucose; gentosamine	3
gentamicin C$_1$		M. purpurea	yes	deoxystreptamine	garosamine, purpurosamine A	4
gentamicin C$_2$		M. purpurea	yes	deoxystreptamine	garosamine, purpurosamine B	4
gentamicin C$_{1a}$		M. purpurea	yes	deoxystreptamine	garosamine, purpurosamine C	4
hygromycin	homomycin; totomycin; 1703-18B	S. hygroscopicus	no	neoinosamine-2 (N-methyl-2-deoxy-streptamine)	none	5
hygromycin B	marcomycin; destomycin A	S. hygroscopicus	no[a]	neoinosamine-2	none	6
hygromycins C, D, E, F		S. hygroscopicus	no	neoinosamine-2	none	7
kanamycin A		S. kanamyceticus	yes	deoxystreptamine	3-aminoglucose, 6-aminoglucose	8
kanamycin B		S. kanamyceticus	yes	deoxystreptamine	3-aminoglucose, neosamine C	9

Name	Synonym	Organism		Cyclitol	Amino sugar	No.
kanamycin C		S. kanamyceticus	yes	deoxystreptamine	3-aminoglucose, d-glucosamine	10
kasugamycin		S. kasugaensis	no[a]	amidine	2,4-diamino-2,3,4-6-tetradeoxymannose	11
neomycin B	streptothricin BII	S. fradiae	yes	deoxystreptamine	2,6-diaminodideoxy-d-glucose	12
neomycin C	streptothricin BI	S. fradiae	yes	deoxystreptamine	2,6-diaminodideoxy-d-glucose	13
paromomycin I	aminosidine; hydroxymycin zygomycin A$_1$ catenulin	S. rimosus forma paromomycinus; S. pulveraceus	yes	deoxystreptamine	d-glucosamine; 2,6-diaminodideoxy-l-idose (neosamine B)	14
paromomycin II	zygomycin A$_2$	S. rimosus forma paromomycinus; S. pulveraceus	yes	deoxystreptamine	d-glucosamine; 2,6-diaminodideoxy-d-glucose (neosamine C)	15
streptomycins streptomycin	streptomycin A	S. griseus	yes	streptidine	N-methyl-l-glucosamine	16
mannosido-streptomycin	streptomycin B	S. griseus	no	streptidine	N-methyl-l-glucosamine	17
hydroxystreptomycin	reticulin	S. griseocarneus	no	streptidine	N-methyl-l-glucosamine	18
mannosido-hydroxystreptomycin		S. griseocarneus	no	streptidine	N-methyl-l-glucosamine	19
dihydrostreptomycin		S. humidus[b]	yes	streptidine	N-methyl-l-glucosamine	20

[a] Agricultural use.   [b] Also produced by chemical reduction of streptomycin.

partly "free" in the cellfree liquor.   The portion of the streptomycin that is in the cells can be released by treatment of the cells with dilute acid.

Recovery of streptomycin from the fermented media was first accomplished by adsorption on carbon, followed by elution with acidified methanol; precipitation as the helianthate, picrate, or reineckate; chromatography on alumina; and finally crystal-

Table 2. Some Pharmaceutical Formulations Containing Aminoglycoside Antibacterial Antibiotics

Antibiotic	Trade name	Active ingredients	Manufacturer
kanamycin	Kantrex	kanamycin sulfate	Bristol Laboratories
neomycin	Amcort	amphomycin; neomycin	Texas Pharmacal Co.
	Bacimycin	neomycin; bacitracin	National Drug Co.
	Biomydrin	neomycin; gramicidin; thonzylamine; phenylephrine; thonzonium bromide	Warner-Chilcott Laboratories
	Biotres	neomycin; bacitracin; polymyxin B; benzalkonium chloride	Central Pharmacal Co.
	Biozyme	neomycin palmitate; trypsin; chymotrypsin	Armour Pharmaceutical Co.
	Caldecort	neomycin; calcium undecylenate; hydrocortisone acetate	Strasenburgh Laboratories
	Coly-Mycin S	neomycin; colistin	Warner-Chilcott Laboratories
	Cortisporin	neomycin; bacitracin; polymyxin B; hydrocortisone	Burroughs Wellcome & Co.
	Mycifradin	neomycin sulfate	The Upjohn Co.
	Mycolog	neomycin; gramicidin; nystatin; triamcinolone acetonide	E. R. Squibb & Sons
	Neo-Cortef	neomycin; hydrocortisone acetate	The Upjohn Co.
	Neo-Decadron	neomycin; dexamethasone 21-phosphate	Merck, Sharp & Dohme
	Neo-Medrol	neomycin; methylprednisolone acetate	The Upjohn Co.
	Neo-Nysta-Cort	neomycin; nystatin; hydrocortisone	Dome Laboratories[a]
	Neosporin	neomycin; bacitracin; polymyxin B	Burroughs Wellcome & Co.
	Otobiotic	neomycin; gramicidin; propesin	White Laboratories, Inc.
	Otobione	neomycin; prednisolone acetate; sodium propionate	White Laboratories, Inc.
	Trisocort	neomycin; gramicidin; polymyxin B; hydrocortisone; phenylephrine; hydroxyamphetamine	Smith Kline & French Laboratories
paromomycin	Humatin	paromomycin sulfate	Parke Davis & Co.
streptomycin		streptomycin sulfate	Eli Lilly and Co.; The Upjohn Co.; Pfizer Laboratories;[b] Wyeth Laboratories
	Strep-Distry-cillin A.S.	streptomycin; procaine; penicillin	E. R. Squibb & Sons
	Cer-o-strep	streptomycin; chloroprocaine penicillin	The Upjohn Co.
dihydro-streptomycin	Tribiotic	dihydrostreptomycin; penicillin; bacitracin	Wyeth Laboratories; Pfizer Laboratories;[b]
		dihydrostreptomycin sulfate	E. R. Squibb & Sons

[a] A div. of Miles Laboratories.
[b] A div. of Charles Pfizer & Co., Inc.

Table 3. In Vitro Antibacterial Activity of Selected Aminoglycoside Antibiotics, Minimal Inhibitory Concentration, μg/ml

Bacteria tested	Strepto-mycin	Mannosido-strepto-mycin	Blueno-mycin	Hygro-mycin B	Neo-mycin B	Paro-momycin	Kanamy-cin A	Kanamy-cin B	Genta-micin
Staphylococcus aureus	0.8	5.6	0.8	25	0.1	1.2	1.3	0.6	0.1
Streptococcus pyogenes	11.7	83		3.1	0.5	3	25	12.5	2.4
Bacillus subtilis	0.1	0.4	50	100	0.26	2	0.3	0.1	0.01
Escherichia coli	6	25	3.2	100	0.06	4.7	6.25	0.12	1.5
Salmonella typhi	12	12	6.4		0.03	4.7	6.25	3.1	2.5
Salmonella schottmuelleri	10	14			1.6	8.2			1.3
Salmonella gallinarum	29	13	6.4	100	6.6				
Shigella sonnei	7.4	31		6.2	8.1	9.2	6.25	1.6	3.0
Aerobacter aerogenes	2.7	10.8		12.5	0.06	4.7	0.78	0.39	0.6
Klebsiella pneumoniae	1.8	6.38	6.4	12.5	1.0	0.7	0.78	0.19	0.2
Proteus vulgaris	0.4		3.2	12.5	3.3	23	25	12.5	1.6
Pseudomonas aeroginosa	1		6.4	100	1.6	37.5	2.5	0.3	1.2
Mycobacterium tuberculosis	2	5.5		50	0.1	0.06	0.78	3.1	0.15

lization of a complex formed between streptomycin hydrochloride and calcium chloride. Ion-exchange resins are used as a convenient means of isolation and also for interconversion of the soluble salts; both the hydrochloride and sulfate have been used clinically in addition to the calcium chloride complex. Antibiotic productivity in some fermentations, as reported in the patent literature, has been on the order of 6 g per liter of fermented medium.

Streptomycin, $C_{21}H_{39}N_7O_{12}$, is an optically active tribasic compound possessing an aldehydic carbonyl group. The molecule contains a proportion of oxygen characteristic of a carbohydrate and was shown, eventually, to be composed of three glycosidically linked units: streptidine, streptose, and N-methyl-L-glucosamine (see Fig. 1a). The evidence leading to the elucidation of its structure (shown in Fig. 1b) was obtained by four groups of workers and has been reviewed by Brink and Folkers (23).

Table 4. Some Manufacturers of Aminoglycoside Antibiotics

Aminosidine: Farmitalia

Gentamicin: Schering Corp.

Hygromycin B: Eli Lilly and Co.

Kanamycin: Bristol Laboratories; Pérrel S.p.A.; Rhône-Poulenc; S.I.F.A. (Soc. Industrielle de Fermentation Antibiotique); Takeda Chemical Industries; Banyu Seiyaku; Nikken Chemicals; Meiji Seika

Kasugamycin: Nihon Kagaku; Banyu Seiyaku; Sanraku Shuzo

Neomycin: S. B. Penick & Co.; Chas. Pfizer & Co. Inc.; E. R. Squibb & Sons; The Upjohn Co.; Rhône-Poulenc; S.I.F.A.; Roussel-UCLAF; Boots Pure Drug Co.; Nikon Kagaku; Takeda Chemical Industries

Streptomycin: Merck & Co.; Chas. Pfizer & Co. Inc.; E. R. Squibb & Sons; Dista Products Ltd.; Glaxo Laboratories Ltd.; Farmitalia; Roussel-UCLAF; Leo Pharmaceuticals; Rhône-Poulenc; S.I.F.A.; A/S Novo Industri; Recherche Industrie Thérapie

Biogenetic studies (26) have shown the incorporation of glucose into all the carbons of streptomycin except for the two guanidino carbons, which come from carbon dioxide (by biological fixation), and the N-methylcarbon of N-methyl-L-glucosamine, which comes from L-methionine (27). Evidence has been found for the direct incorporation of D-glucose into N-methyl-L-glucosamine (28) and streptose (29,30). In streptose, the C-3 of glucose is believed to become the C-formyl group. Streptidine is derived from glucose via *myo*-inositol (26,31).

In the presence of dilute aqueous alkali, streptomycin undergoes a degradative transformation to give maltol,

the γ pyrone derived from the streptose portion of the molecule. The maltol can be readily estimated colorimetrically and its formation affords a convenient method for the chemical assay of the antibiotic. The bioassay used in various laboratories is based on inhibition of growth of *Klebsiella pneumoniae*, *Bacillus subtilis*, or *Escherichia coli*.

Dihydrostreptomycin, $C_{21}H_{41}N_7O_{12}$. The aldehyde group of streptomycin is readily reduced by catalytic hydrogenation to the corresponding carbinol, dihydrostreptomycin. The antibacterial spectra of dihydrostreptomycin and streptomycin are similar, but dihydrostreptomycin is more stable to alkali and does not degrade to yield maltol. Dihydrostreptomycin is also produced commercially in Japan by direct fermentation using *Streptomyces humidus*. **Deoxydihydrostreptomycin,** $C_{21}H_{41}N_7O_{11}$, a derivative produced from dihydrostreptomycin by reduction with sodium amalgam, has been used clinically in Japan and is said to be less toxic than the parent compound.

Mannosidostreptomycin, $C_{27}H_{49}N_7O_{17}$ (see Fig. 1a), a minor product in certain *S. griseus* fermentations, was separated from streptomycin by chromatography and

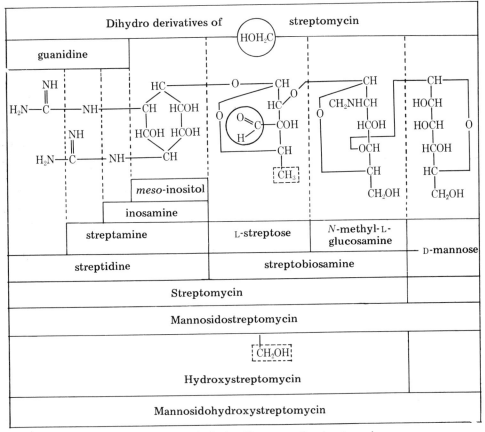

Fig. 1a. Structural relationship among the streptomycins.

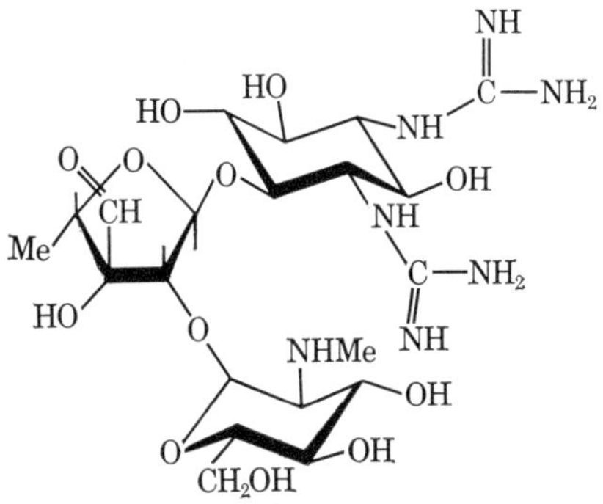

Fig. 1b. Structure of streptomycin.

purified as the crystalline reineckate. Its physical and antibacterial properties resemble those of streptomycin, and it was shown to be a tetrasaccharide formed by the biosynthetic addition of a D-mannose residue to the C-4 atom of the N-methyl-L-glucosamine residue. It is degraded to streptomycin by mannosidostreptomycinase, an enzyme isolated from cultures of S. griseus (24,25).

Hydroxystreptomycin, $C_{21}H_{39}N_7O_{13}$, a third analog of streptomycin, which contains an additional atom of oxygen, was isolated from S. griseocarneus fermentations. It differs from streptomycin (see Fig. 1a) only in having a hydroxymethyl group in place of the methyl group in the streptose portion of the molecule. The biosynthesis of the corresponding *mannosidohydroxystreptomycin* was reported in 1968 (19).

USES

The Mycobacteria are the most important group of organisms which are sensitive to streptomycin, and the antibiotic is indeed used chiefly in the treatment of tuberculosis (caused by *Mycobacterium tuberculosis*). Streptomycin was employed at first in all kinds of Gram-negative microbial infections but, because of the ease with which organisms developed resistance during therapy, many of these applications were abandoned when the "broad spectrum" antibiotics became available. Streptomycin is still used alone or in combination with other antimicrobial agents for the treatment of meningitis and urinary tract infections. Combination formulations with penicillin or the sulfonamide drugs are available for the treatment of certain infections (see also Penicillins; Sulfonamides).

Drug resistance is an especially serious problem in the treatment of tuberculosis since the antibiotic must be given for long periods of time. Experience has shown that 70–80% of all tuberculosis patients harbor resistant organisms after a course of treatment lasting 100–120 days. Other tuberculostatic drugs, including p-aminosalicylic acid, isoniazid, and ethambutol, are now used alternately, or in combination therapy with the antibiotic. Combination therapy not only decreases the chances that resistant forms become established, but also reduces the frequency and intensity of undesirable side reactions since smaller quantities of the antibiotic can be employed (see also Vol. 3, pp. 29–31).

Toxicity. The prolonged use of *streptomycin* (and some of the other aminoglycoside antibiotics) may lead to permanent damage of the eighth cranial nerve. Either or both of the branches of the nerve may be involved. Damage to the auditory branch is associated with permanent impairment of the sense of hearing, vestibular damage with equilibrium problems. These effects were encountered with alarming frequency when streptomycin was first employed as a therapeutic agent until it was found that the recommended dosage was too large. Because of these limitations, streptomycin is regarded in some circles as an adjunct to the nonchemotherapeutic forms of treatment for tuberculosis. Its use is not recommended for benign cases which respond to such treatment.

Dihydrostreptomycin was shown to affect the auditory branch of the eighth nerve, whereas streptomycin appears to be more toxic for the vestibular branch. The toxicity of dihydrostreptomycin is more difficult to guard against than that of streptomycin since the effect is likely to be of an insidious delayed nature. For a number of years a formulation containing equal parts of streptomycin and dihydrostreptomycin was employed on the assumption that it would be less toxic than the corresponding curative dose of either component; this practice has now been abandoned in the clinical treatment of tuberculosis in the United States but is still being used elsewhere.

The Neomycins and Paromomycins

Neomycin, the antibacterial agent group produced by certain strains of *Streptomyces fradiae*, was first described in 1949 by Waksman and Lechevalier (32). This basic, water-soluble complex was soon separated by chromatographic procedures into *neomycins B and C* (neomycin A was shown to be a degradation product of both neomycins B and C) (12,33). Neomycins B and C were found to be isomeric compounds, $C_{23}H_{46}N_6O_{13}$, with structural relationships as shown in Figure 2. Treatment of either with methanolic HCl gave the same amorphous amine hydrochloride, but different accompanying glycosides (34). The common degradation product neamine, also called neomycin A (30), was eventually obtained in crystalline form as the hydrochloride and shown to be neosamine C (2,6-diamino-2,6-dideoxyglucose), linked α-1, 4 to 2-deoxystreptamine (35). Rinehart et al. (36) have obtained evidence from biosynthetic studies on the incorporation of 1-^{14}C glucose, 6-^{14}C glucose, and 1-^{14}C glucosamine that both of the neosamine units and 2-deoxystreptamine are derived from D-glucose according to the scheme in Figure 3.

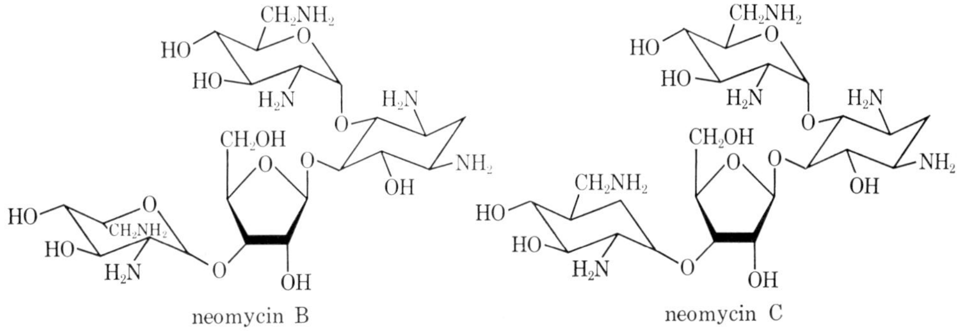

Fig. 2. Structures of the neomycins.

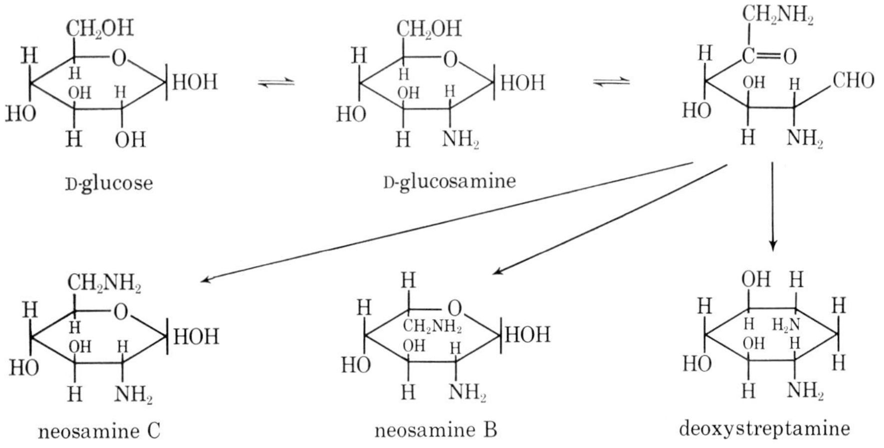

Fig. 3. Rinehart's biosynthesis scheme for neomycin (34).

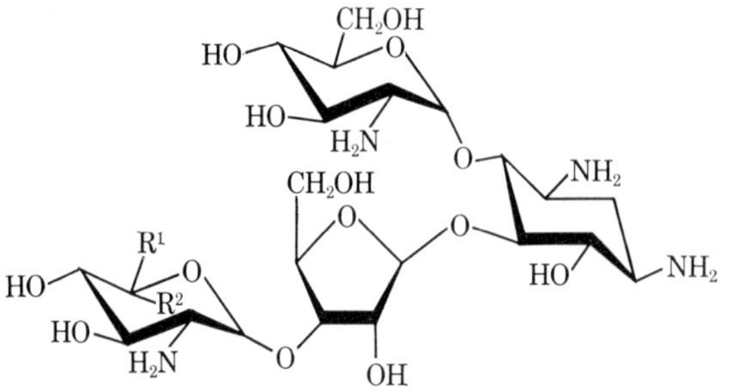

Fig. 4. Structures of the paromomycins.

Neomycins B and C effectively inhibit the growth in vitro of Gram-positive and Gram-negative bacteria as well as Mycobacteria (see Table 3).   They are also effective in vivo in certain laboratory infections.   As in the case of the streptomycins, however, prolonged systemic administration affects the eighth cranial nerve, and the use of neomycins has thus been largely restricted to topical application or to situations where they are not absorbed into the blood stream, eg oral administration to eliminate micro-organisms from intestine and bowel.   Allergic responses have recently been observed in a significant group of patients receiving topical treatment with neomycin-containing ointments, and the widespread use of such formulations may be restricted in the future. The commercial product contains mainly neomycin B with lesser amounts of neomycin C, as determined by quantitative paper chromatographic analyses (37).   A list of some of the commercial producers is included in Table 4 and some of the combinations with other antibiotics are shown in Table 2.

Paromomycins. These antibiotics are antibacterial agents produced by strains of *Streptomyces rimosus* forma *paromycinus* and are chemically related to the neomycins. Methanolysis of paromomycin I (Fig. 4) gives the base paromamine, and a mixture of anomeric glycosides, α- and β-methyl parobiosaminides.   Paromamine is joined to parobiosamine, a disaccharide identical with neobiosamine B (13).   Paromomycin II (Fig. 4) contains paromamine, and neobiosamine C moieties.   Aminosidine, a product from *Streptomyces chrestomyceticus*, appears to be identical with paromomycin 1, but the structure has not been completely elucidated.

The paromomycins, in addition to inhibiting Gram-positive and Gram-negative bacteria, as well as Mycobacteria (see Table 3), are effective against *Endamoeba histolytica* and have been effectively used in controlling amebic dysentery and shigellosis (38,39).

The Kanamycins

The kanamycins are produced by selected strains of *Streptomyces kanamyceticus* (8).   Paper chromatography and ion-exchange chromatography have been used to separate the crude fermentation product into *kanamycin A*, *kanamycin B*, and *kanamycin C* (Fig. 5).   The structures of these compounds have been deduced from chemical degradations (40–42), from x-ray crystallography (43), and by total chemical synthesis. The synthesis of kanamycin A utilized 2-deoxystreptamine as a starting material (44), while that for kanamycin C used paromamine (45).

The kanamycin complex is absorbed rapidly on intramuscular injection but poorly absorbed on oral administration.   It has a degree of ototoxicity but may be employed

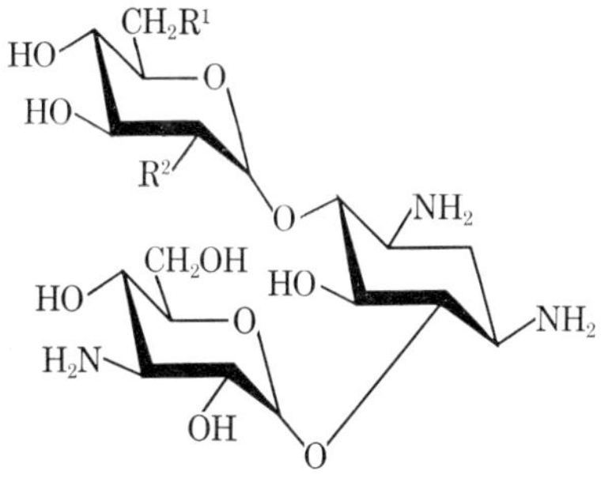

kanamycins A, B, and C
A: $R^1 = NH_2$, $R^2 = OH$
B: $R^1 = NH_2$, $R^2 = NH_2$
C: $R^1 = OH$, $R^2 = NH_2$

Fig. 5. Structures of kanamycins.

with discretion where a lack of cross resistance with other antibiotics is needed. Thus, it is useful against staphylococcal as well as urinary infections that have not responded to other chemotherapeutic agents. The in vitro antibacterial spectrum is summarized in Table 3.

The Gentamicins

The gentamicins, products of two species of *Micromonospora*, include *gentamicins* C_1, C_{1a}, C_2, and A (45a). These chemically related substances can be separated by chromatography (4,46). Chemical degradations (3,47) have shown relationships to the neomycin group, as can be seen from the structure of gentamicin A (Fig. 6) (3). The clinically available material is a mixture of gentamicins C_1, C_{1a}, and C_2.

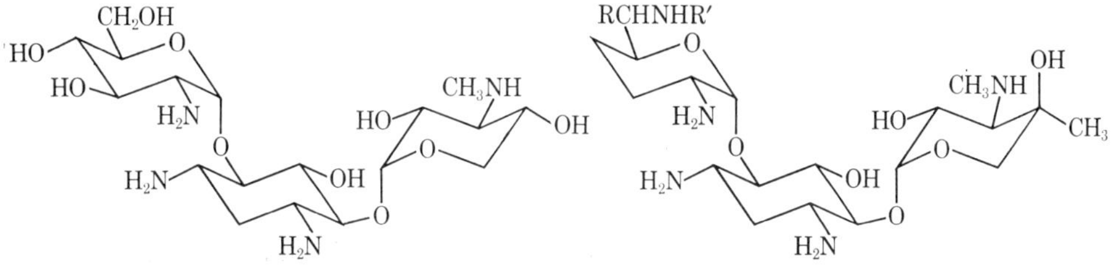

gentamicin A   other gentamicins

gentamicins C_1, C_2, and C_{1a}
C_1: R = CH_3, R′ = CH_3
C_2: R = CH_3, R′ = H
C_{1a}: R = H: R′ = H

Fig. 6. Structures of the gentamicins.

The gentamicins effectively inhibit the growth of Gram-positive and Gram-negative bacteria (see Table 3) and are especially useful in the treatment of infections caused by *Pseudomonas* and *Proteus*. Although ototoxicity has been reported on continued intramuscular administration (48), the antibiotic is effective at such low doses (eg a dose of 10 mg/50 kg patient as compared with a 1-g dose for kanamycin) that there usually is a considerable margin of safety in the treatment of *Pseudomonas* infections.

The Hygromycins

The hygromycins, products of a strain of *Streptomyces hygroscopicus* (5), are a mixture of two types of chemical substances. *Hygromycin A* (Fig. 7) has antibacterial potency against Gram-positive bacteria, mycobacteria, and actinomycetes. It inhibits endameba and also has antiviral action in mice infected with meningopneumonitis. *Hygromycin B*, supposedly closely related to destomycin A (Fig. 8) (6), has structural features in common with the deoxystreptamine antibiotics (49). It has a broad antibacterial spectrum (see Table 3) and inhibits the growth of fungi and a number of helminths. It is used in animal husbandry to control ascaris in swine. *Hygromycins C, D, E,* and *F* are partially characterized compounds containing 3,4-dihydroxy-α-methylcinnamic acid and neoinosamine-2 (*N*-methyl-2-deoxystreptamine) linked via an amide bond. The carbohydrate component of hygromycin C is L-fucose, that of hygromycin F is D-glucose, and 5-keto-6-deoxyarabohexose is found in hygromycins D and E (7).

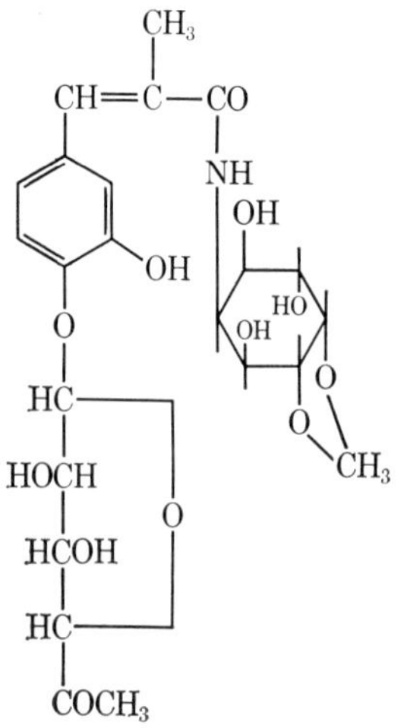

Fig. 7. Structure of hygromycin A.

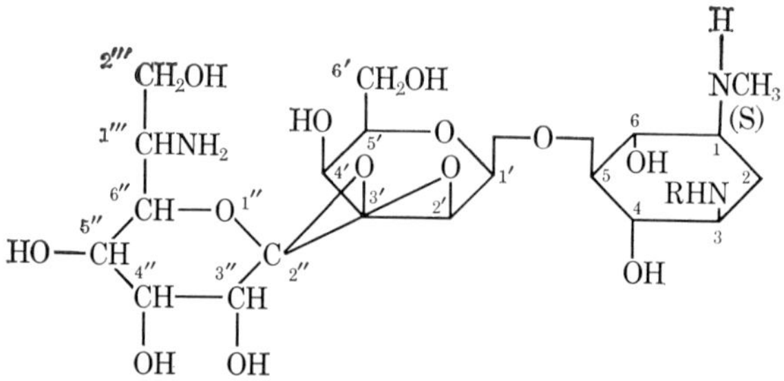

Fig. 8. Structure of destomycin A.

Kasugamycin

Kasugamycin, a metabolite from *Streptomyces kasugaensis,* was discovered in a test system screening for antibiotics effective against the rice blast organism, *Piricularia oryzae* (50). It has weak antibacterial activity. Many common Gram-positive and Gram-negative bacteria were not inhibited at concentrations greater than 100 μg/ml, and those Gram-negative organisms that were inhibited at this concentration were often resistant to 50μg/ml; a few organisms were sensitive to 12.5 μg/ml (51). The antibiotic has extremely low toxicity to mice, rats, rabbits, monkeys, and fish (52). It has been used successfully in Japan to treat *Pseudomonas* infections of the urinary tract (53). Commercial preparations are available in Japan for the control of rice blast.

Hydrolysis of crystalline kasugamycin, $C_{14}H_{25}N_3O_9 \cdot H_2O \cdot HCl$, with barium hydroxide gave methylkasugaminide, oxalic acid, and ammonia (54). The sugar known as kasugamine was identified as 2,3,4,6-tetradeoxy-2,4-diamino-D-mannose (55). The structure (Fig. 9) was deduced from chemical degradations and x-ray crystallography (56,57).

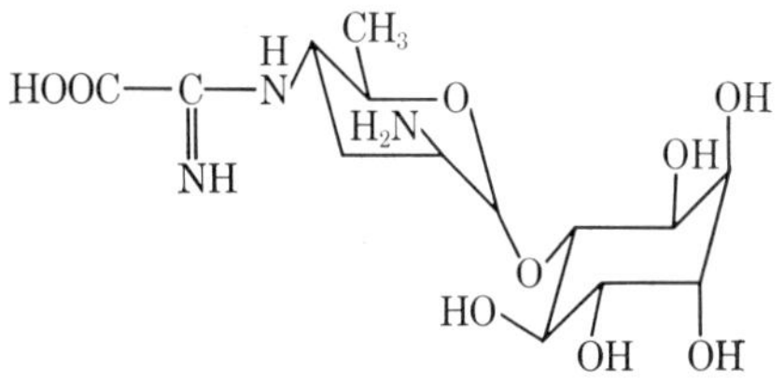

Fig. 9. Structure of kasugamycin.

Other Antibacterial Aminoglycosides. More than twenty-five years have passed since the first observations on streptomycin's antibacterial properties were published, and an intensive search for new antibiotics in the intervening years has resulted in the discovery of a large number of related compounds (see Table 1). Nevertheless, new aminoglycoside antibacterial antibiotics continue to be reported. One of the new groups is *nebramycin*, a mixture of 7 deoxystreptamine related compounds with potential activity against Gram-negative and Gram-positive bacteria (58,59). These and other as yet undiscovered deoxystreptamine antibiotics will undoubtedly find use in the topical control of infections, as well as in the control of systemic problems in special circumstances. The proclivity of causing ototoxicity on prolonged treatment limits the use of these antibiotics in many infections.

The aminoglycoside antibiotics are also finding some laboratory use as a biochemical tool. Notwithstanding the lack of definitive proof, and in spite of some experimental results to the contrary, the bulk of the evidence available (both genetic and biochemical) suggests that the aminoglycoside antibiotics kill bacteria by interfering with the function of ribosomes in protein synthesis. Interference with ribosome function presumably leads to misreading of the code or inhibition of protein synthesis, or both, by one of several mechanisms; such effects may not in themselves be enough to kill the cell, but the combination of these effects with the fact that the aminoglycosides bind irreversibly to the ribosome constitutes a reasonable hypothesis for killing action. The structure–activity relationships among the aminoglycoside group show that small variations in structure have no marked effect on the change in specific activity in inhibiting protein biosynthesis (60).

Bibliography

"Streptomycin Antibiotics (Survey; Streptomycin; Neomycin)" in *ECT* 1st ed., Vol. 13, pp. 57–81 and 90–94, by S. A. Waksman and H. A. Lechevalier, Institute for Microbiology, Rutgers University.

1. F. Arcamone, C. Bertazzoli, M. Ghione, and T. Scotti, *Giorn. Microbiol.* **7,** 251 (1959).
2. B. Bannister and A. D. Argoudelis, *J. Am. Chem. Soc.* **85,** 234 (1963). T. Ohmori, M. Okanishi, and M. Kawaguchi, *J. Antibiotics (Tokyo) Ser. A* **15,** 21 (1962).
3. H. Maehr and C. P. Schaffner, *J. Am. Chem. Soc.* **89,** 6787 (1967).
4. M. J. Weinstein, G. M. Luedemann, E. M. Oden, and G. H. Wagman, *Antimicrobial Agents and Chemotherapy-1963*, American Society for Microbiology, Ann Arbor, Mich., 1964, p. 1.
5. R. L. Mann and D. O. Woolf, *J. Am. Chem. Soc.* **79,** 120 (1957).
6. R. L. Mann and W. W. Bromer, *J. Am. Chem. Soc.* **80,** 2714 (1958). S.-I. Kondo, E. Akita, and M. Koike, *J. Antibiotics (Tokyo) Ser. A* **19,** 139 (1966).
7. J. A. Holowczak, H. Koffler, H. R. Garner, and A. D. Elbein, *J. Biol. Chem.* **241,** 3276 (1966).
8. H. Umezawa, M. Ueda, K. Maeda, K. Yagishita, S. Kondo, Y. Okami, R. Utahara, Y. Osato, K. Nitta, and T. Takeuchi, *J. Antibiotics (Tokyo) Ser. A* **10,** 181 (1957).
9. H. Ogawa, T. Ito, S. Inoue, and S. Kondo, *J. Antibiotics (Tokyo) Ser. A* **11,** 72 (1958).
10. *Ibid.*, 166 (1958).
11. Y. Suhara, K. Maeda, H. Umezawa, and M. Ohno, *Tetrahedron Letters* **1966,** 1239.
12. J. D. Dutcher, N. Hosansky, M. N. Donin, and O. Wintersteiner, *J. Am. Chem. Soc.* **73,** 1384 (1951).
13. K. L. Rinehart, Jr., M. Hichens, A. D. Argoudelis, W. S. Chilton, H. E. Carter, M. P. Georgiadis, C. P. Schaffner, and R. T. Schillings, *J. Am. Chem. Soc.* **84,** 3218 (1962).
14. T. H. Haskell, J. C. French, and Q. R. Bartz, *J. Am. Chem. Soc.* **81,** 3482 (1959).
15. S. Horii, H. Hitomi, and A. Miyake, *J. Antibiotics (Tokyo) Ser. A* **16,** 144 (1963).
16. R. U. Lemieux and M. L. Wolfrom, *Adv. Carbohydrate Chem.* **3,** 337 (1948).
17. J. Fried and H. E. Stavely, *J. Am. Chem. Soc.* **74,** 5461 (1952).
18. F. H. Stodola, O. L. Shotwell, A. M. Borud, R. G. Benedict, and A. C. Riley, Jr., *J. Am. Chem. Soc.* **73,** 2290 (1951).
19. F. Arcamone, G. Cassinelli, G. d'Amico, and P. Orezzi, *Experientia* **24,** 441 (1968).
20. F. Kavanagh, E. Grinnan, E. Allanson, and D. Tunin, *Appl. Microbiol.* **8,** 160 (1960).
21. A. Schatz, S. A. Waksman, and E. Bugie, *Proc. Soc. Exptl. Biol. Med.* **55,** 66 (1944).
22. S. A. Waksman, ed., *Streptomycin*, Williams and Wilkins Co., Baltimore, Md., 1949.
23. N. G. Brink and K. Folkers in S. A. Waksman, ed., *Streptomycin*, Williams and Wilkins Co., Baltimore, Md., 1949, p. 55 ff.
24. D. Perlman and A. F. Langlykke, *J. Am. Chem. Soc.* **70,** 3968 (1948).
25. D. J. D. Hockenhull, M. Herbert, A. D. Walker, G. D. Wilkin, and F. G. Winder, *Biochem. J.* **56,** 73 (1954).
26. J. Mendicino and J. M. Picken, in J. F. Snell, ed., *Biosynthesis of Antibiotics* Vol. 1, Academic Press, Inc., New York, 1966, p. 121.
27. D. J. Candy, M. L. Blumson, and J. Baddiley, *Biochem. J.* **91,** 31 (1964).
28. J. Bruton, W. H. Horner, and G. A. Russ, *J. Biol. Chem.* **242,** 813 (1967).
29. D. J. Candy and J. Baddiley, *Biochem. J.* **96,** 526 (1965).
30. J. Bruton and W. H. Horner, *J. Biol. Chem.* **241,** 3142 (1966).
31. R. M. Bruce, H. S. Ragheb, and H. Weiner, *Biochim. Biophys. Acta* **158,** 499 (1968).
32. S. A. Waksman and H. Lechevalier, *Science* **109,** 305 (1949).
33. J. D. Dutcher and M. N. Donin, *J. Am. Chem. Soc.* **74,** 4320 (1952).
34. K. L. Rinehart, Jr., *The Neomycins and Related Antibiotics*, John Wiley & Sons, Inc., New York, 1964.
35. H. E. Carter, J. R. Dyer, P. D. Shaw, K. L. Rinehart, Jr., and M. Hichens, *J. Am. Chem. Soc.* **83,** 3723 (1961).
36. K. L. Rinehart, Jr., M. Hichens, J. L. Foght, and W. S. Chilton, *Antimicrobial Agents and Chemotherapy-1962*, 1963, p. 193.
37. S. C. Pan and J. D. Dutcher, *Anal. Chem.* **28,** 836 (1956).
38. S. Bell and A. W. Woodruff, *Am. J. Trop. Med. Hyg.* **9,** 155 (1960).
39. K. O. Courtney, P. E. Thompson, R. Hodgkinson, and J. R. Fitzsimmons, *Antibiot. Ann.* **1959–1960,** p. 304.

40. M. J. Cron, D. L. Evans, F. M. Palermiti, D. F. Whitehead, I. R. Hooper, P. Chu, and R. U. Lemieux, *J. Am. Chem. Soc.* **80**, 4741 (1958).

41. K. Maeda, M. Murase, H. Mawatari, and H. Umezawa, *J. Antibiotics (Tokyo) Ser. A* **11**, 163 (1958).

42. S. Tatsuoka, S. Horii, K. L. Rinehart, Jr., and T. Nakabayashi, *J. Antibiotics (Tokyo) Ser. A* **17**, 88 (1964).

43. G. Koyama, Y. Iitaka, K. Maeda, and H. Umezawa, *Tetrahedron Letters* **1968**, 1875.

44. M. Nakajima, A. Hasegawa, N. Kurihara, H. Shobata, T. Ueno, and D. Nishimura, *Tetrahedron Letters* **1968**, 623.

45. S. Umezawa, S. Koto, K. Tatsuat, and T. Tsumura, *J. Antibiotics (Tokyo) Ser. A* **21**, 162 (1968).

45a. K. L. Rinehart, Jr., *Paper Intern. Symp. Gentamycin, Univ. Ill., Coll. Med., Chicago, Oct., 1968*.

46. H. Maehr and C. P. Schaffner, *J. Chromatog.* **30**, 572 (1967).

47. D. J. Cooper and M. K. Yudis, *Chem. Commun.* **1967**, 821.

48. R. L. Jao and G. G. Jackson, *J. Am. Med. Assoc.* **189**, 817 (1964).

49. P. E. Wiley, M. V. Sigal and O. Weaver, *J. Org. Chem.* **27**, 2793 (1962).

50. H. Umezawa, Y. Okami, T. Hashimoto, Y. Suhara, M. Hamada, and T. Takeuchi, *J. Antibiotics (Tokyo) Ser. A* **18**, 101 (1965).

51. M. Hamada, T. Hashimoto, T. Takahashi, S. Yokoyama, M. Miyake, T. Takeuchi, Y. Okami, and H. Umezawa, *J. Antibiotics (Tokyo) Ser. A* **18** 104 (1965).

52. T. Takeuchi, M. Ishizuka, H. Takayama, K. Kureha, M. Hamada, and H. Umezawa, *J. Antibiotics (Tokyo) Ser. A* **18**, 107 (1965).

53. T. Ichikawa, *Antimicrobial Agents and Chemotherapy-1965*, 1966, p. 758.

54. Y. Suhara, K. Maeda, H. Umezawa, and M. Ohno, *J. Antibiotics (Tokyo) Ser. A* **18**, 187 (1965).

55. *Ibid.*, 184 (1965).

56. H. Umezawa, M. Hamada, Y. Suhara, T. Hashimoto, T. Ikekawa, N. Tanaka, K. Maeda, Y. Okami, and T. Takeuchi, *Antimicrobial Agents and Chemotherapy-1965*, 1966, p. 753.

57. T. Ikekawa, H. Umezawa, and Y. Iitaka, *J. Antibiotics (Tokyo) Ser. A* **19**, 49 (1966).

58. W. M. Stark, M. M. Hoehn, and N. G. Knox, *Antimicrobial Agents and Chemotherapy-1967*, 1968, p. 314.

59. R. Q. Thompson and E. A. Presti, *Antimicrobial Agents and Chemotherapy-1967*, 1968, p. 332.

60. J. Davies, *Antimicrobial Agents and Chemotherapy-1967*, 1968, p. 297.

General References

S. A. Waksman, ed., *Streptomycin*, Williams and Wilkins Co., Baltimore, Md., 1949.

S. A. Waksman, ed., *Neomycin, Its Nature and Practical Application*, Williams and Wilkins Co., Baltimore, Md., 1958.

Kenneth L. Rinehart, Jr., *The Neomycins and Related Antibiotics*, John Wiley & Sons, Inc., New York, 1964.

Kenji Maeda, *Streptomyces Products Inhibiting Mycobacteria*, John Wiley & Sons, Inc., New York, 1965.

T. Korzybski, Z. Kowszyk-Gindifer, and W. Kurylowicz, *Antibiotics*, PWN-Polish Scientific Publisher and Pergamon Press, Inc., New York, 1967.

Patents

The following are some patents on processes for producing streptomycin and other aminoglycoside antibiotics:

Aminosidine. Brit. Pat. 880,035 (1961), Società Farmaceutici Italia.

Gentamicin. U.S. Pat. 3,091,572 (1963), G. M. Luedeman and M. J. Weinstein (to Schering Corp.).

Hygromycin. U.S. Pat. 3,018,220 (1962), J. M. McGuire and R. L. Mann (to Eli Lilly and Co.).

Kanamycin. U.S. Pat. 2,931,798 (1960), H. Umezawa, K. Maeda, and M. Ueda.

Neomycin. U.S. Pat. 2,799,620 (1957), S. A. Waksman and H. A. Lechevalier (to Rutgers Research and Educational Foundation).

Paromomycin. U.S. Pat. 2,916,485 (1959), R. P. Frohardt, T. H. Haskell, J. Ehrlich, and M. P.

Knudsen (to Parke, Davis & Co.); U.S. Pat. 2,895,876 (1959), J. W. Davisson and A. Finlay (to Chas. Pfizer & Co., Inc.).

Streptomycin. U.S. Pat. 2,449,866 (1948), S. A. Waksman and A. Schatz (to Rutgers Research and Endowment Foundation).

Dihydrostreptomycin. U.S. Pat. 2,498,574 (1950), R. L. Peck (to Merck & Co.); U.S. Pat. 2,717,236 (1955), M. A. Dolliver and S. Semenoff (to E. R. Squibb & Sons); U.S. Pat. 2,663,685 (1953), G. B. Levy (to Schenley Industries, Inc.); U.S. Pat. 2,931,756 (1959), K. Nakazawa, M. Shibata, K. Tanabe, and H. Yamamoto (to Takeda Pharmaceutical Industries, Ltd.).

Hydroxystreptomycin. U.S. Pat. 2,617,755 (1952), R. G. Benedict and F. H. Stodola (to U. S. Dept. of Agriculture).

D. Perlman
University of Wisconsin

STRONTIUM

Strontium is in group IIA between calcium and barium, in the group generally known as the alkaline earth metals. Its abundance (1) in igneous rocks is 375 ppm (2), but some deposits exist of the carbonate, strontianite, and the sulfate, celestine. The name derives from the lead mines of Strontian, Argyleshire, Scotland (1), where T. C. Hope in 1792 noted a peculiar species of earth differing from the heavy spar (barytes). The identification as a compound of a new metal soon followed, to which the name strontium was eventually assigned.

The metal was first produced by Sir Humphry Davy in 1808, but only in the form of a mercury amalgam. R. Bunsen some fifty years later was able to produce a few grams by electrolysis of the chloride.

Properties

Strontium is a fairly hard white metal with physical properties as shown in Table 1. Its chemical properties are intermediate between those of calcium and barium,

Table 1. Physical Properties of Strontium (1–3)

melting point, °C		770–791		
boiling point, °C		1350–1387		
density		2.6		
crystal system		face-centered cubic		
lattice constant		6.05		
latent heat of fusion, kcal/g atom		2		
latent heat of vaporization, kcal/g atom		42.3		
electrical resistivity, $\mu\Omega$/cm		22.76		
stable isotopes[a]	*84*	*86*	*87*	*88*
abundance, %	0.56	9.86	7.02	82.56

[a] Strontium-90 is a radioisotope which is a product of nuclear fission. Its half-life is 28 yr; it releases no γ radiation, but emits β radiation of 0.54 MeV. It has caused concern because it may be a product of the "fall-out" of nuclear explosions, and when ingested by animals it may accumulate in the bone tissues.

exhibiting greater reactivity than calcium but less than barium. It reacts with H_2 to form SrH_2 at reasonable speed at 300–400°C. It reacts with H_2O, O_2, N_2, S, and halogens to produce compounds corresponding to its valence of 2. At elevated temperatures, it reacts with CO_2 according to the reaction (2)

$$5 \text{ Sr} + 2 \text{ CO}_2 \rightarrow \text{SrC}_2 + 4 \text{ SrO}$$

In common with calcium, but not with magnesium, strontium metal reacts with carbon at elevated temperatures to produce the compound SrC_2, that reacts with water, giving acetylene.

Metallic strontium dissolves in liquid ammonia to give colored solutions. Both the metal and its salts impart a brilliant red color to flames.

Production

Following the work of Bunsen, many attempts have been made to produce the metal by electrolysis of appropriate fused salts. While some success has been achieved, the ready solubility of the metal in the electrolyte makes this a poor method of recovery. The most effective method is that first used by Guntz and Galliot (4). The oxide is heated in the presence of aluminum, and a relatively low pressure of strontium gas is produced according to the reaction

$$x \text{ SrO(s)} + 2 \text{ Al(l)} \rightarrow \text{Sr(g)} + y \text{ SrO}_2 . \text{Al}_2\text{O}_3\text{(s)}$$

If the operation is conducted in vacuo, the gaseous metal may be condensed in a cooler part of the apparatus, and the removal of Sr(g) displaces the reaction to the right. This operation is carried out commercially in apparatus similar to that used for the production of magnesium (5).

Uses

No commercial uses for strontium metal are known. There is a small demand for the metal for experimental purposes. A number of alloy systems involving strontium have been investigated. Hansen (6) lists equilibrium diagrams for strontium with Ag, Al, Cd, Hg, Mg, and Pb. Intermetallic compounds are listed and occasionally other information is given for the systems Sr–B, Sr–Bi, Sr–C, Sr–Ca, Sr–Te, Sr–Th, and Sr–Zn.

The metal is produced by Dominion Magnesium Limited, Toronto, Ontario, Canada. A price of $10.80/lb is quoted for small lots.

Bibliography

"Strontium" treated in *ECT* 1st ed. under "Alkaline Earth Metals," Vol. 1, p. 463, by C. L. Mantell, Consulting Chemical Engineer.

1. C. Smithells, *Metals Reference Book*, 4th ed., Butterworth & Co., Ltd., London, 1967.
2. *Gmelins Handbuch der anorganischen Chemie*, System Number 29, Verlag Chemie, Weinheim/ Bergstr., Germany, 1964.
3. *Metals Handbook*, 8th ed., American Society for Metals, Metals Park, Ohio, 1964.
4. M. Guntz and M. Galliot, *Compt. Rend.* **151**, 813 (1910).
5. L. M. Pidgeon and W. A. Alexander, *Trans. AIME* **159**, 315 (1944).
6. M. Hansen, *Constitution of Binary Alloys*, McGraw-Hill Book Co., Inc., New York, 1958.

L. M. Pidgeon
University of Toronto

STRONTIUM COMPOUNDS

Strontium forms compounds in which its valence is $+2$, its compounds resembling those of the other alkaline earth metals. See also Barium compounds; Calcium compounds. As a rule, strontium salts are less soluble than those of barium. Strontium salts give a brilliant crimson flame color that is used to detect strontium, and in pyrotechnics (qv). Strontium is determined by weighing as the sulfate after separation from barium (see Vol. 3, p. 81).

Strontium compounds were long confused with those of barium. In 1790 Crawford stated that a mineral believed to be a barium mineral was actually a "new species of earth." This was confirmed in 1792 by Hope. The new mineral, strontianite, $SrCO_3$, was so named because it was found in a lead mine at Strontian, Argyleshire, Scotland.

Although many strontium compounds are known, only a few have any industrial importance and they are less important than compounds of the other alkaline earth metals. The principal applications include pyrotechnics, lubricants, and driers, and there are minor applications in medicine. The most important industrial compounds are the peroxide, the hydroxide, the oxide, and the sulfate.

Occurrence and Production

The chief strontium minerals are celestite, $SrSO_4$, and strontianite, $SrCO_3$. Celestite is used in a modern U.S. process for the production of strontium compounds. Two grades of ore are used: a high-grade ore containing 92% $SrSO_4$, and a beneficiated impure celestite which contains 84–92% $SrSO_4$. The impure ore is first treated with 10% hydrochloric acid and then with water, thus removing calcium carbonate and a large part of the calcium sulfate, these being the chief impurities. Either the beneficiated ore or the high-grade 92% celestite ore is slowly added to a solution of soda ash at 150–160°F. The solution is contained in wooden reactor tanks equipped with rubber-covered agitators. The solution is agitated for 6 hr, at the end of which time 86% of the celestite has been converted to strontium carbonate. Part of the supernatant solution is decanted off, more soda ash solution is added, and the solution is agitated for another 10 hr and then allowed to settle for 4 hr. The clear supernatant solution is decanted off and the precipitate of strontium carbonate is washed by decantation three times with hot water. Hydrochloric acid is then added to dissolve the carbonate, and the strontium chloride solution is decanted to a second tank. Here strontium carbonate is reprecipitated by the addition of more soda ash and pumped through a Bird filter. The solids, strontium carbonate plus entrained sodium chloride, are made into a slurry with wash water and washed through a system of six Dorr continuous settling and washing tanks. The strontium carbonate from the last tank is dewatered by means of a Bird continuous steel centrifuge, dried in a gas-fired rotary drier, ground in a Micronizer or similar pulverizer, and packaged. Strontium carbonate so prepared (or sometimes naturally occurring strontianite) is the raw material for other strontium compounds.

Celestite can also be reduced, by heating with coke, to the sulfide, from which the hydroxide (see p. 52) can be obtained (compare the technology of barium compounds, Vol. 3, p. 81).

COLLEGE OF THE SEQUOIAS
LIBRARY

STRONTIUM ACETATE. Strontium acetate, $Sr(C_2H_3O_2)_2$, is a white crystalline salt, soluble in water, 36.4 g dissolving in 100 ml of water at 97°C. It crystallizes as the tetrahydrate, or as the pentahydrate below 9.5°C. When heated, strontium acetate decomposes. The specific gravity of the anhydrous product is 2.099.

STRONTIUM CARBONATE. Strontium carbonate, $SrCO_3$, occurs naturally as the mineral strontianite in orthorhombic crystals, isomorphous with aragonite, $CaCO_3$, and witherite, $BaCO_3$. The chief locality for its occurrence in the U.S. is at Schoharie, Schoharie County, New York. It is found in commercially important deposits in Westphalia, Germany, and in smaller amounts at many other locations. It is associated with barite, $BaSO_4$, celestite, $SrSO_4$, and calcite, $CaCO_3$, most commonly in veins in marl or limestone. Strontianite has the following properties: sp gr approximately 3.7; Mohs hardness 3.5; color, colorless to gray or greenish, yellowish, or reddish.

Strontium carbonate is a white crystalline solid, having a rhombic structure below 926°C, and a hexagonal structure above this temperature. It has a specific gravity of 3.70, a melting point (at 60 atm) of 1497°C, and decomposes to the oxide on heating. The "temperature of decomposition" (temperature at which the dissociation pressure of carbon dioxide is one atmosphere) is reported as 1289°C (1), but published figures vary.

Strontium carbonate is insoluble in water but readily reacts with acids and, like calcium carbonate, will react with and therefore dissolve in carbonic acid. It is also soluble in solutions of ammonium salts. It is sold as a fine white powder of varying grades of purity for the manufacture of other strontium salts. Its manufacture is described above.

Recent tests of color television tubes indicate moderate radiation is getting through the barium glass of the TV tube. Work has indicated that strontium glass will stop this radiation more efficiently at certain wavelengths. Investigation by the glass manufacturers as to the use of strontium carbonate as a replacement for barium carbonate is now under way, and some changes may be in evidence within the next year.

STRONTIUM FORMATE. Strontium formate, $Sr(CHO_2)_2$, mp 71.9°C, forms rhombic crystals. It forms a dihydrate which converts to the anhydrous salt at 65°C. It is soluble in water, insoluble in alcohol and ether.

STRONTIUM HALIDES. **Strontium fluoride,** SrF_2, forms cubic, colorless crystals, or a white powder, sp gr 4.24, mp 1190°C. It is insoluble in water, but soluble in hot hydrochloric acid. It is isomorphous with fluorite, CaF_2.

Strontium chloride, $SrCl_2$, is similar to calcium chloride, but less soluble in water (100.8 g in 100 ml water at 100°C). It forms mono-, di-, and hexahydrates. The anhydrous salt, mp 873°C, forms cubic colorless crystals, sp gr 3.052. It can be prepared by dissolving the carbonate in hydrochloric acid, concentrating the solution, and crystallizing the salt.

Strontium bromide, $SrBr_2$, forms white hygroscopic needlelike crystals, very soluble in water (222.5 g in 100 ml water at 100°C) and soluble in alcohol. A hexahydrate is stable up to 88.6°C, where a dihydrate is formed. The anhydrous salt melts at 643°C and has sp gr 4.216_4^{24}. It can be prepared by treating the carbonate

COLLEGE OF THE SEQUOIAS
LIBRARY

with hydrobromic acid or bromine in the presence of a reducing agent. Strontium bromide has occasionally been employed as a sedative instead of sodium or potassium bromides.

Strontium iodide, SrI_2, forms colorless crystals which decompose in moist air. It is very soluble in water (383 g in 100 ml water at 100°C). It forms hexa-, di-, and monohydrates. The anhydrous salt has a specific gravity of 4.549^{25}, mp 402°C. Strontium iodide can be prepared by treating the carbonate with hydriodic acid. It has been used to some extent in medicine as an alternative to other iodides.

STRONTIUM NITRATE. Strontium nitrate, $Sr(NO_3)_2$, exists in the anhydrous form as colorless, cubic crystals, mp reported to be 570–645°C and sp gr 2.986. A white monoclinic tetrahydrate, $Sr(NO_3)_2.4H_2O$, also exists, having a density of 2.2. The anhydrous salt is soluble in water as shown in Table 1. The anhydrous salt is the main one produced commercially. Methods reported for making strontium nitrate are by (*1*) treating strontianite with nitric acid, (*2*) digesting celestite with soda ash followed by treatment with nitric acid, and (*3*) heating celestite with coal in a rotary kiln to form a soluble sulfide, followed by treatment with nitric acid. Strontium nitrate solutions so formed are purified and a commercial anhydrous strontium nitrate crystal of high purity is prepared by crystallization.

Table 1.   Solubility of Anhydrous Strontium Nitrate in Water

Temp, °C	$Sr(NO_3)_2$, g/100 g water	Temp, °C	$Sr(NO_3)_2$, g/100 g water
0	39.5	60	94.0
10	59.0	80	97.2
20	68.0	100	101
40	91.3		

The main use for strontium nitrate is for producing red colors in pyrotechnics (qv) and railroad fuses. An allied use is in tracer bullet compositions. In these uses a high degree of purity is required, for the contamination of $Sr(NO_3)_2$ with sodium salts, as well as calcium salts, tends to lighten the scarlet red flame of the fuses to a reddish yellow flame. Since most of the $Sr(NO_3)_2$ has sodium salts as contaminants, due to the method of manufacture, purification is necessary.

STRONTIUM OXIDE AND HYDROXIDE. **Strontium oxide,** SrO, is a white powder, similar to calcium and barium oxides, having like them the sodium chloride lattice and a high melting point (2430°C). It is prepared from the carbonate by heating with carbon in an electric furnace similarly to the preparation of barium oxide (see Vol. 3, p. 89). Its sp gr is 4.7. It readily combines with water to form strontium hydroxide. It is used as a source of strontium compounds, especially strontium peroxide.

Strontium hydroxide, $Sr(OH)_2$, is a white, deliquescent solid, sp gr 3.62 and mp 375°C. Its solubility in water is greater than that of calcium hydroxide and less than that of barium hydroxide. The solubility at 0°C is 0.41 and at 100°C is 21.83 g per 100 g of water (2–4). Owing to the large variation of solubility with temperature, it is relatively simple to separate strontium hydroxide from barium or calcium hydroxides by crystallizing from aqueous solutions. Unlike barium hydroxide, the octahydrate, a white tetragonal crystal, sp gr 1.90, reverts to the monohydrate on standing in dry air, or is dehydrated to the anhydrous at 100°C. The crystals, as with all strong alkalis, absorb CO_2 from the air to form the carbonate.

The hydroxide forms insoluble soaps with organic acids and forms insoluble complexes with sucrose and glycerol.

Commercially, only small amounts of strontium hydroxide are produced, approx 100 ton per yr. There is some research activity in its use in the preparation of oil additives and diesel-oil additives, replacing the barium compounds. Its high price, and the relatively low availability of strontium ores, has inhibited this work (5–7).

Strontium hydroxide is produced by two methods: (1) The reduction of celestite to strontium sulfide, which is subsequently treated with caustic soda and the hydroxide crystallized out on cooling. (2) Strontium sulfate is converted to strontium carbonate which is then converted to the chloride with hydrochloric acid. Addition of caustic soda to the chloride solution, and cooling, produces the hydroxide crystal (1).

The commercial grade contains 1.5–5.0% barium hydroxide, which originates in the celestite and a small amount of strontium carbonate which results from contact with atmospheric carbon dioxide. It is shipped in small steel drums or fiber drums containing a moisture barrier.

The strontium greases produced from strontium hydroxide and various soap stocks are useful because of their special properties (see Vol. 12, p. 582). They are structurally stable and resistant to oxidation and to breakdown over a wide temperature range, resistant to disintegration by water at ordinary or elevated temperature, and resistant to the leaching action of hydrocarbons. They give superior protection against moisture or salt corrosion, and the grease structure shows good stability when subjected to mechanical working (5,6).

Strontium hydroxide will form metallic soaps with organic acids. Long-chain hydrocarbon by-products (mahogany oils) are sulfonated and reacted with strontium hydroxide to form strontium organic compounds. By-products of the coal tar industry are also treated with strontium hydroxide to form stabilizers for many vinyl plastics. These compounds are mixtures of various organic acids, and in many cases the use of stabilizers is an art rather than a science.

Strontium hydroxide has been widely used in Europe for beet-sugar refining. It forms an insoluble disaccharate which may be separated and refined. Addition of carbon dioxide regenerates the sucrose together with insoluble strontium carbonate. See Sugar manufacture.

Strontium hydroxide has been used to improve the drying characteristics of oils and paints.

STRONTIUM PEROXIDE, SrO_2. See Vol. 14, p. 750.

STRONTIUM PHOSPHATE, $SrHPO_4$. See Vol. 15, p. 247.

STRONTIUM SALICYLATE. See Vol. 17, p. 729.

STRONTIUM SULFATE. Strontium sulfate, $SrSO_4$, forms colorless or white rhombic crystals, sp gr 3.96. It decomposes when heated to 1580°C. It is more soluble in water than barium sulfate and less soluble than calcium sulfate ($SrSO_4$, 0.0113 g per

100 ml water at 0°C; BaSO$_4$, 0.000336 g per 100 ml water at 30°C; CaSO$_4$, 0.209 g per 100 ml water at 30°C). Strontium sulfate can be prepared from celestite by purification, as described above. Its chief use is as a source of strontium compounds.

Strontium sulfate occurs as celestite chiefly in sedimentary rocks where it is associated with other minerals, including sulfur, strontianite, calcite, and gypsum. In the U.S., large lake-bed deposits and massive beds are found in California. Other locations in the U.S. include Maricopa County, Arizona, and western New York. It occurs widely in smaller deposits. Its properties include sp gr, approx 3.97; Mohs hardness 3–3.5; color, colorless to pale blue.

STRONTIUM SULFIDES. In addition to strontium sulfide, SrS, a tetrasulfide (polysulfide), SrS$_4$. 6H$_2$O, and the hydrosulfide, Sr(HS)$_2$, are known.

Strontium sulfide, SrS, occurs as colorless or light-gray cubic crystals or powder, with a sodium chloride lattice, mp above 2000°C, sp gr 3.70. It is practically insoluble in water, but is soluble in acids with decomposition. If heated with water it decomposes to form the hydrosulfide and the hydroxide. It can be prepared by reduction of the sulfate with carbon. It has some use as a depilatory and in luminous paints.

Strontium hydrosulfide, Sr(SH)$_2$, is prepared as described under strontium sulfide. It is soluble in cold water, and decomposes on heating or on boiling with water.

Strontium tetrasulfide, SrS$_4$, forms the hydrate SrS$_4$. 6H$_2$O which occurs as reddish crystals, mp 25°C, soluble in water and alcohol. The tetrasulfide is prepared by heating the monosulfide with sulfur, leaching, and evaporating the resulting solution in vacuo in the cold.

STRONTIUM SULFITE. Strontium sulfite, SrSO$_3$, forms colorless crystals, practically insoluble in water but soluble in alcohol and very soluble in sulfurous acid. It decomposes on heating to give sulfur dioxide.

Bibliography

"Strontium Compounds" in *ECT* 1st ed., Vol. 13, pp. 113–118, by Louis Preisman, Barium Reduction Corporation, and Desmond M. C. Reilly, Food Machinery and Chemical Corporation.

1. N. V. Sidgwick, *Chemical Elements and Their Compounds*, Vol. 1, Oxford University Press, Inc., New York, 1950.
2. J. W. Mellor, *A Comprehensive Treatise on Inorganic and Theoretical Chemistry*, Vol. III, John Wiley & Sons, Inc., New York, 1922, p. 678.
3. J. F. Thorpe and M. A. Whiteley, *Thorpe's Dictionary of Applied Chemistry, Fourth Edition*, Vol. II, John Wiley & Sons, Inc., New York, 1938.
4. G. Brauer, *Handbook of Preparative Inorganic Chemistry*, 2nd ed., Vol. 1, Academic Press, Inc., New York, 1963.
5. *Chem. Met. Eng.* **53** (1), 152–155 (1946).
6. "Strontium, A Material Summary," *U.S. Bur. Mines Inf. Circ. 7933* (1959).
7. *Gmelins Handbuch der anorganischen Chemie*, 8th ed., Deutsche Chemische Gesellschaft, Verlag Chemie, Berlin, 1960.

Louis Preisman
Pittsburgh Plate Glass Co.

STYRAX. See Resins, natural, Vol. 17, p. 390.

STYRAX OILS. See Oils, essential.

STYRENE

Styrene (phenylethylene, vinylbenzene, styrol, cinnamene), $C_6H_5CH\!=\!CH_2$, is the common name for the simplest and by far the most important member of a series of unsaturated aromatic monomers. Styrene is used extensively for the manufacture of plastics, including polystyrene, rubber-modified impact polystyrene, acrylonitrile–butadiene–styrene terpolymer (ABS), styrene acrylonitrile copolymer (SAN), and for the production of SBR-type synthetic rubber (styrene–butadiene). See also Styrene polymers.

Commercial manufacture of the monomer began on a small scale shortly before World War II. Since that time the production of the monomer has shown enormous growth and is expected to reach 5 billion lb annually by 1970. Several factors have contributed to this success. (*1*) Styrene (bp, 145°C) is a liquid which can be handled easily and safely; (*2*) the activation of the vinyl group by the benzene ring makes styrene easy to polymerize and copolymerize under a variety of conditions; (*3*) polystyrene is one of the least expensive thermoplastics on a cost-per-in.³ basis.

Styrene was first isolated in the nineteenth century from the distillation of storax (see Vol. 17, p. 390), a natural balsam. Although styrene was known to polymerize, no commercial applications were attempted for many years because the polymers were brittle and cracked easily. The simultaneous development of a process for the manufacture of styrene by the dehydrogenation of ethylbenzene by The Dow Chemical Company and Badische Anilin- und Soda-Fabrik A.G. (BASF) represented the first real breakthrough in styrene technology. In 1937 both of these companies were manufacturing a high-purity monomer which could be polymerized to a stable, clear, colorless plastic. During World War II, styrene became very important in the manufacture of synthetic rubber and large-scale plants were built. Later, peacetime uses of styrene-based plastics have accounted for the continuing rapid growth of the industry. Although many producers have since entered the market and new routes to styrene have been tried, the basic manufacturing technique of ethylbenzene dehydrogenation still accounts for virtually all of the styrene being manufactured today.

Properties

The physical properties of styrene monomer are given in Table 1. Polymerization or copolymerization is the only reaction of styrene that is of commercial significance. Virtually all of the monomer manufactured is consumed by these processes.

Styrene monomer can be polymerized by all the common methods employed in plastics technology. See Polymerization mechanisms and processes. Techniques of mass, suspension, solution, and emulsion polymerization have been used for the manufacture of polystyrene and styrene copolymers, but processes relating to the first two methods account for most of the polymers manufactured today. A free-radical polymerization of the monomer initiated thermally or with catalysts is generally employed (1–6).

In addition to polymerization, styrene also undergoes all of the normal reactions of a typical unsaturated compound. Many of these are listed in key references on the monomer (1,8).

Table 1. Physical Properties of Styrene Monomer

Property	Value
boiling point, at 760 mm Hg, °C	145.0
freezing point, °C	−30.6
flash point, °F, Tag open-cup	94.0
Cleveland open-cup	88.0
fire point, °F, Tag open-cup	94.0
Cleveland open-cup	94.0
autoignition temperature, °F	914.0
explosive limits in air,[a] %	1.1–6.1

vapor pressure, Antoine equation

$$\log_{10} p \text{ (mm Hg)} = 6.95711 - \frac{1445.58}{209.43 + t°C}$$

Property	Value
critical pressure, P_c, atm	37.6
critical temperature, t_c, °C	369.0
critical volume, V_c, cm³/g	3.55

refractive index

temp, °C	n_D	temp, °C	n_D
15	1.5495	30	1.5410
20	1.5467	35	1.5382
25	1.5439		

viscosity

temp, °C	cP	temp, °C	cP
0	1.040	80	0.385
20	0.763	100	0.326
40	0.586	120	0.278
60	0.470	140	0.243

surface tension

temp, °C	dyn/cm	temp, °C	dyn/cm
0	31.80	80	28.08
20	30.86	100	27.15
40	29.93	120	26.23
60	29.01	140	25.30

density

temp, °C	g/cm³	temp, °C	g/cm³
0	0.9237	60	0.8702
10	0.9148	80	0.8524
20	0.9059	100	0.8346
30	0.8970	150	0.7900
40	0.8880		

Manufacture

Many different techniques have been investigated for the manufacture of styrene monomer. Of these, the following methods have been used or considered for commercial production:

1. The dehydrogenation of ethylbenzene.

2. Oxidative conversion of ethylbenzene to α-phenylethanol via acetophenone and subsequent dehydration of the alcohol.

3. Side chain chlorination of ethylbenzene followed by dehydrochlorination.

4. Side chain chlorination of ethylbenzene, hydrolysis to the corresponding alcohols, followed by dehydration.

5. Pyrolysis of petroleum and recovery from various petroleum processes.

6. Oxidation of ethylbenzene to ethylbenzene hydroperoxide which is reacted with propylene to give α-phenylethanol and propylene oxide. The alcohol is then dehydrated to styrene.

Table 1 (*continued*)

Property	Value			
specific heat, liquid	*temp, °C*	*cal/(g)(°C)*	*temp, °C*	*cal/(g)(°C)*
	0	0.3910	80	0.4510
	20	0.4039	100	0.4739
	40	0.4178	120	0.5029
	60	0.4329	140	0.5349
specific heat, vapor, at 25°C, C_p, cal/(g)(°C)	0.2818			
latent heat of vaporization, ΔH_v, cal/g				
at 25°C	102.4			
at 145°C	84.69			
heat of combustion, gas at const pressure, at 25°C, ΔH_c, kcal/mole	1018.83			
heat of formation, liquid, at 25°C, ΔH_f, kcal/mole	35.22			
heat of polymerization, kcal/mole	17.8			
Q value	1.0			
e value	-0.8			
volumetric shrinkage upon polymerization, %	17.0			
cubical coefficient of expansion, per °C				
at 20°C	9.710×10^{-4}			
at 30°C	9.805×10^{-4}			
at 40°C	9.902×10^{-4}			
solubility at 25°C, %				
monomer in H_2O	0.032			
H_2O in monomer	0.070			
solvent compatibility				
acetone	∞			
carbon tetrachloride	∞			
benzene	∞			
ether	∞			
n-heptane	∞			
ethanol	∞			

[a] See also Figure 10.

At present all of the styrene manufactured commercially is made by the dehydrogenation of ethylbenzene. The oxidation process 2. was practiced by Union Carbide for a number of years, but has been abandoned in favor of dehydrogenation. Processes 3. and 4., involving chlorine, have generally suffered from the high cost of the raw materials and from the chlorinated contaminants in the monomer. Manufacture of styrene directly from petroleum streams 5. is difficult and costly. The Halcon process 6. is a recent innovation in styrene technology.

In discussing the details of styrene manufacture, it is convenient to consider the following three primary steps in the process separately: (a) the manufacture of ethylbenzene; (b) the conversion of ethylbenzene to styrene (dehydrogenation); and (c) the finishing of the monomer by fractional distillation.

ETHYLBENZENE MANUFACTURE

All of the styrene monomer produced in the United States in 1965 was manufactured from ethylbenzene. About 91% of the ethylbenzene was obtained by alkylation of benzene with ethylene in the presence of a catalyst and the remainder was fractionated from petroleum streams (9). The latter process involves superfractionation employing three 200-ft columns operated in series with high reflux rates. The Badger Company joined with Cosden Petroleum in 1957 to build a plant for Cosden, incorporating such a series of columns. The key distillation in that unit separates ethylbenzene from *p*-xylene, which differ only by 3.9°F in boiling points. Cosden has an ideal case for this application since their West Texas crude oil can be refined to produce a mixed xylene stream that contains 28% ethylbenzene (10). Although an ethylbenzene content of 20% is more common, there are at least seven commercial plants in the United States, including Humble Refining Company at Baytown, Tex., and Sinclair-Koppers at Houston, Tex., recovering ethylbenzene by fractionation. In 1965 a total of 324 million lb of ethylbenzene was manufactured by this method in the United States. Since supplies of mixed xylenes are limited, many producers are adding alkylation units to supplement their ethylbenzene production.

The chemistry of the manufacture of ethylbenzene by the alkylation of benzene with ethylene is shown below:

$$C_6H_6 + CH_2{=}CH_2 \rightarrow C_6H_5CH_2CH_3$$

Two processes are used for this step, one of which involves a *low-pressure liquid-phase reaction* using aluminum chloride catalyst while the other operates in the *vapor phase at high pressure* with various solid catalysts. The earliest commercial example of the latter process was the plant built for the Koppers Company in Kobuta, Pa., during World War II. In this unit, the reaction occurred when the mixture of ethylene with excess benzene passed through a fixed-bed catalyst case. The catalyst was alumina deposited on a silica-gel carrier (11,12), and at the inlet the pressure was 900 psig and the temperature 310°C. One of the major difficulties with this process is its failure to dealkylate the (polyethyl)benzenes that are also produced in the reaction. In order to achieve the normal ethylbenzene yields of above 98% based on both ethylene and benzene, it was necessary to use small auxiliary dealkylation units with aluminum chloride catalyst. (Polyethyl)benzene formation is minimized in commercial production by using increased ratios of benzene to ethylene. This reduces the need for dealkylation, but increases the distillation load in the ethylbenzene purification step.

A new solid phosphoric acid catalyst is used in the fixed-bed reactors at El Paso Natural Gas Company's Odessa plant (13). Sherwood noted (14) that earlier phosphoric acid catalysts on a kieselguhr carrier had achieved only a 13–15% conversion of the ethylene to ethylbenzene at 100 psig and 230°C, but an 80% conversion in a single pass at 600 psig and 325°C, and 95% conversion at 900 psig. Ipatieff indicated (15) that an increase in the benzene-to-ethylene mole ratio in the reactor feed from 3:1 to 5:1 would increase the ethylbenzene concentration in the alkylate from 87 to 93%. Recycling of the diethylbenzene and higher (polyethyl)benzenes tended to form deposits on the catalyst and to reduce its activity so it was essential to keep these components at a minimum (16). However, the savings obtained by higher monoethylbenzene yields when benzene feed concentrations are increased must again be balanced against the increased cost of fractionation of the excess benzene which must be recycled.

The Alkar process (17), first offered by Universal Oil Products Company (UOP) in 1958, is also a high-pressure alkylation process and offers the advantage of less corrosion than the conventional aluminum chloride process. In addition, it was de-

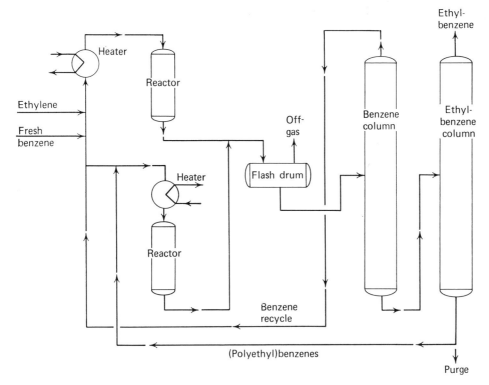

Fig. 1. The Alkar ethylbenzene process.

signed to operate on refinery gas streams containing 8–10% ethylene (18). A simplified flowsheet of the Alkar process is shown in Figure 1. Fresh benzene is mixed with recycle benzene and ethylene and, after heating, is introduced into the fixed-bed alkylator. The high-pressure effluent is then flashed and fed into the benzene recycle column where the benzene is recovered as overhead product. The bottoms become the feed to the following column where the product ethylbenzene is separated from the (polyalkyl)benzenes. Most of the (polyalkyl)benzenes are recycled to a separate dealkylator along with the necessary benzene for conversion back to ethylbenzene. The dealkylator effluent is then combined with the alkylator effluent for flashing (19). Universal Oil Products Company reports substantially complete ethylene conversions for feed ethylene ranging from 5 to 100% purity and an essentially quantitative yield of ethylbenzene with respect to benzene after transalkylation of the (polyethyl)benzenes. A small purge of bottoms is required for removal of traces of other alkylates formed from propylene and acetylene in the feed. The improved catalyst for the alkylation is apparently a boron trifluoride–modified anhydrous γ alumina, BF_3 being added also in the alkylator feed (20). The dealkylator presumably uses the identical catalyst and operates under less severe conditions (202°C and 500 psig) (21,22).

Union Carbide's Linde Division offers a type Y molecular sieve (SK-500) as a catalyst for vapor-phase alkylation, which claims to offer unusual selectivity and milder operating conditions (23,24).

Friedel-Crafts Alkylation. Most of the ethylbenzene in this country and in Europe is made by liquid-phase Friedel-Crafts alkylation using aluminum chloride

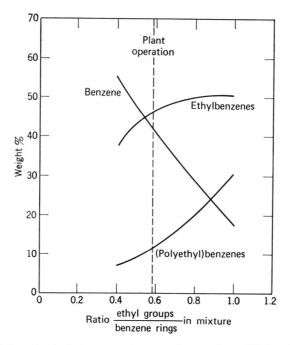

Fig. 2. The effect of the ratio of ethyl groups to benzene rings on the equilibrium in the manufacture of ethylbenzene (1). Courtesy Reinhold Publishing Corp.

as catalyst with ethyl chloride or hydrogen chloride as the promoter. The process is carried out in a brick-lined steel tower or a glass-lined reactor operating at the boiling point of the reaction mixture (80–100°C at atmospheric pressure). Higher pressure operation allows higher temperatures and increases the rate of reaction, but introduces the disadvantages of pressure operation of a corrosive system. However, the reaction is exothermic and it is possible to generate steam if the reaction is run under pressure. The original Union Carbide plant at Institute, W. Va., operated at pressures up to 125 psig and temperatures of 80–130°C (16,25). The new process, licensed by a collaboration of The Badger Company, Cosden Oil and Gas Company, and Union Carbide Corporation, may operate similarly. When alkylating under pressure it is often desirable to reduce residence time by using mechanically agitated glass-lined reactors.

The conventional reactor, which operates at about atmospheric pressure, is a lined vessel filled to approx 35 ft with the liquid reactants which overflow through a line near the top. Ethylene is introduced at the bottom, often through a sparger. Fresh benzene, recycle benzene, recycle (polyethyl)benzenes, and the catalyst, in the form of a complex, are also introduced at the bottom. This complex is an oily, reddish-brown addition compound consisting of about 25–30% aluminum chloride chemically combined with 70–75% of various alkylator product components. The complex is heavier than the reactants but is slowly carried by them up through the reactor. The mechanism of the reaction is discussed in depth in Olah's treatise (26).

The product composition depends, in part, on the ratio of ethyl groups to benzene rings in the total feed (including the complex), as shown graphically in Figure 2. In the past this ratio, ϵ, has been optimized at about 0.5–0.6 to produce a reactor product containing about 46% ethylbenzene, 42% benzene, 10% diethylbenzene, and 2%

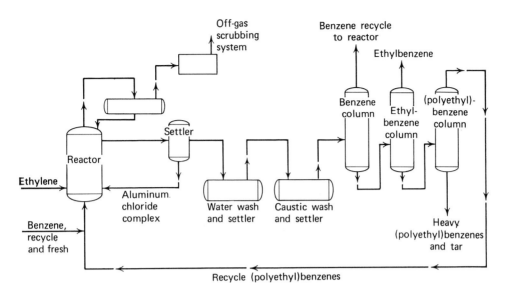

Fig. 3. The manufacture of ethylbenzene employing aluminum chloride as catalyst.

higher-molecular-weight products. As in the case of the high-pressure vapor-phase alkylation, higher ratios of benzene to ethylene (ie, lower ϵ) produce less polymers and tar but require larger equipment and higher operating costs in fractionating the benzene recycle. The choice of ϵ is then governed by economic consideration. Newer heat recovery and exchange techniques in the fractionation of ethylbenzene may allow these lower ϵ's to be used.

The process, shown schematically in Figure 3, is used both in the United States and Germany and has remained essentially unchanged for many years. The benzene used is known as "styrene grade," which defines a benzene with a boiling range of 1°C and a minimum freezing point of 4.85°C (this ordinarily corresponds to a purity slightly above 99%). The purity of the ethylene is not a prime consideration, except that it must be free of acetylene, other unsaturates, and moisture. In general, ethylene at least 90% pure is used. Aluminum chloride is added to a reactor feed stream as a solid and forms the complex in the reactor. Benzene, both feed and recycle, enters the process through a benzene drying column. Hydrogen chloride in the form of HCl or ethyl chloride is also added to the reactor.

The gaseous products, unreacted ethylene, some benzene, hydrogen chloride, and the inerts that were introduced with the ethylene leave the top of the alkylator and enter a condenser from which recovered benzene flows back to the alkylator. The off-gas is scrubbed for final benzene recovery, using recycle (polyethyl)benzenes as absorbent, and then is washed with water for the removal of HCl before venting or before compression for use as fuel.

The liquid products from the alkylator are cooled and pass through a settler where the complex is removed and returned to the alkylator. The alkylate is then washed with water (which breaks any residual complex) and scrubbed with 20% caustic for neutralization, after which it is separated into components in a series of distillation columns. The first column removes the benzene, the second the ethylbenzene, and the third the lighter (polyethyl)benzenes as overheads. The bottoms product of the third tower are the heavy (polyethyl)benzenes and tars, which are partially dealkylated at high temperature; the final tar residue is burned. The distillation system is constructed of steel and little corrosion is experienced. One operating precaution is to remove the diethylbenzene from the monoethylbenzene as completely as possible. If this is not done, divinylbenzene will be formed in the subsequent dehydrogenation step and, on distillation, can polymerize with styrene to a cross-linked polymer which is very hard to remove. Isopropylbenzene (cumene) should also be removed to prevent contamination of the styrene with α-methylstyrene and unreacted cumene.

The production of ethylbenzene using the aluminum chloride route has the advantage that the alkylator also acts effectively to dealkylate the recycled (polyethyl)benzenes. This is now possible in some of the newer vapor-phase processes in a separate reactor, whereas the (polyethyl)benzenes formed in the alumina–silicate process of Koppers had to be dealkylated by aluminum chloride. The vapor-phase process has advantages in the lack of corrosion, but this is offset at present by the disadvantages of pressure equipment, and the need of larger amounts of excess benzene in the feed.

STYRENE MANUFACTURE

There are many possible methods of making styrene and several of these have been tried commercially (27). The direct dehydrogenation of ethylbenzene is the only method used at present, although interest in oxidation techniques is being revived with many new variations, such as Halcon's oxidation–epoxidation process (28).

Oxidation Processes.   The oxidation process of Union Carbide (25) had the dual purpose of manufacturing styrene and acetophenone. In this operation, ethylbenzene was oxidized to acetophenone over a catalyst of manganese acetate at 115–145°C and pressures up to 50 psig, as shown in the following reaction:

$$C_6H_5CH_2CH_3 + O_2 \rightarrow C_6H_5COCH_3 + H_2O$$

The oxidation was followed by the reduction of the ketone to α-phenylethyl alcohol (see also Vol. 1, p. 168), using hydrogen over a copper–chrome–iron catalyst at 150°C and pressures up to 150 psig, as shown below:

$$C_6H_5COCH_3 \xrightarrow{H_2} C_6H_5CH(OH)CH_3$$

The process was concluded with the dehydration of the alcohol to styrene, using a titania catalyst at 250°C and atmospheric pressure, as follows:

$$C_6H_5CH(OH)CH_3 \rightarrow C_6H_5CH{=}CH_2 + H_2O$$

Reaction products in the oxidation step include some phenylethyl alcohol and small amounts of organic acids. When additional acetophenone was required for sale or use, the second reaction was reversed to oxidize the phenylethyl alcohol to acetophenone. This process had the disadvantages of corrosion in the oxidation step and gave approx 10% lower yields than the conventional dehydrogenation process of ethylbenzene. Union Carbide subsequently switched to the latter technique when they built their large styrene plant at Seadrift, Tex., in the 1960s.

A new variation of the oxidation route is Halcon International's process to produce styrene and propylene oxide. In this technique ethylbenzene is oxidized to ethylbenzene hydroperoxide, as follows:

$$C_6H_5CH_2CH_3 + O_2 \rightarrow C_6H_5CH(OOH)CH_3$$

This product is reacted with propylene to form propylene oxide and α-phenylethyl alcohol (29–31), as shown below:

$$C_6H_5CH(OOH)CH_3 + CH_3CH{=}CH_2 \rightarrow C_6H_5CH(OH)CH_3 + CH_3\overset{O}{\overset{\triangle}{CHCH_2}}$$

The alcohol can be dehydrated to styrene as in the Carbide process or it can be reduced to ethylbenzene for recycle if styrene is not desired. Halcon formed a joint company, Oxirane Corporation, with Atlantic Richfield to exploit this process (32,33). Oxirane is considering the construction of a plant with a propylene oxide capacity of 160 million lb/yr. Halcon is reported to be planning a joint venture styrene–propylene oxide plant in Spain with Imperial Chemical Industries and others (28,34). Little information on the technology is publicly available but Halcon reveals (35) that control of the partial pressure of oxygen is important to improve yields.

Literature on direct oxidation of ethylbenzene to styrene has grown rapidly in recent years. Distillers Company, Ltd. (36) reports a direct oxidation process using air and a catalyst containing antimony oxide. Petro-Tex Chemical Company (37,38) states that addition of halogens to the oxygen improves yields. One example of the latter process involves vapor-phase oxidation at 450–650°C with 0.5–1.5 moles of oxygen per mole of ethylbenzene and 0.02–0.075 mole of iodine per mole of ethylbenzene. These processes also cover vinyltoluene and α-methylstyrene. Scientific Design reports the use of bromine in oxidation processes (39). In addition to direct catalytic oxidation with air or oxygen, with or without halogens, a Shell Oil patent (40) declares that ethylbenzene may be reacted with sulfur dioxide in the presence of a metal phosphate catalyst at 450–600°C and pressures from atmospheric to 350 psig. In most of these direct oxidation processes, high conversions per pass (approx 80–90%) are claimed, with styrene yields (or selectivities) on the same order of magnitude. This compares with the 40–60% conversions of the conventional process which has somewhat higher yields. At present there are no major commercial styrene plants utilizing this technique. The problems of corrosion and recovery of halogens, as well as the lower yields, require further study if the method is to be economically feasible. In addition, the major coproducts in the conventional dehydrogenation process are benzene, toluene, and hydrogen, which have considerable value, in comparison to the oxides of carbon, the by-products of oxidative processes.

Dehydrogenation Processes. Direct dehydrogenation of ethylbenzene is the only commercial process presently employed for the manufacture of styrene. This method has been developed along the following two major routes: (1) the *adiabatic cracking process* developed by The Dow Chemical Company and others in the United States and (2) the *isothermal process* developed by BASF in Germany. The reaction is endothermic requiring, at the usual conditions, about 540–570 Btu/lb of ethylbenzene converted, including side reactions. The two processes differ in the manner in which the heat necessary for the reaction is supplied. Both ethylbenzene and styrene are subject to thermal decomposition at temperatures in excess of 610°C (at normal residence times), but it is desirable to maintain temperatures approaching this figure in the reactor to maximize conversion per pass. In the adiabatic reactor the sole source of heat is provided by mixing superheated steam with the ethylbenzene prior to contact with the catalyst. In order to maintain a high temperature throughout the dehydrogenation reaction, the feed mixture is generally introduced at temperatures above 630°C. This results in some thermal cracking of the hydrocarbons. In the isothermal process, heat

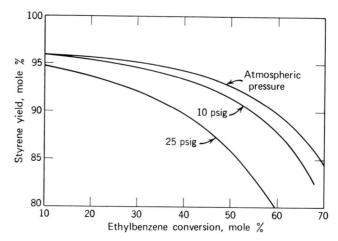

Fig. 4. The effect of pressure on yield and conversion in the dehydrogenation of ethylbenzene.

is provided indirectly in a tubular reactor. Thus in the isothermal reactor, temperatures may be uniformly maintained at 580–610°C throughout the catalyst bed. Consequently little thermal cracking is experienced in the isothermal process, resulting in a 92–94% yield of styrene at 40% conversion vs an 88–91% yield for adiabatic techniques. Therefore, the isothermal process has about a 3%-yield advantage over the adiabatic and requires only about half as much steam. These advantages are partially offset by the higher capital investment necessary for the isothermal process reaction system.

The *adiabatic cracking* (dehydrogenation) process has often been described and there are many recent variations which are discussed below (see p. 66). As Mitchell has pointed out (41), a volume increase accompanies the reaction and decreased pressure is therefore desirable. Operation under vacuum has been avoided both from the safety aspect and because of the cost of the product compression involved. Most adiabatic reactors, therefore, operate as close to atmospheric pressure as the pressure drop through the catalyst bed and the heat exchange equipment allows. This generally means reactor pressures on the order of 5–15 psig. Since 2–3 lb of superheated steam per lb of ethylbenzene are normally used in adiabatic reactors to provide the heat of reaction, the partial pressure of the reactants is reduced.

Figure 4 shows the effect of pressure and higher ethylbenzene conversions in reducing the yields of styrene. Conversion is defined as the fraction of the ethylbenzene fed that is converted to styrene or other products—in essence, the disappearance of ethylbenzene per pass. Inconsistent definitions of the terms "yield" and "conversion" have resulted in considerable confusion in the literature. Yield is herein defined as the net moles of styrene produced per mole of ethylbenzene that disappears in the reactor.

A flowsheet of a typical adiabatic dehydrogenation step is presented in Figure 5. Liquid ethylbenzene (both fresh and recycle) along with about 10% of the steam is heat exchanged with the reactor product. This vaporizes the ethylbenzene and superheats it to about 520–550°C. The remaining 90% of the steam is superheated to about 720°C in the tubes of a fired heater and the mixture of this steam with the superheated ethylbenzene provides a reactor feed at about 650°C. The reactor is a chrome-steel

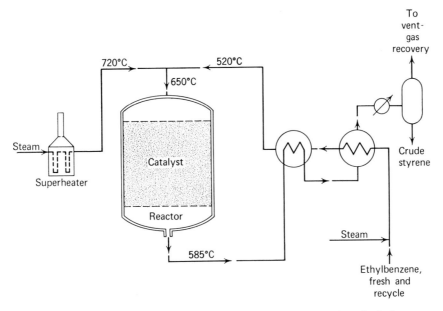

Fig. 5. The manufacture of styrene by the adiabatic dehydrogenation of ethylbenzene.

vessel (nickel may catalyze undesirable side reactions) containing a bed of catalyst pellets (or extrudate) in the form of small cylinders $3/16$ or $1/8$ in. in diameter. Many catalysts are possible, but the major constituent is usually iron oxide. Since the same catalysts are used in the isothermal process, details are discussed below (see p. 67). The modern reactors are usually designed for reactant downflow through the catalyst bed instead of the older upflow variety. The catalyst is supported on a screen and grating through which the product gases pass. Space velocities of 25–35 lb/hr of ethylbenzene fed per ft³ of catalyst space are normal. Single reactor capacities up to three million lb of styrene per month produced at the 40% conversion level are usually employed. As shown in Figure 5, the reactor effluent leaves the reactor at about 585°C and is then cooled by heat exchange with the ethylbenzene feed, followed by condensation using air or water-cooled condensers or both. A typical product composition is shown in Table 2. After condensation of most of the hydrocarbons and the steam, the vent gas is separated, compressed, and refrigerated for maximum recovery of benzene and higher boiling components. The residual vent gas which is usually about 90% hydrogen and 10% carbon dioxide, with small quantities of ethylene and methane, is used as fuel or for its hydrogen value. The crude styrene is then forwarded to the finishing section.

The *isothermal process* has been described by Ohlinger of BASF (2,42). The major difference between this isothermal process and the adiabatic lies in the means of supply-

Table 2. Composition of the Crude Liquid Product from the Adiabatic Dehydrogenation of Ethylbenzene

Product	Percent	Product	Percent
benzene	1.56	ethyl-benzene	57.05
toluene	2.64		
styrene	38.50	"highers"	0.25

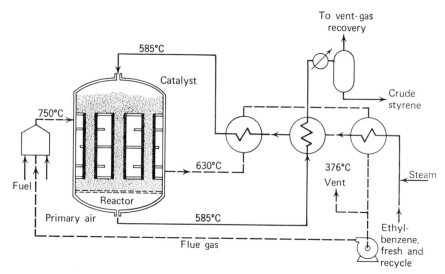

Fig. 6. The manufacture of styrene by the isothermal dehydrogenation of ethylbenzene (42).

ing the heat for the cracking reaction. There are a number of possible variants, both in the source of heat, and in the heat-exchange systems for the feed-product and the heating agent. BASF uses flue gas for heat as indicated in the flowsheet in Figure 6. In this isothermal process, the ethylbenzene is vaporized and superheated along with the steam by heat exchange, partly with the reactor product and partly with the circulating flue gas. As noted before, this process has the following two immediate advantages: (1) only 1 lb of steam is required per lb of ethylbenzene; and (2) the reactor feed temperature is kept below the level at which thermal cracking begins, thereby increasing the yield of styrene. The reactor is built like a shell-and-tube heat exchanger with hot flue gas on the shell side and the ethylbenzene feed passing through the tubes which also contain the catalyst. The catalyst bed is supported, as in the adiabatic process, on a screen and grid below the bottom tube sheet through which the reactor effluent can flow. In order to reduce void volume, part of the section above the tube sheet is also filled with catalyst. The reactor can have tubes 8–12 ft long and 4–8 in. in diameter. BASF reported (42) single reactors with up to four million lb per month styrene capacity (at 40% conversion) and, if the trend toward single large-scale plants continues, even larger reactors will undoubtedly be built. In Figure 6, the flue gas leaves the reactor at 630°C and is cooled by heat exchange to 376°C after which some of it is recirculated by a blower. The recirculated flue gas is reheated to about 750°C by acting as the secondary air for a burner. An amount of flue gas equivalent to the fuel and primary air is vented at the blower suction. As is evident from Figure 6, many variations on the heat-exchange system are possible. Reactor construction also has many possibilities, such as BASF's technique of including the flue-gas reheat furnace as part of the reactor. Unquestionably, the isothermal reactor with its flue-gas circulation system involves more capital than the adiabatic, and this must be offset by the steam and yield advantages.

There have been many other modifications to the basic adiabatic and isothermal reactors (43). One which has been used commercially involves a modification of the heat-exchange section. In this process all the ethylbenzene and all the steam are combined and the final heating of the mixture to reaction temperature is accomplished in a direct-fired tubular superheater before introduction into the reactor (44,45). This design requires very short residence times in the coil to avoid thermal cracking of the ethylbenzene. Adiabatic reactors with reduced pressure drop have been designed in which the reactants flow radially outward through an annular catalyst bed from a central supply pipe, and the product is collected at the reactor wall (46). Another modification employs two adiabatic reactors in series. The reaction mixture is reheated between them by further addition of superheated steam or by a fired heater (47–52). This concept has been extrapolated to more than two beds in series with reheating in between (53). The technique of using adiabatic beds in series is simply an approximation of the isothermal reactor, especially as the number of stages increases. With more stages, maximum temperatures decrease and the yield of styrene increases and, if direct-fired reheat is used, the quantity of steam required decreases. These advantages, which are typical of the isothermal reactor, are again offset by the increased capital investment of the multiple adiabatic system. Recently most of the series adiabatic reactor designs have involved an attempt to economically increase the conversion from 40 to 60%. This has definite advantages in reducing the subsequent cost of separating the crude styrene into the pure product and recycle ethylbenzene, but the yield is reduced, as shown in Figure 4.

The catalyst for the dehydrogenation step is self-regenerative, because it contains sufficient potassium salts to promote the removal of by-product carbon, coke, and tars by reaction with the steam (the "water-gas" reaction). Thus, the catalyst need not be regenerated periodically since these residues only build up to an equilibrium level. Kearby (54) published an excellent summary of the earlier catalysts and emphasized the importance of the addition of the potassium salt (usually as carbonate or oxide) to the iron oxide which is the major component of the catalyst. He also noted the poisoning effect of chlorides in the feed but recently Monsanto has claimed that small amounts of chlorides enhance the reaction (55). Kearby (54) also notes that the addition of chromic oxide results in a longer life of the catalyst. One of the common catalysts used commercially is Shell Chemical's Shell 105 which contains about 87% Fe_2O_3, 11% KOH, and 2% Cr_2O_3 (56–61).

Other catalysts have also been used (42,54,62). Monsanto proposed the use of a "high-selectivity" catalyst in the first of two adiabatic reactors in series, followed by a "high-activity" catalyst, such as Shell 105, in the second bed where the higher conversion slows the reaction (63). Smaller-sized catalyst particles have been shown to have greater activity but have the disadvantage of increased pressure drop.

Thermal cracking of ethylbenzene in the absence of catalysts at 700–800°C results in styrene conversion of 20–30% but with very poor yields (50–60%) (64). Extensions of studies of this type are important in the design of the standard dehydrogenation reactors since they demonstrate that the residence time of styrene and ethylbenzene in void spaces and zones without catalyst must be kept at a minimum. This represents one of the sources of yield loss that occurs in the adiabatic dehydrogenation reactors.

The kinetics of the dehydrogenation of ethylbenzene were studied in detail by Wenner and Dybdal in 1948 (65) and Carra and Forni in 1965 (66), and several process simulations have been made (67).

Styrene Finishing. The third step in the manufacture of styrene is the purification of the styrene in the dehydrogenation reactor effluent. This is done by vacuum distillation to keep the tower temperatures low and minimize the polymerization of styrene. In most cases the first distillation separates the benzene, toluene, and residual water as overhead product; the second takes the ethylbenzene overhead; and the third separates the styrene from tars and polymers. One variation removes all the ethylbenzene along with the benzene and toluene in the first tower. This mixture is subsequently separated, which has the disadvantage that the most difficult separation, that of ethylbenzene from styrene, is done with the probability of poor vacuum control because of the variable water content and dissolved gases in the feed stream.

In the normal procedure the benzene and toluene separated in the first distillation tower are redistilled in a small column and the benzene is recycled to the ethylbenzene plant's drying tower. The ethylbenzene–styrene mixture from the first tower is then separated, with the ethylbenzene (containing about 2% styrene) going overhead and being recycled to the dehydrogenation step. The styrene bottoms, containing about 0.1% ethylbenzene, are then ready for final finishing to remove tars and polymers. This final finishing can be done in batch stills, but more often a continuous distillation tower is used as in the preceding separations. The overhead from this tower is styrene and the bottoms are tars and polymers. These bottoms are usually redistilled in a separate short column to recover as much styrene as possible, and this is recycled to the finishing tower.

To reduce polymerization, sulfur or dinitrophenols are used as inhibitors in the purification stills and p-tert-butylcatechol (TBC) is used in small concentrations in the final finishing still and in storage. It is important to keep the temperature low wherever styrene is stored in appreciable concentrations. Since polymerization is also a function of time, towers of special designs have been used to reduce styrene hold-up (68–72). This is particularly true where styrene is the bottom product in a distillation, as in its separation from ethylbenzene. It has been good practice to hold this temperature below 105°C. The tower overhead temperature is limited to about 45–55°C to obtain condensing of the overhead vapor using air or water-cooled condensers. This requires a vacuum of about 50 mm Hg absolute at the top of the tower. With a bottoms temperature of 105°C, a total pressure drop in the tower of 160 mm Hg or less is needed (ie, a bottoms pressure of 200–210 mm Hg abs). Until recently it has not been possible to make this separation in one tower. General practice has involved two towers in series, each with an absolute overhead pressure of 50 mm Hg. The bottoms from the first tower are fed as reflux to the second tower and the overhead vapor from the second is condensed, pumped to the bottom of the first tower, and revaporized. With two reboilers operating, the demand for reboiler steam for this separation alone is 2.5–3.0 lb steam per lb of styrene for a feed containing 40–45% styrene. With the advent of new distillation tower trays, especially the sieve trays licensed by the Linde Division of Union Carbide Corporation, a single tower is now possible and steam demands are cut almost in half (73). Patents are also available citing means of achieving heat economies, in particular the use of the heat of condensation of the large amount of steam in the dehydrogenator effluent (74–76).

Economic Aspects

The history of styrene production in the United States is shown in Table 3. In the 1930s styrene production was limited to a small output by The Dow Chemical Company's original plant. The sudden increase in the early 1940s was the result of a joint effort of many firms through the government-controlled Rubber Reserve Company to provide styrene for use in synthetic rubber during the war. Following this period, requirements for synthetic rubber decreased and consequently the production of styrene was reduced. Gradually, however, new uses for the monomer, such as styrene plastics, were devised and began to fill the gap created by the reduced demand for rubber. Production of styrene plastics has shown remarkable growth and they now account for the majority of the monomer market.

Table 3. Production of Styrene Monomer[a]

Year	Million lb	Year	Million lb
1940	2	1960[b]	1745
1944	349	1964[c]	2571
1948	377	1965[c]	2864
1952	670	1966[c]	3192
1956[b]	1176	1967[c]	3278

[a] The data for the years 1940–1952 were compiled from the reports of the Chemical Division of the U.S. Tariff Commission.
[b] Reference 76a.   [c] Reference 76b.

With new applications for styrene came increased production and competition which has resulted in a gradual reduction of the price of the monomer, as illustrated in Figure 7. All styrene is made from ethylbenzene and nearly all ethylbenzene is made

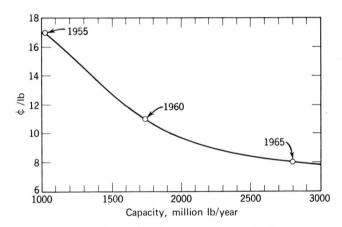

Fig. 7. Price–volume relationship of styrene monomer in the United States.

by the alkylation of benzene. Since the manufacture of styrene has been developed to a highly efficient degree, the cost of benzene is the single most influential factor on the price of the monomer. It should also be noted that styrene is the largest single market for benzene. In Figure 8, the prices of styrene and benzene since 1945 are shown. Many of the styrene manufacturers are not large benzene producers and must purchase this raw material on the market. Since technology for styrene manufacture has been refined to the point at which further improvements would result in only minor gains, competition in the industry has relied heavily on engineering for cost savings. These improvements have taken the form of large streamlined plants which offer savings over smaller individual units. Consequently, styrene is a market in which only large companies, that are willing to invest substantial sums of money in a sizable operation,

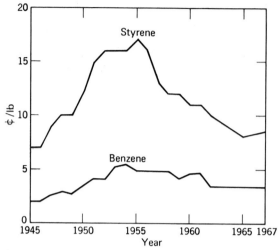

Fig. 8. List price for styrene monomer and benzene in the United States.

can compete.   The trend to large-volume production is evident from the capacities of the United States styrene manufacturers given in Table 4.

Table 4.   U.S. Styrene Manufacturers and Annual Capacities (79,80)

Producer and location	Capacity,[a] million lb
Amoco Chemicals Corporation, Texas City, Tex.	800[b]
Borg-Warner Corporation (Marbon Chemical Division), Baytown, Tex.	125
Cosden Oil and Chemical Company, Big Spring, Tex.	110
Cos-Mar Company, Carville, La.	500
The Dow Chemical Company, Freeport, Tex., and Midland, Mich.	1000
El Paso Natural Gas Products Company, Odessa, Tex.	86
Foster Grant Company, Inc., Baton Rouge, La.	200
Monsanto Company, Texas City, Tex.	750[c]
Shell Chemical Company, Torrance, Calif.	210
Sinclair-Koppers Company, Houston, Tex., and Kobuta, Pa.	270
Suntide Refining Company, Corpus Christi, Tex.	60
Union Carbide Corporation, Institute, W.Va., and Seadrift, Tex.	410
total	4521

[a] As of mid-1967.

[b] Includes a 550-million-lb/yr expansion scheduled for completion in 1969.

[c] Includes a 100-million-lb/yr expansion scheduled for 1968.

Specifications and Analysis

No formal specifications for the purity of styrene monomer have been agreed upon by the industry although the American Society for Testing and Materials (ASTM) has published a set of proposed standards (77). Careful quality control resulting in high-purity, uniform monomer is a necessary prerequisite for survival in the highly competitive styrene market. The purity of a typical sample of top-quality-grade styrene monomer is shown in Table 5.

Table 5. Analysis of a Representative Lot of Polymerization-Grade Styrene

Assay	ppm[a]	Assay	ppm[a]
purity	99.6[b]	chlorides as Cl	10
polymer	none	sulfur as S	10
aldehydes as CHO	10	TBC	12
peroxides as H_2O_2	5	color	<5[c]

[a] Unless otherwise indicated.   [b] Percent.   [c] APHA scale.

Gas chromatography has largely superseded wet methods for analysis of ethylbenzene and styrene during the manufacturing process. However, analytical methods for impurities in the finished monomer still rely heavily on individual chemical and physical tests (78). Styrene content of the product is best determined by careful freezing-point measurements. The results are accurate to within 0.05% which is slightly better than can be obtained by gas chromatography or titration of the double bond. The color of the monomer, particularly that monomer which is to be used for clear polystyrene, is very important. Color is routinely measured in terms of APHA (American Public Health Association) color standards or the Saybolt color scale. Both of these may be determined with standard colorimeters. Pure styrene tends to polymerize slowly on storage. To prevent polymerization, an inhibitor, p-tert-butylcatechol (TBC), is added. Analysis of TBC is conducted by extracting the monomer with aqueous sodium hydroxide and measuring the reddish color of the resulting quinone colorimetrically. Styrene monomer cannot be marketed today unless the polymer content is extremely low. The older tests of monomer viscosity are not sufficiently sensitive to detect polymer concentrations on the order of ppm. At present, polymer impurity is measured by diluting samples of monomer with methanol which precipitates the polymerized material. The samples are then measured for turbidity using a photoelectric colorimeter and are compared with standards prepared from freshly distilled styrene and very pure polystyrene.

The chief impurities of an oxidative origin are aldehydes (principally benzaldehyde and formaldehyde) and peroxides. Aldehydes are determined by reacting a neutral solution of styrene in methanol with neutralized hydroxylamine hydrochloride. Hydrochloric acid is released in direct proportion to the formation of the oxime by the aldehydes and can be titrated. Peroxides are determined by reacting a sample of the monomer with potassium iodide in isopropyl alcohol. The iodine liberated by oxidation is titrated with standard sodium thiosulfate to a colorless end point. Peroxides are one of the most objectionable of the oxidation impurities. Small concentrations have a drastic effect on the polymerization rate of the monomer. Analysis for chlorine and sulfur is carried out by burning samples of the monomer in an oxy–hydrogen flame, collecting the resulting chloride and sulfate ions, and determining them by standard techniques. With present-day cracking and finishing procedures, phenylacetylene in the monomer is virtually nonexistent and is no longer tested for. For safety purposes, gas chromatography is used to monitor the concentration of styrene vapors in the air.

Health and Safety Factors

Styrene is somewhat toxic, it is flammable, and it can be made to react violently under polymerization conditions. However, none of the hazards is unusually severe and the monomer is considered a relatively safe organic chemical. Experience has shown that if proper safeguards and precautions are employed, styrene may be handled, stored, and reacted without difficulty. Styrene monomer is considered low in single-dose oral toxicity. No problem should be encountered from amounts ingested in normal industrial procedures. Contact of the liquid with the eye is painful and irritating. Transient irritation of the conjunctival membranes, as well as minor transient injury to the cornea, may result from such an exposure. No skin irritation is generally observed in brief exposures (5 min or less). However, longer or repeated contact with the monomer may produce irritation and should be avoided.

The effects of inhalation of styrene vapor at various concentrations are shown in Table 6. Generally, overexposure to the vapors may cause eye and nasal irritation and, if exposure is excessive, central nervous system depression (anesthesia). The odor of styrene vapors can be detected at about 60 ppm and is quite strong at 100 ppm. It is unlikely that a person would voluntarily inhale toxic amounts, since concentrations of 200–400 ppm have a disagreeably strong odor and at 600 ppm the vapors are quite irritating. The American Conference on Governmental Industrial Hygienists has adopted a threshold-limit value for styrene vapor in air of 100 ppm. Styrene is detoxified in the body by oxidative cleavage of the double bond.

Table 6. The Effect of Styrene Vapor on Various Test Animals

Concn, by vol, ppm	Effects
10,000	approximately the max concn obtainable under normal room conditions; exposures of 30–60 min are dangerous to life
2,500	max concn tolerated for 60 min without serious systemic effects
1,300–2,000	slight symptoms noted after several hours
650	although this concn is irritating to nose and eye, it can probably be tolerated by man in normal working conditions without serious effects. This level caused no detectable effects to test animals repeatedly exposed

Styrene liquid and vapors are flammable, and appropriate precautions should be taken to see that contact with open flames, hot spots, arcing motors and switches, etc, is avoided. Equipment should be properly grounded to prevent sparks from static electricity. Styrene does not possess sufficient vapor pressure at room temperature to form explosive mixtures with the atmosphere. However, only a slightly elevated temperatures is necessary to raise the vapor concentration to potentially explosive levels (see flash point and fire point in Table 1). Figure 9 shows the approximate explosion limits of styrene.

Pure styrene polymerizes slowly at room temperature and more rapidly under warmer conditions. The polymerization is an exothermic process and the reaction could become self-accelerating. A run-away polymerization can create dangerously

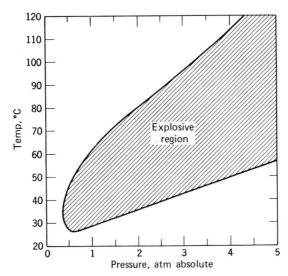

Fig. 9. The approximate explosive limits of styrene monomer vapor in equilibrium with liquid styrene in air. Courtesy of The Dow Chemical Company.

high temperature and pressure within a storage vessel. The polymerization of the monomer is retarded during storage by maintaining an inhibitor level of 10–15 ppm TBC and by avoiding storage in excessively high temperature.

Oxygen tends to degrade styrene. However, it has been shown that some oxygen is necessary for the effective action of the inhibitor (8). Therefore, it is not recommended that styrene be blanketed with an inert gas during storage. Properly inhibited and attended, styrene can be stored at ambient temperatures for extended periods of time. However, in climates where temperatures in excess of 80°F are common, bulk storage of monomer should be refrigerated.

Copper or copper-bearing alloys should not be used in the handling or storage of styrene. It has been found that copper dissolved in the monomer can result in colored impurities and interfere with polymerization. Other common materials, such as iron, steel, magnesium, and aluminum, do not affect the purity of styrene and are quite satisfactory.

Uses

Although styrene was originally used principally for SBR synthetic rubber, styrene plastics are now the major outlet for the monomer. These products, including polystyrene, rubber-modified polystyrene, styrene–butadiene copolymer, styrene–acrylonitrile copolymer (SAN), and acrylonitrile–butadiene–styrene terpolymer (ABS), rank third in volume in the plastics field behind polyethylene and polyvinyl chloride. A breakdown of the amount of styrene consumed in the manufacture of these products in the United States for the year 1965 is shown in Table 7. See also Elastomers, synthetic. Styrene homopolymer accounts for about one quarter of the monomer production and is widely used in packaging, toys, housewares, appliances, etc. It is a clear, inexpensive plastic which can be easily molded or extruded into practically any shape or form. Expanded foams of polystyrene have excellent heat-insulating and flotation properties and find application in construction and refrigeration, as well as numerous uses in packaging. See Foamed plastics. Polystyrene is more sensitive to breakage from impact than many other plastics, however. To correct this fault, a number of copolymers have been formulated to provide increased shock resistance. Rubber-modified polystyrene, which is generally referred to as "impact polystyrene," is not transparent like the homopolymer but is much more durable. It is manufactured either by blending an SBR rubber with polystyrene, by dissolving rubber in the monomer and polymerizing, or by polymerizing styrene in the presence of small granules of the rubber. The latter technique is known as graft polymerization. The styrene content of this product generally ranges from 88 to 97%. It is used in appliances, luggage, and other products that require increased breakage resistance. ABS polymers serve much the same purpose as impact polystyrene and are becoming increasingly popular. They are widely used in automotive applications such as

Table 7. Styrene Monomer Consumption in Plastics [a] (82)

Plastic	Million lb
conventional polystyrene	710
impact polystyrene	640
ABS, SAN, and miscellaneous plastics	190
styrene–butadiene copolymer	100

[a] 1965 data.

instrument panels, and in refrigerator interiors and telephone housings. SAN plastics offer excellent chemical resistance and clarity along with almost unlimited color possibilities. These resins generally contain between 70 and 75% styrene and are harder and more rigid than conventional polystyrene. Styrene–butadiene copolymer, which contains upward of 50% styrene (as compared to synthetic styrene–butadiene rubber which is made from the same ingredients but is only about 20% styrene), is a latex material used as an emulsion in the manufacture of paint and surface coatings for cloth and paper. Chemically modified copolymers of styrene–divinylbenzene are the basis of many ion-exchange resins.

Derivatives

A great many ring- and side-chain-substituted styrene monomers have been reported in the literature. Of these hundreds of compounds only three, divinylbenzene, vinyltoluene, and α-methylstyrene, are produced on a commercial scale. Some interest has also been shown in the production of chlorostyrene. In general these products are used in specialty applications and do not begin to rival styrene in volume or importance.

Divinylbenzene, $C_6H_4(CH{=}CH_2)_2$, is a specialty monomer used to produce cross-linked polystyrene resins. The monomer is manufactured by dehydrogenation of mixed isomeric diethylbenzenes. Commercial divinylbenzene monomer generally consists of diluted mixtures of m- and p-divinylbenzene.

The properties and analyses of two commercial grades of divinylbenzene are shown in Tables 8 and 9, respectively. Divinylbenzene is very easily polymerized to give brittle insoluble resins. To minimize this reaction, the product is heavily inhibited with TBC and is sold as a mixture with ethylvinylbenzene. The diethylbenzenes used in the manufacture of divinylbenzene are side products in the manufacture of ethylbenzene by the alkylation of benzene. Normally, these higher alkylated products are separated and recycled for dealkylation. However, it is a simple matter to retain some of the diethylbenzene stream for the manufacture of divinylbenzene. In a typical commercial alkylation, this crude fraction consists of a mixture of the three possible isomers of diethylbenzene in the proportions shown below and some *sec-* and *iso-*butylbenzenes, which are usually separated from the diethylbenzene before cracking.

Table 8. Physical Properties of Two Divinylbenzene Mixtures (7)

	Value	
Property	DVB-22[a]	DVB-55[a]
boiling point, at 760 mm Hg, °C	180.0	195.0
freezing point, °C		−45.0
flash point, Cleveland open-cup, °F	135.0	165.0
fire point, Cleveland open-cup, °F	135.0	165.0
explosive limits, in air, %	1.1–6.2	1.1
refractive index, n_D^{25}	1.5326	1.5585
viscosity, at 25°C, cP	0.883	1.007
density, at 25°C, g/cm³	0.8943	0.9126
surface tension, at 25°C, dyn/cm	30.55	32.10
critical pressure, P_c, atm	24.3	24.3
critical temperature, t_c, °C	348.0	369.0
latent heat of vaporization,		
at boiling point, ΔH_v, cal/g	76.6	83.8
solubility		
monomer in H₂O at 25°C, %	0.0065	0.0052
H₂O in monomer at 25°C, %	0.051	0.054
solvent compatibility		
acetone		∞
carbon tetrachloride		∞
benzene		∞
ethanol		∞

[a] Dow Chemical Company's designations for 22 and 55% divinylbenzene, respectively.

Table 9. Chemical Analysis of Two Divinylbenzene Mixtures (7)

Assay	DVB-22	DVB-55
	Parts per million	
polymer	100	100
aldehydes as CHO	40	40
peroxides as H₂O₂	5	5
sulfur as S	20	230
TBC	1000	1000
	Percent	
total unsaturation[a]	83.3	149.4
divinylbenzene		
meta	17.1	36.4
para	8.2	18.6
total	25.3	55.0
ethylvinylbenzene		
meta	23.1	25.0
para	10.0	13.0

[a] As ethylvinylbenzene.

Diethylbenzene	Boiling point, at 760 mm Hg, °C	Isomer formed in alkylation, %
ortho	184.4	9.4
meta	180.7	61.5
para	182.8	29.1

Dehydrogenation of the three isomers is carried out in an apparatus very similar to that used for styrene. Preheated vapors of the hydrocarbons are mixed with superheated steam and passed over catalysts of mixed metal oxides at temperatures around 600°C. The presence of two ethyl groups on the aromatic ring greatly increases the number of possible products. The major portion of the reaction effluent consists of *m*- and *p*-divinylbenzene, the corresponding ethylvinyl compounds, and some unreacted diethylbenzene. Essentially all of the *o*-diethylbenzene is isomerized to naphthalene in the dehydrogenation process. Minor contaminants also found are benzene,

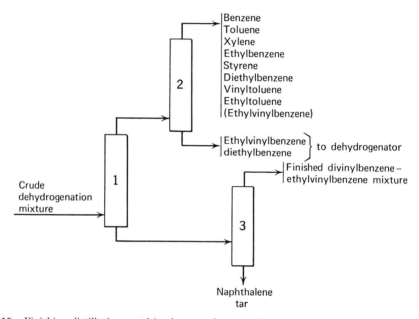

Fig. 10. Finishing distillations used in the manufacture of commercial divinylbenzene monomer.

toluene, vinyltoluenes, ethyltoluenes, xylenes, ethylbenzene, and styrene. The distillation and finishing of this mixture is an extremely sensitive procedure since divinylbenzene polymerizes very readily even at moderate temperatures. The finishing may be carried out in a series of three columns as shown in Figure 10. In the first column a rough separation of the monomers from the lighter materials is accomplished. Benzene, toluene, xylene, ethylbenzene, styrene, diethylbenzene, vinyltoluenes, ethyltoluenes, and some ethylvinylbenzenes are collected as distillates and subjected to further fractionation in column 2, where the lower-boiling materials are taken overhead to be sold as solvent or burned. It is impractical to recover styrene from this stream due to the likelihood of contamination with divinyl materials. The bottoms product of column 2, which is primarily diethylbenzene with some ethylvinylbenzene, is returned to the dehydrogenation reactor. Bottoms product from column 1, which contains most of the ethylvinylbenzene and the divinyl compounds plus some higher-boiling materials, is taken to column 3. Here, under a vacuum of 10–15 mm, a final distillation to remove the naphthalene and tars is carried out. Appropriate inhibitors are employed throughout this step to limit the polymerization of the monomers. For commercial production no attempt is made to further purify the monomer and it is generally sold as a mixture of components, chiefly divinylbenzene and ethylvinyl-benzene. For most applications divinylbenzene is used in low concentrations as a crosslinking agent and additional purification is neither necessary nor desirable. Ethylvinylbenzene is much like vinyltoluene and is easily incorporated into polymers of styrene.

Divinylbenzene can be readily produced by anyone who manufactures ethylben-zene. At present, however, only three companies, The Dow Chemical Company, Sinclair-Koppers Company, and The Foster Grant Company offer the monomer for sale. No production figures are available but it is estimated that no more than 3.0–3.5 million lb/yr of actual divinylbenzene are manufactured domestically. The current price for the 55%-grade monomer is 80–90¢/lb based on the pure divinylbenzene content.

The analytical techniques for trace impurities in divinylbenzene are the same as those mentioned for styrene. Analysis of the various hydrocarbons in the mixture is performed by gas chromatography (83,84).

Divinylbenzene is very closely related to styrene monomer in its toxicological properties. The precautions listed in the section on styrene should serve as a guide to the safe use of this monomer as well. Because of the ease with which it undergoes polymerization, however, additional precautions must be taken for the storage of divinylbenzene mixtures. Usually the monomer is heavily inhibited with about 1000 ppm of TBC to prevent polymerization and oxidation. This, in addition to storing the product at ambient or cooler temperatures, should provide a shelf life of one month or more.

Homopolymerized divinylbenzene formulations result in brittle, unsatisfactory polymers. However, if divinylbenzene is copolymerized in low concentrations with styrene, polymers are obtained which have the appearance of polystyrene but possess higher heat distortion temperatures, greater hardness, and slightly better impact and tensile strength qualities. Polymers formulated with divinylbenzene are used in applications where additional heat resistance and strength are required. The increased thermal distortion temperatures allow the plastics to be machined more easily and permit broader use of the material in electrical insulation applications. Suspension-polymerized beads of styrene–divinylbenzene are used as the basis of ion-exchange resins. (The ionic sites are formed later by substitution of the aromatic nuclei.) The crosslinks in the bead structure help stabilize them and minimize swelling. Ion-exchange resins consume a large fraction of all divinylbenzene production. Divinyl-benzene also finds application in styrene–butadiene rubber. The swelling, shrinkage, and extrusion properties of the product are improved by adding small amounts of the monomer to the formulation.

Vinyltoluene, $CH_3C_6H_4CH{=}CH_2$, is a specialty monomer with properties very similar to those of styrene. It was originally developed to replace styrene when benzene supplies began to dwindle after World War II. It is more difficult to manufacture than styrene and, with the development of new sources of benzene from petroleum, styrene retained its lead position.

Table 10. Physical Properties of a 60/40 Mixture of *m*- and *p*-Vinyltoluene (7)

Property	Value
boiling point at 760 mm Hg, °C	172.0
freezing point, °C	−77.0
flash point, Cleveland open-cup, °F	140.0
fire point, Cleveland open-cup, °F	155.0
autoignition temperature, °F	1067.0
explosive limits, in air, %	1.9–6.1
vapor pressure, at 20°C, mm Hg	1.15
critical pressure, P_c, atm	41.5
critical temperature, t_c, °C	382.0
critical volume, V_c, ml/g	3.33
refractive index, n_D^{20}	1.5422
viscosity, at 20°C, cP	0.837
surface tension, at 20°C, dyn/cm	31.66
density, at 20°C, g/ml	0.8973
specific heat, vapor, at 25°C, C_p, cal/(g)(°C)	0.2936
latent heat of vaporization, H_v, cal/g	
at 25°C	101.84
at boiling point	83.47
heat of combustion, gas at const pressure, at 25°C, ΔH_c, kcal/mole	1151.18
heat of formation, liquid, at 25°C, ΔH_f, kcal/mole	27.60
heat of polymerization, kcal/mole	16.0 ± 1.0
Q value	0.95
e value	−0.89
volumetric shrinkage upon polymerization, %	12.6
cubical coefficient of expansion, at 20°C, per °C	9.361×10^{-4}
solubility, at 25°C, %	
monomer in H_2O	0.0089
H_2O in monomer	0.047
solvent compatibility	
acetone	∞
carbon tetrachloride	∞
benzene	∞
ether	∞
n-heptane	∞
ethanol	∞

Physical properties of the commercial product, a 60/40 mixture of *m*- and *p*-vinyltoluene, produced by The Dow Chemical Company, are shown in Table 10.

Chemically, the manufacture of vinyltoluene is analogous to the styrene process with toluene substituted for benzene. The actual production of the monomer, which is described in detail in a patent to Amos and Coulter (85), is somewhat more complicated than the styrene operation, however.

A mixture of ethyltoluenes is produced by reacting toluene and ethylene in the presence of aluminum chloride in a reactor similar to that used for ethylbenzene manufacture. Unlike the alkylation of benzene, the reaction with the higher-boiling toluene cannot be run effectively under reflux conditions at atmospheric pressure. External

Table 11. Composition of the Unrefined Product Obtained in the Manufacture of Ethyltoluene

Compound	Wt %	Compound	Wt %
benzene and "lights"	0.2	p-ethyltoluene	11.9
toluene	48.3	m-ethyltoluene	19.3
ethylbenzene		o-ethyltoluene	3.8
and xylenes	1.2	(polyethyl)toluenes	14.4
		tar	0.9

cooling is required to keep the reaction temperature below 100°C; this minimizes the side reactions. The crude product from the alkylation is cooled and washed with alkali. A typical analysis of this mixture is shown in Table 11. A series of five fractional distillations is used to purify the alkylation product (8). Toluene and the (polyethyl)toluenes are recycled back to the alkylator. Benzene, ethylbenzene, and other valuable products are reclaimed for use elsewhere.

In the final distillation the mixture of ethyltoluene isomers is fractionated to remove the ortho isomer (bp, 165.1°C) from the m- and p-isomers (bp, 161.3°C and 162°C, respectively). It is essential to minimize the content of ortho isomer of the dehydrogenation mixture because this isomer can undergo ring closure to indene and indane in the cracking process. These contaminants cannot be easily removed from the vinyltoluene and their presence results in inferior polymers from the monomer. In practice, about 94% of the m- and p-ethyltoluenes is recovered in the overhead of the final distillation with an ortho content of less than 0.2%. The residue, which consists of the bulk of the ortho product and the remainder of the other two isomers, is returned to the alkylator where the ortho compound serves to suppress the formation of more of this unwanted substance and is isomerized to the m- and p-isomers.

The dehydrogenation of the mixture of m- and p-ethyltoluene is very similar to that of ethylbenzene. The vapors are heated to 450–500°C, mixed with two to three times their weight of superheated steam, and passed over a dehydrogenation catalyst. The separation of the vinyltoluenes from the crude dehydrogenation mixture and the final finishing of the monomer pose a substantial technical problem due to the high boiling point of the monomer and its rapid rate of thermal polymerization. In addition, a variety of side products, which are formed in the cracking procedure, must be removed. The first and most difficult distillation separates ethyltoluene and the lower boiling materials from vinyltoluene and higher boiling compounds by employing three distillation columns in series operating as a single unit. In this manner, it is possible to keep the bottom temperatures of these stills below the point at which polymerization is a serious problem. Operating pressures can be as low as 20 mm Hg, and polymeriza-

Table 12. Chemical Analysis of Commercial Vinyltoluene

Assay	ppm[a]	Assay	ppm[a]
purity	99.6[b]	peroxides as H_2O_2	5
polymer	none	chlorides as Cl	5
phenylacetylene	58	TBC	12
aldehydes		m-vinyltoluene	60[b]
as CHO	10	p-vinyltoluene	40[b]

[a] Unless otherwise indicated.   [b] Percent.

tion inhibitors are employed. A final finishing column is used to distill the monomer from residual contaminants, affording vinyltoluene of greater than 99% purity.

All of the vinyltoluene currently manufactured is made by The Dow Chemical Company using this process. The capacity of this operation has not been reported. The price of vinyltoluene in 1968 was approx 13–16¢/lb. The analysis of commercial vinyltoluene is given in Table 12.

Vinyltoluene is very similar to styrene in toxicological properties. Vapor tests with animals have shown that atmospheric concentrations of 600 ppm can be tolerated for repeated 7-hr exposures over prolonged periods of time without adverse effect. Concentrations of this magnitude are very irritating to the eyes and nasal passages, however. The odor of vinyltoluene can be detected below 10 ppm and is quite apparent at 100 ppm. One hundred ppm is the maximum level recommended (86) as reasonable for a normal working environment. Vinyltoluene is somewhat less flammable than styrene due to its lower volatility. The monomer is more easily polymerized, however,

Table 13. Physical Properties of α-Methylstyrene (7)

Property	Value
boiling point at 760 mm Hg, °C	165.0
freezing point, °C	-23.2
flash point, Cleveland open-cup, °F	136.0
fire point, Cleveland open-cup, °F	136.0
explosive limits in air, %	0.7–3.4
vapor pressure, at 20°C, mm Hg	1.90
critical pressure, P_c, atm	43.2
critical temperature, t_c, °C	384.0
critical volume, V_c, ml/g	3.26
refractive index, n_D^{20}	1.53864
viscosity, at 20°C, cP	0.940
surface tension, at 20°C, dyn/cm	32.40
density, at 20°C, g/ml	0.9106
specific heat, liquid, at 40°C, cal/(g)(°C)	0.489
specific heat, vapor, at 25°C, C_p, cal/(g)(°C)	0.29534
latent heat of vaporization, ΔH_v, cal/g	
at 25°C	96.69
at boiling point	78.0
heat of combustion, gas at const pressure,	
at 25°C, ΔH_c, kcal/mole	1162.46
heat of formation, liquid, at 25°C,	
ΔH_f, kcal/mole	27.00
heat of polymerization, kcal/mole	9.5
Q value	0.76
e value	-1.17
cubical coefficient of expansion, at 20°C, per °C	9.744×10^{-4}
solubility, at 25°C, %	
monomer in H_2O	0.056
H_2O in monomer	0.010
solvent compatibility	
acetone	∞
carbon tetrachloride	∞
benzene	∞
n-heptane	∞
ethanol	∞

and should be inhibited with 10–50 ppm of TBC. Storage of bulk quantities at temperatures below 50°F is preferred.

Although vinyltoluene is readily polymerized at elevated temperatures to give colorless polymers of high clarity, it is generally used in copolymers and as a specialty monomer for paint, varnish, and polyester preparations. The increased solubility in aliphatic solvents and the faster reaction rates resulting from the added methyl group are properties which make this monomer particularly well suited to these specialty applications.

α-Methylstyrene, $C_6H_5CCH_3{=}CH_2$, is an aromatic monomer with polymerization characteristics considerably different from those of styrene or vinyltoluene. It is produced commercially by the dehydrogenation of isopropylbenzene (cumene) and also as a by-product in the manufacture of phenol and acetone by the cumene oxidation process. The physical properties of α-methylstyrene are given in Table 13.

The addition of the α-methyl group to the vinyl side chain of styrene considerably alters its chemical reactivity. Radical polymerization of the pure monomer proceeds very slowly and is not a practical technique. The monomer can be copolymerized in this fashion, however. Homopolymers of α-methylstyrene may be prepared by ionic catalysis of the monomer.

The Dow Chemical Company produces α-methylstyrene directly by dehydrogenating cumene (qv). In this process, cumene is manufactured by the liquid-phase alkylation of benzene with propylene using an aluminum chloride catalyst. The reaction proceeds more readily than the analogous addition of benzene to ethylene and, therefore, reaction temperatures are generally lower (40–100°C).

Propylene streams can be of varying concentration with respect to this reactant but must be essentially free of ethylene and other unsaturated hydrocarbons. The crude reaction mixture consists primarily of unreacted benzene, cumene, and some (polyisopropyl)benzenes. A series of distillations are used to remove the benzene and (polyisopropyl)benzenes from the product. These materials are recycled back to the alkylator where, through alkylation and transalkylation, they are converted to more cumene. An 88% overall yield of cumene is generally obtained at 40% conversion with respect to benzene.

In addition to aluminum chloride, cumene manufacturers have found that a variety of other catalysts are also applicable to the alkylation process (87). One of the largest cumene manufacturers employs phosphoric acid under adiabatic conditions at elevated temperatures and pressures (88). In this operation, it is necessary to use a high benzene-to-propylene ratio to minimize the polymerization of the propylene. A nonswellable, bentonite-based catalyst has also been used for the alkylation of benzene and the dealkylation of (polyisopropyl)benzenes (89). More recently, catalysts containing boron trifluoride have been investigated for this reaction (90–92). Some of the more specialized materials exhibit a substantial degree of selectivity for propylene over ethylene in the alkylation procedure. Thus, alumina, modified by treatment with thiophene and BF_3, gives conversions of 88.3% with respect to propylene and only 3.5% with respect to ethylene when both are present in appreciable amounts (93). Most of the cumene manufactured is used in the production of phenol and acetone.

The direct dehydrogenation of cumene can be accomplished under conditions very similar to those employed in the manufacture of styrene from ethylbenzene. In a typical operation, a mixture of three parts steam to one part cumene is passed rapidly over an iron oxide dehydrogenation catalyst, such as Shell 105, at temperatures in the range of 550–600°C. The crude dehydrogenation mixture consists of cumene and α-methylstyrene, as well as small amounts of benzene, toluene, ethylbenzene, styrene, etc. The economical operation of this process demands that all of these components be separated and purified for reuse. This is accomplished through a series of fractional distillations.

The purification of small amounts of α-methylstyrene formed as a by-product in the cumene–phenol process is another important industrial source of the monomer. α-Methylstyrene generally represents about 1.7% of the total cumene conversion. In order to recycle cumene in the oxidation process, it must be essentially free of α-methylstyrene. Therefore, the hydrocarbon streams from the reaction must be subjected to a series of fractional distillations to remove this unwanted material. At present, some phenol manufacturers employing the cumene process find it more economical to hydrogenate the α-methylstyrene back to cumene and convert it to more phenol and acetone. Others have chosen to install additional finishing facilities for the monomer and market the compound in their product line. Monomer manufactured by this process is more likely to be contaminated with oxygen-containing compounds than α-methylstyrene produced directly by cumene dehydrogenation.

Propylene is in ready supply and therefore the production economics of α-methylstyrene could compare quite favorably with those of styrene if the former monomer were manufactured on a similar scale. The slow rate of thermal polymerization relegates the monomer to specialty applications, however, and total production amounts to only a small fraction of the volume of styrene monomer manufactured.

The price of α-methylstyrene varies from about 5–20¢/lb depending upon the quality and quantity of material. The following companies are the major U.S. manufacturers: The Dow Chemical Company, Midland, Mich., 10 million lb/yr; Allied Chemical Corporation, Frankford, Pa., 10 million lb/yr; Hercules Inc., Gibbstown, N.J., 3 million lb/yr. (The capacity data refer to July 1965.)

A chemical analysis of α-methylstyrene prepared by the dehydrogenation of cumene is given in Table 14.

Table 14.   Chemical Analysis of α-Methylstyrene Prepared by the Dehydrogenation of Cumene (7)

Assay	ppm[a]	Assay	ppm[a]
purity	99.3^b	peroxides as H_2O_2	3
polymer	none	TBC	15
aldehydes		β-methylstyrene	0.5^b
as CHO	10	cumene	0.2^b

[a] Unless otherwise indicated.   [b] Percent.

Toxicity studies with α-methylstyrene vapor indicate that repeated exposures of 200 ppm can be tolerated over prolonged periods of time without adverse effects. The American Conference of Governmental Industrial Hygienists has recommended a level of 100 ppm as a maximum limit for general working conditions (86). The odor of the monomer can be detected at concentrations below 10 ppm. This fact, plus the irritating nature of the vapor at high levels, serves as a convenient warning against the accumulation of dangerous concentrations in working areas. The higher boiling point of this compound raises the flash point to 136°F and reduces the possibility of explosive concentrations of vapor in the atmosphere. The low polymerization rate makes the monomer easier to store and virtually eliminates the dangers of a run-away thermal polymerization. Violent polymerizations initiated by ionic catalysts are still possible, however. TBC is added to the finished monomer to reduce oxidation on storage.

α-Methylstyrene is used widely in modified polyester and alkyd resin formulations where its distinctive properties, such as light color, are valuable. Copolymers of α-methylstyrene and methylmethacrylate have high heat-distortion properties and have been approved for use in food applications. Low-molecular-weight α-methylstyrene polymers are viscous liquids that are used as plasticizers in paints, waxes, adhesives, and plastics (95).

Chlorostyrene, $ClC_6H_4CH{=}CH_2$, is a reactive monomer produced in developmental quantities by The Dow Chemical Company. The monomer is manufactured from chloroethylbenzene by an oxidation technique. Both o- and p-chloroethylbenzene are used as a starting material and it is possible to produce monomer consisting of either pure o- or p-chlorostyrene or a mixture of the two.

Chlorostyrene monomer is more reactive than styrene and is easily polymerized under thermal conditions. (Polychloro)styrene is a clear, colorless plastic with good heat distortion and foaming properties. Reduced flammability is a further advantage of chlorostyrene polymers. The use of chlorostyrene in polyester formulations allows shorter cure schedules for resins. The properties of higher heat distortion and flame resistance are also incorporated into polyesters formulated with chlorostyrene.

Bibliography

"Styrene" in *ECT* 1st ed., Vol. 13, pp. 119–146, by A. L. Ward and W. J. Roberts, Pennsylvania Industrial Chemical Corporation.

1. R. H. Boundy and R. F. Boyer, eds., *Styrene, Its Polymers, Copolymers, and Derivatives*, Reinhold Publishing Corp., New York, 1952.
2. H. Ohlinger, *Polystyrol*, Springer-Verlag, West Berlin, 1955.
3. J. Elly, R. N. Haward, and W. Simpson, *J. Appl. Chem.* (*London*) **1**, 347 (1951).
4. C. H. Basdekis, "Styrene Polymers," in W. M. Smith, ed., *Manufacture of Plastics*, Reinhold Publishing Corp., New York, 1964.
5. H. Fikentscher, H. Gerrens, and H. Schuller, *Angew. Chem.* **72**, 856 (1960).
6. C. E. Schildknecht, *Polymer Processes*, Interscience Publishers, Inc., New York, 1956, Chap. 4.
7. *Styrene-Type Monomers*, Tech. Bull. No. 170-1514M-762, The Dow Chemical Company, Midland, Mich., July, 1962.
8. K. E. Coulter, H. Kehde, and B. F. Hiscock, "Styrene and Related Monomers," in E. C. Leonard, ed., *Vinyl Monomers*, Interscience Publishers, a div. of John Wiley & Sons, Inc., New York, 1969.
9. R. B. Stobaugh, *Hydrocarbon Process. Petrol. Refiner* **44** (12), 137 (1965).
10. E. V. Anderson, R. Brown, and C. E. Belton, *Ind. Eng. Chem.* **52**, 550 (1960).
11. F. R. Garner and R. L. Iverson, *Oil Gas J.* **63** (43), 86 (1965).
12. A. L. Foster, *Petrol. Engr.* **25** (11), C-3 (1953).
13. E. K. Jones, *Oil Gas J.* **58** (9), 80 (1960).
14. P. W. Sherwood, *Petrol. Refiner* **32** (1), 97 (1953).
15. V. N. Ipatieff and L. Schmerling, *Ind. Eng. Chem.* **38**, 400 (1946).
16. P. W. Sherwood, *Ind. Chemist* **30**, 25 (1954).
17. H. W. Grote and C. F. Gerald, *Chem. Eng. Progr.* **56** (1), 60 (1960).
18. H. W. Grote, *Oil Gas J.* **56** (13), 73 (1958).
19. R. E. Cosner, *European Chem. News* (*London*) (*Large Plant Suppl.*) **1966**, 29 (Sept. 30).
20. U.S. Pat. 3,200,163 (1965), E. R. Fenske (to Universal Oil Products Co.).
21. U.S. Pat. 3,183,233 (1965), H. S. Bloch (to Universal Oil Products Co.).
22. Brit. Pat. 905,051 (1962), Universal Oil Products Co.
23. *Chem. Week* **98** (7), 80 (1966).

24. *A Report on Linde Molecular Sieve Catalyst SK-500*, Union Carbide Corp., Linde Division, 1967.
25. H. J. Sanders, H. F. Keag, and H. S. McCullough, *Ind. Eng. Chem.* **45** (1), 2 (1953).
26. G. A. Olah, ed., *Friedel-Crafts and Related Reactions*, Interscience Publishers, a div. of John Wiley & Sons, Inc., New York, 1964.
27. J. N. Hornibrook, *Chem. Ind.* (*London*) **1962**, 872.
28. *Chem. Week* **99** (21), 115 (1966).
29. *Chem. Week* **97** (20), 49 (1965).
30. Belg. Pat. 641,452 (June 18, 1964), Halcon International, Inc.
31. Belg. Pat. 644,090 (Feb. 20, 1964), Halcon International, Inc.
32. *Chem. Week* **99** (6), 19 (1966).
33. *Chem. Week* **99** (5), 49 (1966).
34. *Chem. Week* **100** (4), 60 (1967).
35. Neth. Appl. 6602321 (1966), Chai Y. Choo (to Halcon International, Inc.).
36. Neth. Appl. 6409211 (1964), Distillers Co., Ltd.
37. U.S. Pat. 3,247,273 (1966), R. M. Mantell and L. Bajars (to Petro-Tex Chemical Corp.).
38. Belg. Pat. 617,890 (1962), L. Bajars (to Petro-Tex Chemical Corp.).
39. U.S. Pat. 3,024,053 (1962), A. Saffer and R. S. Barker (to Scientific Design Co., Inc.).
40. U.S. Pat. 3,299,155 (1967), C. R. Adams (to Shell Oil Co.).
41. J. E. Mitchell in reference 1, p. 35.
42. H. Ohlinger and S. Stadelmann, *Chem. Ing. Tech.* **37**, 361 (1965).
43. M. Sittig, *Chemical Processes Monograph No. 24, Vinyl Monomers and Polymers*, Noyes Development Corp., Park Ridge, N.J., 1966.
44. U.S. Pat. 2,831,907 (1958), F. D. Mayfield and J. C. Shaw.
45. U.S. Pat. 2,813,089 (1957), W. W. Twaddle, A. A. Harban, and V. W. Arnold (to Standard Oil Co.).
46. Neth. Appl. 6606930 (1966), Shell International Research Maatschapij N. V.
47. Belg. Pat. 664,144 (1965), H. A. Huckins, Jr., H. Gilman, and T. W. Stein (to Halcon International, Inc.).
48. Neth. Appl. 6507180 (1965), Halcon International, Inc.
49. U.S. Pat. 3,100,807 (1963), C. G. Hatfield and G. H. Lovett (to Monsanto Chemical Co.).
50. U.S. Pat. 3,118,006 (1964), G. H. Lovett and E. M. Jones (to Monsanto Chemical Co.).
51. Belg. Pat. 618,932 (1962), H. A. Huckins, Jr. (to Scientific Design Co., Inc.).
52. U.S. Pat. 3,330,878 (1967), H. A. Huckins, Jr., H. Gilman, and T. W. Stein (to Halcon International, Inc.).
53. Belg. Pat. 617,881 (1962), H. A. Huckins, Jr., T. Q. Elliot, and H. Gilman (to Scientific Design Co., Inc.).
54. K. K. Kearby, *Ind. Eng. Chem.* **42** (2), 295 (1950).
55. U.S. Pat. 3,306,942 (1967), E. H. Lee (to Monsanto Chemical Co.).
56. Shell Chemical Corporation, Tech. Bull. SC: 55–24, April 1955.
57. U.S. Pat. 2,461,147 (1949), E. P. Davies and F. T. Eggertsen (to Shell Development Co.).
58. U.S. Pat. 2,785,991 (1957), L. M. Bennetch (to C. K. Williams & Co.).
59. U.S. Pat. 2,460,811 (1949), E. P. Davies and E. T. Eggertsen (to Shell Development Co.).
60. U.S. Pat. 2,408,140 (1946), C. L. Gutzeit (to Shell Development Co.).
61. U.S. Pat. 2,449,295 (1948), C. L. Gutzeit (to Shell Development Co.).
62. U.S. Pat. 3,084,125 (1963), F. J. Soderquist, L. K. Frevel, and H. D. Boyce (to The Dow Chemical Co.).
63. U.S. Pat. 3,223,743 (1965), A. C. MacFarlane (to Monsanto Chemical Co.).
64. G. A. Webb and B. B. Corson, *Ind. Eng. Chem.* **39**, 1153 (1947).
65. R. R. Wenner and E. C. Dybdal, *Chem. Eng. Progr.* **44** (4), 275 (1948).
66. S. Carra and L. Forni, *Ind. Eng. Chem. Process Design Develop.* **4** (3), 281 (1965).
67. B. Davidson and M. J. Shah, *IBM Journal* **1965**, 388 (Sept.–Nov.)
68. K. E. Coulter, *Petrol. Refiner* **31** (8), 95 (1952).
69. *Ibid.* (10), 145 (1952).
70. *Ibid.* (11), 156 (1952).
71. *Ibid.* (12), 137 (1952).
72. U.S. Pat. 3,309,295 (1967), R. P. Cahn and F. J. Herrmann (to Esso Research & Engineering Co.).

73. U.S. Pat. 3,282,576 (1966), W. Bruckert and D. I.-J. Wang (to Union Carbide Corp.).

74. U.S. Pat. 3,294,856 (1966), H. A. Huckins, Jr. (to Halcon International, Inc.).

75. Belg. Pat. 632,163 (1962), H. Gilman and J. J. Kirman (to Scientific Design Co., Inc.).

76. Belg. Pat. 610,408 (1962), H. Aldinger and E. Kissel (to Badische Anilin- und Soda-Fabrik A.G.).

76a. R. B. Stobaugh, *Hydrocarbon Process. Petrol. Refiner* **44**, 137 (1965).

76b. *Oil, Paint Drug Reptr.* **193** (25) 3 (June 17, 1968).

77. *1967 Book of ASTM Standards with Related Materials, Part 20*, American Society for Testing and Materials, Philadelphia, Pa., 1967, p. 1155.

78. *Ibid.*, p. 970.

79. *Oil, Paint, Drug Reptr.* **189** (16), 9 (1966).

80. *Chem. Week* **100** (11), 25 (1967).

81. H. C. Spencer, D. D. Irish, E. M. Adams, and V. K. Rowe, *J. Ind. Hyg. Toxicol.* **24**, 295 (1942).

82. *Chemical Economics Handbook*, Stanford Research Institute, Menlo Park, Calif., 1968.

83. E. Blasius and J. Beushausen, *Z. Anal. Chem.* **197**, 228 (1963).

84. R. H. Wiley and R. M. Dyer, *J. Polymer Sci.* **2A**, 3153 (1964).

85. U.S. Pat. 2,763,702 (1956), J. L. Amos and K. E. Coulter (to The Dow Chemical Co.).

86. *J. Occupational Med.* **5**, 491 (1963).

87. M. Sittig, *Chemical Processes Monograph No. 9, Chemicals from Propylene*, Noyes Development Corp., Park Ridge, N.J., 1965, p. 57.

88. *Chem. Eng.* **70** (9), 92 (1963).

89. U.S. Pat. 2,945,072 (1960), G. G. Toris (to Allied Chemical Corp.).

90. U.S. Pat. 3,197,522 (1965), H. L. Dimond and A. C. Whitaker (to Gulf Research & Development Co.).

91. U.S. Pat. 2,442,342 (1948), R. E. Burk and E. C. Hughes (to Standard Oil Company of Ohio).

92. U.S. Pat. 3,046,315 (1962), H. L. Dimond (to Gulf Research & Development Co.).

93. U.S. Pat. 3,086,998 (1963), G. L. Hervert and C. B. Linn (to Universal Oil Products Co.).

94. *Oil, Paint, Drug Reptr.* **188** (1), 9 (1965).

95. L. Crampton and S. S. Drake, in H. R. Simons and J. M. Church, eds., *The Encyclopedia for Basic Materials for Plastics*, Reinhold Publishing Corp., New York, 1967.

K. E. Coulter, H. Kehde, and B. F. Hiscock
The Dow Chemical Company

STYRENE OXIDE. See Epoxides, Vol. 8, p. 289.

STYRENE PLASTICS

This article describes the properties and uses of the principal products based on styrene polymers and copolymers. A fuller account, dealing also with the important subjects of commercial processes, polymerization and copolymerization kinetics, degradation, melt rheology, polymer physics, and physical constants will appear in the *Encyclopedia of Polymer Science and Technology* (Wiley-Interscience).

The first commercial process for producing styrene monomer in the United States was operated by Naugatuck Chemical Company in 1925, but owing to many difficulties manufacture was soon discontinued. At about the same time, I. G. Farbenindustrie began development work in Germany which was carried through to successful commercial conclusion. In 1930 The Dow Chemical Company entered the styrene field and ultimately became the first company in the United States to produce commercial styrene successfully. With the advent of World War II and the resulting loss of natural-rubber resources, the combined efforts of Carbide and Carbon Chemical Company, Koppers Company, Monsanto Company, and The Dow Chemical Company supplied up to 200 million lb of styrene monomer per year to be polymerized with butadiene in the production of GR-S rubber. See also Elastomers, synthetic; Styrene.

The tremendous expansion of styrene monomer production facilities, and the wealth of experience obtained by the above companies, laid the groundwork for the postwar development of polystyrene and styrene copolymer plastics. Latexes for paints and paper coatings, styrenated drying oils, styrenated alkyds as a base for many protective coatings, and styrene–polyester resins for laminated structures of exceptional strength, etc, illustrate still further uses for styrene. This chemical has become basic to many factors of our economy, ranging from synthetic-rubber automobile tires to high-impact polystyrene refrigerator parts and styrene-based latex paints. More information about styrene monomer is given by Coulter et al.   (see General references).

The following have been some of the major developments in the technology of styrene polymers in recent years:

1.   Advances in the understanding of thermal initiation and other mechanisms of styrene polymerization and depolymerization have occurred, along with the increased use of computers for simulating polymerization and copolymerization.

2.   There have been tremendous advances in the use of rubber-modified styrene systems and in our basic understanding of the molecular mechanisms involved. The advent of new tools and techniques, such as dynamic mechanical spectroscopy, phase-contrast microscopy, and osmium tetroxide staining in conjunction with electron microscopy, has aided greatly in the study of the rubber phase in impact polystyrenes.

3.   Two new forms of polystyrene have been prepared. They are the Ziegler-Natta isotactic crystalline polystyrene, readily obtainable as a quenched amorphous or as a partially crystalline polymer, and the Szwarc anionic polystyrene with $\bar{M}_w/\bar{M}_n$ in the range 1.05–1.10 with controlled molecular weight.

4.   A better knowledge of the radiation chemistry of styrene includes grafting, crosslinking, degradation, and polymerization.

5.   The use of foamed polystyrenes, in general, and, more specifically, of foamed objects made from foamable polystyrene beads has greatly increased.

6.   The knowledge and understanding of polystyrene has been vastly extended through the combined use of standard as well as new tools of physics and physical chemistry.

7.   New fabrication techniques have evolved, such as screw injection molding, automated vacuum forming, direct addition of glass fibers and polystyrene granules to injection-molding machines, blow molding of injection-molded parisons, and orientation of injection-molded parts.

8.   Formed parts can now be decorated by vacuum aluminizing, painting, and electroplating, with the latter two processes especially important for ABS polymers.

9.   Glass fibers are being used in injection-molded parts, particularly large moldings of SAN or SAN–ABS mixtures for automotive parts.

10.   Large end users of fabricated parts, such as appliance and automotive companies, have tended to become major producers.

11.   The image of polystyrene has improved, partly through better design of molds and dies, better fabricating procedures and, finally, through the tailoring of engineering properties into specialty polymers such as SAN and ABS.

12.   Packaging and furniture have become new major end uses for polystyrene-type products.

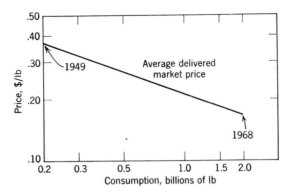

Fig. 1. Relationship of total domestic polystyrene consumption vs market price (1949–1968) (U.S. Tariff Commission and industry sources).

13. The worldwide increase in the consumption and production of styrene and polystyrene has been spectacular.

The production of styrene-based plastics has grown from less than 1 million lb in 1937 to about 2.8 billion lb in 1968 (including paint and foam). In 1948, when the 100-million-lb mark was achieved, general-purpose polystyrene was the main product. Today (1969) rubber-modified styrene homopolymers and copolymers are the biggest subgroup in this family of plastics. Corresponding to this growth, the price per pound of polystyrene has dropped from 89¢ in 1937 to 32.5¢ in 1953 and to 15.5¢ in 1968 (1). For illustration, the polystyrene price-volume relationship is shown in Figure 1. Polystyrene prices have remained relatively constant during the period 1966–1968. Much of the growth of polystyrene has been due to a combination of its favorable characteristics. Styrene-based plastics are easily fabricated, are one of the least-expensive families of plastics, and are amenable to many modifications. All of these factors have made possible a tremendous growth in new applications. Uses of styrene-based plastics in packaging and appliances, and as engineering plastics in the automotive industry, are just a few examples of significant growth.

All styrene-based plastics designed for use in extrusion or molding are available in granular form in a wide variety of shapes and sizes, in a wide range of colors, and with various additives. The nature and the amount of the additives depends on the specific application and/or method of fabrication. For example, materials for extrusion applications generally require little or no additives, while those for molding may require both internal and external lubricants. Also, depending on the end use of these plastics, additives for extending the material or for modifying the mechanical properties can be incorporated. Such additives are inorganic fillers, glass fibers, etc.

The general mechanical properties of these polymers are given in Table 1. It can be seen that considerable differences in performance can be achieved by using the various styrene plastics. Within each group, of course, additional variation is expected. In choosing an appropriate resin for a given application, other properties and polymer behavior during fabrication must be considered. These factors depend on the combination of inherent polymer properties, the fabrication technique, and the devices (mold, vacuum forming, blow mold, etc) used for obtaining the final object. Accordingly, consideration must be given to such factors as the surface appearance of the part, the development of anisotropy—and its effect on mechanical strength—long-term

Table 1. Mechanical-Property Guide for Main Classes of Styrene-Based Plastics (2) (Injection-Molded Specimens)

Property	PS	SAN[a]	Glass-filled[b] PS (3)	Medium HIPS	HIPS	Super[d] HIPS	Medium ABS		Standard ABS	Super ABS
							Type 1	Type 2		
specific gravity	1.05	1.08	1.20	1.05	1.05	1.02	1.05	1.05	1.04	1.04
Vicat softening point, °F	205	225	218	217	203	195	210	226	218	226
tensile yield, psi	6,100	10,000	19,000	5,750	4,300	2,600	4,500	7,800	6,000	5,000
elongation, rupture, %	1.8	3.5	1.5	15	58	60	55	<10	~20[c]	~60[c]
modulus, psi	460,000	550,000	1,100,000	390,000	310,000	240,000	380,000	380,000	300,000	260,000
impact strength, notched Izod, ft-lb/in.	0.4	0.4	1.5	1.8	2.5	8	3.6	3.5	5	8
dart-drop impact strength	very low	very low	medium high	low	medium high	high	medium high	high	very high	very high
relative ease of fabrication	excellent	excellent	poor	excellent	excellent	excellent	excellent	good	good	medium good

[a] 24% acrylonitrile.
[b] 20% glass fibers.
[c] Data supplied by Borg-Warner Corp.
[d] Data supplied by Union Carbide Corp.

resistance of the molding to external strain and stresses, etc. Table 1 is somewhat limited in value and should be consulted only in a general sense.

Polystyrene and Copolymers

General-Purpose Polystyrene. Polystyrene (PS) is a high-molecular-weight (hmw) ($\bar{M}_w = 2\text{--}3 \times 10^5$) crystal-clear thermoplastic which is hard, rigid, and free of odor and taste. Its ease of heat fabrication, thermal stability, low specific gravity, and low cost, result in moldings, extrusions, and films of very low unit cost. In addition, PS materials have excellent thermal and electrical properties which make them useful as low-cost insulating materials.

Commercial polystyrenes are normally rather pure polymers. The amounts of styrene, ethylbenzene, and styrene dimers and trimers are minimized by effective devolatilization or by the use of catalysts for the mass and suspension processes, respectively. Polystyrenes with low overall volatile content have *high heat*-deformation temperatures. The very low monomer and other solvents (eg, ethylbenzene) containing PS's are useful in the packaging of *food*. The negligible level of extraction of organic materials from PS is of crucial importance in this application.

When additional lubricants, such as mineral oil, butyl stearate, etc, are added to PS, *easy-flow* materials are produced. Improved flow is usually achieved at the cost of lowering the heat-deformation temperature. *Stiff-flow* PS has a high molecular weight and a low volatile level and is useful for extrusion applications.

Specialty Polystyrenes. Specialty polystyrenes are available for both commercial and scientific use. While these polymers are essentially pure PS, their molecular structures and/or additives are so adjusted as to make them useful in special applications.

Standard polystyrenes are carefully prepared and characterized PS materials available from the National Bureau of Standards and the Pressure Chemical Company. Materials of both extremely narrow and relatively broad molecular-weight distribution are available. Pressure Chemical Company has narrow-range polystyrenes ranging in molecular weight from 600 to 2,000,900.

Monodisperse polystyrene latexes are produced by The Dow Chemical Company. Latex particle size ranges between 900 and 20,000 Å are available. Initially these latexes were primarily used for calibration in electron microscopy and in the mechanism studies of emulsion polymerization. More recently, however, diagnostic medical use has been predominant, along with calibration for scientific measurements (eg, light scattering, ultracentrifuge, filter pore size).

Isotactic polystyrene may be obtained by the polymerization of styrene with stereospecific catalysts of the Ziegler-Natta type (4,5). As a result of the regular isotactic structure, it can be crystallized and has a threefold helix-chain conformation. The isotactic polymer can exist in the amorphous or crystalline state. Samples quenched from the melt are amorphous but become crystalline if annealed for some time at a temperature slightly below the crystalline melting point. The rate of crystallization is relatively slow compared with other crystallizable polymers, such as polyethylene or polypropylene. In the amorphous state, isotactic polystyrene has properties very similar to those of conventional atactic polystyrene.

Crystalline polystyrene has a high melting temperature showing a first-order transition temperature of approx 240°C. It is insoluble in most common polystyrene solvents, and, as a result of the spherulitic structure of the crystalline phase, is opaque. The density of the 100% crystalline polymer is calculated to be 1.12 from x-ray data. Although polystyrene with a high degree of isotacticity has been prepared, only partially crystalline polymers have been obtained, generally with less than 50% relative crystallinity (6,7). The lack of commercial interest in isotactic polystyrene may be due in part to its low degree of crystallinity and its slow crystallization rate.

Stabilized polystyrenes are materials with low volatile content and with added light stabilizers, uv screening agents, antioxidants, and synergistic agents.

Stabilized polystyrenes are materials with low volatile content and with added light stabilizers, uv screening agents, antioxidants, and synergistic agents.

Early stabilization systems for PS utilized alkanolamines (qv) (8) and methyl salicylate. In recent years, improved stabilizing systems have been developed. These utilize a uv-radiation absorber (eg, Tinuvin P) together with a phenolic antioxidant. Iron as a contaminant, even at a very low concentration, can cause color formation during fabrication. This color formation can be appreciably retarded by using tridecyl phosphite as a costabilizer, with the uv-radiation absorber and the antioxidant (9). Rubber-modified styrene polymers are heat-stabilized with nonstaining rubber antioxidants (eg, Ionol).

Moldings for lighting fixtures are the main use for these polystyrenes.

Flame-retardant polystyrenes have also been developed through the use of additives. While the primary commercial developments are in the area of PS foams (see Foams), numerous general formulations have been suggested. Both inorganic (hydrated aluminum oxide, antimony oxide) and organic (alkyl and aryl phosphates) additives have been used (10). Synergistic effects between halogen compounds and free-radical initiators have been reported (11). Several new halogenated compounds, along with corrosion inhibitors, have been found to be effective additives to render styrene-based polymers self-extinguishing (12).

In the use of these polymers the manufacturer's recommendations with regard to maximum fabrication temperature should be carefully observed to avoid discoloration of the molded part or corrosion of the mold or the machine.

Antistatic polystyrenes have been developed through the internal-additive or coating approach to cope primarily with dust-collecting problems in storage. Large lists of commercial antistatic additives have been published (10). For styrene-based polymers, hmw alkyl and/or aryl amines, amides, quaternary ammonium compounds, anionics, etc, are used. See Antistatic agents.

PS resins are brittle, lmw polystyrenes which are sold in flake form. For instance, PS-2 resin (The Dow Chemical Company) has $\bar{M}_w = 32,000$, $\bar{M}_n = 11,000$. These resins find considerable use in the coating and lacquer industries.

Styrene Copolymers. Acrylonitrile, butadiene, α-methylstyrene, methyl methacrylate, and maleic anhydride have been copolymerized with styrene to yield commercially significant copolymers. Many other styrene copolymers have been prepared and studied, but they do not fall within the scope of this article.

Acrylonitrile copolymers with styrene (SAN) have been available for some time (13). Most of these polymers have been prepared at the crossover composition, which is about 24 wt % acrylonitrile. These copolymers are transparent, and, in comparison to PS, more solvent- and craze-resistant and relatively tough. They also constitute the rigid matrix phase of the ABS engineering plastics.

Other than crossover-composition copolymers are available from continuous-stirred low-conversion processes, where the composition drift does not cause loss of transparency. Copolymers with over 30% acrylonitrile are available.

Butadiene copolymers are mainly prepared in the composition range to yield rubbers (see Elastomers, synthetic). Many commercially significant latex paints are based on styrene–butadiene (weight ratio usually 60:40, high conversion) copolymers (see Coatings; Paints). Most of the block copolymers, prepared by anionic catalysts (eg, butyllithium), also fall in the category of elastomers. However, some of these block copolymers are thermoplastic rubbers which behave like crosslinked rubbers at room temperature but show regular thermoplastic flow at elevated temperatures (14). Some styrene–butadiene block copolymers are useful as polymeric oil-in-oil emulsifiers for rubber–polystyrene solutions (15). These block copolymers represent a class of new and interesting polymeric materials and are receiving considerable attention in the scientific literature (16). Of particular interest are their morphologies (17–19), solution properties (20), and mechanical behavior (19,21).

α-Methylstyrene in styrene copolymers or terpolymers is useful in stiffening the polymer chain and improving the heat-deformation temperature. Usually, higher polymer-fabrication temperatures are required for these materials.

Methyl methacrylate copolymers with styrene are clear materials which when properly stabilized are similar in their light stability to poly(methyl methacrylate). About 60 wt % of methyl methacrylate is needed in the polymer for markedly improved light stability over that of polystyrene.

Maleic anhydride copolymers with styrene tend to have an alternating structure. Accordingly, equimolar copolymers are normally produced, corresponding to 48 wt % of maleic anhydride. However, by utilizing continuous-stirred, low-conversion processes, copolymers with a low maleic anhydride content can be produced (22). Depending on their molecular weights, these can be used as chemically reactive resins (eg, epoxy systems, coating resins, etc) for PS-foam nucleation (23), or as high-heat-deformation molding materials.

Graft copolymers utilizing styrene are reported in numerous publications and are summarized in several textbooks (24–26). In addition to the styrene or styrene–acrylonitrile grafting onto butadiene elastomers, which is the basis of high-impact styrene polymers, many other grafting systems have been studied. Polyethylene, cellulose, and poly(vinyl chloride) are examples of other substrate polymers for styrene grafting.

The grafting of styrene onto poly(vinyl chloride) (PVC) is a good example of the use of simultaneous irradiation of a radiation-sensitive polymer and a radiation-insensitive monomer (27). In a composition range from 10 to 30% styrene, the reaction occurs in the gel phase, and no excess of monomer is employed. Measurements of physical properties reveal that the PVC–styrene-graft copolymer system is easily fabricated before irradiation, while the cured product has improved tensile strength, elongation, and flexural strength compared to pure PVC or pure polystyrene. These properties are at a maximum in the composition range that corresponds to a maximum in the density of the graft copolymer.

Polymers of Styrene Derivatives

Many styrene derivatives have been synthesized (28) and the corresponding polymers and copolymers prepared. Differences in a series of substituted styrene

Table 2. Glass-Transition Temperature and Limiting Softening
Points of Substituted Polystyrenes

Substituent	Glass transition, °C (31)	Limiting softening point, °C (32)
none	100	105
o-methyl	136	125
m-methyl	97	82
p-methyl	93	101
2,4-dimethyl	112	130
2,5-dimethyl	143	134
2,4,6-trimethyl		162
p-tert-butyl	130	128 (132)
p-chloro	110	128
2,5-dichloro	106	137
2,5-difluoro		101
α-methyl	170	192

polymers are shown in Table 2, which gives glass-transition temperatures (T_g) and limiting softening-point data for comparison. The highest glass temperature is that of poly-α-methylstyrene $(T_g = 170°C)$, which can be prepared by anionic polymerization. Unfortunately, since it has a low (61°C) ceiling temperature (29), depolymerization can occur during fabrication, with the formed monomer acting as a plasticizer and lowering the heat distortion to 110–125°C. The polymer is difficult to fabricate because of its high melt viscosity (stiff chains) and is more brittle than PS, but can be toughened with rubber.

In addition to altering the softening point of styrene polymers, substitution brings about changes in solubility and chemical reactivity. For instance, water solubility is achieved in poly(sodium styrenesulfonate), while reactivity is enhanced in poly-p-bromostyrene. The latter can be metalized with Na or K to establish sites for graft polymerization (30).

Some polymers from styrene derivatives seem to meet specific market demands and to have the potential to become commercially significant materials. For instance, narrow-molecular-weight-distribution poly-p-tert-butylstyrene is effective in improving the viscosity index of motor oils (36), and also exhibits an excellent heat-deformation temperature as a molding polymer. Poly(chlorostyrene) can be readily rendered self-extinguishing, while maintaining a good balance of desirable mechanical properties. Monomeric chlorostyrene is useful in glass-reinforced-polyester recipes since it polymerizes several times as fast as styrene (28). Poly(sodium styrenesulfonate) is a versatile water-soluble polymer and finds use in water-pollution control and as a general flocculant (34,35). Poly(vinylbenzylammonium) chloride has been found useful as an electroconductive resin (37).

In addition to the polymerization of styrene derivatives, PS can be chemically modified to produce more reactive species. Jones (33) has reviewed such reactions.

Rubber-Modified Styrene Polymers

Rubber-Modified Polystyrene. Rubber has been incorporated into polystyrene primarily to impart toughness. The resulting materials are commonly called high-impact polystyrenes (HIPS) and have become available in many different varieties.

In 1964, HIPS production in the United States accounted for over 50% (685 $\times$ 10^6 lb) of all polystyrene produced (1). General-purpose polystyrene, however, has grown faster than HIPS, although HIPS has most of the advantages of PS, such as rigidity, ease of fabrication, and the variety of colors and granule sizes available. In addition, these impact polymers are tough and resistant to abuse. Being a two-phase system, they are not available in transparent forms; however, some translucent varieties in the medium-impact-strength range can be obtained.

In rubber-modified polystyrenes, the rubber is dispersed in the polystyrene matrix in the form of discrete particles. The nature of these particles, and the particle-matrix interface, involve some complex questions concerning the true crosslink density of elastomers, occlusions, particle size and distribution, etc, which are not fully understood. However, some fundamental work on several special aspects of HIPS has been carried out. For instance, works on the mechanism of rubber-particle formation (38) and rubber reinforcement (39–42) have been published. Several general reviews of HIPS and other heterogeneous polymers have also appeared (43–45).

The photomicrographs in Figure 2 are representative of the morphology of the presently available HIPS materials (46,48) showing rubber-particle sizes ranging from less than 1 μ to as high as about 10 μ. If particles much larger than this are found, poor surface appearance of moldings, extrusions, and vacuum-formed parts are usually noted. It should also be pointed out that while most commercial HIPS contains approx 3–10 wt % of polybutadiene or styrene–butadiene copolymer rubber, the presence of PS occlusions within the rubber particles gives rise to a volume fraction of the reinforcing rubber phase of 10–40% (40,47). Accordingly, a significant portion of the PS matrix is filled with rubber particles. New techniques have been published for evaluating the morphology of HIPS (48,50,78).

Torsion-pendulum characterization of these typical HIPS's also reveals their heterogeneous nature by showing two distinct damping peaks, viz, the rubber peak (-60 to $-80°C$) and the polystyrene peak at about 90–100°C (46). The glass temperature of the rubber is also shown by these data.

For further comparison, the molecular-weight distribution of the soluble portion of these HIPS's is shown in Table 3 (46).

For effective toughening of otherwise brittle polystyrene with rubbers, the following generalizations can be made:

1. For good impact strength over a wide temperature range, the glass temperature of the rubber must be below $-50°C$, as measured, for example, by the torsion pendulum at 1 cps (Fig. 3). In the case of butadiene copolymers, this means that the vinyl comonomer should not exceed about 25 wt %.

2. The use of butadiene rubbers is particularly effective when the rubber is present during the polymerization of styrene. Grafting of some styrene to rubber takes place, and occlusion of polystyrene extends the volume fraction of the dispersed, reinforcing, rubber phase.

3. The rubber phase in the final product is crosslinked to some degree for the most effective reinforcement. Since the rubber phase exists in the form of discrete rubber particles, the degree of crosslinking does not significantly influence the melt flow, which is that of a linear (uncrosslinked) thermoplastic polymer. A variation in the degree of crosslinking may be needed to optimize product properties for different applications.

4. Depending on the process and rubber concentration used, there is some lati-

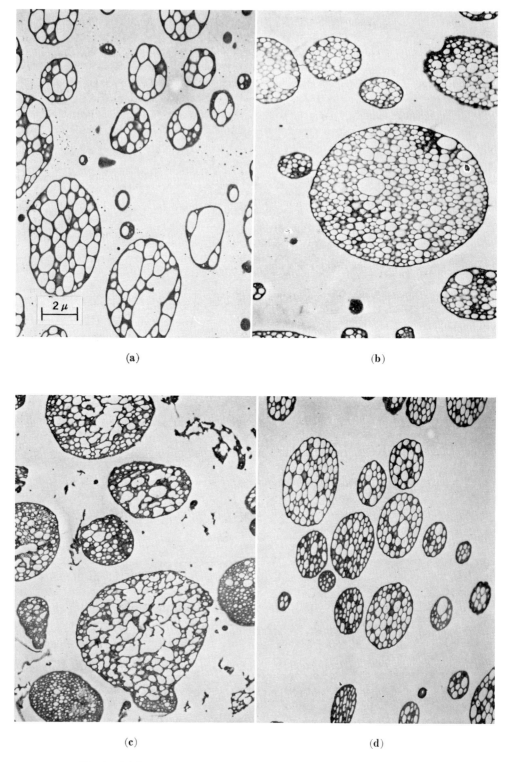

Fig. 2.   (a) Styron 456; (b) Hi-Test 88; (c) TGD-6600; (d) Elrex 422.

Table 3. Molecular-Weight Data of Commercial HIPS (Soluble Portion)

Material	Gel, %	$\bar{M}_z \times 10^3$	$\bar{M}_w \times 10^3$	$\bar{M}_n \times 10^3$	$\bar{M}_w/\bar{M}_n$
Dow, Styron 456	23.1	394	209	84	2.5
Monsanto, Hi-Test 88	20.7	587	251	73	3.4
Union Carbide, TGD-6600	19.4	466	252	104	2.4
Rexall, Elrex 422	23.1	299	164	73	2.2

tude in the size of the rubber particles that will result in a good balance of properties. This range may extend from <1 to >5 μ.

5. Mechanical blending of either gum rubbers or crosslinked rubber-latex solids and polystyrene does not give the most effective reinforcement, particularly if uncrosslinked gum rubber is used (51). This may be due to the fact that a relatively low volume fraction of rubber (no PS occlusions) is available and a less than optimum interface exists between the rubber and the PS matrix.

Medium-Impact Polystyrene. Medium-impact polystyrenes are available in a variety of granule sizes and colors. Also, translucent colors are available. This is possible because of the relatively low rubber concentration present in these polymers. Medium-impact polystyrenes exhibit properties between those of general-purpose and high-impact materials. Relatively little stress whitening is observed when they are deformed.

These polymers are used when only a moderate increase in impact strength over that of polystyrene is required and where the other desirable properties of polystyrene are to remain unaltered. Although all types of fabrication techniques are possible with these polymers, generally injection molding is used for packaging, housewares, toilet seats, enclosures, light diffusers, etc.

High-Impact Polystyrene. The high-impact polystyrenes are available in opaque, naturally white granules or in pigmented formulations. These polymers usually contain about 5–10% polybutadiene or copolymer rubber. However, special grades of higher-impact materials, containing up to 25% rubber, are available. The high-impact materials, like polystyrene, are available in high-heat, easy-flow, etc, formulations and are used for injection molding, extrusion, thermoforming, and blow molding.

Usually many different formulations are offered by the manufacturers as tailor-made polymers to meet the specific fabrication and property requirements of a given application.

Rubber Modified Copolymers

Acrylonitrile–Butadiene–Styrene (ABS) Polymers. ABS polymers have become important commercial products since the mid-1950s. The development and properties of ABS polymers have been discussed in some detail by Basdekis (52). It is shown that the use of ABS plastics in the United States grew from less than 20×10^6 lb in 1958 to over 100×10^6 lb in 1964 and to 290×10^6 (53) in 1967. The growth of ABS polymers abroad has been equally dramatic. Prices in 1968 ranged from 25¢/lb for the medium-impact polymer to 40¢/lb. The high-impact varieties were about 36¢/lb. ABS polymers possess an excellent combination of mechanical and physical properties. Accordingly, they are generally considered engineering plastics with a high strength-to-weight ratio.

ABS polymers, like rubber-modified polystyrene, are two-phase systems in which

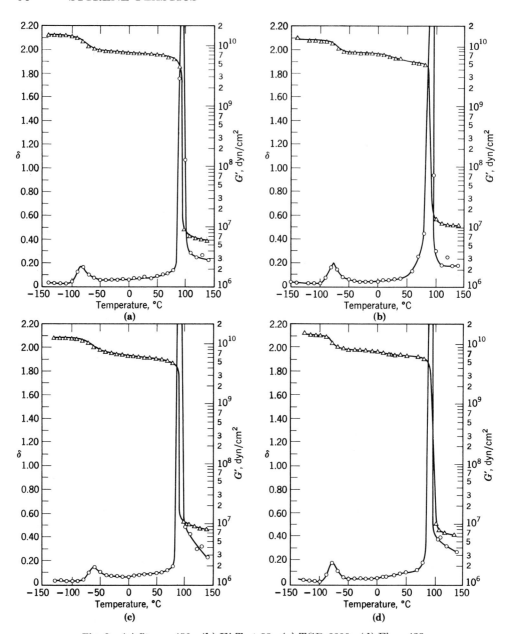

Fig. 3. (a) Styron 456; (b) Hi-Test 88; (c) TGD-6600; (d) Elrex 422.

the elastomer component is dispersed in the rigid styrene–acrylonitrile (SAN) copolymer matrix.   The four electron photomicrographs in Figure 4 show examples of the morphology of the commercially available ABS polymers (46).   The differences in structure of the dispersed phases are primarily a result of differences in the production processes, the types of rubber used, and the variation in rubber concentrations.

As with typical HIPS's, torsion-pendulum characterization of the four representative ABS polymers is presented (Fig. 5).   In addition to indicating the two-phase nature of these polymers, the glass temperature of the rubber is revealed,

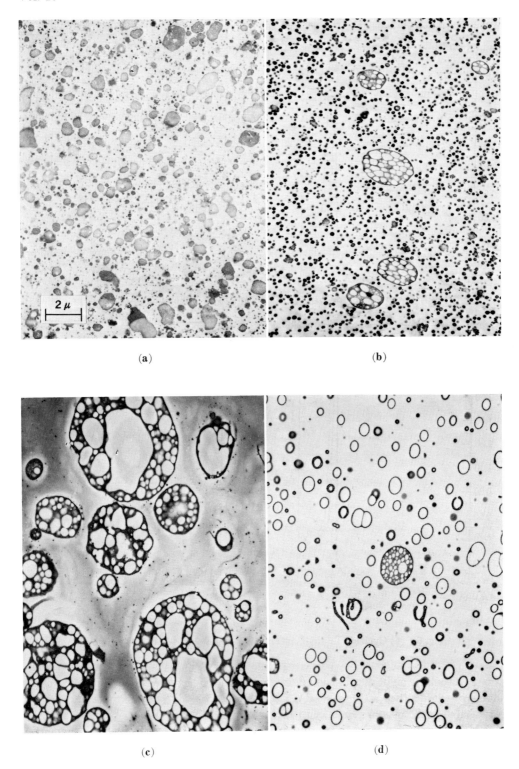

Fig. 4. (a) Cyclolac T; (b) Lustran I-440; (c) Tybrene 213; (d) TH resin.

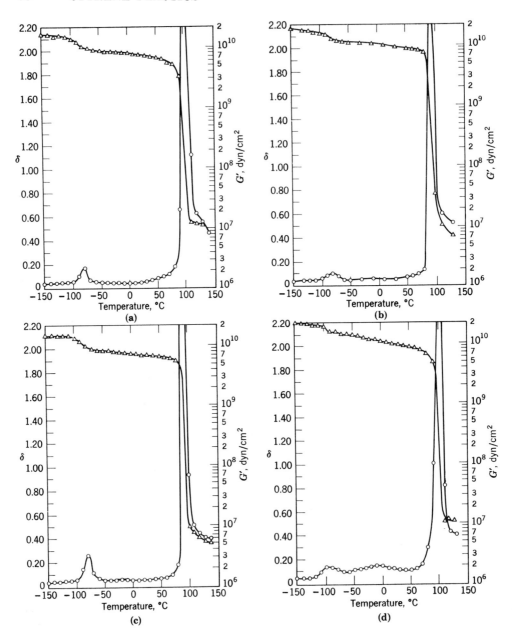

Fig. 5. (a) Cyclolac T; (b) Lustran I-440; (c) Tybrene 213; (d) TH resin.

Molecular-weight distribution data are not given for the ABS polymers because of numerous difficulties arising from the presumed process variations and the drift in copolymer composition. It is known, however, that some ABS polymers have relatively low molecular weights (on the order of $\bar{M}_w = 69,000$ (54)), while others have molecular weights in the range given in Table 3.

Because of the possible changes in the nature and concentration of the rubber phase, a wide range of ABS polymers is available. Generally they are rigid (modulus range at room temperature 2.5–4.5 × 10⁵ psi) and have excellent notched impact strength both at room temperature (2–8 ft-lb/in.) and at lower temperatures (eg, 0°F, 1–4 ft-lb/in.). This combination of stiffness, impact strength, and solvent resistance makes ABS polymers particularly suitable for high-abuse applications. Another important attribute of several ABS polymers is a minimum tendency to orient or develop mechanical anisotropy (55,56) during molding. Accordingly, uniformly tough moldings are obtained.

In addition, ABS polymers exhibit good ease of fabrication and produce moldings and extrusions which have excellent gloss and can be decorated by many techniques. Lacquer painting (57), vacuum metalizing (58), and electroplating (59,60) are the main techniques of decorating. In the case of electroplating, the strength of the molded piece is significantly improved (56). When an appropriate decorative coating or a laminated film is applied, ABS polymers are considered for outdoor uses (61).

Not only are ABS polymers useful engineering plastics, but some of the high-rubber compositions are excellent impact modifiers for PVC. The use of styrene–acrylonitrile-grafted butadiene rubbers as modifiers for PVC has been known since 1957 (62).

Medium-Impact ABS. Medium-impact ABS polymers are available for a variety of applications. The mechanical properties of polymers within this group can vary appreciably (Table 1). Both high- and low-tensile-strength materials corresponding to high and low melt viscosity, respectively, are available. Also, heat-deformation temperatures in different materials vary over a considerable range. These polymers are used in the packaging, automotive, and refrigeration industries. Many of the polymers are especially tailored for specific uses, where such considerations as oil resistance, the ability to decorate a molded part, heat-deformation temperature, or surface gloss are important.

High-Impact ABS. The standard high-impact ABS materials constitute the bulk of the ABS used. These materials, though more expensive, have several advantages over other styrene polymers. They have found extensive use because of their good surface appearance, relative ease of fabrication, good balance of mechanical properties (viz, excellent toughness, rigidity, and hardness), craze resistance, and ability to be decorated by several techniques. ABS moldings and extrusions resist considerable abuse. This is one of the main reasons for their wide acceptance.

ABS polymers are described as solvent-resistant plastics. Indeed, they are unaffected by water, inorganic salts, alkalis, and many acids. It should be remembered, however, that they are readily soluble in such organic solvents as ketones, esters, etc. They are resistant to many common stress-cracking liquids (eg, vegetable oils, some alcohols) and have good resistance to staining by foodstuffs.

ABS polymers can be fabricated by most of the techniques available for plastics and also by some metal-fabricating techniques. Cold forming is one such technique. Uses of ABS polymers vary from such demanding applications as golf-club heads, safety headgear, and luggage, to such large-scale uses as appliance housings, automotive parts, telephones, pipe, etc.

New Rubber-Modified Styrene Copolymers. Rubber modification of styrene copolymers other than HIPS and ABS has been useful for specialty purposes. Transparency has been achieved with the use of methyl methacrylate as a comonomer. TH resin is one such transparent high-impact polymer; other styrene–methyl methacrylate copolymers have also been successfully modified with rubber (119). Improved weatherability, permitting extended outdoor exposure of the material, is achieved by modifying styrene–acrylonitrile copolymers with a saturated, aging-resistant elastomer (120).

Glass-Reinforced Styrene Polymers

Glass reinforcement of polyesters and epoxy resins has become the basis of large industries. Also, the growth of the glass-reinforced thermoplastics (RTP, reinforced thermoplastics (63)) business has been outstanding. Styrene-based plastics have significantly contributed to this growth.

Glass reinforcement of PS and SAN markedly improves their mechanical properties. The strength, stiffness, and fracture toughness are generally at least doubled. Creep and relaxation rates are significantly reduced and creep rupture times increased. The coefficient of thermal expansion is reduced by more than one-half, and generally response to temperature changes is minimized (3). Normally, about 20% glass fibers (eg, 0.25 in. long, 0.00035 in. diam, "E" glass) can be used to achieve the above-mentioned improvements. Polystyrene, styrene–acrylonitrile copolymer, HIPS, and ABS, have all been used with glass reinforcement.

Four approaches are currently available for producing glass-reinforced parts: (1) use of a preblended reinforced molding compound, (2) blending of reinforced concentrates with virgin resin, (3) a direct process, in which the glass is cut and weighed automatically and blended with the polymer at the molding machine, and (4) general in-plant compounding (63). The choice of any of these processes depends primarily on the size of the operation and the corresponding economics.

The use of concentrates (eg, 80% glass, 20% polystyrene) for the subsequent blending to about 20% glass in the final product has many attractive features and seems to be appropriate for a medium-size operation, while the direct process is emphasized in very large scale operations.

The glass-reinforced thermoplastics are molded to many different shapes and sizes, and there seems to be no particular limit to these moldings. The 9-lb glass-filled SAN injection-molded instrument-panel assembly may serve as an example (64).

Characterization of Styrene-Based Plastics

Fractionation and Chemical Analysis. Before an adequate characterization of styrene-based polymers is possible, an effective fractionation must be carried out. A separation is also necessary for polystyrene in order to determine the nonpolymeric components, such as volatiles, lubricants, antioxidants, pigments, fillers, etc. For copolymers or blends, further fractionation may be required to determine if there is variation in the copolymer composition or if blends are present. These fractionations are considerably more involved than the simple fractionations for the separation of additives. Fractionation (eg, sand-column) for the purpose of molecular weight distribution studies is of less need because of the development and extensive use of gel-permeation chromatography (GPC).

For a homogeneous polymer or copolymer, the separation is relatively simple. The first step involves dissolving the polymer in an appropriate solvent (eg, methyl ethyl ketone, xylene, etc). The polymer is recovered by precipitation from the solution by addition of a nonsolvent (eg, methanol) after insoluble fillers have been removed. The lmw additives (also some very lmw polymers) remain in solution and are ready for further analysis.

A scheme for rubber-modified polymers is necessarily more complicated. A general method requires the separation of the elastomeric component from the rigid styrene polymer and additives. The dispersion of the whole polymer in an appropriate solvent system, followed by high-speed centrifugation at low temperature (54), effects this separation. The analysis of the elastomer phase, which in most cases is a pure graft copolymer or a mixture with the original rubber, is rather involved, and the possibility for error exists. For example, care must be exercised that all the occluded and chemically unbound polystyrene or copolymer is removed from the rubber particles before attempting to determine the quantity of grafted polymer. Unsaturation in the elastomer is determined by infrared (65,66), the peroxybenzoic acid method (65,67), or titration with iodine monochloride (68,69). An estimate of the graft level could be obtained from the difference between the unsaturation calculated as polybutadiene and the total weight of the gel. The composition of the original elastomer (it may have been a pure polybutadiene or a butadiene copolymer) can be estimated from the glass temperature of the rubber (44). However, more reliable methods for rubber–vinyl polymer graft determination involve chemical destruction of butadiene segments by ozonolysis (54,70,71), cleavage by periodic acid of rubber after treatment with peroxyformic acid (65), or cleavage by osmium tetroxide (72). Here, again, care is necessary. Control experiments with the pure graft component must be carried out so that degradation of the graft during the rubber destruction need not be a concern. Analyses of the polybutadiene fragments and the graft have been reported (54).

Molecular-Weight Determinations. The thermal and solvolytic stability of polystyrene, its solubility in a wide variety of solvents, freedom from structural anomalies such as branching and crystallinity, freedom from association, ease of fractionation, and, more recently, its ability to be made into narrow fractions, have resulted in polystyrene being the most extensively characterized polymer there is.

For industrial purposes in the United States, the 10%-solution viscosity is widely used as a measure to control molecular weights (Fig. 6).

Intrinsic viscosity is a widely used secondary standard; the constants K and a in the Mark-Houwink equation,

$$[\eta] = K\bar{M}_v{}^a$$

are determined on fractions by osmotic pressure and/or light scattering. Some fifty different sets of constants are listed in one tabulation. Of these, we have chosen one as illustrative, based on our own experience:

$$[\eta] = 11.0 \times 10^{-5} [M]^{0.725} \tag{73}$$

Molecular-weight distributions of polystyrene are generally studied by fractional precipitation (74b), velocity ultracentrifuge (74a), or gel-permeation chromatography (GPC) (74c,75). All of these techniques have been used with polystyrene and styrene copolymers. In the case of rubber-modified polymers, the gel phase usually has to be separated before determining the molecular weight of the soluble polymer, particularly when using light scattering or GPC (54). Molecular weight distribution measurements of copolymer systems are open to question because of possible composition drift.

Morphology. The two-phase nature of rubber-modified styrene polymers was first shown microscopically by Claver and Merz (76). A method for phase-contrast microscopy was reported by Traylor (77). Subsequently, a vapor etching and double-

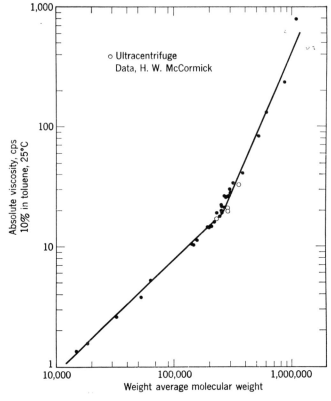

Figure 6.

replicating technique using an electron microscope was developed (50).   More recently, excellent resolution has been achieved by Kato (48), using osmium tetroxide (OsO_4)-staining of the rubber-containing heterogeneous polymers (eg, ABS).   Williams and Hudson (78) used this technique successfully with HIPS to reveal the inner structure of the rubber particle.   In addition to OsO_4, they used ionic radiation for the hardening of the rubber particles.   The electron photomicrographs shown in this article were obtained using the techniques of OsO_4 hardening.

Mechanical Behavior of Styrene-Based Plastics

Stress-Strain Properties.   Tensile measurements of styrene-based plastics are usually conducted by the ASTM procedure D638-61T.   The brittle PS or styrene copolymers and the more ductile rubber-modified polymers are all extended at 0.2–0.25 in./min.   The stress-strain data (tensile and elongation at yield and rupture, and modulus) are usually reported for room-temperature measurements (23 ± 1°C, 50 ± 2% rh).   Figure 7 depicts the stress-strain curves of some styrene-based plastics.   The data in Table 1 show some typical values.

When considering the stress-strain behavior of a plastic in detail, a more comprehensive study is needed.   In determining the strength of a material, the important variables are (1) the rate of extension, (2) the temperature, (3) the shape and the method of fabrication of the specimen, and (4) polymer orientation.

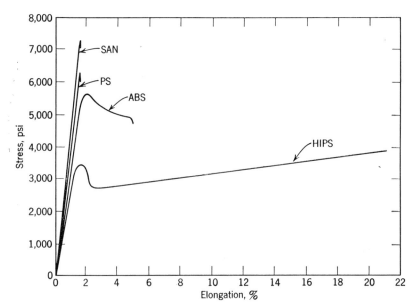

Fig. 7. Typical stress-strain curves of styrene-based plastics (compression-molded specimens). NOTE: There is considerable variation in ABS elongation data from different sources.

A change in the rate of extension can give rise to significant changes in a stress-strain curve. With increasing rate of extension, the tensile strength and modulus increase (79,80). However, the elongation at break tends to decrease, particularly in the case of HIPS (79–81). Therefore, it is important that careful consideration be given to the conditions of testing when using stress-strain data for designing or predicting the toughness of a material. The strain energy, derived from the area under the stress-strain curve, is considered to indicate the level of toughness of a polymer. From Figure 7, it is apparent that a HIPS has a higher strain energy than an ABS. When using different impact-testing techniques, it is found that many ABS materials are tougher than HIPS (55,82). The failure of the stress-strain curve to reflect this ductility can be related to the fact that ABS polymers tend to show only localized flow (necking tendency) at low rates of extension and hence produce a failure at low elongation. HIPS extends uniformly during such tests, and the test specimen whitens over all of its length, while extending well beyond the yield elongation. At higher testing speeds, ABS polymers also deform more uniformly and give high elongations (82).

The effect of temperature on the tensile strength of styrene polymers is rather significant. Increased temperature lowers the strength. Tensile modulus, on the other hand, in the temperature region of most such tests (−40 to 50°C), is affected only slightly. The elongations of PS and styrene copolymers do not vary much with temperature (−40 to 50°C), but the elongation of rubber-modified polymers at first increases with increasing temperature and ultimately decreases at high temperatures.

The orientation of the polymer in a fabricated specimen can significantly alter the stress-strain data as compared with the data obtained on an isotropic specimen (eg, obtained by compression molding). For instance, tensile strengths as high as 18,000 psi (83,84) have been reported for PS films and fibers. PS tensile strengths below 2000 psi have been obtained in the direction perpendicular to the flow.

Testing in compression and flexure also involves stress-strain measurements. Compression and flexural testing are usually performed in accord with ASTM D695-63T and D790-66, respectively. The general interpretation given in connection with the tensile testing above is considered appropriate. However, in flexural measurements, where the calculations are based on the outer-fiber stress, the calculated flexural-stress values can be significantly different from those calculated from tensile or compression measurements.

Creep, Stress Relaxation, and Fatigue. The long-term engineering tests on plastics in use environments and temperatures are considered very helpful in predicting the overall performance of a polymer in a given application.

Creep tests involve the measurement of deformation as a function of time at a constant stress (load). The creep rate increases with increased load and temperature. Accurate data for specific materials are needed for design purposes. In addition, accelerated tests are needed to predict the long-term behavior. For styrene-based plastics, many such studies have been carried out (85,86). Creep curves for styrene and its copolymers at room temperatures show low elongation, with only small variation with stress, while the rubber-modified polymers exhibit a low-elongation region, followed by crazing and increasing elongation, usually to about 20%, before failure (Fig. 8).

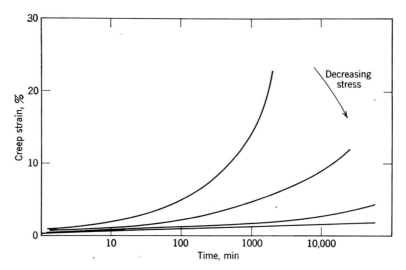

Fig. 8. Typical creep behavior of rubber-modified styrene polymers.

Creep tests are ideally suited for the measurement of long-term polymer properties in aggressive end-use environments. For example, creep is measured for HIPS and ABS specimens while they are exposed to vegetable oil to simulate a possible situation in a refrigerator. Both the time to failure and the ultimate elongation in such creep tests tend to be reduced. Another test to determine plastic behavior in a corrosive atmosphere is a prestressed creep test (87) in which the specimens are prestressed at different loads, lower than the creep load, before the final creep test.

Stress-relaxation measurements, where stress decay is measured as a function of time at a constant strain, have also been used extensively to predict the long-term behavior of styrene-based plastics (79,85). These tests have also been adapted to measurements in aggressive atmospheres (88). Stress-relaxation measurements are further used to obtain modulus data over a wide temperature range (89).

Fatigue is another property which is of considerable interest to the design engineer. Cyclic deflections of a predetermined amplitude, short of giving immediate failure, are applied to the specimen, and the number of cycles to failure is recorded. In addition to mechanically induced periodic stresses, fatigue failure can be studied when developing cyclic stresses by fluctuating the temperature.

Fatigue in polymers has been reviewed by Andrews (90). Detailed theory and practice of fatigue testing are covered. Fatigue tests are carried out for two main reasons: (*1*) to learn the inherent fatigue resistance of the material, and (*2*) to study the relation of the specimen design and fatigue failure. Fatigue tests are carried out both in air and in aggressive environments (91).

Impact Strength. Polystyrene and styrene copolymers are brittle polymers under normal-use conditions. A high-speed blow at temperatures below the glass temperature will cause catastrophic failure, without significant deformation, crazing, or yielding in the polymer. Rubber-modified styrene polymers, on the other hand, are significantly more impact resistant. Generally, both HIPS and ABS polymers exhibit ductile failure at room temperature when dealt an impact blow. These polymers are characterized by significant whitening (39) of the specimen during the test, due to craze formation (39) (see below under Crazing), separation of the rubber phase from the matrix polymer (40), and cracks. It should be pointed out, however, that the rubber-modified polymers exhibit brittle failure under certain test conditions and with certain specimen types, and then do not show the otherwise characteristic whitening.

When considering the toughness of a polymer, it is important to know at what conditions the specimen will give a brittle fracture (92). The change from ductile to brittle failure is usually accomplished by increasing the test speed or lowering the test temperature. The importance of knowing the point of incipient brittle fracture relates to the fact that most failures in plastics practice occur by a brittle mechanism, ie, whitening or yielding is seldom observed (92).

Accordingly, when testing a material for toughness by a notched impact test, the effect of both test temperature and notch radius should be investigated. Three-dimensional plots of such data have been reported (93). In addition to the comprehensive notched impact test, various dart-drop tests are of considerable use. Here again, brittle fracture can be induced if the test conditions are properly varied. It has been found with rubber-modified polymers that brittle fracture can be induced by lowering the test temperature and by reducing the radius of the dart tip (94).

A brittle fracture of a styrene polymer can also be brought about by producing uniaxially oriented moldings. Measuring the strength in these moldings across the flow direction, or by biaxial loading, such as in a dart-drop test, will show this embrittlement of an otherwise tough polymer. Injection moldings of HIPS produced at low temperatures have been shown to be particularly prone to brittle fracture, while the ABS polymers in general are less subject to fabrication-induced anisotropy and the consequent embrittlement (55). However, Cleereman (95) has shown that tough moldings of PS can be obtained through the introduction of balanced, multiaxial orientation. One way this orientation can be achieved is by molding objects with rotational symmetry at low molding temperatures and by rotating one half of the mold during and after filling, and until the polymer in the mold is cool enough to resist molecular relaxation. In addition to enhanced toughness, craze resistance is improved manifold in such moldings.

Embrittlement of otherwise tough rubber-modified styrene polymers occurs through aging of these polymers. Bucknall and Street (96) have studied the effects of outdoor aging of rubber-modified thermoplastics. They were able to simulate outdoor aging by laminating a brittle film onto a virgin rubber-modified polymer molding. These experiments showed that aging reduces the energy of crack initiation, so that the final impact strength is determined by the inherent crack-propagation energy of the rubber-modified polymer.

Specimens in Mechanical-Property Testing. In order to understand the mechanical behavior of styrene-based polymers, the effect of the method of specimen preparation should be taken into account. In considering this effect, it is fortunate that the styrene-based polymers are not subject to crystallization or thermal degradation under heat-fabrication conditions. Accordingly, the effect of the molding technique and conditions can be observed with relatively few complications and should be applicable to other amorphous thermoplastic materials. Both compression- and injection-molding techniques should be considered.

Compression molding produces a relatively isotropic molding, ie, there is no specific orientation, other than the memory of the extruded granules or some flow orientation produced while pressing out the molten polymer. In compression molding, care must be exercised not to produce moldings with voids, sink marks, or improper fusion. A satisfactory technique involves premelting the styrene-based polymers at 400–425°F for 3–5 min before applying the full pressure for 2 min. The best moldings are obtained when they are slowly cooled in the press. The properties of these moldings are independent of molding temperature as long as specimens without imperfections are obtained and proper fusion takes place.

In addition to compression molding, fairly thick extruded sheet (>0.1 in.) is also suitable for obtaining relatively isotropic specimens for mechanical-property testing. Because a large amount of polymer is required, extrusion does not lend itself to laboratory preparation of test specimens.

Specimens prepared by injection-molding techniques vary considerably. Injection moldings are generally anisotropic (118). The highest level of orientation is achieved at low molding temperatures; at high temperatures, more nearly isotropic moldings are produced (94). Moldings (eg, ⅛-in. thick dumbbell-shape test specimens) which are end-gated are particularly prone to give varying mechanical properties as functions of molding temperature. From large side-gated molding specimens in the direction parallel (‖, equivalent to the end-gated molding) as well as perpendicular (⊥) to the flow direction can be obtained.

As seen from Figure 9, the properties of specimens cut parallel to the flow are the best; those specimens cut perpendicular to the flow are the poorest. Compression moldings tend to give intermediate properties. In the case of biaxial loading, such as in a dart-drop test, it appears that the high strength of oriented, low-temperature moldings is of no desirable consequence. In fact, HIPS moldings prepared at low molding temperatures exhibit brittle fracture (55,94), although moldings of the same material molded at higher temperatures are ductile. Accordingly, if the judgment of a polymer is based on the high strength of a low-temperature molding, misleading conclusions could be drawn as to the real strength and toughness of the material.

End-gated, relatively thick, ¼- to ½-in. injection-molded specimens can be

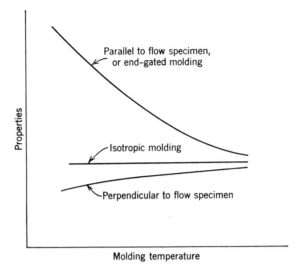

Fig. 9. Effect of orientation on properties (notched Izod impact strength, tensile strength, etc).

used with reduced effects of anisotropy (97). The normally used thickness of ⅛ in. is not sufficient for reducing the effects of uniaxial orientation. Figure 10 shows electron photomicrographs of the surface layer and the center of a ⅛-in.-thick injection-molded specimen at 400 and 550°F. In the case of thick specimens, the surface orientation is of relatively smaller consequence. Also, less orientation at the center is found because of the longer freezing time, particularly at high molding temperatures. Annealing of oriented specimens is used to improve the heat-distortion temperature and craze resistance, but for the purpose of significantly changing other mechanical properties of the ⅛-in. thick specimens, it is not usually successful. Accordingly, the use of compression moldings or relatively thick (¼ to ½ in.) injection moldings is recommended for the mechanical-property testing of styrene-based polymers.

Effect of Radiation on Styrene-Based Plastics

Polystyrene is one of the most stable polymers to irradiation, and very large doses are required to produce any noticeable change. The behavior of other styrene-based polymers is controlled to a large extent by the type of comonomers present.

While several studies of the effects of irradiation on polystyrene have been carried out, styrene copolymers have not been studied extensively. The gas evolution and the rate of crosslinking during irradiation have been measured. Also, some mechanical-property studies have been reported.

Upon irradiation, polystyrene evolves essentially pure hydrogen. The initial yield corresponds to G (H_2) = 0.03–0.04 (G = moles of gas produced per 100 eV of absorbed energy). The G value for crosslinking has been found to average about 0.04 (98). In a later study, the γ-ray-produced crosslinking yielded the expected G (crosslinking) value, but crosslinking brought about in a nuclear reactor was equivalent to G (crosslinking) = 0.096 ± 0.015. The ratio of scissions to formation of crosslinked units was 0.14 for both cases (99).

It has been found that trapped radicals of considerable lifetime are produced during irradiation. They become active when polystyrene is heated above the glass

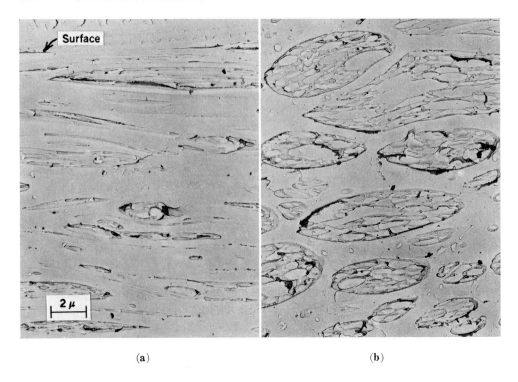

(a)   (b)

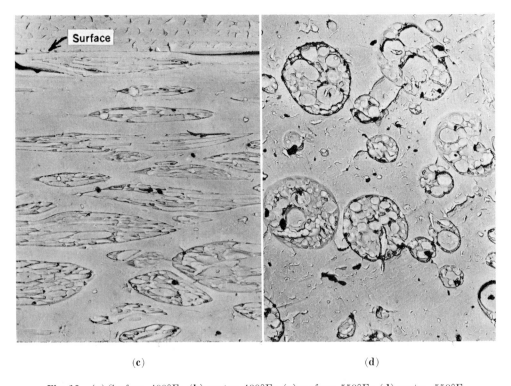

(c)   (d)

Fig. 10. (a) Surface, 400°F; (b) center, 400°F; (c) surface, 550°F; (d) center, 550°F.

temperature or treated with a solvent. Irradiation in air gives rise to degradation of polystyrene.

Substituted polystyrenes show different effects when irradiated. Poly-p-isopropylstyrene produces a crosslink yield 2.7 times higher than that of polystyrene (98). On the other hand, with many other electronegative and electropositive substituents in the para position of polystyrene, it becomes more stable to radiation (100).

During irradiation, polystyrene expands. This is distinct from the thermal expansion which also occurs (101). In the study of creep rates during irradiation, it was found that the polystyrene creep rate increases by a factor of about 5 over that of the unirradiated sample. This increase is significantly less (10–43 times) than that for poly(methyl methacrylate) (101). Radiation crosslinking causes the polystyrene specimens to remain coherent and solid with gradually decreasing internal friction. High irradiation doses cause it to maintain a high dynamic modulus beyond 227°C (102).

Fabrication of Styrene-Based Plastics

The fabrication of styrene polymers into desired objects involves a combination of temperature, time, and pressure. The styrene polymers are available in a granular form which is ideally suited for extrusion and molding. Extruded sheet and film are widely used in forming. See also Plastics technology.

Injection Molding. By far the largest proportion of styrene polymers is fabricated by injection molding. Today molding machines with up to a 25-lb shot capacity (of polystyrene) exist (103). For example, a molding of an entire 17-ft^3 refrigerator food liner has been accomplished in one operation. Most molding machines built in recent years are of the reciprocating-screw type (104). Large machines of this design can be built. Uniform melt of the polymer is achieved, as well as good control of the filling process in reciprocating-screw machines.

The injection-molding process is basically the forcing of melted polymer into a relatively cool mold where it "freezes" and is removed in a minimum time. The shape of a molding is defined by the cavity of the mold. Quick entry of the material into the mold, followed by quick setup, results in a significant amount of orientation in the molded part. The polymer molecules, and, in the case of heterogeneous rubber-modified polymers, the rubber particles, tend to be highly oriented at the surface of the molding. Orientation at the center of the molding tends to be significantly less, due to the relaxation of the molten polymer (Fig. 10).

The anisotropy which develops during the molding operation is detrimental to the performance of the fabricated part in several ways. First, highly oriented moldings, which result particularly if low melt temperatures are used, exhibit poor gloss, have an abnormally narrow use-temperature range (early warping) and, perhaps most importantly, tend to be brittle even though the material is inherently capable of producing tough parts (94). However, this development of polymer orientation during molding can also be used to an advantage, as in the case of rotational orientation during the molding operation (95).

The achievement of isotropic moldings is also important when the molded part is to be decorated (painted, metalized, etc). Parts which are highly oriented and have a high frozen-in internal stress memory tend to give rise to rough or distorted surfaces, due to the relaxing effect of the solvents and/or heat. For electroplating ABS moldings, it is particularly important to obtain isotropic moldings. Isotropy can be achieved by the use of a high melt temperature, a slow fill speed, a low injection pressure, and a high mold temperature (59,60,105,117).

Injection molding of styrene-based plastics is usually carried out between 400 and 600°F. For ABS polymers, the upper limit may be somewhat less, since these polymers tend to yellow somewhat if too high a temperature and/or too long a residence time are imposed.

To obtain satisfactory moldings with good surface appearance, contamination, including moisture, must be avoided. For good molding practice, particularly with the more polar styrene copolymers, drying must be part of the molding operation. A maximum of 0.1% of moisture can be tolerated before surface imperfections become apparent.

For achieving appropriate economics, injection-molding operations are now highly automated (104) and require only minimal operating personnel. Loading of the hopper is usually done by an air-veying system; the pieces are automatically ejected, and the rejects and sprues are ground and reused along with the virgin polymer. Also, hot probes or manifold dies are being used to eliminate sprues and runners.

Extrusion. Extrusion of styrene polymers is one of the most convenient methods of fabrication, particularly for obtaining sheet, pipe, irregular profiles, and films. Relatively small extruders (eg, $4\frac{1}{2}$-in. diam) can produce well over 1000 lb of polymer sheet per hour. Extrusion is also the method for plasticizing the polymer in modern injection-molding machines and is used to develop the parison for blow molding.

Extrusion of plastics is also one of the most economical methods of fabrication, since it is a continuous method with relatively inexpensive equipment. The extrusion process has been studied in some detail and has been reported widely (106,107). Single-screw extruders work satisfactorily with styrene-based plastics. Machines with an L/D ratio of 20:1 to 24:1 are normally recommended for obtaining a uniform polymer melt. As in molding, careful drying (0.03–0.05% max) of the polymer before extrusion is essential for obtaining high-quality sheet.

A large portion of rubber-modified styrene plastics is fabricated into sheet by extrusion, primarily for subsequent thermoforming operations. Much consideration has been given to the problem of achieving good surface quality in extruded sheet (108,109). Excellent surface gloss and sheet uniformity can be obtained with these polymers.

Lamination of other polymer films for protection or for decorative purposes can be carried out during the extrusion step. For example, an acrylic film can be laminated to ABS sheet during extrusion for producing such items as thermoformed camper sections and canoes, which require good outdoor weatherability (61).

Calendering. Calendering is not extensively used in connection with styrene-based plastics. Extrusion appears to produce the desired results, and at lower cost.

ABS polymers, particularly when blended with PVC, are often calendered. To be satisfactory for calendering, the materials must have low nerve and low shear sensitivity for obtaining a smooth sheet. High viscosity is also desirable for successful calendering. ABS can be calendered to obtain sheet up to a thickness of about 0.060 in. (109).

Thermoforming and Orientation. Thermoforming of HIPS and ABS extruded sheet is of considerable importance in several industries. In the refrigeration industry, large parts are obtained by the vacuum forming of extruded sheet. In fact, vacuum forming of HIPS sheet for refrigerator-door liners was one of the most significant early developments which promoted the rapid growth of the whole family of rubber-modified polystyrene.

When a thermoplastic polymer film or sheet is heated above its glass temperature it can be formed or stretched. Under controlled conditions, new shapes can be obtained; also, various amounts of orientation can be imparted to the polymer film or sheet for altering its mechanical behavior.

Thermoforming is usually accomplished by heating a plastic sheet above its softening point and forcing it against a mold by applying vacuum, air, or mechanical pressure. On cooling, the contour of the mold is reproduced in detail. In order to obtain the best reproduction of the mold surface, carefully determined conditions for the plastic-sheet temperature, ie, heating time and mold temperature, must be maintained.

Several modifications of thermoforming of plastic sheet have been developed. In addition to straight vacuum forming, these are vacuum snapback forming, drape forming, and plug-assist-pressure-and-vacuum forming. Some combinations of these techniques are also practiced. Such modifications are usually necessary to achieve more uniform wall thickness in the finished deep-draw sections. Vacuum forming can also be accomplished continuously, using the sheet as it is extruded.

Thermoforming is perhaps the process giving the lowest unit cost. Examples of thermoformed articles are refrigerator-door and food-container liners, containers for dairy products, luggage, etc. Some of the largest formed parts are camping-trailer covers and liners for refrigerated-railroad-car doors (110).

Orientation of styrene-based copolymers is usually carried out at temperatures just above the glass temperature. Biaxially oriented films and sheet are of particular interest. Such orientation increases tensile properties, flexibility, toughness, and shrinkability. Polystyrene produces particularly clear and sparkling film after being oriented biaxially (for envelope windows, decoration tapes, etc).

Oriented films and sheets of styrene-based polymers are made by the bubble process and by the flat-sheet or tentering process. Fibers and films can be produced by uniaxial orientation (111). See also Film materials.

Blow Molding. Blow molding is a multistep fabrication process for manufacturing hollow symmetrical objects. The granules are melted, and a parison, a cylindrical tube, is obtained by extrusion or by an injection-molding technique. The parison is then enclosed by the mold, and pressure or vacuum is applied to force the material to assume the contour of the mold. After sufficient cooling, the object is ejected.

Styrene-based plastics have found some use in blow molding, but not to an extent comparable to linear polyethylene and PVC. Rubber-modified polystyrene and ABS have found use in specialty bottles and containers. ABS is also used as one of the impact modifiers for PVC. Clear, tough bottles with good barrier properties are blow-molded from these formulations.

PS or copolymers have not found much use in blow molding, because without balanced molecular orientation the toughness and craze resistance are borderline. However, tough and craze-resistant PS containers have been made recently by multiaxially oriented injection-molded parisons (112). This process permits the design of blow-molded objects with a high degree of controlled orientation, independent of blow ratio or shape.

Special Fabrication Techniques. Several additional fabrication techniques can be used with styrene-based plastics. Some of these techniques seem to have considerable potential.

Expansion-cast or *molded* objects of reduced density and of considerable strength are made. These objects can be made to resemble various textures, including wood. A contour chair frame has been made from expansion cast and *rotationally molded* ABS foam (113).

Cold forming or solid-phase forming, normally associated with high-speed forming of metals, appears to be suitable with some ABS polymers and some other thermoplastic materials (114). A deep-drawing technique has been developed which permits cold forming of ABS parts at considerable speed (115). Significant savings over thermoforming can be visualized.

Because of reduced pressure and injection-time requirements, an *injection-stamping* process permits production of large injection-molded articles. The injection-stamping process is a modification of conventional injection molding. The improved mold filling is achieved by permitting breathing of the mold while it is being filled (116).

The special fabrication techniques presented above are not meant to be a comprehensive list but rather to illustrate that the more recent plastics-fabrication techniques are striving toward higher speeds and larger objects and toward replacing existing materials in many applications.

Uses of Styrene-Based Plastics

As a class, styrene-based plastics are one of the most widely used polymers because of their ease of fabrication and the wide spectrum of properties possible. The main industries using styrene-based plastics are the packaging, appliance, construction, automotive, radio and TV, furniture, toy, houseware, and luggage industries.

There are numerous methods of fabricating styrene-based plastics, and the choice among several materials for a specific use is a complicated matter. The questions of size, shape, mechanical-property requirements, and such things as the need for a highly glossy surface, or perhaps the possibility of decoration, must all be considered before a choice of a particular material can be made. Table 4 can be used to obtain a general picture of uses and fabrication methods.

Table 4. Examples of Uses of Styrene-Based Plastics[a]

Process	Use
extrusion	pipe (ABS), wall covering, profiles, films, multilayer films
extrusion and forming	refrigerator and freezer parts, luggage (ABS), food containers, trays, container lids, camping-trailer covers (ABS)
injection molding	housings, kitchenware, containers, cigarette packages, telephone sets (ABS), shoe heels, radio and TV cabinets, automotive parts, drinking cups, pipe fittings (ABS), safety helmets, furniture, golf-club heads (ABS), light diffusers, toys
specialty (blow-, roto-) molding	bottles, cups, containers, furniture

[a] Major ABS end uses are noted.

Styrene-Based Latexes

Miller (121) has published a comprehensive review covering the history, science, and technology of styrene–butadiene latexes in protective and decorative coatings.

Styrene-containing latex systems of commercial significance can be divided into a small number of categories:

1. Styrene–butadiene with less than about 30% styrene. See Elastomers, synthetic.

2. 60-Styrene–40-butadiene latexes used in paper coatings, water-based paints, and additives for portland cement mortars and concrete (121).

3. Same as 2 except modified with one or more additional monomers, usually a carboxylic acid, for use in paint, paper coating, and textile applications. The fourth monomer, if present, may serve as a comonomeric emulsifier (121).

4. Copolymers of styrene with alkyl acrylates having low glass temperature (eg, 2-ethylhexyl acrylate), for use in water-based paints, self-polishing floor polishes, and, more importantly, as binders for improved light and heat stability in paper coatings.

5. High-butadiene copolymers of the SBR type with a carboxylic acid replacing part of the styrene, to be used in making rubbery foams by nonsulfur vulcanization, as taught in the Dunn patent (122). For example, a carboxylated S/B latex is foamed in the presence of a polyfunctional reactive material like melamine formaldehyde and cured with heat. Such foams are not as soft as the SBR types and are used largely as coating foams on fabrics, etc.

6. α-Methylstyrene–alkyl acrylate latexes for use in outdoor water-based paints, with the α-methylstyrene replacing methyl methacrylate. Thus far this has not been a significant use.

7. Polystyrene latexes to be used, among other things, as a hardening additive for softer latexes; to impregnate cloth with the latex, which is then dried and subsequently fused with heat and/or solvents; and as an additive for floor waxes.

8. Uniform polystyrene latex particles used in medicine and in size calibration.

Miller's review article puts special emphasis on categories 2 and 3 above. Some of the important end-use trends in S/B latexes may be summarized as follows:

1. The use of S/B latexes for paper-coating applications has grown substantially as more and more coated paper is employed. S/B latexes replace part of the natural binders, such as starch, protein, and casein.

2. A system has been developed for making rubber foams without sulfur vulcanization, as already mentioned above.

3. There has been extensive testing of S/B latex in concrete for repairing bridge decks where thin, lighter-weight resurfacing sections are needed, as well as experimental use in highways. S/B latex improves the mechanical properties of the cured concrete.

4. Carboxylated S/B latex has been used extensively in carpet backing to bind the carpet fibers within the yarns and to the backing. One large manufacturer (Dow) has built a plant and technical service laboratory in Dalton, Ga., which is near the center of the carpet industry.

5. A growing world shortage of casein, a common ingredient of coating formulations containing S/B latexes, has led to an active search for "synthetic caseins" (124). General Tire and Rubber (125) has a patent on the use of alkali-swellable latexes. which can function as synthetic caseins.

6. Electrodeposition serves to deposit latex coatings on metals. See Electrophoretic deposition.

7. Smog-control regulations are placing greater emphasis on the use of water-based coatings.

8. The desire of large paint companies to manufacture their own latexes, combined with a reluctance to handle butadiene, has led to a widespread use of poly(vinyl acetate) latexes.

In addition to the technological trends noted above, reference might be made to a representative group of scientific advances in understanding S/B latexes. The mechanism of film formation from latexes continues to generate interest. Miller (121) has reviewed the older hypotheses. A new approach by Sheetz (126) seems worthy of mention. Older theories visualized that surface-tension forces caused coalescence of the latex particles and expulsion of the water. Sheetz suggests that, although this process is important during the first half of film formation, the energy for forming the final highly coherent film comes from evaporation of water which has diffused through the latex particles. A series of ingenious experiments were carried out to test this hypothesis.

Vanderhoff and his co-workers (127) have been able to prepare clean polystyrene latexes by treatment with rigorously purified, mixed anion–cation exchange resins. These ion-exchanged latexes appear to be stabilized by some strong acid groups, presumably sulfate end groups, which cannot be removed by ion exchange. Thus it is possible to prepare a dispersion of particles (either monodisperse or polydisperse) with a known surface-charge density.

Wagner (128) has made an exhaustive study of the effects of latexes in portland cement mortars and concrete. While many different factors are involved, he finds that an S/B latex functions to improve the physical properties of the cured concrete by giving good workability of the wet cement at lower than normal, and closer to stoichiometric, water contents, where optimum strength properties are achieved. A reduced rate of water loss during curing, and increased entrainment of air, are also shown to be beneficial factors.

The article by Stagg (129) gives U.S. production of all types of S/B latexes for the year 1963. See also below under Global aspects.

Styrene-Unsaturated Polyesters

These are discussed under Unsaturated polyester resins. Mention may be made here of the newer trends, such as these:

1. Emphasis on newer developments using styrene derivatives as well as various polymeric additives which reduce shrinkage during cure of glass-fiber-reinforced styrene–polyester systems. Reduced shrinkage from the so-called "low profile" resins results in much improved surface finishes and a greatly reduced need for sanding and polishing, thus improving the economics.

2. Special fast catalysts to speed up the cure of styrene, inherently fast curing monomers, such as chlorostyrenes, and automation of matched die molding, all of which are promising trends to reduce costs still further.

3. Use by the automotive industry of increasing amounts of matched die molded parts on standard large-production-run cars in addition to limited-production-run sports cars. It is also using slush-molded parts based on styrene polyesters.

4.   A new technique called "injection molding of thermosets," in which styrene–polyester systems will undoubtedly find increasing use.

5.   The electron-beam curing of surface coatings, especially for the factory finishing of wood. This is a promising new technique. Styrene–polyester systems are among the possible coating materials, at least for indoor usage.

6.   The advent of new types of unsaturated lmw polyesters, known also as vinyl esters, as exemplified by the Derakane (Dow) family of resins.

7.   Greater use of styrene derivatives such as vinyltoluene, which permits a higher cure temperature (hence faster rate) because of the higher boiling point, and of *tert*-butylstyrene, which minimizes shrinkage because of the bulky *tert*-butyl group.

8.   An increasing trend toward fire-retardant polyester systems.

9.   Development of chemically resistant polyesters for use in chemical-process equipment.

10.   Filament winding as a technique for making glass-fiber-reinforced pressure vessels, piping systems, and tanks.

The Methylstyrenes

Crampton and Drake (130) have reviewed sources and uses of two commercially available methylstyrenes: α-methylstyrene and mixed (*m,p*)-vinyltoluenes. Both monomers are made by The Dow Chemical Company by the styrene-type synthesis using the propylation of benzene for α-methylstyrene and the ethylation of toluene for vinyltoluene. α-Methylstyrene is also available as a by-product from the cumene phenol process, and Foster Grant supplies an impure vinyltoluene obtained from refinery streams.

American Cyanamid has discontinued its manufacture of mixed (*o,p*)-vinyltoluenes by addition of two moles of toluene to acetylene to give 1,1-ditolylethane, followed by the cracking out of one mole of toluene. Molding powders from this monomer were supplied on a semicommercial basis by American Cyanamid but have since been discontinued. The high softening point of the (*o,p*)-polymer was a definite advantage over polystyrene. Presumably the unfavorable raw material and conversion costs for an acetylene-based monomer, and the small scale of operation for a new monomer, proved insurmountable obstacles to the commercial success of this monomer–polymer family.

The higher cost (about twice that of styrene) and lowered heat distortion of polymers based on (*m,p*)-vinyltoluenes rules them out for molding-powder uses, although they have had moderate use as a route to poly(vinylbenzyl chloride).

The mixed (*m,p*)-isomers were originally used mainly to make styrenated drying oils. However, they are now finding increasing use in unsaturated polyester systems where the higher boiling point reduces odor and permits higher molding temperatures (faster rates) without porosity. The electrical properties of vinyltoluene-diluted unsaturated polyesters are generally superior to those of their styrene counterparts.

Poly-α-methylstyrene was carried through the pilot-plant stage by Dow and then discontinued because of its poor thermal stability (low ceiling temperature). A styrene copolymer containing approximately 20% α-methylstyrene was discontinued by Dow because of higher cost and greater difficulty in molding, both of which offset the advantage of a higher heat-distortion temperature. α-Methylstyrene is used in some copolymer systems and to prepare the dimer, which is a very active hydrocarbon chain transfer agent.

Polystyrene Foams

These are discussed under Foamed plastics.   An older review by Kennedy (131) gives the early history of foamed polystyrene.   A later book by Benning on plastic foams has a full chapter on polystyrene foams (132).

Going back to 1954, the major source of foamed polystyrene then was extruded logs and planks made from polystyrene and methylchloride and used for low-temperature thermal insulation, buoyancy, floral display, and novelty applications. Foamable polystyrene beads developed by Badische Anilin- u. Soda-Fabrik (BASF) (133–135) under the trademark of Styropor were then relatively new.   These beads, made by suspension polymerization in the presence of blowing agents such as pentane or hexane, or by post pressurization with the same blowing agents, have had an almost explosive growth in the past fifteen years.   Table 5 lists physical properties of these

Table 5.   Characteristic Properties of Some Rigid Foams

| Type | Thermoplastic polystyrene | | | | Thermoset polyurethan, Thurane^a-cast |
	Styrofoam^a-extruded		Beadboard-molded		
density, lb/ft^2	1.8	3.3	1	2	1.9
compressive strength, psi	30	120	10	30	25
tensile strength, psi	70	225	35	70	55
bending modulus, psi	2200	2000			460
K factor^b at 40°F	0.24	0.19	0.245	0.225	0.15
heat distortion, °F	170	170	185	185	225
max temp for continuous use, °F	165	165			200
burning characteristics	SE	burns	SE	SE	SE

^{a} Registered trademark of The Dow Chemical Co. ^{b} Btu/(hr)(ft^2)(°F/in.).

two types of foam in comparison with rigid polyurethan foam.   At present (1969) there are at least ten types of foamed polystyrenes which are significant to varying degrees:

1.   Extruded planks and boards in the density range of 1.8 lb/ft^3 and largely self-extinguishing, used for low-temperature thermal insulation, buoyancy, floral display, novelty, packaging, and construction purposes.

2.   Foamed boards and shapes from foaming-in-place (FIP) beads, in the density range of 1–2 lb/ft^3, for packaging, buoyancy, insulation, and numerous other uses. Batch molding of boards and shapes, as well as automated molding of continuous planks, are used.

3.   Extruded foamed polystyrene sheet in the thickness range of 5–20 mils and densities from 4 to 10 lb/ft^3, used largely in packaging applications.   Extremely fine cell size is required for both texture and strength.   Special nucleating agents are employed for this purpose, such as copolymers of styrene and maleic anhydride (136a), citric acid–sodium bicarbonate mixtures (136b), and hexabromocyclohexane (136c).

4.   High-density extruded planks, usually in the range of 2.2–4 lb/ft^3, for heavy-duty structural applications.

5.   Styrene copolymer foams (as with acrylonitrile) for gasoline resistance, made either by extrusion or from beads.

6.   High-density, 30–50 lb/ft^3 injection-molded objects made from mixtures of

FIP beads and polystyrene granules. These moldings have a high-density skin of essentially polystyrene and a foamed core.

7. Foamable ABS systems, usually in the form of laminates with ABS skins and a heat-foamable core for structural applications, as in car body parts (137).

8. Combinations of foamable beads with an exothermic (usually thermoset) resin such as epoxy or phenolic so that heat evolved as the resin cures causes expansion of the beads. This is a type of syntactic foam (138,139).

9. Sandwich panels made either by foaming beads between the skin materials or by adhering skins to planks cut to precise dimensions.

10. Foamed polystyrene beads admixed with concrete for lightweight masonry structures (147).

This list does not exhaust the possibilities but merely suggests the versatility of foamed polystyrene systems.

Extruded Rigid Polystyrene Foam. The end-use pattern for extruded foam has changed drastically to embrace more diverse applications in the construction industry. In addition to low-temperature thermal insulation, foamed polystyrenes are now used for insulation against ambient temperatures in the form of perimeter insulation, insulation under floors and in walls and roofs. Best (140) has patented a new concept, the "upside-down roof system," in which a foamed plastic such as Styrofoam-brand plastic foam is above the tar-paper vapor seal, thereby protecting the tar paper from extreme thermal stresses which cause cracking. The foam is covered with gravel or some other wear-resistant topping.

In addition to these thermal-insulation uses in buildings, there is a potentially tremendous new area in the form of highway underlayment to prevent frost damage. Damage to roadways, roadbeds, and airfields because of frost action is a costly and aggravating problem in those parts of the world where frost-susceptible soils and free water exist at freezing temperatures. Conventional treatments to prevent such damage are expensive and unreliable. During the 1960s an improved and more economical solution to the problem was developed (141). It is based on the use of thermal insulation to reduce the heat loss in the frost-susceptible subgrade soil to the extent that no freezing occurs.

Well over two dozen insulated pavements have been built in the United States, Canada, Europe, and Japan. The concept has proved valid, and the performance of extruded polystyrene foam has been completely satisfactory. It is expected that the use of this concept will continue to grow as nature's road-building materials continue to become more scarce and expensive, and as the weight and speed of land and airborne vehicles continue to increase.

One-half inch of Styrofoam-brand plastic foam with a K factor (see Table 5) of about 0.23 is equivalent to one foot of gravel. Any synthetic foam having compressive strength sufficiently high and thermal conductivity sufficiently low will work. However, the resistance of polystyrene-type foams to water, frost damage, and microorganisms in the soil makes them especially desirable.

In addition to thermal insulation, there are two new areas where foam is used as a load-bearing material in addition to contributing insulation, namely, sandwich panels and spirally generated structures. One brand of sandwich panels (142) uses $\frac{1}{4}$-in. plywood faces bonded with a phenol–formaldehyde adhesive to an extruded polystyrene foam core whose thickness can be chosen in the range of 2–8 in. Such panels permit a rapid simplified construction of low-temperature-storage space (with or

Fig. 11. Final stage in erection of a spirally generated dome from Styrofoam-brand foam. The dome rests on vertical sandwich panels which also contain foamed polystyrene as core material.

without controlled atmosphere) erected either inside existing buildings or as a separate outside structure.

The spiral-generation concept patented by Wright (143,144) permits the semi-automated erection of domed structures through the thermoplastic welding of strips of extruded polystyrene foam into a monolithic structure. Free-standing, load-bearing domes (wind and snow loads) require a foam thickness proportional to the radius of the dome. A 100-ft dome requires 8-in. thickness of foam for structural purposes. Thermal insulation is a plus factor. Thinner foam sections can be used if a load-bearing covering of reinforced cement is placed on the outside of the dome. This also provides a weathering surface.

Figure 11 shows the construction of one of two 90-ft diam side-by-side domes resting on vertical walls of sandwich panels of the type mentioned earlier with cores of Styrofoam-brand plastic foam. The boom arm and operator's platform for applying the foam are protruding from the top of the dome. The Styrofoam-brand plastic foam will be covered with a styrene–butadiene latex modified, steel-wire-grid-reinforced concrete as a load-bearing and weathering coating. This is a sophisticated example of new technology which permits the use of polystyrene-containing materials in the construction industry. These two domes were intended for the low-temperature storage of poultry. However, the principal use of such foam domes at the moment is as a cover for trickling filters in waste-treatment plants to reduce problems with odor, spray drift, and cold-weather fog production.

Rigid Polystyrene Foam from Foaming-in-Place (FIP) Beads. In 1954, the total U.S. production of general-purpose polystyrene was between 200 and 300 million lb, with a negligible amount going into foams. In 1969, approx 200 million lb of general-purpose polystyrene will be used in making foams, with perhaps 160 ± 5 million in FIP beads, and the balance in various types of extruded foam. A growth curve presented several years ago (145) shows this remarkable growth for FIP beads.

Ingram and Wright (146) have analyzed a large number of factors which influence the foaming of foamable polystyrene beads, such as the molecular weight of the polymer, polymer type, blowing-agent type and content, bead size, and others. They suggest that at least part of the pentane blowing agent is present in microvoids in the glassy polystyrene. Thus the density of beads containing 5.7% n-pentane was 1.08, compared to a value of 1.05 for pure polystyrene beads, and compared with a calculated density of 1.02 for a simple mixture in which n-pentane was dissolved in the polystyrene. If all of the pentane were in voids, they calculate a density of 1.12. They estimate that about 60% of the pentane is held in voids, with the balance presumably dissolved.

n-Pentane present in voids will have a reduced vapor pressure which depends on the effective microcapillary diameter; dissolved n-pentane in polystyrene will also have a reduced vapor pressure, by an amount depending on the thermodynamic interaction between solvent and polymer.

Ingram and Wright show the importance of polymer structure by pointing out that an unspecified experimental styrene copolymer (possibly with acrylonitrile) shows a greatly reduced tendency to lose blowing agent on aging at 23°C. Rubens of Dow finds that FIP beads from chlorostyrene likewise have a greatly enhanced ability to retain blowing agent, as indicated in Table 6. The higher heat distortion of this polymer requires steam pressures of 30–50 psi for blowing.

Table 6. Loss of Isopentane[a] from 40-Mesh FIP Beads,[b] %

Temp, °C	20 hours		300 hours	
	Polystyrene	Polychloro-styrene	Polystyrene	Polychloro-styrene
25	18	1.3	40	10
50	38	12	72	33
80	48	24	80	54

[a] Initial concentration 6%.   [b] Open storage.

Rubens (147a) has studied various other factors which influence the foaming of polystyrene, especially crosslinking. Rubens treats foaming as a viscoelastic process in which there is competition between the blowing pressure, which increases with temperature, and the thinning out and rupture of cell walls with consequent collapse of the foam. The presence of crosslinks reduces the tendency for cell wall rupture. Figure 12, taken from the paper by Rubens, shows foam volumes attained as a function of temperature for various amounts of divinylbenzene. Rubens also discusses the effect of temperature and crosslinking on the kinetics of foaming.

The largest type of expandable polystyrene is in the form of spherical beads. However, The Dow Chemical Company pioneered an elongated shape called Pelaspan-Pac which expands into a wormlike shape ideally suited as a loose fill for packaging. Items packed in spherical beads will settle to the bottom of the container during shipping. The irregular elongated form prevents this settling.

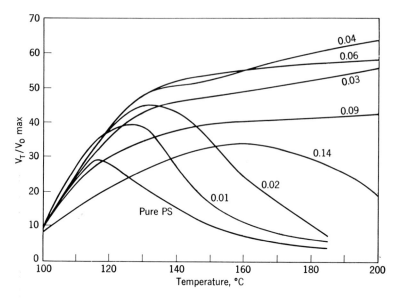

Fig. 12. Maximum foaming volume of styrene–divinylbenzene copolymers containing 8.8% CO_2 as a function of DBV content and temperature, after Rubens. Numeral beside curve indicates percent OVB.

Hohwiller and Köhling (147b) have described the rapidly growing use in Germany of lightweight concrete made from prefoamed Styropor beads, portland cement, and organic binders. Precast shapes are being used to provide structural strength, thermal insulation, and sound deadening.

Expandable ABS Polymers. Woollard (137) has described two types of expandable ABS polymers. One is an injection-moldable grade, giving average densities in the range of 30–60 lb/ft^3, with a dense high-strength surface layer possessing a woodlike texture. The other is an expansion casting grade which can produce molded parts having densities in the range of 30–35 lb/ft^3. In this process, pellets of ABS are placed in a closed mold which is then placed in a heating chamber capable of reaching temperatures of 375–450°F. On completion of the expansion, the mold is cooled with a water spray.

Self-Extinguishing Polystyrene Foams. The growing use of polystyrene foams in the construction industry has provided impetus for continuing research on additives which will make the foam self-extinguishing (SE) while not detracting unduly from its physical properties. Organic bromine compounds such as acetylene tetrabromide have long been used for this purpose in extruded polystyrene foam. It is also an advantage to use hexabromocyclodecane as an organic nucleating agent.

Eichhorn (148) has described in detail a new synergistic SE principle which permits a significant reduction in the amount of halogen compound needed if a free-radical generator is present. Figure 13 illustrates one simple case, dicumyl peroxide and acetylene tetrabromide. The 5% acetylene tetrabromide needed for SE in the absence of peroxide will seriously lower the heat-distortion temperature (softening point) of the foam; but merely 0.5% of the same bromine compound will suffice for SE if 0.5% of dicumyl peroxide is present.

Eichhorn presents evidence to suggest that free radicals generated from the

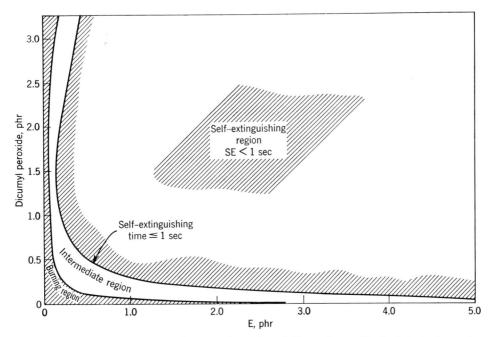

Fig. 13. Synergistic action of acetylene tetrabromide and dicumyl peroxide (both in parts per hundred) in making polystyrene foam self-extinguishing, after Eichhorn (148).

peroxide attack the polymer, which then reacts with the halogen compound. This consecutive reaction delays loss of the halogen compound from the polymer and hence increases the efficiency of its utilization.

Numerous peroxides, hydroperoxides, azo compounds, quinone imines, benzothiazole sulfenamides, and disulfides show this synergistic action. Eichhorn lists the patents obtained by him and numerous colleagues in this field. While such systems are ideal for use with foams of either the extruded or FIP types, they have not proved feasible as yet for polystyrene molding granules because of the more severe thermal history during extrusion or injection molding.

Poly(chlorostyrene) contains 26.5% of ring chlorine, which is thermally stable, and it is therefore very close to the minimum of 28% needed for SE. Thus, poly-(chlorostyrene) is much easier to render SE with small amounts of additives than is polystyrene. However, foams from polychlorostyrene are not commercial.

Eichhorn (149) has reviewed the general problem of the combustion of thermoplastics.

Polystyrene as a Raw Material for Rigid Thermoplastic Foams. It is interesting to consider the reasons for the unique position which polystyrene has attained in the field of rigid thermoplastic foams. The low cost of the polymer, and its high thermal stability (giving good recycle efficiency), as well as the possibility of using low-cost blowing agents, are all important. The heat-distortion point of about 80°C (in contrast to 65°C for PVC foam) permits its use in most construction applications. The low sensitivity of the polymer to moisture is another important factor. The ability of FIP beads to retain simple blowing agents such as *n*-pentane over an adequate shelf life and then be foamable with hot air or low-pressure steam are both very important desiderata.

According to Rubens, another important factor affecting the foaming of poly-styrene beads is the differential rate of diffusion of n-pentane compared to steam and air. He estimates that the quantity of n-pentane normally used is sufficient to produce a foaming volume of 30-fold and hence a foam of no more than 2 lb/ft³. However, the steam and/or air which diffuses into the beads contributes to further expansion so that foaming volumes of 60-fold or more are commonly achieved. This aspect of diffusion has been discussed in some detail by Skinner, Baxter, and Grey (150a) as well as by Hinselmann (150b). Rubens has experimented with so-called "cycle foam-ing" in air, in which beads are allowed to equilibrate with air after each heat-foaming step through a series of stages. Foaming volumes of 200 have been achieved in this manner, with densities down to 0.2–0.3 lb/ft³.

Because of all of the above, and possibly for other reasons, polystyrene has been the dominant material used in rigid thermoplastic foams. PVC has good economics and good physical properties and is self-extinguishing, but it is marginal on heat distortion for some end uses and does not readily lend itself to the continuous extrusion process used for polystyrene foam. Thus far, no FIP bead system based on PVC has been perfected. This could well be a result of its high vapor barrier compared to poly-styrene. Polyethylene is too permeable to retain blowing agent and hence is ruled out as a FIP bead material.

Logistics of Manufacturing, Shipping, and Storing Foams. We have already com-mented on the explosive growth of polystyrene foam from FIP beads compared to that of extruded foam. The latter process has been controlled by one manufacturer on the basis of some process patents. The FIP beads have been available from Sinclair-Koppers, Dow, United Cork (now BASF), and Monsanto, all under license from Badische. Aside from these important differences, there are some simple logistical factors which favor FIP bead systems.

The high-bulk (low-weight) characteristic of foams imposes limitations on how far they can be economically shipped. One solution is to build a series of manufac-turing plants to make extruded foams near large consuming regions (see section on Global aspects). Other solutions are liquid foaming systems such as polyurethans, and FIP beads. FIP beads can be shipped in the condensed or unfoamed state and then converted to foam at or near the point of use by a relatively simple, low-capital-cost process. This fact accounts for the tremendous growth of FIP beads during the past fifteen years. Their use in packaging gave extra impetus by saving shipping and inventory costs. Finally, FIP beads can be molded to precise profiles, in contrast to the wasteful cutting operations required with extruded foam.

The greater cost of FIP beads as compared to general-purpose polystyrene feed-stock used in making extrudable foam offsets to some extent the shipping-cost ad-vantages. However, foamed objects from FIP beads usually have a lower density than extruded foam to compensate for the cost of the beads. For packaging applica-tions, this lower density may be advantageous. The greater friability and porosity can be disadvantageous for some end uses.

Basic patents on both extruded foams and foams molded from FIP beads will expire over the next five years (from 1969), and then the relative growth of the two types can take place solely on the merits of cost and properties. Meanwhile, rigid polyurethan foams are making rapid progress. Self-extinguishing thermoset foams for the construction industry might well displace much of the polystyrene foam from this end use.

(NOTE: The assistance of Messrs. R. N. Kennedy, L. C. Rubens, R. E. Skoch-dopole, and R. C. Warner of The Dow Chemical Company and Dr. H. Willersinn of BASF in preparing this foam section is acknowledged.)

Oriented Polystyrene Film and Sheet. While precise statistics are not available, informed opinion indicates that at the present time approximately 100 million lb/yr of polystyrene is being used in the form of film and sheet, both of them biaxially oriented. Film is defined as being ≤ 3 mils in thickness, whereas sheet is > 3 mils in thickness. The material is predominantly general-purpose polystyrene supplemented with only modest amounts of styrene–acrylonitrile copolymer and rubber-modified (impact) polystyrene. This usage does not include the foamed sheet discussed in the section on foamed polystyrene.

Oriented polystyrene film, in addition to having the lowest cost of any of the rigid plastic materials, offers a high degree of optical clarity, high surface gloss, excellent dimensional stability (particularly with regard to relative humidity), and the capability of being heat-shrinkable. It is not a barrier film; in fact, one of its biggest end uses, that of packaging field-fresh produce, depends upon its having a relatively high permeability to both oxygen and water vapor (see Table 7).

Table 7. Gas and Water-Vapor Permeabilities of Polystyrene-Type Films

Material	Composition	Gas permeabilities			Water-vapor permeability
		O_2	CO_2	N_2	
Styron[a] 683	unmodified polystyrene	300[b]	1150[b]	53[b]	7–8[d]
		(4650)[c]	(17,800)[c]	(820)[c]	(110–125)[e]
Tyril[a] 767	72:28 styrene/VCN	80	380	8.5	13
		(1250)	(5,900)	(130)	(200)
poly-o-chlorostyrene		65	180	15	2
		(1000)	(2,800)	(230)	(31)
Styron[a] 700	79:21 styrene/α-methylstyrene	280	950		7–8
		(4300)	(14,700)		(110–125)
Zerlon[a] 150	35:65 styrene/methyl methacrylate	30	90		6–7
		(470)	(1,400)		(93–110)

[a] Registered trademark of The Dow Chemical Co.

[b] cm³(STP)/(day)(100 in.²)(atm/ml) at 23°C.

[c] cm³(STP)/(day)(m²)(atm/ml) at 23°C.

[d] g/(day)(100 in.²)(ml) at 37.8°C and 90% rh.

[e] g/(day)(m²)(ml) at 37.8°C and 90% rh.

Pinsky (152) has written a specific review on polystyrene film as part of a larger study on films of all types, edited by Sweeting (151). Park (154) deals with film generally, but devotes considerable attention to polystyrene. Eichhorn (155) has a recent review article giving comparative information on a large number of plastic films, again with the inclusion of information on polystyrene. Saikaishi (156) has presented a study on the potential for synthetic plastic paper in Japan, with special emphasis on both polystyrene and polyolefin films.

Historically, it appears that Germany was the first to work with biaxially oriented film, the end product going largely into dielectric use as a wrapping material for high-voltage cables, where its high dielectric strength of 5000 V/mil at 60 cycles is utilized. There is a modest use in this area both in Germany and in the United States. The

Plax Corporation, now a part of Monsanto Company, began development work in the United States during the late 1940s on polystyrene sheet, using the tenter-frame method of developing biaxial orientation. The Dow Chemical Company also began work in the late 40s, but on film material. As of 1969 many others have been active in polystyrene film in the United States, and there are at least six producers of polystyrene sheet, having a total of seventeen tenter frames, each with the rated capacity of approx 5 million lb/yr. More companies are entering this market as the end-use development expands. It is believed that there is a current potential shortage of 40 million lb/yr.

In Europe the film market appears to be dominated by PVC, so that polystyrene film has still only a very modest use. At the moment, it appears that Japan may launch a major effort on polystyrene film as a type of synthetic paper.

Although polystyrene is normally considered a rather brittle material, the act of biaxial orientation imparts some extremely desirable properties, particularly in regard to an increase in elongation. Thus the 1.5–2% of elongation normally associated with unoriented polystyrene can become as high as 3 or even 10%, depending on the exact conditions of preparation. Park and Conrad (157) have reviewed the subject of biaxial orientation in regard to films in general, with frequent mention of polystyrene films. Karam (153) gives his main emphasis to melt rheology as related to achieving biaxial orientation.

There have been four principal methods of preparing biaxially oriented polystyrene film. The oldest one was that employed by the Germans, namely, a parabolic or horseshoe-shaped stretcher over which an extruded tube of polystyrene was drawn. Perhaps the second method to gain use was the so-called tenter-frame method, in which the edges of a polystyrene sheet are gripped continuously and pulled sidewise as the sheet is drawn lengthwise in the machine direction by takeup rolls. The Dow Chemical Company later began experimenting with the bubble process and is currently in commercial production with this method. Dow also experimented with a so-called eight-sided or pancake stretcher which had a fair amount of promise but has now been abandoned (153,157,158).

The high softening point, coupled with the tendency of oriented film to shrink above 185°F, makes heat sealing difficult. Solvent and adhesive sealing are used in most applications. Scratch resistance, impact strength, and crease resistance are low.

Although the bubble process superficially resembles the common bubble process for making polyethylene, polypropylene, and Saran film, yet there are a number of substantive differences, and the polystyrene process is considerably more difficult to achieve. In the case of polyethylene, for example, crystallinity is acting to stabilize the blown bubble; whereas with a true thermoplastic, such as polystyrene, one must rely upon cooling the molten polymer to the glass transition point to ultimately stabilize the blown film. This involves extremely careful control of temperature in the blowing process.

As a general rule of thumb, it can be said that there is an economic break-even point at about 3 mils which coincides with the defined difference between film and sheet; film is made more economically by the bubble method, sheet by the tenter-frame method. The exact thickness for break-even is obviously dependent on technological improvements which can be made in both processes, in the degree of control which is used in regulating them, and in quality requirements.

Polystyrene film contains no plasticizers, absorbs negligible moisture, and exhibits exceptionally good dimensional stability. It does not become brittle with age nor distort when exposed to low or high humidity. Excellent machinability (this means ability to run through packaging machinery at high speeds and to be cut and heat-sealed, etc), clarity, and stability are central factors in the use of oriented polystyrene in window envelopes. These same characteristics have also led to applications of film for window cartons. An antifog film 1–1.5 mils in thickness has been used extensively for the windows of cartons for bacon. Substantial amounts of film are also employed for sheet protectors and for inserts in wallets. A thickness of 2.5–4.75 mils is customary for these applications. Polystyrene film can be printed by means of flexographic, rotogravure, and silk-screen methods. A lamination of reverse printed film and paper has been used for an attractive, high-sparkle package for hand soap. The film is an excellent base for metalizing because of the almost complete absence of volatiles.

For polystyrene sheet, the big end use responsible for its rapid growth is in meat trays, where the merchandising value is important, ie, the transparency of the package, in addition, of course, to its resistance to moisture and its dimensional stability. A smaller but growing use is for a photographic-film base where dimensional stability at all humidities, and low gel count, are both important. The thermoplastic nature of polystyrene, and the memory effects built into it through biaxial orientation, make it especially suitable for packaging applications. It must be processed in pressure rather than vacuum-forming equipment to avoid the shrinkage which would otherwise result from the high level of orientation.

For polystyrene two of the important uses are as windows in envelopes, etc, as mentioned above, and secondly, for produce overwrap. High optical clarity is required for mechanized reading of characters through envelope windows, a significant technological trend which is certain to enhance the use of polystyrene film. In regard to produce overwrap, the transmission characteristics of polystyrene for both water vapor and oxygen coincide more or less with the metabolic requirements of the produce being packaged, such as lettuce, so that in addition to giving mechanical protection to something like a head of lettuce, the produce is able to metabolize in a normal manner. Low cost, and the high optical clarity, or see-through characteristics, are both important here. In addition, the feel of polystyrene film gives an impression of crispness as far as the product is concerned. This end use has been reviewed by Scott, Butt, and Eichhorn (159).

One of the potential large-volume uses for film is in the preparation of overhead transparency slides used more and more widely in visual-aid equipment. Polyester film has been the dominant material here. However, the excellent dimensional stability of polystyrene film, as well as its high optical clarity and low cost, is making it look more attractive all the time.

Polystyrene film also has potential use as a type of synthetic paper (156). It is perhaps natural that this type of end use should first receive serious attention in Japan, which must import each year tremendous quantities of wood pulp to use in the manufacture of paper. Even though Japan must also import petroleum that would be needed for any synthetic plastics, there is a net favorable balance toward the use of plastic materials. Consequently Japan is not only looking seriously at synthetic papers, but the government is subsidizing and encouraging effort in this direction. Saikaishi estimates that synthetic-paper production ten years hence could be as much as 3,500,000 tons, or something in excess of 7 billion lb. The Japanese Government is currently offering subsidies to companies which are working on the production of synthetic paper.

Currently (1969), all types of synthetic plastics are being considered, although economic factors would naturally favor polyolefins, poly(vinyl chloride), and polystyrene. Both general-purpose and impact polystyrene are under investigation. General-purpose polystyrene needs some kind of treatment to give it opacity, and this can take the form of either pigmentation, mechanical abrasion, or a surface treatment such as a chemical etch. The impact-polystyrene material already is reasonably opaque. Polystyrene film, of course, can be given a suitable coating, such as a latex-clay coating, of the kind that is used on ordinary paper for the purpose of achieving a good printable surface.

As regards their properties, polystyrene-type papers have such extremely good dimensional stability that unbelievably good four-color printing has been achieved because of the precise registry possible in color printing.

Table 7 lists the gas and water-vapor permeabilities of polystyrene, one derivative, and three copolymers. For a discussion of gas permeabilities in plastic films in general, one can consult references 151, 154, and 155, as well as reviews by Yasuda et al. (160) or Rogers (161). Experimental, combined with theoretical, studies on polystyrene have been reported in papers by Schulz and Gerrens (162), as well as by Vieth et al. (163).

(NOTE: The assistance of Messrs. J. Eichhorn, W. R. R. Park, J. A. Radford, G. V. Schulz, and J. W. Thorsberg of The Dow Chemical Company in preparing this section is acknowledged.)

Global Aspects of the Styrene Family

Styrene monomer is a truly global commodity product. It is manufactured in many countries throughout the world and is freely shipped by commercial tankers between countries as well as by truck and rail between producers in several nations.

It can be shipped more readily than either ethylene or vinylchloride because of its high boiling point of 146°C. This factor gives styrene monomer a substantial advantage in national and international trade. International availability has permitted any country the opportunity to enter production of polystyrene, rubber, and latex, using purchased styrene. A monomer plant may come later, after internal usage justifies construction of a minimum economic-sized plant.

The rate at which styrene grew from a specialty product to commodity status was accelerated by several factors: (1) development, by chemical manufacturers of styrene and its polymers and copolymers, of extensive internal uses as well as new global markets, (2) a trend by most major chemical companies to become self-sufficient in styrene raw materials, and (3) a trend toward forward integration by many major oil companies into the production of ethylbenzene, styrene, and polymers and copolymers of styrene.

Another factor that hastened styrene's status as a commodity was the availability of turnkey monomer plants, as for instance one resulting from the collaboration of Union Carbide, Cosden Petroleum, and The Badger Company. Universal Oil Products and Scientific Design also have set up plants at several locations throughout the world. Lummus and Monsanto now offer the Monsanto know-how.

As styrene approached commodity status, the economics of commodity prices

Table 8. Product Integration in the Styrene Family at The Dow Chemical Company

styrene
  monomer
  (by 1934
  Dow process)
	homopolymer	molding granules—1938
		foamed polystyrene—1943
		    (Styrofoam)
		biaxially oriented film—1955
		    (Trycite)
		foaming-in-place beads—1960
		foamed sheet—1964

	copolymers	styrene–butadiene latexes:
		    for paper—1946
		    for paint—1948
		    for foam—1964
		    for carpet—1963
		
		styrene–acrylonitrile—1949
		
		rubber-modified polystyrene:
		    molding granules—1948
		    cottage cheese tubs—1961
		rubber-modified styrene—1964
		    (ABS) (Tybrene)

forced manufacturers to construct modern, highly engineered production units, with capacities in the range of 0.25–1.0 billion lb/yr, and located conveniently near raw materials as well as water transportation. In January 1969 The Dow Chemical Company announced plans to build a 1 billion-lb/yr styrene monomer facility in Freeport, Texas, to be onstream in 1971. Frequent trading of monomer between producers has become commonplace in an effort to optimize the effects of plant outages, under- and overcapacity, strikes, and shipping costs.

Since The Dow Chemical Company pioneered in the global development of styrene and its polymeric products, a brief description of this company's international operations may serve to illustrate the evolutionary order of growth. Table 8 sketches in condensed form the vertical integration which has taken place within Dow in the United States during the past thirty years. Note the development first of the monomer, secondly of the polymer, and subsequently of other forms, including the copolymers and related products.

This pattern of forward integration was somewhat modified during the course of establishing the styrene family in many countries. In several cases, these countries were first introduced to styrene-based products through the import of polystyrene resins for use by fabricators. The logical steps that followed were the building of polymer production units using imported styrene, and then a further step in backward integration—the construction of styrene monomer plants wherever and whenever the economics of volume justified a plant.

Table 9. Global Activities of The Dow Chemical Company
(number of production sites)

| Country | Styrene family of products | | | |
	Styrene monomer[a]	Poly- styrene[b]	Styro- foam	S/B latex
United States	2	4	6	5
Canada	1	1	1	1
Japan	1	2	1	2
England		1	1	1
Spain		1		
Holland	1	1		1
Italy		1		1
France		1		
Germany			1	1
Greece		1		
Australia	1	2		1
India		1		
Colombia		1		
Argentina				1
total	6	17	10	14

[a] The parent plant in Midland, Mich., produces α-methylstyrene, divinylbenzene, and (m,p)-vinyltoluene; it has an active development program in (o,p)-chlorostyrene, $p\text{-}tert$-butylstyrene, and other styrene derivatives.

[b] Biaxially oriented polystyrene film is produced at three sites in the U.S. and at one location in Japan.

Table 9 shows the worldwide current status of Dow's production facilities for key products in the styrene family. Some production facilities are part of a basic Dow production complex, some are isolated plants (ie, they are not a part of a Dow multiple-product complex), and still others are in association with a joint company or a combination thereof. This table is not intended to reflect the history of how Dow arrived at its indicated global position, only its present status. But, for example, the English polystyrene facility was originally jointly owned with Distillers, using monomer made in England by another Distillers' joint company. When Distillers sold its plastics interest to British Petroleum, Dow acquired full ownership of the Distrene polystyrene facility, which now operates on Dow-produced monomer.

Another aspect which Table 9 does not capture is the product mix. For example, styrene–butadiene latex is not one single well-defined product, but rather a product family which may have thirty members at a given time. There are these considerations: (1) In an advanced country like the United States, older latex formulations are either being improved constantly or completely displaced by new types of latexes. (2) This changing technology is exported globally, although overseas plants, especially in lesser developed countries, will probably never require the broad product line inherent to the United States.

Similar remarks can be made about the breadth and dynamic nature of polystyrene resin, which really consists of several lines of product subcategories. These include the general-purpose and impact grades, as well as the copolymers, each in a number of varieties. It also happens that slightly different end-use technology for countries outside the United States is forcing the development of species peculiar to that country. In addition, encouragement of synthetic paper by the Japanese govern-

Table 10. World Production of Styrene Monomer, million lb (estd)

Country	1966		1972	
	Capacity	Consumption	Capacity[a]	Consumption
United States	3200.0	2800.0	5400.0	4800.0
Canada	338.8	191.4	338.8	1500.4
Japan	660.0	539.0	1876.1	1500.4
India	44.0	26.4	66.0	79.2
Australia	55.0	22.0	59.4	66.0
France		292.6		
Netherlands		116.6		
West Germany		660.0		
Spain		6.6		
Belgium		68.2		
United Kingdom		354.2		
Italy		352.0		
other West Europe and Africa		22.0		
total[b]	1652.2			3388.0
Mexico		44.5		
Argentina		36.3		
Brazil		46.2		
Chile		3.3		
Colombia		6.6		
total Latin America[b]	136.4			308.0–440.0

[a] Includes only announced capacities through 1968.
[b] Includes only those countries individually listed here.

Table 11. Estimated End-Use Pattern of Styrene Monomers for the U.S., 1966–1972

End use	Production, million lb (estd)	
	1966	1972
polystyrene[a] general-purpose impact (including beads, foam, etc) copolymers	1614	2860
SBR rubber	580	634
S/B latex	165	277
styrene for paint and polyesters	136	268

[a] According to the October 1968 Tariff Commission Report, the distribution of products within the polystyrene family is as follows:

End use	Million lb	Percent
general-purpose	89	36
high-impact PS	73	30
ABS and SAN	44	18
S/B latex	29	12
all other	12	5
total	247	100

ment could lead to an astronomical production of polystyrene and biaxially oriented film therefrom, if that should be the preferred material.

A dramatic aspect of the worldwide development of polystyrene concerns a Dow U.S. patent covering an improved method of making impact polystyrene. The Dow invention covers the use of shearing agitation at a critical stage during the solution polymerization of rubber in styrene to give a product with superior properties. This process is widely imitated, and Dow is currently engaged in numerous countries in complex patent suits alleging infringement. Some companies, both before and after the suit, have obtained licenses; others are attacking the validity of the patent on the grounds that stirring is obvious. This is undoubtedly a precedent-setting case of patent infringement.

Table 10 shows estimated capacities and consumptions of styrene by country, and Table 11 gives the estimated end-use pattern in the United States.

Bibliography

"Styrene Resins and Plastics" in *ECT* 1st ed., Vol. 13, pp. 146–179, by J. A. Struthers, R. F. Boyer and W. C. Goggin, The Dow Chemical Company.

1. U.S. Tariff Commission Reports; *Mod. Plastics* **46** (1) (1969).
2. *Plastics Technol.* **12** (10), 32 (1966); **13** (13), 38 (1967).
3. W. E. Brown, J. D. Striebel, and D. C. Fuccella, *Automotive Eng. Congr. Paper 680059*, Jan. 8, 1968.
4. G. Natta and F. Danusso, *Stereoregular Polymers and Stereospecific Polymerization*, Pergamon Press, Inc., New York, 1967.
5. N. E. Gaylord and H. F. Mark, *Linear and Stereospecific Addition Polymers*, Interscience Publishers, Inc., New York, 1959.
6. A. S. Kenyon, R. C. Gross, and L. A. Wurstner, *J. Polymer Sci.* **40**, 159 (1959).
7. J. N. Hay, *J. Polymer Sci.*, [A]**3**, 433 (1965).
8. U.S. Pat. 2,287,188 (June 23, 1942), L. A. Matheson and R. F. Boyer (to The Dow Chemical Co.).
9. U.S. Pat. 3,406,143 (Oct. 15, 1968), C. L. Stacy, W. J. Hanson, and T. C. Wallace (to The Dow Chemical Co.).
10. *Mod. Plastics Encyclopedia for 1968–69* **45** (14A) (1968).
11. J. Eichhorn, *J. Appl. Polymer Sci.* **8**, 2497 (1964).
12. U.S. Pat. 3,324,076 (June 6, 1967), M. E. Elder, R. T. Dickerson, and W. F. Tousignant (to The Dow Chemical Co.).
13. G. P. Ziemba "Acrylonitrile–Styrene Copolymers," in *Encyclopedia of Polymer Science and Technology*, Vol. 1, Interscience Publishers, a division of John Wiley & Sons, Inc., 1964, pp. 425–435.
14. U.S. Pat. 3,265,765 (Aug. 9, 1966), G. Holden and R. Milkovich (to Shell Oil Co.).
15. G. E. Molau, *J. Polymer Sci.* [A]**3**, 1267, 4235 (1965); Can. Pat. 754,636, G. E. Molau and H. Keskkula.
16. J. Moacanin, G. Holden, and N. W. Tschoegl, eds., *Polymer Symp.* **26** (*J. Polymer Sci.*, Part C) (1969).
17. E. Vanzo, *J. Polymer Sci.* [A1]**4**, 1727 (1966).
18. H. Hendus, K. H. Illers, and E. Ropte, *Kolloid-Z.* **216–217**, 110 (1967).
19. M. Matsuo, T. Ueno, H. Horino, S. Chujyo, and H. Asai, *Polymer* **9**, 425 (1968).
20. G. E. Molau, *Publication 1573*, Natl. Acad. Sci., Washington, D.C., 1968, pp. 245–258.
21. J. T. Bailey, E. T. Bishop, W. R. Hendricks, G. Holden, and N. R. Legge, *Rubber Age* **98**, 69 (Oct. 1966).
22. U.S. Pat. 3,336,267 (Aug. 15, 1967), R. L. Zimmerman and W. E. O'Connor (to The Dow Chemical Co.).
23. U.S. Pat. 3,231,524 (Jan. 25, 1966), D. W. Simpson (to The Dow Chemical Co.)

24. H. A. J. Battaerd and G. W. Tregear, *Graft Copolymers*, Interscience Publishers, a division of John Wiley & Sons, Inc., New York, 1967.

25. R. J. Ceresa, *Block and Graft Copolymers*, Butterworth Inc., Washington, D.C., 1962.

26. W. J. Burlant and A. S. Hoffman, *Block and Graft Copolymers*, Reinhold Publishing Corp., New York, 1960.

27. D. E. Harmer, "Irradiation of Polymers," in R. F. Gould, ed., *Advan. Chem. Ser.* Vol. 66, *Am. Chem. Soc. Publ.* **1967,** pp. 203–213.

28. R. H. Boundy and R. F. Boyer, *Styrene*, ACS Monograph Series No. 115, Reinhold Publishing Corp., New York, 1952, p. 736.

29. H. W. McCormick, *J. Polymer Sci.* **25,** 488 (1957).

30. A. Dondos and P. Rempp, *Rev. Gen. Caoutchouc* **41,** 1361 (1964).

31. W. A. Lee and G. J. Knight, in J. Brandrup and E. H. Immergut, eds., *Polymer Handbook*, Interscience Publishers, a division of John Wiley & Sons, New York, 1966, p. III-70.

32. W. G. Barb, *J. Polymer Sci.* **37,** 515 (1959).

33. G. D. Jones, in E. M. Fettes, ed., *Chemical Reactions of Polymers*, Interscience Publishers, a division of John Wiley & Sons, Inc., New York, 1964, p. 273.

34. U.S. Pat. 3,206,445 (Sept. 14, 1965), H. Volk (to The Dow Chemical Co.).

35. U.S. Pat. 3,340,238 (Sept. 5, 1967), W. E. Smith and H. Volk (to The Dow Chemical Co.).

36. U.S. Pat. 3,318,813 (May 9, 1967), H. W. McCormick and W. R. Nummy (to The Dow Chemical Co.).

37. U.S. Pat. 3,011,918 (Dec. 5, 1961), L. H. Silvernail and M. W. Zembal (to The Dow Chemical Co.).

38. G. E. Molau and H. Keskkula, *J. Polymer Sci.* [A1]**4,** 1595 (1966).

39. C. B. Bucknall and R. R. Smith, *Polymer* **6,** 437 (1965).

40. J. A. Schmitt, *J. Appl. Polymer Sci.* **12,** 533 (1968).

41. S. Strella, in E. Baer, ed., *Engineering Design for Plastics*, Reinhold Publishing Corp., New York, 1964, pp. 795–814.

42. R. F. Boyer, *Polymer Eng. and Sci.* **8,** 161 (1968).

43. S. L. Rosen, *Polymer Eng. and Sci.* **7,** 115 (1967).

44. E. M. Fettes and W. N. Maclay, *Appl. Polymer Symp.* **7,** 3 (1968).

45. H. Willersinn, *Makromol. Chem.* **101,** 297 (1966).

46. H. Keskkula, S. G. Turley, and R. F. Boyer, to be published; H. Keskkula and S. G. Turley, *Polymer Letters*, to be published.

47. D. A. Walker, *Mod. Plastics Encyclopedia for 1968–69* **45** (14A), 334 (1968).

48. K. Kato, *J. Electron-Microscopy* (*Japan*) **14** (3), 220 (1965); *Polymer Eng. Sci.* **7,** 38 (1967).

49. H. Keskkula and W. C. Taylor, to be published.

50. H. Keskkula and P. A. Traylor, *J. Appl. Polymer Sci.* **11,** 2361 (1967).

51. S. G. Turley, *J. Polymer Sci.* [C]**1,** 101 (1963).

52. C. H. Basdekis, *ABS Plastics*, Reinhold Publishing Corp., New York, 1964.

53. *Mod. Plastics* **45** (1) (1968).

54. L. D. Moore, W. W. Moyer, and W. J. Frazer, *Appl. Polymer Symp.* **7,** 67 (1968).

55. H. Keskkula, G. M. Simpson, and F. L. Dicken, *SPE* (*Soc. Plastics Engrs.*) *Preprints Ann. Tech. Conf.* **12,** XV-2 (1966).

56. *Brit. Plastics* **38,** 708 (Dec. 1965).

57. G. M. Kraynak, *SPE Preprints Ann. Tech. Conf.* **13,** 896 (1967).

58. *Vacuum Metallizing Cycolac*, Technical Report P 135, Borg-Warner Corp., Chicago.

59. E. N. Hildreth, *Mod. Plastics Encyclopedia* **43,** 991 (1966).

60. K. Stoeckhert, *Kunststoffe* **55,** 857 (1965).

61. *Mod. Plastics* **45,** 84 (August 1968).

62. U.S. Pat. 2,802,809 (Aug. 13, 1957), R. A. Hayes (to The Firestone Tire and Rubber Co.).

63. J. E. Hauck, *Mod. Plastics* **45,** 80 (July 1968).

64. *Rubber Plastics Age* **46,** 1271 (Nov. 1965).

65. J. A. Blanchette and L. E. Nielsen, *J. Polymer Sci.* **20,** 317 (1956).

66. R. R. Hampton, *Anal. Chem.* **21,** 923 (1949).

67. I. M. Kolthoff and T. S. Lee, *J. Polymer Sci.* **2,** 206 (1947).

68. T. T. Crompton and V. W. Reid, *J. Polymer Sci.* [A]**1,** 347 (1963).

69. A. R. Kemp and H. Peters, *Anal. Chem.* **15,** 453 (1943).

70. D. Barnard, *J. Polymer Sci.* **22,** 213 (1956).
71. N. Rabjohn, C. E. Bryan, G. E. Inskeep, H. W. Johnson, and J. K. Lawson, *J. Am. Chem. Soc.* **69,** 314 (1947).
72. I. M. Kolthoff, T. S. Lee, and C. W. Carr, *J. Polymer Sci.* **1,** 429 (1946).
73. G. Natta, F. Danusso, and G. Moraglio, *Makromol. Chem.* **20,** 37 (1956). F. Danusso and G. Moraglio, *J. Polymer Sci.* **24,** 161 (1957).
74. M. J. R. Cantow, ed., *Polymer Fractionation*, Academic Press, Inc., New York, 1967; (a) H. W. McCormick, pp. 251–284; (b) A. Kotera, pp. 44–66; (c) K. H. Altgelt and J. C. Moore, pp. 123–179.
75. J. F. Johnson, R. S. Porter, and M. J. R. Cantow, *Rev. Macromol. Chem.* **1** (2), 393 (1966).
76. G. C. Claver, Jr. and E. H. Merz, *Offic. Dig., Federation Paint Varnish Prod. Clubs* **28,** 858 (1956).
77. P. A. Traylor, *Anal. Chem.* **33,** 1629 (1961).
78. R. J. Williams and R. W. A. Hudson, *Polymer* **8,** 643 (1967).
79. W. E. Brown, *Performance of Plastics in Building*, No. 1004, Building Research Inst., Inc., Washington, D.C., 1963.
80. S. Strella, *High Speed Testing*, Vol. 1, Interscience Publishers, Inc., 1961, pp. 27–40.
81. J. A. Schmitt and H. Keskkula, *J. Appl. Polymer Sci.* **8,** 132 (1960).
82. F. J. Furno, R. S. Webb, and N. P. Cook, *Prod. Eng.* **35,** 87 (August 17, 1964); V. E. Malpass, *SPE Preprints Ann. Tech. Conf.* **13,** 618 (1969).
83. Ref. 28, p. 1160.
84. W. E. Brown, *International Plastics Congr.* 1966, N. V. t'Raedthuys, Utrecht, Netherlands, 1967.
85. R. L. Bergen and W. E. Wolstenholme, *SPE J.* **16,** 1235 (1960).
86. G. B. Jackson and J. L. McMillan, *SPE J.* **19,** 203 (1963).
87. S. G. Turley and H. Keskkula, *Polymer Eng. Sci.* **7,** 1 (1967).
88. R. McFedries, Jr., *Plastics World* **21,** 34 (October 1963).
89. E. Scalco, T. W. Huseby, and L. L. Blyler, Jr., *J. Appl. Polymer Sci.* **12,** 1343 (1968).
90. E. H. Andrews, in J. V. Schmitz and W. E. Brown, eds., *Testing of Polymers*, Vol. 4, Interscience Publishers, a division of John Wiley & Sons, Inc., 1969, p. 237.
91. W. H. Haslett, Jr. and L. A. Cohen, *SPE J.* **20,** 246 (1964).
92. P. I. Vincent, *Plastics Inst. Transactions J.* **30,** 157 (1962).
93. R. H. Shoulberg and J. J. Gouza, *SPE J.* **23,** 33 (1967).
94. H. Keskkula and J. W. Norton, Jr., *J. Appl. Polymer Sci.* **2,** 289 (1959).
95. K. J. Cleereman, *SPE J.* **23,** 43 (Oct. 1967); **25,** 55 (Jan. 1969).
96. C. B. Bucknall and D. G. Street, *J. Appl. Polymer Sci.* **2,** 289 (1959).
97. C. H. Adams, G. B. Jackson, and R. A. McCarthy, *SPE Preprints Ann. Tech. Conf.* **2,** 121 (1956).
98. A. Chapiro, *Radiation Chemistry of Polymeric Systems*, Interscience Publishers, a division of John Wiley & Sons, New York, 1962, p. 446.
99. W. W. Parkinson, C. D. Bopp, D. Binder, and J. E. White, *J. Phys. Chem.* **69** (3), 828 (1965).
100. W. Burlant, J. Neerman, and V. Serment, *J. Polymer Sci.* **58,** 491 (1962).
101. J. P. Bell, A. S. Michaels, A. S. Hoffman, and E. A. Mason, *Advan. Chem. Ser.* Vol. 66, *Am. Chem. Soc. Publ.* **1967,** pp. 79–112.
102. D. E. Kline, *J. Appl. Polymer Sci.* **4,** 191 (1961).
103. J. E. Hauck, *Mod. Plastics* **46** (1), 100 (1969).
104. W. O. Elliott, *Mod. Plastics Encyclopedia*, **45** (1A), 720 (1967).
105. P. A. M. Ellis, *Plastics Inst. J. Trans.* **35** (117), 537 (1967).
106. H. R. Jacobi, *Screw Extrusion of Plastics*, Iliffe Books, Ltd., London, 1963.
107. J. P. Goslin, R. M. Bonner, *Mod. Plastics Encyclopedia* **45** (1A), 743 (1967).
108. R. Giuffria, R. O. Carhart, and D. A. Davis, *J. Appl. Poly. Sci.* **7,** 1731 (1963).
109. E. P. Weaver, *Polymer Eng. Sci.* **6,** 172 (1966).
110. *Cycolac Brand ABS Polymers*, sales Bull., Marbon Chemical Division of Borg-Warner Corp., Chicago.
111. W. R. R. Park and J. Conrad, "Biaxial Orientation," in *Encyclopedia of Polymer Science and Technology*, Vol. 2, Interscience Publishers, a division of John Wiley & Sons, Inc., New York, 1965, p. 339.
112. K. J. Cleereman, W. J. Schrenk, and L. S. Thomas, *SPE J.* **24,** 27 (1968).
113. *Mod. Plastics* **45,** 79 (Feb. 1968).

114. P. M. Coffman, *Soc. Automotive Engrs., Automotive Eng. Congr. 680063, Detroit, Jan. 1968.*

115. R. G. Royer and W. R. Meadors, *SPE Preprints Ann. Tech. Conf.* **14,** 231 (May 1968).

116. J. Harreis, *SPE J.* **24,** 61 (April 1968).

117. E. Zahn and K. Wiebusch, *Kunststoffe* **56,** 773 (1966).

118. H. J. Orthmann and B. Schmitt, *Kunststoffe* **55,** 779 (1965).

119. L. A. Landers and W. C. Meisenhelder, *SPE J.* **20,** 621 (July 1964).

120. BASF, to be published in *J. Appl. Polymer Sci.,* 1969.

121. F. A. Miller, in R. R. Meyers and J. S. Long, eds., *Treatise on Coatings,* Vol. 1, Part 2, Marcel Dekker, Inc., New York, 1968, pp. 1–57.

122. U.S. Pat. 3,215,647 (Nov. 2, 1965), Edwin R. Dunn (to The Dow Chemical Co.).

123. R. L. Zimmerman, B. B. Hibbard, and H. R. Bailey, *Rubber Age* **98** (1968).

124. W. J. Van Essen, D. E. Erickson, and M. A. Rolik, *Tappi* **50,** 622 (1967).

125. U.S. Pat. 3,409,596 (Nov. 5, 1968), R. E. Lane and J. E. Carmichael (to General Tire and Rubber Co.).

126. D. P. Sheetz, *J. Appl. Polymer Sci.* **9,** 3759 (1965).

127. J. W. Vanderhoff, H. J. van den Hul, R. J. M. Tausk, and J. Th. G. Overbeek, *Proc. Symp. Clean Surfaces,* Marcel Dekker, Inc., in press.

128. H. B. Wagner, *Ind. Eng. Chem. Prod. Res. Develop.* **4,** 191 (1965); **5,** 149 (1966); **6,** 223 (1967); **7,** 259 (1969).

129. R. Stagg, "Latexes" in *Encyclopedia of Polymer Science and Technology,* Vol. 8, Interscience Publishers, a division of John Wiley & Sons, Inc., New York, 1968, pp. 164–195.

130. L. Crampton and S. S. Drake, in H. R. Simonds and J. M. Church, eds., *The Encyclopedia of Basic Materials for Plastics,* Reinhold Publishing Corp., New York, 1967.

131. R. N. Kennedy, in R. J. Bender, ed., *Handbook of Foamed Plastics,* Lake Publishing Co., Libertyville, Ill., 1965.

132. Calvin Benning, *Plastic Foams,* John Wiley & Sons, Inc., New York, 1969.

133. U.S. Pat. 2,681,321 (June 15, 1954), F. Stasny and R. Gaeth (to Badische Anilin- u. Soda-Fabrik).

134. U.S. Pat. 2,744,291 (May 8, 1956), F. Stasny and K. Buchholtz.

135. U.S. Pat. 2,787,809 (April 9, 1957), F. Stasny.

136. a. U.S. Pat. 3,231,524 (Jan. 25, 1966), D. W. Simpson (to The Dow Chemical Company); b. U.S. Pat. 3,089,875 (April 12, 1960), C. H. Pottenger (to Koppers Co., Inc.); b. U.S. Pat. 3,093,599 (Aug. 16, 1960), H. Müller-Tamm (to BASF).

137. D. C. Woollard, *paper 12th Annual SPI Conf., Washington, D.C., Oct. 16–18, 1967.*

138. U.S. Pat. 2,958,905 (Nov. 8, 1960), R. F. Newberg and R. O. Newman, Jr. (to The Dow Chemical Co.).

139. Can. Pat. 762,531 (July 4, 1967), J. L. M. Newnham and D. J. Simcox (to Dunlop Rubber Co.).

140. U.S. Pat. 3,411,256 (Nov. 19, 1968), J. S. Best (to The Dow Chemical Co.).

141. U.S. Pat. 3,250,188 (May 10, 1966), G. A. Leonards (to The Dow Chemical Co.); *Highway Insulation,* Technical Bull., The Dow Chemical Co., Nov. 1967.

142. *Low Temperature Panel Structures,* Technical Bull., The Dow Chemical Co., Jan. 1969.

143. U.S. Pat. 3,206,899 (Sept. 21, 1965), D. R. Wright (to The Dow Chemical Co.).

144. U.S. Pat. 3,377,384 (Aug. 22, 1967), D. R. Wright (to The Dow Chemical Co.).

145. *Chem. Eng. News* **41** (2), 23 (1963).

146. Alvin R. Ingram and Harold A. Wright, *Mod. Plastics* **41** (3), 152 (Nov. 1963).

147. a. L. C. Rubens, *J. Cellular Plastics* **1,** 3 (1965). b. F. Hohwiller and K. Köhling, *Betonstein Ztg.* **2, 3,** 3 (1968).

148. J. Eichhorn, *J. Appl. Polymer Sci.* **8,** 2497 (1964).

149. J. Eichhorn, in S. Atlas and H. Mark, eds., *Chemical Aftertreatment of Textiles,* Interscience Publishers, a division of John Wiley & Sons, Inc., New York, under preparation.

150. a. S. J. Skinner, S. Baxter, and P. J. Grey, *Trans. J. Plastics Inst.* **32,** 180 (1964). b. I. K. Hinselmann, *Kunststoffe,* in press.

151. O. Sweeting, ed., *Science and Technology of Polymer Films,* Vols. 1 and 2, Interscience Publishers, a division of John Wiley & Sons, Inc., New York, 1968–1969.

152. J. Pinsky, Ref. 151, Vol. 2, in press.

153. J. Karan, Ref. 151, Vol. 1, pp. 227–253.

154. W. R. R. Park, ed., *Plastics Film Technology,* Reinhold Publishing Corp., New York, in press.

155. J. Eichhorn, "A Study of the Manufacture and Market for Packaging and Industrial Films," in R. H. Mosher and D. S. Davis, *Industrial and Specialty Papers,* Vol. 2, 1968.

156. Choji Saikaishi, *Japan Chem. Quart.* **1**, 49–54 (1968).
157.   W. R. R. Park and J. Conrad, "Biaxial Orientation," in *Encyclopedia of Polymer Science and Technology*, Vol. 2, Interscience Publishers, a division of John Wiley & Sons, Inc., 1965, pp. 339–373.
158. R. J. McCormick, *Packaging Eng.* **3**, 1 (June 1958).
159. C. R. Scott, F. J. Butt, and J. Eichhorn, *Mod. Packaging* **38**, 135 (1965).
160. H. Yasuda, H. G. Clark, and V. Stannett, "Permeability," in *Encyclopedia of Polymer Science and Technology*, Vol. 9, Interscience Publishers, a division of John Wiley & Sons, Inc., 1968, pp. 794–807.
161. C. E. Rogers, in E. Baer, ed., *Engineering Design for Plastics*, Reinhold Publishing Corp., New York, 1964, pp. 609–688.
162. G. V. Schulz and H. Gerrens, *Z. Physik. Chem.* **1**, 182 (1956).
163. W. R. Vieth, P. H. Tam, and A. S. Michaels, *J. Col. Interface Sci.* **22**, 360 (1966).
164. T. Surprenant, "Film Materials," in *Encyclopedia of Chemical Technology*, Vol. 9, Interscience Publishers, a division of John Wiley & Sons, Inc., New York, 1966, pp. 220–224.

General References

K. E. Coulter, Howard Kehde, and B. F. Hiscock, "Styrene and Related Monomers," in E. C. Leonard, ed., *Vinyl Monomers*, Interscience Publishers, a division of John Wiley & Sons, Inc., New York, in press.
"Styrene Polymers," in N. Bikales, ed., *Encyclopedia of Polymer Science and Technology*, Interscience Publishers, a division of John Wiley & Sons, Inc., New York, in press.

HENNO KESKKULA,
ALAN E. PLATT, AND
RAYMOND F. BOYER
The Dow Chemical Co.

SUBERIC ACID, $HOOC(CH_2)_6COOH$.   See Acids, dicarboxylic, Vol. 1, p. 249.

SUCCINIC ACID AND SUCCINIC ANHYDRIDE

Succinic acid, $HOOCCH_2CH_2COOH$, occurs widely in nature in both plant and animal matter. It may be present in the form of esters. The acid and its anhydride have many unique properties; the most interesting of these is the reactivity of the methylene groups. As in maleic or fumaric acid (see Maleic anhydride, maleic acid, and fumaric acid), the unsaturated acids from which succinic acid may be derived, each group can react in some manner under suitable experimental conditions. Succinic acid has therefore been used as an intermediate in the synthesis of a wide variety of complex organic compounds. It is important in the manufacture of pharmaceuticals and also in the synthesis of plastics, protective coatings, and many other industrial products.

Succinic acid can be obtained in 3–8% yields by the distillation of amber (*succinicum*, in Latin). Agricola, in 1550, was the first to use this method. The acid is also found in some varieties of lignite, in resins, in turpentine oils, and in animal fluids. It is formed in both the chemical and biochemical oxidation of fats, in the fermentation of calcium malate or ammonium tartrate, and in the alcoholic fermentation (qv) of sugar. Its presence in both plant and animal matter has led to extensive phytochemical and zoological studies, especially those directed toward its role in various metabolic and other vital processes. It is formed, for example, in a metabolic cycle of certain microorganisms which can derive their carbon requirements from two-

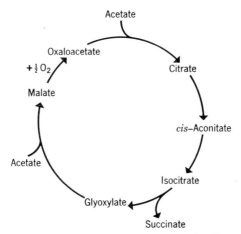

Fig. 1. Main stages of the "glyoxalate cycle" (1). Courtesy *Nature*.

carbon compounds (ie, acetates). The "glyoxalate cycle," described by Kornberg and Krebs (1), presents a pathway of synthesizing one molecule of succinic acid from two molecules of acetic acid, as shown in Figure 1.

$$2 \text{ CH}_3\text{COOH} + \tfrac{1}{2}\text{ O}_2 \rightarrow \begin{array}{l}\text{CH}_2\text{COOH} \\ | \\ \text{CH}_2\text{COOH}\end{array} + \text{H}_2\text{O}$$

Physical and Chemical Properties

The acid occurs both as colorless triclinic prisms (α form) and as monoclinic prisms (β form). The monoclinic crystals are triboluminescent and are stable up to 137°C; the triclinic crystals are stable above 137°C. Both forms dissolve in water, alcohol, diethyl ether (2), anhydrous glycerol, acetone, and various aqueous mixtures of the last two solvents. Succinic acid sublimes when heated below its melting point under reduced pressure (for an example, see Table 1). It is readily absorbed from solution by charcoal.

Succinic anhydride forms rhombic pyramidal or bipyramidal crystals. It is relatively insoluble in water and ether, but soluble in chloroform and alcohol. The physical properties are listed in Table 1.

Succinic acid undergoes most of the reactions characteristic of dicarboxylic acids (see also Acids, dicarboxylic). In addition many interesting reactions occur at the active methylene group.

On heating, loss of water causes succinic acid to form an internal anhydride with a stable ring structure, as shown below:

$$\begin{array}{l}\text{CH}_2\text{---COOH} \\ | \\ \text{CH}_2\text{---COOH}\end{array} \xrightarrow{-\text{H}_2\text{O}} \begin{array}{l}\text{CH}_2\text{---C} \\ | \\ \text{CH}_2\text{---C}\end{array}$$

On further heating, the dilactone of γ-ketopimelic acid is produced (9), which can also be obtained at a lower temperature in the presence of alkali:

$$\begin{array}{c}\text{CH}_2\text{---CH}_2 \\ | \\ \text{CO---O}\end{array} \mathrm{C} \begin{array}{c}\text{O---CO} \\ | \\ \text{CH}_2\text{---CH}_2\end{array}$$

Table 1. Physical Properties (2–8)

Property	Succinic acid	Succinic anhydride
melting pt, °C	181–185	119.6
boiling pt, °C	(dehydrates at 235°C)	261
sublimation pt at 2 mm, °C	156–157	90
sp gr	1.552–1.577	1.572
solubility, g/100 g soln, in		
water, at 0°C	2.88	
at 100°C	121	
96% alcohol, at 15°C	9.99	
ether, at 15°C	1.25	
dissociation constant		
$K_1 \times 10^{-5}$	6.52–6.65	
$K_2 \times 10^{-6}$	2.3	
pKA (in molten ethylpyridinium bromide)	8.45	
sp heat at 0–35°C, av, cal/g	0.2965	
heat of combustion, kcal/mole	356.2–357.4	369.9–373.1
heat of solution in 60 pts of water, cal/mole	6528	
dipole moment at 20°C, esu $\times 10^{-18}$		4.20
magnetic susceptibility, esu	−57.47	−43.85
dielectric constant at 3–97°C, 5 kc	2.29–2.90	

Allen and Caldin (10) reported that, like other dicarboxylic acids, the β form of succinic acid, due to hydrogen bonding, associates to an extended polymer structure:

$$\ldots O \qquad OH\ldots O \qquad OH\ldots$$
$$\text{C—CH}_2\text{—CH}_2\text{—C} \qquad \text{C—CH}_2\text{—CH}_2\text{—C}$$
$$\ldots HO \qquad O\ldots HO \qquad O\ldots$$

Halogenation. The reactivity of the methylene group is shown in the reactions of succinic acid and its anhydride with halogens. *Monochlorosuccinic acid* can be prepared by the addition of hydrogen chloride to fumaric acid.

Monofluorosuccinic acid was prepared by Bean and Pattison (11) by the following route:

$$\text{EtOOCCH}_2\text{CH}_2\text{COOEt} \xrightarrow[\text{KOEt}]{\text{EtOOCCOOEt}} \text{EtOOCCH}_2\overset{\text{COOEt}}{\underset{\text{COCOOEt}}{\text{CK}}} \xrightarrow[\text{EtOH}]{\text{ClO}_3\text{F}}$$

$$\left[\text{EtOOCCH}_2\overset{\text{COOEt}}{\underset{\text{COCOOEt}}{\text{CF}}}\right] \xrightarrow{\text{KHCO}_3} \text{EtOOCCH}_2\text{CHFCOOEt} \xrightarrow{\text{dil H}_2\text{SO}_4} \text{HOOCCH}_2\text{CHFCOOH}$$

The ethoxalyl grouping promotes the fluorination by the perchloryl fluoride, and the strongly electronegative character of the introduced fluorine atom facilitates the alkaline cleavage of the β-keto ester.

When heated in a sealed vessel at 100°C, succinic acid yields *meso-dibromosuccinic acid* almost quantitatively (2):

$$\overset{\text{CH}_2\text{—COOH}}{\underset{\text{CH}_2\text{—COOH}}{|}} \xrightarrow{\text{2 Br}_2} \overset{\text{CHBr—COOH}}{\underset{\text{CHBr—COOH}}{|}} + \text{2 HBr}$$

When more than one equivalent amount of water is present, brominated hydrocarbons are produced and the yield of dibromoacid is reduced.

α,α-*Difluorosuccinic acid* (mp, 144–145°C) can be obtained by oxidizing 1-chloro-2,3,3-trifluorocyclobutene with permanganate (12).

$$\begin{array}{c} \text{CH}_2\!\!-\!\!\text{CCl} \\ | \quad\quad \| \\ \text{CF}_2\!\!-\!\!\text{CF} \end{array} \xrightarrow{\text{KMnO}_4} \begin{array}{c} \text{CH}_2\!\!-\!\!\text{COOH} \\ | \\ \text{CF}_2\!\!-\!\!\text{COOH} \end{array}$$

Middleton (13) reported the preparation of *trifluorosuccinic acid* (mp, 111.2°C), by the reduction of *chlorotrifluorosuccinic* acid with the aid of zinc and sulfuric acid in dioxane. The product was extracted with ether, washed with methylene chloride, and recrystallized from ether–chloroform. This treatment led to a complex of two molecules of trifluorosuccinic acid, $HOOCCHFCF_2COOH$, with one molecule of dioxane.

Tetrachlorosuccinic acid anhydride is obtained directly by the chlorination of the acetic anhydride or its mono- or dichloro derivatives (14):

$$\begin{array}{c} \text{CH}_3\text{CO} \\ \quad\quad\quad \diagdown \\ \quad\quad\quad\quad \text{O} + 5\ \text{Cl}_2 \\ \quad\quad\quad \diagup \\ \text{CH}_3\text{CO} \end{array} \xrightarrow{150°\text{C}} \begin{array}{c} \text{CCl}_2\!\!-\!\!\text{CO} \\ | \quad\quad\quad \diagdown \\ \quad\quad\quad\quad\quad \text{O} + 6\ \text{HCl} \\ | \quad\quad\quad \diagup \\ \text{CCl}_2\!\!-\!\!\text{CO} \end{array}$$

Diethyl succinate treated with excess chlorine in sunlight is chlorinated completely, yielding small needles of *bis(pentachloroethyl) tetrachlorosuccinate*, Cl_3CCl_2-$OOCCCl_2CCl_2COOCCl_2CCl_3$.

Succinic acid reacts with an equimolecular amount of phosphorus pentachloride at 120–130°C to yield succinoyl chloride. Thionyl chloride may also be used for this reaction.

Condensation with Ketones and Aldehydes. Succinic esters condense with aldehydes and ketones in the presence of bases (eg, sodium alkoxide, piperidine) to form half-esters of alkylidenesuccinic acids. This reaction, known as the *Stobbe condensation* (15,16,16a), is peculiar to succinic esters and substituted succinic esters. The reaction takes place in three steps: (1) formation of an aldol or a ketol; (2) loss of alcohol to give a γ-lactone ester (paraconate); and (3) rearrangement to the alkylidenesuccinic acid half-ester. A typical Stobbe condensation is that of acetone and diethyl succinate:

ethyl 2,2-dimethylparaconate
(ethyl terebate)

monoethyl isopropyl-
idenesuccinate
(ethyl teraconate)

Dialkylidenesuccinic acids and anhydrides (fulgides) are highly unsaturated, intensely colored compounds, which may be formed in a similar manner from aromatic aldehydes:

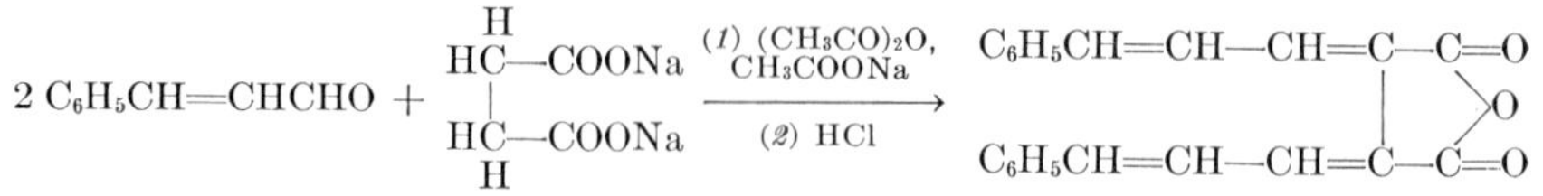

$$2\,C_6H_5CH=CHCHO + \begin{array}{c} H \\ HC-COONa \\ | \\ HC-COONa \\ H \end{array} \xrightarrow[\text{(2) HCl}]{\text{(1) }(CH_3CO)_2O,\ CH_3COONa} \begin{array}{c} C_6H_5CH=CH-CH=C-C=O \\ \diagdown O \\ C_6H_5CH=CH-CH=C-C=O \end{array}$$

cinnamaldehyde α,δ-distyrylfulgide (2,3-dicinnamylidenesuccinic anhydride)

Diketones. Ketones containing reactive methyl or methylene groups condense with succinates in the presence of sodium hydride (17,18) to form diketones by a Claisen mechanism competing with the Stobbe condensation. For example, *tert*-butylsuccinate and acetophenone give (besides a mixture of the half-esters of γ-methyl-γ-phenylitaconic acid and its isomers) a 19–34% yield of 1,8-diphenyl-1,3,6,8-octanetetraone (1,6-dibenzoyl-2,5-diketohexane):

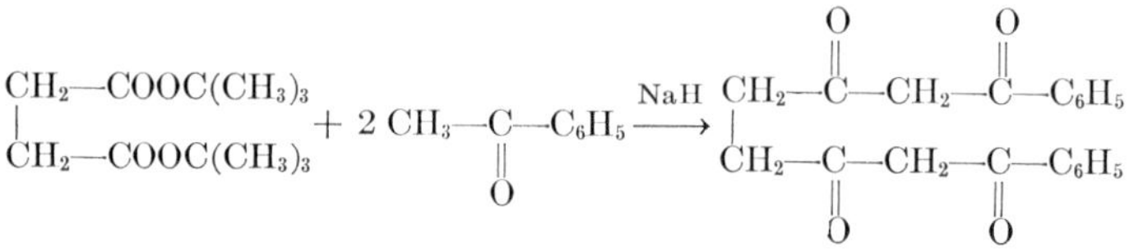

$$\begin{array}{c} CH_2-COOC(CH_3)_3 \\ | \\ CH_2-COOC(CH_3)_3 \end{array} + 2\,CH_3-\underset{\underset{O}{\|}}{C}-C_6H_5 \xrightarrow{NaH} \begin{array}{c} CH_2-\overset{\overset{O}{\|}}{C}-CH_2-\overset{\overset{O}{\|}}{C}-C_6H_5 \\ | \\ CH_2-\underset{\underset{O}{\|}}{C}-CH_2-\underset{\underset{O}{\|}}{C}-C_6H_5 \end{array}$$

The Stobbe half-ester is not formed when the sodium derivative of the ketone reacts with a monoacid chloride of a succinic half-ester at low temperature (19):

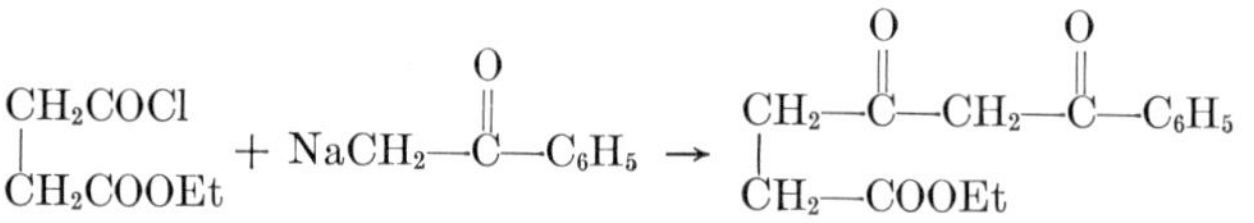

$$\begin{array}{c} CH_2COCl \\ | \\ CH_2COOEt \end{array} + NaCH_2-\overset{\overset{O}{\|}}{C}-C_6H_5 \rightarrow \begin{array}{c} CH_2-\overset{\overset{O}{\|}}{C}-CH_2-\overset{\overset{O}{\|}}{C}-C_6H_5 \\ | \\ CH_2-COOEt \end{array}$$

Thorpe Reaction. Johnson and co-workers (20) reported an interesting reaction between dimethylsuccinate and 2-cyano-1,2,3,4-tetrahydro-2-methyl-1-oxophenanthrene (in the presence of potassium *tert*-butoxide). Apparently, the cyano group takes part in the reaction leading to a cyclic compound via an intramolecular Thorpe reaction, as shown in the following equations:

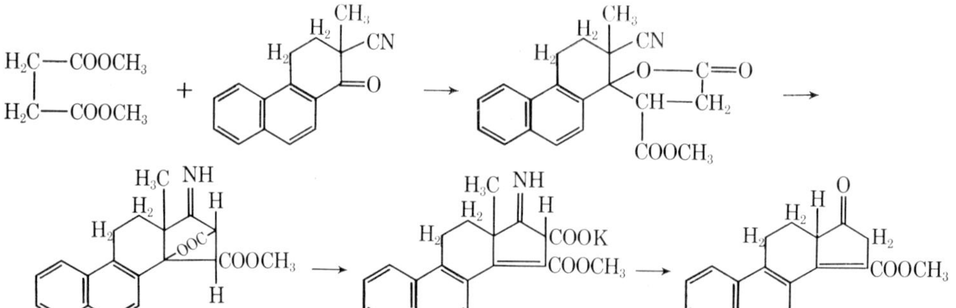

Friedel-Crafts Reactions. Succinic anhydride reacts with alkylbenzenes in the presence of anhydrous aluminum chloride to form alkylbenzoylpropionic acids (21) and it readily adds to fused polycyclic compounds (such as indane) to form various derivatives of 4-oxobutyric acid (22). Fieser and Seligman showed that the succinoylation takes place in the 5 position (23), as shown below:

indan

With acenaphthene diacylation takes place (24):

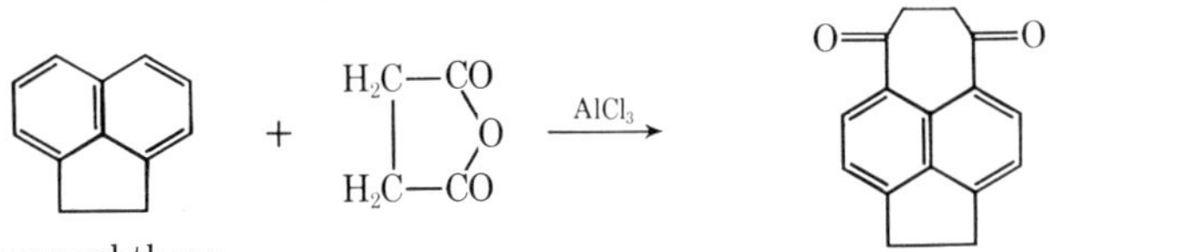

acenaphthene

1,4-acepleidanedione
(*peri*-succinoylacenaphthene)

Phenol esters of succinic acid undergo the *Fries rearrangement* (25,26), as shown in the following equations:

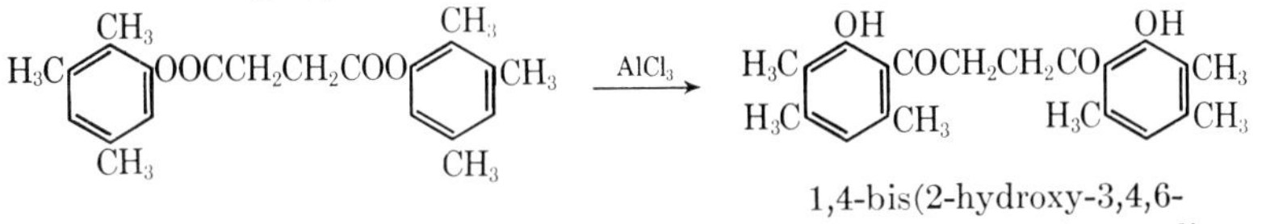

1,4-bis(2-hydroxy-3,4,6-
trimethylphenyl)-1,4-butanedione

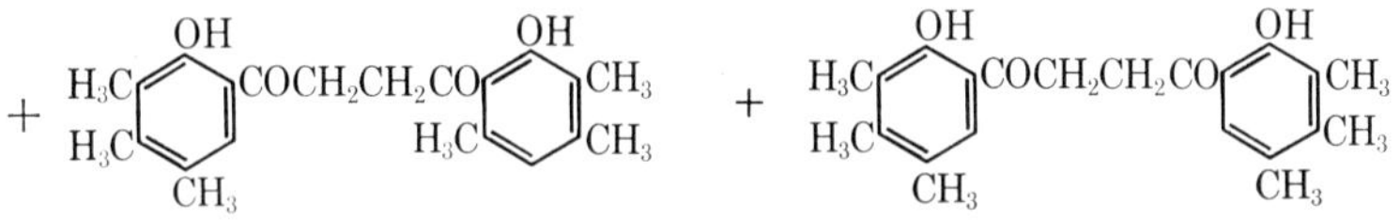

1-(2-hydroxy-3,4,5-trimethyl-
phenyl)-4-(2-hydroxy-3,4,6-trimethyl-
phenyl)-1,4-butanedione

1,4-bis(2-hydroxy-3,4,5-trimethyl-
phenyl)-1,4-butanedione

Esterification. Monomethylsuccinate (mp, 58°C) and dimethylsuccinate (mp, 19°C) are easily prepared from acetylene, methanol, and carbon monoxide (27). Diethyl succinate undergoes self-condensation in the presence of sodium to form diethyl 2,5-diketocyclohexane-1,4-dicarboxylate (28):

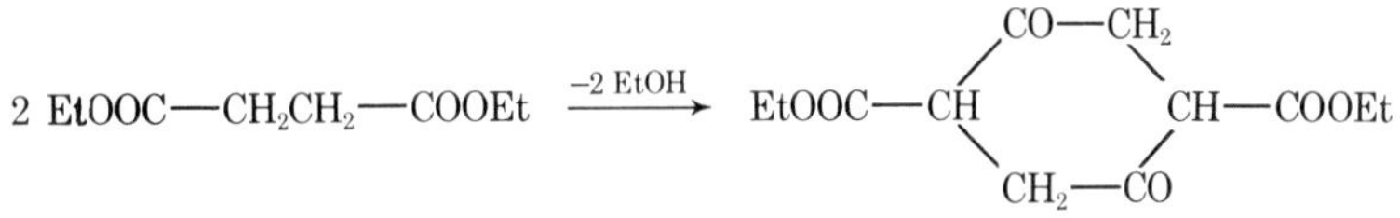

Similarly, ethyl formate and diethyl succinate react to yield diethyl 2-formyl succinate (29):

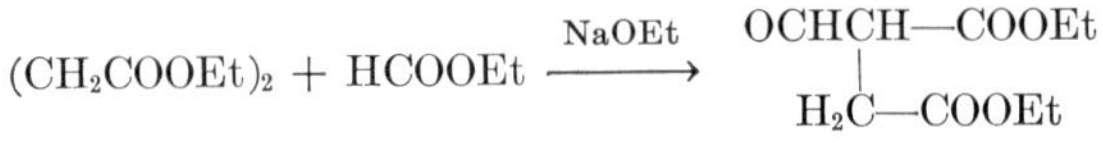

Succinic anhydride reacts with polyhydric alcohols and with cellulose to yield a variety of polyesters. In the presence of stannous chloride, the glycol polyesters can be depolymerized to polymembered ring products. For example, a 16-membered cyclic dimer, 1,5,9,13-tetraoxacyclohexadecane-4,8,12,16-tetraone, is obtained from polyethylenesuccinate (30).

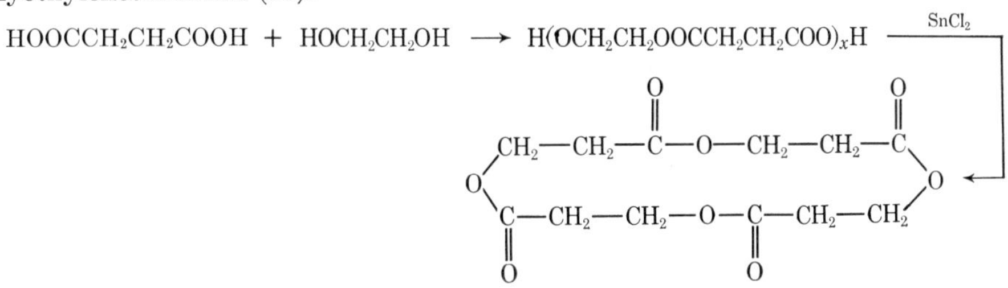

Nitrogen Derivatives. Succinic acid and succinic anhydride react with amino compounds to form a variety of products. An important derivative is *succinimide* (mp, 126°C), which is prepared from succinic acid or dialkyl succinates at elevated temperature with ammonia (31), urea, or some isocyanates.

$$\begin{array}{c} H_2C\text{---}COOH \\ | \\ H_2C\text{---}COOH \end{array} \xrightarrow{NH_3} \begin{array}{c} H_2C\text{---}CO \\ | \quad\quad\;\; NH \\ H_2C\text{---}CO \end{array}$$

The corresponding alkyl- or arylsuccinimides are obtained from the appropriate amino compounds. Succinimide can also be prepared by hydrogenation of maleimide.

N-Alkylsuccinimides can be prepared from *N*-alkylacrylamides and carbon monoxide (32), as follows:

$$\begin{array}{c} \quad\quad O \\ \quad\quad \| \\ CH\text{---}C\text{---}NHR \\ \| \\ CH_2 \end{array} + \;\; CO \;\; \longrightarrow \begin{array}{c} CH_2\text{---}CO \\ | \quad\quad\;\; NR \\ CH_2\text{---}CO \end{array}$$

Halogen-substituted succinimides can be obtained by reacting hypobromous or hypochlorous acid with succinimides, or iodine with silver succinimide (33).

N-Bromosuccinimide (mp, 176–177°C), is the most important member of this group. It is prepared by the addition of bromine to a sodium hydroxide solution of succinimide in the cold (34) and is frequently used for bromination and oxidation in the synthesis of cortisone and other hormones (qv) (see also Steroids) (35).

This product has the unique property of facilitating a selective halogen substitution at methylene groups adjacent to unsaturated bonds without an addition reaction (36). By varying the reaction conditions, it can be used for synthesizing many compounds and even saturated substances. The Wohl-Ziegler bromination with *N*-bromosuccinimide can be applied to a variety of reactions, such as the substitution of side chains attached to aromatics; controlled dehydrogenation; nuclear addition to aromatic compounds; formation of bromohydrins; and selective oxidation of alcohol groups. The reaction proceeds via a free-radical chain mechanism through the following steps (37): (a) thermal dissociation of *N*-bromosuccinimide;

$$\begin{array}{c} CH_2\text{---}CO \\ | \quad\quad\;\; NBr \\ CH_2\text{---}CO \end{array} \xrightarrow{\Delta} \begin{array}{c} CH_2\text{---}CO \\ | \quad\quad\;\; N\cdot \\ CH_2\text{---}CO \end{array} + Br\cdot$$

(b) abstraction of hydrogen from the methylene group adjacent to an unsaturated bond by the free radical; (c) propagation; and (d) chain termination.

N-Chlorosuccinimide (mp, 150–151°C), forms orthorhombic crystals and has a chlorinelike odor. It is a powerful germicide, used for disinfecting drinking water in military camps; to a limited extent, it is also used as a chlorinating agent.

N,N'-Disuccinimides can be prepared by heating ethylenediamine with two moles of succinic anhydride:

$$H_2NCH_2CH_2NH_2 \;\; + \;\; 2 \begin{array}{c} H_2C\text{---}CO \\ | \quad\quad\;\; O \\ H_2C\text{---}CO \end{array} \xrightarrow{\Delta} \begin{array}{c} H_2C\text{---}CO \quad\quad\quad CO\text{---}CH_2 \\ | \quad\quad\;\; NCH_2CH_2N \quad\quad\; | \\ H_2C\text{---}CO \quad\quad\quad CO\text{---}CH_2 \end{array}$$

Derivatives of succinimides are frequently used in the pharmaceutical industry as very effective anticonvulsants (see Hypnotics, sedatives, anticonvulsants).

Succinamic acid, NH₂CO—CH₂CH₂—COOH, is obtained by adding ammonia to the anhydride or by partial hydrolysis of succinimide. The latter reaction can be reversed, and the succinamic acid dehydrates to succinimide upon heating with a dehydrating agent, such as phosphorus pentachloride.

Succinamide, (CH₂.CONH₂)₂ (mp, 268–270°C), may be obtained by reacting succinoyl chloride with ammonia or by partial hydrolysis of succinonitrile. When succinimide is warmed with a primary amine, *N*-alkylsuccinamides are formed:

$$\begin{matrix} CH_2—CO \\ | \quad\quad\ \ \diagdown NH \\ CH_2—CO \diagup \end{matrix} + 4\ RNH_2 \longrightarrow \begin{matrix} CH_2—CONR_2 \\ | \\ CH_2—CONR_2 \end{matrix} + 3\ NH_3$$

The formation of succinamic acids and succinamides by the usual procedures with various amines has been extensively used in the synthesis of dyes, insecticides, and drugs; for example, *N-p*-arsonosuccinanilic acid is obtained by heating atoxyl (sodium hydrogen arsanilate) with succinic anhydride and hydrochloric acid:

$$\underset{NH_2}{\underset{|}{\bigcirc}}\ AsO_3HNa + \begin{matrix}CH_2—CO\\|\quad\quad\ \diagdown O\\CH_2—CO\diagup\end{matrix} \xrightarrow[\Delta]{HCl} \underset{NHCOCH_2CH_2COOH}{\bigcirc}\ AsO_3H_2$$

Succinonitriles. The mononitrile, β-cyanopropionic acid, CN—CH₂CH₂—COOH (mp, 50°C), is prepared from propiolactone with sodium cyanide (38). The dinitrile succinonitrile, NC—CH₂CH₂—CN (mp, 57.2°C), is obtained by the usual preparative methods, or from acrylonitrile with hydrogen cyanide.

Nitrosuccinic acid esters may be obtained by reacting α-bromosuccinic esters with sodium nitrite (39).

Sulfur Derivatives. Diethyl (or diphenyl) succinate reacts with potassium hydrogen sulfide to form dipotassium *dithiosuccinate*, which loses hydrogen sulfide upon acidification and yields *dithiosuccinic anhydrosulfide* (dihydro-2,5-thiophenedione):

$$\begin{matrix}CH_2—COOEt\\|\\CH_2—COOEt\end{matrix} \xrightarrow{KHS} \begin{matrix}CH_2—COSK\\|\\CH_2—COSK\end{matrix} \xrightarrow{H_2SO_4} \begin{matrix}CH_2—CO\\|\quad\quad\diagdown S\\CH_2—CO\diagup\end{matrix}$$

This compound can also be obtained by the reaction of phosphorus pentasulfide with succinic acid, or sodium sulfide with succinoyl chloride.

Sulfosuccinic Acids and Esters. Sulfur trioxide reacts with both methylene groups of succinic acid and yields 2,3-disulfosuccinic acid:

$$\begin{matrix}CH_2—COOH\\|\\CH_2—COOH\end{matrix} + 2\ SO_3 \longrightarrow \begin{matrix}HSO_3CH—COOH\\|\\HSO_3CH—COOH\end{matrix}$$

Monosulfosuccinate esters are widely used as wetting agents. In the cosmetic, pharmaceutical, and food industries, they are applied as solubilizing and dispersing agents for hydrophilic colloids. The *dioctyl sodium sulfosuccinate*, NF XII (41), is a waxlike, white solid with a characteristic odor suggesting octyl alcohol. It can be prepared by esterifying maleic anhydride with 2-ethylhexanol followed by the addition of sodium bisulfite:

$$
\begin{array}{c}
\text{CH—CO} \\
\quad\quad\ \ \ \text{O} \\
\text{CH—CO}
\end{array}
\xrightarrow[\text{HOCH}_2\text{CH(CH}_2)_3\text{CH}_3]{\overset{\text{C}_2\text{H}_5}{|}}
\begin{array}{c}
\text{CH—COOC}_8\text{H}_{17} \\
\| \\
\text{CH—COOC}_8\text{H}_{17}
\end{array}
\xrightarrow{\text{NaHSO}_3}
\begin{array}{c}
\overset{\text{C}_2\text{H}_5}{|} \\
\text{CH}_2\text{COOCH}_2\text{CH(CH}_2)_3\text{CH}_3 \\
| \\
\text{NaSO}_3\text{—CHCOOCH}_2\text{CH(CH}_2)_3\text{CH}_3 \\
| \\
\text{C}_2\text{H}_5
\end{array}
$$

It is a component of polymer emulsions for the paper and textile industries (42), and is also used as ionic surfactant in photographic emulsions (43) and in antioxidant compositions (44).

MISCELLANEOUS REACTIONS

Hydration. Succinic anhydride is converted to the acid almost instantaneously with boiling water.

$$
\begin{array}{c}
\text{CH}_2\text{—C} \overset{\text{O}}{\overset{\|}{}} \\
| \quad\quad\quad \text{O} \\
\text{CH}_2\text{—C} \\
\quad\quad \|\\
\quad\quad \text{O}
\end{array}
+ \ \text{H}_2\text{O} \ \longrightarrow \
\begin{array}{c}
\text{CH}_2\text{—COOH} \\
| \\
\text{CH}_2\text{—COOH}
\end{array}
$$

Oxidation. Hydrogen peroxide and succinic acid, according to experimental conditions, yield *peroxysuccinic acid*, $(\text{CH}_2\text{COOOH})_2$, 2,2-dihydrosuccinic acid, malonic acid, or a mixture of acetaldehyde and malonic and malic acids. Hydrogen peroxide and succinic anhydride form *succiboyl peroxide*, $(\text{COOH}.\text{CH}_2\text{CH}_2\text{CO}.\text{O})_2$ (mp 133°), which explodes upon heating, and decomposes with water to monopersuccinic acid, $\text{HOOC}.\text{CH}_2\text{CH}_2\text{CO}.\text{O}.\text{OH}$ (mp 107°C). The cyclic succinoyl peroxide, a very explosive product, is obtained by the reaction of sodium peroxide on succinoyl chloride:

$$
\begin{array}{c}
\overset{\text{H}_2}{\underset{}{\text{C}}} \\
\text{H}_2\text{C} \quad \text{CO} \\
| \quad\quad | \\
\text{OC} \quad \text{Cl} \\
\ \ \text{Cl}
\end{array}
\xrightarrow{\text{Na}_2\text{O}_2}
\begin{array}{c}
\overset{\text{H}_2}{\underset{}{\text{C}}} \\
\text{H}_2\text{C} \quad \text{CO} \\
| \quad\quad | \\
\text{OC} \quad \text{O} \\
\ \ \text{O}
\end{array}
+ \ 2\ \text{NaCl}
$$

Reduction. The *N*-methylanilide of succinic acid can be reduced with lithium aluminum hydride to succinaldehyde at 0°C (45):

$$
\begin{array}{c}
\text{CH}_2\text{COOC}_6\text{H}_5\text{NCH}_3 \\
| \\
\text{CH}_2\text{COOC}_6\text{H}_5\text{NCH}_3
\end{array}
\xrightarrow[0°\text{C}]{\text{LiAlH}_4}
\begin{array}{c}
\text{CH}_2\text{—CHO} \\
| \\
\text{CH}_2\text{—CHO}
\end{array}
$$

This compound is commercially available in its stable, water-soluble acetal form, 2,5-diethoxytetrahydrofuran, $\text{C}_2\text{H}_5\text{OCHCH}_2\text{CH}_2\text{CHOC}_2\text{H}_5$ (bp, 196°C at 5 mm Hg).

Degradation Reactions. Succinic acid and its salts, when heated under various conditions, yield a variety of compounds, such as γ-ketopimelic dilactone, 1,4-cyclohexanedione, a mixture of propionic acid and acetaldehyde, acrylic acid and acrolein, oxalic acid, cyclopentanone, and furan. Electrolysis of succinic acid produces ethylene and acetylene.

Manufacture

Hydrogenation. Succinic acid is generally produced by the hydrogenation of maleic anhydride or fumaric acid (see Vol. 12, p. 828) and is isolated either as the free acid or as the anhydride. Several different processes are available for this purpose. They include, for example, treating an aqueous solution of sodium maleate with hydrogen gas at 100°C under 2500 psi pressure in the presence of a Raney-nickel catalyst; reduction with hydrogen at room temperature with colloidal palladium as catalyst; electrolytic reduction; and reduction with sulfuric acid and zinc. The equipment, hydrogen quality, and catalysts used for the catalytic hydrogenation of maleic anhydride are similar to those used for fat hardening (see Vol. 8, pp. 801–805).

In a typical hydrogenation, molten, distilled maleic anhydride is charged to a hydrogenator. The vessel is purged and filled with hydrogen. The catalyst (nickel or a noble metal) is added as a slurry, agitation is started, and the temperature is raised to 130–140°C. Moderate hydrogen pressure is maintained until the reaction is complete (4–6 hr). The catalyst is then removed and the product is distilled under conditions practically identical with those used for phthalic anhydride, which melts very near to succinic anhydride and is also sold in the form of white flakes (see Vol. 15, p. 452).

The acid may also be produced by hydrolyzing succinonitrile with either aqueous alkali or acid. Numerous other methods have also been employed.

Oxidation. Succinic acid is obtained in various yields when spermaceti and other waxes (qv) (46), butanediol, butyric acid, γ-butyrolactone, sebacic acid, stearic acid, cycloparaffins, tetrahydrofuran, or 3-formylpropionic acid are treated with nitric acid (47,48). Small amounts are also formed in the oxidation of cyclohexane to adipic acid (see Vol. 1, p. 411). Other oxidation methods include treating glutamic acid or butyrates with hydrogen peroxide, or acetic acid and potassium peroxysulfate, $K_2S_2O_8$, or acetyl peroxide. Furfural has been oxidized to succinic anhydride with Caro's acid, H_2SO_5. The vapor-phase oxidations of petroleum wax and of butyrolactone have also been recommended. These methods use a vanadium oxide or copper oxide catalyst and yield a mixture of both the acid and the anhydride. Electrolytic oxidation has been employed with ethyl potassium malonate, tetrahydrofurfuryl alcohol, or tetrahydrofuran.

Fusion. Included here is the treatment of lactose, gum arabic, or cinnamic acid with hydrated lime; of cellulosic materials (such as corn cobs) with caustic alkali (49); and of pyrrole (qv) with caustic and hydroxylamine. This last method gives first an oxime, which may then be converted to the acid.

Catalytic Addition. Acetylene and some of its substituted derivatives, such as ethyl, phenyl, or diphenyl acetylene, react with carbon monoxide and water at elevated temperatures (80–250°C) and at pressures of 30–500 atm in acid medium to yield succinic acid derivatives, according to the reaction shown below:

$$\begin{array}{c} R_1\!-\!C \\ \quad \||| \\ R_2\!-\!C \end{array} + 2\,CO + 2\,H_2O \xrightarrow{\text{catalyst}} \begin{array}{c} R_1\!-\!CH\!-\!COOH \\ \quad | \\ R_2\!-\!CH\!-\!COOH \end{array}$$

A flow diagram for a continuous process (50) is shown in Figure 2.

The reaction is carried out in reactor *5* in a single homogeneous liquid phase, containing the reactants and a suitable catalyst, eg $(Co(CO)_4)_2$. Carbon monoxide and acetylene are introduced through compressors *1* and *2*, respectively. Succinic

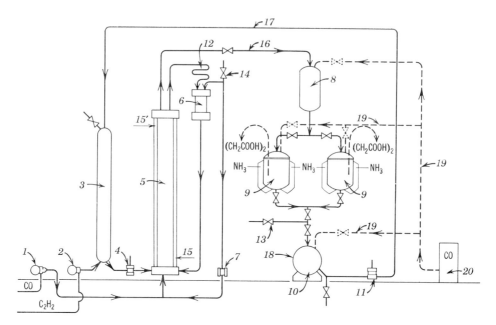

Fig. 2. Flow diagram for a catalytic addition process for the manufacture of succinic acid.

acid, the main reaction product, is precipitated on one of the filters *9* and removed. The gasometer *20* maintains a carbon monoxide atmosphere which prolongs the efficiency of the catalyst. Under optimal conditions, the yield of succinic acid may be as high as 75–80%, calculated on the acetylene.

Miscellaneous. The action of carbon monoxide on ethylene glycol (51) or on acrylic acid in oleum (52) may also be utilized in the manufacture of succinic acid. Other methods include treatment of various products with potassium cyanide, followed by hydrolysis; the reaction of ethyl cyanoacetate and formaldehyde cyanohydrin; the reaction of hydrocyanic acid and ethylene (53); the reduction of malic or tartaric acid with hydroiodic acid; the controlled decarboxylation of ethanetricarboxylic acid; various fermentation processes; and recovery from spent liquors of the pulping industry (54,55).

Preparation of Succinic Anhydride. The anhydride has been obtained by the dry distillation of maleic acid; the dehydration of succinic acid at elevated temperatures; and by treating succinic acid with diketene, succinyl chloride, or acetic anhydride. It may also be prepared from the diethyl ester with boron chloride in a closed flask at 250°C.

Prices and Specifications

Little information is available on the production of succinic acid and its derivatives. The price of succinic acid and succinic anhydride was 61–62¢/lb and 51–52¢/lb, respectively, in 1969 (tank-car quantities). Specifications of commercially available products are listed in Table 2.

N-Bromosuccinimide, containing a minimum of 44.5% active bromine, and *N*-chlorosuccinimide, with a chlorine content of 25% or more, are available in 50-lb drums.

Table 2. Specifications of Succinic Acid (56) and Succinic Anhydride (57)

Property	Succinic acid	Succinic anhydride
melting pt, °C, min	187.0	118.3[a]
physical appearance	clean, small, white crystals	clean, white flakes
total acidity, %, min	99.0[b]	99.5[c]
unsaturates,[d] %, max		0.5
ash, %, max	0.1	
chlorides, %, max		0.15
iron (as Fe), ppm, max	10	
lead (as Pb), ppm, max	5	
sulfates (as SO_4), %, max	0.05	0.04
heavy metals, ppm, max	10	20
contamination	nil	
turbidity, 5% aq soln, nephelos units,[e] max	20	10
fineness, 10-mesh, %, min	100	

[a] Solidification pt. [c] As succinic anhydride. [e] Coleman Instruments Corp.
[b] As succinic acid. [d] As maleic anhydride.

Uses

Due to their unique chemical and physical properties, succinic acid, succinic anhydride, and their derivatives find extensive industrial application. The toxicity of succinic acid is very low, and therefore it is widely used in foods and drugs. Its use in food products has been cleared by the FDA (*Fed. Register* **26** (19), 938 (1961)). A list of applications includes adhesives, coatings, elastomers, lubricants, pesticides, pharmaceuticals, plastics, and many other items (17).

Adhesives. A synthetic adhesive resin is obtained from succinic anhydride with glycerol and an aromatic diamine (58), or with an alkylenimine derivative and water (59). Succinic dihydrazide can be used to improve the adhesive strength, and the fungus and water resistance of casein glues (60).

Coatings. Succinic acid or its anhydride are used in the manufacture of alkyd resins (qv) to impart flexibility, elasticity, and water resistance. A copolymer of polyglycol succinates and styrene yields hard, clear products suitable for commercial finishes (61). Plasticized glycerol succinates are used in cellulose nitrate lacquers (62). Succinic acid itself acts as a viscosity stabilizer for phenolic varnishes (63). The condensation product of triethylenemelamine with succinamide is used for water-repellent coatings (64). Silicone–alkyds containing succinic acid (65) give coatings with a high resistance to deterioration at elevated temperatures. Monoallyl succinate mixed with the hexamethyl ether of hexamethylolmelamine forms a thermosetting coating composition (66).

Dyestuffs. The dibenzyl ester of succinic acid has been employed in the dyeing of vinyl yarn (67); anthraquinone dyes, obtained from reacting diethyl succinate or succinic anhydride with aminoanthraquinones, can be applied to nylon or acetate rayons (68,69).

Elastomers. *N,N′*-Diisopropyldithiosuccinamide and succinamic acid and some of its derivatives can be used as vulcanization accelerators (70,71); succinic anhydride condensed with glycols yields rubberlike substances with high resistance to heat and oils; they can be used for special tubings, cable coverings, and extruded articles (72). Diallyl succinate and 1,3-butadiene also form a synthetic rubber (73).

Lubricants. Alkenylsuccinic anhydrides, prepared by the reaction of maleic anhydrides with olefins, have been used in preparing additives for lubricants (74,75). The condensation product of succinic anhydride, methylamine, and acetoacetic esters exhibit properties of drying oils (76). A moisture-resistant lubricant is made by mixing a glycerol monostearate–succinic acid resin with cellulose (77).

Paper. Succinic acid derivatives are applied as fire-retardants for paper and other cellulose products (78), and in paper coatings (79).

Pesticides. Dialkylsuccinates and N,N'-dialkyl derivatives of succinic acid are used as repellents against black flies, sand flies, mosquitoes, roaches, and ants (24, 80–85). The di-n-butyl succinate was found effective against termites and *Drosophila* (86). The 2,4,5-trichlorophenyl ester is used for seed treatment. 2-(2,4-Dichlorophenoxy)ethyl succinate inhibits the growth of weeds (87).

Pharmaceuticals. Sodium succinate has an analeptic effect in coma (88); it acts as an antidote for barbiturate poisoning (89) and also prolongs the duration of anesthesia with thiopental (90). The calcium salt of the benzyl ester has been employed as an antispasmodic and also in rheumatic fever treatment. Ammonium salts are used internally for controlling spasmodic pains, labor pains, uterine contractions, and delirium tremens (91). Succinic acid and anhydride are used in the manufacture of sulfa drugs (qv) (92,93). Succinylsulfapyrazine reduces the count of coliform bacteria (94); N-succinylsulfanilamidodiazines are efficient intestinal antiseptics (95). N-Methyl-2-phenylsuccinimide, N-2-dimethyl-2-phenylsuccinimide, and 2-methyl-2-ethylsuccinimide are very effective anticonvulsants in the treatment of epilepsy (Vol. 11, p. 522). The n-butyl ester of succinic acid has been used as a solvent in parenteral injections (96); other derivatives serve as muscular relaxants (97) and tuberculostatic agents (98); succinylcholine is a curarelike compound with a neuromuscular blocking effect (99).

Both the Stobbe-synthesis and the Friedel-Crafts reactions (see pp. 137 and 138, respectively) have been extensively used in the synthesis of polynuclear aromatic compounds. A good example is the synthesis of various substituted benzanthracenes, reported as having carcinogenic properties, which have been of interest in cancer studies (100). Succinic acid and its anhydride have been used in the synthesis of vitamins A (101) and B_6 (102), cortisone derivatives (103,104), antihemorrhagic drugs (105,106), ketohydroxyacids of the steroid series (107,108), arsenicals (109), salts of sulfur–gold and sulfur–antimony derivatives of mercaptosuccinic acid (110,111), α-tocopheryl acid succinate (112), and chloramphenicol monosuccinate (113); the acid was reported to inhibit the growth of *Micrococcus pyogenes* var. *aureus* (114), and also the multiplication of certain types of influenza virus in chicken embryo (115).

Photographic Chemicals. Condensation products of succinates with 2,6-diaminopyridine are employed for fixing acid dyes in photographic plates (116). Gelatin heated with succinic anhydride forms an improved vehicle for silver halide photographic emulsions (117). Vinyl acid succinate copolymers were used as gelatin hardeners (118).

Plasticizers. Esters of succinic acid are used as plasticizers for poly(vinyl chloride) polymers and copolymers (119–123), and for cellulose derivatives (124,125). Dioctyl succinate has been used as an effective plasticizer for cellulose nitrate lacquers stable at low temperatures (126).

Plastics and Resins. Succinic anhydride-based alkyd resins have outstanding electrical insulating properties. Vinyl succinate and diallyl succinate copolymerized with other unsaturated monomers give casting, molding, and laminating resins (127, 128). Succinic anhydride serves as a crosslinking agent for ion-exchange membranes (129), and for epoxy resins made from epichlorohydrin and 1,4-butanediol (130). Various plastic materials can be prepared from succinic anhydride and partially hydrolyzed cellulose acetate (131), or from ethylcellulose and polyvinyl alcohol. Condensates of succinic acid with polyhydric alcohols are used in producing safety glass (132). Tough flexible epoxy resins are prepared from ester adducts of polyethylene glycol, glycerol, and polybutylene glycol combined with derivatives of succinic anhydride (133); the latter is also applied in curing epoxy resins (134).

Surface-Active Agents. Derivatives of succinic acid have been used as components of detergents (135,136), soaps (137), and demulsifying agents (138).

Synthetic Fibers and Textiles. In preparing polyethylene terephthalates used for synthetic fibers, manganese, zinc, and cadmium succinates have been applied as catalysts (139). Cellulose fabrics gain shrink-resistant, creaseproof properties when treated with a combination of succinaldehyde with a polyepoxide or a pentaerythritol derivative (140,141); wool fabrics are crease- and feltproofed by compositions containing succinic acid derivatives (142). Reinforced fibers were made from mixtures of linear polyesters, polyamides, and succinic anhydride (143).

Miscellaneous Uses. Succinic acid or its derivatives have been used in the leather industry to improve water repellency and wet strength (144–147); to improve the froth in the flotation of various ores (148); as vehicles for printing inks (149); as a filter material for tobacco smoke (150); as flavoring in the food industry (151) and gelating agent for marmalades (152); as coalescing agent for emulsion paints (153); and for a wide variety of other industrial applications.

Bibliography

"Succinic Acid and Succinic Anhydride" in *ECT* 1st ed., Vol. 13, pp. 180–191, by Wm. Howlett Gardner and Lawrence H. Flett, National Aniline Division, Allied Chemical & Dye Corporation.

1. H. L. Kornberg and H. A. Krebs, *Nature* **179,** 988 (1957).
2. *Beilstein*, 4th ed., Vol. II, pp. 601–606; 1st Suppl., pp. 259–262; 2nd Suppl., pp. 542–546; 3rd Suppl., pp. 1643–1656; Vol. XVII, p. 407; 1st Suppl., p. 228; 2nd Suppl., p. 429; Vol. XXI, p. 380.
3. T. L. Hill, *J. Chem. Phys.* **12,** 56 (1944).
4. M. Kushner and S. Weinhouse, *J. Am. Chem. Soc.* **71,** 3558 (1949).
5. G. D. Pinching and R. G. Bates, *J. Res. Natl. Bur. Std.* **45,** 444 (1950).
6. B. K. Singh, K. M. S. Mahain, S. L. Agarwal, N. Hog, and M. Singh, *Proc. Indian Acad. Sci.* **A22,** 163 (1945).
7. J. Oldham, "Dicarboxylic Acids and Related Compounds," in S. Coffey, ed., *Rodd's Chemistry of Carbon Compounds*, 2nd ed., Vol. ID, Elsevier Publishing Co., Amsterdam, 1965, pp. 305–363.
8. J. Vedel and B. Tresmillon, *Bull. Soc. Chim. France* **1966,** 220–227.
9. U.S. Pat. 2,302,321 (1941) (to H. Griesshaber).
10. G. Allen and E. F. Caldin, *Quart. Rev. (London)* **7,** 267 (1953).
11. F. H. Dean and F. L. M. Pattison, *Can. J. Chem.* **41,** 1833 (1963).
12. M. S. Raasch and J. E. Castle, *Org. Syn.* **42,** 44–47 (1962).
13. U.S. Pat. 2,831,835 (Apr. 22, 1958), Wm. J. Middleton (to E. I. du Pont de Nemours & Co., Inc.).
14. H. Klug and K. Kuchinka, *Ann. Chem.* **677,** 77–83 (1964).
15. H. Stobbe, *Ber.* **26,** 2312 (1893).
16. R. Adams et al., eds., *Organic Reactions*, Vols. 1–15, John Wiley & Sons, Inc., New York, 1942–1967.
16a. W. S. Johson and G. H. Daub, "Stobbe Condensation," in reference 16, Vol. 6, 1951, pp. 2–73.

17. *Succinic Anhydride*, Tech. Bull. I–11, Allied Chemical Corp., Plastics Division, New York, 1963.
18. G. H. Daub and W. S. Johnson, *J. Am. Chem. Soc.* **72**, 501–504 (1950).
19. C. R. Hauser and B. O. Linn, *J. Am. Chem. Soc.* **79**, 731–734 (1957).
20. W. S. Johnson, J. W. Petersen, and C. D. Gutsche, *J. Am. Chem. Soc.* **69**, 2942 (1947).
21. A. G. Peto, "Acylation with Di- and Polycarboxylic Acid Derivatives," in G. A. Olah, ed., *Friedel-Crafts and Related Reactions*, Vol. III, Part 1, Interscience Publishers, a div. of John Wiley & Sons, Inc., New York, 1964, p. 550.
22. E. Berliner, in reference 16, Vol. 5, 1949, pp. 230–289.
23. L. F. Fieser and A. M. Seligman, *J. Am. Chem. Soc.* **59**, 833 (1937).
24. V. Boekelheide, W. E. Langeland, and C. T. Liu, *J. Am. Chem. Soc.* **74**, 2432 (1952).
25. L. J. Smith and R. R. Holmes, *J. Am. Chem. Soc.* **73**, 3847 (1951).
26. A. Gerecs, "The Fries Reaction," in reference 21, p. 499.
27. P. Pino and A. Miglierina, *J. Am. Chem. Soc.* **74**, 5551 (1952).
28. Brit. Pat. 742,949 (1954) (to D. W. Ingram).
29. E. Carriere, *Ann. Chim.* **17** (9), 38–132 (1922).
30. E. W. Spanagel and W. H. Carothers, *J. Am. Chem. Soc.* **57**, 929–931 (1935).
31. H. T. Clarke and L. D. Behr, in A. H. Blatt, ed., *Organic Syntheses*, Coll. Vol. II, John Wiley & Sons, Inc., New York, 1943, p. 562.
32. J. Falbe and F. Korte, *Ber.* **95**, 2860 (1962).
33. W. R. Benson, E. T. McBee, and L. Rand, *Org. Syn.* **42**, 73 (1962).
34. L. Horner and E. H. Winkelmann, *Angew. Chem.* **71**, 349 (1959).
35. C. Djerassi, *Chem. Rev.* **43**, 271 (1948).
36. J. H. Incremona, *Diss. Abstr.* **B, 27** (7), 2295 (1967).
37. G. F. Bloomfield, *J. Chem. Soc.* **1944**, 114.
38. T. L. Gersham, et al., *J. Am. Chem. Soc.* **74**, 1323 (1952).
39. R. Gelin and S. Gelin, *Compt. Rend.* **256**, 3705 (1963).
40. Brit. Pat. 1,054,957 (Jan. 11, 1967) (to K. R. Dutton et al.).
41. The *National Formulary*, 12th ed., American Pharmaceutical Association, Washington, D.C., 1965.
42. Brit. Pat. 1,045,535 (Oct. 12, 1966) (to Monsanto Co.).
43. V. M. Uvarova et al., *Ref. Zh. Khim.* **1966** (13), Pt. II, Abstr. No. 13N587; (through) *Chem. Abstr.* **66** (6), 24413a (1967).
44. Fr. Pat. 1,437,037 (Apr. 29, 1966) (to Monsanto Chemicals, Ltd.).
45. F. Weygand et al., *Angew. Chem.* **65**, 525–531 (1953).
46. T. Hsi et al., *Sci. Abstr. China, Chem. Chem. Technol.* **4**, 18–19 (1966).
47. U.S. Pat. 2,771,482 (Nov. 20, 1956), G. P. Brown et al. (to Gulf Research & Development Co.).
48. U.S. Pat. 2,452,741 (Nov. 2, 1948), H. W. Fleming (to Phillips Petroleum Co.).
49. Can. Pat. 302,784 (Aug. 5, 1930), L. C. Swallen (to Commercial Solvents Corp.).
50. U.S. Pat. 2,851,456 (Sept. 9, 1958), G. Natta and P. Pino (to Lonza Electric and Chemical Works, Ltd.).
51. W. Reppe et al., *Ann.* **582**, 72 (1953).
52. L. Weintraub, J. F. Vitcha, and R. Leinon, *Chem. Ind.* (*London*) **1965**, 185.
53. Japan. Pat. 153,150 (Nov. 21, 1942), (to Nippon Chemical Industries Co.).
54. T. Enkvist and T. Lindfors, *Finska Kemistamfundets Medd.* **75**, 1–21 (1966).
55. T. Enkvist and T. Lindfors, *Paperi Puu* **48**, 639–646 (1966).
56. *Technical Data Bulletin D55*, Allied Chemical Corp., New York, 1966.
57. *Technical Data Bulletin AA-5*, Allied Chemical Corp., Plastics Division, Morristown, N.J., Oct., 1965.
58. Japan. Pat. 145 (1951), S. Watanabe (to Ryoka Industries Co.).
59. U.S. Pat. 3,223,681 (Dec. 14, 1965), G. M. Rambosek (to Minnesota Mining & Manufacturing Co.).
60. U.S. Pat. 2,668,154 (Feb. 2, 1954), G. O. Orth, Jr. (to Mathieson Chemical Corp.).
61. U.S. Pat. 2,570,269 (Oct. 9, 1951), E. E. Parker (to Pittsburgh Plate Glass Co.).
62. U.S. Pat. 1,886,242 (Nov. 1, 1932), C. Ellis (to Ellis-Foster Co.).
63. U.S. Pat. 2,785,144 (March 12, 1957), J. J. Wachter (to Westinghouse Electric Corp.).
64. U.S. Pat. 2,582,594 (Jan. 15, 1952), E. L. Kropa and H. P. Wohnsiedler (to American Cyanamid Co.).

65. U.S. Pat. 2,576,486 (Nov. 27, 1951), J. L. Speier (to The Dow Corning Corp.).
66. Can. Pat. 729,729 (March 8, 1966), I. H. McEwan (to Canadian Industries, Ltd.).
67. U.S. Pat. 2,362,376 (Nov. 7, 1944), K. Heymann (to American Viscose Corp.).
68. Indian Pat. 31,437 (Aug. 14, 1947) (to J. D. Billmoria).
69. Brit. Pat. 652,453 (1951) (to Ciba Ltd.).
70. M. C. Throdahl, R. O. Zerbe, and D. J. Beaver, *Ind. Eng. Chem.* **43,** 926 (1951).
71. U.S. Pat. 2,723,969 (Nov. 15, 1955), R. A. Naylor and E. O. Hook (to American Cyanamid Co.).
72. "Polyester Elastomers" in *Encyclopedia of Plastics,* Plastics Catalog Corp., New York, 1944, p. 898.
73. U.S. Pat. 2,384,572 (Sept. 11, 1945), W. L. Semon (to B. F. Goodrich Co.).
74. U.S. Pat. 3,234,131 (Feb. 8, 1966), A. J. Morway (to Esso Research & Engineering Co.).
75. Brit. Pat. 1,011,313 (Nov. 25, 1965) (to Esso Research & Engineering Co.).
76. U.S. Pat. 1,419,091 (June 6, 1922) (to R. Willstätter, O. Wolfes, and H. Maeder).
77. U.S. Pat. 2,682,506 (June 29, 1954), A. F. Siriani and I. E. Puddington (to National Research Council, Canada).
78. U.S. Pat. 2,692,203 (Oct. 19, 1954), D. X. Klein and M. N. Curgan (to Heyden Chemical Corp.).
79. U.S. Pat. 3,245,816 (Apr. 12, 1966), H. C. Schwalbe (to Mead Corp.).
80. J. Develotte, *Ann. Chim.* **5** (12), 215 (1950).
81. K. H. Applewhite and H. F. Cross, *J. Econ. Entomol.* **44,** 19 (1951).
82. R. M. Altman and C. N. Smith, *J. Econ. Entomol.* **48,** 67 (1951).
83. B. V. Travis, *Proc. N.J. Mosquito Exterm. Assoc.* **37,** 154 (1950).
84. Swiss Pat. 287,140 (1953) (to Ciba Ltd.).
85. R. N. Chakravarti and R. C. Dhar, *J. Indian Chem. Soc.* **30,** 751 (1953).
86. "New Products," *J. Agr. Food Chem.* **5,** 466 (1957).
87. U.S. Pat. 2,765,224 (Oct. 2, 1956), J. A. Lambrech (to Union Carbide & Carbon Corp.).
88. E. M. Trautner and E. R. Trethewie, *Med. J. Australia* **2,** 848 (1953).
89. S. Soskin and M. Taubenhaus, *J. Pharmacol.* **78,** 49 (1943).
90. N. J. Giarman, R. P. Rowe, and J. F. Young, *Anesthesiology* **15,** 122 (1954).
91. *The Merck Index,* 4th ed., Merck & Co., Rahway, N. J., 1930, p. 75; 8th ed., 1968, p. 196.
92. E. C. McCulloch, *Disinfection and Sterilization,* 2nd ed., Lea & Febiger, Philadelphia, Pa., 1945, p. 300.
93. U.S. Pat. 2,576,825 (Nov. 27, 1951), G. S. Delmar and E. N. Macallum (to Sharp & Dohme (Canada), Ltd.).
94. P. T. Callomon and G. F. Raiziss, *J. Pharmacol.* **79,** 200 (1943).
95. U.S. Pat. 2,533,033 (Dec. 5, 1950), M. L. Moore (to Sharp & Dohme, Inc.).
96. E. G. Gross, *Proc. Soc. Exptl. Biol. Med.* **56,** 172 (1944).
97. Swed. Pat. 143,592 (1954), E. L. Larsson and B. K. F. Sjögren (to Aktiebolaget Astra).
98. L. Katz, *J. Am. Chem. Soc.* **73,** 4007 (1951).
99. J. O. Hoppe, *Anesthesiology* **16,** 91–124 (1955).
100. M. S. Newman and R. Gaertner, *J. Am. Chem. Soc.* **72,** 264 (1950).
101. U.S. Pat. 2,414,722 (Jan. 21, 1947) (to B. C. Cornwell).
102. U.S. Pat. 2,440,218 (Apr. 20, 1948), F. Bergel and A. Cohen (to Hoffmann-La Roche, Inc.).
103. U.S. Pat. 2,786,835 (March 26, 1957), E. R. Pinson, Jr., and G. D. Laubach (to Chas. Pfizer & Co., Inc.).
104. B. B. Brown and H. W. Werner, *Ann. Allergy* **6,** 122 (1948).
105. B. R. Baker and G. H. Carlson, *J. Am. Chem. Soc.* **64,** 2657–2664 (1942).
106. Brit. Pat. 541,138 (1941) (to Hoffmann-La Roche & Co.).
107. U.S. Pat. 2,447,325 (Aug. 17, 1948), T. F. Gallagher (to Research Corp.).
108. E. M. Chamberlin et al., *J. Am. Chem. Soc.* **75,** 3477 (1953).
109. H. Eagle et al., *J. Am. Chem. Soc.* **65,** 1236 (1943).
110. H. E. Hornby, *J. S. African Vet. Med. Assoc.* **12,** 90–93 (1941).
111. F. R. Heilman, *Science* **91,** 366 (1940).
112. Brit. Pat. 1,114,150 (May 15, 1968) (to Eisai Co., Ltd.).
113. Hung. Pat. 154,759 (May 29, 1968), J. Rakoczi and J. Torok (to Egyesult Gyogyszer es Tapszergyar).
114. K. Öblom, *Physiol. Plantarum* **4,** 563 (1951).

115. B. Fauconnier, *Ann. Inst. Pasteur* **89,** 101 (1955).
116. U.S. Pat. 2,671,071 (March 2, 1954), T. T. M. Laakso and D. D. Reynolds (to Eastman Kodak Co.).
117. U.S. Pat. 2,525,753 (Oct. 10, 1950), H. C. Yutzy and G. F. Frame (to Eastman Kodak Co.).
118. U.S. Pat. 3,277,030 (Oct. 4, 1966), L. M. Minsk and H. L. Cohen (to Eastman Kodak Co.).
119. U.S. Pat. 2,779,783 (Jan. 29, 1957), R. H. Hayes (to Firestone Tire and Rubber Co.).
120. U.S. Pat. 2,755,262 (1956), M. H. Dilke et al. (to Distillers Co., Ltd.).
121. G. J. van Veersen and A. J. Meulenberg, *Kunststoffe* **56** (1), 23–29 (1966).
122. Fr Pat. 1,405,778 (July 9, 1965) (to Lonza Ltd.).
123. U.S. Pat. 2,686,200 (Aug. 10, 1954), J. C. Lo Cicero and C. L. Leveque (to Rohm and Haas Co.).
124. U.S. Pat. 2,689,863 (Sept. 21, 1954), A. E. Broderick and C. R. W. Morison (to Union Carbide & Carbon Corp.).
125. U.S. Pat. 1,939,217 (Dec. 12, 1933), L. P. Kyrides (to Monsanto Chemical Co.).
126. A. Kraus, *Farbe Lack* **60,** 185 (1954).
127. U.S. Pat. 2,521,303 (Sept. 5, 1950), H. T. Neher et al. (to Rohm and Haas Co.).
128. Brit. Pat. 398,173 (1933).
129. E. Selegny et al., *Bull. Soc. Chim. France* **1966,** 2400.
130. R. Reichherzer and R. Rosner, *Oesterreich. Chemiker-Zt.* **57,** 126 (1956).
131. U.S. Pat. 2,794,799 (June 4, 1957), G. D. Hiatt and J. Emerson (to Eastman Kodak Co.).
132. Ger. Pat. 624,462 (1936) (to Degea AG.).
133. U.S. Pat. 3,299,008 (Jan. 17, 1967), A. C. Mueller (to Shell Oil Co.).
134. Neth. Pat. Appl. 6,415,332 (July 1, 1965) (to Gulf Research & Development Co., Inc.).
135. U.S. Pat. 2,362,041 (Nov. 7, 1944), J. S. Reichert et al. (to E. I. du Pont de Nemours & Co.).
136. U.S. Pat. 2,374,187 (Apr. 24, 1945), L. H. Flett (to Allied Chemical and Dye Corp.).
137. U.S. Pat. 2,792,348 (May 14, 1957), R. D. Aylesworth (to Emery Industries, Inc.).
138. U.S. Pat. 2,743,293 (Nov. 26, 1956), M. De Groote (to Petrolite Corp.).
139. Brit. Pat. 753,880 (Aug. 1, 1956) (to Chemstrand Corp.).
140. U.S. Pat. 2,774,691 (Dec. 18, 1956), C. W. Schroeder and R. W. Sumers (to Shell Development Co.).
141. U.S. Pat. 2,785,996 (March 19, 1957), B. H. Kress (to Quaker Chemical Products Corp.).
142. Neth. Pat. Appl. 6,514,930 (May 18, 1966) (to International Synthetic Rubber Co., Ltd.).
143. Neth. Pat. Appl. 6,600,608 (July 19, 1966) (to Allied Chemical Corp.).
144. U.S. Pat. 2,795,517 (June 11, 1957), A. Lowe and G. Williams (to Imperial Chemical Industries, Ltd.).
145. F. P. Luvisi et al., *J. Am. Leather Chemists' Assoc.* **61,** 384–393 (1966).
146. *Ibid.,* 585–593 (1966).
147. L. Seligsberger, *J. Am. Leather Chemists' Assoc.* **62,** 346–362 (1967).
148. U.S. Pat. 2,689,043 (Sept. 14, 1954), A. H. Fischer (to Minerec Corp.).
149. U.S. Pat. 2,778,806 (Jan. 22, 1957), W. M. Hutchinson (to Phillips Petroleum Co.).
150. U.S. Pat. 2,780,228 (Feb. 5, 1957), G. P. Touey (to Eastman Kodak Co.).
151. T. Take and H. Itsuka, *Kaseigaku Zasshi* **17,** 213–217 (1966).
152. Neth. Pat. Appl. 6,607,121 (Nov. 28, 1966) (to Pfeiffer & Laugen K.G.).
153. Brit. Pat. 1,033,466 (June 22, 1966), J. J. Huitson (to Distillers Co., Ltd.).

PAUL TURI
Sandoz, Inc.

COLLEGE OF THE SEQUOIAS
LIBRARY

SUGAR

PROPERTIES OF SUCROSE

Sucrose, *USP* XVII (α-D-glucopyranosyl β-D-fructofuranoside), $C_{12}H_{22}O_{11}$, is a disaccharide composed of D-glucose and D-fructose. Its use was at first restricted to the wealthy, owing to its early high price, but ancient Chinese doctors and those of other early people prescribed it as a medicinal. Today our syrups, elixirs, and pills are still compounded with sugar. Queen Elizabeth I is credited with introducing sugar to the table, a custom which has spread throughout the world.

Sucrose is said to be the first pure carbohydrate to separate from the photosynthetic process. As such, it is the progenitor of all plant and animal substances and the origin of coal and petroleum, our principal sources of heat and power. Sucrose is found in almost all land plants, in the juice, seeds, flowers, leaves, stems, and roots.

Commercially, sucrose is produced in the tropics and semitropics from the juice of the sugar cane (*Saccharum officinarum* L.). In temperate zones sources are the sugar beet (*Beta vulgaris*), sorghum (*Sorghum vulgare*), and the sugar maple (*Acer saccharum*). Beets provide much of the sugar for Europe and the central and western United States. Cane supplies the sugar requirements of almost all of the rest of the world. Sorghum, repeatedly suggested as a source, continues to be used to a limited extent, mostly to produce a syrup. Maple sugar has a limited production which is practical only because the product commands a premium price. Neither sorghum nor maple sugar is a serious competitor for the sugar market.

Synthesis of sucrose defied efforts until 1943, when Hassid, Doudoroff, and Barker found that a phosphorylase enzyme from *Pseudomonas saccharophilia* D. would combine glucose-1-phosphate with fructose to give sucrose (14). The active intermediate has since been identified as *uridinediphosphoglucose* (uridine 5′-pyrophosphate glucose ester) (25). In 1953, Lemieux and Huber reported the first strictly chemical synthesis of sucrose, from tri-O-acetyl-D-glucosan <1,5>α<1,2>, or $CH_2(OAc)$-

$CH(OAc)CH.CH(OAc).\overline{CH.CH}.CHO$, and 1,3,4,6-tetra-$O$-acetyl-D-fructofuranose (26).

Because of the highly specialized molecular configuration of sucrose it appears unlikely that an economically practical commercial synthesis is possible in the near future (16).

Physical and Chemical Properties

Sucrose is a water-soluble substance which crystallizes in a characteristic monoclinic form (6). Additional forms have been studied, including the hemiheptahydrate, $C_{12}H_{22}O_{11}.5\frac{1}{2}H_2O$ (20), and an unstable amorphous form (29,32), which rapidly crystallizes in the presence of water vapor. Sucrose melts with some decomposition at 184°C. The decomposition of heated, dry sucrose has been the subject of several

COLLEGE OF THE SEQUOIAS
LIBRARY

studies, and many products have been identified, including two kestoses and many other carbohydrates (8,9,39). (Kestoses are trisaccharides. An example is 1-kestose, which has the structure β-D-fructofuranosyl-$(2{\rightarrow}1)$-β-D-fructofuranosyl-$(2{\rightarrow}1)$-α-D-glucopyranoside.)

Sucrose crystals are triboluminescent (24). The specific gravity of monoclinic sucrose, $d_{17.5}^{17.5}$, is 1.58056. The surface energy has been estimated by a number of methods, and it has been found that the most probable value for the surface energy of solid sucrose is 224 ergs/cm^2 (43).

The most outstanding physical property of sucrose is its sweet taste. In comparing sweetness, sucrose is frequently used as the standard substance with a value of 100 (see Table 1). The relative sweetness of fructose is dependent upon temperature and concentration. At 5°C fructose is 1.437 times as sweet as sucrose; at 40°C they have equal sweetness; while at 60°C fructose is only 0.79 times as sweet as sucrose.

Table 1. Relative Sweetness of Sugars in 10% Solutions at 20°C (31)

fructose	120	galactose	67
sucrose	100	mannitol	64
glycerol	77	lactose	39
glucose	69		

The second most important property of sucrose is its solubility in water (7,19,22).

Extensive tables of optical properties of sucrose have been compiled because of the importance of the refractive index and optical rotation in sugar manufacture (5,10, 17–19,41,42).

Sucrose has two predominating chemical properties: it is *nonreducing* and *readily hydrolyzed*.

Sucrose is called nonreducing since it fails to reduce copper in Fehling's or equivalent tests inasmuch as the reducing groups of both moieties are tied up as glycosides. More vigorous reagents, however, readily attack the sucrose molecule and account for some use of sucrose as an antioxidant, for example, in jams and jellies. Fermentation and other degradations of sucrose are the most important industrial (nonfood) applications.

Sucrose is very soluble in water (7,19,33,45). It is readily soluble in dilute ethyl alcohol and ammonia, and practically insoluble in anhydrous ethanol, ether, chloroform, and anhydrous glycerol (20,35,38). An abbreviated table of solubility in water is given in Table 2.

Table 2. Solubility of Sucrose in Water (16)

Temperature, °C	Sucrose, wt %	Sucrose, g per 100 g water
0	64.40	180.9
10	65.32	188.4
20	66.60	199.4
30	69.18	214.3
40	70.01	233.4
50	72.04	257.6
60	74.20	287.6
70	76.45	324.7
80	78.74	370.3
90	81.00	426.2

Hydrolysis. Although the glycosidic linkage is relatively stable in dilute alkali, and in neutral solutions, maximum stability occurs at about pH 9. Sucrose is easily hydrolyzed in the presence of hydrogen ion, ammonium ion, and certain enzymes—all acting as catalysts—to a mixture of D-glucose and D-fructose, called "invert sugar" because of a reversal of the direction of optical rotation (12,30).

In the inversion reaction, sucrose unites with a molecule of water, and then decomposes into glucose and fructose, as follows:

$$C_{12}H_{22}O_{11} + HOH \rightarrow C_6H_{12}O_6 + C_6H_{12}O_6$$
$$\text{sucrose} \qquad\qquad \text{glucose} \quad \text{fructose}$$

This is a bimolecular reaction, sucrose and water being the molecules involved. In dilute solution the change in the amount of water as the reaction proceeds is insignificant, and the reaction is effectively monomolecular and irreversible.

At 20°C the specific rotation of sucrose is +66.4. Glucose has a specific rotation of +52.5 and fructose of −88.5. Thus, the change in the direction of rotation of the plane of polarized light from dextro to levo inspired the word "inversion" for the reaction, and the designation of the individual monosaccharides as "invert sugars."

In the sucrose manufacturing process only a small amount of inversion is permitted to occur, and the sucrose concentration may be considered constant. Since hydrogen ion is the catalyst, the inversion rate, c, is proportional to the hydrogen ion activity,

$$c = c_0[\text{H}^+]$$

where c_0 is a constant independent of the hydrogen ion activity, which increases rapidly with temperature, as shown in Table 3.

Table 3. Sucrose Inversion Constants, c_0 (40)

Temp, °C	c_0	Temp, °C	c_0
50	0.1145	80	3.303
60	0.3806	90	8.922
70	1.182	100	26.797

Knowing the value of c, the quantity of invert formed in any time t is given by the following relation:

$$i = cs_0t$$

where s_0 is the starting concentration of sucrose, expressed as 1 or 100, and i is the quantity of invert formed.

When invert sugar is to be intentionally produced, by acid hydrolysis under extreme conditions, a loss of 7–8% of the fructose may occur. The lost fructose can, to some extent, be identified as fructose dianhydrides. Enzymic (invertase) inversion can compete with the acid process because similar losses are not sustained. Invertase inversion also finds favor by those who are prejudiced against chemical alteration of a food substance.

Although invert-sugar syrup is a common item of commerce, many consumers prepare their own by adding 1 part of citric or tartaric acid to 800 parts of sucrose in 33–35% solution and heating at 80°C for half an hour.

The hydrolysis of sucrose in alkaline solutions has been the subject of thorough studies by Heidt and co-workers (15).

Oxidation.   Vigorous oxidation of sucrose with strong nitric acid produces equimolar quantities of oxalic acid and tartaric acid. When the oxidation with nitric acid is carried out in the presence of sodium metavanadate, high-purity oxalic acid is produced (28).

Hydrogenation.   In the presence of a Raney-nickel catalyst, inverted sucrose is hydrogenated to a mixture of sorbitol and D-mannitol. See Vol. 1, p. 581.

Hydrogenolysis.   Under more drastic conditions the sugar chains are severed and good yields of glycerol and propylene glycol are formed.

Alkaline Degradation.   Sucrose autoclaved with aqueous calcium hydroxide yields up to 70% of lactic acid.

Acid Degradation.   Hot mineral acids convert sucrose to 5-(hydroxymethyl)-furfural. By variations, the reaction can yield equimolar amounts of levulinic and formic acids.

Other Organic Compounds of Sucrose.   Compounds or adducts are formed with some difficulty with the acetate ion, and sucrose sodium acetate, $NaC_2H_3O_2 . C_{12}H_{22}O_{11}$ (46), and a series of sucrose acetoacetates (11,23) have been reported. Studies have resulted in the preparation of octamethyl sucrose (27), and of silyl (4), and nitrophenyl-azobenzoyl derivatives (2). Alkyloxymethyl ethers can be made from reaction with alkyl halogenomethyl ethers (1).

Inorganic Sucrose Compounds.   Sodium sucrates that have the general formula $C_{12}H_{22-x}O_{11} . Na_x$ have been prepared by reacting sucrose in liquid ammonia solution with metallic sodium (3,34). Sucrose reacts slowly with halides or oxides of alkali and alkaline earth elements to form true compounds (21,27,36,37,44). A sucrose–borax complex with a molecular ratio of 1:1, used in analytical chemistry, has been described (13).

Sucrose Fatty Acid Esters.   Sucrose esters of fatty acids, such as lauric, palmitic, oleic, and stearic, have excellent detergent properties, and are biodegradable. See under Sugar derivatives.

Bibliography

"Sucrose" under "Sugars (Commercial)" in *ECT* 1st ed., Vol. 13, pp. 247–251, by J. L. Hickson, Sugar Research Foundation, Inc.

1. G. R. Ames, M. Blackmore, and T. A. King, *J. Appl. Chem.* **14,** 503–506 (1964).
2. E. S. Amin, *J. Chem. Soc.* **1961,** 5544–5545.
3. P. C. Arni, W. A. P. Black, E. T. Dewar, J. C. Patterson, and D. Rutherford, *J. Appl. Chem.* **9,** 186–197 (1959).
4. S. A. Barker, J. S. Brimacombe, M. R. Harndon, and J. A. Jarvis, *J. Chem. Soc.* **1963,** 3403–3406.
5. F. J. Bates, et al., "Polarimetry, Saccharimetry and the Sugars," *Natl. Bur. Std. (U.S.), Circ. C440* (1942).
6. C. A. Beevers, T. R. R. McDonald, J. H. Robertson, and F. Stern, *Acta Cryst.* **5,** 689 (1952).
7. A. Benrath, *Z. Anorg. Allgem. Chem.* **249,** 245 (1942).
8. H. Bergström, *Jernkontorets Ann.* **135,** 176 (1951).
9. D. Bollman and S. Schmidt-Berg, *Z. Zuckerind.* **15,** 179–184, 259–265 (1965).
10. D. F. Charles, *Intern. Sugar J.* **62,** 126 (1960).
11. L. K. Dalton, *J. Appl. Chem.* **13,** 277–281 (1963).
12. J. G. Dawber, D. R. Brown, and R. A. Reed, *J. Chem. Educ.* **43,** 34–35 (1966).
13. J. Fernandez-Bertran and J. Marinello, *Cuba Azucar* **1,** 2–8, 41E (May 3, 1966).
14. W. Z. Hassid, M. Doudoroff, and H. A. Barker, *J. Am. Chem. Soc.* **66,** 1416 (1944).
15. L. J. Heidt, C. M. Colman, and J. Dayan, *Abstr. Papers, Am. Chem. Soc. 121st Meeting, Milwaukee, Wisc., April 1952,* p. 12P.

16. G. Henseke, *Zuckererzeugung* **7**, 64–66, 78 (1963).
17. S. Hill and W. J. H. Orchard, *Intern. Sugar J.* **63**, 42–44 (1961).
18. *Ibid.*, **64**, 100–102 (1962).
19. P. Honig, ed., *Principles of Sugar Technology*, Vol. 1, Elsevier Publishing Co., New York, 1953.
20. F. T. Jones and F. E. Young, *Anal. Chem.* **26**, 421 (1954).
21. F. H. C. Kelly, *Intern. Sugar J.* **58**, 128–129 (1956). (A review.)
22. F. H. C. Kelley, *Sugar J.*, **20** (8), 14,15,28,29 (1957–1958).
23. O. K. Kononenko and J. L. Kestenbaum, *J. Appl. Chem.* **11**, 7–10 (1961).
24. H. Kürten and H. Rumpf, *Chem. Ing. Tech.* **38**, 331–342 (1966).
25. L. F. Leloir and E. Calib, *J. Am. Chem. Soc.* **75**, 5445 (1953).
26. R. U. Lemieux and G. Huber, *J. Am. Chem. Soc.* **75**, 4118 (1953).
27. N. N. Lichtin and M. H. Saxe, *Abstr. Papers, Am. Chem. Soc. 126th Meeting, New York, N. Y., Sept. 1954*, p. 29D.
28. K. I. Lu and R. D. Luo, *Chemistry (Taipei)* **1966** (2), 76–84.
29. B. Makower and W. B. Dye, *J. Agr. Food Chem.* **4**, 72–76 (1956).
30. G. Mantovani and A. Indelli, *Zucker* **17**, 593–597 (1964).
31. R. W. Moncrieff, *Flavours* **11** (6), 5–11 (1949).
32. K. J. Palmer, W. B. Dye, and D. Black, *J. Agr. Food Chem.* **4**, 77–81 (1956).
33. G. Pidoux, *Ind. Aliment. Agr. (Paris)* **79**, 93–97 (1962).
34. V. Prey and F. Grundschober, *Monatsh. Chem.* **91**, 1185–1191 (1960).
35. L. A. Reber, *J. Am. Pharm. Assoc. Sci. Ed.* **42**, 192–193 (1953).
36. J. A. Rendleman, Jr., *J. Org. Chem.* **31**, 1839–1845 (1966).
37. J. A. Rendleman Jr., *Adv. Carbohydrate Chem.* **21**, 209–271(1966). (A review.)
38. R. Rossi, *Boll. Chim. Farm.* **93**, 297–298 (1954).
39. A. R. Sapronov, *Izv. Vysshikh Ucheb. Zavedenii Pishchevaya Tekhnol.* **1963** (1), 33–37.
40. P. M. Silin, *Technology of Beet-Sugar Production and Refining*, Pishchepromizdat, Moscow, 1958; Israel Program for Scientific Translations, Jerusalem, 1964, p. 62.
41. G. L. Spencer and G. P. Meade, *Cane Sugar Handbook*, 8th ed, John Wiley & Sons, Inc., New York, 1944, p. 354.
42. J. M. Thoburn, *Intern. Sugar J.* **68**, 205–207 (1966).
43. A. vanHook and E. J. Kilmartin, *Z. Electrochem.* **56**, 302–305 (1952).
44. G. Vavrinecz, *Elelm. Ipar* **11**, 133–137 (1957).
45. G. Vavrinecz, *Cukoripar* **11**, 326–327 (1958).
46. G. Vavrinecz, *Elelm. Ipar* **13**, C5 (1959); also in *Zucker* **11**, 545–548 (1958).

R. A. McGinnis
Spreckels Sugar Co.

SUGAR ANALYSIS

All sugars are polyhydroxy compounds that either contain an aldose or a ketose residue, or are capable of forming such a group on hydrolysis. On this basis the former, the aldoses and ketoses, are called reducing sugars, since they have reducing power, and the latter are nonreducing sugars. Solutions of a reducing sugar consist of mixtures of tautomeric forms of the sugar, and the physical and chemical properties of the solutions depend upon establishment of an equilibrium. Nonreducing sugars exist only in one form, and, consequently, these solutions are stable. Glucose, fructose, lactose, and maltose are representative of reducing sugars; sucrose is nonreducing.

General Physical Methods

All sugars are white, crystalline, water-soluble substances. Measurements of optical rotation, density, and refractive index of their aqueous solutions are used for determining concentration of pure sugar solutions. In addition, optical-rotation

Table 1. Physical Properties of Some Sugars

Sugar	Mp, °C	$[\alpha]_D^{20}{}^a$
Monosaccharides		
α-D-ribose	95	−23.1 to −23.7 ($c = 4$)
β-L-arabinose	160	+190.6 to +104.5
α-D-xylose	145	+93.6 to +18.8 ($c = 4$)
D-xylulose		+33.1 ($c = 2$)
α-D-glucose	146	+112.2 to +52.7 ($c = 4$)
α-D-glucose monohydrate	83	+102.0 to +47.9 ($c = 4$)
β-D-glucose	148–150	+18.7 to +52.7 ($c = 4$)
α-D-mannose	133	+29.3 to +14.2 ($c = 4$)
β-D-mannose	132	−17.0 to +14.2 ($c = 4$)
α-D-galactose	167	+150.7 to +80.2 ($c = 5$)
β-D-galactose		+52.8 to +80.2 ($c = 4$)
α-D-fructose	102–104	−132.2 to −92.4 ($c = 4$)
β-L-sorbose	159–161	−43.7 to −43.4 ($c = 12$)
β-D-epirhamnose	139–140	+73.3 to +29.7 ($c = 8$)
α-L-fucose	145	−152.6 to −75.9 ($c = 4$)
α-L-rhamnose mono- hydrate	93– 94	−8.6 to +8.2 ($c = 4$)
β-L-rhamnose	123–125	+38.4 to +8.9
D-*manno*-heptulose	152	+29.0
D-heptulose		+2 to 3 ($c = 10$)
Disaccharides		
β-cellobiose	225	+14.2 to +34.6 ($c = 8$)
α-gentiobiose dimethanolate	85–86	+21.4 to +8.7 ($c = 5$)
β-gentiobiose	190–195	−11.0 to +9.6
α-lactose monohydrate	202	+85.0 to +52.6 ($c = 8$)
β-lactose	252	+34.9 to +55.4 ($c = 4$)
β-maltose monohydrate	102–103	+111.7 to +130.4 ($c = 4$)
β-melibiose dihydrate	82–85	+111.7 to +129.5 ($c = 4$)
sucrose	160–186[b]	+66.53 ($c = 26$)
α,α-trehalose dihydrate	97	+178.3
turanose	157	+27.3 to +75.8 ($c = 4$)
gentianose	209–211	+31.5
Tri- and tetrasaccharides		
melezitose dihydrate	153–154	+88.2 ($c = 4$)
raffinose pentahydrate	80	+105.2 ($c = 4$)
stachyose tetrahydrate	167–170	+148

[a] The solvent in all cases is water, and the concentration is expressed in grams per 100 milliliters of solution.

[b] Depending upon solvent from which crystallized: H_2O, 186°; CH_3OH, 170°.

measurements of solutions of known concentration are a means of identifying the individual sugars.

Optical Rotation. The plane of polarized light is rotated to the left or to the right as it passes through a sugar solution. When measured under known conditions, the amount and direction of rotation is characteristic for each sugar and hence is a means of identification. Observed or direct rotations are converted to specific rotations by the formula

$$[\alpha]_\lambda^t = \frac{\alpha}{l \times c}$$

where α is the observed rotation (circular degrees), l is the length of tube containing the sugar solution (decimeters), c is the concentration (grams of sugar per 100 ml solution), λ is the wavelength (Angstrom units), and t is the temperature (°C). Molecular rotation is the specific rotation multiplied by the molecular weight.

The saccharimeter is a polarimeter modified for the sugar industry by having the scale read directly in percent sucrose (sugar degrees) for the standard concentration and tube length. This instrument is used for factory control and in trade transactions.

Since aqueous solutions of the reducing sugars contain a mixture of their tautomeric forms, optical rotation is constant only when equilibrium is established within the solution. The change in rotation that takes place while equilibrium is being established is called mutarotation.

Optical rotations of some sugars are given in Table 1.

Mutarotation. Determinations of optical rotation are complicated by changes in rotations of many sugars with the age of the solution. This phenomenon, called mutarotation, is caused by the establishing of an equilibrium among the possible forms of a sugar. Two of these forms are cyclic hemiacetals formed by reaction of the carbonyl with a hydroxyl of the chain; the resulting five- or six-membered (furanose or pyranose) rings are stable in the solid state but labile in solution, particularly in the presence of acids or bases. The formation of the ring creates a new point of asymmetry at the carbonyl carbon. In the case of aldoses, two additional forms (α- and β-) have been isolated, whereas no α form is known for ketoses.

The mutarotation of the aldoses therefore comes from equilibration of α- and β- as well as furanose and pyranose forms. However, with ketoses, the mutarotation observed is ascribed to the furanose–pyranose equilibration. Some, but by no means all, of the possible components of an aldose equilibrium are shown in equation 1 for

(1)

D-glucose. A D-sugar which upon mutarotation increases in positive optical rotatory power is the β-anomeric form. An increase in the negative direction is evidence of the α-anomer.

Density (qv). Density measurements are widely used in the sugar industry for the determination of sugar concentrations, particularly in connection with transactions involving syrups and molasses. The density is usually expressed in grams per milliliter. Closely related to density is specific gravity, which is a comparison between the masses of equal volume of the substance in question and of water, the temperature of both being stated, as d_{18}^{25}. Since at 4°C, the temperature of its maximum density, 1 ml of water weighs 1 g, specific gravity d_4^t is numerically equal to density.

The following terms are used in the literature in connection with density measurements of sugars:

$$\text{true density} = \frac{\text{wt (in vacuum) of given vol of soln at temp } t}{\text{wt (in vacuum) of same vol of water at 4°C}}$$

$$\text{apparent density} = \frac{\text{wt (in air) of given vol of soln at temp } t}{\text{wt (in air) of same vol of water at 4°C}}$$

$$\text{true specific gravity} = \frac{\text{wt (in vacuum) of given vol of soln at temp } t}{\text{wt (in vacuum) of same vol of water at temp } t}$$

$$\text{apparent specific gravity} = \frac{\text{wt (in air) of given vol of soln at temp } t}{\text{wt (in air) of same vol of water at temp } t}$$

In order to facilitate the conversion of the density of a sugar solution to percentage sugar content, standard tables are available for use with the common sugar, sucrose, and with other sugars such as glucose, maltose, and fructose. Because of the commercial importance of sucrose, tables of sucrose density have been prepared for use over wider ranges of temperatures and concentration than have those for the other sugars. In general, these tables apply to pure sugar solutions and the results obtained by their use are strictly correct only when they are thus employed. However, much of the material that naturally occurs along with a sugar is found to have a similar density. Therefore, the tables are used for determining the concentration of various syrups and sugar mixtures such as molasses with little error. A comparison of the densities of 10% solutions of the following sugars when measured at 20°C is indicative of the accuracy that can be expected when using the sucrose table for other sugars: arabinose, 1.0379; glucose, 1.0377; fructose, 1.0385; galactose, 1.0379; sorbose, 1.0381; sucrose, 1.0381; maltose, 1.0386; lactose, 1.0376; and raffinose, 1.0375.

Density measurements of sugar solutions are made by the methods generally applicable to the determination of densities of liquids. Hydrometers, graduated on the basis of percentage (by weight) of sucrose in a pure sucrose solution, are used by the sucrose industry. The graduations are referred to as *degrees Brix* and standardization is generally made at 20°C. A solution of 45° Brix, therefore, has the same density as does 45% sucrose solution. Hydrometers graduated in degrees Baumé are also used, particularly when molasses and sugar syrups of both sucrose and dextrose are concerned. This is an arbitrary scale which is related to specific gravity by the following equation:

$$\text{degrees Baumé} = 145 - (145/d_{20}^{20})$$

Refractive Index (see Refraction). The index of refraction is another physical measurement that can be related to the sugar concentration of a solution, but since this relationship varies somewhat for different sugars, tables such as Table 2 have been constructed for a number of sugars of commerce. The most widely used of these is the *International Scale of Refractive Indices of Sucrose Solutions at 20°C*, adopted by the International Commission for Uniform Methods of Sugar Analysis.

Table 2. Refractive Indexes of Sugar Solutions at 20°C

Composition, g sugar/100 g soln	Refractive indexes					
	Sucrose	Glucose	Fructose	Invert sugar	Maltose.H_2O	α-Lactose.H_2O
0	1.33299	1.33299	1.33299	1.33299	1.33299	1.33299
10	1.34782	1.34775	1.34764	1.34764	1.34739	1.34758
20	1.36383	1.36356	1.36331	1.36341	1.36284	
30	1.3811	1.38052	1.38029	1.38040	1.37947	
40	1.3998	1.39872	1.39857	1.39866	1.39736	
50	1.4200	1.41826	1.41817	1.41827	1.41659	
60	1.4419	1.43918	1.43912	1.43928	1.43723	
70	1.4654	1.46156	1.4615	1.46172		
80	1.4907	1.48542	1.4851	1.48564		
85	1.5040		1.4974			

In 1966, this organization adopted the table based on recent work carried out at the Physikalisch-Technische Bundesanstalt. This table covers the range from 0 to 85 percent sucrose and reports refractive indexes to the sixth decimal place over the entire range. For accurate work, such a table is applicable only to solutions of the pure sugar. In less precise work, the sucrose table is used with impure solutions and sugar mixtures for approximate values. Corrections have been devised to compensate for the effect of impurities, thus increasing the accuracy in such cases.

Chemical Methods for Reducing Sugars

The reducing action of the aldose and ketose sugars is the basis for a large number of methods that have been devised for their quantitative and qualitative determination (Table 3). In general the reagents comprise: alkaline copper solutions stabilized by tartrate, citrate, or carbonate ions; copper acetate; potassium ferricyanide; tungstates; and phenolic reagents in strong acid solution. The principal problem in the application of any of the methods arises from the fact that the reducing reaction is not quite stoichiometric, so the accuracy of the method depends upon strict adherence to conditions of pH, temperature, concentration, and time. This also causes the chemical equivalence factor to be different for each sugar and each method.

MACROMETHODS

The alkaline copper–tartrate reagent devised by Fehling and modified by Soxhlet is used in a number of macromethods. The soluble copper–tartrate complex ion present in this reagent is deep blue in color. Cuprous ions resulting from reduction of the copper do not form a complex with the tartrate but are precipitated from the alkaline solution as cuprous oxide.

Table 3. Methods of Analysis for Reducing Sugars

Method	Application	Reagent	Reaction conditions	Size of sample, ml	Amount of sugar in sample, mg
Munson and Walker	glucose, fructose, invert sugar, lactose, and maltose	Soxhlet	boil 2 min	50	5–240
Quisumbing and Thomas	glucose, fructose, invert sugar, lactose, and maltose	copper–alkali–tartrate	30 min at 80°C	50	50–150
Lane and Eynon	glucose, fructose, invert sugar, lactose, and maltose	Soxhlet	boil 2 min	0–50	100–800 mg/100 ml
Luff-Schoorl	glucose, fructose, invert sugar, lactose, and maltose; invert sugar in presence of sucrose	copper–carbonate	boil 10 min	50	2.4–62.2
Spengler, Tödt, and Scheuer	invert in beet sugars	copper–tartrate–carbonate	10 min in boiling water bath	100	0–20
Sichert and Bleyer	glucose in presence of maltose	copper–acetate	20 min in boiling water bath	20	26.5–99
Somogyi	glucose in blood	copper–carbonate	15 min in boiling water bath	5	0–2
Somogyi	glucose; used for analysis	copper–phosphate	10 min in boiling water bath	5	0–3
Hagedorn and Jensen	glucose in blood	alkaline ferri-cyanide	15 min in boiling water bath	12	<0.38
Folin and Malmros	glucose in blood	ferricyanide–carbonate	8 min in boiling water bath	4	0–0.2
Folin and Wu	glucose in blood	copper–carbonate–phosphomolybdic acid	8 min in boiling water bath	2	0–8

Many methods using this reagent have been devised. They differ in time and temperature of heating, amount of reagent used, and method for the determination of the reduced copper. The method of Lane and Eynon is unique in that a measured quantity of sugar solution is added to the hot reagent until the copper is completely reduced. In the other procedures an excess of reagent is used, and the cuprous oxide is separated by filtration and subsequently determined gravimetrically or volumetrically. Details of these procedures and their applicability are to be found in the general textbooks on sugar analysis. The method of Lane and Eynon follows in detail. Although more rapid, this method gives results whose accuracy compares favorably with other procedures using copper alkali reagent; therefore it has been generally adopted by industry.

Lane and Eynon Method. The following reagents are used—Soxhlet's modification of Fehling's solution: (a) copper sulfate solution: dissolve 34.639 g of pure $CuSO_4.5H_2O$ in water and dilute to 500 ml; (b) alkaline tartrate solution: dissolve 173 g of Rochelle salt and 50 g of NaOH in water and dilute to 500 ml (carbonate-free NaOH); (c) methylene blue solution, 1% aqueous.

Standard Method of Titration. 10 or 25 ml of mixed Soxhlet's reagent is placed in a 300–400-ml flask. The sugar solution is placed in a 50-ml buret. The outlet of the buret must be so designed that neither the stopcock nor the sugar solution is heated by the steam evolved during the reaction. Almost all of the sugar solution that will be required to completely reduce the copper is added to the cold reagent. The additional sugar solution required should be 0.5–1 ml. The flask containing the reaction mixture is heated over an asbestos gauze plate. After the liquid has begun to boil, it is kept in moderate ebullition for 2 minutes, and then without removing from the flame, 3–5 drops of methylene blue solution is added, and the titration is completed in 1 additional minute, so that the reaction mixture boils for approximately 3 minutes without interruption. The intense blue color of the methylene blue indicator, in the absence of air, almost instantly disappears when excess reducing sugar has been added. Duplicate determinations should agree within 0.1 ml in the volume of sugar solution required.

Usually the sugar concentration is not known with sufficient certainty to add the proper amount to the cold copper reagent. Consequently, Lane and Eynon advise performing a preliminary titration in order to determine the approximate volume of sugar solution required. This is most conveniently accomplished by adding an initial volume of 15 ml of the sugar solution to the measured volume of the copper reagent, boiling for 15–20 seconds, and then adding further increments of sugar until the blue color of the copper solution has nearly disappeared. This point can be judged within 1 or 2 ml of sugar solution. Methylene blue is then added and the titration completed dropwise, the period of operation occupying as close to 3 minutes as possible. In the analysis of solutions of hexoses, this incremental method is nearly as reliable as the standard method, but with solutions of the disaccharides it is desirable to repeat the titration by the standard method.

Calculation. Lane and Eynon determined the weight of each sugar required to reduce the copper completely. These weights, which vary with the nature of the sugar and with its concentration, constitute a table of factors (Table 4) from which the proper one may be selected when the titer is known. The concentration of sugar is then:

$$\frac{(\text{factor} \times 100)}{\text{titer}} = \text{mg of sugar in 100 ml}$$

It is desirable for the analyst to determine the factor for a known sugar solution similar to the solutions to be analyzed.   In this way he may apply any slight correction that should be made to the tabulated factors.   By properly diluting the solution under investigation so that the total volume at the end of analysis is the same as that when a standard solution is used (within 1 ml), the titration may be converted directly to milligrams of sugar.   This is the basis of the so-called constant-volume modification. When sucrose is present, allowance is made for reduction due to its hydrolysis by including it in the standard.   Tables for invert sugar in the presence of sucrose are also available.

Table 4. Factors for Use with the Lane and Eynon Method[a]

Titer, ml	Sugar				
	Invert	Glucose	Fructose	Maltose	Lactose.H$_2$O
25	124.0	120.5	127.9	194.5	169.9
30	124.3	120.8	128.1	192.8	168.8

[a] 25 ml of reagent.

Other Methods.   Copper reagents of lower pH than that of Fehling's solution are less sensitive to sucrose at 100°C.   The *Luff-Schoorl method*, which uses a carbonate-buffered copper reagent, belongs to this group.   The reduced copper is determined iodometrically or by methylene blue indicator and final addition of reducing sugar to the boiling reaction mixture as in the Lane and Eynon method.

Nyn's selective method for the determination of fructose is based upon the fact that, at 55°C, fructose has thirteen times the reducing power of glucose when reacted with a copper carbonate–bicarbonate reagent.

Benedict's copper carbonate reagent is used for the detection of glucose in urine. (The solution is made up of 17.3 g $CuSO_4.5H_2O$, 173 g sodium or potassium citrate, and 100 g anhydrous Na_2CO_3 dissolved in water and diluted to a final volume of 1 liter.)

Aldoses react with *iodine* in dilute alkaline solution to form the corresponding monobasic acids, whereas ketoses and nonreducing sugars are only slightly affected by this reagent.

Under specific conditions *copper acetate reagent* is selective for glucose in the presence of maltose and the higher-molecular-weight saccharides produced by starch hydrolysis (see Dextrose).

MICROMETHODS

Micromethods of sugar analysis are used in medical and biological laboratories, in carbohydrate research work, and by the sugar industry when small quantities of sugar are to be determined.

These methods for the determination of reducing sugars fall into three major categories, depending upon the type of reagent used: (a) the reduction of ferricyanide to ferrocyanide, (b) the reduction of cupric sulfate to cuprous oxide, and (c) the development of color when the sugar reacts with phenols in concentrated acid solution. As a rule the copper reagents are more selective in their oxidizing action on the sugars than are the ferricyanide reagents.   The latter have the advantage of not being easily reoxidized by air.   The amount of reduction with either ferricyanide or copper reagents may be determined by iodometric titrations or colorimetrically. In general, the former procedure is applicable to larger sugar samples.

Ferricyanide is reduced to ferrocyanide by reducing sugars in hot alkaline solution. The resulting ferrocyanide is stabilized in a zinc complex and the quantity of reduced ferricyanide is determined iodometrically. The difference between the quantity of ferricyanide in the original reaction mixture and that after reduction has taken place is correlated to the reducing sugar present. The procedure introduced by Hagedorn and Jensen in 1923 is useful in determining a maximum of 380 μg of glucose or its equivalent.

Hagedorn and Jensen Method. The reagents used are: (*1*) 1.65 g $K_3Fe(CN)_6$ (recrystallized and dried at 50°C) and 10.6 g anhydrous Na_2CO_3 contained in 1 liter of water solution. (*2*) 10 g $ZnSO_4.7H_2O$, 50 g NaCl dissolved in 200 ml water. At time of using, add solid KI in the proportion of 2.5 g per 100 ml. This solution should be colorless. (*3*) Acetic acid 3 ml per 100 ml solution. (*4*) Starch indicator solution. (*5*) 0.005N $Na_2S_2O_3$ prepared daily from 0.1N solution.

In a large test tube (30 × 90 mm) containing 12 ml of sugar solution, add 2 ml of ferricyanide reagent. Heat in a boiling water bath exactly 15 minutes. Cool and add 3 ml of reagent (*2*) and 2 ml reagent (*3*). Titrate the liberated iodine with the 0.005N thiosulfate solution using starch indicator to determine the end point. Determine a blank in which no sugar is added. Reduction of ferricyanide by the sugar sample is equivalent to the difference between the thiosulfate required for the analysis and that used in the blank. Each analyst should establish the relationship between sugar and thiosulfate by analyzing known quantities of pure sugar. An accuracy of ±2% is to be expected.

Somogyi's Method. Copper reagents are more specific for sugars and are thus often preferred for biological work. Most consistent results are attained when the copper reagent is deaerated and when the mixing and heating are carried out under an inert atmosphere, to prevent reoxidation of reduced copper. Many methods have been proposed; however, those of Somogyi are used most extensively. His phosphate-buffered reagent (1945) is preferred when amylases are involved since with this reagent they stay in solution. His carbonate-buffered copper reagent (1952) is more stable and is, therefore, more widely used. The reduction is carried out by heating for a prescribed period of time in a boiling water bath. The quantity of copper reduced is determined iodometrically. For details of these procedures, reference 2, p. 998, and reference 5, p. 383. Boiling times most suitable for a number of sugars are given.

Colorimetric Methods. The reduction of yellow ferricyanide solutions to colorless ferrocyanide involves a color change that can be equated to reducing sugar present. This reaction is used extensively in conjunction with an AutoAnalyzer (manufactured by Technicon International) in clinical laboratories for blood sugar determinations as well as by the sugar industry for monitoring waste water for sugar losses.

Nelson modified Somogyi's procedure by replacing the iodometric titrations with a colorimetric scheme based on the reaction of arsenomolybdate with the unreduced copper. Absorbance is read at 500 mμ. The precision is comparable with that of the original method; the range is more limited.

Folin and Wu's procedure, which has been widely used in clinical work, depends upon copper reduction when a sugar solution is heated in a boiling water bath with a copper–carbonate reagent. Subsequently a tungstate color reagent is added to the cooled reaction mixture. The final color is compared with that of a series where known quantities of dextrose are carried through the same procedure.

Phenolic compounds in concentrated acid solution react with sugars to give colors that can be measured and correlated to the quantity of sugar. Color is produced by reaction of the phenolic compound with furfural derivatives that result from breakdown of sugar in the strong acid solution. All sugars do not give the same color. Phenol, orcinol (5-methylbenzene-1,3-diol), resorcinol (benzene-1,3-diol), and 1-naphthol are representative phenolic reagents. Phenolic reagents are very useful for qualitative tests because the results are easily and rapidly obtained.

Careful adherence to an exact procedure is required when doing quantitative work with these methods since considerable heat is generated when the concentrated sulfuric acid is added to the aqueous phenol–sugar solution.

The anthrone (9,10-dehydro-9-oxoanthracene) method also depends upon the reaction of sulfuric acid on sugars to give furfural derivatives, which in turn react with anthrone. The method has been studied extensively; its greatest use is in the analysis of uncontaminated solutions of hexoses and their polymers. The color produced varies with the individual sugar and is affected by many chemicals including generally used solvents.

Small changes in procedures are continuously being proposed in colorimetric methods in order to adapt them for particular analyses; however, standard references contain basic procedures for their use in sugar analysis.

Enzymic Methods (6). D-Glucose aerodehydrogenase is a specific oxidant for D-glucose. The resulting gluconolactone is hydrolyzed to gluconic acid which can be titrated with standard alkali. As an alternative, oxidation may be determined colorimetrically by determining the quantity of hydrogen peroxide which is produced in molar equivalents to the glucose oxidized. This method has been used in an Auto-Analyzer where a 92–97% recovery of 1–3 mg of added glucose to solutions containing 65–140 mg/100 ml was reported. It is used in test papers for detecting glucose in urine. Selective fermentation methods have been studied for different sugars; however, difficulties in obtaining and keeping pure enzymes limit the use of these methods.

Isotope Dilution. Sugars containing carbon-14 or tritium (^{3}H) have been used in analytical work. This is possible because the rate of radioactivity in μCi/mg in a sample purified by repeated recrystallization is the same as that in the total sugar prior to purification. For details on general applications of isotope dilution to sugar analysis see reference 7; for application to sugar beets and refinery products see references 8 and 9.

Chromatography

Chromatographic separation techniques have revolutionized qualitative analysis of complex sugar mixtures and have greatly increased the accuracy of their quantitative analysis (10,11). Columns, paper chromatography, electrophoresis, gas–liquid chromatography (GLC), and thin-layer chromatography (TLC) have all been used for sugar analysis. Excellent reviews are available on these rapidly expanding fields.

After using *columns* to separate sugars, the quantity of sugar in the separate fractions is determined by standard physical or chemical procedures. Continuous monitoring of the eluent from a column may be done instrumentally by noting changes in refractive indexes, optical rotation, or by chemical analysis. A specific procedure based on column separation is that for the determination of sugars in honey (ref. 2, p. 511).

After separation by *paper chromatography* the sugars may be eluted and analyzed by appropriate procedures; the area of paper containing the sugar may be cut out and introduced into the reaction mixture for sugar analyses; or the density of color produced when the spot is treated with a color-producing reagent may be measured. The accuracy of results is limited in these procedures but for some purposes it is adequate.

Electrophoresis of sugars depends upon their conversion to charged complexes, generally borate. Good separations are accomplished by using $0.02M$ sodium borate solution (pH 9.2). Voltage gradients of 100 V/cm give excellent sugar separations in 30 minutes with this buffer using apparatus described by Gross (12,13). Here the paper is clamped between plastic sheets on water-cooled metal plates. Much of the work has been done with lower voltage gradients (20–25 V/cm), for which a longer time is usually required. Tables that give the relative movement of different sugars are available (13).

Gas–liquid chromatographic separations of sugars require their conversion to volatile compounds; the ones most used are trimethylsilyl derivatives (15–17) (see under Silicon compounds). These are prepared by reacting the sugar with hexamethyldisilazane and trimethylchlorosilane in pyridine solution. The reaction time is 5–6 minutes and the reaction mixture is ejected into the gas chromatograph. Both quantitative and qualitative results are reported. A number of different columns have been used successfully.

Thin-layer chromatography is a rapid technique for qualitative analyses. The separation of sugars on kieselguhr G layers with a solvent system of ethyl acetate, isopropyl alcohol, and water has been found satisfactory. Advantage is taken of sugar borate complexing for separating sugars on plates of silica gel G containing $0.1N$ boric acid. Different developing mixtures can be used. For detailed procedures see reference 18.

Bibliography

"Sugar Analysis" in *ECT* 1st ed., Vol. 13, pp. 192–203, by Emma J. McDonald, National Bureau of Standards.

1. G. P. Meade, *Cane Sugar Handbook*, 9th ed., John Wiley & Sons, Inc., New York, 1963.
2. W. Horwitz, ed., *Official Methods of Analysis of the Association of Official Agricultural Chemists*, 10th ed., Association of Official Agricultural Chemists, Washington, D.C., 1965.
3. F. J. Bates et al., "Polarimetry, Saccharimetry and the Sugars," *Natl. Bur. Stds. (U.S.), Circ. C440*, 1942.
4. C. A. Browne and F. W. Zerban, *Sugar Analysis*, John Wiley & Sons, Inc., New York, 1941.
5. R. L. Whistler and M. L. Wolfrom, eds., *Methods of Carbohydrate Chemistry*, Vol. 1, Academic Press, Inc., New York, 1962.
6. L. Hough and J. K. N. Jones in R. L. Whistler and M. L. Wolfrom, eds., *Methods of Carbohydrate Chemistry*, Vol. 1, Academic Press, Inc., New York, 1961, p. 400.
7. H. S. Isbell and H. L. Frush in R. L. Whistler and M. L. Wolfrom, eds., *Methods of Carbohydrate Chemistry*, Vol. 1, Academic Press, Inc., New York, 1962, p. 409.
8. H. Horning and H. Hirschmuller, *Z. Zuckerind.* **9**, 16 (1959).
9. M. J. Sibley, F. G. Eis, and R. A. McGinnis, *Anal. Chem.* **37**, 1701 (1965).
10. G. N. Komkabany in E. Heftmann, ed., *Chromatography*, Chap. 19, Reinhold Publishing Corp., New York, 1961.
11. Reference 5, pp. 13–58, 395.
12. D. Gross, *J. Chromatog.* **5**, 194 (1961).
13. D. Gross, *The Analyst* **90**, 379 (1965).
14. A. B. Foster in R. L. Whistler and M. L. Wolfrom, eds., *Methods of Carbohydrate Chemistry*, Vol. 1, Academic Press, Inc., New York, 1962, p. 51.

15. C. C. Sweeley, M. Makita, and W. W. Wells, *J. Am. Chem. Soc.* **85**, 2497 (1963).

16. H. E. Brower, J. E. Jeffery, and M. W. Folsom, *Anal. Chem.* **38**, 362 (1966).

17. J. S. Saneardiker and J. H. Sloneker, *Anal. Chem.* **37**, 945 (1965).

18. E. Stahl and N. Kaltenbach in E. Stahl, ed., *Thin-Layer Chromatography*, Academic Press, Inc., New York, 1965, p. 461.

Emma J. McDonald

U.S. Department of Agriculture

CANE SUGAR

Sugar is the common name for sucrose (or saccharose), a carbohydrate classified as a disaccharide, with the chemical formula $C_{12}H_{22}O_{11}$. Sugar occurs in many plants and is an important food, valued for its sweet taste and the texture and consistency it imparts to other foods. For the purpose of establishing standards of identity for foods, the U.S. Food and Drug Administration has defined the term "sugar" as "refined sugar (sucrose)." Refined sugar, whether of cane or beet origin, is the organic substance produced in pure form in the greatest volume, and is one of the purest of all substances produced in considerable volume. Its analysis is, approximately: sucrose, 99.90%; invert sugar, 0.01%; ash (inorganic material), 0.03%; moisture, 0.03%; organic material, 0.03%. There is a slight variation in the nonsucrose components between the cane refined and beet refined, but this is relatively insignificant.

It is the material of greatest food value economically, in the sense that an acre devoted to the cultivation of sugar, whether beet or cane, is capable of producing more calories than any other food crop. It is the cheapest source of calories known. However, sugar is all energy (calories) and contains no proteins, virtually no minerals, and no vitamins, which must come from supplementary diet materials.

The two principal sources of table granulated are varieties of (*1*) the sugar cane, a giant grass of the genus *Saccharum*, and various hybrids, and (*2*) the sugar beet (*Beta vulgaris*). See under Beet sugar.

Raw cane sugar is usually produced in areas of relatively low population density, but the *refined* product is consumed in densely populated areas. Thus, it is the universal practice, with very few exceptions, to ship the raw sugar to refineries (most of which are located on the sea coasts), where it is refined and then shipped to consumers. In the United States, the table grade of beet sugar is produced directly from the beet without an intermediate stage, although in Europe some raw beet sugar is still produced. This raw sugar is then refined in much the same way as cane raw sugars.

The per capita consumption of sugar is an excellent indicator of the degree of economic advancement of a country. Modern transportation systems aid the distribution of the product because of the comparatively low value of a large volume of refined sugar (a 100-lb bag of refined sugar, costing about $10.00, occupies 2.25 ft^3). The countries with the greatest per capita consumption are Scandinavia, Australia, the Netherlands, the United Kingdom, and the United States, whereas those countries with a low standard of living, eg, China, India, and the African countries, are at the bottom of the list.

Sugar cane is grown in tropical and semitropical countries. Beets are grown in temperate climes, all in the Northern Hemisphere.

The total production of sugar in the world for the year 1967–1968 was 66,887,300 metric tons. This amount was divided thus: 36,887,100 tons from cane (56%) and 29,337,200 tons from beet sources (44%) (see Table 1).

Table 1. World Sugar Production

Cane sugar		Beet sugar	
Country	Amount, %	Country	Amount, %
North America and Hawaii	43	Western Europe	39
South America	21	Eastern Europe	19
Asia	24	U.S.S.R.	27
Africa	8	Asia	5
Australia and all others	4	U.S.A.	9
		all others	1

There are other commercial sources of sugar, although in much smaller quantities. Two of the better known are the sugar maple (*Acer saccharum*) and sorghum (*Sorghum vulgare*). However, maple sugar is of too great value as a confection ever to be refined to table granulated. Sorghum is produced mainly for the manufacture of table syrups, and attempts to produce a raw sugar from this source have met with little success. The soft or brown sugars are varieties of refined cane sugar, and will be discussed later. (For chemical and physical properties of sugar see Carbohydrates; Sugar analysis.)

History. The origin of sugar cane is lost in antiquity, although the newest studies by Artschweger and Brandes (1,2) indicate that "the garden sugar canes of Melanesia constitute the original base from which our present-day varieties of sugar cane derive." Sugar cane originated in New Guinea, and not in India as has been believed. It was probably taken from island to island in the South Pacific, and thence, during a period of some 3000 years, to the Malay Peninsula and to Indochina. It was eventually carried to northern Africa by the Arabs, from where it spread to southern Europe.

By around 400 BC sugar cane was known throughout most of the subcontinent of India. During the incursion of Alexander the Great into India sugar cane came to his attention, and he brought some to Greece early in the fourth century BC; however, it was not cultivated until many years later. By the first century BC, sugar cane was growing in China, and the art of sugar manufacture was well known there in the seventh century AD.

The conquests of the Arabs in the seventh century of the Christian era resulted in their bringing the cane which they discovered growing in the region of the Tigris-Euphrates and Indus rivers into Egypt, Cyprus, Morocco, Spain, Crete, Malta, Rhodes, and Sicily, by the end of the ninth century. By the beginning of the twelfth century, sugar cane had been brought into Europe, and Venice had become an important sugar-refining center. Sugar cane was introduced into the islands of Madeira, the Azores, Cape Verde, and the Canaries by the middle of the fifteenth century and, on his second voyage to the New World, Columbus brought cane to Hispaniola (now the Dominican Republic and Haiti). From there it spread to the other islands of the West Indies, which area became the major source of sugar for many years.

Although cane was first brought to the mainland of South America in 1532 and to the mainland of North America (Mexico) in 1519, the major step in the industry occurred when the Jesuit missionaries took it to Louisiana in 1751.

The production and refining of raw sugar reached impressive proportions in the eighteenth century, notably in the West Indies, from where tremendous fortunes flowed to England and France (3,4).

The first successful production of sugar in the United States was in 1795 by Etienne deBore, although the universally held claim that he was the first to make sugar granulate is false; sugar had been produced commercially in the hemisphere for 200 years. During the nineteenth century, Louisiana was the leader in raw-sugar technology, contributing to the world the tandem (series) of steam-driven horizontal roller mills, shredders and crushers, multiple-effect evaporation, the green bagasse burner, and other innovations contributing to the efficiency of the process. The first school of chemical engineering in the United States, the Audubon Sugar School, the prototype of all such experimental stations, was founded in the 1890s. The first polariscope to be used anywhere in the Western Hemisphere was imported from France in 1849. The first experiments with what is now known as diffusion were performed in the early 1880s by Spencer.

Advances were being made at about the same time in refining, with England predominating. The vacuum pan was invented by Howard (a scion of the house of Norfolk) in 1813; the centrifugal by Weston in 1852, and applied to sugar-house work in 1867; bone char decolorization in about 1820; the crystallizer in 1881; and the granulator in 1878. These advances, together with the application of the multieffect evaporator of Rillieux, made modern refining possible.

The principal tools of the sugar technologist date from the middle of the nineteenth century. The first practicable polariscope and sugar scale were invented by Ventzke in 1842; the "Brix" hydrometer by Balling in 1854; and Fehling's method for determining reducing sugars and Clerget's method for the accurate determination of sucrose when in combination with other sugars in about 1846. The latest basic analytical procedure, and one of the most important, stemmed from the work of Brewster with pH around 1923. See Sugar analysis.

The filter press, invented by Needham around 1820, was improved around 1916 when the so-called leaf filters (Kelly, Vallez, and Sweetland) came into use. The first of the frothing clarifiers was invented in 1918 in Louisiana and carbonation in England late in the nineteenth century.

At that time, the sugar was refined by first dissolving (melting), then defecating by the addition of limewater, oxblood, egg whites, and so on, and finally boiling to grain. The mixture of crystals and syrup was poured into porous clay cones, the syrup draining through, with the remaining sugar being washed to remove most of the adhering syrup. The clay forms were dried by heating in a hot room; when the clay forms were removed, the sugar loaves resulted.

With the advent of steam boiling, the use of vacuum, the use of phosphoric acid as a clarifier (filtration being done by means of the Taylor bag filter), and the centrifugal and the granulator, tremendous increases in the capacity of the refineries occurred. In 1861, the Havemeyer & Elder refinery in Brooklyn was the largest in the world, processing 35 tons of raw sugar daily. Today the largest refinery in the world melts over 4000 tons daily.

The production of refined sugar from beets is comparatively recent. In 1747 Andreas Marggraf demonstrated that sugar is contained in the juice of the beet. In 1787 Karl Achard, also in Germany, succeeded in increasing the sugar content of beets by cultivation, and made some beet sugar in a modestly practical way. A beet sugar factory of some size was constructed in 1802, and by 1811 it had become evident that sugar could be made relatively economically from beets. Napoleon gave beet sugar manufacture its first important impetus in 1811 by establishing a beet sugar industry by edict when the English blockade cut off France's supply of sugar from the tropics. The industry grew steadily (except for a hiatus immediately after Waterloo) throughout Europe. By the time of World War I most continental countries were producing sufficient beet sugar for their needs, with some left over for export.

World War II seriously affected the production of sugar, both beet and cane; many of the mid-European beet-growing regions became battlefields; in the United States beet-field workers abandoned the fields for jobs in defense industries. Java, one of the most important raw-sugar producers at the time, was overrun by the Japanese, and to this day has not reached its former status. Ships were in demand for other carriage, more important to the war effort.

Today, about 40–45% of the total sugar production of the world comes from beets. Most of the sugar produced is either consumed where it is produced (eg, Russia, mid-Europe, etc) or committed through special agreements between countries (eg, raws imported into the United States and England from the tropics); only about 15% enters free trade as uncommitted supplies.

Cultivation and Harvesting (5,6)

The principal source of raw sugar for many years, in fact, until the 1920s, was the so-called noble cane, *Saccharum officinarum*. The stalks were thick barrelled and of moderately soft rind. However, in time these canes began to succumb to diseases such as mosaic, caused by virus and insects such as the cane borer. In attempts to produce a cane resistant to these factors, the more famous experimental stations, those of Java, Demerara (Guyana), Barbados, and Hawaii, and later the United States Experimental Station at Canal Point, Florida, as well as those in India, Argentina, Australia, and others, succeeded in developing many varieties able to withstand the onslaught of the borer and mosaic. The characteristics of these new varieties are many and widely varied, and their use depends upon the nature of the land, the climate, and other factors. Most of the cane grown in the world today consists of those hybrids.

These newer seedling varieties are designated by initials and numerals, the best known being POJ (Proefstation Ost Java, East Java Experimental Station). Others bear such initials as D (Demerara), PR (Puerto Rico), H (Hawaii), B (Barbados), CP (Canal Point), CO (Coimbatore, India), and others.

The length of the crop season varies widely. In Louisiana, for example, cane is planted early in the year and is usually cut before the end of the year; it is imperative to have the crop in before freezes cause deterioration of the cane in the fields. In other areas, Hawaii, for example, cane might be allowed to grow two years before cutting. Hence, in Louisiana and other such subtropical areas, cane never comes to full maturity, whereas the long growing season in fully tropical areas results in greater tonnage of cane per acre, and greater yield of sugar per ton of cane.

The cane is planted by dropping cuttings into furrows, and then covering with earth. Each node of the cane stalk so planted produces a clump or "stool."

The cane is cut at the ground level and from the undisturbed root system a varying number of crops will sprout. In Louisiana, one planting results in only three cuttings, the third of which (second-year stubble or ratoon), is at times of such little economic value that it is not worthwhile cutting. Other areas (eg, Florida) may get six or more cuttings, and it has been said that in certain tropical countries cane is being cut from plantings over twenty years old. Commercial cane is all grown from such cuttings, but if allowed to flower (or arrow) it can be grown from seed. In this manner varieties are developed.

Harvesting (7). Harvesting of the cane is accomplished by many different methods. The traditional method, still practiced in many parts of the world, consists of manually cutting the cane with cane knives (machetes), stripping off the leaves, and "topping" the upper joints where the juice is not of sufficient richness to warrant saving. This produces cane of the very best quality for the mills, but is obviously becoming too expensive under modern economic conditions. However, several important areas still retain this method (as of 1968); these include Cuba, Florida, the Dominican Republic, and probably other areas of low labor cost.

In recent years, several successful mechanical harvesters have been developed. These have found application especially in Louisiana, Australia, and Hawaii. They are machines mounted on large rubber-tired wheels, or truck tractors, which move along the rows of cane, cutting the stalks close to the ground, trimming off the sugar-poor upper joints, and then stacking the cane into piles or pushing it into windrows for subsequent loading into cane carriers that bring the cane to the mills.

These systems operate efficiently where there is a high tonnage of cane, but they produce cane which is high in occluded dirt and requires cleaning before milling. This is done by washing the cane, usually with water from the condensers. This will be discussed later.

Because any form of mechanical harvesting leaves much of the foliage of the cane, which is undesirable later in the milling process, it is now the universal custom to burn the cane before mechanical harvesting to remove the greater part of the foliage. One exception is Louisiana, where the cane is burned in the windrows after cutting. When the cane is dry, this burning goes forward easily, is readily controlled, and if the cane is promptly milled, results in virtually no damage to the juice constituents. Even in those parts of the world where hand harvesting is the practice, burning is used to facilitate the cutting and eliminate the stripping of the foliage.

Washing the Cane (8,9). Because of the large amount of dirt and trash resulting from mechanical harvesting, it is mandatory to wash the cane before milling. This has been a regular practice in Louisiana and Hawaii, and is now becoming universal. It is an expensive, although necessary process, both because of the additional equipment required in the form of conveyors, pumps, and the like, and because the operation leaches out some of the sugar from the cane. This loss is in the range of 0.15 to 0.20% on weight of cane, or about 1.5% of the sugar in the cane. (Washing is necessary for sugar beets also, but here the loss is very much less, around 0.04 to 0.05% on weight of beets.)

Manufacture (Raw Sugar)

Extraction of the Juice. The juice may be extracted from the cane by one of two methods: *milling*, where the cane is pressed between heavy rollers to express out the

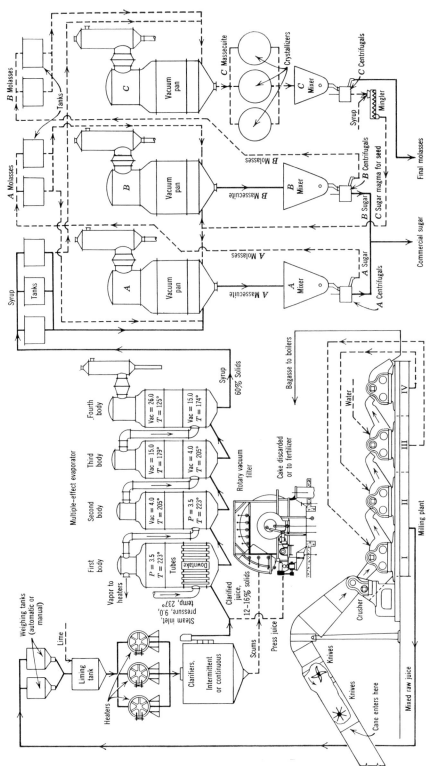

Fig. 1. Flow diagram of a raw-sugar factory (P = pressure; Vac = vacuum; T = temperature).

juice, or *diffusion*, where the sugar is leached out by water and thin juices. At present, by far the greatest percentage of cane is milled, although diffusion is making serious inroads.

In both processes, the cane must first be prepared by breaking up the stalks into shorter pieces, and rendering them into as small fragments as feasible. This can be done by crushers which are similar to mills, but equipped with large teeth, widely spaced, to break the cane so that it feeds into the following mills more easily, after having been cut into short sections by knives. Also used are the so-called shredders, which shred the cane into smaller chips without extracting much juice. In both milling and diffusion, a combination of any or all of these may be used. Magnets should be installed in the cane feed system to remove tramp iron which would ruin the knives, crushers, or shredders.

Milling (10,11). The cane thus prepared goes to a series of mills (called a tandem or train) (see the flow diagram in Fig. 1). These mills are massive horizontal cylinders, in groups of three, with one roller on top and two on the bottom in a triangular formation. These rollers are grooved to permit the extracted juice to flow into troughs beneath for collecting the extracted juice. There may be anywhere from three to five or more of these combinations of rollers in series. The juice from the first mill is richer than that from the second, that from the second richer than that from the third, and so on. In order to exhaust the pressed bagasse (qv) (the fibrous residue of the extracted cane), a system of imbibition, usually (but incorrectly) called compound maceration, is practiced in one form or another. This consists of spraying the bagasse going to the final mill with water, which tends to extract whatever sucrose remains in the bagasse; the resultant juice from the last mill is then sprayed on the bagasse mat going to the penultimate mill, and so on.

The combination of all these juices collected from the first mill (and any from the crusher) is known as mixed juice, and it is on this material that the technical figures of the factory are based. It must be weighed and clarified before going to the evaporators. The Brix (percent solids) of this mixed juice will usually be about 16°, and the purity (percent sucrose on solids) between 70 and 85%, depending upon geographical location, age of cane, variety of cane, climate during the growing season, cultivation, condition of the mill train, and other factors. It will contain about 12–14% sucrose, and from 0.5 to 1.0% (and more) invert sugar, depending upon the maturity of the cane. It will also contain salts of both organic and inorganic acids, free acids (some of these being amino acids), and other nonsugar organic materials, such as protein, starch, gums, waxes, fats, and other unidentified nonsugars (see reference 6, p. 24).

Diffusion (11). The concept of extracting the juice from the cane by diffusion (as is done with beets) is now widespread, and has proved successful. It is entirely possible that it will outrank conventional milling in the future.

Many of the large manufacturers of conventional mills have begun the production of diffusers. Dorr-Oliver is producing the Silver Engineering Works Inc. diffuser in the Western Hemisphere, and Mitsubishi Heavy Industries, Ltd. in the Eastern. Farrel, the largest mill manufacturer in the United States, has taken on the exclusive rights for the production of the DDS diffuser and Fulton Iron Works Co. for the Extraction De Smet diffuser.

The history of diffusion goes back at least to 1884 when Spencer experimented with it in Louisiana. There are references to even earlier trials, eg, on the Kock plantation in Louisiana in 1874. The use of diffusion in batch was practiced commercially in Egypt fifty years ago.

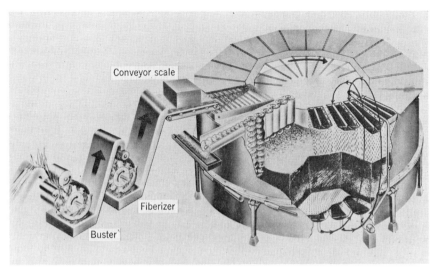

Fig. 2. The Silver ring diffuser. Courtesy Silver Engineering Works Inc.

The present rapidly growing use of diffusion (now entirely in continuous systems) is in fact a revival due to the development since World War II of continuous diffusers in beet sugar manufacture.

The term diffusion is actually a misnomer, since the process involves a combination of lixiviation (leaching) and osmosis. It is accomplished by subjecting the cane, rendered into as small portions as possible, to soaking in hot water and thin juices. The optimum temperature for this system is between 150 and 167°F. This is desirable because the high temperature kills the unopened cells, permitting diffusion through the cell walls, and reduces sucrose losses from bacterial and enzymic action. The sucrose is leached out into the solvent, and that portion retained in the unopened cells passes through the cell membrane by osmosis.

The breakdown of the cane into fragments by various means, eg, by shredders, crushers, hammer mills, etc, is even more important in diffusion than in milling. In the earlier installations, the cane was partly milled, going through the conventional shredder–crusher and through some mills before entering the actual diffusion cells. Such combinations of milling and diffusion characterize the diffusers of Braunschwei-gische Maschinenbauanstalt (BMA) (Egyptian), De Smet, and De Danske Sukker-fabriken.

In continuous systems, the mat of bagasse moves on some form of conveyor the entire length of the diffuser, progressing through richer juices to thinner ones and finally to the extraction water added in countercurrent flow. In others, the bagasse moves upward in a scroll conveyor against the downward flow of the lixiviating solvent, which starts as water at the top, and becomes mixed juice at the bottom. In one, the bagasse moves in an annulus against the countercurrent flow of the solvent (the Silver diffuser, Fig. 2). The principle of countercurrent flow is universal in juice extraction, both in diffusion and in milling.

The Silver diffuser is a quite successful development in sucrose extraction, as has been proved in Hawaii, Mexico, Venezuela, Okinawa, and Taiwan (Formosa). The cane is prepared by being chopped into fragments, first by knives and then by a fibri-dizer (or cane buster), a form of hammer mill. The prepared cane is fed into a ring with a perforated bottom. The cane–bagasse bed is undisturbed as it slowly rotates under juice distributors and over juice compartments. Juice is circulated counter-current to the flow of cane from the juice compartment to the next distributor, the juice passing through the cane to the next forward juice compartment. Water is added to the last distributor before the cane is removed from the diffuser. Extractions of over 97% are obtained from this ring diffuser. The resultant juice is much freer of suspended solids than conventional mixed juice from a mill train because it has, in effect, been filtered through successive layers of fiber in the ring.

None of the diffusion processes produces a final bagasse sufficiently dry to permit its combustion in the furnaces, and as this is essential to the economics of the industry, it must be dried to about 50% moisture before being sent to the boilers. This is generally accomplished as in the regular milling process, for example, by using the last two sets of mills of a conventional mill train. The Silver process uses a cone press specifically designed for the dewatering of bagasse. As in conventional milling, the press water is returned to the process.

The advantages claimed, and substantially proved, by advocates of the diffusion process over conventional milling are: (1) better sucrose extraction (which, however, is accompanied by excessive extraction of nonsugars); (2) higher juice purity for a given degree of extraction; (3) easier clarification owing to the cleaner juice (some claims are made that the juice can be sent directly to the evaporators); (4) less bacterial action owing to the higher operating temperatures; (5) lower investment (because less power is required, a smaller steam plant is needed); and (6) easier maintenance.

Weighing the Juice (13,14). The properly operated sugar factory keeps an accurate materials balance. (Sugar manufacture was the first of the large industries to adopt this now universal practice.) To this end, in order to keep a close check on such important operations as recovery, boiling-house efficiency, mill extraction, loss in process, etc, it is necessary to weigh the mixed juice. (The cane had already been weighed.) The weights and analyses of the discarded filter-press mud, bagasse, maceration (or imbibition) water, etc, are desirable, but in practice actual weights are difficult to obtain so these figures are in part calculated.

There are many types of automatic juice scales in use, all satisfactory provided they are maintained properly. Although it is possible to arrive at juice weights by means of volume measurements and Brix determinations, automatic scales far outperform such methods. See Weighing and proportioning.

Clarification. The mixed juice requires clarification. This is accomplished by a combination of liming, heating, and settling. The sequence of heating and liming is not fixed. The historical method was to add lime and then to heat rapidly to the desired temperature, usually around the boiling point. In modern practice, much higher temperatures are used (around 240°F), which requires heating under pressure. The combination of the increased alkalinity and temperature results in the precipitation of certain colloids in the juice, and the formation of a floc which entraps the inert solids in the juice.

Good clarification is of the utmost importance; too much emphasis cannot be laid on this point. Improperly clarified juice will result in turbid meladura (the thickened juice from the evaporators which constitutes the pan feed), and this in turn will mean a raw sugar with occluded impurities in the grain, making refining difficult. To achieve good clarification, the cane should be cleaned as much as possible, liming must be carried out at the proper pH, and the juice kept at a predetermined fixed pH level.

The temperature of the juice should be raised to the proper level (eg, 220°F) in the shortest possible time and kept in the clarifier as short a time as is consistent with good clarification. Even with excellent clarification, there will be some carryover of fine particles of bagasse fiber (bagacillo) and close screening of the clarified juice is desirable before it goes to the evaporators.

In some geographical areas, it is advantageous to add phosphates or other electrolytes to the juice to improve the formation of a desirable floc. The sequence of liming and heating is also widely variable. An important innovation some years ago was the adoption of FL and DH (fractional liming and double heating) (Fig. 3). In this process the juice is limed to an intermittent pH (eg, 6.4), the temperature raised to boiling, the juice then relimed to 7.6 pH, again boiled, and settled.

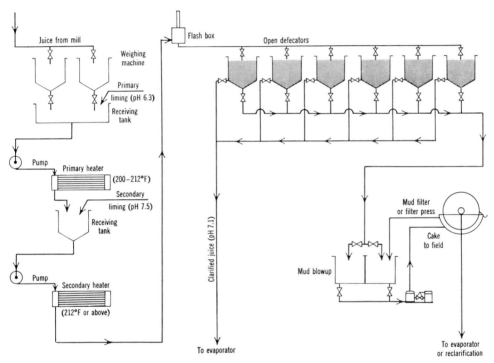

Fig. 3. Fractional liming and double heating (with intermittent clarification).

A fairly recent development, which has not yet gained general acceptance because of its cost, is the use of magnesium hydroxide instead of lime in clarification. These alkalis may also be used in combination. With lime, a hard scale of calcium sulfate forms on heating surfaces, which must be cleaned frequently. The principal advantage of magnesium is that it largely avoids this problem; in addition, it produces less muds. Disadvantages in the use of magnesium, in addition to cost, are (1) its slower rate of reaction and (2) poorer clarification, giving a more turbid juice.

In those raw factories which make a direct-consumption sugar (see p. 184) there has been good success with the use of sodium carbonate to maintain pH; conventional liming is used to precipitate the impurities, but any further maintenance of pH is effected by the sodium ion. However, sodium salts must be used with care in the production of cane sugar, since they are known to produce color.

Clarifiers (9,14).   The removal of the entrapped impurities is accomplished by means of vessels called clarifiers; this is done after preliminary screening to remove large particles, unbroken fibers, and the like.   The original method of removal was to boil the limed juice vigorously and then run into flat tanks.   The froth carried the impurities to the top of the juice and was brushed off, leaving the clear juice below.

Clarifiers are all variations of this method, ie, some form of decantation.   Perhaps the most widely used clarifier today is the one by Dorr-Oliver Inc., a vertical cylindrical vessel composed of a number of trays, stacked one over the other.   The treated juice is run into the trays, the impurities settle to the bottom of each tray, and the clear juice rises to the top and overflows into a header.   A sweep arm in each tray, moving quite slowly, moves the settled muds into the central mud takeoff (see Sedimentation).   The clarified juice then goes to the evaporators.   There are many other types of clarifiers in use throughout the world, for example, the Deming (Deming Division, Crane Co.), Graver (Graver Water Conditioning Co.), Bach subsider, Fortier, BMA, Prima-Sep; in all these, the principle is the same, the separation of the floc from the clear juice by settling.

As mentioned above, there is at least the possibility that this station of the factory may in time be eliminated by means of some form of diffuser where the juice is, in effect, filtered out on the bagasse.

Reclamation of Scums (Muds).   The scums from the clarifiers contain sugar which must be reclaimed.   This is accomplished by treatment with additional lime, heating, and settling (not shown in Fig. 1 for simplicity).   The supernatant liquor from this settling is usually cloudy, and is returned to the clarifiers for treatment with the incoming raw juice.   The remaining bottoms are diluted with water and filtered on some form of press, either conventional plate-and-frame or a rotating drum type such as the Eimco or Oliver.   The clear juice from this filtration goes along with the clarified juice from the mills to evaporators, the muds (the remaining solids after filtration) having value as fertilizer.

Evaporation (15).   The screened and clarified juice then goes to the evaporators. Evaporation is carried out in multiple effect, in which two, three, usually four, but in some places as many as six, bodies (effects) successively concentrate the solids in the juice from under 20% solids to over 60%.   The multiple-effect principle utilizes the latent heat of steam as many times as there are bodies in the effect.   The steam enters the calandria of the first body, and the vapor therefrom, which is at say, 5 in. of mercury vacuum, will enter the calandria of the second body and boil the liquor there, where the vapor is at, say 15 in. of vacuum; this vapor then enters the calandria of the third body to boil syrup in the liquor belt where the vacuum is at, say 25 in. of vacuum (see Evaporation).   The thin juice is pumped into the first body, and the gradually thickened syrup is taken successively to the following bodies, where the vacuum increases; the boiling point therefore decreases.   The thickened juice (called variously meladura, mill syrup, etc) is finally pumped at about 60–65 Brix to the pan feed tanks.

Although most of the evaporators in the raw cane sugar industry are of the conventional type described above, there are other types which have found acceptance. Among these are the climbing film types, such as the Kestner, a semi-Kestner variety, and a forced-flow evaporator produced by Maschinenfabrik Buckau R. Wolf.   The advantage of this type of evaporator lies in the short time the liquors remain in the bodies, so color buildup due to long exposure to the high temperature is reduced.

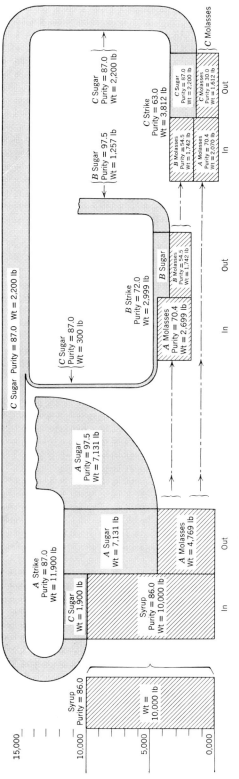

Fig. 4. Pan flow diagram showing a three-boiling system.

Crystallization (16,17). The raw sugar of commerce is first produced in the vacuum pans. It is desirable that all the sugar be of uniformly sized grain, and of as nearly uniform chemical composition as possible. To this end various schemes known as boiling systems are used; Figure 4 shows one example, a three-boiling system. The particular scheme adopted depends upon various factors, possibly the most important of which is the purity of the juice; this, in turn, depends largely upon the ripeness of the cane when harvested and processed. The basic principle of crystallization is to bring the solution to a concentration at which it contains crystal nuclei and is ready to crystallize of its own accord, and then to maintain it in a supersaturated state so the crystals will grow. The growth is promoted by introducing a supply of sugar in solution from which the crystals can take additional sucrose.

The pan man (sugar boiler) takes into the pan a quantity of syrup or molasses which he knows from experience will produce the amount of crystal nuclei which, at full growth, will be of the proper size for commercial raw sugar, and which, when such size has been reached, will result in a full pan of massecuite. By means of a device in the side of the pan known as a proofstick he draws samples until he notes the formation

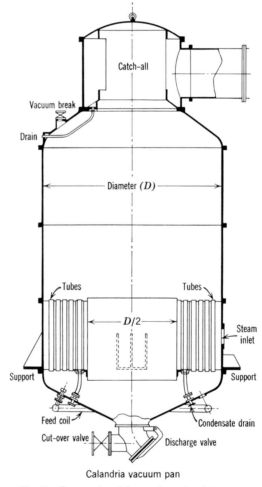

Calandria vacuum pan

Fig. 5. Conventional form of a calandria pan.

of minute crystals of sucrose. By careful manipulation of pan temperature (controlled by the vacuum level), steam, and rate of feed of the syrups, he keeps the crystals growing until the pan is full. At this point the sugar crystals will be of the desired size if the pan-boiling operation has been done properly. The resultant mass will contain about half the solids in the form of crystals and half in solution.

The proofstick samples are taken at intervals throughout the operation to enable the pan man to check on the development of the crystal growth, and at the end of the

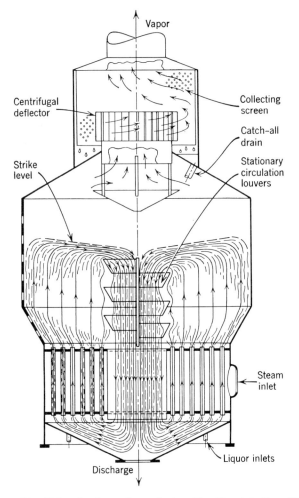

Vapor

Centrifugal
deflector

Collecting
screen

Catch–all
drain

Strike
level

Stationary
circulation
louvers

Steam
inlet

Liquor inlets

Discharge

Fig. 6. Hamill low-head pan (manufactured by Honolulu Iron Works).

strike to determine the proper time to drop (strike) the pan. There should be no crystals of widely different size than the desired average, since mixtures of crystals of different sizes make future refining difficult.

At this point the vacuum is released, and the pan is dropped or struck; the resulting mixture of grain and syrup (known as massecuite or fillmass) is run out of the pan into crystallizers, where the crystallization continues further, or directly into mixers, from which it is fed to the centrifugal machines.

Vacuum Pans (18,19). Vacuum pans are usually vertical cylindrical vessels which are equipped with heating elements such as steamcoils, or chests containing vertical tubes known as calandrias (Fig. 5). Steam entering the coils or calandrias causes the syrup to boil, the circulation almost universally being up the sides and down the middle.

The vacuum in the pan is maintained by the condensation of the vapors in a leg-pipe (Torricellian) condenser; it is also necessary that the pan be equipped with a vacuum pump for the removal of such noncondensable gases as enter through leaks in the pan, or with the syrup feed. In some forms of condensers, the water for condensation is pumped downward into the condenser in the form of jets at high pressure, which act as ejectors for the removal of these noncondensable gases, thus eliminating the need for a vacuum pump. Presently the vacuum pump is being largely replaced by steam ejectors, which have the advantages of economical installation, small space requirements, low first cost, and fairly easy maintenance. They must not, however, be operated at less than the specified steam pressure.

Types of Vacuum Pans. The basic vacuum pan described above has been altered in many ways, especially toward improving the circulation of the mass being boiled. If no auxiliary aid to circulation is employed, it is essential for the central open portion of the pan (the downcomer) to be of sufficient diameter to allow easy and unrestricted flow. The pan made by Honolulu Iron Works accomplishes this free flow without the use of mechanical circulation; in this pan the section immediately above the calandria widens out, the central section, or well, being fenced in by a series of downward louvers designed to channel the massecuite flow into the downcomer (Fig. 6). This is conceded to be an important advance.

Mechanical Circulator. In order to improve pan circulation, the mechanical circulator has been widely accepted. The modern circulator is a large scroll conveyor with a downward thrust into the center of the pan powered by a quite large (50–75 hp) electric motor located above the pan, through a shaft extending downward through the entire height of the pan. This provides positive movement of the massecuite, eliminating crosscurrents, and permitting circulation of the mass without the necessity of ebullition. This is very desirable during the period when the supersaturation of the boiling liquor is in the metastable zone, ie, at the time the grain is being brought in or formed and until it has grown to the point where feed can be introduced. In addition, the overall time required to boil a strike is reduced. This circulator is used virtually exclusively with calandria pans.

The final dropping "proof" or concentration of solids in the strike is usually 93–96 Brix. There are instances where even heavier massecuites are desirable, and these are boiled in pans with very large ratios of heating surfaces to volume. The massecuites may be of such density that the final mass must be sluiced out by heavy liquor or syrup. Among the innovations recently introduced are the Fives Lille-Cail horizontal pan and the Segura high-speed pan. The latter reverses the flow of massecuite by having the downcomer around the periphery of the pan instead of in the center. The heating surface is of the calandria type.

Boiling Systems (9). It is the aim of the raw-sugar producer to make a raw sugar of uniform character, that is, sugar which is virtually of the same color and test. This is done by what are known as two-, three-, or even four-boiling systems. The adoption of one of these over another depends upon various factors, the most important of which is possibly the purity of the juice from the mills and the desirability (or necessity) of producing final molasses of the lowest purity. Figure 4 shows how the syrups are boiled back in a three-boiling system (see also Fig. 10). The sugar from the last boiling is usually mingled with syrup to form seed, or beginning grain, for the first two or three strikes.

A usual procedure in a three- or four-boiling system is to use the last massecuite as footings for the first ones. The last massecuite, however, must make its own grain; this is usually induced by the introduction of fine sugar crystals. To do this the syrup in the pan must be brought to and kept in the metastable zone until the crystals thus formed have grown to a size which will enable them to resist any tendency to dissolve in the less saturated pan feed. If a Webre-type circulator is used, this is a simple procedure. The steam is turned off the pan (eliminating evaporation) and circulation is mechanically maintained until the crystals grow to the desired size. If the pan does not have such a circulator, circulation must be maintained by ebullition, and great care must be exercised by the pan man (sugar boiler) during this stage.

Once the crystals are formed, feed is introduced at a controlled rate until the proper size has been attained, at which time, if properly managed, the pan will be full and the strike will be ready to drop.

Because apparatus now exists which can determine the degree of saturation of the contents of the pan at all times, control of this phase has now gone past the point of being an art. In the past, a sugar boiler learned his business by long apprenticeship, whereas now good pan men can be trained in a very short time, provided they have been properly taught the use of their instruments and will learn to depend upon them. It is often true that it is easier to train a "green" man to boil sugar with instruments than to convert an "old hand" to their use.

Among the various methods used to control pan boiling are: (1) conductivity methods (Suma); (2) determination of vapor-pressure difference between material in the pan itself and that in a pilot pot outside the pan under identical vacuum (Ditmar-Jansse); and (3) viscosity measurements of the boiling mass, determined by the power necessary to drive a small propeller in the pan at constant speed, etc.

Recovery—Crystallizers (19,20). The lower the purity of the mother liquor, the slower is the rate of crystallization. It is usual to drop the massecuite into crystallizers, where additional crystallization takes place at gradually reducing temperatures and with increased time. In the case of a well-run factory using a four-boiling system, the first massecuite might remain in the crystallizer for 6–8 hr, the second for 12–16 hr, the third for 30–36 hr, and fourth for maybe 72 hr before being sent to the mixers prior to centrifugation to remove the adhering mother liquor. (The mixer serves as a feed box for the centrifugal; it is necessary to keep the mass in motion to prevent the crystals from settling out.) The syrup running off the final strike in a boiling cycle after it has been in the crystallizer is the by-product of the factory, and is known as blackstrap molasses (Dutch, black syrup). It is very heavy, possibly in the neighborhood of 90° Brix or even more, extremely viscous, and with an apparent purity of about 30% (percent pol. in total solids determined as Brix). See Molasses.

Centrifuging (21). After aging in the crystallizer, the massecuite is "dried" or centrifuged in centrifugal machines to separate the crystals from the mother liquor. These centrifugals may be either batch or continuous. See Centrifugal separation.

The batch centrifugals are of various sizes and run at various speeds. An excellent all-around centrifugal, the Western States G-8, has a diameter of 48 in. and a depth of 40 in. and operates at 1200–1600 rpm. The thickness of massecuite against the wall of the basket at the start of the cycle is 7 in., but after syrup has been centrifuged off, only the solid crystals remain and the thickness is reduced.

Possibly the best known of the batch centrifugals are those manufactured by Western States, Broadbent, The Squier Corp., Fives Lille-Cail, BMA, Salzgitter Maschinen A.G., and Asea-Landwerk.

The baskets of greater diameter turn slower, those of narrower diameter turn faster, in order to give approximately equal centrifugal force. In some areas, such as Peru, Hawaii, and possibly others, speeds of over 2000 rpm have been used, in spite of the inherent danger of such high kinetic energy.

Most continuous centrifugals are essentially vertical cones of strong screen with the apex at the bottom. The massecuite is fed into the bottom of the cone, and is thrown out against the screen by centrifugal force. The massecuite then progresses upward in a thin layer, hopefully only one crystal thick, so that as the diameter of the basket increases, the centrifugal force increases also. The syrup or molasses passes through the screen, and as the purged sugar crystals get to the top of the cone, they are thrown off to be collected below the centrifugal machine.

Continuous centrifugals with well-known names are the Silver, BMA, Western States, and Buckau-Wolf. A few, such as those made by Esscher-Wyss and Allis-Chalmers Manufacturing Co., are horizontal.

In the centrifuging process, water is usually added to assist in the removal of the mother liquor adhering to the crystals. Steam may be used for the same purpose. This improves the rate of purging and quality of sugar, but some sugar is dissolved and the molasses purity suffers (ie, it is too high, for ideally there should be no sugar in the final molasses).

For the first massecuite, possibly little or no water is needed, but with each successive lower-purity massecuite more water must be used to wash off the ever-increasingly viscous syrup. The sugars from all boilings should be reasonably similar, and when blended give a fairly homogeneous raw product. In no case must so much water be used that all the molasses is rinsed off the crystal, since this thin film of mother liquor acts as a protective barrier against fermentation. The resultant sugar must be dried to a point where the percentage of moisture in the whole raw sugar is not more than 25 or at most 30% of the total nonsucrose components of the raw sugar. (This 25% factor, known as the safety factor, was developed in Australia, and has proved to be an excellent indicator of the keeping quality of a raw sugar.)

For example, a typical analysis of raw sugar might show polarization of 97.0°, moisture of 0.70%, ash (inorganic material) of 0.75%, invert (reducing sugars) of 0.78%, and organic materials (determined by difference) of 0.77%. In this case the safety factor would be 0.23 and the raw would be expected to keep well. This factor is calculated thus: $0.70 \div (100.0 - 97.0) = 0.233$. If another raw, also polarizing 97.0°, had an analysis of 0.95% moisture, 0.68% ash, 0.68% invert, and 0.69% organic material, the safety factor would be $0.95 \div (100.0 - 97.0) = 0.316$ and its keeping quality would be questionable. The higher this figure, the poorer will be the keeping quality; the lower it is the better. There is no minimum safety factor, but usually a figure of 0.20–0.25 is obtainable with good raws.

The last massecuite in the cycle (eg, the third in the three-boiling system shown in Fig. 4) is never washed, because it is desirable not to dissolve any of the sucrose from the crystals and wash it into the final molasses. The sugar in the three-boiling system under consideration is mingled with syrup to make a footing for the first two strikes, but if these strikes are to be seeded in some other way, the sugar is improved by double purging. This molasses is the principal by-product of the raw-sugar factory, and is very viscous and black and of such purity that further crystallization of sucrose from it is economically impossible.

There are additional techniques used to improve centrifuging, such as hot mingling and double purging; the type used depends on the pan-boiling system employed. For details see references 6, 8, and 28.

Batch versus Continuous Centrifugals. There has been a great deal of study on the matter of application of continuous centrifugals to work formerly done by batch types. In general, it may be stated that when massecuites of very low purity are to be handled, one conventional continuous centrifugal can replace three conventional batch machines; but for massecuites of refined sugar purity, the ratio is no better than one to one, and the resultant sugar from the batch types is superior to that from the continuous. The very great advantages of continuous centrifugals are in the area of original costs as well as in maintenance and power. In addition, they are said to be able to purge badly "smeared" massecuites (ie, continuing very fine crystals along with the regular sized ones) which batch centrifugals cannot adequately handle.

Storage (22,23). Although at one time all raw sugar was packed in individual containers of various sizes and materials (jute bags, cotton bags, hogs-heads, straw mats, etc, with individual packages weighing from 40 to 400 lb most of the raw sugar received in the United States today is in bulk form. Off-shores (raw sugars imported into the United States from overseas) come in bulk in the holds of steamers (and occasionally barges), and domestic raws (ie, from Louisiana and Florida) come in bulk box cars or trucks. The trucks and cars are weighed on railroad or truck scales, in and out (and by internal scales for checking and technical control); the off-shore raws are weighed in bulk hopper scales at the point of discharge. If duty payment is required, the Government weighs the raw; settlement is usually made on weights and tests determined at this point.

Storing the raws in the producing country until sufficient volume is accumulated for shipment is usually done by piling in dry, well-ventilated warehouses; this is done by means of overhead belts equipped with diverters or cross-belts or by means of a slinger such as the Sinden piler, which throws the sugar off a very high-speed belt in a strong stream onto a pile which may be as high as thirty feet or more. There is an attendant advantage to such a slinger, because some cooling and drying is effected in the throwing.

The raws so stored should adhere to the safety factor delineated above. The material should be cooled as much as feasible, because warm raw sugar in a pile, especially if at all moist, tends to pack into a very hard mass, and worse, to increase in color due to caramelization at the elevated temperature.

Attention must be paid to the possibility of fire. For a long time it was generally thought that normal raw sugar in a bulk pile would not support combustion, but a serious conflagration in Australia disabused sugar producers of this fallacy (24).

Raws stored in bags should be given the same care as bulk piles; the susceptibility to fire is very much greater; the jute and other containers support combustion, and the voids between the units provide a free flow of air for combustion. In a fire in bulk raw, if caught reasonably soon, damage caused by the sprinklers is usually light, because the surface sugar packs, permitting the water to flow off. Similar sprinkler damage in a pile of raw in bags results in a sad mess, because the water runs down between the bags, permeating the entire stack to the ground, and serious fermentation results if the raws are not refined quite promptly.

The piled raws from bulk storage are handled like any other bulk product, by bulldozers, Athey-type loaders, dump trucks, elevators, and belt systems; this applies both to the loading and the receiving ends.

By-Products of Raw-Sugar Manufacture (25,26). The cellular residue of the grinding of the cane after the extraction of the juice is called bagasse and is used principally as fuel for the factory. A well-operated sugar mill, once started, is usually able to operate with no supplemental fuel, and in many cases, has sufficient bagasse left over to permit its combustion for the production of electric power. In some areas, and at certain times, the bagasse is manufactured into various products, eg, wallboard, plastics, furfural, etc.

It is customary in such cases for the mill to sell the bagasse in return for the value in fuel. Where the fuel is natural gas, as for example in Louisiana, this is a definite advantage to the mill because of the greater ease and cleanliness of burning gas over bagasse, which requires huge combustion chambers (Dutch ovens) (see Bagasse).

The shiny and smooth cuticle on cane is a wax, and this has been recovered from the muds (cachaza) and refined into a commercial wax well able to compete with other vegetable waxes such as carnauba and candelilla (see Waxes).

The final molasses was formerly used exclusively for fermentation into alcohol and for cattle feed, and in the tropics this is still the case. However in those countries with a well-developed petroleum technology, alcohol can be synthesized more cheaply than it can be produced by fermentation, so the cattle-feed outlet is the more important one.

Direct-Consumption Sugars (31). Many raw-sugar mills produce in addition to, or even instead of, the raw sugar that is sent to the refinery a semirefined product which can be consumed as ordinary table granulated, although it will not have the same degree of purity or whiteness of color. For one such product, the sugar is treated at the mill with vegetable carbon to decolorize it; the result is, for all practical purposes, a refined sugar.

Turbinados. The thickened juice (meladura) may be filtered clear by means of filter aids and boiled to grain; the sugar is then washed in the centrifugal and dried (still in the centrifugal) with a jet of steam. This product, being of somewhat larger grain size than ordinary table granulated, dries rapidly and keeps well. The color is decidedly off-white, but its polarization generally exceeds 99°. It has many uses, for example, in the manufacture of certain foods not requiring good color. The product can also be made without the preliminary filtration for the removal of solids impurities and detritus, but the resulting material is not as desirable.

Other Types. Other off-white sugars can be made by subjecting the syrups or juices at an early stage of the process to bleaching agents such as chlorine, sulfur dioxide, or hydrogen peroxide, but they are not of as good quality as those produced by decolorization with carbon.

A "whole" sugar can be made from the syrup, without elimination of any impurities, by boiling, and one, well-received in Brazil, is known as terzeira. It is a moist, soft, and yellow product. Another type is called rapadura. All these are what are called the noncentrifugal sugars, since they are not subjected to the process of separating crystals from mother liquor. The gur of India is produced in quite large quantities for consumption locally. Other noncentrifugal sugars go by such picturesque names as panela, areado, pilé, piloncillo, papelon, and chancaca. Unlike turbinados they are of little economic importance internationally.

Refining (27–30)

The raw sugar which comes to the refinery consists of a crystal of practically pure sucrose, to which adheres a very thin film of the mother liquor from which the sugar was boiled (molasses). For example, a raw sugar testing 97.0° contains on an average 0.75% of moisture (safety factor = 0.33) and 2.25% impurities (invert sugar, inorganic ash, and organic matter), practically all of which are in the film of molasses. Refining is the process of separating the sucrose from the impurities as soon and as completely as possible. In doing this it is necessary to avoid reversing the process by mixing back lower-purity products with those of higher purity at any subsequent point.

Quality of Raws. Historically, raw sugar has been bought on the basis of polarization, although lately there have been efforts on the part of the refiners to take into account other factors of importance to them (see reference 6, p. 4). These include: (1) the safety factor; (2) color, which is an important factor in refining costs; (3) ash, especially sulfates, which tend to precipitate out on heating surfaces; (4) grain characteristics, eg, size, and more importantly, evenness of grain size (which affects the affination process) and lack of "mounted" or "double-crystals"; and (5) filterability, especially in the case of a refiner who filters the washed raw sugar through a filter medium before char filtration.

Affination. The first step in refining raw sugar is to wash off the molasses film on the crystals. This operation is called affination (see Fig. 7 for a flow diagram of the refining process).

After weighing (almost invariably done automatically by such scales as Servo-Balans, Parsons, or others) and sampling the raws entering the refinery, the raw sugar is sent to a mingler, where it is made into a thick artificial massecuite called a magma by thoroughly mixing with a warm, high-Brix syrup (the washings from previously affined sugar). The purpose of this step is to moisten the syrup on the surface of the crystal, and to put the raw sugar into a flowable state so it can be run into the affination machines. These are centrifugals (usually of the batch type although continuous types are applicable) in which the adhering softened syrup is spun off along with the mixing syrup. After spinning, the wall of sugar is washed with water to remove the residual syrup remaining on the crystals. In modern refineries completely automatic batch machines are gaining favor. The sugar is "cut out" into a scroll or vibrating conveyor below and conveyed to a melter, ie, a dissolver. A portion of the syrup spun off comes back to mingle with more raw sugar, the surplus going to the bone char or the recovery system (to be explained later), or for clarification and char filtration for soft sugars or refiners syrup.

At this point, a very large part of the refining has been accomplished; the resulting washed raw sugar is around 98+ purity, and about three-fourths of the color and two-thirds of the chemical impurities have been separated from the crystal.

Melting. In the sugar industry, the term "melting" means "dissolving"; sugar is never actually melted in any part of the process. The washed raw sugar is melted, usually with light sweet waters from other stations of the refinery. These solvents must have approximately the same purity as the washed sugar to eliminate, as much as possible, recirculation of impurities through the factory. Hence, the low-purity sweet

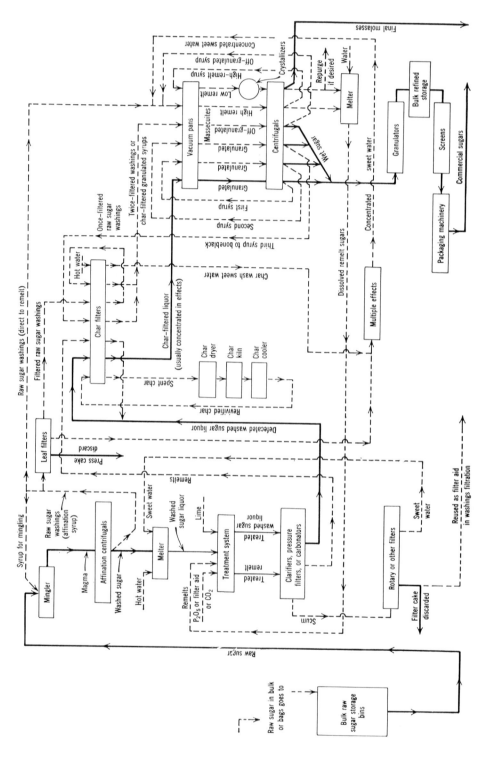

Fig. 7. Flow diagram of the bone char refining process.

waters from char washing are undesirable but those light sweet waters from reclamation of sugar dust, or from reclamation of sucrose from clarifier muds and the like, can be used.

The melted sugar is coarsely screened to remove the coarser forms of foreign matter and then heated to the desired temperature, which depends on the clarification method to follow. The Brix is adjusted by controlling the amount of solvent sweet water, or by adding water. This adjustment is almost universally done by automatic means.

The melted sugar is then screened again to remove the larger dirt particles, the operation being called prescreening, and sent to clarifiers.

Clarification. The melted washed sugar is clarified before char treatment so that (*1*) the liquor will be clean when it goes to the bone char, thus eliminating possible blockup of the char surface and (*2*) to enhance the decolorizing power of the char by the use of a cleaner liquor. There are at present three major systems for clarification:

1. *Pressure filtration* with inert filter aids. (Some systems include small percentages of phosphate in order to obtain some decolorization. However, the calcium phosphate precipitate is gelatinous and adversely affects filtration rates.)

2. *Phosphatation* in frothing clarifiers utilizing tricalcium phosphate floc.

3. *Carbonation* using lime and carbon dioxide from scrubbed stack gases.

Pressure filtration was used almost universally in the refining industry until the 1920s, but it has not been installed in any new refineries and is now used mainly as an adjunct to frothing clarifiers and carbonation systems. In this process, the melted washed sugar is filtered through some form of filter press, assisted by an inert filter aid of diatomaceous earth. Its principal advantage lies in the complete clarity of the outflow liquor. However, no improvement in the color of the liquor is gained. It has the additional disadvantage of being a batch process. Usually, some form of leaf filter is used, such as Vallez, Kelly, or Sweetland, automated as much as possible so as to save labor.

The *frothing clarifiers* (32) depend on the formation of a gelatinous floc, which, when floated to the surface of the clarifier by means of occluded air and subsequent heating, entraps the impurities. The system of treating the liquor with phosphoric acid and lime is a very old one, and was utilized for many years, but until the development of the floc-flotation system, the tricalcium phosphate precipitate had to be removed by filtration with Taylor bag filters, which was slow, laborious, and productive of excessive amounts of sweet water.

Frothing clarifiers properly operated produce a liquor of adequate clarity for char filtration (although some refineries follow with pressure filtration to insure complete clarity) and greatly reduced color, amounting to 30–45% removal. This greatly reduces the color load on the char. These clarifiers are quite sensitive to variations in the quality of the raw and work better on high-quality raws than on inferior raws. They produce a comparatively large amount of scums and about 5% of the entering sucrose must be recovered from these scums. If such recovery is rapid and efficient, no appreciable inversion occurs and the resultant sweet water is utilizable for melting. These clarifiers have the advantage of complete continuous operation, and are readily adapted to automation.

Since the mid-1920s, all new refineries built over the world have adopted this system, with few exceptions, and with only few exceptions all refineries which have changed over from pressure filtration have favored phosphatation.

The third important system of clarification, *carbonation* (33), was developed in Europe, especially England, and is gaining favor each year. Three important Western Hemisphere refineries have changed over to this system.

In this process, the washed sugar liquor is limed and then treated with carbon dioxide (obtained by scrubbing stack gases (see Vol. 4, p. 357) followed by compression) to form a precipitate of calcium carbonate, which is removed in filter presses. The principal advantage of this system is quite high color removal, up to 60%. Chemical costs are low. The press cake remaining is easily washed free of the residual sugar. The disadvantages of carbonation stem from the fact that the filtration operation is noncontinuous; thus, the same type of problems are encountered as in pressure filtration. Compressor costs and maintenance costs are high.

The problem of choosing between phosphatation (frothing clarifiers) and carbonation continues to occupy the attention of modern refiners.

Recovery of Sugar from Frothing-Clarifier Scums. Because of the high percentage of sugar in the scums, its recovery is obviously important. Various methods have been used; for example, a series of dilutions reducing the Brix each time, settling, decanting the clear solution, and finally filter-pressing the bottoms or solids remaining. The disadvantage of this method is that the solutions remain at high temperatures and thin Brixes for too long a time, so that appreciable inversion takes place.

Filtration of the scums on rotary vacuum drum filters is possible, but requires a high percentage of filter aid, which is expensive. The best method used now consists of removing the solids from the diluted scums by means of supercentrifuges. These are smaller than the regular centrifugals, but operate at a much higher speed. Well-known makes are the Titan (A. S. Titan Co.), the Westphalia, the De Laval (The De Laval Separator Co.), and others. They offer important advantages, eg, labor savings and reduced sugar loss in sweet waters due to reduced time in process. Usually, less sweet water is produced. The principal disadvantages of the supercentrifuge are the relatively high maintenance costs and the initial cost.

Decolorization (34,35). The principal refining tool is char (boneblack, bone char). It consists of the calcined fragments of animal bone, of size such that it usually passes through 8–10 mesh and is retained on 16–28 mesh. Fresh bone char consists of a basic structure of calcium phosphate (apatite), which is a very porous material with a large ratio of exposed surface to weight. The surfaces of the crystal are covered with a thin film of carbon with high absorbent properties. Although the normal char appears to be all black in color, in actual fact it contains only between 6 and 8% of carbon when new. With use, the carbon content of the char changes. If the revivifying atmosphere is oxidizing, the content will drop; this is usually not disadvantageous, since bone char with carbon percentages as low as 2 or 3% can decolorize quite well. If the carbon content of the char rises in use above its original level, this is an indication that the carbonaceous compounds removed in the filtration have been reduced to carbon. This carbon is inert and not only does it not have any decolorizing power, it blankets the activated carbon on the surface of the char.

The bone char has the valuable properties of removing from the clarified liquor the color bodies, ash (inorganic constituents), and some colloidal material, all in varying degrees. After the bone char has removed the practical amount of these impurities, it can be revivified for reuse some hundreds of times.

The adsorbed mineral materials are desorbed when the char is washed free of the remaining sugar after the decolorizing phase of the process; the organic materials are distilled off from the char in the kilns at the end of the char cycle.

Because the adsorbed inorganic materials are not completely desorbed and washed away, the bone char gradually picks them up and in time grows heavier and must be replaced. Also, since bone char is a friable material and is gradually reduced in size, it must be continually screened before reuse to maintain flow characteristics. This finer fraction, removed by screening, has better color-reducing properties than the larger grain, so a compromise must be worked out between loss of color removal and reduction of flow.

The heavier fractions of the char are not as active as the lighter ones, and should be eliminated, because they displace the more active fractions in the filter, and also tend to abrade them to dust. The Sutton, Steele, and Steele table is most valuable in removing these heavy grains, as well as other heavy, inert material which may have found its way into the char, such as pieces of refractory, mortar, rock, and the like (see Vol. 10, p. 719).

During a period around World War II when bone char became difficult to obtain, efforts to produce a synthetic bone char resulted in a product known as "Synthad." It matches the characteristics of true animal bone char very well, although there are both advantages and disadvantages when compared with the natural product (36).

Decolorizing carbons (12) come in two forms, powdered and granular. All such carbons are derived from gaseous, liquid, or solid carbonaceous substances by one of two general methods, both of which include thermal decomposition of the starting material. The surface areas and porosities are determined by the type of raw material and by activation method. The two general methods of activation are: (*1*) high-temperature oxidation of a previously charred carbonaceous substance (coke, coal, charcoal, etc), and (*2*) lower-temperature chemical dehydration and/or chemical reaction of a carbonaceous raw material.

In the United States, the bulk of current production is by the high-temperature steam process, although chemical activation is used to some extent. In continental Europe, chemical activation is more widely used. Precise control of both reaction temperature and reaction time is very important in steam activation to impart the desired properties. Temperatures usually range upwards from 800°C. Almost any carbonaceous substance can be used as a raw material for steam activation, eg, lignite (commonly used), wood charcoal, coke, coal, peat, etc.

For both the powdered and the granular carbons, the surface area is very large, being on the order of 450–1800 m²/g.

Because of the much higher percentage of carbon in these materials than in bone char or Synthad, they have much longer decolorizing cycles. Their principal disadvantage is their inability to remove inorganic matter.

Powdered activated carbons have been, and still are widely used for decolorizing of sugar liquors, although of late they are being replaced by the granular carbons. The powdered carbons (50–98% minus 325 mesh) are used by mixing in the feed liquor as well as by forming a bed for throughflow in the filter presses. They are generally used on a throw-away basis, although it is possible to revivify them; however, this is not standard practice. Their principal advantage lies in reduced first cost; all that is needed to produce a white liquor suitable for boiling to refined material are some tanks and filter presses, whereas bone char refineries require massive installations in a large char house, many char filters and kilns, more labor, and systems for handling both the dry (revivified) and wet (exhausted) chars.

Granular activated carbons are of approximately the same grain size as bone char, the common grades being screened 4 × 12, 12 × 20, and 20 × 40 United States standard mesh sizes. Their use costs fall between those of the powdered carbons and bone char, because of their long decolorizing cycle, eg, twenty days as compared to forty to seventy hours for bone char. The life of a unit of granular carbon is about twenty cycles. Hence, fewer cisterns, less conveying machinery, less regeneration apparatus, etc, are required.

These granular carbons are becoming increasingly important in the refinery industry. Although their inability to remove inorganic matter is a detriment, this lack can be remedied by the use of ion-exchange resins.

Ion-Exchange Resins. These are of value to remove inorganic material when no bone char is used in the system, and a combination of ion-exchange resins with either granulated carbon or powdered carbon is advantageous. These resins are revivified by means of acid (usually H_2SO_4) and alkali (usually $NaOH$).

In addition to removal (exchange) of inorganic matter, some types of resins remove color; these are being increasingly used for this purpose. Such resins are customarily revivified by salt ($NaCl$) with occasional intermediate treatments with acid. Also available are resins for the specific purpose of removing iron salts.

Types of Filtration Equipment. There are several types of filtration equipment. As mentioned above, powdered vegetable carbons are removed by filter presses. Liquors for decolorizing treatment by means of granular carbons are treated in the same manner as liquors for treatment by bone char.

There are two broad systems for using bone char or granular carbon; fixed beds and movable beds. Movable beds in turn fall into two classes: expanded beds and slug beds.

By far the greatest volume of liquor decolorized by bone char is handled in fixed beds. Large vertical cylindrical cisterns, usually of 1000–1200 ft³ capacity and about 20 ft in height and 10 ft in diameter, called char filters are filled with bone char, through which liquor is percolated until further decolorization is no longer considered economical. Then the remaining sugar liquor is pushed out by introducing water into the top of the filter; rodlike flow should be maintained and mixing in the filter avoided as much as possible. The remaining sugar is washed out (leached) with water, this sweet water being reclaimed until its concentration of sugar makes further recovery uneconomical. (This sweet water contains a high percentage of ash (inorganic) which has been desorbed in the process, and is undesirable for melting, etc; it it concentrated and reboiled to remelt (see Fig. 1), which is a raw-sugar type of product that goes back again through the refining process.)

After all economically reclaimable sugar has been saved, the bone char continues to be washed with wash water to the sewer, both to assure the complete removal of sugar (which would caramelize and carbonize in the char kilns) and to permit the optimum desorption of the adsorbed inorganic matter from the char. The char is then sent to the char-revivification cycle (p. 192). Normally, animal bone char in modern refineries can be used for three or more years.

Movable Beds—Slug Beds. In the conventional char filter the liquor to be decolorized is fed into the top of the filter and percolated downward through the bed. The bottom of the filter is equipped with woven blankets of cloth or metal which permit passage of the decolorized liquor in a relatively clean state.

In the movable beds, which utilize filters or cisterns of roughly similar size and configuration as the fixed-bed systems, the char (or granular carbon) enters the top of the filter at fixed intervals and in fixed amounts; the liquor to be filtered is introduced

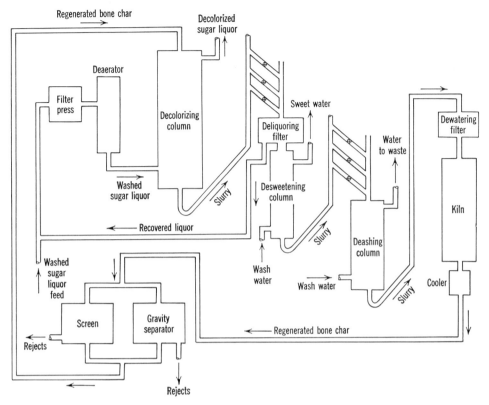

Fig. 8. Continuous adsorption process (CAP) applied to bone char.

into the bottom of the filter at a steady rate; each time fresh char is added to the top of the filter, an equivalent amount of used char is drawn from the bottom.

The char taken from the bottom of the filter is then leached free of sugar (sweetened off) and if it is bone char, washed additionally to desorb the adsorbed ash constituents. Since granular carbon adsorbs no ash, it is necessary only to free the carbon of sugar. The washed carbon or granular char is revivified in one of the systems described later.

CAP (Continuous Adsorption Process). This is a movable-bed process developed and patented by the American Sugar Company (Fig. 8). The particular feature of this unique process lies in the fact that the char bed is at all times "expanded" so that all faces of the individual char particles are exposed to the liquor. The exhausted char is removed at a uniform rate from the bottom of the filter and goes to a screening system where most of the free liquor is removed. It then goes to another similar but much smaller movable-bed system. The heavily-sugar-laden char enters at the top of the column, the washing water at the bottom. Thus, the less-sugar-laden char is met at the bottom of the column by the fresh wash water, and the sugarfree char leaves the bottom. The sugarfree char then goes to the deashing column, where the same procedure is followed, the char going into the top of the column, the water entering the bottom in the same countercurrent flow. As with the slug beds, if the decolorant is granular washing beyond the point of removal of sugar is unnecessary.

Advantages and Disadvantages of Movable-Bed Columns. The principal advantage of the movable beds is due to the fact that they are continuous, and thus have greatly reduced labor requirements. Further, the countercurrent flow pattern is said to effect better utilization of the char in the decolorization phase, and better utilization of the wash water in the deashing phase.

The principal disadvantage is that the decolorized liquor carries with it the fines from the char (or carbon) because these fines are not filtered out by the char itself as in the fixed beds. Therefore the decolorized liquor must be filtered before going to the pans, which is not necessary with fixed beds. Furthermore, only one grade of liquor can be handled on each filter, in contrast to conventional fixed-bed down-flow columns in which a liquor of lower purity can follow one of higher purity with more efficient use of char.

Removal of Exhausted Char. In fixed beds, the conventional method of removing the exhausted char, which is very wet (containing some 50% or more moisture by weight) is to open a port in the bottom of the filter. Some of the wet char runs out, but much must be raked out. Because of the expense of a modern char house, it has become increasingly essential to get as much use from each char filter as possible; hence, dead time such as this must be reduced to a minimum.

To this end, some advanced refineries remove the remaining char by hydraulic means, sluicing out the bone char by hoses and reducing the volumn of water by a combination of settling and filtering before sending the char to the driers and kilns. In this connection it should be mentioned that char filters, for both conventional char and granular carbon, can be filled as well by such hydraulic means. However, a char or carbon filter so filled must be sweetened on as well as sweetened off, with attendant increased volume of sweet water.

Char Cycle. This is a separate cycle within the char-house operation. After the char has been exhausted, it is washed as described above, then fed into hoppers from whence it goes through dryers. By the time the char reaches the dryers it contains 25% or less moisture. Some residual moisture is desirable in the char that goes to the kilns.

Bone char is revivified in two types of kilns: pipe (or retort) kilns and multiple-hearth kilns. Pipe kilns consist of a number of vertical retort tubes through which the char passes, gradually being heated in the absence of air to around 1000°F. Little or no air is allowed to enter these retorts, although in some cases a small amount is permitted to decarbonize the char, that is, to burn off the amorphous carbon formed from the organic matter in the filtration operation. A form of kiln in which the individual retorts rotate so as to continually heat all sides of the tube equally, known as the Buchanan kiln, was once in wide use in England. This type is now giving way to hearth kilns, as indeed are most of the existing retort-type kilns when replacement is required.

Another type of retort kiln is known as the Stordy, whose principle approximates the conventional pipe kiln, but with better facilities for decarbonizing the revivified char, and with better heat conservation in drying the entering wet char.

Herreshoff Char Kiln. This is a multiple-hearth vertical cylindrical kiln, in which actual revivification is accomplished in the lower hearths, where the hot gases from the heat source (gas or oil burner) enter (Fig. 9). These gases progress upward through the successive hearths, finally concluding the drying of the char as they enter the top hearth, which has been previously partly dried. By close control of the air feed, decarbonization can be accomplished to a very exact degree; the kiln lends itself excellently to automation. The char particles are moved across the successive hearths by means of rabble arms which turn slowly around a central shaft; the char particles drop

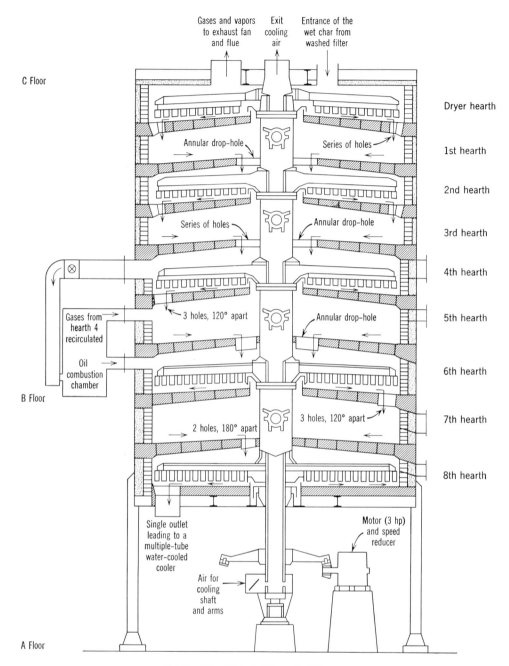

Fig. 9. The Nichols-Herreshoff furnace.

from the periphery of one hearth to the center of each successive hearth, where dropping ports are located (see Sulfuric acid). The efficiency of the kiln is very good; heat transfer and heat efficiency are excellent because some of the air from the upper hearths is returned to the combustion chamber of the burner. The principal objection to this kiln is the loss of grain by attrition; however, with ease of control, conservation of space, fuel efficiency, etc, it is very likely that it will become the principal char revivifier of the industry in time.

Revivification of Granular Carbon. The Herreshoff kiln is very well adapted to the revivification of granular carbon, and its operation for this product is much the same as for animal bone char. Because of the high carbon content of granular carbon, the excellent control of the gases of combustion makes it especially appealing for use with this product.

Granular carbon is also revivified in horizontal kilns. Close control of excess air is necessary to avoid combustion of the carbon to carbon dioxide; for this reason the exiting carbon, which is at red heat, must be immediately quenched with water. The quenched carbon–water complex is hydraulically transferred to the next filter in the cycle.

Revivification of Powdered Carbon. Revivification of powdered carbon is possible, but it is barely economical, and such carbon is usually used on a throw-away basis.

Treatment of Revivified Char. After the char has been revivified, it is sent over a Sutton, Steele, and Steele table (see Vol. 10, p. 719). This apparatus separates the char into fractions of varying densities. The heavier fractions (which may weigh up to 80 lb/ft³ or more) are discarded; these are the char grains which have adsorbed excessive inorganic material. New animal bone char has a density of less than 50 lb/ft³, sometimes as low as 40 lb/ft³, largely depending on size of grain.

Before the char is run into the filters, the fines are usually separated, either by means of air separation or screens. See Size separation.

Crystallization (38,39). The decolorized liquor, generally known as no. 1 liquor, is the starting point for the boiling sequence leading to the finished refined sugar. In those refineries where a down-flow fixed-bed system is used the liquor customarily goes directly to the pans; but in many modern refineries the liquor is "polished" by pressure filtration, with filter aids, in order to give a clear liquor free of haze, and one which will tend to result in reduced floc when the sugar is used by bottlers. Of course, when the liquor comes from upward-flow beds it contains a large amount of char fines, so that polishing by pressure filtration is mandatory.

The liquor from the char house varies in different refineries from a low of about 60° Brix to as high as 67° Brix. Preevaporation in single- or multiple-effect before going to the first boiling is desirable and is widely practiced.

Vacuum Pans (see section under Raw sugar, p. 180). The vacuum pans used in the refining industry are the same as those described above under raw-sugar production. Automation is more widely practiced than in the raw-sugar factories. The massecuites are "dried" or centrifuged in the same fashion, except that the wall of crystals is invariably washed with water to assist in removing the remaining syrup.

Following the principle of separation of impurities stated earlier, the syrups may be divided into run-offs or greens, the first discharge of syrup through the screens, and wash, the wash waters containing the syrup remaining on the crystals after the first purge, plus the small amount of sucrose dissolved from the grains. Because of the small ratio of water to sugar, the volume of sugar actually so dissolved is very small. The run-off syrup goes to the next pan in the cycle, and the wash, if significantly higher in purity, goes back to the same pan for the next similar strike.

Usually, four such strikes can be boiled, each successive one being inferior to the preceding one in color, and with a higher content of invert sugar and ash. The blending of all four together results in the commercial designation of extra fine granulated.

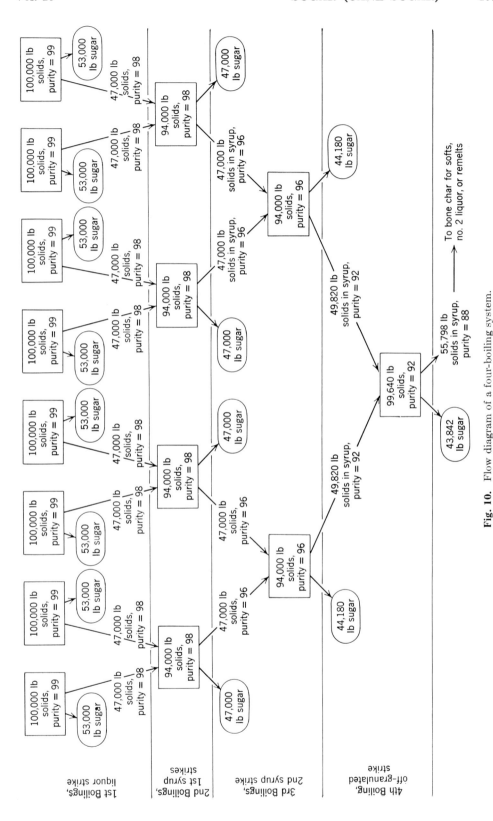

Fig. 10. Flow diagram of a four-boiling system.

Roughly, then, the final product of the normal refinery will be composed of eight parts of first sugar, four parts of second-boiled sugar, two parts of third-boiled sugar, and one part of fourth-boiled sugar (or off-granulated). In practice, each successive strike produces a smaller percentage of grain (both because of the lower purity of the mother liquor, and because more water is needed to wash off the syrup from the crystals). Where the boiling is properly done in well-automated pans, an average "yield" of 50% or more sugar in the bag on sugar solids entering the pans should be expected (see Fig. 10 and Table 2).

Table 2.   Calculation of Average Yields of Sugar Solids for Figure 10

Produced		Boiled	
lb	*lb*	*lb*	*lb*
$8 \times 53{,}000$ =	424,000	$8 \times 100{,}000$ =	800,000
$4 \times 47{,}000$ =	188,000	$4 \times\ \ 94{,}000$ =	376,000
$2 \times 44{,}180$ =	88,360	$2 \times\ \ 94{,}000$ =	188,000
$1 \times 43{,}842$ =	43,842	$1 \times\ \ 99{,}640$ =	99,640
	744,202		1,463,640

Average yield, % sugar produced on solids boiled = 50.8%

Salt (see Sodium compounds) is crystallized in continuous vacuum pans, and although there is much interest in this system in the refinery industry, only batch pans are used at present.

Centrifuging.   The white sugar massecuite emerging from the pan is usually between 90 and 95° Brix at 150–160°F, and of a purity varying from 99 for the first strike to 88 for the final strike. It is centrifuged in centrifugals similar to those described in the section on raw sugars, although a higher percentage is spun in batch than in continuous centrifugals. (Whereas with low-purity massecuites it has been claimed that one continuous centrifugal will replace three batch type, this ratio reduces as the purity of the massecuite rises.) This operation is being automated in modern factories.

The sugar "cut" (plowed) from the machines contains a small amount of moisture, eg, from 0.75 to over 2.00%, depending upon the type and condition of the centrifugal, the character of the grain, the purity of the massecuite, etc. It is conveyed to an elevator for transporation to the drying station. Various forms of conveyors are in wide use. Possibly the most popular is the scroll conveyor, although vibrating conveyors have demonstrated that they do an excellent job.

Drying Granulators (38,40). The drying apparatus by far most widely used in the world is the granulator, so called (and misnamed) because it separates the grains from one another, although the actual granulation, of course, has been done in the vacuum pans. The granulator is a cylindrical vessel, with an almost horizontal long axis, through which the wet sugar flows countercurrent to the drying air. The granulator drum contains a series of shelves with serrated edges which carry the sugar up and then allow it to be strewn down through the drum in a continuous curtain of sugar as the drum turns on its axis. Thus, each crystal is bathed in the drying air. The air is heated before entering, so that hotter air is presented to the more-nearly dry sugar and the moister, cooler air to the entering wet sugar. The sugar must be dried slowly enough to prevent the formation of a crust of dry crystals over a thin film of syrup on the sugar grains. This entrapped moisture will later cause the sugar to cake or harden.

Usually, these granulators are operated in pairs, the upper drum effecting most of the drying and the lower acting as a cooler, the air entering this drum being at ambient temperature; however, many variations of this procedure are possible. Some factories, eg, in England and Canada, do the cooling and drying in the same drum, utilizing a pattern of single-pass drums, which is effective. Then too, the sugar from one or a number of granulator sets may be combined and run through a cooler drum and subjected to chilled and dehumidified air. This drum may not effect a large drop in temperature, but it replaces the ambient air entering with the sugar with dehumidified air, reducing the tendency of the sugar to cake later.

Roto-Louvre. The Link-Belt Company produces a variation of the typical granulator known as the Roto-Louvre, which has made considerable impact on the industry; one of the largest refineries in the world, the Thames refinery of Tate and Lyle in London, uses this type exclusively.

The principal feature of the Roto-Louvre is its double shell, the inner one of which is made up of louver plates attached to full-length radial plates, tapered so that the inner shell increases in diameter from the entering end to the discharge end. The drying hot air is introduced through the louvers from between the two shells. There are no lifting trays in this granulator, the sugar sliding gently down the trays of the inner shell where it is warmed and subjected to the drying action of the air. Because of the design of the Roto-Louvre, the bed of sugar is thinnest at the entering end, where the sugar is wettest and where the least resistance is offered to the drying air.

The bed grows correspondingly thick at the discharge end, where it is cooled. The emerging sugar is dry and cooled to the desired temperature, and because it has not been subjected to the scratching action of grain against grain, has a brighter, more polished appearance.

Dryers of this type have advantages in the production of the big-grained sugars for which the appearance and sparkle of the crystal are important. "Sanding" sugars which have application in the "sanding" of candies such as gum drops, cookies, and the like, are sensitive to appearance. Tray dryers are also of value in this regard.

Tray Dryers. Tray dryers depend upon the exposure of the crystals to the drying air on a constantly changing surface on a series of beds, one above the other. The sugar is gently stirred by scrapers or rabble arms and so removed downward from one tray to the other. It is claimed that the resultant crystals are less scratched, resulting in a sparkling appearance. The wet sugar from the centrifugals can be (and usually is) partially predried in a conventional horizontal drum dryer. This type (one of which is the Büchner-Werke) has not had wide acceptance in the Western Hemisphere, but has attained favor in Europe.

Screening. Although the approximate size of the sugar crystals is generally determined in the pan, it is necessary to remove the larger and the finer fractions; the dried granulated sugar must therefore be screened. The size of the standard table granulated varies widely from country to country and even from one area to another. The separation of the various sized grains is usually accomplished by mechanical screens, although some auxiliary separation by pneumatic action is done; for example, the finer crystals are removed from the sugar by the air stream in the drying process. Such finer crystals find their way into the dessert-type products.

The coarser crystals are milled to form powdered sugar (see p. 198). The efficiency of the mills is improved in proportion to the size of the crystals fed to them. The unusable fine dust is redissolved and goes back through the process.

Dust Collecting. Obviously, the dust formed in the granulators must be reclaimed, and this is done by dust collectors, of which there are several types. These may be either wet or dry types. Wet types are on the whole more efficient, and require less space, but the resultant thin sweet waters are ideal breeding grounds for certain undesirable microorganisms, of which *Leuconostoc mesenteroides* is particularly undesirable. Very careful control of sanitation is necessary when wet-type collectors are used.

Big-Grain Sugars, Specialty Sugars, etc. There are many different sizes of granulated sugar produced by the modern refineries. These include very large grains (eg, with crystals the size of ice cream salt) known as coarse, medium, etc. Some refineries produce a grain intermediate in size between these large-grained crystals and the conventional standard fine granulated; these intermediate sizes are known as "manufacturers" and similar designations. These large-grained specialty sugars are in demand by candy manufacturers and producers of quality products who require a sugar of extremely high quality. These sugars are boiled from first-run liquor, carefully selected for the finest color.

Another product having wide demand is the small-grained variety known as dessert, berry, or fruit granulated sugar; their fine grain dissolves easily and quickly in cold beverages, and on fruit such as berries and grapefruit.

Some refineries produce other specialties, such as cube sugars and tablets (both wrapped and unwrapped) packed in small packages (1 or 2 lb) or in somewhat larger bulk (3- and 5-lb polyethylene bags). These are produced by special equipment and are quite expensive to make, so that they are priced much higher than table granulated.

Powdered Sugar. This product is a milled sugar, the grain being ground to powder by means of various kinds of mills, hammer mills for example, followed by screening in some cases, and for very, very fine sizes, by air separation. Corn starch (3% or more) is added to inhibit caking. Depending upon the degree of fineness, it may be designated as 4X, 6X, 10X, 12X, etc. The very finest are called by some trade name, such as fondant, because a commercial fondant can be made from the product by admixture with a liquid such as water without the necessity of boiling the fine grain in pans. Some of these superfine types contain other adjuncts, such as dextrose crystals, to improve their properties. See also Confectionery.

Soft Brown Sugars. Softs, which are true refined sugars that are boiled from syrups selected for certain characteristics such as flavor and color, are produced in almost all bone char refineries. Beet sugar factories, and cane refineries that do not have a decolorant with ash-adsorbing properties, find it impossible to produce such true softs, but they may produce a synthetic product made by mingling their finest dusty grain with cane syrups. Although these have the appearance of natural soft sugars, they usually lack the flavor.

The bases for the production of soft sugars in the bone char refinery are the affination syrups and the off-granulated syrups, ie, the syrup from the final boiling of white sugars. By filtration with inert filter aids, assisted by various adjuncts such as phosphates to remove the iron ion, and multiple char filtration, a liquor is produced which has low purity (about 80–88%) and light color. The sugar is boiled in pans under the highest vacuum obtainable, under conditions which produce a badly mixed grain; the resultant centrifuged product, which is not washed with water, will retain much of the mother liquor, which contains the flavor and color. The run-off from the centrifuging of softs is boiled back into subsequent strikes, since it is the principal source of flavor and color.

Softs have colors designated by numbers, the lightest being possibly as low as no. 4 or 5, the darkest no. 16, although each producer has his own trade name, such as Golden C, Canary Yellow, Light Golden Brown, Old Fashioned Brown, etc.

Packing and Storing (17). The storage of refined sugar is of the utmost importance and continues to receive the keenest study by the industry. Obviously, a product like sugar must be kept in dry bins. Ventilation is important; in order to prevent moisture pickup (or loss) the relative humidity of the air between the crystals should be close to 50%.

The problem in keeping refined sugar lies in the infinitesimally small amount of bound moisture, that is, the moisture in the crystal itself, entrapped between the various layers of sucrose laid down during the crystallization process in the pan. If the sugar is warm, and the walls of the storage bin are cold, the moisture present in the air surrounding the crystals tends to condense on the cold surface; here a partial vacuum is formed, and more moist ambient air moves to the side walls. This moisture dissolves a small part of the crystal surface, and the resultant syrup glues the crystals together, causing caking (41). At the same time the bound moisture in the crystals is slowly released, and contributes to the problem.

If the sugar is packed subsequently into small units, this action is not of great importance unless exaggerated, in which case even very small packages can become hard. With the rapidly increasing demand for bulk shipments of refined sugar, in trucks and railroad cars carrying up to 100 tons, it is vital that the sugar be cured so that it will travel well without hardening or "setting up."

Several ways of curing sugar have been developed. The simplest is to dry the sugar as well as possible, and then permit it to age for about three or four days, during which time the bound moisture will be released. Then, as the sugar is circulated, the moisture escapes.

This process can be expedited by ventilating the sugar during the aging process, by blowing air (preferably dehumidified) through it. This reduces the time necessary to cure by about half. In such case, the sugar is put into the bins relatively warm so the inherent heat can assist in the evaporation of the moisture.

Another, and possibly the best procedure, is to run the air through the sugar constantly in a countercurrent fashion. The sugar as produced from the granulators is fed into the top of a cylindrical silo, care being taken to distribute it evenly over the entire surface. Sugar is removed from the bottom at the same rate, with the same care being taken to remove it evenly across the cross section of the bin to achieve as nearly as possible rodlike flow through the bin. The (evenly distributed) drying air is blown upward through the bottom of the bin. The resultant sugar may contain as little as 0.008% moisture, and will keep and ship into the most severe climatic conditions with no danger. This system permits the curing of the sugar in the shortest possible time, maybe in as little as 24 hr.

Packing. The refined sugar is packed in containers of various sizes and materials, ranging from individual packets containing a teaspoonful to 100-lb bags. Mention has been made above of bulk trucks and rail cars, and some sugar has been shipped in bulk in barges.

The usual material for sugar packages, especially in the United States and Canada, is paper. A 100-lb bag made of three to five plies of kraft paper, with a total basis weight of betwen 170 and 250 lb (depending on distance to be shipped, amount of handling necessary, etc) is an excellent container. (Basis weight is the weight in pounds of 500 sheets of 24 in. × 36 in. paper.) It is cheap, strong, and protects the product well. The empty bags handle well in automatic filling and sewing equipment. They stack well. (To assist this quality, the outer ply is treated so that the bags do not slip one over the other easily.) A grade of extensible paper which has a degree of stretch greatly decreases the incidence of breakage.

The consumer-sized packages are also made of paper, naturally lighter in weight. Consumer goods are packed in units of 60 lb in the United States, eg, thirty 2-lb bags, twelve 5-lb bags, six 10-lb bags, etc. The enclosing "baler" is also of paper, with a basis weight of about 120 lb.

During excessively cold and wet weather the 100-lb bags and the balers making up the bundles of small bags contain a ply of polyethylene between two of the kraft paper plies, acting as a most effective moisture barrier, and protecting the sugar from absorbing moisture from the outer atmosphere. It will not, however, guarantee that the sugar will not set unless it has been properly conditioned before packing.

Some table granulated sugar is packed in cartons; this is true of small capacities, usually not over two pounds. The softs and confectioners' (powdered sugar) for household trade are packed in 1-lb cartons in waxed paper or other protective liners to prevent migration of moisture. Polyethylene bags of 2 lb, $2\frac{1}{2}$ lb, and possibly other sizes, are finding wider acceptance for these household sizes; they offer excellent protection for the product, and their transparency has advantages.

The packing department of the modern refinery offers excellent opportunities for mechanization, and the increasing cost of labor demands such. The smaller items, such as cartons, are made entirely mechanically; the liner is formed from roll stock, the flat carton stock is formed around the liner, and the adhesive applied. The sugar is weighed automatically into the carton, which is automatically sealed. Before going to the final shipping unit, the corrugated board container or case, in most instances, is automatically palletized for warehousing and/or shipping. The weights of individual cartons, and possibly the final container, are automatically check-weighed, units beyond the admissible tolerance being rejected.

Filling and closing of the 2-, 5-, and 10-lb bags, packing into the baler, and palletizing are all now done automatically. Such automation extends even to the 100-lb bags.

Shipping. Shipments of granulated sugar are made by rail, truck, and where available, by water in barges. An important innovation in this area is the growing tendency to ship in larger units, such as full pallets. Palletizing of bags, bundles, and containers is simple and economical, reducing labor demands both in the refiner's warehouse and shipping department, and in the customer's receiving station and warehouse as well. The conventional wooden pallet is in some places replaced by disposable fiberboard pallets; these, however, require special fork-truck equipment for handling.

Liquid Sugar (42)

The term liquid sugar is used for commercial products such as solutions of sucrose, and solutions containing varying percentages of invert sugar. Their compositions range from pure sucrose (at a saturation concentration of 67% solids) to "full invert," which actually contains 4–6% remaining uninverted sucrose on a solids basis. Full invert is normally marketed at 70–72% solids, although when somewhat higher storage and handling temperatures are available, it can be sold at as high as 75% solids. (Full invert at 75–77% solids and normal temperatures is sold in drums and pails as partially crystallized semisolid invert.)

An important grade of liquid sugar is "medium invert" in which 50% of the sucrose has been converted to invert. This grade is shipped at a saturation concentration of 76–78% solids. It has particular appeal to industrial customers because of its excellent keeping qualities; its high osmotic pressure inhibits bacterial growth. It will be noticed that a higher concentration is possible with mixed sucrose and invert than with either alone, and it must be remembered that invert, with its smaller molecules, gives a higher osmotic pressure, for the same concentration, than sucrose.

Such liquid products appeal to manufacturers who use sufficient quantities of sugar to warrant installation of the relatively simple and low-cost storage and handling equipment required to automate the receipt, storage, and use of the product. (Similar installations for dry granulated sugar are more elaborate and expensive.) The advantages are savings in handling costs, elimination of the melting and filtration step, improved plant cleanliness, and better process and inventory control. The manufacturer saves the costs of crystallization, drying, screening, packing, and handling of the finished package products.

A disadvantage is increased freight cost (because of the water content; hence, such sugar is usually derived from a nearby supplier). Extreme care must be taken to ensure good sanitation, and to provide proper storage and handling conditions. Special care must be taken to avoid the formation of a layer of thin-Brix solution due to condensation on the surfaces of the holding tanks, because fermentation progresses rapidly under such circumstances. This is avoided by continually removing vapors with exhaust fans, the entering air being carefully screened to eliminate air-borne spores and bacteria. Ultraviolet lamps treat the entering air, and installed in the tank top air space, give some antibacterial protection to the top surface of the liquors in the tanks.

Manufacture. Liquid sugar was first produced in about 1925. The initial process consisted of decolorization of high-grade raw cane sugar by filtration with powdered activated carbon, inversion by acidifying and heating, and evaporation.

Liquid sugars may be produced in plants specifically designed for their exclusive production, or they may be produced in the ordinary sugar refinery as part of the process.

If the refinery is to produce the liquid sugar exclusively, it may start by the usual methods of affination, melting, clarification, and decolorizing, using the processes described above. In such cases, it is necessary to recover the sucrose going to affination, and one or two remelt boilings are required, the remelt sugars returning to the process as in the case of the dry refinery. Usually, it is difficult to reduce the final syrup to acceptably low purities, and it must be sold as an intermediate product, possibly to a syrup blender.

After the decolorization process, it is necessary to reduce the inorganic content of the liquors, because in the absence of the boiling house, no purification by crystallization is accomplished and the ash must be removed by other means. This is done by ion exchange, as was described above; as part of this process further reduction of color is gained.

The liquors are then concentrated in evaporators to the desired final Brix, given a final "polish" by the use of vegetable carbons to improve the color further, and pumped into storage.

If the liquid-sugar refinery is able to purchase raws of sufficiently high purity, the steps of affination and subsequent remelt recovery may be eliminated; however, in this case, premium prices must be paid for the improved raws.

The normal refinery producing dry granulated sugar may also put part of its production into liquid sugar. It has two principal paths to follow, or a combination of the two; one is to take a part of the liquor stream from the char house, and by further decolorization and ash reduction (by means of ion-exchange resins), process the solution to the desired quality of liquid sugar. The second approach, followed by many, is to use the final boilings of granulated, plus tailings (screenings) from the dry granulated, dissolve them, concentrate to final Brix, and polish with the use of vegetable carbons to attain the desired final color. Because most of the inorganic materials have been left in the syrups after boiling and centrifugation, the ash level may be low enough to require no further deashing. Which system is used depends upon the individual refinery, the quality of the raws (and so the color of the char-filtered liquor), the efficiency of the bone char, etc.

Invert Level. There are endless combinations of sucrose and invert produced. Since the entering sugar is virtually all sucrose, some must be inverted at some part of the process. If the ion-exchange resins are operated separately, ie, individually as anions or cations, the liquor stream can be permitted to invert in its passage through the cation column, by (1) increasing its temperature, and/or (2) increasing the contact time. If little inversion is desired, and if the resins are used separately, reduction in temperature and rapid throughput will keep inversion down to a minimum.

Inversion may also be effected by treating the sucrose liquor with acid, usually hydrochloric, and controlling the degree of inversion by means of time and temperature.

After the sugar has been inverted to the desired degree, it is partially neutralized by the use of a base such as sodium hydroxide (caustic soda). The neutralization is usually brought to a pH no higher than 5.5, and ordinarily to a lower pH, between 4.5 and 5.0; a higher pH tends to allow the formation of color, and a lower pH is undesirable to many users because of detrimental effect to equipment and/or product.

The amount of the residual salt formed, eg, sodium chloride, is so low that it is undetectable in the presence of the extreme sweetness of the product.

Uses. The baking, canning, candy, fruit concentrate, flavor, pharmaceutical, confectionery, and soft drink manufacturers are the principal users of liquid sugar. Because the refiners can vary the concentration of invert, special benefits accrue to certain manufacturers; they derive the increased sweetness of invert, the improved shelf life of baked goods because of the hygroscopicity of invert, the prevention of crystallization in preserves, the improvement of smoothness of ice creams, etc.

Further, because some manufacturers desire other sweeteners in their products in addition to sucrose and the other blends of liquid sugars, in the early 1950s blends of liquid sugar and corn syrups (see Dextrose and starch syrups) became available, structured to customers' specifications. Currently, many suppliers of liquid sugar offer blends of liquid sugar and various corn syrups, as well as of liquid sugar and liquid dextrose.

Bibliography

"Sugar Manufacture" in *ECT* 1st ed., Vol. 13, pp. 203–227, by L. A. Wills, Consultant.

1. E. Artschweger and E. W. Brandes, "Sugar Cane Classification," *U.S. Department of Agriculture Handbook No. 122*, 1958.
2. N. Deerr, *History of Sugar*, Chapman and Hall, Ltd., London, 1949.
3. W. K. Aykroyd, *Story of Sugar*, Quadrangle Books, Chicago, 1967.
4. A. Van Hook, *Sugar*, Ronald Press, New York, 1947.
5. H. G. Sorensen, in V. E. Baikov, ed., *Manufacture and Refining of Raw Cane Sugar*, Elsevier Publishing Co., Amsterdam, 1967, Chap. 1.

6. G. P. Meade, *Cane Sugar Handbook*, 9th ed., John Wiley & Sons, Inc., New York, 1963.
7. F. A. Beale, Chap. 2 in reference 5.
8. Reference 5, Chap. 3.
9. Reference 6, Chaps. 7–9.
10. Reference 6, Chap. 5.
11. Reference 5, Chap. 4.
12. *A Symposium on Activated Carbon*, Technical Brochure, Atlas Chemical Industries, Inc., 1968.
13. Reference 6, Chaps. 7 and 8.
14. Reference 5, Chaps. 6 and 7.
15. A. L. Webre, Chap. 11 in reference 6.
16. A. L. Webre, Chap. 12 in reference 6.
17. Reference 5, Chap. 10.
18. Reference 6, Chap. 12.
19. E. C. Gillett, Chap. 13 in reference 6.
20. Reference 5, Chap. 11.
21. Reference 5, Chap. 12.
22. E. F. Rice, Chap. 13 in reference 5.
23. Reference 6, Chap. 14.
24. A. R. King, "Fire in Bulk Stores," *Proc. Tech. Session, Cane Sugar Refining Res., New Orleans, La., Oct. 10–11, 1966*, p. 24.
25. Reference 6, Chap. 15.
26. Reference 5, Chap. 14.
27. O. Lyle, *Technology for Sugar Refinery Workers*, Chapman and Hall, Ltd., London, 1941.
28. G. H. Jenkins, *Introduction to Cane Sugar Technology*, Elsevier Publishing Co., Amsterdam, 1966.
29. P. Honig, *Principles of Sugar Technology*, Elsevier Publishing Co., Amsterdam, 1953.
30. Reference 6, Chaps. 18ff.
31. Reference 5, Chap. 25.
32. Reference 6, Chap. 18.
33. F. M. Chapman, Chap. 19 in reference 5.
34. F. M. Chapman, Chap. 20 in reference 5.
35. V. R. Deitz and F. G. Carpenter, Chap. 19 in reference 6.
36. E. P. Barrett, J. M. Brown, and S. M. Oleck, *Ind. Eng. Chem.* **43,** 639–654 (1951).
37. V. E. Baikov, Chap. 20 in reference 5.
38. Reference 6, Chap. 20.
39. Reference 5, Chap. 22.
40. Reference 5, Chap. 23.
41. H. E. C. Powers, *Intern. Sugar J.* **58,** 246 (Sept. 1956).
42. P. X. Hoynak and G. N. Hollenback, *This Is Liquid Sugar*, 2nd ed., Refined Syrups & Sugars, Inc., Yonkers, N. Y., 1966.

H. G. GERSTNER
Colonial Sugars Company

BEET SUGAR

If one draws two lines around the globe, following approximately the north and south latitudes of 33°, the tropical and semitropical zones between them contain all of the sugar-cane growing areas of the world, and all of the cane raw-sugar mills. In the western hemisphere there are the plantations of the southeastern United States, Mexico, Central America, the West Indies, Peru, Brazil, Bolivia, and northern Argentina. In the eastern hemisphere are the plantations of Africa, except in the extreme northern and southern portions, and of India, southern China, southern Korea, southern Japan, and the East Indies.

On the other hand, if we consider the rest of the world not in the warm zone, that is, all the land north of north latitude 33° and south of south latitude 33°, we find that all the sugar-beet growing areas of the world are in the temperate to cold areas and so are all the beet-sugar factories. In the northern areas are most of the United States and Canada; Europe, with an active industry in the British Isles, Sweden, Denmark, Finland, the Netherlands, Belgium, France, Germany, Spain, Italy, Austria, Hungary, Czechoslovakia, U.S.S.R., and Turkey; northern Africa with beet industries in Algeria, Tunis, and Morocco; the near East represented by Syria, Israel, Afghanistan, and Iran; and Asia including the U.S.S.R., China, and northern Japan. In the southern hemisphere beet-growing areas are found at present only in Uruguay, Argentina, and Chile, although it would appear possible to grow sugar beets successfully in South Africa and southern Australia, from a climatic point of view (1).

Sugar beets thrive in temperate to relatively cold climates. *Beta vulgaris* is a biennial plant, accomplishing its vegetative growth in the first year, and its seed production in the second. Thus, for sugar production purposes, it is harvested at the end of the first year's growth. It may be noted that the sugar beet, var. *crassa*, is white, as opposed to the familiar red color of var. *cruenta*. Growth requires a frostfree period of five or six months, and the equivalent of an annual rainfall of about 20 in. It has been observed that the sum of the daily mean temperatures during the beet-growing period should average about 2500°C. Lack of sufficient rainfall during the growing period can be remedied by irrigation. The harvest season, normally in the fall of the year, should be dry to permit mechanical harvesting and transportation (2).

Agronomically, the sugar beet requires a soil texture intermediate between light and heavy, with a good structure and considerable humus. Sufficient lime, phosphates, nitrogen, and traces of various inorganic substances are needed. However, sugar beets are grown with profit in almost every type of soil to which remedial measures have been applied, such as enrichment with fertilizers, and the introduction of humus by planting grasses in the crop rotation. Acid soils are frequently neutralized by the addition of pond lime, a calcium-carbonate waste material from the beet-sugar factory. Fertilization is not a standardized procedure, but must be adapted to the properties and requirements of the particular soil.

Sugar beets are often profitable crops in areas where few other crops, except potatoes, can be grown successfully. Sugar beets are an excellent crop to fit into a crop-rotation scheme, as their culture tends to improve the soil. Beets are deep-rooted, and consequently bring up plant food from a considerable depth, that is thus made available to other shallow-rooted crops. Usually sugar beets cannot be planted in the same field more often than once every three or four years, since they are attractive hosts to certain nematodes, and thus must be alternated with other crops not attractive to these nematodes.

Because sugar beets are grown in temperate climates, it is possible to plant them in many of the most heavily populated areas and to manufacture the sugar relatively close to the areas of consumption. This fact, plus the relative simplicity of the process of manufacture, has resulted in production in single factories, ie, in plants where the final product is made from the raw vegetable material in a single process.

Manufacture of Beet Sugar

The manufacture of beet sugar is a seasonal operation, since factory operations are confined to the time intervals during which sugar beets are harvested, plus the additional time the beets can be sorted in piles without undue loss of sucrose. In most areas of the United States and Canada, except for California and Arizona, the harvest period

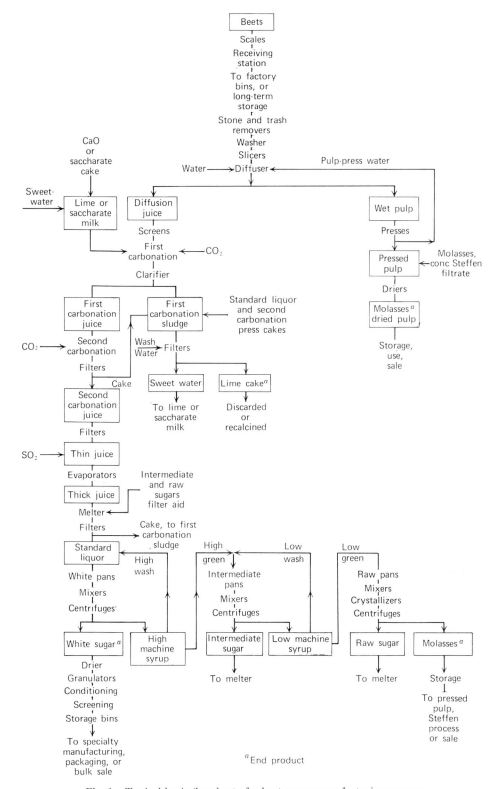

Fig. 1. Typical basic flowsheet of a beet-sugar manufacturing process.

lasts from about the first of October until the end of November, by which time the harvest must be completed to avoid the freezing of the beets in the ground. It is customary to build storage piles of beets and to continue factory operations for about two more months, resulting in campaign lengths (operating season) on the order of 120 days. In northern California, where there are separate fall and spring plantings and harvests, factory operations may total 250 days a year. In southern California and Arizona factory operations start about May 1 and continue into July. In Arizona there is an additional fall campaign for beets harvested in southeastern Arizona and western New Mexico.

In order to extend their operating seasons, a few factories are built to be specially large at the beet end, so that excess concentrated, purified thick juice (see Fig. 1) can be produced and stored in suitable tanks. The beet end includes the parts of the factory from the point of entry of the sugar beets through the extracted, purified, and concentrated thick juice, while the sugar end comprises the balance, or crystallization part of the process. At factories with facilities for storing excess thick juice, when the fresh beet supplies are used up, the sugar end continues operations, crystallizing sugar from the supplies of stored thick juice.

Sugar Beet Supplies (3). Growers are paid for their beets by procedures which involve a degree of profit-sharing, being partly based on what is termed the net selling price of the sugar. This is, in essence, the wholesale price of sugar minus sales expenses. In many cases, also, the minimum payment per ton the grower receives for his beets is keyed to the price of raw cane sugar at the nearest point of entry. Sliding scales of payments are used, varying in details, so that proportionally more money is paid for beets which contain higher percentages of sugar. In most areas each grower is paid according to the results of sugar and tare analyses of samples of the beets he has delivered. The tare material consists of dirt, stones, weeds, beet tops, and the low-purity beet crowns that are found in the loads of delivered beets. In decreasingly fewer areas growers are paid for the campaign-average sugar percentage of all the beets sliced, the individual grower's payments being corrected to the weight of beets he delivered, minus the weights of tare materials. The laboratories in which samples of beets are analyzed for grower payment purposes are known as tare laboratories (4). Individual tare laboratories are capable of processing from 500 to 5000 samples in an 8-hr period. These laboratories are rapidly being automated, as, at best, their operation is expensive.

Growers deliver their truck loads of beets to beet-receiving stations located either at the factory, or at convenient rail-side locations in the harvesting areas (5). At the latter, the beets are transferred to railcars or transport trucks for shipment to the factory site. On arrival at a receiving station the loaded truck is weighed and its beets are discharged into a hopper, from which they are moved to screens which remove most of the dirt, rocks, and trash. Leaving the screens, the stream of beets is sampled by insertion of a sampling pan. The tare material removed by the screens is weighed, and the empty truck is weighed out of the station, or, in some cases, the tare material may be returned to and weighed with the empty truck. The original gross weight of the truck, less the weights of tare and empty truck, is the *first net weight*. At the tare laboratory the sample is weighed in, the beets are either washed and dried in hot air, or brushed free of dirt, the low-purity beet-crown material is trimmed off in accordance with agreed-on procedures, and all leaves, petioles, and trash are removed. The cleaned and trimmed beets are weighed, and the percentage of the original sample weight is calculated. The first net weight, multiplied by this percentage, gives the *second net weight* of beets delivered and, after further multiplication by the percentage of sucrose, yields the weight of sucrose on which the grower's payment is based.

Sugar-Beet Composition (6). Sugar beets consist of about 92% juice, which is a solution of sugar and nonsugars, about 5% insoluble matter, called *marc*, and about 3% of bound water. The percentage of soluble solids in the beets may vary from 11 to 25%. The purity (percentage of solids which is sucrose) of the juice may be about 87.5%. Thus the percentage of sucrose in the whole beet may vary from 10 to 22%. The estimates of nonsugars given in the following paragraph are typical of certain beets.

The nonsugar solubles in the juice contain about 44% organic–nitrogen substances, about 36% nitrogenfree organics, and about 20% inorganic compounds. Of the nitrogenous compounds, about 58% is protein which is removed by the factory process. Of the other nitrogen compounds betaine constitutes 40%, which carries through to the molasses, and the remainder are amino acids and purines, and amides and ammonium salts; the latter cause difficulties in processing. The nitrogenfree organic substances other than sucrose are about half organic acids, and the balance consists of varying amounts of other carbohydrates, including raffinose and invert sugar, and small amounts of fats and saponin. The major acid is oxalic, which is eliminated as the insoluble calcium oxalate in the purification stage. Most of the other organic acids have soluble lime salts, and are not eliminated in the process. The invert sugar is almost completely destroyed in liming. Purification removes 95% of the saponin, which is a glycoside chiefly composed of oleanolic and glucuronic acids. A small portion of the balance is frequently found as a trace impurity in the product sugar. Of the soluble inorganic salts, the major cations are potassium, calcium, magnesium, and sodium. The major anions are phosphate, sulfate, and chloride. There are traces of iron, silicon, and aluminum. Phosphates are eliminated in purification, while most of the other inorganics pass through to the molasses.

The beet marc consists of the individual cell membranes, of which cellulose makes up about 24%, hemicellulose 22%, and pectic substances about 48%. The cell walls also contain small amounts of protein and inorganic matter.

Beet Preparation for Diffusion (7). Since sugar beets have about the same specific gravity as water, it is convenient to move them from factory bin or slab storage to the factory in water flumes. Located in these flumes are rock and stone removers, vegetation-trash catchers, and beet washers. At the factory the beets are elevated to a higher point by a conveyor belt, elevator, or "beet pump," where they are deposited in supply hoppers over the beet-slicing mechanisms. In the United States horizontal-axis, rotating-drum slicers are normally used. Serrated knives are set in the periphery of the drum and the beets, entering the interior of the drum, are sliced into *cossettes*, which are long thin strips, of either V-shaped or square cross section. Typical cossettes may be 2 or 3 mm thick, and up to 15 cm long.

Diffusion (8). A typical flow diagram of a beet-factory process is shown in Figure 1. The sugar is extracted from the cossettes in the diffuser. Batch diffusers or batteries, once universally used, have now nearly disappeared. The most commonly emplayed continuous diffuser is the DdS slope diffuser, illustrated in Figures 2a and 2b, which is essentially a covered, sloping trough, from 13 to 24 ft wide, and from 52 to 63 ft long, depending on the designed capacity, up which the cossettes are carried by perforated scroll flights. Hot water enters at the upper end, flowing down countercurrent

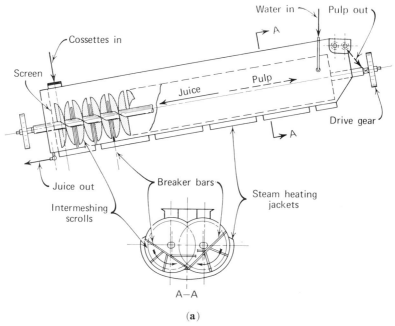

(a)

(b)

Fig. 2. (a) Flow diagram and (b) side view of a DdS slope diffuser.

to the direction of cossette movement, and leaving the lower end of the diffuser as *diffusion juice* or *raw juice*. The diffuser is equipped with steam jackets for heating.

The sugar in the sugar beet is contained within the parenchyma cells, shown in Figure 3, which are the most common type of cells in vegetable tissue. The parenchyma cells are enclosed by cell walls, made of about equal quantities of celluloses and protopectin. The interior of the cell, or *vacuole*, holds the cell sap, a water solution usually containing about 17.5% sucrose and 2.5% nonsucrose. The walls of the mature cell vacuole are lined with protoplasm composed of proteins, chiefly albumins. On heating

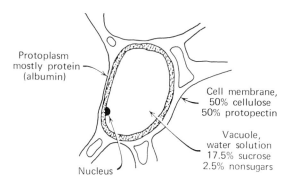

Protoplasm
mostly protein
(albumin)

Cell membrane,
50% cellulose
50% protopectin

Vacuole,
water solution
17.5% sucrose
2.5% nonsugars

Nucleus

Fig. 3. Mature beet-parenchyma cell.

to a sufficiently high temperature (60°C), the protoplasm is clotted or slowly coagulated. On heating to 70–80°C, the clotted protoplasm forms a stringy network, through which diffusion of dissolved molecules can take place. Small molecules presumably pass through most readily, followed by sucrose, and later the large alkaline earth complexes and colloids. Extraction rates are actually slightly different, as shown in Table 1.

Table 1. Rates of Extraction of Various Substances in Killed Beet Tissue (8a)

	Extraction, %		Extraction, %
sucrose	98	total ash	70
"harmful" nitrogen[a]	95	magnesium	60
chloride	90	sodium	60
potassium	80	total nitrogen	57
phosphate	75	proteins	30
sulfate	70	calcium	10

[a] Mostly amides.

The unexpectedly low extraction of the small sodium and potassium ions is due to the electrostatic retarding effect of the high-molecular-weight polymeric anions. The low calcium extraction is due to its presence in insoluble salts.

With the countercurrent flow of leaching water, at any point in the diffuser the concentration of sucrose is lower in the liquid outside the cossettes than it is in the liquid within the beet cells, thus providing the necessary gradient for sucrose extraction. From the point of maximum temperature at the lower end, to the elevated end of the diffuser, the temperatures are gradually lowered, with the diffuser supply water entering at the top at about 60°C. The temperature pattern adopted is set relatively high as the cossettes enter the diffuser, mainly to kill the beet cells so that diffusion of sugar into the surrounding liquid phase can start. The high temperature kills also most of the soil microorganisms entering with the cossettes. The temperature at the cossette inlet end of the diffuser may range from 75 to 80°C and ideally the balance of the diffuser is held within 70–73°C, dropping off at the top end to the temperature of the battery supply water. If the temperature pattern of the diffuser is too high, or if the diffuser supply water is too alkaline, peptic substances within the beet cells are extracted, causing difficulties later in the processing of the juice, and in pressing the water from the exhausted cossettes or *pulp*. On the other hand, if the temperature pattern is too low, microbial or enzymatic inversion of sucrose and fermentations by lactic acid-producing and other microorganisms are increased, with resulting serious losses of sucrose. Thus a compromise median-temperature pattern is used, usually with resort to periodic addition of chemical sterilizing agents to limit microbial action. Formaldehyde is often employed for this purpose, being prepared at the time of use by hydrolysis of paraformaldehyde, with the aid of steam and caustic soda. In a typical single addition, 15 lb of hydrolyzed paraformaldehyde is added in "shots" to the part of the diffuser where the infection appears to be centered. Continuous addition is not effective, as the microorganisms acquire a tolerance. The formaldehyde is completely destroyed in liming and carbonation (8b). The enriched diffusion juice leaving the lower end of the diffuser is screened to remove small pieces of cossettes, and at that point may contain about 14.5% of total solids, which, with a sucrose content of 12%, have a purity of about 83%.

Dried Pulp (9). The pulp leaving the diffuser with a water content of about 95% is pressed in screw-type presses until it contains from 75 to 80% moisture. The water pressed out of the pulp, which still contains some sucrose, is returned to the diffuser at a point somewhat below the elevated end, usually after heat sterilization. The pressed pulp is enriched by the addition of molasses or concentrated Steffen filtrate (see under Steffen process) or both, to a maximum of about 35% on the final dried product. This enriched pulp is dried in rotary dryers, fired by natural gas or fuel oil, and is cooled and stored for sale or use with a final moisture content of 6–10%. The once common practice of storing and selling wet pulp is no longer followed, the fermentation odors being disagreeable to the community, and the losses of solids in storage expensive. Molasses–dried-beet-pulp is an excellent cattle food (see Vol. 8, p. 867) and its sale contributes appreciably to the profits of the factory. Dried pulp produced amounts to 6–8% of the weight of beets sliced, curiously enough increasing as the percentage of sugar in the beets increases.

Purification with Lime and Carbon Dioxide (10). The method of purifying the extracted sugar juice used in the beet-sugar factory, while similar in principle to that used in the raw-cane-sugar mill, differs considerably in detail. This difference depends primarily on the differing amounts of invert sugar in the juices of the sugar-cane stalk and the beet root. In cane juice the percentage of present invert on a sucrose basis is about 5–10%, while in the healthy sugar beet it is less than 1%. Enough invert sugar is present in the cane-sugar juice to make its destruction uneconomical. Its destruction in large amounts would result in the formation of color bodies that would be expensive to remove, and would reduce the invert content of the final blackstrap molasses. Thus the lime used in cane processing is only about 10% of that in beet processing. In a beet-sugar factory only about 8% calcium oxide based on sucrose is added in a *straight house* (a factory not using the Steffen process for desugaring molasses, see p. 216) and about 13% in a *Steffen house*. In a raw-cane mill this amount is about 1% based on sucrose. Throughout the cane mill and the cane refinery the pH values of the process juices must be kept near or slightly on the acid side of neutrality to avoid the destruction of invert sugar. In a beet-sugar factory, the small amount of invert present is destroyed by massive liming, the coloring matter being adsorbed on the surfaces of the fine calcium carbonate crystals formed in first carbonation. The end molasses contains about 50% total sugars in both beet and cane processing, but in cane blackstrap as much as one-third of the total sugar may be invert, whereas in beet discard molasses the invert content seldom exceeds 4% of the total sugars.

Chemistry of the Process. All American beet-sugar factories use lime and carbon dioxide for juice purification. The effectiveness of this process is due to reactions of two different types: those involving direct action of the lime with impurities, and those involving the special adsorptive properties of the calcium carbonate precipitate formed after carbonation.

The reactions with lime, in turn, comprise those leading to the formation of precipitates, and those leading to the formation of soluble products. Of the nonsugars removed by precipitation, 60–70% are acids having insoluble calcium salts. Oxalates are almost completely removed. Other acid anions substantially removed are hydroxycitric, citric, tartaric, phosphoric, and some sulfuric. The other 30–40% of nonsugars are removed through coagulation by calcium or hydroxyl ions. The substances coagulated are proteins, saponins, and various vegetable coloring matters. In addition, the small amounts of iron, aluminum, and magnesium are precipitated in the alkaline medium as the hydroxides.

The reactions leading to soluble products are mostly caused by the hydroxyl ions introduced with the lime. Any free acids are neutralized. Ammonium salts evolve ammonia gas. Asparagine and glutamine are converted to the respective amides, which are hydrolyzed also with evolution of ammonia, and, as undesirable by-products, calcium salts accumulate in the juices. Allantoin decomposes slowly in several steps; ammonia, carbon dioxide, calcium glycolate, and a precipitate of calcium oxalate are the end products. Oxamic acid also decomposes rather slowly, similarly yielding free ammonia and solid calcium oxalate. Likewise, as a result of action in the hot, alkaline medium, the invert sugars dextrose and levulose are decomposed in a complex fashion, resulting in yellowing or browning of the juices, with formation of acids or their salts, such as brown glucinic ($C_{12}H_{22}O_{11}$?), reddish apoglucinic ($C_9H_{10}O_5$?), brownish saccharummic ($C_{14}H_{18}O_{11}$?), brown molassic ($C_6H_6O_3$), and various, dark-colored, so-called humic acids, of which a typical formula is $C_{60}H_{52}O_{24}(COOH)_4$; formic, acetic, lactic, and carbonic acids may also be present. The small amount of fats extracted from the beets is saponified, leaving glycerine in solution, and precipitating the calcium salts of fatty acids. Pectin precipitates as calcium pectinate, but this further decomposes in the alkaline solution to methyl alcohol and pectic acid. The latter forms a gelatinous precipitate of calcium pectate, a substance which causes difficulties in the filtration of the juice later.

On passing carbon dioxide through the limed mixture, either simultaneously with, or after, liming, calcium carbonate is precipitated. The second phase of the purification is the adsorption of nonsugar materials, particularly colloids, on the surface of the calcium carbonate crystals. Thus physical conditions in carbonation are adjusted to favor the production of a precipitate with a high surface area, which involves high pH (about 10.2) and high supersaturation of calcium carbonate. In practice the calcium carbonate precipitate formed in first carbonation has a very large total surface area, and adsorption on this positively charged surface is the essence of the purification taking place in carbonation. The nonsugars adsorbed are negatively charged colloids, such as gums, calcium salts of various inorganic and organic compounds, including especially amino acids, and the colored products which resulted from the decomposition of the invert sugar.

The fine calcium carbonate crystals, with their adsorbed impurities, tend to cluster around bits of coagulated organic matter, which are so large in size that they settle readily in tray clarifiers, and can be removed satisfactorily from the under-

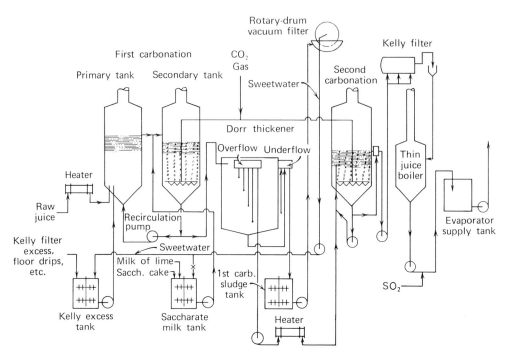

Fig. 4. Dorr-system continuous first and second carbonation.

flow by vacuum filters. The clear overflow from the tray clarifier is again carbonated in second carbonation, which is strictly a deliming operation, conducted to the vicinity of 9 pH. The calcium carbonate crystals thus formed are relatively coarse, and are easily removed in leaf-type pressure filters. Occasionally small amounts of milk of lime are added to second carbonation. This addition may act as a safety factor, partially rectifying errors in purification resulting from faulty first carbonation. Figure 4 shows a flowsheet of first and second carbonation of a typical Dorr-system, a process which is used by a majority of American beet-sugar factories.

Modifications of Liming and Carbonation. A very large number of alternate liming and carbonation procedures have been proposed, and many are being used. The most common alternate, which has been adopted in some modification by most European factories and by some American factories, involves *predefecation* or *preliming*, and *main liming* in advance of carbonation. By gradually adding to the diffusion juice about a tenth of the total lime to be used, over a period of approx 20 min, many nitrogenous substances are precipitated at their isoelectric points, and are not later redispersed on main liming. This predefecation sludge is slimy and is not easily removed. In order to give it a more granular character, some sludge from the first carbonation clarifier may be returned and mixed with the predefecation mixture, or other special measures may be taken.

In separate main liming the remainder and largest part of the lime is added all at once after predefecation, and the mixture is given a 10- or 20-min detention to allow completion of precipitation and destruction reactions. Since lime is more soluble in cold than in hot juice, a "vigorous" defecation involves the addition of the lime to cold juice, followed by heating to about 80°C. In a "mild" defecation the lime is added to hot juice. In the Dorr-system defecation, which is very mild, the hot juice is simultaneously limed and carbonated with the aid of 700% recirculation, and high alkalinities are avoided. Mild defecation has the advantage that the first carbonation sludge is less gummy, and is easier to separate, and the sugar is easily removed by washing in the filters. However, it has the disadvantage that defecation is not as complete, and in particular the destruction reactions are not complete, so that the resultant thin juice may be thermolabile, and may increase in color excessively while in the concentration and crystallization stages.

Alternative Purification Methods. The most promising alternatives or supplements to liming and carbonation use activated carbon (11), or ion-exchange resins. For many decades it has been the practice in some beet-sugar factories to supplement normal defecation with the use of powdered, activated carbon of vegetable origin, to assist in the removal of colloidal substances, in amounts of ca 0.5 lb per ton of beets sliced. A common method has been to add the carbon to the thick juice after the evaporators, and to remove it in the standard liquor filters. The filter cake might then be reslurried in clear first-carbonation juice, being finally removed in the second-carbonation filtration. With the development of efficient granular carbons, such as those made from bituminous coal with suitable binders, the exhausted carbon can be regenerated in kilns, making it possible to use the carbon much more economically. Using Herreshoff-type kilns (see under Sulfuric acid), total carbon losses are 3–6% per cycle. Common dosages are on the order of 4.5 lb per ton of beets, or 1.5 lb per 100-lb bag of sugar manufactured. Activated carbons remove coloring matter and other troublesome colloidal impurities, particularly traces of saponins, which may be present in the final sugar product to the extent of several ppm. Here they may be the cause of unsightly flocs in acidified carbonated beverages.

Many attempts have been made to use ion-exchange resins (12) in the beet-sugar industry. Some use has been found for deliming resins, which lower the lime-salts contents of the thin juice. These cation-exchange resins are used in the sodium-ion form, and are regenerated with salt. High-lime salts in the thin juices cause scaling of the evaporator heating surfaces, may lead to turbidity in water solutions of the final product, and may increase the amount of molasses formed.

Some successful use has also been made in the United States of the European Quentin process, in which the intermediate machine syrup is treated with cation-exchange resin in the magnesium form, replacing potassium and sodium ions with magnesium ions. Magnesium salts are far less *melassigenic* (molasses-forming) than sodium or potassium salts, and a lowering of the purity of the final molasses (which, of course, is desirable) of as much as 3 or 4 percentage points can be accomplished. The economic viability of this process is dependent on the availability of a cheap source of magnesium brine, with which the resin is regenerated. Ion-exchange treatment supplementing the purification by liming and carbonation had extended trials some years ago in at least three factories, without economic success. Primary problems are the costs of the regenerating chemicals, loss of sugar, increased fuel costs due to water dilution, and waste disposal. As of early 1969, one large experimental installation is in use in which ion exchange supplements lime and carbon dioxide defecation by a mixture of thin juice and intermediate machine syrup.

Sulfitation (13). A small quantity of sulfur dioxide (usually from burning elemental sulfur) is added to the thin juice. The sulfur may sometimes be supplied from purchased liquid sulfur dioxide. This is not for the purpose of bleaching the juice, but to catalytically inhibit the *Maillard* or *browning* reaction between reducing sugars and amino acids. The browning reaction is the chief cause of increased coloration of the process juices during evaporation and crystallization. Only about 25 ppm of sulfur dioxide in the thin juice is required for this purpose, although usual dosages are between 100 and 200 ppm, since sulfur dioxide is gradually oxidized to sulfate as it passes through the sugar end. Occasionally additional small amounts of sulfur dioxide are added to the thick juice to maintain a concentration of at least 25 ppm in the pan boiling. After sulfitation the thin juice is sent to the evaporators, sometimes with an intervening filtration.

Evaporation and Heat Economy (14). For maximum fuel economy in the beet-sugar factory, four general principles are followed as completely as possible: (1) all high-pressure steam from the boilers is expanded to exhaust-steam pressure through turbines driving electric generators and engines; (2) all exhaust steam is used in the first effect of the evaporator; (3) all possible evaporation is done in the evaporator to reduce the load on the vacuum pans; and (4) for all factory heating, such as vacuum pans, heaters, and melters, vapors are used from one of the evaporator effects at the lowest possible pressure. It is customary to heat the beet-end juices gradually, using portions of the latter-effect vapors to start, and finishing with first effect vapors. Thus in the case of a quintuple-effect evaporator, diffusion juice may be heated with fourth vapor and then third vapor; juice after carbonation may be heated with second vapor, and then juice on its way to the evaporator first effect with second vapor and then with first vapor. Similar arrangements are made for heating in the sugar end. The use of portions of the vapors for other purposes than heating the next effect achieves excellent heat economy and requires adjustment of the amount of heating surface for the individual effects, the heating surface areas decreasing from the first to the last effect. Table 2 illustrates the use of heat from a five-effect evaporator, with four Kestner, long-tube, single-pass effects, and a fifth calandria effect which normally has little function, but may be used when other bodies are temporarily out of service for descaling or other maintenance. See Evaporation.

Crystallization (15). Two remelt sugars are dissolved in the thick juice from the evaporators (see Fig. 1), filter aid is added—usually diatomaceous earth—and a tight filtration follows. The filtered liquor, or *standard liquor*, provides the feed material for the vacuum-pan boiling of the first product. Pan boiling is very similar to the same unit process in the cane refinery, excepting that the beet materials have somewhat different crystallizing characteristics (see also under Cane sugar).

Sufficient feed liquor is taken into the vacuum pan to permit its concentration to a critical supersaturation of sucrose, where it still covers the heating element, and where

Table 2. Distribution of Steam between Evaporator and Process Heating

Vapor	To next effect for evaporation, %	For process heating, %	Pressure, psig
exhaust steam	100		40
first	73	27	30
second	33	67	17
third	5	95	5
fourth	0	100	8^a

NOTE: In a typical run, thin juice entering the evaporator at 13.5% dry substance may emerge from the last effect at about 64%.

[a] Inches Hg abs.

crystal nucleation may be induced by adding a small amount of powdered sugar. In this case, when sufficient crystals have been formed, the supersaturation is dropped to the point where spontaneous nucleation will not further occur. Alternatively, the charge of feed liquor may be concentrated to a supersaturation suitable for growing crystals, and a carefully measured and prepared mass of seed crystals is added, so that when the crystals are fully grown there are the same number of final crystals as there were seed crystals added. Following either starting procedure, the crystals are grown to full size with additions of feed liquor. The content of a vacuum pan is known as a *strike*. This *fillmass, massecuite,* or *magma* (all terms are in use) consists of a mass of crystals and of mother liquor, and is discharged into mixer tanks for temporary storage to supply the centrifugals. In the centrifugals the sugar is spun free of syrup, and is then washed briefly with hot water. This sugar, after drying and screening, is the final product, white granulated sugar.

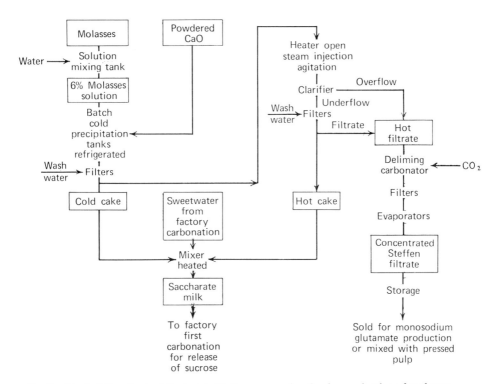

Fig. 5. Typical flowsheet of the batch Steffen process for the desugarization of molasses.

The syrup spun off is known as *green syrup* (although it is brown, not green, in color), and provides the vacuum-pan feed for the second, or *intermediate* boiling. The wash syrup is returned to the *white* or first-boiling feed. The centrifuging of the intermediate fillmass provides intermediate sugar, which becomes a part of the standard liquor. The green syrup from the intermediate boiling (*low machine syrup*) provides the feed supply for the third, or raw boiling. The intermediate wash syrup is recycled to the intermediate pan feed supply. The fillmass from the low raw boiling is held from 16 to 74 hr in crystallizers where the temperature is gradually lowered, allowing time for the slow rates of crystallization in this low-purity material to crystallize out all the sugar possible. The sugar from the low raw boiling becomes a part of the standard liquor, while all of the syrup spun from the sugar is called *molasses*.

Desugaring Molasses with the Steffen Process (16). Many factories in the United States are using the Steffen process for desugaring molasses. The Steffen process, illustrated in the flowsheet of Figure 5, is a highly empirical one. Its mechanism is not well understood, and it is not even known for certain if the calcium saccharate precipitates formed by the process are colloidal micelles of variable composition, or are true compounds. It seems probable that the precipitates may contain compounds or aggregates of the general formula $(C_{12}H_{22}O_{11}.3CaO)_n$. In the Steffen process about 95% of the sugar in the molasses is recovered. Normal molasses, containing about 50% sucrose, is diluted with water to about 6% sucrose, and cooled to about 6°C, or in any case, well below 18°C. A little more than 100% lime on sugar (weight for weight) is added. In this process two competing reactions, ie, the slaking of the quicklime and the formation of the calcium saccharate, both occur. Therefore at first only about one-fifth of the lime is added as milk of lime, presumably to repress the slaking reaction and to favor the calcium saccharate formation. The latter is known to be a function of the physical surface area of the quicklime particles. The balance of the lime is then added as a finely powdered quicklime, and very quickly mixed with the cold, limed molasses solution. After formation of the saccharate precipitate, the cold saccharate cake is removed in rotary vacuum filters and the cold filtrate is heated by steam injection, resulting in the precipitation of more saccharates. The mixture is thickened in a small clarifier and the underflow is filtered in rotary vacuum filters to remove the *hot saccharate cake*. The final, hot filtrate may be carbonated to reduce the lime content, filtered, and concentrated to about 60% solids. In this form it is added to the pressed pulp before drying, or it may be used for monosodium glutamate production (see Vol. 2). At some factories the *hot Steffen filtrate* is sewered to waste. The cold and hot saccharate cakes are slurried in sweet water, to form the *saccharate milk*, which serves as the liming agent for carbonation. On carbonation these saccharates are decomposed, yielding free sucrose and calcium hydroxide, which latter is then converted to calcium carbonate.

The trisaccharide, raffinose, is present in sugar beets in appreciable quantities (in greater amount in beets which have been subjected to cold temperatures, either in the ground or in piled storage). Calcium raffinates are precipitated along with the saccharates in the Steffen process and the raffinose is freed in first carbonation. In the factory it appears in the molasses to be sent again to the Steffen process. Thus raffinose tends to build up in the Steffen factory. Since its specific rotation at 20°C is +105.2°, considerably greater than that of sucrose (+65.5°), its presence leads to appreciable errors in the polarization analysis for sucrose. In addition, large amounts of raffinose influence the sucrose crystals to assume needlelike shapes to such an extent that 100 lb of sugar may no longer fit in a normal 100-lb bag. Thus, because of the buildup of raffinose and some other impurities, molasses is discarded in Steffen factories, for a 24-hr period every week or so. Sometimes a small amount of molasses may be discarded all the time. This *discard molasses* is either put on the pressed pulp, or is sold for yeast production or other purposes. It has a somewhat higher content of nitrogenous substances than cane blackstrap molasses.

The Barium Process (17). At Johnstown, Colo., an installation exists for treating discard molasses for further sugar recovery with the aid of barium hydroxide. This process has the advantage that it does not precipitate as much raffinose as does calcium hydroxide, and the disadvantage that the barium saccharates are not as insoluble as the calcium saccharates, when economically practical amounts of barium reagent are used. Thus the barium saccharates are of higher purity, but the sucrose recovery is not as complete.

The barium saccharate process is made economically possible by recovery of the barium used as barium carbonate, and by recycling this through the presses to produce barium hydrate. The specific process used followed the discovery that if a mixture of barium carbonate and silica, in the ratio of $3:1$, is heated in a kiln, the carbon dioxide is driven off and a clinker is obtained from which two thirds of the barium oxide may be leached with water. The leached residue of $BaO.SiO_2$ is rekilned with 2 moles of $BaCO_3$ to produce the same clinker as before. In factory practice operations are started with witherite (barium carbonate) and sand, fed to a rotary kiln. The clinker from the kiln goes to a ball mill slurried with water and the effluent from the ball mill proceeds to a series of five Dorr thickeners in which a countercurrent flow of sludge and overflow is maintained. The overflow from the first Dorr thickener, on cooling, yields crystals of barium hydrate, which are filtered off, and the filtrate and wash are again run to the ball mill with fresh clinker. The sludge leaving the final thickener is mixed with barium carbonate returned from the sugar factory, sufficient barium sulfate is added to make up losses, and the mixture is filtered on a rotary drum filter. The filter cake is used as the feed to the rotary kiln. The molasses is diluted, the barium hydroxide is added, and the saccharate is filtered off, slurried, and carbonated to liberate the sucrose. Filtration of the resulting solution, which now carries barium carbonate in suspension, furnishes a sugar solution of about 95% purity, from which white sugar is obtained by processing it similarly to the refining of raw cane sugar, including treatment with bone-black or granular vegetable carbon. The barium carbonate cake is regenerated or re-converted to the hydroxide by calcining with silica and leaching out as already described.

Final Granulated Product (18). The granulated sugar produced in beet-sugar factories is dried, screened, and bagged or stored in bulk for later packaging or bulk sale, or for manufacture into secondary products, such as liquid and powdered sugars. There is more use of large-scale storage of bulk sugar in the beet then in the cane industry, due to the seasonal production. (Raw cane sugar production is also seasonal but the refinery is able to operate continuously by storing raw sugar.) Bulk-storage capacities as high as 75 million lb of sugar are not uncommon at individual factories.

Quickly dried granulated sugar frequently requires additional aeration, or storage with occasional movement, to permit the escape of traces of moisture. If this is not done, there is a tendency for the sugar to cake in bags or in bulk storage from the exuding and drying off of these traces. Thus, it is common to pass warm or dried air through freshly manufactured sugar, or to recirculate the sugar between two bins.

Beet-sugar processing equipment, such as filters, vacuum pans, centrifuges, granulators, dryers, and screens, is similar to that found in cane refineries. Beet-sugar products as manufactured in the United States are, for all practical purposes, identical with refined cane sugar products. In the past, a rather widespread prejudice against beet sugar was caused by the fact that in the earlier days of the beet-sugar industry much of the product turned out was not properly processed. This has not been true since the introduction of the three-boiling system in the early 1930s with two remelt sugars, instead of two-boiling system previously used with only one remelt sugar.

In Europe it was formerly the custom to manufacture a raw beet sugar in factories near the beet fields, and then to send the raw sugar to refineries for processing into white sugar. This practice still persists in some localities. Also, cane refineries in England and on the European continent process considerable quantities of beet raw sugar, sometimes actually mixed with raw cane sugar.

Control

Control of Yields and Losses (19). The sugar industry led the chemical industry in its early development of the control and accounting of factory yields and losses of product. Sucrose is a relatively fragile material when in solution. Its ready inversion to dextrose and levulose under the influence of frequently encountered catalysts, its fermentation by many microorganisms whenever the conditions are favorable for their growth, and its caramelization at only moderately high temperature, make rigid chemical accounting a necessity to avoid insidious and expensive losses.

A description has already been given of the procedures for the measurement of the sugar content of the sugar beets delivered by the farmer to determine how much he should be paid (see p. 206). This determination of the sugar in the beets purchased is the first of five relatively accurate measures of sugar content throughout the manufacturing process, around which the factory *statement of yields and losses* is constructed: (*1*) sugar in beets as purchased, entering preprocessing storage; (*2*) sugar in beets sliced, entering factory; (*3*) sugar in molasses worked in Steffen process (if any); (*4*) sugar in molasses produced; (*5*) granulated sugar produced.

Sugar in Sliced Beets. This is determined by weighing all the beet cossettes, usually in continuously integrating moving-belt scales, or in batch scales. Representative samples of cossettes are taken at ca hourly intervals and immediately analyzed for their sugar content. The product of the weight of the cossettes and their percent sugar content gives the weight of sugar entering the factory in this form.

Sugar in Molasses. In measuring molasses produced, analysis for sugar is made of representative samples. The weight of molasses is found either with the use of batch scales, or the amount may be estimated approximately through the use of volume flowmeters, or by setting up a material balance, including the amounts of molasses in storage tanks as determined manometrically, the amounts added to the pulp to be dried, and the amounts sold.

The molasses worked in the Steffen process are usually weighed into the process in scales, or measured with volumetric tanks accompanied by suitable sample analysis.

Granulated Sugar Produced. The granulated sugar is accurately weighed out of the factory in bucket scales, in which each load of about 500 lb is determined to within 0.5%, and the sum of many weighings is accurate to the next decimal.

Yields and Losses Statements. These statements are made up for time intervals of one day to one month, depending on individual company practice. Losses of sugar in the beets between the time of purchase and the time of slicing are known as the *outside-factory losses*. A part of these losses is from metabolic changes in the beets while in transit to the factory, or while in the factory bins awaiting immediate processing, or in long-term storage in piles. There are also direct physical losses of beet tails or broken pieces of beets, and there are some losses from leaching out of sucrose while in the water flumes. Outside-factory losses may involve 1–5% of the sugar purchased, depending on circumstances. The total outside loss, or *shrink*, is found by the difference between the sugar in beets purchased and beets sliced.

Inside-factory losses are found in total by subtracting the weight of granulated sugar produced from the amount of sugar in the beets sliced, with correction for sugar in molasses worked, if any. An effort is made to account for all losses. The readily accountable losses include the sugar in molasses (which is a gain if more molasses is worked than produced), in the exhausted beet pulp, in the lime flume, in the Steffen hot filtrate, and in the factory waste waters. Often estimates are also made of inversion in the sugar end of the factory based on the amount of invert in the molasses produced, and of fermentation in the diffuser through measures of the increases of lactic acid and invert contents from the cossettes to the diffusion juice. The difference between the total inside-factory losses and the total accounted losses is the *unaccounted loss*. With good operations, the sugar loss in molasses produced varies between 16 and 18% of the sugar in the cossettes. The total of the other accounted losses varies between 2 and 5%, and the unaccounted losses are usually 1.5–3.0% of the sugar in the cossettes.

By *extraction* is meant the percentage of sugar recovered as granulated of the total sugar in the beets, when purchased or when entering the factory. For a straight house, the extraction varies between 78 and 85%. The extraction of a Steffen house is, of course, enhanced by the sugar recovered in the Steffen process, and may amount to from 88 to 94% of the sugar in the beets purchased, depending on the amount of molasses worked.

Chemical Control (20). The important analyses of the process materials are based on the use of the refractometer or Brix hydrometer for measuring total solids in solution; on the use of the polariscope for the determination of sucrose; and on copper-reduction methods for invert sugars. It is customary to determine purity and total dissolved solids in the diffusion juice, standard liquor, intermediate and raw fillmasses, wash and green syrups, and molasses. Sucrose alone is determined in cossettes, diffusion juice, lime flume, Steffen filtrates, saccharate cakes, and molasses. pH values of process liquors are measured throughout the factory, since the liquors are kept basic to prevent inversion, and low pH values in diffusion juices indicate fermentations. First and second carbonations are controlled by titrated alkalinities. Calcium oxide is determined in carbonation juices, and total lime salts in thin juice. Sulfur dioxide addition is controlled by iodimetric analyses of the thin juice and white fillmass. Detailed analyses are required of quicklime produced, coke, carbon dioxide gas, granular carbon, and saccharate cakes. Many analyses must be made for the quality control of the sugar product to follow such factors as color and turbidity of the solution, sediment, specks, odor, taste, ash, sulfite sulfur, particle size by sieve test, saponins, and solution foam grade (a measure of the tendency of dissolved sugar to foam when boiled). The products, dried pulp, and molasses require many control tests. Many determinations must be made of both mesophilic and thermophilic microorganisms, as there are strict limits which must be met for bottlers of carbonated beverages, and for canners and other industrial food manufacturers.

Automation (21). The newer beet-sugar factories are using the principle of central control. Indicating and recording instruments covering all the important variables in the factory are grouped in one room on panel boards, together with visual process-flow diagrams. Also in this control room are placed the controls for most of the equipment units, and all are under the control of one operator. It is but a few steps, not yet taken, to semi- or complete computer control, which is anticipated by the whole industry. Automation has markedly reduced labor costs.

Bibliography

"Beet Sugar" under "Sugar Manufacture" in *ECT* 1st ed., Vol. 13, pp. 217–227, by L. A. Willis, Consultant.

In the brief treatment given in this article references are made to the following five general treatises, which are all readily accessible:

J. Dubourg, *Sucrerie de Betteraves*, Librairie J.-B. Baillière et fils, Paris, 1952, 416 pp.
This is an older text, which primarily describes French and Western European technology.

P. Honig, ed., *Principles of Sugar Technology*, 3 vols., Elsevier Publishing Co., New York, 1953, 1959, 1963, 2045 pp.
A comprehensive treatise, dealing primarily with cane-sugar manufacture. There are sections of interest to the beet-sugar industry, including those on Properties of sucrose, Sucrose crystallography and crystallization fundamentals, Heat transfer, Centrifugation, and Microbiology.

R. A. McGinnis, ed., *Beet-Sugar Technology*, Reinhold Publishing Corp., New York, 1951, 574 pp.
An older text primarily describing North American technology, containing extensive bibliographies. Second edition to be published in 1970.

F. Schneider, ed., *Technologie des Zuckers*, 2nd ed., Verein der Zuckerindustrie, M. and H. Schaper, Hannover, 1968, 1067 pp.
The most recent text, dealing almost entirely with the beet-sugar industry; very large and comprehensive, describing primarily German and European technology. Contains extensive bibliographies.

P. M. Silin, *Technology of Beet-Sugar Production and Refining*, Pishchepromizdat, Moscow, 1958; Israel Program for Scientific Translations, Jerusalem, 1964, 482 pp.

1. J. Baxa and G. Bruhns, *Zucker im Leben der Völker*, Verlag Dr. Albert Bartens, Berlin, 1967, 402 pp.
2. J. Dubourg, *op. cit.*, pp. 18–29; R. A. McGinnis, *op. cit.*, Chap. 2; F. Schneider, *op. cit.*, Chap. 2; P. M. Silin, *op. cit.*, pp. 15–28.
3. McGinnis, pp. 84–91.
4. McGinnis, Chap. 3.
5. Dubourg, pp. 34–40; McGinnis, pp. 79–102; Schneider, Chap. 3; Silin, pp. 32–39.
6. Dubourg, pp. 11–18; Schneider, Chap. 1; Silin, pp. 43–87.
7. Dubourg, pp. 79–90; McGinnis, pp. 123–133, 170–174; Schneider, Chap. 4; Silin, pp. 89–114, 154–158.
8. Dubourg, pp. 90–143; McGinnis, Chap. 6; Schneider, Chap. 5; Silin, pp. 114–175.
8a. K. Andrlik, *Z. Zukerind. (Böhmen)* **28,** 10 (1903–1904).
8b. A. Carruthers and J. F. T. Oldfield, *J. Am. Soc. Sugar Beet Technologists* **13,** 105–115 (1964).
9. Dubourg, pp. 143–150; McGinnis, Chap. 17; Schneider, pp. 869–874; Silin, pp. 376–379.
10. Dubourg, Chap. 5; McGinnis, Chaps. 7, 8 and pp. 247–278; Schneider, Chap. 6; Silin, pp. 179, 258.
11. McGinnis, pp. 278–289; Schneider, pp. 589–591, 630–631; Silin, pp. 258–263.
12. McGinnis, pp. 289–311; Schneider, pp. 593–629; Silin, pp. 263–271.
13. Dubourg, pp. 226–230, 294–295; McGinnis, pp. 245–246; Schneider, pp. 319–322; Silin, pp. 255–258.
14. Dubourg, Chap. 6; McGinnis, Chaps. 11, 19; Schneider, Chap. 7 and pp. 643–684; Silin, section IV.
15. Dubourg, pp. 297–373; McGinnis, Chap. 12; Schneider, pp. 379–483; Silin, section V.
16. McGinnis, pp. 438–452; Schneider, pp. 983–989; Silin, pp. 388–393, 395–398.
17. McGinnis, pp. 452–458; Schneider, pp. 991–994.
18. McGinnis, Chap. 13; Schneider, pp. 482–487, 501–514.
19. McGinnis, Chap. 20.
20. Dubourg, pp. 66–77.
21. Schneider, pp. 764–775, 800–844.

R. A. McGinnis
Spreckels Sugar Co.

SUGAR DERIVATIVES

Sucrose has found a broad spectrum of industrial nonfood applications over the years, ranging from electroplating to embalming fluids. In most cases sugars have been used to modify the properties of aqueous solutions. For example, for many years they were used in adjusting the viscosity of printing pastes for the textile industry. Yet, with a few notable exceptions, they have not come into general usage as starting materials for conversion to industrially significant compounds.

The disaccharide sucrose has perhaps received more organized attention, under a program of research called "sucrochemistry," than has been applied to any other of the simple sugars. The following remarks, based on the experience gained in this program of industrial nonfood markets, are perhaps applicable to some extent to the other sugars.

Sucrochemistry

In the first place, sucrose hydroxyls are less reactive than water; therefore, it is comparatively difficult to make derivatives of sugar in aqueous media. The high ratio of oxygen to carbon, on the other hand, greatly limits the number of organic solvents which are of potential use. Pyridine has been a standby solvent for the carbohydrate chemists for many years, but it is expensive and noxious. Comparatively recently, the chemical industry has produced a few solvents of potential value: N-N-dimethyl-formamide (see Vol. 10, p. 109), dimethysulfoxide (see Sulfoxides), and N-methyl-2-pyrrolidone (see Vol. 16, p. 852). These substances dissolve significant quantities of sucrose, contain only comparatively unreactive hydrogen, and, while moderately expensive, offer some promise of providing useful reaction media for sucrochemical conversions.

A second factor of importance is that sucrose is an exceedingly fugitive molecule in the presence of Lewis acids, although it is essentially stable at pH's up to 9 or 10 at moderate temperatures. Reducing sugars, on the other hand, are subject to degradation in such alkaline conditions.

Third, sucrose is a metastable molecule thermodynamically, and when maltreated it readily decomposes to caramel or worse. Generally, however, it is sufficiently stable below 100°C so that useful reactions can be carried out.

From among the million or so organic compounds, the few score that are of significant tonnage fall conveniently into fifteen application groups, as follows:

1. Foods	6. Fibers	11. Adhesives
2. Fuels	7. Paper	12. Plasticizers
3. Explosives	8. Pesticides	13. Plastics
4. Elastomers	9. Soil conditioning agents	14. Surfactants
5. Lubricants	10. Solvents	15. Surface coatings

Five items can be eliminated from this list, for a variety of reasons, as shown:

1. *Foods*, because it is hardly likely that any *other* large-scale food use can be found for sugar.

2. *Fuels* and 3. *Explosives*, because sugar is 58% by wt water and is therefore a comparatively expensive and low-energy fuel.

4. *Elastomers* and 5. *Lubricants*, because the high percentage of oxygen, favoring strong hydrogen bonding, keeps sugar and its derivatives from having the requisite properties.

Five of the remaining target areas seem unlikely prospective outlets, according to the current state of knowledge.   These include the following:

6. *Fibers* call for long, linear polymers.   The differences between the rates of reaction for most of the eight hydroxyl groups of sugar is so very small that the reaction products of sugar are more likely to be branched rather than linear polymers.   Hence, the incorporation of sugar into polymer chains has not been achieved.   Even so, sugar has been degraded to di- or oligofunctional polymerizable molecules such as carboxy acids, amines, or glycols.   Most attempts to date, however, have been found to be comparatively expensive mechanisms for obtaining products which can be supplied more easily from other carbon sources.

7. *Paper* production and paper conversion are major outlets for many organic substances.   Although sugar seems to be too expensive to have a significant application here, some sugar derivatives might be useful as components in special coatings, in augmenting the wet-strength, or in the resins employed in the printing media.

8. *Pest control chemicals* constitute a rapidly growing market for organic chemicals. The biodegradability of sugar suggests that if the toxic moieties of known pesticides could be combined with sugar through ether or ester linkages, some benefits might accrue.   One research attempt was fruitless; whether this was due to faulty chemistry or to the nature of the sugar derivatives obtained was not determined.

9. *Soil conditioners* had much promise, but the difficulties encountered in obtaining economical high-molecular-weight, long-lived sugar polymers have made the achievement of this goal unlikely.

10. *Solvents*.   Probably the oldest sucrochemical reaction is fermentation to alcohol.   Other solvents based on furfural, glycols, and polyamines might be produced from sugars, but cursory analysis suggests that petrochemical sources are destined to be more economical.   Indeed, in recent years several chemical companies of significance have developed processes for degrading hexoses to hydroxymethylfurfural and the further derivatives (alcohols and amines), but little or no commercial interest in the products could be generated.

Sucrochemical Targets in Sight.   The preceding conclusions reduced the list of target areas for sucrochemical research by two thirds, and the areas left for study are 11–15.   Of these topics little work has been done on 11. *Adhesives*, except as an application of phenolics.

12. *Plasticizers*, likewise, have received minimal attention.   Some fatty acid esters have achieved commercial usage, such as SAIB (sucrose diacetate hexaisobutyrate).   Sucrose distearate hexaacetate is a prototype of the property modifications that can be achieved.

13. *Plastics* markets were estimated by the Paley Committee in 1962 as likely to grow to approx 8 million tons by 1975.   This estimate was later demonstrated to be conservative; however, it spurred efforts to seek mechanisms by which the sugar could enter this burgeoning market.   The multiplicity of sugar's reactive sites suggested that bulk polymers rather than linear polymers might be the best objectives.   Some promising applications have been described in (a) replacing up to half of the phenol in phenolic resins as plywood adhesives and (b) replacing 10–25% of the melamine in

laminating and surface coating compounds. Both these processes have been commercialized to some extent. Some polymerizable derivatives, such as carbonate esters, have been described. More recently, limited reaction at selected reactive sites has been achieved, producing *p*-toluenesulfonyl or amine group replacements for hydroxyls.

Table 1. Naturally Occurring Sugar Acids

Structure	Name	Natural source
CHO $\|$ HCOH $\|$ HOCH $\|$ HOCH $\|$ HCOH $\|$ COOH	D-galacturonic acid	combined in pectins, karaya gum, and gum tragacanth
CHO $\|$ HOCH $\|$ HOCH $\|$ HCOH $\|$ HCOH $\|$ COOH	D-mannuronic acid	combined in alginic acid
CHO $\|$ HCOH $\|$ HOCH $\|$ HCOH $\|$ HCOH $\|$ COOH	D-glucuronic acid	combined in animal urine, pneumococcus type III polysaccharide, hyaluronic acid, chondroitinsulfuric acid, heparin, mesquite gum, and gum arabic
COOH $\|$ C=O $\|$ HOCH $\|$ HCOH $\|$ HCOH $\|$ CH_2OH	2-keto-D-gluconic acid	combined in carageenin, the polysaccharide of Irish moss (*Chondrus crispus*); see Seaweed colloids.

None of these modifications has yet achieved commercialization, but the results are sufficiently promising for the search to continue.

14. *Surfactant* markets presented an interesting challenge because of the obvious hydrophilicity of sugar. The higher fatty acid esters can be synthesized under potentially economic conditions to produce interesting surfactants that are quite desirably biodegradable. The process has achieved commercialization in Japan in food surfactant applications and in Germany as an additive for photographic emulsions. A

variety of other long-alkane-chain derivatives such as acetals or ethers have received research attention and are covered by patent literature, but there is no known commercialization of these products to date.

15. *Surface Coatings*. This area of research has been deemed as promising a one as surfactants. This, to a large degree, is attributable to the higher functionality of sucrose and its low cost, as compared to other polyols, such as glycerol, pentaerythritol, or sorbitol. Early efforts attempted to prepare polymerizable acrylate esters or allyl ethers. Recently, interest has centered on the polyunsaturated fatty acid esters such as "linseedates." No commercialization has been achieved, but the research results indicate that the research is a fruitful one.

Degradation Products

Derivatives that are manufactured may be arbitrarily divided into those formed by degradation and those formed by combining reactions. The many degraded products may be subdivided into those produced by fermentation and those produced by chemical degradations.

FERMENTATION DEGRADATION

Fermentation of sugars and other carbohydrates leads to a wide variety of products ranging from carbon dioxide to antibiotics to yeasts. Several fermentative reactions have been the source of organic chemicals of considerable industrial significance, such as acetone and 1-butanol. Except for potable ethyl alcohol, and citric, gluconic, glutamic, and lactic acids, however, production from petroleum or by electrochemical methods has for the most part supplanted the fermentation processes. In several areas, molasses is converted to food or feed-grade proteins by *Torulopsis utilis* (15). It is interesting to conjecture on the future competition, as protein suppliers, between the sugar and petroleum residues (10). Many other substances have been reported to be products of fermentation reactions (12). See also Fermentation.

CHEMICAL DEGRADATION

Sucrose, dextrose, and lactose, when heated, lose water and darken in color. The product is caramel (qv), which is useful for coloring and flavoring foods and beverages. More severe thermal degradation in the presence of acids produces furfural (qv) from pentose sugars and aldohexuronic acids. This degradation is performed on a large scale with pentosan-containing raw materials such as oat hulls, corn cobs, and sugar cane bagasse. Hexose sugars, including cellulose, by the same treatment yield 5-(hydroxymethyl)furfural, which upon further degradation produces levulinic acid.

Sucrose, when heated in the presence of calcium hydroxide, degrades and rearranges to yield a variety of products, including lactic acid (qv) and the saccharinic acids.

Dextrins, in which part of the sugar residues are dehydrated, are obtained by thermal degradation of starch (qv).

Levulinic acid, $CH_3CO(CH_2)_2COOH$, small colorless leaflets; mp, 37.2°C; d_4^{20}, 1.1395; is very soluble in water, ethyl alcohol, and ether. It is produced along with formic acid when a hexose sugar is heated in the presence of oxalic acid or a mineral acid, decomposing in several steps of dehydration and degradation:

hexose   5-(hydroxymethyl)furfural   levulinic   formic
                                                  acid   acid

A process has been reported which gives a 70% conversion of a 3% sucrose solution (4,7,14). One manufacturer produces levulinic acid from corn starch in about 50% yield. It is also a by-product of furfural production.

Several heterocyclic compounds (such as (1), (2), and (3)) have been prepared from levulinic acid (21), but none has provided a significant outlet, although calcium levulinate may be used medicinally as a source of calcium. The acid was proposed as an additive in cattle feeding to improve the digestibility of the cellulose, but markets have not yet developed (39). In general, the production potential of levulinic acid greatly exceeds the demand at present high prices.

α-angelica lactone   3-methyl-6-ketotetrahydropyridazine   2-methyl-3-indole-
                     (6-methyl-4,5-dihydro-3(2H)-pyridazinone)   acetic acid
       (1)   (2)   (3)

A variety of nitrogen-containing heterocyclics, (4), (5), and (6), have been produced by degrading sugars in the presence of ammonia. Critical factors, including catalyst, pressure, and temperature, determine whether the reactions will be relatively simple replacements or complex fragmentations followed by recombinations into heterocyclics.

1-aminosorbitol   2-methylpiperazine (18)   4-methylimidazole (25)
     (4)   (5)   (6)

Products of Combining Reactions

Few sugar derivatives outside of the degradative derivatives have attained any sizable market. Two important hydrogenation products, sorbitol and mannitol (see Alcohols, polyhydric) are useful as humectants and can be converted to other useful products including surface-active agents and alkyd-type resins. Mannitol forms the primary explosive mannitol hexanitrate (see Vol. 8, p. 610). Dextran produced from sucrose by fermentation held some promise as a blood plasma expander, but markets failed to meet expectations because the medical profession has preferred blood products as long as they were available. Industrial applications, such as textile sizing, have failed to materialize.

ESTER DERIVATIVES

The essentially hydrophilic character of sugar can be modified (that is, usually, reduced) to a degree dependent upon the type and number of acid groups introduced. At the same time a considerable change in other properties occurs. For example, sucrose, one of the sweeter of the natural products, becomes less sweet as it is acetylated. The octaacetate is bitter enough to be used as an alcohol denaturant.

Some of the esters of sucrose are listed in Table 2. This list does not include the large number of partially esterified products. In contrast to the unsubstituted sugars, the acetates and propionates of mono- and dissaccharides are distillable at 0.001 mm Hg. The monoacetate of sucrose has been reported (19) to be a humectant.

Table 2. Totally Esterified Sucrose Esters

Ester	Mp, °C	Ester	Mp, °C
acetate	72.3	p-nitrobenzoate	150 (dec)
propionate	44–46	p-bromobenzoate	114–117
palmitate	54–55	cinnamate	87–88
stearate	57	nitrate	85.5

Nitrates of sugars have received repeated attention as explosives, but they are less stable than the nitrates of glycerol and the sugar alcohols. Lactose octanitrate and, to a lesser extent, sucrose octanitrate have found use when glycerol was in short supply, but they do not compete on a free market.

Phosphate esters are intermediates in sugar metabolism and in vivo synthesis of carbohydrates. The calcium salt of sucrose orthophosphate has been suggested as a dietary source of phosphate of significance in reducing dental caries rates (13).

The hydrophilic character of some sugar derivatives has suggested their use in surface-active agents. Sucrose esters have been commercialized in Japan as food additives, in Germany in photographic emulsions, and in France in reconstituted milks. The biodegradability of the detergent products continues to focus attention on these products as agents in reducing problems of water pollution (5,6).

Examples of derivatives proposed for use as wetting agents are di-O-lauroyl-D-glucosyl sulfate (33) and sugar phosphate dioleate (32). N-Cetyl-N-methylglucamine (32) and N-cetyl-N-D-glucosyl-N-methylammonium iodide (31) are among those suggested as emulsifiers. The esters of sucrose formed by reaction with the acid chlorides of China wood or perilla oils are drying oils. Some success has also been achieved with corresponding derivatives of linseed oil (2,3).

Acetates. Franchimont, in 1879, reacted sodium acetate and acetic anhydride with D-glucose. With but slight modifications, this is the currently recommended method for preparing completely reacted acetates. The reaction is general for sugars and carbohydrates. Other reagents which have been recommended include acetic anhydride and pyridine, acetic anhydride and sulfuric acid, and acetic anhydride and zinc chloride. As a rule, mild reagents and low temperatures (below 50°C) favor the α-configuration if the α-form is taken at the outset, while high temperatures (100–130°C), and stronger catalysts favor the β-derivatives regardless of the original configuration. In intermediate ranges, mixtures result.

Sucrose octaacetate, $C_{12}H_{14}O_{11}(C_2H_3O)_8$, white needles from alcohol; mp, 72.3°C; $[\alpha]_D^{22}$, +59.6° (CHCl₃); is soluble in ethyl alcohol, ether, and common organic solvents, and very slightly soluble in water. It is one sucrose derivative that has considerable commercial production. The octaacetate is prepared with sodium acetate and acetic anhydride by the Franchimont method. Sucrose octaacetate is commercially available in 200-lb drums and in January 1969 was selling at $1.10/lb.

About twenty tons of the acetate is consumed annually in denaturing ethyl alcohol. The compound imparts an exceedingly bitter taste to the alcohol but is nontoxic. Mixed with glucose pentaacetate, it finds use as an adhesive, as does sucrose-modified polyvinyl alcohol. These materials have achieved some use in laminated glass. Sucrose octaacetate is also used as a plasticizer in dialkyl succinate and maleic anhydride–styrene resins. In phenol–formaldehyde or phenol–furfural polymers, it produces a plastic particularly useful in bonding asbestos brake linings.

Plasticizer usage of sucrose esters as the diacetate hexaisobutyrate (SAIB) and the octabenzoate has attained significant commercialization in ester and acrylic polymers. No present penetration into vinyl or the polymerized olefin series has been achieved.

ACID DERIVATIVES

Of the many sugar acids (glyconic, glycuronic, and glycaric) only the most important are described here. See also Citric acid; Lactic acid; Maleic and fumaric acids; Itaconic acid.

D-*Gluconic acid*, $C_6H_{12}O_7$, fine needles; mp, 125–126°C; $[\alpha]_D^{20}$, −6.7° → +11.5° (H₂O, c = 5); is soluble in water and insoluble in ethyl alcohol and ether. No natural source has been reported for D-gluconic acid, but, because its salts have been of interest, some has been prepared by aerobic fermentation of D-glucose. In shallow pans, *Penicillium chrysogenum* will give a 60% conversion in 8–10 days. *Aspergillus niger* NRRL 3 or 67 in rotating fermenting drums is said to give a 95% conversion if boric acid is added to complex the D-gluconic acid as it is formed. D-Gluconic acid is usually prepared by aerobic fermentation of D-glucose with *Acetobacter suboxydans*. It may also be prepared in good yield by electrolytic oxidation (16) and more recently has been prepared by catalytic air oxidation (1). (Sugars may be oxidized to aldonic acids in the presence of a soluble bromide electrolyzed with carbon anodes in an undivided cell. The aldonic acid is usually recovered as the calcium salt by adding calcium carbonate to the cell. In this reaction the hypobromite is evidently the oxidizing agent. A modification of this process is in industrial operation at present, but a description of it has as yet not been released.)

The acid of commerce is a 50% aqueous solution (22). Sales reached 3.5 million lb in 1965. In January 1969, the acid was selling for 14.5 to 48¢/lb in drum lots or tanks. Sodium gluconate is available in the technical grade and in January 1969 was selling for 32¢. Sales reached 8.1 million lb in 1965. Calcium gluconate in barrels or drums sold for 69¢/lb (USP) and for 75¢/lb (AA) in January 1969 and potassium gluconate sold for $1.67/lb in drum lots.

Gluconic acid is used in cleaning metal containers, particularly in the dairy industry to remove milkstone. Salts of D-gluconic acid have found interest in pharmacy as a means of administering calcium or iron (see Table 3). The sodium salt in the presence of caustic alkali is a sequestrant for iron or calcium as in boiler water conditioning. It is claimed to be superior to sodium citrate or tetrasodium ethylenediaminetetraacetate (9,35). See Complexing agents.

Table 3. Salts of D-Gluconic Acid

Salt	Appearance	Mp, °C	Solubility
ammonium	fine, white needles	154 dec	31.6 g/100 ml H_2O/25°C; sl s EtOH; i organic solvents
sodium	irregular, colorless		59 g/100 ml H_2O/25°C; i organic solvents
potassium	fine, white cryst powder	180 dec	readily s H_2O
calcium	fine, white needles		3.5 g/100 ml H_2O/25°C; i Et_2O, EtOH
magnesium, monohydrate	white powder		10.6 g/100 ml H_2O/25°C; i organic solvents
ferrous, monohydrate	fine, yellowish-green powder		8.5 g/100 ml H_2O/100°C; sl s EtOH; i Et_2O (solutions are reduced by light owing to a photochemical reaction) (see Vol. 2, p. 35)
cupric	light bluish-green		30 g/100 ml H_2O/25C°; i organic solvents

Another use proposed for D-gluconic acid involves Ruff degradation of the calcium salt to D-arabinose:

$$
\begin{array}{cc}
\begin{array}{c}
\text{COOH} \\
| \\
\text{HCOH} \\
| \\
\text{HOCH} \\
| \\
\text{HCOH} \\
| \\
\text{HCOH} \\
| \\
\text{CH}_2\text{OH} \\
\text{D-gluconic acid}
\end{array}
\quad + \text{Ca(OH)}_2 \xrightarrow[\text{Fe(OOCCH}_3)_3]{\text{H}_2\text{O}_2}
\quad
\begin{array}{c}
\text{CHO} \\
| \\
\text{HOCH} \\
| \\
\text{HCOH} \\
| \\
\text{HCOH} \\
| \\
\text{CH}_2\text{OH} \\
\text{D-arabinose}
\end{array}
\end{array}
$$

The D-arabinose can be used as such or after oxidation to D-arabonic acid (see below) in one method of synthesizing riboflavine (qv).

Heating D-gluconic acid under reduced pressure drives off one molecule of water, producing D-glucono-δ-lactone, $C_6H_9O_6$, long prisms; mp, 146°C; $[\alpha]_D^{20}$, +67.5° → +17.7° (H_2O, c = 14); soluble in water.

D-Gluconic acid in aqueous solution comes to an equilibrium with D-glucono-δ-lactone and D-glucono-γ-lactone. When such a solution is slowly evaporated under reduced pressure, the δ-lactone crystallizes. This lactone is used to some extent as the acidulant in baking powders. See Vol. 3, p. 58.

D-*Glucuronic acid*, $C_6H_{10}O_7$, crystallizes from water in the β-configuration; mp, 154–156°C; $[\alpha]_D^{24}$, +11.7 → 36.3° (H_2O); it is soluble in water. There are several natural polysaccharides which contain D-glucuronic acid (a hexuronic acid), such as gum arabic, heparin, and hyaluronic acid, although these are not employed as sources.

D-*Glucose* is the common source and several methods have been announced for the conversion (20). One procedure (34) employs the isopropylidene derivative to protect the carbonyl group. The primary hydroxyl is then oxidized with air in the presence of a platinum–carbon catalyst (eq. 1). Alternative methods employ the methyl glucoside (eq. 2). Oxidants have included permanganate, said to give a 50–60% yield (37); nitrogen dioxide, about 30% yield (36); and nitric acid, 27–33% yield (26). D-Glucuronic acid is recovered from the lactone by acid hydrolysis and crystallization from water. Methyl α-D-glucoside can be oxidized with oxygen and platinum black in the presence of sodium bicarbonate to the sodium salt of methyl α-D-glucuronic acid in 87% yield (8). Methyl α-D-glucoside is available commercially in 100-lb bags.

1,2-isopropylidene-
D-glucofuranose   D-glucuronic acid   (1)

methyl α-D-glucopyranoside   methyl α-D-glucopyranosidurono-6,3-lactone   (2)

The sodium, potassium, and calcium salts of D-glucuronic acid have been suggested for use as sequestering agents. They are available in limited quantities. A polyanhydro-D-glucuronic acid (oxidized cellulose, USP XIV (cellulosic acid, NNR) obtained by oxidation of cellulose with nitrogen dioxide is an effective hemostatic glucurono-γ-lactone, $C_6H_8O_6$, mp, 175–178°C; $[\alpha]_D^{20}$, +19.2° (H_2O). It is soluble in water and slowly hydrolyzes to form an equilibrium with the acid. The lactone is available in limited quantities, to some extent satisfying the requirements for pantothenic acid. See Vitamins.

D-*Glucaric Acid* (saccharic acid). Oxidation of D-glucose with nitric acid produces D-glucaric acid, tartaric acid (qv), oxalic acid (qv), and carbonic acid. Under controlled conditions, nitrogen tetroxide in chloroform will give a 40% conversion of D-glucose to D-glucaric acid. The acid has been used to a limited extent as a sequestering agent.

$$
\begin{array}{c}
\text{COOH} \\
| \\
\text{HCOH} \\
| \\
\text{HOCH} \\
| \\
\text{HCOH} \\
| \\
\text{HCOH} \\
| \\
\text{COOH}
\end{array}
$$

D-glucaric acid
(7)

D-*Galacturonic Acid.* The widespread occurrence of pectins (see Pectic substances) in plants makes D-galacturonic acid a common sugar derivative (see Table 1.) Sugar beet pulp and citrus waste have been proposed as sources for D-galacturonic acid if a commercial demand develops. It is present to the extent of 22% in gum arabic and has been recovered from the sulfite liquors from pulping of white pine. The chief use for D-galacturonic acid is as pectin (the polyuronide).

D-*Arabonic acid,* $C_5H_{10}O_6$, is very soluble in water. It can be obtained in 70% yield by air oxidation of D-glucose or D-fructose in alkaline solution (eq. 3). Nitrobenzene or methylene blue exerts a positive catalysis upon the reaction. Invert sugar is a common starting material, and molasses is also a possibility. A limited market for D-arabonic acid has developed as an intermediate (through epimerization to D-ribonic acid) in preparing the ribitol portion of synthetic riboflavine (see Vol. 17, p. 449).

$$
\begin{array}{c}
\text{CHO} \\
| \\
\text{HCOH} \\
| \\
\text{HOCH} \\
| \\
\text{HCOH} \\
| \\
\text{HCOH} \\
| \\
\text{CH}_2\text{OH}
\end{array}
\xrightarrow{\text{OH}^-}
\begin{array}{c}
\overset{\text{H}\;\;\;\text{OH}}{\underset{\|}{\text{C}}} \\
\text{COH} \\
| \\
\text{HOCH} \\
| \\
\text{HCOH} \\
| \\
\text{HCOH} \\
| \\
\text{CH}_2\text{OH}
\end{array}
\xrightarrow[\text{OH}^-]{\text{O}_2}
\left[
\begin{array}{c}
\text{OH} \\
| \\
\text{HC—O} \\
| \quad | \\
\text{HOC—O} \\
| \\
\text{HOCH} \\
| \\
\text{HCOH} \\
| \\
\text{CH}_2\text{OH}
\end{array}
\right]
\xrightarrow{\text{OH}^-}
\begin{array}{c}
\text{COOH} \\
| \\
\text{HOCH} \\
| \\
\text{HCOH} \\
| \\
\text{HCOH} \\
| \\
\text{CH}_2\text{OH}
\end{array}
+ \;\; \text{HCOOH} \quad (3)
$$

D-arabonic acid

$$
\begin{array}{c}
\text{CH}_2\text{OH} \\
| \\
\text{C=O} \\
| \\
\text{HOCH} \\
| \\
\text{HCOH} \\
| \\
\text{HCOH} \\
| \\
\text{CH}_2\text{OH}
\end{array}
\xrightarrow[\text{H}_2\text{O}]{\text{HCN}}
\begin{array}{c}
\text{CN} \\
| \\
\text{HOC—CH}_2\text{OH} \\
| \\
\text{HOCH} \\
| \\
\text{HCOH} \\
| \\
\text{HCOH} \\
| \\
\text{CH}_2\text{OH}
\end{array}
\xrightarrow{\text{NH}_4\text{OH}}
\begin{array}{c}
\text{CO}_2\text{NH}_4 \\
| \\
\text{HOC—CH}_2\text{OH} \\
| \\
\text{HOCH} \\
| \\
\text{HCOH} \\
| \\
\text{HCOH} \\
| \\
\text{CH}_2\text{OH}
\end{array}
\quad\text{or}\quad
\begin{array}{c}
\text{CO}_2\text{NH}_4 \\
| \\
\text{HOCH}_2\text{—COH} \\
| \\
\text{HOCH} \\
| \\
\text{HCOH} \\
| \\
\text{HCOH} \\
| \\
\text{CH}_2\text{OH}
\end{array}
$$

fructose   fructose cyanohydrin   ammonium
                                            fructoheptonate

Mild heating converts the acid into D-arabo-δ-lactone, $C_2H_8O_5$, mp, 96–98°C; $[\alpha]_D^{20}$, +73.3° (H_2O, $c = 5.8$); soluble in water, ethyl acetate, and ethyl alcohol.

Fructoheptonic acid is produced by the hydrolysis of the HCN adduct to fructose (see p. 230). It is claimed that this acid reduces the rate of scale deposition in alkaline water of dairy and soft drinks equipment (40).

Lactobionic acid and maltobionic acid are examples of aldonic acids that may be obtained from reducing disaccharides, such as lactose and maltose, by means of fermentation and chemical oxidation.

MISCELLANEOUS DERIVATIVES

Sugar derivatives such as sucrose ethers, because of their polyfunctional nature, have received considerable study as components of plastic materials, but none of these suggestions has been put to practical use. Benzyl, ethyl, allyl, and crotyl ethers of sucrose are said to plasticize cellulose ester polymers. The allyl ethers of sucrose appear to be useful as a coating resin with somewhat superior resistance to organic solvents. Allyl sucrose also has received some attention for upgrading semidrying oils (38). Ethylidene sucrose will give vinyl-type polymers when catalyzed with boron trifluoride.

Sucrose, itself, has been studied as a component of a number of systems that produce bulk polymers in the presence of alkaline catalysts. It can be used to extend phenolics for molding and plywood adhesives (11,17), melamines for laminating and textile applications (23,24), and, when modified with polyoxyalkylene side chains, in rigid urethans as thermal insulation (27). Each of these applications has achieved some commercial usage.

If glucose in liquid ammonia is hydrogenated in the presence of Raney nickel at 50–100 atm pressure and 75–125°C, *glucamine* (D-glucitylamine) is formed. When methylated on the nitrogen, the product is *N-methylglucamine*. A variety of applications of this product have been suggested. For example, it is said to facilitate bright-plating with cadmium. With formaldehyde, phenol, and fluosilicic acid, it produces a water-soluble mothproofing substance. With chloroethanesulfonic acid and methylamine, a product is formed which will couple with aromatic diazonium salts to yield dyes. Condensed with cetyl chloride, glucamine yields a detergent.

<pre>
      H   OCH₃   CH₂NHCH₃
       \ / |
        C   HCOH
        | |
      HCOH   HOCH
        | |
      HOCH   O   HCOH
        | |
      HCOH   HCOH
        | |
      HC   CH₂OH
        |
      CH₂I
</pre>

methyl 6-deoxy-6-iodo-	*N*-methylglucamine
α-D-glucopyranoside	
(8)	**(9)**

Bibliography

"Sugar Derivatives" in *ECT* 1st ed., Vol. 13, pp. 261–270, by J. L. Hickson, Sugar Research Foundation, Inc.

1. Anon., "A New Catalytic Air-Oxidation Process," *Chem. Week* **89** (20), 185 (Nov. 18, 1961).
2. Anon., *The Chemistry of Preparation of Sucrose Esters for the Ink, Paint, and Protective Coating Industries*, Sugar Research Foundation, Inc., New York, 1963.
3. Anon., *Engineering and Pilot Plant Data for the Commercial Production of Sucrose Esters for the Ink, Paint, and Protective Coating Industries*, Sugar Research Foundation, Inc., New York, 1963.
4. Anon., "Levulinic Acid Process Goes on Stream," *Chem. Eng. News* **41** (5), 48 (Feb. 4, 1963).
5. Anon., *Sucrose Esters, 1968*, Noyes Development Corp., New Jersey, 1968.
6. Anon., *Sucrose Ester Surfactants, Research Report*, Sugar Research Foundation, Inc., New York, reprinted 1964.
7. *Levulinic Acid and Related Products Produced from Sucrose Including 5-Hydroxymethylfurfural and Formic Acid*, Special Member Report No. 20, Sugar Research Foundation, Inc., New York, 1949.
8. S. A. Barker, E. J. Bourne, and M. Stacey, *Chem. Ind. (London)* **1951**, 970.
9. R. H. Blom, V. F. Pfeifer, A. J. Moyer, D. H. Traufler, N. F. Conway, C. K. Crocker, R. E. Farison, and D. V. Hannibal, *Ind. Eng. Chem.* **44**, 435 (1952).
10. A. Champaynat, "Protein from Petroleum," *Sci. Am.* **213** (4), 13–17 (1965).
11. C. D. Chang and O. K. Kononenko, "Sucrose-Modified Phenolics Resins as Plywood Adhesives," *Adhesives Age* **5** (7), 36–40 (1962).
12. B. S. Gould, *Chemical Compounds Formed from Sugar by Molds*, Sugar Research Foundation, New York, 1947.
13. R. Harris, B. G. Schamschula, G. Gregory, M. Roots, and J. Beveridge, "Observations on the Cariostatic Effect of Calcium Sucrose Phosphate in a Group of Children Aged 5–17 Years," *Australian Dental J.* **12** (2), 105–113 (1967).
14. L. K. Herndon, *Engineering Study of Preparation of Levulinic Acid from Sucrose*, Special Member Report No. 21, Sugar Research Foundation, Inc., New York, 1950.
15. Wan-chun Hsu, "Protein from Sugar on Taiwan," *Sugar* **56** (7), 33–36 (1961).
16. H. S. Isbell and H. L. Frush, *J. Res. Natl. Bur. Std. A* **6**, 1145 (1931).
17. O. K. Kononenko, *A New Adhesive for Exterior Plywood, Research Report*, Sugar Research Foundation, Inc., New York, 1962.
18. O. K. Kononenko, *Reductive Aminolysis of Sucrose*, Final Research Report, International Sugar Research Foundation, Inc., Bethesda, Md., 1969.
19. O. K. Kononenko and I. L. Kestanbaum, "Sucrose Monoacetate," *J. Appl. Chem. (London)* **11**, 7–10 (1961).
20. C. L. Mehltretter, in C. S. Hudson and M. L. Wolfrom, eds., *Advances in Carbohydrate Chemistry*, Vol. 8, Academic Press, Inc., New York, 1953, pp. 231–250.
21. A. A. Morton, *Levulinic Acid as a Source of Heterocyclic Compounds*, Sugar Research Foundation, New York, 1947.
22. F. J. Prescott, J. K. Shaw, J. P. Billello, and G. O. Cragwell, *Ind. Eng. Chem.* **45**, 338 (1953).
23. G. L. Redfearn, W. Flavell, and W. Mikucki, *Invert and Other Sugars as Extenders in Melamine Formaldehyde Resins*, Sugar Research Foundation, Inc., New York, 1963.
24. G. L. Redfearn, *Sugar Modified Melamine Resins for Textile Applications*, Sugar Research Foundation, Inc., New York, 1966.
25. L. F. Wiggins, "Some Recent Studies on Ammoniated Molasses," *Sugar J.* **18** (8), 18 (1956).
26. Brit. Pat. 670,929 (April 30, 1952), (to Corn Products Refining Co.).
27. Brit. Pat. 955,488 (April 15, 1964), (to Pittsburgh Plate Glass Co.).
28. Brit. Pat. 992,833 (May 19, 1965), (to Ajinomoto, Inc.).
29. Brit. Pats. 1,057,824, 1,057,825, and 1,057,826 (Feb. 8, 1967), (to A. V. Kogyo, K.K.).
30. U.S. Pat. 2,052,029 (Aug. 25, 1936), B. R. Harris.
31. U.S. Pat. 2,060,850 (Nov. 17, 1936), W. S. Calcott and R. G. Clarkson (to E. I. du Pont de Nemours & Co., Inc.).
32. U.S. Pat. 2,091,105 (Aug. 24, 1937), H. A. Piggott (to Imperial Chemical Industries).
33. U.S. Pat. 2,212,521 (Aug. 27, 1940), B. R. Harris (to Colgate-Palmolive-Peet Co.).
34. U.S. Pat. 2,562,200 (July 31, 1951), C. L. Mehltretter (to U.S.A.).
35. U.S. Pat. 2,584,017 (Jan. 29, 1952), J. Dvorkovitz and T. G. Hanley, Jr. (to Diversey Corp.).

36. U.S. Pat. 2,592,249 (April 8, 1952), D. H. Couch and E. A. Cleveland (to Corn Products Refining Co.).
37. U.S. Pat. 2,592,266 (April 8, 1952), D. M. Gallagher (to Corn Products Refining Co.).
38. U.S. Pat. 2,606,881 (Aug. 12, 1952), M. Ziet and E. Yanovsky (to U.S.A.).
39. U.S. Pat. 2,831,769 (April 22, 1958), J. Kamlet (to Crown Zellerbach Corp.).
40. U.S. Pat. 2,992,998 (July 18, 1961), J. V. Karabinos and F. J. Quinn.

General References

F. J. Bates et al., *Polarimetry, Saccharimetry and the Sugars*, Circ. C440, Natl. Bur. Std. (U.S.), 1942.
E. F. Degering, *Chemistry of the Carbohydrates*, John S. Swift Co., Cincinnati, Ohio, 1943.
T. H. Evans and H. Hibbert, *Bacterial Polysaccharides*, Sugar Research Foundation, New York, 1947; *Advan. Carbohydrate Chem.* **2**, 203 (1946).
M. Hunt, *Patents on the Reactions of Sugars*, Sugar Research Foundation, New York, 1961.
V. Kollonitsch, *Sucrose Chemicals*, International Sugar Research Foundation, Inc., Bethesda, Md., 1969.
W. W. Pigman, *Carbohydrates, Chemistry, Biochemistry, Physiology*, Academic Press, Inc., New York, 1967.
P. S. Pittenger, *Sugars and Sugar Derivatives in Pharmacy*, Sugar Research Foundation, New York, 1947.
L. A. Underkofler and R. J. Hickey, *Industrial Fermentations*, Chemical Publishing Co., Inc., New York, 1954, Vol. 1.
R. L. Whistler and C. L. Smart, *Polysaccharide Chemistry*, Academic Press, Inc., New York, 1953.

J. L. HICKSON
International Sugar
Research Foundation, Inc.

SUGAR ECONOMICS

Sugar has been an item of international trade since the dawn of recorded history. It was a commodity brought to the Mediterranean community by early caravan. It is

Table 1. World Sugar Production, 1000 short tons[a]

Crop year, ending	Beet	Cane	Total production
1904	6673	6638	13,311
1909	7684	8110	15,794
1914	9959	10,627	20,586
1919	4871	12,597	17,468
1924	6665	14,872	21,537
1929	10,574	18,907	29,481
1934	10,086	16,624	26,710
1939	11,619	19,701	31,320
1944	8366	19,000	27,366
1949	11,084	19,749	30,833
1954	18,267	24,165	42,432
1959	23,778	32,204	55,982
1964	25,946	34,689	60,635
1965	33,867	39,716	73,583
1966	29,827	39,673	69,500
1967	30,903	40,941	71,844
1968	33,427	40,170	73,597

NOTE: From F. O. Licht's *World Sugar Statistics*, 1967/1968, Ratzeberg, W. Germany (May 1968). Courtesy F. O. Licht KG.

[a] Raw value, ie, adjusted to 96% sucrose.

Table 2. Changing World Supply and Demand for Sugar, Raw Value[a]

Crop year, ending	Production	Disappearance	Population[b]	Per capita, lb
	........1000 metric tons........			
1968	67,478[c]	67,688[c]	3485	42.8
1967	65,842	65,616	3420	42.4
1966	63,272	62,932	3355	41.4
1965	67,128	60,063	3295	40.7
1964	55,094	54,262	3239	37.0
1963	51,344	54,550	3179	38.0
1962	52,351	55,602	3119	39.4
1961	56,073	52,734	3061	38.0
1960	49,564	48,858	3004	35.9
1959	51,034	47,561	2948	35.6
1958	45,172	44,704	2892	34.2
1957	42,339	42,228	2836	32.9
1956	39,322	40,443	2782	32.1
1955	38,255	38,254	2730	30.9
1954	38,390	36,892	2680	30.4
1953	35,132	35,200	2631	29.5

[a] *Lamborn Sugar Market Reports*, Nov. 12 and Dec. 17, 1968.
[b] United Nations estimates.
[c] F. O. Licht, *Estimates*, Nov. 21, 1968.

said to have been one of the trade monopolies of the Phoenicians and a prize captured by the Venetians, who added refining to its technology. Cane culture spread along both shores of the Mediterranean as far as the Azores and the Canary Islands to the extent that when the Spaniards started to colonize the new world in 1493, they elected to establish sugar cane culture as one facet of the economy.

The demand for sugar increased over the next four centuries, and when the

Table 3. Sugar as a World Commodity, 1966–1967, 1000 metric tons

Country	Production[a]			Imports	Exports	Consumption
	Beet[b]	Cane[b]	Noncentrifugal[c]			
Austria	363					312
Belgium and Luxembourg	414			32	91	402
Bulgaria	225			94		330
Czechoslovakia	853			165	400	620
Denmark	317			28	42	259
France	1825			523	583	1914
East Germany	687			10	84	665
West Germany	1955			108	21	2228
Great Britain	956			2285	413	2837
Hungary	473				66	400
Italy	1396			127		1512
Yugoslavia	588			150	100	540
Netherlands	586			205	6	762
Poland	1684			22	404	1269

(continued)

Table 3 (*continued*)

Country	Production[a] Beet[b]	Cane[b]	Noncentrifugal[c]	Imports	Exports	Consumption
Rumania	519				100	401
Soviet Russia	9165			1801	1295	11,101
Spain	585	45		105	1	729
Sweden	228			123	7	339
Switzerland	59			266	5	298
Turkey	776				45	584
British West Indies		905		1	750	141
Canada	151			891	18	1011
Cuba		6128			4450	510
Dominican Republic		819			605	117
Mexico		2477	59		602	1626
U.S. (excl Hawaii)	2581	1102		5964	62	9466
Hawaii		1080			1011	42
Puerto Rico		742			595	110
Argentina		1070			62	919
Brazil		4122			1132	3128
Chile	165			195		361
Colombia		596	340		156	388
Peru		732	7		372	345
Venezuela		395	19		2	346
Mauritius		561			503	30
Morocco	72			340		416
Republic of South Africa		1628			879	793
United Arab Republic		388		193		560
Australia		2446			1692	668
China	570	1850	318	880	330	2950
India		2434	2750		252	2999
Indonesia		625	150		150	630
Iran	248			326		600
Iraq	3			305		300
Japan	246	297	7	1598	3	2122
Malaysia				450	25	453
Pakistan	5	422	280	30		513
Philippines		1560	30		997	567
Taiwan		770	11		767	161
totals	37,219	28,093	4228	20,926	21,286	64,559

NOTE: F. O. Licht's *World Sugar Statistics*, 1967/1968, Ratzeburg, W. Germany (May 1968). Courtesy F. O. Licht, KG.

[a] Crop years vary according to climate and geography. [b] Raw value, ie, adjusted to 96% sucrose. [c] 50% sucrose.

Table 4. Pattern of Distribution of Sugar in the United States,[a] 1967

Distribution	Sugar refined, 1000 short tons
Industrial	
beverages	1785
bakery, cereal, and allied products	1286
confectionery and related products	1004
canned, bottled, and frozen foods, jellies, preserves, etc	843
ice cream and dairy products	486
multiple and all other food uses	424
nonfood products	66
subtotal	5894
Nonindustrial	
wholesale grocers, jobbers, and sugar dealers	2176
retail and chain grocers and sugar markets	1888
hotels, restaurants, and institutions	82
all other deliveries, including government	16
subtotal	3594
total	9488

NOTE: From *Sugar Report No. 190*, U.S. Department of Agriculture (March 1968).

[a] Represents 98.5% of deliveries by primary distributors in the continental United States.

British blockaded Napoleonic Europe in the early years of the nineteenth century, a whole new wartime industry was established—sugar beet culture and processing. The battle of Waterloo permitted the abandonment of the blockade, and the ensuing flood of West Indies sugar supplies brought the fledgling beet industry to bankruptcy.

The economic lessons of the blockade and the flood of offshore sugar were not lost on the western world, for it became the practice of governments to foster a domestic supply of sugar, either from beet or cane, by limitations on sugar imports to guarantee that at least some sugar supplies would be available in emergencies. At the same time, they purchased the remainder of their needed supplies in foreign trade.

The sugar plantations of the West Indies provided the first major market for African slaves in the new world. Abolition of this system reduced the ability of the plantation system to compete, so that the beet producers of southeastern Europe who began filling the European sugar bowl almost bankrupted the West Indies operations.

World War I provided the background for a new look at the economics of sugar, and agreements between major consuming countries and their favored suppliers were set up, such as the British Commonwealth Program and equivalent ones centering about the United States, France, and Germany.

As early as 1905, these programs had been built into an International Sugar Agreement in which net importing countries agreed to set aside quotas for their favored suppliers. At the same time, net exporters agreed to limit their production under the control of an International Sugar Council, to the end that there would be some profit for all producers.

Some facets of this world sugar trade are illustrated in Tables 1–4.

JOHN L. HICKSON
International Sugar
Research Foundation, Inc.

SPECIAL SUGARS

Lactose

Lactose, *USP* XIV (4-*O*-β-D-galactopyranosyl-D-glucopyranose, lactobiose) (**1**), $C_{12}H_{22}O_{11}$, was unknown until 1628, when Fabritius Bartolettus of Mantua reported an "essential salt" in milk serum.

lactose (**1**)

Glucose was identified as one of its components in 1812, and galactose in 1855, but the structure of lactose evaded definition until 1927. The ordinary lactose of commerce is α-lactose monohydrate. The sugar was synthesized by Haskins, Hann, and Hudson (1). See also Vol. 13, pp. 514, 565–567.

Lactose occurs in the milk of all species of mammals, including the whale, ranging in amount from 1.8% in rabbit milk to over 7% in ass and elephant milk. Cow's milk contains 2.9–5.3% lactose and human milk 4.0–8.3%. Production of lactose was begun before 1880 in the Swiss canton of Luzern. One New York firm in 1893 reported a production of 250,000 lb (2). In 1967, from a potential of about 2 million short tons in commercial milk, about 37.5 thousand short tons entered the United States market as the sugar lactose.

PHYSICAL AND CHEMICAL PROPERTIES

Lactose is a water-soluble substance prepared in three crystallized forms: α-*Lactose monohydrate* crystallizes from aqueous solution below 93.5°C as rhombic spheroidal crystals, stable in air; mp, 201.6°C; d_4^{20}, 1.525. β-*Lactose anhydrate* is prepared by crystallization from solution above 93.5°C as transparent, colorless crystals of the holoaxial-polar class of the monoclinic system, stable under reasonable humidity conditions; mp, 252.2°C. α-*Lactose anhydrate* is metastable to atmospheric moisture; mp, 222.8°C; d_4^{20}, 1.589. All forms are soluble in water, liquid ammonia, and acetic and formic acids; they are slightly soluble in 85% methanol and pyridine; and insoluble in ethyl alcohol, absolute methanol, ether, and chloroform. Water solubility is the outstanding physical property (see Vol. 13, p. 565). A definite break in the solubility curve at a temperature of 93.5° has been found to occur at the transition point, in solution, for α- and β-lactose.

Somewhat astonishingly, for a sugar, lactose is not very sweet (see Table 1, p. 152) and therefore milk-based desserts usually call for additional sweetening. Unlike sucrose, lactose is a reducing sugar.

Hydrolysis. Lactose hydrolysis is catalyzed by acids or by enzymes (lactases) from many sources. The reaction is monomolecular. Practical preparations of hydrolyzed lactose syrup are made by heating 10–30% solutions adjusted to pH 1.2–1.3 with hydrochloric or sulfuric acid, as well as through the action of lactases.

Lactases, widely distributed throughout microorganisms, plants, and animals, are of two kinds, β-D-galactosidases and β-D-glucosidases. Typical of the β-D-galactosidases are those of the *Torula* yeasts. Emulsin from bitter almonds contains a typical β-D-glucosidase lactase.

Fermentation. The best-known fermentation of lactose occurs in the souring of milk to form lactic acid. A number of organisms cause this reaction; examples are *Streptococcus lactis* and *Lactobaccillus casei* (Vol. 12, p. 175). Propionic acid in 48% yield can be made by a mixed culture of *Propionibacterium shermanii* and *L. casei*. Ethyl alcohol can be produced in 80–83% yield by *Torula lactosa*.

Oxidation. Nitric acid in various concentrations degrades lactose to galactaric and D-glucaric acids or to tartaric, oxalic, and carbonic acids. Milder acid agents produce D-gluconic and D-galactonic acids. Iodine, bromine, or copper in alkaline solutions will give lactobionic acid. Periodic acid yields tartronic, glycolic, glyceric, and formic acids, and formaldehyde.

Reduction. Sodium amalgam was reported, in 1872, to degrade lactose to galactitol, glycerol, ethyl alcohol, isopropyl alcohol, isohexyl alcohol, and sodium lactate. Catalytic hydrogenation has produced *lactitol* (**2**). Under more drastic conditions, such as a copper–chromium oxide catalyst, 300 atm, and 250°C, a variety of reductive degradation products are obtained, including 4-hydroxytetrahydrofurfuryl alcohol, and several hexamethylenetriols.

Degradation. Darkening is encountered to some extent in the pasteurization, evaporation, and drying of milk. *Lactosan* (**3**) has been identified among the intermediate degradation products. Caramel from lactose is a substitute for that from dextrose.

Action of Alkali. This follows the expected pathways varying from epimerization to the formation of saccharinic acids. One new product is *lactulose* (**4**).

lactitol (**2**)   lactosan (**3**)

lactulose (**4**)

Carbonyl Reactions. Lactose phenylosazone was one of the first osazones reported by Emil Fischer in 1884. Considerable study has been made of the structure and the properties of this osazone, for it was obtained from one of the few saccharides higher than monosaccharides that could be prepared in a high state of purity.

Lactoside Formation. Physiologically active substances such as the sterols or sulfa compounds have been solubilized by conversion to the lactosides. The lactosides, however, have received no widespread use in medicine.

Esterification. Acetates, propionates, benzoates, isocyanates, p-nitrobenzoates, nitrates, and phosphates have been described. The octanitrate has received some attention as an explosive (see p. 226).

MANUFACTURE

Industrial sources of lactose include skim milk, whey, and buttermilk (see Milk and milk products). Lactose is produced in four grades selling in January, 1969, at prices of 13.5–26¢/lb. A crude product may contain 2% protein and may develop an odor on standing.

Crude lactose is converted to a technical grade by reducing the protein content by coagulating and precipitating it in a process called defecation. This process is then followed up by decolorization, usually with carbon, to produce a product suitable for infant foods, for animal rations, for fermentation process, and for the production of explosives. A bacteriological grade for culture media meets requirements for freedom from growth factors, such as vitamins and other micronutrients, as well as contaminating organisms. This latter product is suitable for formulation into microbiological assay media for such growth factors.

PHYSIOLOGICAL PROPERTIES

Lactose has been highly recommended in infant formulations, although it may be that interpretation of the evidence has been colored, too frequently, by partisan attitudes. One of the moderately infrequent disturbances of infants is an inability to hydrolyze lactose to its monosaccharides. This is caused by a congenital defect resulting in a failure to produce an enzyme, lactase, a β-galactosidase. The presence of undigested lactose in the intestinal tract causes a high water content, causing a persistent diarrhea that sometimes can lead to fatal complications. Other deficiencies of enzymes, which also can have genetic background, can lead to a high level of blood galactose, called galactosemia. This, in the infant, is believed to lead to irreversible brain damage.

High levels of lactose in the diet (40–80%) cause rats to develop marked changes in the cornea that almost invariably progress to bilateral cataract. In some cases, there is an accompanying excessive calcium content that can be ascribed to the whole lactose molecule. The cataracts are due, however, solely to the galactose moiety. Riboflavine, to some extent, delays the onset of the cataracts, but the complete etiology is not known.

At lower levels, the unabsorbed part of dietary lactose contributes to a change in the nature of the intestinal flora. The change from primarily putrefactive to acidogenic organisms is believed to be favorable in the treatment of some digestive disorders.

Maltose

Maltose (4-O-α-D-glucopyranosyl-D-glucopyranose, maltobiose), $C_{12}H_{22}O_{11}$, is a disaccharide composed of two D-glucose residues (**5**).

maltose (5)

The free sugar rarely occurs in nature. More frequently it is encountered as a component of partially hydrolyzed starch. First preparation has been ascribed to de Saussure in 1819, although the identity of his product was not recognized until 1847 (7).

PHYSICAL AND CHEMICAL PROPERTIES

Maltose (mp, 102–103°C; α_D^{20}, + 111.7 → 130.4° (H_2O, c = 4); d_{20}^{20}, 1.540) is soluble in water, slightly soluble in ethyl alcohol, and insoluble in ether. It crystallizes from water or dilute ethyl alcohol as a stable monohydrate of the β-anomer. It is about a third as sweet as sucrose.

Maltose is a reducing sugar. Emil Fischer, in 1889, oxidized maltose to maltobionic acid and showed that it was a glucosylglucose. Attachment at the fourth carbon was demonstrated by the methylation work of Haworth and Peat in 1926.

Many of the traditional ester, ether, and carbonyl derivatives of maltose have been prepared. Their properties can be found in the compendia of Bates; Elsner; or Vogel and Georg (4,6,8). No derivative has attained commercial significance.

The principal useful properties of maltose are its ready fermentability by most yeast, and its ready digestibility.

MANUFACTURE

There have been several reports of the occurrence of free maltose in the plant world. It has been alleged to comprise 50% of the carbohydrate of *Tropaeolum* leaves and up to 1.25% of those of *Pyrola rotundifolia*, *Populus tremuloides*, and *Linnaea borealis*. Commercially, however, it is produced exclusively by hydrolysis of starch from grains (wheat, barley, or corn) or tubers (potato or manioc). It is a major component of corn syrups (see Dextrose and starch syrups) and malt (see Beer and brewing). Maltose is usually isolated by enzymic (disastase or a β-amylase) hydrolysis from impure forms of the sugar, malt, malt syrup, or maltose syrup.

Malt syrup is essentially a solution of maltose with a characteristic flavor. Refining this syrup removes the malt flavor and the product is *maltose syrup*. β-Amylase enzymes of *Aspergillus niger* or *Aspergillus oryzae* convert wheat flour to maltose to the extent of 75–85%. Removal of protein and carbon treatment give a 75% solution called maltose syrup. Malt syrup was produced to the extent of 200 million lb in 1945 (as a consequence of wartime sugar rationing) (5), but the demand for it has since decreased.

Uses. Untold amounts of maltose are produced by the malting process for captive consumption in the brewing industry. In addition to its presence in beer, malt, and corn syrup, maltose is added to soft drinks, bread doughs, confections, infant and invalid foods, yeast, bee food, printing compositions, snuff, and stamp-pad compositions. Malt syrup finds use as a flavor component in ice cream, particularly in chocolate flavors, and in baking.

Maple Sugar and Maple Syrup

Maple sugar and maple syrup are forms of sugar (sucrose) with a characteristic flavor and aroma. They are prepared by concentrating a sap collected from several varieties of maple, principally the sugar maple (*Acer saccharum*) and the black maple (*Acer saccharum nigrum*) which grow throughout the northeastern United States, southeastern Canada, and, to some extent, in northern Japan.

Average results of analyses of fifty samples of maple sap are: total solids, 3.25%; sucrose, 2.93%; invert sugar, 0.021%; ash, 0.0396%. The characteristic flavor is developed during the concentration. Sap which has been freeze-dried has none of it. By modifying the technique of evaporation, it was found practical to obtain a fourfold intensification of the maple flavor (9). Identity of the flavor component is as yet unknown. There is on the market a "maple-flavor" which is alleged to be 3-methyl-1,2-cyclopentadione. This is of interest because of its structural similarity to a tautomer of reductic acid (3-hydroxy-1,2-cyclopentadione), a product of sugar degradation (10).

Maple syrup is prepared by evaporating maple sap at atmospheric pressure until its boiling point rises to 219°F or until the specific gravity rises to 35.6° Bé at 60°F.

Under these conditions, the syrup will contain not less than 65% total solids and weigh not less than 11 lb per U.S. gal. To produce maple sugar, syrup is concentrated until the boiling point rises to 240–250°F and allowed to crystallize. Yields run about 40 gal of syrup or 300 lb of sugar from 100 trees per season (11). The U.S. Department of Agriculture recognizes three grades of syrup classified principally by color (12).

Consumption in the U.S. during 1967 totaled 29,117,000 lb of maple sugar, including the sugar equivalent of 2,928,000 lb of maple syrup. Of this total, 18,348,000 lb was imported from Canada (13).

Bibliography

"Commercial Sugars" in *ECT* 1st ed., Vol. 13, pp. 244–251, by J. L. Hickson, Sugar Research Foundation, Inc.

Lactose

1. W. T. Haskins, R. M. Hann, and C. S. Hudson, *J. Am. Chem. Soc.* **64**, 1852–1856 (1942).
2. J. R. Klamp, L. Hough, J. L. Hickson, and R. L. Whistler, "Lactose," *Advan. Carbohydrate Chem.* **16**, 150–206 (1961).
3. E. O. Whittier and B. H. Webb, *By-Products from Milk*, Reinhold Publishing Corp., New York, 1950.

Maltose

4. F. J. Bates et al., *Polarimetry, Saccharimetry, and the Sugars*, Circ. C440, U.S. National Bureau of Standards, 1942.
5. A. Effron and R. H. Bloom, *Ind. Eng. Chem.* **40**, 412–415 (1948).
6. H. Elsner, *Kurzes Handbuch der Kohlenhydrate*, Johann Ambrosius Barth, Leipzig, 1935.
7. T. S. Harding, *Sugar* **25**, 350–352 (1923).
8. H. Vogel and A. Georg, *Tabellen der Zucker und ihrer Derivate*, Springer-Verlag, Berlin, 1931.

Maple Sugar and Maple Syrup

9. U.S. Pat. 2,549,877 (April 24, 1951), C. O. Willits and W. L. Porter (to U.S.A.).
10. L. Sattler, private communication to author, 1954.
11. C.O. Willits, *Maple Sirup Pryducers Manual*, Agriculture Handbook No. 134, rev. ed., U.S. Dept. of Agriculture, Washington, D.C., 1965.
12. *U.S. Standards for Grades of Maple Syrup*, 1st issue as amended, effective May 24, 1967, *Fed. Reg.*, May 24, 1967 (32 F. R. 7579).
13. J. C. Lewis, J. J. Stubbs, and W. M. Noble, "Vitamin Synthesis by Totula Yeast," *Arch. Biochem.* **4** (3), 389 (1944).

J. L. HICKSON

International Sugar Research Foundation, Inc.

SULFA DRUGS.   See Sulfonamides.

SULFAMIC ACID AND SULFAMATES

Sulfamic acid, NH_2SO_2OH, is the monoamide of sulfuric acid.   It was a laboratory curiosity for almost 100 years until new and practical methods of manufacture were discovered in 1936.   Rose is credited with the first actual preparation about 1836.   The pure acid was prepared later by E. Berglund.   Sulfamic acid is produced commercially by reacting urea, sulfur trioxide, and sulfuric acid.

In 1957 the IUPAC Commission on the Nomenclature of Inorganic Chemistry recommended the name "amidosulfuric acid" for sulfamic acid;   however, the older name is still in general use.

Principal applications of sulfamic acid are in metal cleaners, scale removers, detergent manufacture, and as a stabilizer for chlorine.   The salts of sulfamic acid are used in flame retardants, weed and brush killers, synthetic sweeteners, and for electroplating.   Production is some thousands of tons annually for the United States.   The selling price for truckloads or carloads in 1968 ranged between $14.75 and $16.00 per 100 lb, depending on grade.

Properties

Sulfamic acid is a dry, nonvolatile, nonhygroscopic, odorless, white, crystalline solid.   Stability is the outstanding physical property of the acid.   In fact, the crystals may be kept in the laboratory for years without change, and are a convenient standard for titrimetry.   Other physical properties of the acid are listed in Table 1 (see also refs. 1 and 2).

Table 1.   Some Physical Properties of Sulfamic Acid

melting point, °C	205
density, g/cm³	2.126
dissociation constant, 25°C	1.01×10^{-1}
refractive indexes, 25 ± 3°C	
α	1.553
β	1.563
γ	1.568

In aqueous solution it is highly ionized and strongly acidic.   The pH of a 1% solution is 1.18.   Sulfamic acid is moderately soluble in water;   14.68 g will dissolve in 100 g of water at 0°C and 47.08 g at 80°C (3). It is soluble in formamide, but insoluble in most other organic liquids.

Sulfamic acid crystallizes in the orthorhombic system with a unit cell of eight molecules. Tablets and compact prisms are obtained from cold aqueous solutions; large, lozenge-shaped plates are obtained on cooling hot aqueous solutions.

Inorganic Reactions. Sulfamic acid begins to decompose at 209°C. At 260°C decomposition produces sulfur dioxide, sulfur trioxide, nitrogen, water, and other products.

Dilute aqueous solutions of sulfamic acid are stable for many months at room temperature. At higher temperatures, however, hydrolysis of the acid and its ammonium salt is comparatively rapid, forming ammonium hydrogen sulfate and ammonium sulfate, respectively.

$$NH_2SO_3H + H_2O \rightarrow NH_4HSO_4$$

$$NH_2SO_3NH_4 + H_2O \rightarrow (NH_4)_2SO_4$$

The rate of hydrolysis is regulated by concentration, temperature, and pH (3). Hydrolysis of various concentrations of sulfamic acid at 80°C is illustrated in Table 2.

Table 2. Hydrolysis of Sulfamic Acid in Aqueous Solutions at 80°C, %

Time, hr	Solution		
	1%	10%	30%
1	4.54	7.75	7.85
2	9.07	15.07	15.14
5	16.86	28.28	27.49
7	24.18	39.51	37.49

The hydrolysis is highly exothermic, and if a concentrated aqueous solution of ammonium sulfamate is heated in a closed container or one with insufficient venting, it can generate sufficient steam pressure to cause an explosion (4). Amine sulfamates behave similarly. For example, a 60% solution of ammonium sulfamate will begin "runaway" hydrolysis at 200°C at pH 5, and at 130°C at pH 2. However, since the boiling point of a 60% solution of ammonium sulfamate in an open container is 107°C, the hazard of a "runaway" hydrolysis is minimal.

Alkali metal sulfamates are stable in neutral or alkaline solutions, even at the boiling point.

In liquid ammonia, sulfamic acid behaves as a dibasic acid; one hydrogen of the amino group and one hydrogen of the sulfonic group are replaceable by sodium, potassium, etc, to give salts of the formula $NaNHSO_3Na$, etc.

Chlorine, bromine, and chlorates oxidize sulfamic acid to sulfuric acid and to nitrogen.

$$2 NH_2SO_3H + KClO_3 \rightarrow 2 H_2SO_4 + N_2 + KCl + H_2O$$

Pure nitrous oxide is obtained by the reaction of concentrated nitric acid with sulfamic acid.

$$NH_2SO_3H + HNO_3 \rightarrow H_2SO_4 + H_2O + N_2O$$

Nitrous acid reacts very rapidly and quantitatively with sulfamic acid, yielding nitrogen gas.

$$NH_2SO_3H + HNO_2 \rightarrow H_2SO_4 + H_2O + N_2$$

Hypochlorous acid at low temperature forms N-chlorosulfamic acid.

$$NH_2SO_3H + HOCl \rightarrow NHClSO_3H + H_2O$$

Sulfamyl chloride is formed by reaction of thionyl chloride with sulfamic acid.

$$NH_2SO_3H + SOCl_2 \rightarrow NH_2SO_2Cl + HCl + SO_2$$

Reaction of certain metal iodides such as those of sodium, potassium, cesium, and rubidium with sulfamic acid forms the triiodides (5).

$$2\ NH_2SO_3H + 3\ CsI + H_2O \rightarrow CsI_3 + Cs_2SO_4 + (NH_4)_2SO_3$$

Organic Reactions. Audrieth and co-workers have reviewed the organic reactions of sulfamic acid (6).

Primary alcohols react with sulfamic acid to form ammonium alkyl sulfates:

$$ROH + NH_2SO_3H \rightarrow ROSO_2ONH_4$$

Secondary alcohols react in the presence of an amide catalyst such as acetamide or urea, but tertiary alcohols do not react (7).

Phenol, cresols, xylenols, naphthols, pyrocatechol, resorcinol, hydroquinone, anisole, phenetole, and phenyl ether are sulfonated when treated with sulfamic acid. In most instances, ammonium aryl sulfates are formed as intermediates and the sulfonate results from a subsequent rearrangement. Thus with phenol:

$$C_6H_5OH + NH_2SO_3H \rightarrow C_6H_5OSO_2ONH_4 \rightarrow HOC_6H_4SO_2ONH_4$$

Phenyl derivatives such as anethole, styrene, and isosafrole with unsaturated alkyl side chains are sulfonated in the side chain by reaction with sulfamic acid.

Amides react in certain cases to form ammonium salts of sulfonated amides. For example, treatment with benzamide yields the ammonium salt of N-benzoylsulfamic acid, $C_6H_5CONHSO_2ONH_4$, and, with ammonium sulfamate, yields diammonium imidodisulfonate, $HN(SO_2ONH_4)_2$.

Aldehydes form addition products with sulfamic acid salts. These are stable in neutral or slightly alkaline solutions, but are hydrolyzed in acid and strongly alkaline solutions. With formaldehyde, the salt of the methylol (hydroxymethyl) derivative, $Ca(O_3SNHCH_2OH)_2$, is readily obtained as a crystalline solid.

Cadmium, cobalt, copper, and nickel sulfamates react with lower aliphatic aldehydes. These stable compositions are reported to be suitable for use in electroplating solutions for deposition of the respective metals.

The N-alkyl and N-cyclohexyl derivatives of sulfamic acid are comparatively stable and may be isolated; the N-aryl derivatives are very unstable and can only be obtained in the form of their salts. A series of stable thiazolylsulfamic acids has been prepared.

Sulfation by sulfamic acid has been used, especially in Germany, in the preparation of detergents from dodecyl, oleyl, and other higher alcohols. Secondary alcohols may be sulfated readily by addition of pyridine.

Cellulose sulfated with sulfamic acid has been reported to show less degradation than the customary product from sulfuric acid (8). Cellulose esters of sulfamic acids are formed by the reaction of sulfamyl halides in the presence of tertiary organic bases.

Analysis

Sulfamic acid or the sulfamate ion may be quantitatively determined by reaction with nitrite ion:

$$NaNO_2 + NH_2SO_3H \rightarrow NaHSO_4 + N_2 + H_2O$$

Bowler and Arnold (9) utilized this reaction in a rapid direct titration method using a starch–iodide external indicator. Accuracy was comparable with that of the older gravimetric methods involving oxidation of sulfamate to sulfate. A gasometric method (10) depending on measurement of the nitrogen evolved can be performed with simple apparatus or can be adapted to micro procedures where the accuracy is $\pm 5\%$ and the operation requires only 20 min. The reaction is specific for the amino group and very few ions interfere.

Sulfamic acid and its salts retard the precipitation of barium sulfate. To determine accurately any sulfate derived from hydrolysis of sulfamic acid, it is essential to let the barium sulfate precipitate stand overnight.

Manufacture

Sulfamic acid is manufactured by the reaction of equimolal quantities of urea, sulfur trioxide, and sulfuric acid (11). The reaction, which is strongly exothermic, may be represented stoichiometrically:

$$NH_2CONH_2 + SO_3 + H_2SO_4 \rightarrow 2\,NH_2SO_3H + CO_2$$

The reaction is considered theoretically to take place in two steps:

$$NH_2CONH_2 + SO_3 \rightarrow HSO_3NHCONH_2 \tag{1}$$
$$\text{carbamidomonosulfonic acid}$$

$$HSO_3NHCONH_2 + H_2SO_4 \rightarrow 2\,NH_2SO_3H + CO_2 \tag{2}$$

Excess liquid sulfur trioxide may be used as a reaction medium. A liquid mixture of equimolar quantities of urea and sulfuric acid is added to a large excess of liquid sulfur trioxide while agitating and cooling to prevent the formation of carbon dioxide. After completion of the initial reaction, the mass is heated further to produce sulfamic acid. The excess sulfur trioxide is removed by either distillation or spray drying, or both, or by flaking.

The salts of sulfamic acid are manufactured by neutralizing the acid with the appropriate hydroxide or carbonate. Ammonium sulfamate is the most important commercial salt. It is manufactured by adding anhydrous ammonia and sulfamic acid to ammonium sulfamate mother liquor from a preceding crystallization until a hot, concentrated solution of ammonium sulfamate is formed (12). The anhydrous ammonia is added slowly with agitation while the heat of reaction is removed by cooling coils. The hot, concentrated ammonium sulfamate solution is then run to crystallizers from which ammonium sulfamate crystals are recovered; the cold mother liquor is returned to the neutralization step.

Health and Safety Factors

Although brief contact of dry crystalline sulfamic acid with the skin causes no noticeable ill effect, precautions should be taken to avoid contact with the eyes, skin, or clothing. The action of sulfamic acid on the skin is limited to the effects of low pH. It is suggested that both goggles and gloves be worn when handling sulfamic acid dry or in solution. In the event of contact, flush skin with water; for eyes, flush with plenty of water and get medical attention.

Sulfamic acid presents no fire or explosion hazard and evolves no fumes.

Ammonium sulfamate, like the more common ammonium salts, such as the chloride or sulfate, is neither very irritating to the skin nor very toxic.

Sulfamates

Sulfamic acid readily forms salts by reaction with oxides, hydroxides, carbonates, or active metals. With the exception of the basic mercury salt, its salts are very soluble, particularly the lead salt.

Precise solubility determinations are available for only a few salts (13). The solubility of sodium sulfamate (14) has been determined from 0 to 55°C. At 0°C, 79.90 g dissolves in 100 g of water; at 55°C, 191.30 g dissolves in 100 g of water. Below the transition point (38.3°C), the solid phase in equilibrium with the saturated solution is the monohydrate, a waxy, difficultly filterable material; above the transition point, the anhydrous salt is formed. The anhydrous salt melts at 250°C.

Ammonium sulfamate is five times as soluble in water as ammonium chloride (200.2 g dissolves in 100 g of water at 20°C) and very soluble in glycerol, glycols, and formamide. The pH of a 5% (0.44N) solution is 5.2. Ammonium sulfamate melts at 132.9°C.

King and Hoopes (15) give comprehensive tables of solubilities for calcium, barium, and magnesium salts from 0 to 100°C. The relative viscosity and relative density of aqueous solutions of the acid and the ammonium, magnesium, calcium, and barium salts have been determined for several concentrations at 25°C (16).

Lead sulfamate gives solutions with high densities (2.18 g/ml at 68.5%) which may be used for determining the density of heavy solids.

Uses

Flame Retardants. Ammonium sulfamate is extensively used in formulated, nondurable, flame-retarding agents for cellulosic materials (17). It does not cause stiffening or otherwise adversely affect the hand and appearance of paper and fabrics. Because the sulfamates are water soluble, retreatment is required whenever fabrics are laundered or otherwise subjected to water leaching.

Flame retardants based on sulfamates are used to treat service clothing, drapes and curtains, decorative materials, blankets, and wearing apparel. See Fire-resistant textiles.

Softening Agents. Certain amine sulfamates have been found to have outstanding properties as softeners for paper and textiles (18,19). Compared with other commonly used softening agents, their softening action is longer lasting and is better at low humidities.

Weed and Brush Killers. Sulfamic acid and certain of its salts have proved to be highly effective weed killers. Ammonium sulfamate is a nonselective killer for weeds, brush, stumps, and trees. See Weed killers.

Acid Cleaning. Sulfamic acid is an outstanding choice for acid-cleaning applications. Because of its dry form it is easy to formulate, transport, and handle. It forms soluble salts with most metals and is generally less corrosive to metals than the common inorganic acids (Table 3).

Table 3. Relative Corrosion Rates of 3% Aqueous Solutions of Acids at $72 \pm 4°F$

| Metal | Relative Corrosion Rate (Sulfamic Acid = 1.0) | |
	H_2SO_4	HCl
1010 steel	2.6	4.2
cast iron	3.2	3.2
galvanized iron	63.0	a
tin plate	81.0	23.0
304 stainless	10.0	a
zinc	2.2	a
copper	1.5	6.7
brass	1.5	2.8
bronze	4.0	7.0
aluminum	0.6	5.3

[a] Very rapid corrosion.

These advantages of sulfamic acid have led to its use in acid cleaners in the following fields: in air conditioning for the removal of rust, algae, and hard-water scales from cooling tower systems and evaporative condensers; in marine equipment for the periodic removal of scales from seawater evaporators (distillation units), heat exchangers, and salt water heaters; for cleaning items such as copper-bottomed kettles, steam irons, dishwashers, silverware, toilet bowls, bricks and tiles; in food and dairy processing equipment for removing hard-water scale and protein deposits on cooking and pasteurizing equipment in meat, vegetable, and dairy processing plants. Sulfamic acid is authorized by the United States Department of Agriculture for use in official meat, poultry, rabbit, and egg processing establishments as an acid cleaner for use in all departments.

Sulfamic acid is also used for cleaning steam boilers, condensers, heat exchangers, jacketed equipment, and piping in the chemical process industries (20–22); in brewery equipment for removal of beerstone in glass-lined tanks, kettle and open beer coolers, and beer kegs (23); for cleaning sugar evaporators in both cane sugar and beet sugar refineries (24); in paper mills for conditioning of papermakers' felts, Fourdrinier wires, and cylinder molds, and for descaling black-liquor evaporators and clad digesters (25). Sulfamic acid is approved by the Federal Food and Drug Administration under section 121.101h, "Substances migrating to food from paper and paperboard products used in food packaging that are generally recognized as safe for their intended use, within the meaning of section 409 of the Act" (Food, Drug, and Cosmetic Act as amended, 1958).

Sulfamic acid is used for cleaning or "acidizing" water, oil, and gas wells (26).

Nitrite Removal. One of the first industrial applications to be developed for sulfamic acid is based on its reaction with nitrous acid. This reaction is rapid and quantitative (see above under Analysis). The reaction is applied commercially in eliminatimg the excess nitrite employed in diazotization reactions for dye and colored pigment manufacture, for piece dyeing of fabrics, and for certain types of leather dyeing. In piece-dyeing procedures, sulfamic acid can eliminate all but one of the rinsings normally carried out, with resultant savings in time and water usage.

Other oxides of nitrogen react similarly and can be removed quantitatively and easily from such materials as sulfuric acid and hydrochloric acid.

Electroplating and Electroforming. Most metal sulfamates are soluble and the solutions conduct electricity well; this makes them useful as electroplating salts.

Deposits from the sulfamates of cadmium, cobalt, copper, indium, lead, nickel, rhodium, or silver, for example, are bright and dense. Plating baths of nickel sulfamate give excellent deposits for electroforming (27).

Baths of aluminum sulfamate are often preferred for the anodic oxidation of aluminum and aluminum alloys. They give abrasion- and corrosion-resistant finishes with good dye receptivity (28).

Sweetening Agents. Salts of cyclohexylsulfamic acid can be prepared directly from sulfamic acid and cyclohexylamine or a substituted cyclohexylamine:

$$2\ RNH_2 + NH_2SO_3H \rightarrow NHRSO_2ONH_3R + NH_3$$

Treatment with sodium or calcium hydroxide gives the corresponding salt, eg $NHRSO_2ONa$ (29). Sodium cyclohexylsulfamate is a well-known sweetening agent. See Sweeteners.

Stabilization of Chlorine. A major use for sulfamic acid is in the broad field of chlorine stabilization. When chlorine gas is dissolved in water, the following equilibrium is established:

$$Cl_2 + H_2O \rightleftarrows HOCl + HCl$$

Upon the addition of sulfamic acid, N-chlorosulfamic acid is prepared:

$$HOCl + NH_2SO_3H \rightarrow NHClSO_3H + H_2O$$

The chlorine here is still active, but the equilibrium with free chlorine is shifted to the right, reducing losses by volatilization; reactivity of the chlorine is also reduced. For these reasons, sulfamic acid is utilized in conjunction with chlorine in such places as swimming pools (30), cooling towers (31), and paper mills (32) to control microorganisms, and in paper pulp for bleaching.

The use of sulfamic acid in paper pulp bleaching is reviewed in a Du Pont Company bulletin (33), and in papers by R. U. Tobar (34), J. M. Robinson and D. Santmyers (35), and L. C. Aldrich (36). Some of the observed benefits include a reduction of pulp degradation, an increase of pulp brightness, and an improvement of bleach plant efficiency.

Analytical Uses. Sulfamic acid has been recommended as a standard of reference in acidimetry (37). The acid is readily purified by recrystallization and air drying to give a stable product analyzing 99.95% pure. A variety of indicators are suitable; bromothymol blue gives a sharp change from yellow at pH 6.4 to blue at pH 7.0.

The procedure for the determination of sulfamic acid with nitrite has been adapted in reverse for the determination of nitrite ion. Sulfamic acid improves the Winkler method for determining dissolved oxygen in water (38). Sulfamic acid is used for removal of nitrites in the Marshall procedure for determining the sulfanilamide content of blood.

Other Uses. Sulfamic acid is used in the sulfation of polyether alcohols. See Sulfonation and sulfation. A number of resins have been prepared by condensing the methylol sulfamates with melamine or urea. Possible uses include water-repellents, sizing materials, and laminating agents. Sulfamic acid has been found to be a good curing agent for phenolics because it has fewer objectionable effects than other inorganic acids and is faster acting than organic acids. Polyamine sulfamates have been shown to produce easier handling crum when used as a coagulating aid for styrene–butadiene rubber (39). Sulfamic acid has been employed as a wash to remove deleterious metallic impurities in the preparation of improved halophosphate phosphors for lamps (40).

Bibliography

"Sulfamic Acid" in *ECT* 1st ed., Vol. 13, pp. 285–294, by Gilberta G. Torrey, E. I. du Pont de Nemours & Co., Inc., Grasselli Chemicals Department.

1. E. G. Taylor, R. P. Desch, and A. J. Catotti, *J. Am. Chem. Soc.* **73**, 74–77 (1951).
2. E. J. King and G. W. King, *J. Am. Chem. Soc.* **74**, 1212–1215 (1952).
3. M. E. Cupery, *Ind. Eng. Chem.* **30**, 627–631 (1938).
4. J. K. Hunt, *Chem. Eng. News* **30**, 707 (1952); *Chem. Week* **69** (11), 2, 4 (1951).
5. P. Sakellaridis, *Bull. Soc. Chem. Biol.*, Nos. 9–10, 610–611 (Sept.-Oct. 1951).
6. L. F. Audrieth, M. Sveda, H. H. Sisler, and M. J. Butler, *Chem. Revs.* **26**, 49–94 (1940).
7. U.S. Pat. 2,452,943 (Nov. 2, 1948), Malkemus et al. (to Colgate-Palmolive-Peet Company).
8. U.S. Pat. 2,511,229 (June 13, 1950), J. C. Thomas (to E. I. du Pont de Nemours & Co., Inc.).
9. W. W. Bowler and E. A. Arnold, *Anal. Chem.* **19**, 336–337 (1947).
10. W. N. Carson, Jr., *Anal. Chem.* **23**, 1016–1019 (1951).
11. U.S. Pat. 2,880,064 (March 31, 1959), M. L. Harbaugh and G. A. Pierce (to E. I. du Pont de Nemours & Co., Inc.); P. Baumgarten, *Ber.* **69**, 1926–1937 (1936); U.S. Pat. 2,102,350 (Dec. 14, 1937), P. Baumgarten (to E. I. du Pont de Nemours & Co., Inc.); U.S. Pat. 2,191,754 (Feb. 27, 1940), M. E. Cupery (to E. I. du Pont de Nemours & Co., Inc.).
12. U.S. Pat. 2,487,480 (Nov. 8, 1949), C. A. Rohrmann (to E. I. du Pont de Nemours & Co., Inc.).
13. J. E. Ricci and B. J. Selekson, *J. Am. Chem. Soc.* **69**, 995–998 (1947).
14. S. H. Lanning and P. A. Vander Meulen, *J. Am. Chem. Soc.* **69**, 1828–1830 (1947).
15. G. B. King and J. F. Hoopes, *J. Phys. Chem.* **45**, 938–942 (1941).; K. A. Craig, *Tappi* **42**, 792–796 (1959).
16. A. F. Schenelezle and J. E. Westfall, *J. Phys. Chem.* **48**, 165–168 (1944).
17. U.S. Pat. 2,723,212 (Nov. 8, 1955), R. Aarons and P. Wilson (to E. I. du Pont de Nemours & Co., Inc.).
18. F. T. Blakemore, *Am. Paper Converter* **23** (6), 11, 29 (1949).
19. U.S. Pat. 2,526,462 (Oct. 17, 1950), O. Edelstein (to Pond Lily Co.).
20. H. E. Graham, et al., *Am. Ry. Eng. Assoc., Bull.* **59**, 524–526 (1957).
21. C. T. Gallinger, *Oil Gas J.* **61** (31), 102–105 (1963).
22. C. T. Gallinger, *Mater. Protect.* **5** (1), 39–42 (1966).
23. J. F. Neumeister, Sr., *Am. Brewer* **86** (10), 43–44 (1953).
24. M. Avaloo and A. G. Keller, *Sugar News* **32**, 398–406 (1956).
25. J. W. Thomas, *Can. Pulp Paper Ind.* **16**, 36–39 (1963).
26. *Oil Gas J.* **57** (23), 178 (1959).
27. R. A. F. Hammond, *Nickel Plating from Sulphamate Solutions*, International Nickel Co. (mond) Ltd., 1964.
28. U.S. Pats. 3,384,561, 3,384,562 (May 21, 1958), C. E. Michelson, H. Montgomery, and D. C. Montgomery (to Olin Mathieson Chemical Corp.).
29. Brit. Pat. 662,800 (Dec. 12, 1951), (to Abbott Laboratories).
30. L. S. Stuart and L. F. Ortenzio, *Soap Chem. Specialties* **40** (8), 79–82, 112–113 (1964).
31. U.S. Pat. 3,170,883 (Feb. 23, 1965), R. W. Owens and S. Thomas, Jr. (to Cortez Chemicals Co.).
32. U.S. Pat. 3,328,294 (June 27, 1967), R. W. Self, J. C. Watkins, Jr., and J. K. Sullins (to Mead Corp.).
33. *The Use of Du Pont Sulfamic Acid in Paper Pulp Bleaching*, Bull. No. 48171, E. I. du Pont de Nemours & Co., Inc.
34. R. U. Tobar, *Paper Trade J.* **150**, 36 (1966).
35. J. M. Robinson and D. Santmyers, *Paper Trade J.* **151**, 52–53 (1967).
36. L. C. Aldrich, *Tappi* **51**, 71A–74A (1968).
37. Sister M. M. Caso and M. Cefola, *Anal. Chim. Acta* **21**, 205–214 (1959).
38. I. Nusbaum, *Water Sewage Works* **105**, 469–471 (1958).
39. U.S. Pat. 3,350,371 (Oct. 31, 1967), D. Santmyers (to E. I. du Pont de Nemours & Co., Inc.).
40. U.S. Pat. 3,384,598 (May 21, 1968), A. I. Friedman and D. H. Beaumont (to General Electric Co.).

DONALD SANTMYERS AND RALPH AARONS
E. I. du Pont de Nemours & Co., Inc.

SULFANILAMIDE.   See Sulfonamides.

SULFANILIC ACID, $p\text{-}H_2NC_6H_4SO_3H$.   See Aniline, Vol. 2, p. 424.

SULFATED ACIDS, ALCOHOLS, OILS, etc.   See Sulfonation and sulfation; Surfactants.

SULFATE PROCESS.   See Pulp, Vol. 16, p. 702.

SULFATES.   See such articles as Ammonium compounds; Barium compounds; also Sulfuric and sulfurous esters.

SULFATION.   See Sulfonation and sulfation.

SULFIDES.   See such articles as Ammonium compounds; Barium compounds; also Thiols.

SULFINOL PROCESS.   See Sulfur compounds.

SULFITE PROCESS.   See Pulp.

SULFITES.   See such articles as Barium compounds; see also Sulfur compounds; Sulfuric and sulfurous esters.

SULFOALKYLATION.   See Sulfonation and sulfation.

SULFOCHLORINATION.   See Sulfonation and sulfation; Sulfurization of oils.

SULFOLANE

Sulfolane (tetrahydrothiophene 1,1-dioxide; tetramethylene sulfone), $C_4H_8O_2$, is a colorless, highly polar, water-soluble compound of outstanding solvent properties and exceptional chemical and thermal stability.

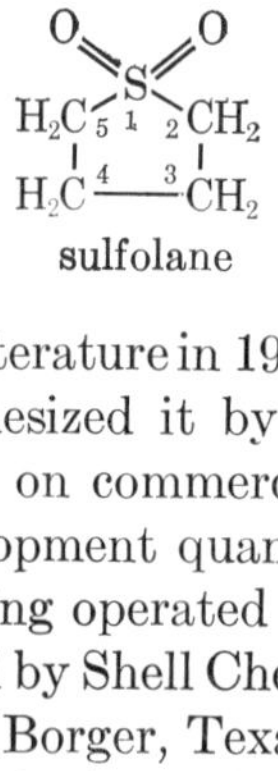

sulfolane

Sulfolane first appeared in the literature in 1916, when it was reported by Grischkevitch-Trokhimovskii (1), who synthesized it by oxidizing tetrahydrothiophene with permanganate.   Development work on commercial sulfolane synthesis was initiated about 1940.   In 1959 market development quantities of sulfolane became available. In 1961 a commercial plant was being operated by Shell at Stanlow, England.   Domestically, sulfolane is manufactured by Shell Chemical Company at Norco, Louisiana, and Phillips Petroleum Company at Borger, Texas.   Sulfolane may be synthesized by several routes (2,3); commercial synthesis can be by the hydrogenation of 3-sulfolene (2,5-dihydrothiophene 1,1-dioxide), which is the cyclic reaction product of butadiene and sulfur dioxide, ie,

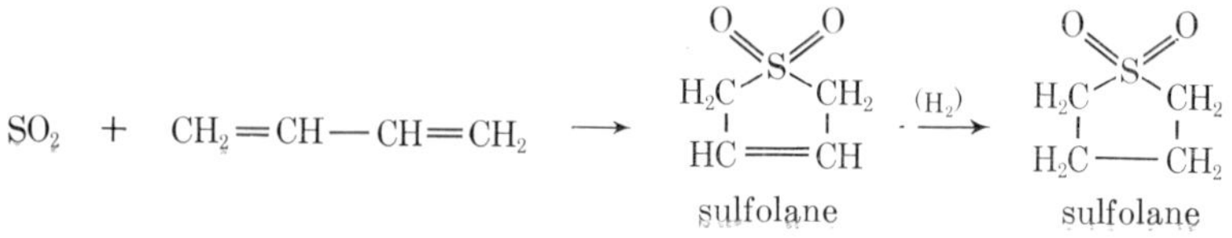

Table 1. Physical Properties

Property	Value
specific gravity at 30/30°C	1.266
boiling point, °C	285
freezing point, °C	27.4–27.8
flash point (Cleveland)	
open cup, °F	350

Table 2. Vapor Pressure, $\log P$ (mm Hg) $= 28.6824 - 4350.7/T$ (°K) $- 6.5633T$ (°K)

t, °C	P, mm Hg
150	14.53
200	85.23
250	333.7

Most classes of organic compounds and polymers are soluble in or miscible with sulfolane. Exceptions are paraffinic and alicyclic compounds and methacrylate, styrene, and vinylidene chloride polymers (4).

Sulfolane exhibits good thermal stability up to temperatures of 220°C. At this temperature it very slowly produces sulfur dioxide and unsaturated, probably polymeric, material which imparts a brownish color to the product (5).

Sulfolane is generally unreactive with chemicals such as acids, mercaptans, and diolefins, and under ordinary conditions will not polymerize or decompose in the presence of acids or bases. During five hours at reflux temperatures, no reaction was observed between sulfolane and potassium carbonate, sodium acetate, 25% aqueous sodium hydroxide, or copper and iron strips. In the temperature range of 140–150C° some reaction occurs between sulfolane 93% sulfuric acid, and there is an appreciable reaction between sulfolane and aluminum chloride with the evolution of hydrogen chloride (4).

Sulfolane is resistant to reduction to the cyclic sulfide, being unaffected by either zinc or acetic and hydrochloric acid reagents. However, a 75% yield of the sulfide is reported with use of lithium aluminum hydride (6), and a 40% conversion is reported with vapor-phase hydrogenation at 350°C and 150 psig over molybdenum sulfide catalyst (7,8).

Corrosion tests on sulfolane itself and with small amounts of water and hydrocarbon gave negligible results at 200°C (392°F) on carbon steel (about 1 mil/yr) (5).

Applications

Applications of sulfolane derive primarily from its unusual solvent properties and chemical and thermal stability.

Acid Gas Removal. Sulfolane has received wide interest as a solvent in the Sulfinol process (Shell Development Company) for the removal of acid gases, such as H_2S, CO_2, COS, and mercaptans, from a variety of sour gas streams. The process combines sulfolane with any one of a number of alkanolamines for simultaneous selective physical and chemical absorption of the acidic components, and their subsequent release at ambient pressure and somewhat elevated temperature. Significant savings over conventional processes are shown for the purification of a variety of sour natural gases, of refinery gases, and of hydrogen streams from synthesis gases.

Extraction of Aromatic Hydrocarbons. Sulfolane is the preferred solvent in a number of liquid–liquid and liquid–vapor extraction applications. A major application of the Sulfolane Extraction Process is in the liquid–liquid extraction of BTX aromatics from reformate or hydrotreated pyrolysis naphtha feeds. It yields purity at 99.9+ with almost 100% recovery. Because sulfolane has high solvency and selectivity for aromatics, utility consumption is minimized and capital investment costs are quickly realized (5,9–13).

The same general scheme has been extensively studied in relation to fractionating gasoline, for enrichment of aromatics with attendant improvement of octane number for automotive fuel, and for producing at the same time a raffinate stream enriched in saturates for jet-engine fuel (5).

Extractive Distillation of Closely Boiling Products. It has been demonstrated that sulfolane effectively separates n-propyl alcohol and sec-butyl alcohol (2-butanol). These alcohols are resistant to separation by fractional distillation, as both their anhydrous and water binary-azeotrope boiling points are within 1.7°C of each other. The separation is readily accomplished through extractive distillation, when sulfolane is used as a reflux liquid to depress the vapor pressure of the 2-butanol for isolation of n-propyl alcohol and any water present in the overhead stream; the butanol and sulfolane are recovered as a bottoms product.

Similar systems have been studied and proposed for separation of other close low-boiling mixtures such as butane and 2-butene (14) and close high-boiling materials such as 1-methylnaphthalene from kerosene streams. Unsaturated fatty acids have been separated by this method at reduced pressure (15).

Fractionation of Fatty Acids and Oils. Fractionation of fatty acids into saturated and unsaturated portions has been effected through liquid-phase extraction with sulfolane. In a single-stage operation a fatty acid mixture of oleic and linoleic acids of iodine number 131 was separated into fractions of iodine isotope 142 in the extract phase and iodine value 125 in the raffinate (16). Hence, multistage extraction should have a pronounced effect and be of value in producing drying and nondrying fractions from semidrying acids, such as from soybean oil, and in the fractionation of the original glycerides into saturates and polyunsaturates.

Recovery of Sulfur Dioxide (17). Sulfur dioxide has been recovered from dilute streams through absorption in sulfolane at atmospheric or higher pressure. It is isolated by increasing temperature and/or reducing pressure. The solubility of sulfur dioxide in sulfolane at 20°C and 1 atm is about 0.65 lb per lb of sulfolane and, at 75°C, about 0.115 lb sulfur dioxide per lb sulfolane. Advantages over water absorption are the recovery of anhydrous sulfur dioxide, the noncorrosive system, the much higher absorptive capacity of sulfolane, and the lower heat requirement for volatilization of sulfur dioxide from sulfolane solution.

Miscellaneous Extraction Applications. Sulfolane has been suggested for fractionating and decolorizing noncellulosic wood products, such as pyroligneous liquids, tars, and tall oil (18). It has been suggested as being applicable in the separation of a wide variety of mixed coal and agricultural chemical products (14). It reportedly did not increase the relative volatility of m- and p-xylene sufficiently to allow practical use in extractive distillation separation (19).

Reaction Solvent. Sulfolane has been studied in a number of cases as a reaction solvent when anhydrous systems were desired and the high polarity and exceptional solvent properties of sulfolane could improve yields and reaction rates. Pyridine,

4-picoline, and 4-isopropylpyridine are quaternized quantitatively in sulfolane solvent with n-butyl bromide at 25, 50, and 75°C, following second-order kinetics. The quaternization starts for poly(4-vinylpyridine) at the same rate as for the monomeric amines, but later decreases. Sulfolane does not give side reactions as do nitrobenzene and dimethylformamide solvents (20).

Sulfolane has also been used as the reaction medium for the preparation of isocyanates from phosgene and amine salts (21).

Polymer Solvent. Considerable studies have been made of the use of sulfolane as a spinning and casting solvent for acrylonitrile (22–30). As an example, a 15% solution of a polyacrylonitrile homopolymer of 120,000 molecular weight is made from 200-mesh polymer by heating at 140°C for 30 min. The solution is clear and has a viscosity of 600 P at this temperature. This solution can be cast at 150°C on polished metal surfaces at 175°C to form thin, tough, transparent, and tear-resistant films, or it can be spun at about 150°C in an evaporative spinning cell to obtain strong flexible fibers (27). Studies have also been made of sulfolane in solvent systems for polyvinyl chloride (31), polyvinyl fluoride (32), and polyvinylidene cyanide (33) for spinning and casting application.

Special Applications. Low-melting mixtures of sulfolane and other sulfones are indicated for use as dielectrics in electrical condensers of high capacity to reduce the size of the condenser (34). The dielectric constant of sulfolane at 30°C is 44, an unusually high value for an organic liquid (35).

The application of sulfolane in hydraulic fluids in admixtures with other liquids, such as castor oil and glycols, has been suggested in view of the good thermal stability, low volatility, noncorrosivity, and low toxicity of the compound (36).

Up to 30% of sulfolane has been incorporated into water-soluble cellulose esters, such as methylcellulose, hydroxyethylcellulose, and carboxymethylcellulose, to act as a flexibilizer. When 30% sulfolane was blended with unmodified methylcellulose, elongation was increased from 10 to 28%—with a retention of 22% after two weeks' bake at 100°C—without serious loss in tensile strength (37).

The compound has been found attractive as a printing assistant in textile-printing paste formulations. Use of some 18% sulfolane in gum-thickened aqueous dye pastes imparts greater depth and brightness of color as well as better leveling in the print dyeing of cotton, rayon, silk, wool, and nylon (38).

Bibliography

1. E. Grischkevich-Trokhimovskii, *J. Phys. Chem. Soc.* **48**, 880 (1916).
2. Belg. Pat. 626,586 (1963), (to Shell Internationale Research Maatschappij N.V.).
3. Ger. Pat. 1,224,749 (1966), P. Feiler, H. Toussaint, and A. Palm (to Badische Anilin- und Soda-Fabrik AG).
4. T. E. Jordan and F. Kipnis, *Ind. Eng. Chem.* **41**, 2635–2637 (1949); *Chem. Abstr.* **44**, 2334 and *Chem. Zentr.* **1950**, II, 2534.
5. C. H. Deal et al., *Petrol. Refiner* **38**, 185–192 (Sept. 1959).
6. F. G. Bordwell and W. H. McKellin, *J. Am. Chem. Soc.* **73**, 2351–2353 (1951); *Chem. Abstr.* **46**, 1536.
7. Can. Pat. 485,948 (1952), R. J. Moore and R. A. Trimble (to Shell Development Co.); *Chem. Zentr.* **1954**, 1953.
8. U.S. Pat. 2,471,077 (1949), R. J. Moore and R. A. Trimble (to Shell Development Co.); *Chem. Abstr.* **43**, 7512.
9. Ger. Pat. 848,192 (1952), G. J. Pierotti and C. L. Dunn (to Bataafsche Pet. Mij.); *Chem. Zentr.* **1953**, 5394.

10. U.S. Pat. 2,496,207 (1950), A. E. Handlos and G. J. Pierotti (to Shell Development Co.); *Chem. Abstr.* **44,** 4509.
11. H. G. Staaterman et al., *Chem. Eng. Progr.* **43** (4), 148–151 (1947); *Chem. Abstr.* **41,** 4142.
12. H. G. Staaterman et al., *Petrol. Process.* **1,** 85–86 (Oct. 1946).
13. U.S. Pat. 2,407,820 (1946), E. L. Durrum (to Shell Development Co.); *Chem. Abstr.* **41,** 477 and *Chem. Zentr.* **1947,** 1148.
14. U.S. Pat. 2,360,859 (1944), T. W. Evans and R. C. Morris (to Shell Development Co.); *Chem. Abstr.* **39,** 2163.
15. U.S. Pat. 2,368,597 (1945), R. C. Morris and A. V. Snider (to Shell Development Co.); *Chem. Abstr.* **39,** 5138.
16. U.S. Pat. 2,360,860 (1944), R. C. Morris and E. C. Shokal (to Shell Development Co.); *Chem. Abstr.* **39,** 2164.
17. U.S. Pat. 2,385,704 (1945), G. W. Hooker et al. (to Dow Chemical Co.); *Chem. Abstr.* **40,** 185 and *Chem. Zentr.* **1946,** I, 2292.
18. U.S. Pat. 2,360,862 (1944), R. C. Morris and E. C. Shokal (to Shell Development Co.); *Chem. Abstr.* **39,** 2164.
19. J. C. Chu et al., *Ind. Eng. Chem.* **46,** 754–761 (1954); *Chem. Abstr.* **48,** 7957 and *Chem. Zentr.* **1955,** 5750.
20. B. D. Coleman and R. M. Fuoss, *J. Am. Chem. Soc.* **77,** 5472–5476 (1955); *Chem. Abstr.* **50,** 2257.
21. Ger. (East) Pat. 4496 (1954), P. Schlack; *Chem. Zentr.* **1956,** 2313.
22. U.S. Pat. 2,706,674 (1955), G. M. Rothrock (to E. I. du Pont de Nemours & Co., Inc.); *Chem. Abstr.* **49,** 10636 and *Chem. Zentr.* **1956,** 12718.
23. Brit. Pat. 698,174 (1953), Wuppertal-Elberfeld; *Chem. Zentr.* **1955,** 3525.
24. U.S. Pat. 2,555,300 (1951), J. G. Calton and Q. J. O'Brien (to Du Pont); *Chem. Abstr.* **45,** 8816 and *Chem. Zentr.* **1953,** 950.
25. Fr. Pat. 961,050 (1947), J. G. Calton and Q. J. O'Brien; *Chem. Zentr.* **1951,** 278.
26. Brit. Pat. 579,887 (1946), (to Du Pont); *Chem. Abstr.* **41,** 1882.
27. U.S. Pat. 2,404,728 (1946), T. G. Finzel (to Du Pont); *Chem. Zentr.* **1947,** 546.
28. U.S. Pat. 2,404,723 (1946), R. R. Merner (to Du Pont); *Chem. Abstr.* **40,** 6887 and *Chem. Zentr.* **1947,** 545.
29. U.S. Pat. 2,404,722 (1946), R. C. Houtz (to Du Pont); *Chem. Abstr.* **41,** 479 and *Chem. Zentr.* **1947,** 544.
30. U.S. Pat. 2,404,713 (1946), R. C. Houtz (to Du Pont); *Chem. Abstr.* **41,** 150 and *Chem. Zentr.* **1947,** 538.
31. U.S. Pat. 2,617,777 (1952), E. Heisenberg and J. Kleine (to Vereinigte Glanzstoff-Fabriken); *Chem. Abstr.* **47,** 4625 and *Chem. Zentr.* **1954,** 6624.
32. U.S. Pat. 2,953,818 (1960), L. R. Barton (to Du Pont); *Chem. Abstr.* **55,** 4052.
33. U.S. Pat. 2,548,169 (1951), F. F. Miller (to B. F. Goodrich Co.); *Chem. Abstr.* **45,** 5975.
34. U.S. Pat. 2,628,265 (1953), W. F. Busse and H. R. Davidson (to General Aniline & Film Corp.); *Chem. Abstr.* **47,** 5827 and *Chem. Zentr.* **1956,** 4569.
35. R. L. Burwell and C. H. Langford, *J. Am. Chem. Soc.* **81,** 3799–3800 (1959); *Chem. Abstr.* **54,** 4114.
36. U.S. Pat. 2,394,251 (1946), R. C. Morris et al. (to Shell Development Co.); *Chem. Abstr.* **40,** 3843 and *Chem. Zentr.* **1946,** I, 2435.
37. U.S. Pat. 2,471,272 (1949), G. W. Hooker and N. R. Peterson (to The Dow Chemical Co.).
38. Brit. Pat. 708,248 (1954), W. Clarke et al. (to Imperial Chemical Industries, Ltd.); *Chem. Zentr.* **1955,** 2783.

G. S. MORROW
Shell Chemical Company

SULFONAMIDES

Sulfonamides have the general formula $RSO_2NR'R''$ where R is an organic radical, and R' and R'' are hydrogen or organic radicals. Depending upon the nature of R the sulfonamides are classified as *aliphatic, aromatic,* or *heterocyclic.* Some representative sulfonamides are listed in Table 1. The aliphatic sulfonamides have not yet become

Table 1. Representative Sulfonamides

Name	Formula	Mp, °C	References
methanesulfonamide	$CH_3SO_2NH_2$	88	1
ethanesulfonamide	$C_2H_5SO_2NH_2$	60	1
N-methylethanesulfonamide	$C_2H_5SO_2NHCH_3$	3–7	1
N,N-dimethylethanesulfonamide	$C_2H_5SO_2N(CH_3)_2$	oil	1
propanesulfonamide	$C_3H_7SO_2NH_2$	52	2
1,3-propanedisulfonamide	$CH_2(CH_2SO_2NH_2)_2$	169	3, 4
		172.5–174.5	
ethylenesulfonamide	$CH_2{=}CHSO_2NH_2$	87	3
benzenesulfonamide	$C_6H_5SO_2NH_2$	156, 153	1, 5
N-methylbenzenesulfonamide	$C_6H_5SO_2NHCH_3$	31	1
p-toluenesulfonamide	$CH_3C_6H_4SO_2NH_2$	156	5
1-naphthalenesulfonamide	$C_{10}H_7SO_2NH_2$	150	5
2-naphthalenesulfonamide	$C_{10}H_7SO_2NH_2$	212	5
3-pyridinesulfonamide	$C_5H_4NSO_2NH_2$	110–111	5
6-quinolinesulfonamide	$C_9H_6NSO_2NH_2$	191–192	6
2-imidazolesulfonamide	$HN.CH{:}CH.N{:}CSO_2NH_2$	236–236.5	7
2-benzimidazolesulfonamide	$HNC_6H_4N{:}CSO_2NH_2$	214	7
1,2,4-triazolesulfonamide	$HN.CH{:}N.N{:}CSO_2NH_2$	224–225.5	7
2-thiazolesulfonamide	$S.CH{:}CH.N{:}CSO_2NH_2$	120.5–121	7
2-pyrimidinesulfonamide	$N{:}CH.CH{:}CH.N{:}CSO_2NH_2$	180.5–181	7

important. Aromatic and heterocyclic sulfonamides, on the other hand, have achieved great commercial significance; they themselves are, or they are the parent substances of, important diuretics, hypoglycemics, uricosurics (gout treatment drugs), and other chemotherapeutics. Their application in bacterial chemotherapy is so well known that the name "sulfonamides" has been used loosely as a general name for sulfanilamide derivatives. (See under Sulfa drugs, p. 261; see also Bacterial infections, chemotherapy, Vol. 3, pp. 2–5.)

Physical and Chemical Properties

The unsubstituted short-chain aliphatic sulfonamides are low melting and water soluble; the simple aromatic and heterocyclic sulfonamides are higher melting and only slightly soluble in water. Generally, sulfonamides are colorless crystalline solids; their melting points are usually lowered by N-alkylsubstitution (see Table 1). Unsubstituted and N-monosubstituted sulfonamides, RSO_2NH_2 and RSO_2NHR', are weak acids and dissolve in aqueous alkali (with occasional exceptions—see p. 260) (1,5). The acidity of sulfonamides increases with increasing electron-withdrawing power of the groups R and R'. This is illustrated by the acidities (given as pK'_a) of the following representative sulfanilamide derivatives (R is —$C_6H_4NH_2$): RSO_2-NH_2, 10.43; $RSO_2NHC_6H_5$, 9.60; $RSO_2NHCH\!:\!N.CH\!:\!CH.CH\!:\!N$, 6.48; RSO_2NH-$COCH_3$, 5.38; RSO_2NHSO_2R, 2.89 (8). Disubstituted sulfonamides, $RSO_2NR'R''$, have no ionizable hydrogen and are neutral compounds.

Simple sulfonamides are quite stable generally, and vigorous methods are usually needed for their hydrolysis. Sulfonamides often are resistant to fusion with 80% sodium hydroxide at 250°C, but negatively substituted derivatives occasionally afford phenols, with destruction of the carbon–sulfur linkage (1,5). Alcoholysis of disubstituted sulfonamides in refluxing isoamyl alcohol with sodium isoamylate has been described, as well as aminolysis with sodium amides (9). Trisulfonamides,

$$ArSO_2N(R)_2 \xrightarrow[150–200°C]{C_5H_{11}ONa} ArSO_2Na + R_2NH$$

$$ArSO_2NR_2 + NaNHR' \rightarrow ArSO_2NR'Na + R_2NH$$

$(RSO_2)_3N$, are cleaved easily with sodium ethoxide or piperidine, in only 1 hr on the steam bath (1).

Aliphatic and aromatic sulfonamides are split on heating with strong hydrochloric or sulfuric acid (5). The drastic conditions of this procedure, however, limit its usefulness. This is especially true where recovery of the amine is desired, as in the Hinsberg procedure for the separation of primary, secondary, and tertiary amines (see Vol. 2, p. 104). Somewhat milder is cleavage in acetic acid and hydrochloric acid with the aid of zinc chloride, or heating with aqueous pyridine hydrochloride (1,10).

Hydrolysis of sulfonamides by acid or base is beset by difficulty and uncertainty but reductive cleavage is often accomplished under mild conditions. The use of a mixture of hydrobromic acid and phenol at reflux temperature (11), or of hydrobromic acid, phenol, and acetic acid at lower temperatures (12), gives good results in many cases. The hydrobromic acid–phenol procedure is not a simple hydrolysis since an oxidation-reduction reaction is involved. The phenol, besides acting as a solvent, serves as a bromine acceptor to protect other components. An explicit example of reductive cleavage is the use of zinc dust in acetic acid (1,13,13a). Cleavage by

$$RSO_2NHR' \xrightarrow[\text{acetic acid}]{\text{Zn dust}} RSH + R'NH_2$$

hydriodic acid is doubtless also a reductive process; it is reported to be so mild that a carboxamide group in the same molecule is unaffected (1). Aliphatic sulfonamides are split reductively by sodium in isoamyl alcohol in 80–90% yields, where sodium alcoholate often fails (14).

Sulfonamides convert at low temperatures with nitric acid–sulfuric acid to nitramides (5). These nitrosulfonamides are strong acids and form stable neutral

$$RSO_2NH_2 + HNO_2 \rightarrow RSO_2NHNO_2$$

salts in water. At higher temperatures aliphatic sulfonamides react explosively with nitric acid (5). Unsubstituted sulfonamides react with nitrous acid in sulfuric acid to

$$C_2H_5SO_2NH_2 + HNO_3 \rightarrow C_2H_5SO_3H + N_2O + H_2O$$

give sulfonic acid and nitrogen (13a). Monosubstituted sulfonamides give N-nitroso-

$$RSO_2NH_2 \xrightarrow[H_2SO_4]{HNO_2} RSO_3H + N_2$$

amides, useful for the preparation of diazoalkanes (eg diazomethane) (13a).

$$RSO_2NHR \xrightarrow{HNO_2} RSO_2N(NO)R$$

p-Toluenesulfonamide is converted quantitatively by chlorination in alkaline solution or by equivalent hypochlorite to N,N-dichloro-p-toluenesulfonamide (*dichloramine T*) (13a).

$$CH_3C_6H_4SO_2NH_2 + 2\ NaOCl \rightarrow CH_3C_6H_4SO_2NCl_2 + 2\ NaOH$$

If less hypochlorite is used the product is sodium N-chloro-p-toluenesulfonamide (*chloramine T*),

$$CH_3C_6H_4SO_2NH_2 + NaOCl \rightarrow CH_3C_6H_4NClNa + H_2O$$

The same product is formed and crystallizes out when dichloramine T is dissolved in warm alkali and the solution then cooled.

Sulfonamides with at least one replaceable hydrogen can be alkylated or acylated. Alkylation is often performed by the action of an alkyl halide on the sodium salt (13a).

$$CH_3C_6H_4SO_2NHNa + ClCH_2CH_2CH_2N(C_2H_5)_2 \rightarrow CH_3C_6H_4SO_2NHCH_2CH_2CH_2N(C_2H_5)_2$$

Acylation of sulfonamides is aided by salt formation and is usually performed in Schotten-Baumann fashion in water with alkali or in anhydrous media with bases like tertiary amines or alkali carbonates (1,5,13a,14).

$$RSO_2NH_2 + R'COCl \xrightarrow{base} RSO_2NHCOR'$$

$$RSO_2NH_2 + R'SO_2Cl \xrightarrow{base} RSO_2NHSO_2R'$$

Sulfonylureas. In salt form, sulfonamides react at low temperature with isocyanates (13a). The resulting sulfonylureas are important hypoglycemic drugs.

$$RSO_2NH_2 + R'NCO \rightarrow RSO_2NHCONHR'$$

Another route leading to the sulfonylureas begins with the reaction of an unsubstituted sulfonamide with phosgene (15). The resulting sulfonyl isocyanate is a stable

$$CH_3C_6H_4SO_2NH_2 + COCl_2 \rightarrow CH_3C_6H_4SO_2NCO + 2\ HCl$$

distillable liquid which reacts vigorously with amines to give sulfonylureas.

$$CH_3C_6H_4SO_2NCO + C_4H_9NH_2 \rightarrow CH_3C_6H_4SO_2NHCONHC_4H_9$$
tolbutamide

Preparation

The sulfonamides, whether aliphatic, aromatic, or heterocyclic, are generally prepared by reacting a sulfonyl chloride with ammonia or an amine (5,13a,14). In the synthesis of aliphatic and particularly heterocyclic sulfonamides, the reaction with

$$RSO_2Cl + R'NH_2 \xrightarrow{base} RSO_2NHR'$$

the amine is usually straightforward, but the difficulty frequently lies in first constructing the appropriate sulfonyl chloride. With certain weak amines and unreactive heterocyclic amines, however, the reaction of the sulfonyl chloride is sluggish or capricious, and special procedures are necessary. (See under Sulfa drugs.) Generally the condensation is performed in pyridine or triethylamine with or without added un-reactive solvent. The pyridine or triethylamine binds the hydrochloric acid which is evolved and which otherwise would inactivate the reacting amine. The reaction often works well in aqueous suspension in Schotten-Baumann fashion when alkali or carbonate is used as the acid-binding agent.

In special cases the heating of the ammonium salt of an aromatic sulfonic acid leads to formation of the sulfonamide, but this procedure is much less effective than the analogous procedure is for carboxamides (5). In another process sulfonamides may be obtained from the action of chlorine on a sulfinic acid and ammonia (16). The oxidation of sulfenamides and sulfinamides to sulfonamides has been described (13a). Alkylation or arylation as discussed above can be used to prepare substituted

$$RSNHR' + O_2 \rightarrow RSO_2NHR'$$

sulfonamides from simple sulfonamides. Alkyl halides, alkyl sulfates, or active aryl halides usually are employed in the presence of alkali (5).

$$RSO_2NH_2 + R'X \xrightarrow{\text{alkali}} RSO_2NHR' + HX$$

Uses

Simple aliphatic sulfonamides have not found extensive commercial use, probably because of their cost. The sulfonamides obtained by the reaction of methanesulfonyl chloride (17) or α-toluenesulfonyl chloride (18) with various amines have been proposed as a means of identifying those amines. The reaction products of methanesulfonyl chloride with amino acids have been suggested for a similar use (5). The aliphatic sulfonamide *carinamide* (1), p-α-toluenesulfonamidobenzoic acid, briefly found medical application in the early years of penicillin therapy. Concomitantly administered carinamide produced high, long-lasting plasma levels of penicillin even when relatively low doses of the antibiotic were given. It produced this effect by interfering in the kidney with the excretion of penicillin (19,19a).

$$\text{CH}_2\text{SO}_2\text{NH}{-}\text{CO}_2\text{H} \qquad (\text{C}_3\text{H}_7)_2\text{NSO}_2{-}\text{CO}_2\text{H}$$

(1)   (2)

Carinamide was displaced for co-administration with penicillin by the more potent *probenecid* (2), p-(dipropylsulfamoyl)benzoic acid (19a). A dramatic lowering of penicillin production costs made these drugs obsolete in the treatment of infectious diseases. (See also Penicillins.) Probenecid, however, during its clinical use, was observed to be effective in the treatment of gout by facilitating the excretion of uric acid (qv). Continued experience has borne this out. Probenecid has thus found an important place in medicine and is the first useful synthetic compound for control of the age-old disease gout (19a).

The anti-infective chemotherapeutic sulfonamides are the most important single applied class of sulfonamides. They are discussed under Sulfa drugs. The clinical experience with sulfa drugs in turn led to important new applications of sulfonamides (19a). The uricosuric drug probenecid (see above) is one such development. The diuretic sulfonamides (see also Vol. 7, p. 259) and hypoglycemic sulfonylureas—two prominent new drug classes—likewise arose out of this vast clinical experience.

The knowledge that the kidney contains carbonic anhydrase and that sulfanilamide inhibits this enzyme in vitro led to the synthesis of various heterocyclic sulfonamides (7,20). This study culminated in the discovery of *acetazolamide* (**3**), 5-acetamido-1,3,4-thiadiazole-2-sulfonamide, a potent carbonic anhydrase inhibitor and the first orally effective and clinically useful sulfonamide diuretic (21). This drug is a

(**3**)

prototype of the carbonic anhydrase inhibitors and, by promoting bicarbonate excretion, causes a loss of sodium and potassium ions. The disulfonamide, *dichlorphenamide* (**4**), 4,5-dichloro-*m*-benzenedisulfonamide, is equally active as a carbonic anhydrase inhibitor but increases chloride excretion over that of acetazolamide (**3**). A new sulfonamide diuretic on the U.S. market in 1966 was *furosemide* (**5**) (22,23).

(**4**)   (**5**)

Deriving from the disulfonamide, diuretics are the thiazides (see also Vol. 7, p. 261), in which one sulfonamide group is incorporated into a ring structure; *chlorothiazide* (**6**) and *hydrochlorothiazide* (**7**) are examples (21). The thiazides cause excretion of

(**6**)   (**7**)

sodium and chloride in equivalent amounts and are referred to as saluretic agents. They are weak carbonic anhydrase inhibitors and in them saluretic activity seems to be separated grossly from carbonic anhydrase activity.

These diuretics have been very effective in the control of electrolyte level and management of congestive heart failure. Additionally, the thiazides control hypertension and have become the basic therapeutics onto which other hypertensive agents are superimposed as needed (21).

The recognition that certain sulfa drugs produce a hypoglycemic side effect has led to the testing of related derivatives. This work culminated in the preparation of the hypoglycemic sulfonylureas (19,19a). These drugs have been eminently successful and in approximately ten years on the U.S. market their production in 1966 had risen to 1,298,000 lb per year (24). There are four sulfonylurea drugs available in the U.S. (25,26), *tolbutamide* (**8**), *chlorpromamide* (**9**), *acetohexamide* (**10**), and *tolazamide* (**11**).

CH_3—⟨ ⟩—$SO_2NHCONHC_4H_9$

(8)

Cl—⟨ ⟩—$SO_2NHCONHC_3H_7$

(9)

CH_3CO—⟨ ⟩—$SO_2NHCONH$—⟨ ⟩

(10)

CH_3—⟨ ⟩—$SO_2NHCONHN$⟨ ⟩

(11)

The solubility of simple sulfonamides in alkali is the basis of the classic Hinsberg procedure for the isolation and identification of amines (1,5) (see also p. 256). There are some exceptions where the salts are insoluble or the sulfonamide is too feebly basic. The *N*-chlorosulfonamides, such as chloramine T and dichloramine T, have served for some time as antiseptics and bleaching agents (see also Antiseptics, Vol. 2, p. 616; Bleaching agents, Vol. 3, p. 557; Chloramines and chloroamines). However, their current use may be slight as no mention of these compounds was found in the U.S. Tariff Commission report for 1966 (24). *Halazone*, *p*-(dichlorosulfamoyl)benzoic acid, has been used with soda (sodium carbonate?) for drinking water sterilization (13). *o*-Sulfobenzoic imide, $C_6H_4.SO_2.NH.CO$, is the well-known sweetening agent *saccharin* (see Sweeteners). Certain nitrobenzenesulfonamides have been used in the treatment of coccidiosis in chickens (27).

Bibliography

"Sulfonamides" in *ECT* 1st ed., pp. 312–316, by M. E. Hultquist, Research Division, American Cyanamid Company.

1. P. A. S. Smith, *The Chemistry of Open-Chain Organic Nitrogen Compounds*, Vol. 1, W. A. Benjamin, Inc., New York, 1965, pp. 186–192. (A good, short, up-to-date overview of sulfonamide chemistry.)
2. M. Duguet, *Bull. Acad. Roy. Belg.* **1902**, 79–92; *Chem. Zentr.* **1902,** 855.
3. P. W. Clutterbuck and J. B. Cohen, *J. Chem. Soc.* **121,** 120–128 (1922).
4. J. W. Griffin and D. H. Hey, *J. Chem. Soc.*, **1952**, 3334–3340.
5. C. M. Suter, *The Organic Chemistry of Sulfur*, John Wiley & Sons, Inc., New York, 1944, pp. 103–175, 575–637. (An extensive but dated review.)
6. C. V. Chelintsev and N. J. Zakonin, *J. Gen. Chem. (USSR)* **11,** 729–730 (1941); *Chem. Abstr.* **36,** 477 (1942).
7. R. O. Roblin, Jr. and J. W. Clapp, *J. Am. Chem. Soc.* **72,** 4890–4892 (1950).
8. P. H. Bell and R. O. Roblin, *J. Am. Chem. Soc.* **64,** 2905–2917 (1942).
9. D. Klamann and H. Bertsch, *Chem. Ber.* **91,** 1688 (1958); **92,** 2610 (1959).
10. D. Klamann and G. Hofbauer, *Ann. Chem.* **581,** 182–198 (1953).
11. D. Weisblat, B. J. Magerlein, and D. R. Meyers, *J. Am. Chem. Soc.* **75,** 3630–3632 (1953).
12. H. R. Snyder and R. A. Heckert, *J. Am. Chem. Soc.* **74,** 2006–2009 (1952).
13. E. Müller, ed., *Methoden der Organischen Chemie (Houben-Weyl)*, Vol. 9, 4th ed., Georg Thieme Verlag, Stuttgart, West Germany, 1955. (A detailed review.)
13a. F. Muth in reference 13, pp. 605–648.
14. M. Quaedvlieg, in reference 13, pp. 398–404.
15. C. King, *J. Org. Chem.* **25,** 355 (1960).
16. P. R. Carter and D. H. Hey, *J. Chem. Soc.* **1948,** 147–149.
17. C. S. Marvel, M. D. Helfrick, and J. P. Belsley, *J. Am. Chem. Soc.* **51,** 1272–1274 (1929).
18. C. S. Marvel and H. B. Gillespie, *J. Am. Chem. Soc.* **48,** 2943–2944 (1926).
19. R. F. Gould, ed., "Molecular Modification in Drug Design," *Adv. Chem. Series* **45,** 1964.
19a. M. Tishler in reference 19, pp. 7–9.
20. W. H. Miller, A. M. Dessert, and R. O. Roblin, Jr., *J. Am. Chem. Soc.* **72,** 4893–4896 (1950).
21. J. M. Sprague in reference 19, pp. 88–97.

22. C. K. Cain, ed., *Annual Reports in Medicinal Chemistry, 1966*, Academic Press, New York, 1967.
23. E. J. Cragoe, Jr. and J. B. Bicking in reference 22, p. 60.
24. United States Tariff Commission, *Synthetic Organic Chemicals, United States Production and Sales, 1966*, 50th ed., U.S. Government Printing Office, Washington, D.C., 1968, p. 33.
25. R. Pinson in C. K. Cain, ed., *Annual Reports in Medicinal Chemistry, 1965*, Academic Press, New York, 1966, p. 168.
26. R. Pinson in reference 22, p. 182.
27. U.S. Pat. 2,531,755 (1950), E. Walelzky (to American Cyanamid Co.).

SULFA DRUGS

Any general definition of sulfa drugs must include both their chemical structure and their biological effects. In the most restricted definition, these drugs are sulfonamides derived simply from sulfanilamide (*p*-aminobenzenesulfonamide). Substitution on the sulfonamide nitrogen is referred to as N^1-substitution and substitution on the *p*-amino group as N^4-substitution. The therapeutically active derivatives usually are N^1-substituted. The structures of sulfanilamide (**1**) and sulfadiazine (**4**) illustrate these relations. The numerals also refer to the compound numbers in Table 1 where

many other N^1-substituted derivatives are listed. The fact that the sulfa drugs are antibacterial agents separates them sharply from the diuretic, hypoglycemic, and uricosuric sulfonamide drugs. It has become customary to include with the sulfa drugs certain related antibacterials in which the formal structural divergence from sulfanilamide is considerable, such as Prontosil (**30**), converted in vivo to sulfanilamide and mafenide (**28**). One important class of sulfanilamide analogs are not sulfonamides. They are the antibacterial sulfones (eg, dapsone (**29**)). They will be included here with the sulfa drugs for completeness.

The action of the sulfa and sulfone drugs is bacteriostatic rather than bactericidal (see Antiseptics and disinfectants) and (with some exceptions) is thought to arise from a derangement of the metabolic conversion of *p*-aminobenzoic acid (PABA) (see Vol. 3, p. 435) to the folic acid–related vitamins (1a,2) (see also Vitamins). The sulfa drugs are still immensely important even though they have been largely displaced by antibiotics (qv) from their original application in systemic disease. They provide a principal treatment of urinary-tract disease for which they not only are cheaper than the antibiotics but actually may be considered superior by some physicians. The sulfa drugs have some application in the treatment of the fungus-related nocardiosis and in the prophylaxis of rheumatic fever under certain circumstances (3a). Certain sulfa drug relatives are used empirically to treat ulcerative colitis although the basis of their action is not understood (3a). The related sulfones have become an accepted treatment for leprosy and have extensive worldwide use for this purpose.

A list of sulfa drugs with their structural formulas and some physical properties is given in Table 1. These compounds include all currently important drugs, a few experimental drugs not yet marketed in the U.S., and a few drugs no longer used but historically important. A complete list of all sulfa drugs at one time of interest would be much longer. Following sulfanilamide (**1**), Table 1 lists the principal classes of derivatives, the N^1-heterocyclic derivatives, (**2**) to (**19**); the N^1-acyl derivatives,

Table 1. Selected Major Sulfa Drugs and Related Compounds

No.	Generic or common name	Structure	Melting pt, °C[a]	Approx solubility in water at 25°C, mg per 100 ml[a]	Approx "half-life," hr[b]	pK'_a[b]
1	sulfanilamide	$H_2NC_6H_4SO_2NH_2$	164.5–166.5	750	6.8	10.08
2	sulfapyridine	$H_2NC_6H_4SO_2NH$—	191–193	30		8.43[c]
3	sulfathiazole	$H_2NC_6H_4SO_2NH$—	200–204	60	3.8	7.25
4	sulfadiazine	$H_2NC_6H_4SO_2NH$—	252–256	8	16.7	6.52
5	sulfachloropyridazine	$H_2NC_6H_4SO_2NH$—		ca. 90[d] at pH 5.5	8.0	6.10
6	sulfadimethoxine	$H_2NC_6H_4SO_2NH$—	201–203	<4.6	ca 33	6.32
7	sulfaethidole	$H_2NC_6H_4SO_2NH$—	185–186	25	4.8	5.65

No.	Name	Structure	mp			pK_a
8	sulfamerazine	$H_2NC_6H_4SO_2NH$— (4-methylpyrimidin-2-yl)	234–238	16	23.5	6.98
9	sulfamethazine	$H_2NC_6H_4SO_2NH$— (4,6-dimethylpyrimidin-2-yl)	176	ca 100	7.0	7.37[c]
10	sulfamethizole	$H_2NC_6H_4SO_2NH$— (5-methyl-1,3,4-thiadiazol-2-yl)	208	25	(short)	5.45
11	sulfamethoxazole	$H_2NC_6H_4SO_2NH$— (5-methylisoxazol-3-yl)	167		11.0	6.03
12	sulfamethoxypyridazine	$H_2NC_6H_4SO_2NH$— (6-methoxypyridazin-3-yl)	182–183	110 at pH 5	40.0	7.20
13	sulfameter (sulfamethoxydiazine)	$H_2NC_6H_4SO_2NH$— (5-methoxypyrimidin-2-yl)	214–216		36.6	7.02
14	sulfamoxole	$H_2NC_6H_4SO_2NH$— (4,5-dimethyloxazol-2-yl)	193–194		10.6	7.40
15	sulfaphenazole	$H_2NC_6H_4SO_2NH$— (1-phenylpyrazol-5-yl, C_6H_5)	179–183		10.0	6.09

(continued)

Table 1 (*continued*)

No.	Generic or common name	Structure	Melting pt, °C[a]	Approx solubility in water at 25°C, mg per 100 ml[a]	Approx "half-life," hr[b]	pK'$_a$[b]
16	sulfapyrazine	H$_2$NC$_6$H$_4$SO$_2$NH—	250–254	5		6.04[c]
17	sulfaquinoxaline	H$_2$NC$_6$H$_4$SO$_2$NH—	247–248	<7.5		
18	sulfisomidine	H$_2$NC$_6$H$_4$SO$_2$NH—	243	ca 250	7.4	7.57
19	sulfisoxazole	H$_2$NC$_6$H$_4$SO$_2$NH—	194	350 at pH 6	6.0	5.0
20	sulfacetamide	H$_2$NC$_6$H$_4$SO$_2$NHCOCH$_3$	182–184	>670	7.0	5.78
21	sulfabenzamide	H$_2$NC$_6$H$_4$SO$_2$NHCOC$_6$H$_5$	181–182	31		4.57[c]
22	sulfaguanidine	H$_2$NC$_6$H$_4$SO$_2$NHC(:NH)NH$_2$	190–193	100		(base)
23	N^1-acetylsulfamethoxypyridazine	H$_2$NC$_6$H$_4$SO$_2$N—	186–187	7[e]		

No.	Name	Structure	mp, °C	Solubility	
24	N^1-acetylsulfisoxazole	$H_2NC_6H_4SO_2N$ (isoxazole, CH_3, CH_3, $COCH_3$)	192–195	7	
25	succinylsulfathiazole	$HO_2CCH_2CH_2CONHC_6H_4SO_2NH$ (thiazole)	184–186 192–195	(soluble pH 7)	(acid)
26	phthalylsulfathiazole	(CO_2H)($CONHC_6H_4SO_2NH$–thiazole)benzene	240–250 effervesces 272–277 decomp	(soluble pH 7)	(acid)
27	salicylazosulfapyridine	(HO_2C)(HO)C_6H_3–N=N–$C_6H_4SO_2NH$–pyridine	240–245 decomp	(soluble pH 7)	(acid)
28	mafenide (homosulfanilamide; α-amino-p-toluenesulfonamide)	$H_2NCH_2C_6H_4SO_2NH_2$	153 (HCl salt 256)	(salt soluble)	(base)
29	dapsone (4,4'-diaminodiphenyl sulfone, DDS)	H_2N–C_6H_4–SO_2–C_6H_4–NH_2	175–176	(soluble)	(base)
30	Prontosil (sulfamidochrysoidine)	$HCl\cdot H_2N$(NH_2)C_6H_3–N=N–C_6H_4–SO_2NH_2			

[a] Unless otherwise noted, source of data is (10).   [c] From (14).   [e] From (13).
[b] Unless otherwise noted, source of data is (11).   [d] Estimated from (12).

(20) to (22); the N^1-acyl-N^1-heterocyclic derivatives, (23) and (24); and the N^4-acyl derivatives, (25) and (26). The remaining compounds, (27) to (30), are not sulfa drugs in the strictest sense but are closely related.

For a review describing over 5000 sulfanilamide derivatives, their preparation, properties, trade names, and biologic applications complete through 1944, see Northey (1). Several thousand additional derivatives have probably been made since 1944 but no comparable review is available. For mode of action see Seydel (2), for a definitive medical overview to 1960 see Weinstein et al. (3), for a review of the experimental antibacterial aspects with some historical background see Neipp (4) and Zbinden (5), and for pharmacology and toxicology see Bagdon (6) and Rieder (11).

History. The discovery and development of the sulfa drugs is by itself a landmark in modern medicine. They were the first drugs in history to control systemic bacterial disease and they still find important application today for this purpose. The sulfa drugs additionally led the way directly or indirectly to a number of the more important therapeutic discoveries of our time. The success of the sulfa drugs in the previously unrewarding treatment of bacterial disease made reasonable the immensely expensive effort which led to penicillin and later the broad-spectrum antibiotics (7). During clinical use it was noted that certain sulfa drugs had unexpected pharmacological effects. These effects, perfected in various derivatives, became the main properties of important new classes of diuretics, hypoglycemics, and uricosurics (drugs for treating gout) (8).

In a sense the sulfa drugs were an outgrowth of Paul Ehrlich's ideas of the mechanism of action of chemotherapeutic agents and can be traced back to him through the unsuccessful early efforts of Julius Morgenroth and R. Levey and of Michael Heidelberger and Walter A. Jacobs. The studies that mark the actual beginning of the sulfa drugs were those of the team Fritz Mietzsch and Joseph Klarer, chemists, and Gerhard Domagk, pharmacologist, at I. G. Farbenindustrie in Germany in the years 1930–1935 approximately. These studies culminated in Prontosil (30) (sulfamidochrysoidine; p-((2,4-diaminophenyl)azo)benzenesulfonamide) the first drug to cure bacterial septicemias (see also Vol. 3, p. 4; Vol. 7, p. 258). A very important factor in this discovery was the use of an animal infection to test for activity; Prontosil (H. Bayer, Leverkusen) is inactive in the test tube. It was

$$H_2N-\langle\rangle-N{=}N-\langle\rangle-SO_2NH_2$$

Prontosil (30)

established by the French scientists Tréfouël, Tréfouël, Nitti, and Bovet and confirmed by others internationally that sulfanilamide was formed from Prontosil in the body and was responsible for the activity of that drug. This discovery marked the beginning of a worldwide research effort in the synthesis and testing of sulfanilamide derivatives (1b). This vast effort produced in less than ten years the over 5000 derivatives listed in Northey's review (1). The primary aim of this early work was to produce more active compounds with a broader spectrum. This objective was reached in the N^1-heterocyclic substituted sulfanilamides exemplified by sulfapyridine, sulfathiazole, and sulfadiazine. In these compounds a maximum activity was reached which was not surpassed substantially by later derivatives if compared drug level for drug level.

Nevertheless most of the early N^1-heterocyclic substituted sulfanilamides are now obsolete (5a); only the sulfapyrimidines (**4**) and (**9**) remain, and these in diminishing use. The second-generation sulfa drugs which now dominate the market are also N^1-heterocyclic substituted sulfanilamides. Although usually not more active, these are less toxic or have pharmacologic advantages (5a).

During the same time the N^1-substituted sulfanilamides were becoming widely accepted for the treatment of systemic disease caused by common bacteria, another class of derivatives showed promise in mycobacterial infections. These were congeners of bis(p-aminophenyl) sulfone, often referred to as 4,4'-diaminodiphenyl sulfone, or DDS. In contrast to the direction of progress in the sulfonamides, sulfone derivatives did not find wide use but today the parent sulfone, dapsone (**29**), is the treatment of choice for the ancient scourge leprosy (9,26,27).

Physical and Chemical Properties

The sulfa drugs are white or nearly white powders melting above 150°C. The azo and nitro derivatives may be yellow. These compounds are not very soluble in cold water but are somewhat soluble in alcohol or acetone. Sulfanilamide (**1**), sulfaguanidine (**22**), sulfacetamide (**20**), and mafenide (**28**) are fairly soluble in hot water (Table 1). N^4-Acetylation generally lowers solubility, but there are exceptions (Table 2).

These drugs are weak acids, the more important ones generally with a pK'_a in the range 5–8. By this acidity the sulfa drugs are generally soluble in basic aqueous solutions. The N^1-acyl substituted and some N^1-heterocyclic substituted sulfas are highly soluble as salts at body pH, for example sulfacetamide (**20**) (pK'_a = 5.38) and sulfisoxazole (**19**) (pK'_a = 5.0). The N^4-acyl derivatives succinylsulfathiazole (**25**) and phthalylsulfathiazole (**26**) contain a free carboxyl and, of course, are entirely soluble at pH 7. As the pH is lowered, the solubility of the N^1-substituted sulfanilamides reaches a minimum, usually in the pH range 3–5. This minimum corresponds to the solubility of the molecular species and approximates to the intrinsic solubility in water as given in Table 1. The sulfa drugs with a free amino group are by virtue of it weak bases, all of about the same strength (approx pK'_a = 2). Consequently, with a further decrease of pH to that of a moderately strong acid, the sulfa drugs dissolve as the cations. They are usually freely soluble in aqueous strong mineral acids such as hydrochloric or sulfuric acid. The sulfa drugs generally are stable in strong alkali and strong acid but there are exceptions. Their solubilities have been studied widely, particularly in body fluids or in buffered solutions, in order to understand their behavior in the body (1d,11,15). The binding of sulfa drugs to blood proteins is important in theoretical interpretations of their systemic activity (6a).

The amino group is readily diazotized with nitrous acid and this is a basis for its assay. Aldehydes react with the amino group to form anils and other condensation products. The yellow product formed with 4-dimethylaminobenzaldehyde is useful for the visualization of sulfa drugs with free amino groups in thin-layer and paper chromatography. Acylation of the amino group occurs readily with agents such as acetic or phthalic anhydride.

Preparation and Manufacture (1c)

By far the most usual method of preparing sulfa drugs is by the reaction of acetylsulfanilyl chloride (ASC) with the appropriate amine. Extra amine or a suitable base is used to neutralize the hydrochloric acid freed in the reaction. The resulting

$$CH_3CONHC_6H_4SO_2Cl + RNH_2 \xrightarrow{\text{base}} CH_3CONHC_6H_4SO_2NHR$$

acetyl product is usually hydrolyzed with aqueous alkali to the free amino compound. On occasion certain other N-acylsulfanilyl chlorides may be used. p-Nitrobenzenesulfonyl chloride can be used instead of ASC; the intermediate nitro sulfa drug can then be converted to the free amino compound by reduction instead of hydrolysis. The nitro intermediate is much more expensive than ASC so that this route is rarely used. ASC is very cheaply obtained by the chlorosulfonation of acetanilide and is a basic raw material for most sulfa drugs.

N^1-Heterocyclic Substituted Sulfanilamides. Sulfanilamide itself is manufactured as above by the reaction of ASC with excess concentrated aqueous ammonia and hydrolysis of the resulting product. Most heterocyclic amines are less reactive and the condensation with ASC is usually done in anhydrous media in the presence of an acid-binding agent. The anhydrous conditions avoid a hydrolytic destruction of ASC. Commonly the solvent and acid-binding role is filled by pyridine alone or by mixtures of acetone and pyridine. Tertiary amines (eg, triethylamine) can be substituted for pyridine. Excess of reactant amine can also be used as the acid-binding agent but since these amines are usually expensive, efficient recovery procedures must be available. The majority of N^1-heterocyclic substituted sulfanilamides are made by the above simple condensation with ASC and hydrolysis.

Sulfisomidine (**18**) is prepared by a variation of this route because of the different character of the amino group in the 4-position in pyrimidines. Two moles of ASC are condensed with one mole of 4-amino-2,6-dimethylpyrimidine in the presence of triethylamine as hydrogen chloride acceptor. The resulting bis(acetylsulfanilyl) derivative is readily hydrolyzed to (**18**). A similar bis(acetylsulfanilyl) derivative has been employed in the synthesis of sulfathiazole (**3**) (1a) and sulfamoxole (**14**) (16) but the direct 1:1 reaction is probably preferable in these latter cases.

Occasionally N^1-heterocyclic substituted sulfanilamides are prepared by an alternate condensation. The sulfonamide nitrogen of sulfanilamide or N^4-acetylsulfanilamide condenses with an active heterocyclic halide in the presence of an acid-binding agent to form the sulfa drug. Sulfapyridine (**2**) (from 2-halopyridine), sulfadiazine (**4**) (from 2-halopyrimidine), and sulfapyrazine (**16**) (from 2-halopyrazine) have been prepared by this method (1c). The most important application, however, is probably in the synthesis of sulfachloropyridazine (**5**) and sulfamethoxypyridazine (**12**) (17).

Finally, N^1-heterocyclic derivatives in some cases can be formed by a ring closure of a simpler sulfanilamide derivative. Sulfadiazine, sulfamethazine, sulfamerazine, and sulfathiazole have been prepared by this method, in addition to their having been synthesized from aminoheterocycle and ASC. The synthesis of sulfamethazine (**9**) from sulfaguanidine (**22**) and acetylacetone is an example.

$$H_2NC_6H_4SO_2NHC(:NH)NH_2 \quad + \quad CH_3COCH_2COCH_3 \longrightarrow H_2NC_6H_4SO_2NH-\!$$

(**22**)

(**9**)

N^1-Acylsulfanilamides. Of this once numerous class of sulfa drugs, only two examples have remained important in the U.S. *Sulfacetamide* (**20**) is prepared by acetylating N^4-acetylsulfanilamide with acetic anhydride or with acetyl chloride in pyridine. The resulting N^1,N^4-diacetylsulfanilamide can be hydrolyzed selectively with mild alkali to the desired product, (**20**). Its isolation and purification from regenerated sulfanilamide is easy because of the greater acidity of sulfacetamide. *Sulfaguanidine* (**22**) is prepared by condensing ASC with guanidine in the presence of sodium hydroxide. The N^4-acetyl group may be removed by acid or alkaline hydrolysis.

N^1-Heterocyclic-N^4-acylsulfanilamide Derivatives. The two important examples in this class are succinylsulfathiazole (**25**) and phthalylsulfathiazole (**26**). They are best prepared by fusing sulfathiazole with either succinic anhydride or phthalic anhydride as required.

N^1-Heterocyclic-N^1-acetylsulfanilamide Derivatives (18). A straightforward but expensive preparation of these compounds starts with the heterocyclic amine (RNH$_2$) and *p*-nitrobenzenesulfonyl chloride and involves acetylating the nitro sulfa drug.

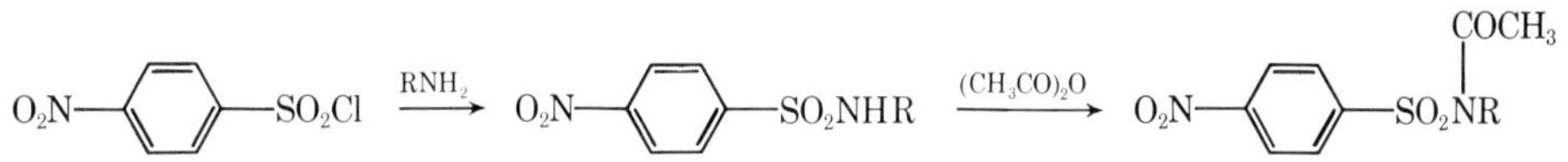

$$O_2N-\!\!\!\!\!\!\!\!\!\!\!\!\!\!\!\!-SO_2Cl \xrightarrow{RNH_2} O_2N-\!\!\!\!\!\!\!\!\!\!\!\!\!\!\!\!-SO_2NHR \xrightarrow{(CH_3CO)_2O} O_2N-\!\!\!\!\!\!\!\!\!\!\!\!\!\!\!\!-SO_2NR$$

The resulting compound reduces under very mild conditions to give the required product.

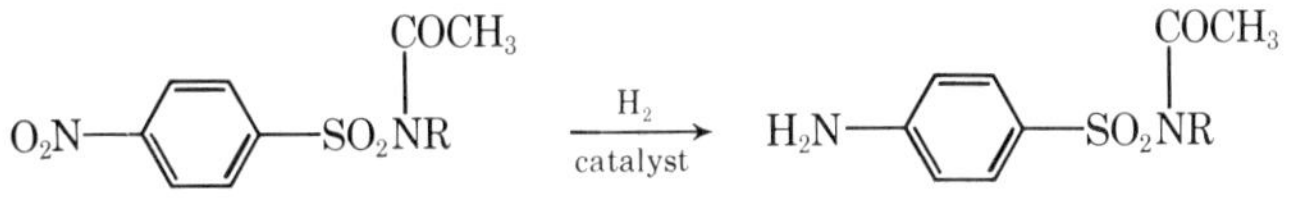

$$O_2N-\!\!\!\!\!\!\!\!\!\!\!\!\!\!\!\!-SO_2NR \xrightarrow[catalyst]{H_2} H_2N-\!\!\!\!\!\!\!\!\!\!\!\!\!\!\!\!-SO_2NR$$

To avoid use of the expensive *p*-nitrobenzenesulfonyl chloride, approaches have been developed which start with the sulfa drug itself. An example is the synthesis of N^1-acetylsulfamethoxypyridazine (**23**) in two effective operations, starting with sulfamethoxypyridazine and benzaldehyde (19).

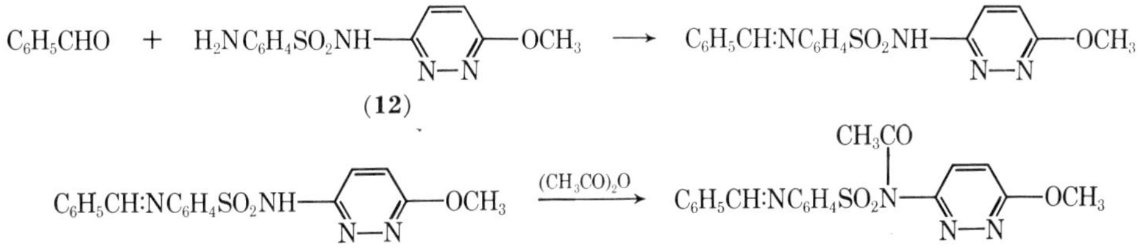

$$C_6H_5CHO \quad + \quad H_2NC_6H_4SO_2NH-\!\!\!\!\!\!\!\!\!\!\!\!\!\!\!\!-OCH_3 \longrightarrow C_6H_5CH:NC_6H_4SO_2NH-\!\!\!\!\!\!\!\!\!\!\!\!\!\!\!\!-OCH_3$$

(**12**)

$$C_6H_5CH:NC_6H_4SO_2NH-\!\!\!\!\!\!\!\!\!\!\!\!\!\!\!\!-OCH_3 \xrightarrow{(CH_3CO)_2O} C_6H_5CH:NC_6H_4SO_2N-\!\!\!\!\!\!\!\!\!\!\!\!\!\!\!\!-OCH_3$$

In the above reaction, the benzaldehyde group protects the N^4-amino group from acetylation. The reaction product need not be isolated, as the mere addition of water causes the removal by hydrolysis of the benzaldehyde covering group.

$$C_6H_5CH\text{:}NC_6H_4SO_2N \underset{\underset{N-N}{}}{\overset{\overset{CH_3CO}{|}}{\diagdown}} OCH_3 \xrightarrow{H_2O} H_2NC_6H_4SO_2N \underset{\underset{N-N}{}}{\overset{\overset{CH_3CO}{|}}{\diagdown}} OCH_3$$

(23)

The simplest route to these derivatives is a selective acetylation of the N^1-nitrogen, leaving the N^4-nitrogen unaffected. Sulfisoxazole suspended in a pyridine–acetone mixture reacts with acetic anhydride to yield N^1-acetylsulfisoxazole (24) (20). The great acidity of sulfisoxazole possibly makes this simple procedure practicable—it is not generally applicable to other sulfa drugs.

Miscellaneous Compounds. *Salicylazosulfapyridine* (27) can be prepared by diazotizing sulfapyridine (2) and coupling it to salicylic acid (21). *Mafenide* (28) has been synthesized by chlorosulfonating N-benzylacetamide, reacting the resultant α-acetamido-p-toluenesulfonyl chloride with ammonia, and, finally, hydrolyzing to remove the acetyl group. *Dapsone* (29) has been prepared by numerous methods (1c,9). Excess sodium sulfide with 1-chloro-4-nitrobenzene gives high yields of 4-amino-4′-nitrodiphenyl sulfide:

$$O_2N\text{—}\diagup\!\!\diagdown\text{—}Cl \xrightarrow{Na_2S} O_2N\text{—}\diagup\!\!\diagdown\text{—}S\text{—}\diagup\!\!\diagdown\text{—}NH_2$$

This sulfide, after acetylation to protect the amino group, can be oxidized with hydrogen peroxide to the sulfone, then the nitro group is reduced to amino and, finally, acidic or basic hydrolysis yields the product bis(p-aminophenyl) sulfone (29).

$$O_2NC_6H_4SC_6H_4NHCOCH_3 \xrightarrow{H_2O_2} O_2NC_6H_4SO_2C_6H_4NHCOCH_3$$

$$\xrightarrow[\text{H}^+ \text{ or OH}^-]{H_2} H_2NC_6H_4SO_2C_6H_4NH_2$$
$$(29)$$

Amination of bis(4-chlorophenyl) sulfone at a high temperature and under pressure is claimed to be a good method.

$$ClC_6H_4SO_2C_6H_4Cl \xrightarrow[\text{ca 200°C}]{NH_3} H_2NC_6H_4SO_2C_6H_4NH_2$$
$$(29)$$

Therapeutic Aspects

Nonchemical Sulfa Drug Classification. In recent years it has become customary to classify sulfa drugs by their persistence in the body (short-, intermediate-, or long-acting) and by their propensity to block the kidney tubules by crystal formation ("soluble," "insoluble"). The clinical testing of the N^1-substituted sulfanilamides available in the early years of sulfa drug research brought out that these drugs differed significantly in these respects.

Sulfamethoxypyridazine (12) was the first truly persistent sulfa drug (4a). Its development focused attention on this property and now many derivatives of long persistence have been synthesized and are available (11). This property is covered in Table 1 as the "half-life," the approximate time needed for the drug blood level to fall to half its maximum after a single dose in the therapeutic range; the dosing for this determination (in contrast to actual clinical usage) is preferably intravenous, since the absorption time for a peroral dose introduces serious error for quickly excreted drugs.

The sulfa drugs are weak acids (see the pK'_a values in Table 1) whose solubility can be markedly lowered during urinary excretion. The excretion begins in the kidney at pH 7 and ends at the urine at pH 5–6. If the blood concentration of drug is already high, then the acidifying and concentrating action in the tubules can cause the drug to precipitate and block the kidney. Some of the early N^1-heterocyclic substituted derivatives—notably sulfapyridine and sulfadiazine—occasionally caused death in this way. No useful sulfa drug is truly soluble, but from experience it has been found that those soluble no less than ca 70 mg per 100 ml at pH 5–5.5 are almost free of this fearsome toxicity (15). Such drugs have been loosely called "soluble" sulfa drugs. Obviously this property is of less importance for the persistent sulfa drugs since they are but slowly excreted, and only low concentrations are achieved in the urine. Correspondingly, it is of critical importance for "short-acting" drugs which are quickly excreted and thereby reach high levels in the kidney.

Systemic Infections. It was in the treatment of bacterial septicemias—blood stream infections—that the sulfa drugs had their spectacular beginning; they have been effective in internal infections, both septicemias and other tissue infections, that are due to *Streptococci*, pneumococci, *Staphylococci*, meningococci, gonococci, *Hemophilis influenza*, and the fungus-related *Nocardia* (1e,3). From the time penicillin was introduced, about 1944, the sulfa drugs have been increasingly displaced from this important field by the antibiotics (3b,4b). Now they are only rarely the treatment of choice and it is controversial whether they should be supplanted altogether by antibiotics except perhaps in rheumatic fever prophylaxis and in nocardiosis (22–24). Nevertheless their low cost, convenience (by oral dosing), and traditional acceptance keep them significant drugs for the treatment of systemic disease, particularly in Europe.

Very early in the clinical use of sulfas, emphasis was given to achieving high blood levels of these drugs, and to maintaining these levels by suitable dosing schedules (25). This emphasis arose because, generally speaking, the sulfonamides are bacteriostatic (not bactericidal, as are many antibiotics). If the level of drug falls too low, the pathogen resumes growth. The need for continued high levels gave the impetus to development of the long-acting sulfa drugs. The "half-life" of a number of drugs is shown in Table 1 and indicates how widely they vary as to persistence in the body. The experimental drug 4-sulfanilamido-5,6-dimethoxypyrimidine (not in Table 1) has the longest persistence to date. It has a "half-life" of over 200 hr. A dose of 200 mg per week produces significant serum levels in humans (6b).

At about the time in the history of sulfa drugs when sulfapyridine (**2**) appeared, a sulfanilamide-related compound, not a sulfonamide, showed equal promise. It was bis(*p*-aminophenyl) sulfone, or dapsone (**29**). This compound and its congeners were decidedly more active than sulfanilamide on experimental streptococcal infections but they were also more toxic (1f). With the outstanding activity of sulfadiazine (**4**) the N^1-heterocyclic substituted sulfanilamide appeared to have won out over the sulfones. But unexpectedly the sulfones proved more active than the sulfonamides against experimental tuberculosis. The sulfones were prevented from attaining clinical usefulness in the treatment of tuberculosis by the appearance of the more active streptomycin (qv), but they did show an effect on the closely related mycobacterial disease leprosy. Neither the sulfonamides nor the antibiotics have shown a comparable effect on leprosy. Although widespread efforts were made to develop further derivatives of the sulfone, as had been done successfully for the sulfonamide, the sulfone derivatives have not found a place in therapy. The parent dapsone (**29**), however, is the treatment of choice for this ancient and previously untreatable scourge (9,26,27). That it is cheap and effective when administered once or twice per week in low doses gives it an outstanding additional advantage, because leprosy is a disease rampant in poor areas of the world where the cost of medication is a serious problem. There are estimated to be three million lepers in the world, primarily in tropical and semitropical countries (27).

Enteric Infections. The sulfa drugs are very effective in the control of bacillary dysentery, particularly that caused by *Shigella*. Originally the poorly absorbed derivatives sulfaguanidine (**22**), succinylsulfathiazole (**25**), and phthalylsulfathiazole (**26**) had been developed for just this application. They were expected to inhibit growth of the pathogenic bacteria because they are highly soluble at the pH of the gut and, being poorly absorbed, build up to high levels in the gut. These drugs were quite successful in this use, and, doubtless, are still employed frequently. However, a return to the better-absorbed sulfa drugs for enteric infections has come with the recognition that the offending bacteria (especially *Shigella*) invade the bowel tissue. The bacteria should be inhibited in this tissue by high levels of drug, which can be achieved only if the drug is well absorbed. The original broad application of the sulfa drugs in enteric infections has been narrowed because antibiotics are often preferable (3a).

Urinary Tract Infections. Despite the rise of the antibiotics the sulfa drugs have kept an important place in this field. Indeed, in the view of many investigators the sulfa drugs are the treatment of choice, especially in acute infections of the urinary tract (3c,4c). There is near consensus that short-acting "soluble" drugs are best in urinary tract disease. Advocates of short-acting drugs point to the high levels in the urine assured by the quick throughput of these drugs (4c). This is probably the prevailing view among practitioners, as the short-acting drugs sulfisoxazole (**19**), sulfamethizole (**10**), and sulfisoimidine (**18**) dominate the entire sulfa drug market (5).

Topical Infections. In general sulfa drugs are not recommended for surface use because of the danger of sensitization (28). Among the exceptions, however, sulfacetamide (**20**) is recommended topically for the treatment of ocular infections. Mafenide (**28**) is not a typical sulfa drug and has no systemic activity at all, but is also used topically. Originally mafenide was used in wounds to prevent gangrene (1g); recently it has been recommended for the topical treatment of burns to prevent growth of the dangerous *Pseudomonas* organisms (29). Both these drugs are weakly active and probably achieve their effects through the overwhelmingly high levels which their solubility permits.

Miscellaneous. Sulfa drugs have an effect in malaria but not enough to compete with the usual antimalarials (1e). Interest in sulfa and sulfone drugs has been revived because these drugs are effective on the resistant malaria which has appeared in Viet Nam during the war (30).

Veterinary uses for sulfa drugs are comparable to medical treatments for humans. The relative cheapness of these drugs is, however, much more important in animal therapy. Sulfaquinoxaline (**17**) and sulfamethazine (**9**) are employed against coccidiosis in turkeys and chickens (31).

The drug salicylazosulfapyridine (**27**) is recommended for ulcerative colitis, for which some say it is the treatment of choice. Its mechanism of action in this disease is obscure. An inhibition of fecal organisms is probably not involved (3a).

Metabolic Inactivation. The sulfa drugs are metabolized in the animal body, primarily in the liver, to inactive derivatives. The kind and extent of metabolic change varies with each drug and species. The two most important changes are acetylation of the primary amino group and conjugation by glucuronic acid of the sulfonamide or associated heterocyclic nitrogen. For example, the glucuronide of sulfadimethoxine comprises approx 80% of the total 24-hr urinary excretion of this drug; some 10% is excreted as the N^4-acetyl derivative, and only 10% is excreted unchanged (6c). This extent of conjugation is far greater than usual and it occurs with this long-acting drug because the greater portion of the unconjugated drug is reabsorbed in the kidney to maintain the blood level. During the same excretion period, some 85% of the sulfadimethoxine exists in the blood in the active unconjugated form. Conjugation is important not only because it decreases activity but also because it can modify toxicity (see below).

Toxicity. A small percentage of patients treated with sulfa drugs have developed symptoms of toxicity such as drug fever, rashes, mild peripheral neuritis, and mental disturbances. The incidence of these reactions may vary considerably from drug to drug. In general, toxicity is higher with higher blood levels and thus often accompanies poor excretion or overdosing (15). In 1966 the Food and Drug Administration required the two long-acting sulfa drugs sulfamethoxypyridazine (**12**) and sulfadimethoxine (**6**) to carry a label warning that the drugs had been implicated in deaths due to Stevens-Johnson syndrome (an extremely severe dermatologic reaction) (32). A later study of this implied association, however, cast doubt on its validity (33).

A more common and generally recognized toxic effect of sulfa drugs is their potential to damage the kidney. The basis of this toxicity and its significance to sulfa drug evolution was discussed under Nonchemical classification. The metabolic acetylation of sulfa drugs adds a degree of complexity to the control and prevention of this toxicity. Usually, but not always, the N^4-acetylated drug is less soluble than the parent. Some "soluble" sulfa drugs, unlikely themselves to precipitate, are converted extensively to the N^4-acetyl derivatives whose solubility lies in a range thought to be dangerous. Lehr arbitrarily selects a solubility of ca 70 mg per 100 ml at pH 5.5 and 37°C as the lower limit of safety (15). Sulfathiazole (**3**) is a drug that illustrates this situation. Judged retrospectively from its solubility of 98 mg per 100 ml, sulfathiazole should be safe. But because of the lower solubility of its acetyl derivative,

Table 2. Renal Safety and Solubility (15)

| Drug | Solubility at 37°C at pH 5.5, mg per 100 ml | | Safety |
	Free drug[a]	N^4-Acetyl drug	
sulfanilamide (**1**)	1500	530	very good
sulfathiazole (**3**)	98	7	very poor
sulfadiazine (**4**)	13	20	poor
sulfamethazine (**9**)	75	115	good
sulfapyrazine (**16**)	5	5	very poor
sulfisoxazole (**19**)	100 est[b]	50 est[b]	good
sulfacetamide (**20**)	1100	215	very good

[a] In general these values are higher than the solubilities given in Table 1 because of the higher temperature. However, some inconsistencies are apparent and are typical of the poor reproducibility of this determination.

[b] From (15b).

only 7 mg per 100 ml, it was found to cause blockage of the kidneys by crystalline deposits (15a). Kidney toxicity was an important factor in the obsolescence of this effective drug. Table 2 summarizes the solubility and presumed safety data of some sulfa drugs and acetylated derivatives. The solubility safety limit of ca 70 mg per 100 ml would apply uncertainly to long-acting drugs. Their slow excretion guarantees that high concentrations will not be reached in the urine from ordinary doses of these drugs.

The danger of kidney blockage is reduced by increasing the fluid intake and by administering sodium bicarbonate. These two measures simultaneously dilute the excreted drug and increase its solubility by alkalinizing the urine. The threat of this toxicity is also reduced by administering mixtures of drugs (15). The therapeutic efficacy of a mixture is presumably equal to the sum of its components but the solubilities of the components also add so that effective levels can be maintained with less likelihood of precipitation. One example, sold as a triple sulfonamide mixture, contained the three sulfa drugs sulfadiazine, sulfamerazine, and sulfamethazine. Numerous other mixtures were at one time sold. Some disadvantages of sulfa mixtures have, however, also been pointed out (4d).

Theoretical Aspects

Biological Mechanism of Action. It is generally agreed that the sulfa drugs act primarily by holding back growth (bacteriostatic) rather than by destroying the pathogen (bactericidal). Curing is then left to the normal defense machinery of the body. The sulfa drugs inhibit bacteria in vitro only if the growth medium is free of inactivating materials, notably peptones and p-aminobenzoic acid derivatives. Had in vitro activity been a prerequisite, neither Prontosil (inactive even in the absence of antagonists) nor its degradation product sulfanilamide would have been tried as a drug, and the rise of bacterial chemotherapy would have been delayed. Prontosil itself and the many sulfanilamide derivatives have been compared in experimental animal infections to determine the superior variants. Northey's compendium lists many of these results.

With the successful entry of the antibiotics into clinical medicine there came a curious contrast. The applicability of an antibiotic in a given clinical case could be checked quickly and accurately by in vitro tests on the particular infecting organism. However, because of the requirement for stringently simplified media to test sulfonamides, no comparable in vitro testing was done. Besides, there was disagreement as to the significance to therapy of the results of such in vitro tests as had been done (4e). This situation may be changing; there is now evidence that there may be a correlation between the clinical effectiveness of sulfa drugs and their bacteriostatic effect against the isolated bacteria in simplified media (34).

Pharmacokinetics and Dose Schedules. With the advent of increasingly persistent sulfa drugs the problem of arriving at an optimal dose schedule came to the fore. If these schedules are arrived at by trial and error, much time is consumed and there is danger to the patient. Persistent sulfa drugs in doses that are too high or too frequently given can lead to levels high enough to be toxic. Too little, of course, leads to levels too low to be effective. The elegant calculations of Krüger-Thiemer have filled in this important gap; his original work should be consulted for this complex matter (35). In general he sets a therapeutic level which should be maintained in the blood for effectiveness and calculates the size and spacing of doses which will achieve this level. The therapeutic level is derived from an in vitro inhibitory level corrected for the inactivating effect of protein absorption. The dosage schedule primarily rests on a determination of half-life—the time needed for an intravenously administered dose to drop to half value.

Biochemical Mechanism of Action. Just as the search for better sulfa drugs led to entirely new classes of practical therapeutics, so pursuit of the mechanism of their action has given new insights into drug theory that have affected even distantly related fields. From Woods' discovery that p-aminobenzoic acid (PABA) (see also Vol. 3, p. 435) reverses sulfa drug inhibition of bacteria arose the Woods-Fildes antimetabolite theory of drug action (1a). Pursuit of this concept in cancer chemotherapy has led the way to the present-day drugs for leukemia; this theory has had an impact also on tropical medicine and parasite chemotherapy.

The *Woods-Fildes theory* of sulfa drug action postulates that PABA is an essential metabolite for the bacteria involved. The primary action of the sulfa drugs is assumed to be a competitive inhibition of one or more enzyme reactions involving PABA. Subsequent work has shown the principal role of PABA to be that of a building block for folic acid and related vitamins (primarily folinic acid). The sulfa drugs prevent this synthesis and are therefore toxic to those bacteria which must synthesize their own folic acid vitamins. Mammals cannot synthesize these vitamins and thus depend on food sources; consequently sulfa drugs are not toxic to them in this sense.

The mechanism of action of sulfa drugs has been the subject of intensive studies from the earliest days. Two good recent reviews are those of Seydel (2) and Rogers (36). The variations of structure compatible with activity as developed from synthesis and testing of derivatives are outlined in the next section. The only rule that holds with certainty is that the primary amino group is necessary for biological action. The best current thinking is that this amino group reacts with a pterin compound (or precursor) involved in the formation of folinic acid from PABA. This competing reaction may be nonenzymatic and involve the accompanying Schiff base with pterin-

aldehyde or the reaction may be with a simpler aldehyde fragment. The competing reaction (aldehyde or not) may, as originally suggested by Woods, be at an enzyme receptor site, which normally handles PABA. Interestingly, as a twist on history, impressive evidence favors the nonenzymatic action as being more important (2).

There have been numerous attempts to organize into one theory the great array of facts which have come from the synthesis and testing of thousands of analogs (1a,2). The earliest was the theory of Bell and Roblin which posited a direct relationship between activity and the electronegativity of the sulfone portion of the sulfonamide group as deduced from the pK'_a. Activity has been correlated with basicity of the amino group, with dipole moments, with spectral data, and has been calculated quantum mechanically (2).

Structure-Activity Relations. The vast field of sulfanilamide-related compounds has been covered in depth by Northey (1) and summarized succinctly by Seydel (2).

If attention is limited to those compounds whose bacteriostatic activity is reversed by PABA, the following formulas summarize the features essential to highest activity:

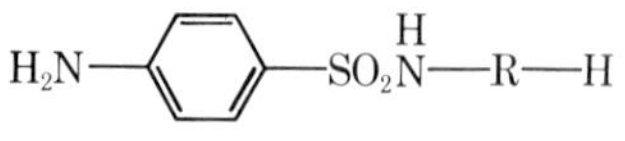

$$H_2N-\!\!\langle\bigcirc\rangle\!\!-SO_2\overset{H}{N}\!-\!R\!-\!H \qquad\qquad H_2N-\!\!\langle\bigcirc\rangle\!\!-SO_2\!-\!R\!-\!NH_2$$

sulfonamide 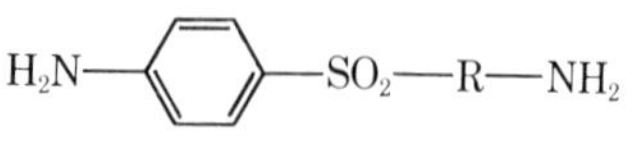   sulfone

Each structure has a p-aminobenzenesulfonyl group unsubstituted either in the ring or on the amino group. N^4-Acylated derivatives are chemotherapeutically active only if the acyl group is removed in the body. In the best sulfonamides R is heterocyclic but can be variously isocyclic or acyl. In the sulfones R can be benzene or a heterocycle; the "parent" dapsone (R = C_6H_4) is the most highly active.

One compound defies the above rules. It is the important tuberculostatic compound PAS (p-aminosalicylic acid). Although it is not a sulfa drug at all, it shares the same mechanism of action since it is reversed by PABA (37,38). The above narrow limits thus are not inviolable since PAS has neither a sulfonyl group nor an unsubstituted benzene ring. However, PAS may be exceptional in all ways. It is highly bacteriostatic but almost unbelievably specific in its action to *Mycobacteria* and often only to virulent ones at that (38).

Violation of the above structure-activity rules does occasionally give compounds active by a different mechanism. Separation of the amino group from the ring by a methyl group in mafenide (**28**) or its replacement by an amidine group (in methyl-p-amidinophenylsulfone) gives active compounds whose action has no known metabolite antagonist (1h).

Economic Aspects

The production of sulfa drugs increased rapidly after their introduction; spurred on by the military needs of World War II, it reached a maximum of 10 million lb in 1943. An abrupt drop to less than half this amount occurred in 1944, concomitant with the commercial development of antibiotics. This led to the belief that the sulfa

Table 3. U.S. Production of Sulfa Drugs and Antibiotics, 1000 lb (39)

Drug	1942	1943	1946	1952	1956	1966
total sulfa drugs	5,435	10,006	5,104	5,786	3,817	5,450
sulfathiazole	1,594	not given	2,016	724	a	a
total antibiotics	0	0	38	1,487	1,967	9,652
penicillins	0	0	35	671	631	2,092

a Probably negligible.

drugs would be quickly replaced, or at least reduced to a very low level of consumption. Their output has, however, been maintained close to the 1944 level, in spite of a very rapid increase in the production of antibiotics. An increased veterinary use, as well as their low cost and general effectiveness, has helped to hold a market for the sulfa drugs. Selected U.S. production figures of sulfa drugs and antibiotics are displayed in Table 3.

Because the total production of sulfa drugs has stabilized since 1944, it might appear that the field had become static. This is far from being the case. Sulfathiazole, at 2 million lb in 1946, was 40% of the entire sulfa drug production. By 1953 this drug had dropped to about 15% and at present (1969) is practically obsolete. A similar drop has occurred with most of the main drugs of 1946. In contrast, sulfisoxazole, a safer "soluble" derivative, not available in 1946, is the major sulfa drug in the U.S. (5a). To some extent the stabilization and even resurgence of the sulfa drugs in recent years come from a recognition that they are not only cheap but, for uncomplicated urinary tract disease, may be superior to the antibiotics (3a).

Pharmaceutical Formulations

The sulfa drugs are usually administered either as tablets or in suspensions of finely divided powder. The suspensions are useful for administration to children. Because some sulfa drugs taste intensely bitter, such formulations are often prepared from the N^1-acetyl sulfa drug. These acetyl derivatives are very insoluble and hence practically tasteless. They are well fitted for incorporation with pleasant-tasting syrups in "pediatric" preparations. N^1-Acetylsulfisoxazole (**24**) and N^1-acetylsulfamethoxypyridazine (**23**) are the principal examples of this application. They are inactive in their unaltered state and depend on rapid hydrolysis in the gut to give the active parent compounds (3). N^1-Acetylsulfisoxazole (**24**) is also marketed as the oil suspension. This preparation is expected to prolong the blood levels of sulfisoxazole. How well the oil suspension does in fact prolong the action of sulfisoxazole is controversial (3).

Formerly, sulfa drugs as solutions of the sodium salts were given by injection to severely ill patients. Since the sulfa drugs usually are relatively weak acids (see Table 1 for pK'_a), these solutions often are quite alkaline and, consequently, irritating to tissue and dangerous. Sulfisoxazole is one of the more acidic sulfa drugs and is available for parenteral use as a concentrated neutral solution of its diethanolamine salt. However, the antibiotics have taken over in precisely those critical diseases requiring parenteral treatment, and such preparations of the sulfa drugs are now of lesser importance.

Analysis and Identification

For most sulfa drugs having a free p-amino group, assay is readily carried out by titration with nitrous acid (40a). For assaying sulfa drugs in body fluids the Bratton-Marshall method is used (41). The basis for this method is the diazotization of the aromatic amino group, followed by coupling with N-naphthylethylenediamine and estimation of the color. After hydrolysis in acid such fluids give an added color response for N^4-acetyl derivatives which may have been formed in vivo. The difference between color readings before and after hydrolysis measures the extent of N^4-acetylation. A variety of simple chemical and physical tests have been used to identify individual sulfa drugs (40b). The multiplicity of metabolic conjugates of sulfa drugs and, also, the deliberate use of mixtures of sulfa drugs in therapy have given rise to great difficulties in identification and assay. Chromatographic separation is invaluable in such complex cases. Separations have been made on paper, and by the use of thin-layer chromatography (42).

Bibliography

"Sulfa Drugs" in *ECT* 1st ed., Vol. 13, pp. 271–285, by M. E. Hultquist, Research Division, American Cyanamid Company.

1. E. H. Northey, *The Sulfonamides and Allied Compounds*, Reinhold Publishing Corp., New York, 1948; (a) Chap. XI, pp. 466–516; (b) pp. 1–6; (c) except where noted, from pp. 11 to 20; (d) pp. 458–459; (e) pp. 517–577; (f) p. 340; (g) pp. 252–253; (h) pp. 510–511.
2. J. K. Seydel, *J. Pharm. Sci.* **57,** 1455–1478 (1968).
3. L. Weinstein, M. A. Madoff, and C. M. Samet, *New England J. Med.* **263,** 793–800, 842–849. 900–907, 952–957 (1960); (a) pp. 900–905; (b) p. 793; (c) pp. 952–957.
4. L. Neipp in R. J. Schnitzer and F. Hawking, eds., *Experimental Chemotherapy*, Vol. II, Academic Press, Inc., New York, 1964, pp. 169–249; (a) pp. 178–179; (b) p. 170; (c) pp. 175–176; (d) pp. 176–177; (e) pp. 231–235.
5. G. Zbinden in R. F. Gould, ed., "Molecular Modification in Drug Design," *Advan. Chem. Ser.* **45,** 25–38 (1964).
6. R. E. Bagdon in R. J. Schnitzer and F. Hawking, eds., *Experimental Chemotherapy*, Vol. II, Academic Press, Inc., New York, 1964, pp. 249–306; (a) pp. 290–292; (b) p. 301; (c) p. 282.
7. The sulfa drugs rarely get this credit. It is in part acknowledged by G. T. Stewart, *The Penicillin Group of Drugs*, Elsevier Publishing Co., New York, 1965, pp. 8–9.
8. M. Tishler in R. F. Gould, ed., "Molecular Modification in Drug Design," *Advan. Chem. Ser.* **45,** 5–9 (1964).
9. L. Doub in W. H. Hartung, ed., *Medicinal Chemistry*, Vol. V, John Wiley & Sons, Inc., New York, 1961, pp. 352–354.
10. P. G. Stecher, ed., *The Merck Index*, 8th ed., Merck & Co. Inc., Rahway, N. J., 1968. (Melting point and solubility data in Table 1 were taken from this reference except where specifically noted.)
11. J. Rieder, *Arzneimittel-Forsch.* **13,** 81–103 (Parts I–III) (1936).
12. L. Neipp and R. L. Mayer, *Ann. N.Y. Acad. Sci.* **69,** 448–456 (1968).
13. U.S. Pat. 2,833,761 (1958), D. M. Murphy and R. G. Shepherd.
14. P. H. Bell and R. O. Roblin, *J. Am. Chem. Soc.* **64,** 2905–2917 (1942).
15. D. Lehr, *Ann. N.Y. Acad. Sci.* **69,** 417–446 (1958); (a) p. 418; (b) estimated from graph on p. 430.
16. Brit. Pat. 819,019 (1959), (to Nordmark-Werke Gesellschaft, Hamburg).
17. J. H. Clark, J. P. English, C. R. Jansen, H. W. Marson, M. M. Rogers, and W. E. Taft, *J. Am. Chem. Soc.* **80,** 890 (1958).
18. Northey (1c) does not discuss this class of derivatives. The information given in this section is from general background of the author and partially extrapolated from cited sources.
19. U.S. Pat. 2,974,137 (1961), G. T. Fitchett, J. E. Gordon, and R. G. Shepherd, (to American Cyanamid Co., New York).
20. U.S. Pat. 2,721,200 (1955), M. Hoffer, (to Hoffman-LaRoche, Nutley, N. J.).
21. U.S. Pat. 2,396,145 (1946), A. Askelof, N. Svartz, and H. C. Willstaedt, (to Aktiebolaget Pharmacia); (through) *Chem. Abstr.* **40,** 3472 (1946).
22. J. M. Murdoch, *The Practitioner* **194,** 26–30 (1965).
23. *The Medical Letter* **7,** No. 16 (July 1965) (published by Drug and Information, Inc., New York). (In this issue the editors recommend that penicillin replace sulfa drugs in the treatment of all bacterial meningitides (including that from meningococcus, for which sulfas were formerly the treatment of choice). They recommend that sulfas be used for urinary tract disease, for *Nocardia, Shigella*, and some *Proteus* infections, for pyogenic conjunctivitis, for the prophylaxis of rheumatic disease, and for the suppression of bowel flora.)
24. Letter, H. L. Ley, Dept. Health, Education, and Welfare, Food and Drug Administration, Jan. 8, 1968. (This letter to the entire medical profession criticizes the use of sulfa drugs in the treatment of streptococcal disease but condones their use in its prophylaxis.)
25. J. T. Litchfield, Jr., reference 1, Chap. X, pp. 434–465.
26. S. G. Browne, *Brit. Med. J.* **1968 *III*,** 725–728.
27. G. Middlebrook and R. J. Dubos in R. J. Dubos, ed., *Bacterial and Mycotic Infections of Man.*, 3rd ed., J. B. Lippincott Co., Philadelphia, 1958, pp. 305–306.
28. Editorial, *Brit. Med. J.* **5380,** 485 (1964).

29. J. A. Moncrief, *Surgery* **63,** 862–867 (1968).

30. A. R. Surrey and A. Yarinsky in C. K. Cain, ed., *Annual Reports in Medicinal Chemistry, 1967,* Academic Press, Inc., New York, pp. 126–139 (1968).

31. E. E. Wehr and M. M. Farr, "Animal Diseases," in A. Stefferud, ed., *The Yearbook of Agriculture 1956,* U.S. Dept. Agriculture, Washington, D.C., 1956, p. 441.

32. Washington News Section, *J. Am. Med. Assoc.* **195,** 27 (1966).

33. J. R. Bianchine, P. J. J. Macaraeg, Jr., L. LaSagna, D. L. Azarnoff, S. F. Brunk, E. F. Hvidberg, and J. A. Owen, Jr., *Am. J. Med.* **44,** 390–405 (1968).

34. A. W. Baver, *Chemotherapia* **10,** 152–163 (1965–1966).

35. E. Krüger-Thiemer, *J. Theoret. Biol.* **13,** 212–215 (1966).

36. H. J. Rogers in R. J. Schnitzer and F. Hawking, eds., *Experimental Chemotherapy,* Vol. II, Academic Press, Inc., New York, 1964, pp. 45–56.

37. R. Knox in R. J. Schnitzer and F. Hawking, eds., *Experimental Chemotherapy,* Vol. II, Academic Press, Inc., New York, 1964, p. 84.

38. G. P. Youmans and A. S. Youmans in R. J. Schnitzer and F. Hawking, eds., *Experimental Chemotherapy,* Vol. II, Academic Press, Inc., New York, 1964, pp. 445–447.

39. United States Tariff Commission, *Synthetic Organic Chemicals, United States Production and Sales,* U.S. Govt. Printing Office, Washington, D.C.; used in Table 3, *1941–1943,* TC Publication 153, 1946; *Preliminary for 1946,* 1947; *1956,* TC Publication 200, 1957; *Preliminary for 1966,* 1967.

40. *The U.S. Pharmacopeia,* 17th Revision, Mack Publishing Co., Easton, Pa., 1965; (a) p. 882; (b) pp. 676–686.

41. A. C. Bratton and E. C. Marshall, *J. Biol. Chem.* **128,** 537–550 (1939).

42. T. Bićan-Fišter and V. Kajganović, *J. Chromatography* **16,** 503–509 (1964). (These authors cite earlier literature on paper-chromatographic separations.)

Leonard Doub

Parke, Davis & Co.

SULFONATION AND SULFATION

The term sulfonation designates any procedure by which the sulfonic acid group, —SO₂OH, or the corresponding salt or sulfonyl halide, is attached to a carbon atom. Included are those methods in which the sulfur, at a lower state of valence, is already attached to the carbon atom; the sulfonation process in these cases comprises oxidation. The term sulfonation is also sometimes loosely used to indicate treatment of any organic compound with sulfuric acid, regardless of the nature of the products formed.

Specialized sulfonation procedures include *sulfochlorination,* ie introduction of a —SO₂Cl group into an alkane, using sulfur dioxide and chlorine or sulfuryl chloride; *chlorosulfonation,* ie, introduction of a —SO₂Cl group into an aromatic or heterocyclic compound with chlorosulfuric acid; *sulfoxidation,* ie, direct sulfonation of an alkane with a mixture of sulfur dioxide and oxygen; and *sulfoalkylation* and *sulfoarylation,* ie attachment of a sulfoalkyl or a sulfoaryl group, respectively, to an organic compound, so as to form a new sulfonate of higher molecular weight and with altered properties.

Sulfation denotes the establishment of an —OSO$_2$OH grouping on carbon.

Sulfamation designates the attachment of the —SO$_2$OH group to nitrogen. This procedure, sometimes called *N*-sulfonation, is also discussed here, although it is of minor importance compared to sulfonation and sulfation.

Types and Uses. Sulfonates, sulfates, and sulfamates can each be differentiated into the following three main chemical types: aliphatic (including alicyclic), aromatic, and heterocyclic. The nature of the group attached directly to —SO$_2$OH determines the classification. Thus, alkanesulfonic acids may also contain aromatic or heterocyclic groupings, for example, α-toluenesulfonic acid, C$_6$H$_5$CH$_2$SO$_2$OH, or pyridylmethanesulfonic acid, (C$_5$H$_4$N)CH$_2$SO$_2$OH.

Three additional types of sulfonates, derived from petroleum fractions, from lignin, and from fatty oils and acids, are important commercially. They are made mostly by empirical procedures and are indeterminate in chemical composition.

Most uses for these compounds depend upon the presence of the hydrophilic, highly polar —SO$_2$OH group. In detergents, and similarly in wetting, emulsifying, and dispersing agents, the water-soluble sulfonate grouping is combined with an oil-soluble organic portion in many possible ways to produce a variety of desired effects. For dyes, mothproofing compounds, and synthetic tanning agents, it serves to make the compound soluble in water, and then to attach the organic molecule firmly to the fiber or leather. Ion-exchange resins function as strong acids that are completely insoluble in water, an unusual combination of properties leading to many applications. On the other hand, water-soluble sulfonated polymers are of interest as synthetic gums and thickening agents. Certain sulfamates are useful as sweetening agents and blood anticoagulants.

Sulfonates and sulfates are also used as intermediates for the preparation of other chemicals. Aromatic and heterocyclic sulfonates form phenols by caustic fusion. Phenol, 4-cresol, resorcinol (1,3-benzenediol), the naphthols and various hydroxyanthraquinones, 3-hydroxypyridine, and 8-hydroxyquinoline are notable examples. For this and other transformations of the sulfonic acid group see the article under Sulfonic acids. Dimethyl sulfate is employed as an alkylating agent; sulfated lower alkenes are converted to alcohols. Sulfonyl chlorides, RSO$_2$Cl, are of special interest as providing a simple route to various sulfonate derivatives, such as amides, esters, thiols, and sulfones. Some alkanesulfonyl chlorides have been employed as tanning agents or to make detergents or elastomers, while the aromatic analogs yield sulfa drugs, dyes, and insecticides. See also such articles as Detergency; Dyes and dye intermediates; Emulsions; Ion exchange; Phenol; Sulfonamides; Sulfonic acids; and Surfactants.

Reagents for Sulfonation

By far the most common procedure for preparing sulfonates, sulfates, and sulfamates involves treatment of an organic compound with sulfur trioxide or a compound thereof. The most important of these reagents are therefore discussed here.

Sulfur Trioxide. This is theoretically the most efficient reagent, since only direct addition is involved, as shown by the following overall equation:

$$RH + SO_3 \rightarrow RSO_2OH$$

Sulfur trioxide (see Sulfuric acid), bp 44.5°C, mp 16.8°C, is a colorless liquid when freshly distilled. It remains liquid if stored warm (at ca 34°C), but at room temperature exposure to even a trace of moisture results in the formation of solid polymers not ordinarily useful for sulfonation. The addition of a small quantity of a suitable compound—especially certain derivatives of boron, silicon, or sulfur—prevents the formation of solid polymer, so that the material "stabilized" in this manner is a practical article of commerce. Sulfur trioxide is miscible with liquid SO_2, and with chlorinated and chlorinated–fluorinated organic solvents. It is usually applied commercially as a 5–10% mixture with dry air or other gas, being obtained by vaporization of the liquid (which is commercially available), by distillation from oleum, by the use of "converter gas" from a sulfuric acid plant, or from a specially installed sulfur burner and catalytic converter. Liquid SO_3 is also sometimes used as a dilute solution in liquid SO_2. This is an almost ideal solvent because of its low price, stability, miscibility with SO_3 and sulfonic acids, and its boiling point (-10°C), which allows it to function as an autorefrigerant during sulfonation. The use of SO_3 for sulfonation has developed steadily since 1947, when the stabilized liquid was first introduced as an article of commerce. Some of its principal uses are for sulfonating aromatic compounds (eg, toluene, nitrobenzene, or detergent alkylate), petroleum oils, and long-chain terminal alkenes, and for sulfating alcohols, ether–alcohols, and dimethyl ether.

Sulfuric Acid and Oleum. These hydrates of SO_3 (see Sulfuric acid) have been the most common reagents for direct sulfonation, according to the following reaction:

$$RH + H_2SO_4 \rightleftarrows RSO_2OH + H_2O$$

The presence of water exerts such a profound influence that sulfuric acid and free SO_3 can be considered as having opposite properties as sulfonating agents, as summarized in Table 1 for the case of aromatic hydrocarbons.

Oleum (a solution of SO_3 in 100% sulfuric acid) has often proved a practical compromise between these two extremes. The advantages of SO_3, and correspondingly of oleums, as noted in Table 1, eg, rapid and complete reaction, minimum reactor capacity, and absence of spent acid (for SO_3 only), have proved increasingly attractive for industry because of the general increase in cost of labor and fixed capital and the necessity for obviating waste acid disposal. On the other hand, the disadvantages, such as high heat of reaction and high viscosity, which taken together can lead to darkening and decomposition, can often be overcome by modern engineering design, choice of conditions, or use of the proper solvent.

Table 1. Comparison of Sulfuric Acid and Sulfur Trioxide
for the Sulfonation of Aromatic Hydrocarbons

Factor compared	Sulfuric acid	Sulfur trioxide
boiling point, °C	290–317	45
reaction rate	slow	instantaneous
heat input	requires heat for completion	strongly exothermic throughout
extent of reaction	partial	complete
side reactions	minor	sometimes extensive
viscosity of reaction mixture	low	sometimes high
required reactor capacity	substantial	minimal
solubility in halogenated solvents	very low	miscible

Chlorosulfuric Acid. This compound has in the past been designated chlorosulfonic acid (qv). However, in accordance with the 1957 recommendation of the IUPAC Commission on the Nomenclature of Inorganic Chemistry, it is now preferably named chlorosulfuric acid.

This reagent, bp 152°C, can be regarded as an adduct of SO_3 with hydrogen chloride, which is released as a gas during sulfonation:

$$RH + ClSO_3H \rightarrow RSO_2OH + HCl\uparrow$$

If excess chlorosulfuric acid is used, sulfonyl chlorides are formed:

$$RSO_2OH + ClSO_3H \rightleftharpoons RSO_2Cl + H_2SO_4$$

Sulfation is effected as follows:

$$ROH + ClSO_3H \rightarrow ROSO_2OH + HCl\uparrow$$

This reagent has also been employed for sulfamation:

$$3 RNH_2 + ClSO_3H \rightarrow RNHSO_2\overset{-}{O}\overset{+}{H_3}NR + RN\overset{+}{H_3}\overset{-}{Cl}$$

Chlorosulfuric acid has been a favored laboratory and commercial reagent for sulfating alcohols, and for preparing sulfonyl chlorides. However, for sulfating alcohols, there has been a trend toward the use of sulfur trioxide. Chlorosulfuric acid is ordinarily used without a solvent, but it dissolves readily in methylene chloride, chloroform, 1,2-dichloroethane, and liquid sulfur dioxide and these have been employed occasionally.

Amidosulfuric Acid. The use of this name, in preference to the usual term "sulfamic acid," was recommended by the 1957 IUPAC Commission on the Nomenclature of Inorganic Chemistry, and is employed here.

Amidosulfuric acid (see Sulfamates), NH_2SO_2OH, is a stable, nonhygroscopic solid melting at 205°C. It is moderately soluble in water, and has an acid strength comparable to that of nitric or sulfuric acids. In sulfation and sulfamation reactions, amidosulfuric acid can be conveniently regarded as ammonia–SO_3 complex, $NH_3.SO_3$, even though it is not so prepared, and even though the formula NH_2SO_2OH more correctly denotes its role as a strongly acidic analog of sulfuric acid. Due to its chemical inertness and its strongly acid character, objectionable decomposition of the organic compound can occur at temperatures necessary to effect reaction, which are often in the range 150–200°C. On the other hand, its inertness is an advantage in sulfating alkylphenol–ethylene oxide condensates, since other reagents give undesirable ring sulfonation:

$$ROH + NH_3.SO_3 \rightarrow ROSO_2\overset{-}{O}\overset{+}{NH_4}$$

Amidosulfuric acid is also used commercially for sulfamating cyclohexylamine:

$$2 RNH_2 + NH_3.SO_3 \rightarrow RNHSO_2\overset{-}{O}\overset{+}{H_3}NR + NH_3\uparrow$$

The addition of weakly basic catalysts, such as urea, substantially accelerates the sulfation and sulfamation reactions with amidosulfuric acid and thus the reaction temperature can be lowered appreciably. This observation has extended the range of usefulness of amidosulfuric acid considerably.

Complexes with Organic Compounds. Sulfur trioxide and chlorosulfuric acid form "adducts" or "complexes" with organic bases and these are finding increasing use for specialized reactions where the more common reagents are unsuitable. *Sulfur* *trioxide–pyridine* is a saltlike solid, insoluble in the common organic solvents, but soluble in dimethylformamide. It is commercially available, and has been used extensively as a laboratory reagent for sulfating alcohols, phenols, sterols, and carbohydrates, for sulfamating amines, amides, and proteins, and for sulfonating acid-sensitive heterocyclic compounds and alkadienes. Sulfur trioxide–pyridine can be reacted with some compounds at moderate temperatures, usually below about 120°C, in the presence of excess pyridine or a solvent such as 1,2-dichloroethane. It reacts with other compounds by melting the two together in the range 150–200°C. Sulfamations and phenol sulfations can be effected in cold aqueous alkaline solution.

Sulfur trioxide trimethylamine is also a stable, saltlike solid with low solubility in common organic solvents except dimethylformamide. It is more stable to hydrolysis than SO_3–pyridine, as a result of the greater basic strength of trimethylamine compared with that of pyridine. This high degree of stability permits its more extensive use in aqueous systems, loss of the reagent by hydrolysis being comparatively minor. It is commercially available, and is used for sulfations and sulfamations like those cited above for SO_3–pyridine. A potential disadvantage of this complex in some cases is the persistent and unpleasant odor of even small residual quantities of the free amine.

Sulfur trioxide–dioxane is an unstable solid which must be prepared immediately before use. It has been employed extensively in the laboratory for sulfonating alkenes and sulfating alcohols.

Sulfur trioxide forms many other complexes which have been used to a lesser extent. A number of powerful solvents, including dimethyl sulfoxide, sulfolane, tetrahydrofuran, dimethylformamide, and acetonitrile, form sulfur trioxide complexes usually soluble in excess solvent. These are beginning to find application for sulfating polymers and other difficultly soluble materials.

Chlorosulfuric acid also forms complexes with weak bases, such as diethyl ether. This system has proved a favored laboratory reagent for sulfating alcohols. Its complexes with urea and dimethylformamide have been employed for sulfating oleyl alcohol and complex phenols, respectively. The chemical composition of these "complexes" is not clear; with pyridine, chlorosulfuric acid simply forms a mixture of sulfur trioxide–pyridine and pyridinium chloride.

Sulfonation Procedures

The principal procedures for preparing sulfonates, sulfates, and sulfamates may be classified as follows: *(1)* direct treatment with SO_3 or a compound thereof; *(2)* oxidative procedures; *(3)* sulfite reactions; and *(4)* condensation and polymerization methods.

Direct treatment with sulfur trioxide or a compound thereof is by far the cheapest and most widely applicable procedure. It involves reaction of an organic compound with one of the reagents listed in the preceding section. This method is designated *direct sulfonation*.

Oxidative procedures are often used in the laboratory to prepare aliphatic and heterocyclic sulfonates from thiols and thiol derivatives. Various types of oxidizing agents can be used, including oxygen, hydrogen peroxide, and nitric acid, the general overall reaction being expressed as follows:

$$RSH + 3\,O \rightarrow RSO_2OH$$

An especially useful variant involves aqueous chlorination to sulfonyl chlorides, which are versatile intermediates:

$$RSH + 3\,Cl_2 + 2\,H_2O \;\rightarrow\; RSO_2Cl + 5\,HCl$$

Sulfite reactions are used considerably for the preparation of aliphatic sulfonates, and to a lesser degree for the preparation of aromatic compounds. Metallic sulfites and bisulfites, especially the sodium, potassium, or ammonium salts, are the most common reagents, although sulfurous acid (sulfur dioxide and water) is sometimes employed. Alkenes, alkylene oxides, aldehydes, and ketones add bisulfites to yield alkanesulfonates in the first case, and hydroxyalkanesulfonates in the other three cases.

The reaction of an alkyl halide with a sulfite (the *Strecker reaction*), as shown below, has proved a useful tool in the laboratory and to some extent industrially.

$$RCl + Na_2SO_3 \;\rightarrow\; RSO_2ONa + NaCl$$

It can be used under more drastic conditions to prepare sulfonates in the benzene and anthraquinone series.

Sulfochlorination involves treatment of an alkane, or alkane derivative, with a mixture of sulfur dioxide and chlorine in the presence of light or other catalysts to form the sulfonyl chlorides as follows:

$$RH + SO_2 + Cl_2 \;\rightarrow\; RSO_2Cl + HCl\uparrow$$

The closely related procedure of *sulfoxidation* proceeds by the following overall reaction:

$$RH + SO_2 + \tfrac{1}{2}\,O_2 \;\rightarrow\; RSO_2OH$$

Condensation and polymerization methods involve the preparation of complex sulfonates from simpler ones, which are used as "building blocks."

Sulfoalkylation is a condensation-type procedure employing as sulfoalkylating agents such materials as the salts of N-methyltaurine ($CH_3NHCH_2CH_2SO_2OH$), 2-hydroxyethanesulfonic acid (isethionic acid), 2-chloroethanesulfonic acid, or propane-sultone, $\overline{(CH_2)_3OSO_2}$. These, and many similar types of sulfonates, have been reacted with diverse materials, such as long-chain acid chlorides, phenols, thiophenols, amines, alcohols, starch, and cellulose. Typical examples of this procedure are the following:

$$RONa + ClCH_2CH_2SO_2ONa \;\rightarrow\; ROCH_2CH_2SO_2ONa + NaCl$$

$$RONa + \overline{OCH_2CH_2CH_2SO_2} \;\rightarrow\; ROCH_2CH_2CH_2SO_2ONa$$

Sulfoarylation denotes the similar use of aromatic sulfonic acids, such a naphthalenesulfonic, phenolsulfonic, sulfanilic, or sulfoisophthalic.

Sulfonated polymers result from the polymerization of salts of ethylenesulfonic acid, $CH_2{=}CHSO_2OH$, or of styrenesulfonic acid, $CH_2{=}CHC_6H_4SO_2OH$. Condensation of formaldehyde with phenolsulfonic or naphthalenesulfonic acids, yields resins with varying degrees of solubility in water, depending upon the conditions. The reactions involved are the standard ones of phenol–formaldehyde resin formation. These products are manufactured as tanning or dispersing agents and as ion-exchange resins.

Aliphatic and Alicyclic (Cycloaliphatic) Sulfonates

Commercial development of these sulfonates is comparatively new, since it is dependent upon the availability of newly accessible raw materials, such as methanethiol, long-chain alkenes or polyethylene, or novel processes of sulfonation, for example, sulfochlorination or sulfoxidation.

Direct Sulfonation. Paraffinic and cycloparaffinic hydrocarbons react with sulfonating agents, but neither easily nor in a clean-cut manner. Oxidation and dehydrogenation are the major primary effects, but secondary reactions occur, yielding complex mixtures containing sulfonic acids, sulfates, carbonyl compounds, carboxylic acids, and other products. This approach has consequently not proved preparatively useful, although it has practical interest in other respects. Sludge formation during the sulfonation of petroleum fractions occurs partially in this manner. The adhesiveness and printability of polyethylene is improved by surface oxidation–sulfonation; reaction undoubtedly occurs mainly at the tertiary carbon atoms. Of the many patents which have appeared on the various procedures for achieving this effect, two may be cited as typical. In one process polyethylene fabric is treated with 3% oleum at 50°C (68) and in the other polyethylene sheeting is treated at room temperature with a solution of SO_3 in tetrachloroethylene (28). Chlorosulfuric acid was the best reagent for sulfonating low-pressure polyethylene film (63). Solvents, such as 1,2-dichloroethane or chloroform, which dissolve SO_3 or chlorosulfuric acid and also promote swelling and penetration of the polymer, greatly facilitate the sulfonation. Although alkanes react with SO_3 and are poor solvents for it, they have been employed

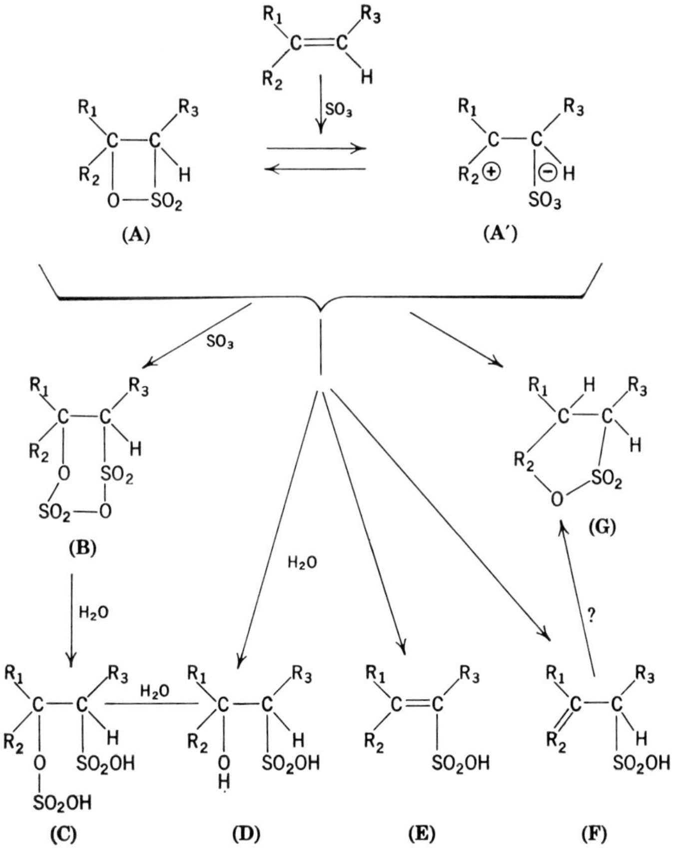

Fig. 1. Alkene sulfonation products.

occasionally as sulfonation solvents for other compounds which react more easily, especially at low temperatures; *n*-butane and *n*-hexane have been used in this manner.

Alkenes and cycloalkenes, on the other hand, react easily with SO₃, or several of its complexes, to yield one or more of various possible products, as illustrated in Figure 1. Sulfuric acid, however, yields sulfates, the formation of which is discussed under Sulfation (see p. 304). A β-sultone (**A**), or the corresponding carbonium ion (**A′**), is considered the primary alkene sulfonation product. These sultones are quite reactive and unstable, and are usually not isolated as such, although they have been obtained at a low temperature from styrene, fluorinated alkenes, and terminal alkenes. Products of type **B** (sulfate–sulfonic anhydride, or a "carbyl sulfate") have been isolated only in the cases of ethylene and 1,1-difluoroethylene (with both of which no other products are formed), of trifluoroethylene and methallyl chloride (which give mixtures), of tetrafluoroethylene and hexafluoropropylene (which give some product **B** with undistilled SO₃, but none with the freshly distilled material), and possibly of cyclohexene. Five-membered ring sultones of type **G** result in fair yield from γ-branched alkenes, such as 3-methyl-1-butene or 4-methyl-2-pentene (10). The usual types of final products, isolated after aqueous neutralization of the reaction mixture, are alkenesulfonates (structure **E** or **F**), or hydroxysulfonates (either of type **D** or of a type resulting from the hydrolysis of sultones of structure **G**). Product structures are quite sensitive to various factors, such as alkene structure, type of sulfonating agent, reaction solvent, time, temperature, and method of isolation.

Commercial availability of straight-chain C_{15-18} 1-alkenes has prompted widespread study of their interaction with SO₃ for the possible preparation of detergents (42,50,69). If the reaction is run below room temperature (69), the product comprises mainly hydroxy-1-sulfonates, of which 64% is the undesirably water-insoluble 2-hydroxy compound and 33% the more soluble 3-hydroxy compound. At higher temperatures (ie 40–60°C), 50–55% mixed unsaturated 1-sulfonates are obtained with the double bond distributed along the chain to as far as C_{11}–C_{12}; the remainder is mostly 3- and 4-hydroxy-1-sulfonates. This reaction is uniquely susceptible to color and by-product formation, but rapid conversion in a continuous reactor, followed by prompt neutralization, yields a product of good quality as a detergent (42). Commercial production of this type of sulfonate was begun in 1967.

Many types of alkenes react with SO₃ according to the above scheme, including terminal-fluorinated alkenes, vinyl ethers and esters, alkadienes, and natural and synthetic rubbers. Steric factors are important in the sulfonation of alkenes since they often determine the structure of the product or even whether or not reaction occurs. Thus, 1,1-diphenyl-2-methyl-1-propene, $(CH_3)C{=}C(C_6H_5)_2$, and tetrachloroethylene do not form sulfonates. Internal olefins are much less reactive than terminal ones. For example, polybutylene mixtures sulfonate only to the extent of about 25%, the remainder apparently being sterically too hindered to react, since the double bonds are internally situated. Perfluorocyclohexene fails to react with SO₃ even at 200°C, though cyclohexene and tetrafluoroethylene react easily at room temperature.

Chlorosulfuric acid dissolved in ethyl ether also reacts easily with olefinic compounds. The primary product is apparently a chlorinated sulfonic acid, but the halogen is often so labile that the olefinic sulfonate is the compound actually isolated:

$$RCH{=}CHR' \xrightarrow[\text{Et}_2\text{O}]{\text{ClSO}_3\text{H}} RCHClCH(R')SO_2OH \xrightarrow{-HCl} RCH{=}C(R')SO_2OH$$

With a nonpolar solvent, or without solvent, no sulfonic acid is formed; instead the chlorosulfonic acid organic ester, $ClSO_2OR$, is obtained by sulfation.

Alkenes undergo sulfonation with a mixture of acetic anhydride and sulfuric acid ("acetyl sulfate"), forming products of the structure $RCH(OCOCH_3)CH_2SO_2OH$. A mixture of octadecenes has been thus converted to a commercial detergent; removal of the acetyl group as acetic acid was effected by steaming.

Acetylene reacts with four moles of sulfur trioxide, forming a product of type **B** (see Fig. 1), which upon hydrolysis yields acetaldehydedisulfonic acid, $(HO)_2CHCH(SO_2OH)_2$, in its hydrated or dihydroxy form, which is a compound of type **D**. This acid has been used experimentally as a source of the sulfoethylidene group, $=CHCH_2SO_2OH$, in the preparation of ion-exchange resins and other sulfonated compounds, one of the sulfonic groups being lost by cleavage during reaction of the aldehyde group (27).

Aliphatic aldehydes and ketones are easily sulfonated on the carbon atom adjacent to the carbonyl group with SO_3, usually applied as the dioxane complex. The procedure is simple, the yields are generally good, mono- or disulfonic acids can be obtained depending upon the proportions used, and the reaction is widely applicable. Saturated aliphatic acids (C_9 and higher) likewise are easily sulfonated in good yield on the C_2 with SO_3, used either as liquid or vapor (60). Yields from the lower fatty acids are poor, although chloroacetic acid is monosulfonated smoothly with SO_3 vapor in 95% yield. Sulfur trioxide–dioxane selectively sulfonates phenylalkanoic acids on the carbon atom adjacent to the carboxyl group, rather than on the easily sulfonated phenyl group; ring sulfonation is, however, observed with other reagents, such as sulfuric acid. Esters readily undergo scission with SO_3, but fair yields of sulfo esters can be obtained under special conditions (58).

Oxidative Procedures. The oxidation of thiols, and of many thiol derivatives (disulfides, thiosulfates, thioacetates, isothiouronium salts, thiocyanates, etc), is a widely applicable approach for the preparation of sulfonic acids and of sulfonyl halides. Various oxidizing agents have been used, including nitric acid (65), hydrogen peroxide (57), oxygen in the presence of bases (67), and oxygen in the presence of a small quantity of NO_2 (49), as follows:

$$RSH \xrightarrow{3\ O} RSO_2OH$$

This type of reaction is used industrially in a high-speed process for dehairing hides (53); the disulfide linkages in the hair are oxidized by treatment with ClO_2 to form water-soluble sulfonic acids. Sulfonic acid formation is similarly the principal reaction occurring during the bleaching of human hair with hydrogen peroxide.

Chlorination of a thiol, or its derivatives, in aqueous acetic acid is a favored laboratory procedure for preparing sulfonyl chlorides (20), as shown below:

$$RSH + 2\ H_2O + 3\ Cl_2 \rightarrow RSO_2Cl + 5\ HCl$$

Methane- and n-octanesulfonyl chlorides are prepared by this method industrially. The sulfonyl chlorides are convenient intermediates for the preparation of various sulfonate derivatives, such as esters and amides.

Sulfite Reactions. Aldehydes and a few ketones add sulfurous acid or bisulfites to form α-hydroxysulfonates, $R_2C(OH)SO_2OMe$. Formaldehyde–sodium bisulfite is a useful sulfomethylating agent, as discussed below (see p. 290). The water-soluble sulfurous acid adduct of polyacrolein, $—(CH_2CH(CH(OH)SO_2OH))_x—$, is a strong polyelectrolyte with interesting surface-active properties (54), which can react with other polymers through residual aldehyde groups, forming novel "composite polymers." Copolymers of acrolein, eg, with acrylonitrile, also form water-soluble bisulfite adducts. It is therefore possible to modify ordinarily insoluble polymers by copolymerization of the suitable monomer with a sufficient proportion of acrolein so that the bisulfite adduct is water-soluble.

Epoxides react easily with bisulfites. In the case of ethylene oxide the product, sodium isethionate, is a useful sulfoalkylating agent (see p. 290).

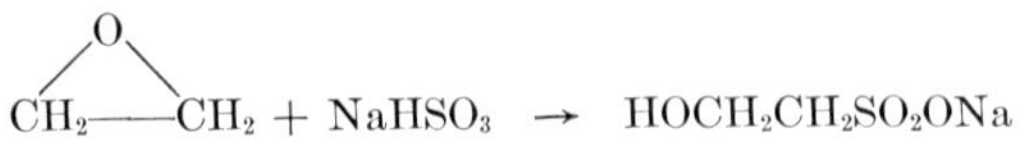

$$CH_2 \overset{O}{\diagdown} CH_2 + NaHSO_3 \rightarrow HOCH_2CH_2SO_2ONa$$

The free-radical-catalyzed addition of bisulfites to long-chain terminal alkenes has been studied industrially (16) as a possible approach to biodegradable detergents:

$$RCH{=}CH_2 + NaHSO_3 \rightarrow RCH_2CH_2SO_2ONa$$

The yields are 95% or better, provided several process conditions are observed. These include control of pH between 7 and 9, use of air or peroxides as initiator, presence of an alcoholic solvent (methanol, ethanol, or 2-propanol), gradual addition of bisulfite, and efficient mixing. The addition of bisulfite to allyl alcohol is the first step in preparing 1,3-propanesultone, an important sulfoalkylating agent, as shown in the following equation:

$$CH_2{=}CHCH_2OH \xrightarrow{NaHSO_3} NaO_3SCH_2CH_2CH_2OH \xrightarrow[(2) \ -H_2O]{(1) \ H^+} O_2\overset{\frown}{S(CH_2)_3O}$$

Heteroconjugate systems (ie, conjugate systems involving noncarbon atoms as well as carbon atoms) add bisulfites with ease, and no catalyst is required since the reaction is ionic. This reaction, shown below, is used commercially to prepare wetting agents of the "aerosol" type from various long-chain esters of maleic acid. Sulfosuccinate esters of corn starch are made similarly.

$$\begin{matrix} CHCOOR \\ \| \\ CHCOOR \end{matrix} + NaHSO_3 \rightarrow \begin{matrix} CH_2COOR \\ | \\ CH(SO_2ONa)COOR \end{matrix}$$

The *Strecker reaction*, ie, substitution of organic halogen with a sodium sulfonate grouping (see p. 284), has been studied extensively. Usually a primary organic halide is refluxed with an aqueous inorganic sulfite solution for periods of time which may vary from one hr to several days, depending upon the compound reacted. Water-miscible cosolvents (eg alcohols, glycols, or dimethylformamide) are sometimes added to promote mutual solubility or to permit higher reaction temperatures. Reaction under pressure at 160–200°C is often advantageous. Commercially the Strecker procedure has been employed to prepare sodium 2-chloroethanesulfonate, a useful sulfoalkylating agent, according to the following reaction:

$$ClCH_2CH_2Cl + Na_2SO_3 \rightarrow ClCH_2CH_2SO_2ONa + NaCl$$

Another commercial application is for the manufacture of surface-active agents, such as the Triton (Rohm and Haas Co.) types, as shown below:

$$C_8H_{17}C_6H_4OC_2H_4OC_2H_4Cl + Na_2SO_3 \rightarrow C_8H_{17}C_6H_4OC_2H_4OC_2H_4SO_2ONa + NaCl$$

The wetting agent sodium lauryl sulfoacetate is similarly prepared from lauryl chloroacetate.

The *sulfochlorination* reaction (5) was patented by Reed in 1936, when he observed that a —SO_2Cl group could be placed on an aliphatic carbon atom by using a mixture of sulfur dioxide and chlorine in the presence of a chain-initiating catalyst, such as actinic light, in the series of reactions shown below:

$$Cl_2 \xrightarrow{\text{catalyst}} 2\ Cl.$$

$$Cl. + RH \rightarrow R. + HCl$$

$$R. + SO_2 \rightarrow RSO_2.$$

$$RSO_2. + Cl_2 \rightarrow RSO_2Cl + Cl.$$

This procedure seemed at the time to provide the long-sought method for easy sulfonation of cheap paraffinic petroleum fractions, which (as discussed above, see p. 285) cannot be effected with SO_3 or its compounds. It was therefore accorded immediate and intensive study by the E. I. du Pont de Nemours & Co., Inc., in the United States and by I. G. Farbenindustrie in Germany. The raw materials were, respectively, a petroleum white oil and a hydrogenated gas oil obtained by the Fischer-Tropsch process. These yielded sulfonate detergents by alkaline hydrolysis of sulfonyl chlorides; annual production in Germany of a detergent of this type reached 80,000 tons by the end of World War II.

Chlorination and disulfochlorination occur as side reactions which can be reduced, but not eliminated, by resorting to partial conversion of the organic compound, and by using a considerable molar excess of SO_2 relative to chlorine. The consequent necessity for raw material recovery and recycle, the high cost of raw material (ie, the consumption of unproductive chlorine), the need for specialized equipment (because of the formation of corrosive hydrogen chloride and the requirement of photochemical activation), and the necessity for a final saponification step, have put this process in an unfavorable position for commercial detergent production as compared to sulfoxidation and the direct sulfonation of dodecylbenzene.

Sulfochlorination is employed commercially for the conversion of polyethylene to an elastomer which can be cured by reaction with various inorganic or organic agents to a synthetic rubber of outstanding abrasion resistance and durability on exposure to oxygen, ozone, heat, and weather (13a,59). Chemically, the elastomer is a high-molecular-weight chlorinated polysulfonyl chloride. (See Vol. 7, p. 695.) A second commercial application is the production of 2-chloroethanesulfonyl chloride by the combined chlorination–sulfochlorination of ethane (18). This compound is a versatile sulfoalkylating agent. Long-chain alkanesulfonyl chlorides achieved semicommercial acceptance as specialized tanning agents; during tanning, sulfonamides are formed by interaction with the amino groups of the leather. All three of these applications involve reactions of the sulfonyl chloride group other than simple hydrolysis.

Sulfoxidation resembles sulfochlorination in being a free-radical chain process for the sulfonation of paraffin hydrocarbons:

$$RH + SO_2 + O_2 \xrightarrow{\text{light}} RSO_2OOH \xrightarrow[H_2O]{SO_2} RSO_2OH + H_2SO_4$$

However, this process (9) has the important advantage of not requiring chlorine. It has been employed commercially since 1968 for the production of biodegradable detergents from C_{14-17} petroleum-based *n*-alkanes.

Long-chain alkyl hydroperoxides, prepared by the air oxidation of paraffinic petroleum fractions, yield sulfonates by reaction with an excess of aqueous metallic bisulfite:

$$ROOH + 2\,NaHSO_3 \;\rightarrow\; RSO_2ONa + NaHSO_4 + H_2O$$

This reaction has been studied by several industrial groups interested in making cheap petroleum-based detergents (44). It has also been employed experimentally for sulfonating polyethylene. The raw materials (hydrocarbon, SO_2, and oxygen) and the products (organic sulfonate and sulfate ion) are the same for this process as for sulfoxidation, but this method is operated stepwise.

Condensation and Polymerization Methods. *Sulfomethylation*, ie, introduction of the $—CH_2SO_2ONa$ group using formaldehyde–sodium bisulfite, has proved a simple and mild procedure for sulfonating compounds containing active hydrogen atoms such as phenols, ketones, amines, amides, and sulfonamides. The first two types of compounds sulfomethylate on carbon, the last three on nitrogen. This reaction has been applied industrially to prepare azo dyes for cellulose acetate. Condensation with phenols and excess formaldehyde yields ion-exchange resins; these can be regarded as phenol–formaldehyde resins containing sulfomethyl groups. Although this type of resin is no longer manufactured in the United States, a chemically similar product is made by treating crushed phenol–formaldehyde polymer with sulfite. Sulfomethylation on nitrogen has been used to enhance the water solubility of pharmaceuticals, the nuclear sulfonates being in contrast less effective and more toxic (46).

Sulfoethylation is commonly effected with four reagents. Sodium 2-chloroethanesulfonate, $ClCH_2CH_2SO_2ONa$, has been employed experimentally to sulfoalkylate amines, long-chain amides, starch, and cellulose. Sodium 2-hydroxyethanesulfonate (isethionate, see p. 288) reacts with acids or acid halides; the wetting agent Igepon A (GAF Corp.) is thus made from oleic acid or its chloride. Sodium *N*-methyltaurine similarly forms the surface-active agent Igepon T by reaction with oleoyl chloride, as follows:

$$RCOCl + CH_3NHCH_2CH_2SO_2ONa \;\xrightarrow{\;NaOH\;}\; RCON(CH_3)CH_2CH_2SO_2ONa + NaCl + H_2O$$

Sodium ethylenesulfonate (38), $CH_2{=}CHSO_2ONa$, unlike the other sulfoalkylating reagents cited above, forms no secondary products, such as water or hydrogen chloride, during sulfoalkylation. It is a highly reactive compound, combining easily with amines or alcohols. The most efficient procedure for sulfoethylating cellulose is said to involve the use of sodium ethylenesulfonate at 67–75°C with an organic solvent, such as 2-propanol, *tert*-butyl alcohol, or dioxane, in the presence of aqueous alkali. The acid and several of its derivatives have been polymerized and copolymerized with various other monomers to water-soluble and insoluble polymers of types not accessible by other preparative methods. A homopolymer has been on the market for several years as a blood anticoagulant.

1,3-Propanesultone (26) is a highly reactive and versatile sulfoalkylating agent capable of combining, often without using a solvent, with many different types of compounds, including alcohols, phenols, amines, thiols, carboxylic acid salts, amides, sulfonamides, and even inorganic salts. Sodium oleate forms a derivative, shown below, with good foaming and detergency:

$$RCOONa + \overline{O(CH_2)_3}SO_2 \;\rightarrow\; RCOO(CH_2)_3SO_2ONa$$

Many other sulfoalkylating agents are known, but they are generally less widely applicable or less easily available than those mentioned above. Such compounds contain carbonyl (aldehyde and ketone), carboxyl, ester, cyano, or organometallic groups in addition to the sulfonic acid moiety.

Aromatic Sulfonates

This group comprises the most important industrial sulfonates, including detergents, tanning agents, ion-exchange resins, and intermediate sulfonates for preparing dyes, pharmaceuticals, and phenolic compounds. The hydrocarbon sulfonates are the outstanding category within this group, and direct sulfonation is by far the most useful procedure for preparing these compounds.

DIRECT SULFONATION

Physicochemical Factors. A predominant characteristic of the aromatic sulfonation reaction is the requirement that, if sulfuric acid is used, the acid must be maintained above a certain strength for a reaction to proceed. This means that water must be removed to complete sulfonation:

$$RH + H_2SO_4 \rightarrow RSO_2OH + H_2O$$

This is usually accomplished by distilling the water out of the reaction mixture as an azeotrope with excess hydrocarbon. Much more complete utilization of aqueous acid can be effected by the use of elevated temperatures and pressures. The water can also be removed chemically, for example by adding thionyl chloride, as shown below:

$$RH + H_2SO_4 + SOCl_2 \rightarrow RSO_2OH + 2\,HCl\uparrow + SO_2\uparrow$$

Anhydrous sulfonations go to completion:

$$RH + SO_3 \rightarrow RSO_2OH$$

$$RH + ClSO_3H \rightarrow RSO_2OH + HCl\uparrow$$

The position taken by a sulfonate group entering an aromatic compound is strongly influenced by temperature and by acid strength. Thus, toluene with 85% sulfuric acid at 120°C forms 20.1% *ortho-*, 5.0% *meta-*, and 74.5% *para*sulfonic acid isomers, but at 160° the percentages are 12.7, 4.4, and 82.3, respectively. At 25°C, 80.6% acid gives 25% ortho sulfonic acid, but 98.5% acid gives 49.4% of the ortho isomer. These data were obtained after short times of reaction.

Aromatic sulfonation is reversible in the presence of excess sulfuric acid provided the temperature is high enough. In addition, the initially formed (ie, kinetically

Table 2. Kinetic vs Equilibrium Orientation, Isomer Distribution, %

	Initial			At equilibrium		
Compound	ortho	meta	para	ortho	meta	para
toluene	52	5	43	3	60	37
chlorobenzene	low	low	>95	0	54	46
phenol	39	0	61	low	38	61
benzene[a]	0	>95	low	0	66	34

[a] Disulfonate.

oriented) sulfonates are usually not the most stable ones thermodynamically. These two characteristics taken together mean that mild sulfonation conditions (ie, short reaction times, low temperatures) give different products from those obtained at equilibrium involving more drastic conditions. Several examples are given in Table 2. It will be noted that different products are obtained not only with compounds easy to sulfonate (eg, phenol or toluene), but also with those which react with difficulty (ie benzenesulfonic acid).

Nitro, sulfonyl, carbonyl, and trihalomethyl groups are largely meta directing and make sulfonation difficult, while alkyl, alkoxy, alkylthio, and hydroxy groups render sulfonation easy and are primarily ortho-para directing. Amino and halogen are anomalous. The former is ortho-para directing under some conditions, but meta directing under others; it facilitates sulfonation. Halogen retards sulfonation, but is ortho-para directing. (The orientation effects mentioned refer to the products obtained in a short time under mild conditions, and not to those produced under drastic conditions, as indicated in Table 2.)

Another practical consequence of the reversibility of aromatic sulfonation is the process of steaming a sulfonic acid to recover the aromatic compound, known as *hydrolytic desulfonation*, a useful technique in its own right. (See Sulfonic acids.)

Table 3. Relative Rates of Sulfonation with H_2SO_4 in Nitrobenzene[a]

Compound	Rate ratio	Compound	Rate ratio
o-xylene	1775[b]	benzene	100
naphthalene	910	chlorobenzene	69
m-xylene	752	bromobenzene	61
toluene	507	*m*-dichlorobenzene	43
ethylbenzene	482[b]	4-nitrotoluene	21
isopropylbenzene (cumene)	335[b]	*p*-dibromobenzene	7
tert-butylbenzene	284[b]	*p*-dichlorobenzene	6
1-nitronaphthalene	169	1,2,4-trichlorobenzene	5
4-chlorotoluene	110	nitrobenzene	2

[a] Based on data in reference 61, unless otherwise indicated.
[b] Based on data in reference 45.

As shown in Table 3, relative ease of sulfonation, as reflected by the reaction rate, increases with increasing methylation of the benzene ring, and with an increase in the number of fused rings. The introduction of nitro or halogen groups reduces the rate, but this can be counteracted by methylation. With the monoalkylated benzenes, increasing the size of the alkyl group reduces the rate. Isomeric di- and polysubstituted benzenes can vary greatly in relative ease of sulfonation, an important factor being the tendency of an entering sulfonate group to avoid, because of its large size, a position adjacent to another group. The sulfonic acid group resembles *tert*-butyl in its shape and bulk; steric factors are therefore important in sulfonation.

Polycyclic ring systems, such as anthracene or phenanthrene, sulfonate so easily that polysulfonates are formed even under such mild conditions that some of the hydrocarbon remains unsulfonated. As in the case of toluene cited above, the products of initial polycyclic sulfonation are different from those obtained under more drastic conditions. As a result of these complications such sulfonations have been studied very little.

The major side reactions noted in the sulfonation of aromatic compounds are sulfone formation, polysulfonation, oxidation, dealkylation, and rearrangement. The last three side reactions often occur together when alkyl groups are involved. It was recognized only about 1960 that sulfonic anhydrides can be formed in high yield by the direct reaction of various aromatic hydrocarbons with SO_3 or strong oleum (15,41), as shown below.

$$2\,RH + 3\,SO_3 \;\rightarrow\; (RSO_2)_2O + H_2SO_4$$

This reaction occurs to some extent in the commercial sulfonation of detergent alkylate with SO_3 and will no doubt be noted in other cases as the trend toward stronger detergents continues.

Kinetic and mechanistic studies of aromatic sulfonation have led to the conclusion that it is an S_E2 reaction with monomeric SO_3 as the effective reacting species, not only with SO_3 itself, but also when sulfuric acid or oleum is used. In low-strength oleums, the rate expression is $K \propto (ArH)(SO_3)$. As the SO_3 content of the oleum is increased, the order with respect to SO_3 increases steadily, approaching 2 for pure SO_3, and is $K \propto (ArH)(SO_3)^2$.

Benzene. The monosulfonation of benzene is of commercial importance because it is an intermediate to a process for producing phenol (qv), although this approach to phenol is now considered less economical than the air oxidation of cumene. There are several methods for preparing benzenesulfonic acid (qv); the Tyrer process is favored in the United States. In a preferred form, this operation comprises the liquid-phase treatment of benzene with low-strength oleum, followed by continuous removal of water at an elevated temperature (eg, 180°C) by countercurrent treatment with benzene vapor in a multiple-unit cascade system substantially to complete the reaction of the sulfuric acid. The simplest possible preparative procedure, namely, direct reaction of benzene with SO_3, is rendered impractical by the formation of excess by-product sulfone. In a procedure without sulfone formation the benzene is reacted with sulfuric acid; the latter, diluted by water of reaction, is then refortified by adding SO_3 and recycled. This Dennis-Bull process, however, involved too many processing difficulties to achieve commercial acceptance.

The disulfonation of benzene is a significant intermediate step in the only established commercial process for making resorcinol (see Vol. 11, p. 472). The introduction of a second sulfonic acid group into the benzene ring is much more difficult than that of the first. Treatment of the monosulfonic acid with oleum for a comparatively short time (eg, 8 hr or less) at a moderate temperature (ie, 35–85°C) yields the desired *meta* isomer as practically the only product. (More drastic conditions give increasing quantities of undesired *para* disulfonate isomer, as indicated in Table 2.) This procedure yields a large quantity of spent sulfuric acid. The acid is separated commercially by neutralization, but laboratory studies have shown that it can be removed by vacuum distillation. The disulfonic acid has also been prepared commercially by treating the monosulfonic acid with SO_3. This approach has the advantage of largely eliminating the formation of spent acid, but the yield is reduced as the result of sulfone formation.

Toluene. Interest in the preparation of toluenesulfonic acid (see Sulfonic acids) has been stimulated by the availability of toluene in large quantities from petroleum sources, combined with a shortage of *p*-cresol. The first step in the production of saccharin (see Sweeteners) is the low-temperature chlorosulfonation of toluene, discussed in more detail below (see p. 299). As indicated previously, the isomer yields obtained in toluene sulfonation are quite sensitive to temperature, reaction time, and reagent strength (see p. 291). In the laboratory a total yield of 95% is obtained by adding 96% sulfuric acid to the hydrocarbon as fast as compatible with control of the reaction, followed by the removal of water by distillation with excess toluene to complete the sulfonation. A commercial process of this type (48) employs 98% acid, requires 7 hr, and gives a product comprising 75% para and 25% ortho isomers. Toluene can form undesirable quantities of sulfone and/or disulfonic acid with SO_3. However, by using liquid SO_2 as reaction solvent, and by simultaneously adding the two reagents dissolved in SO_2 to the reactor, both of these side reactions can be minimized, and the product comprises over 90% para isomer. Several U.S. companies employ this type of process. Most synthetic cresol is prepared using this procedure as the first step.

Detergent Alkylate. The sulfonation of "detergent alkylate" is very important for the large-scale manufacture of household and industrial detergents. This hydrocarbon mixture is made by chlorinating a mixture of kerosene-based straight-chain hydrocarbons, averaging about C_{12}, followed by reaction of the halide with benzene. Annual world production of this and similar long-chain alkylated benzenesulfonates is about one million tons, making it the major one in production by a large margin, except for lignosulfonates. The hydrocarbon mixture is easily sulfonated by a variety of procedures to yield a detergent of good color, odor, and performance. For these reasons it is widely used by detergent manufacturers.

Detergent alkylate has been sulfonated commercially with 98% acid, oleums of various strengths, and SO_3. However, the presence of the long alkyl chains in such compounds leads to different behavior during sulfonation than that noted with benzene or toluene. Dealkylation can occur, forming long-chain olefins, with a tendency which varies inversely with the reagent strength. Although the quantity of olefin formed is small, a noticeable difference in product odor results, which can be important in household detergents. Vaporized SO_3 gives the least dealkylation and the best odor; sulfuric acid behaves oppositely and oleums are intermediate. On the other hand, liquid SO_3 cannot be added directly to undiluted detergent alkylate without prohibitive dealkylation, although excellent results are obtained when liquid SO_2 is employed as reaction solvent. The partial-pressure distillation method cannot be used with these compounds, as a result of their high boiling points, and because dealkylation would occur in the presence of hot sulfuric acid. Unlike benzene or toluene, detergent alkylate forms only small amounts of sulfone with SO_3. However, it does give sulfonic anhydrides, but these are easily hydrolyzed to the desired sulfonic acid. Steric factors determine that detergent alkylate, unlike toluene, forms almost entirely the para sulfonic acid. The type of process chosen depends upon the desired production rate (which may determine whether the operation is batch or continuous), product quality requirements (eg inorganic sulfate content, odor level), availability of reagents, and whether or not several products are to be produced in the same plant.

The usual commercial reagents are 20% oleum and SO_3. The use of oleum involves a cost for the sulfonating agent of approx $40–45 per ton of alkylate, relatively simple equipment and processing, and the need for spent acid disposal or the formation of a final product with a high content of sodium sulfate. The use of SO_3 entails a reagent cost of about $20 per ton of alkylate when using stabilized SO_3, but less than that if the SO_3 is obtained from other sources (eg converter gas), or by burning sulfur. Equipment and processing are somewhat more complex than with oleum, but there is no spent acid disposal problem. The final product has a lower content of sodium sulfate and a better odor than that prepared with oleum.

Initial commercial operation was effected batchwise. When employing 20% oleum, a typical process might comprise addition of the oleum (1.05–1.20 lb/lb of hydrocarbon) gradually to the alkylate with stirring and cooling over a period of about 1.5 hr at 25–35°C, after which the mixture is digested for about 2 hr at 35–50°C to complete the reaction. Water is then added to cause stratification into layers of sulfonic acid and spent sulfuric acid; the sulfonic acid layer is neutralized to a product containing 88–90% sodium sulfonate and 10–12% sodium sulfate; the lower layer of sulfuric acid is discarded. An alternative working-up procedure involves neutralization of the entire sulfonation mixture to yield a "low active" product containing approx 60% sulfonate and 40% sulfate.

Batch procedures were also developed using SO_3. It is ordinarily employed in vapor form, diluted with 90–95% of dry air or other gas. The gas mixture is bubbled into the alkylate at about 50°C; efficient stirring is essential, since more heat is evolved than with 20% oleum, and the reaction mixture is more viscous (32). After a short period of digestion, 1–2% water is added to hydrolyze sulfonic acid anhydrides, and the reaction mixture is neutralized. Another commercial batch procedure involves the use of liquid SO_2 at its boiling point ($-10°C$) as the reaction solvent.

Commercial interest in continuous processing developed corresponding to the rapid growth in the production of detergent alkylate sulfonate. The batch process based on oleum was adapted to continuous operation by employing a centrifugal pump or other similar device for mixing the oleum and alkylate. The reaction product is continuously bled off to a digestion vessel. The "acid mix" was next diluted with water with external cooling, to make subsequent layer separation possible. Since this step required several hours, the overall process was in effect only semicontinuous. The discovery that layer separation occurs in only a few minutes if the sulfonation product is added to a large mass of recycled spent acid, made fully continuous operation possible, and is the basis of the Chemithon process (22). The throughput time was thus reduced from 5–6 hr to 35 min.

Attention was also given to continuous processes involving the use of SO_3 (14). It was recognized that it is inherently more suitable than oleum for continuous operation, since it reacts virtually instantaneously, and no acid separation step is involved. Several commercial procedures were developed, following a successful demonstration of once-through continuous operation in a scraped-wall reactor (3), with reaction and heat removal occurring in a thin film on the cooled reactor surface. The process of the Chemithon Corp. is similarly based on reaction in a thin film (11). The processes of the Marchon Products Ltd. (24) and by Ballestra (8) employ a cascade series of reactors, with SO_3 being added in portions to each unit. Unlike these procedures, the Allied Chemical Corp. (62) and the Stepan Chemical Co. (37) procedures involve vertical film-type reactors without moving parts, the former utilizing a quiescent film, and the latter a film with high turbulence. All of these processes employ SO_3 vapor diluted with a carrier gas. The Jergens process (Andrew Jergens Co.) also employs dilute SO_3 vapor, but the reduction in concentration is effected by operation in vacuum rather than by using a diluent gas (23).

"Polydodecylbenzene." The high-boiling alkylated benzene fraction, obtained as a by-product in the manufacture of detergent alkylate, or prepared from benzene and "tetrapropylene" (see Propylene), is sulfonated commercially for the preparation of lubricant additives (33). This hydrocarbon mixture is rich in long-chain dialkylated benzenes, which undergo partial dealkylation during sulfonation with oleum, but remains unchanged when employing SO_3 vapor (30). The para isomers are so sterically hindered as to completely resist sulfonation with the latter reagent.

Petroleum Oils. The long-chain alkylated aromatic hydrocarbons naturally occurring in petroleum have long been important as raw materials for oil-soluble sulfonates used as lubricant additives and for many other industrial applications. Sulfuric acid has been used to refine petroleum fractions for over a century, but it was not until 1875, when the manufacture of white mineral oils by drastic treatment of lubricant fractions with oleum was initiated, that the sulfonates thus obtained as by-products became available in quantity. The two types of these sulfonates were named after their characteristic colors: oil-soluble *mahogany acids*, and oil-insoluble, or water-soluble *green acids* isolated from the acid layer. The use of oil-soluble sulfonates has steadily increased since then as emulsifiers, rust-proofing agents, and additives for heavy-duty engine lubricants to such an extent that by World War II the demand exceeded the supply of by-product, and manufacture of the sulfonates as primary products began. The water-soluble sulfonates have not proved useful.

Since petroleum is a complex mixture of many types of hydrocarbons of largely unknown composition and with extreme variation in ease of sulfonation from highly reactive to inert, it is not surprising that the sulfonation process, and to an even greater degree the subsequent isolation procedure, are empirical in nature and are under constant study toward improvement. The following three steps are involved: (*1*) preliminary purification of the sulfonation stock to remove sludge and color-producing constituents either by a light treatment with sulfuric acid or, more often, by solvent extraction; (*2*) the sulfonation and sludge separation step; and (*3*) the isolation procedure.

A typical industrial process (13) involves continuous mixing of a solvent-refined lubricant raffinate at 50°C with about 60% by wt of 20% oleum in a 12-plate orifice mixer. The mixture is next digested in a holding vessel where most of the reaction occurs, followed by continuous centrifugal separation of the acid oil layer and the sludge layer. An optimum reaction time of 10 min elapses from the time of mixing to the separation of the layers. The acid is applied in six equal portions ("treats" or "dumps"); sludge is separated after each treat, and the sulfonate product is extracted from the acid oil layer after each group of three treats. About 80% of the possible sulfonation is accomplished by the first three treats; the second group of three is required for further purification to white oil, and might be omitted if sulfonate is the sole desired product. The yield of mahogany sulfonate may be 5–10 g per 100 g of oil treated.

Although 20% oleum has been the traditional reagent, laboratory (29) and commercial (36) studies have shown that, in comparison with oleum, dilute SO_3 vapor gives higher yields of petroleum sulfonates, lower chemical costs, and reduced sludge formation. Sulfur trioxide has, in fact, been used increasingly for petroleum oil sulfonation.

In the third step, the mahogany sulfonates are neutralized to the desired metallic salt, which for some purposes need not be separated from the residual unsulfonated oil. Extraction with alcohol, followed by removal of the solvent, gives a mixture of about equal parts of sulfonate and oil. This extraction step is often operated continuously (13). Further purification, yielding a metallic sulfonate, essentially free of oil, can be realized by treating the alcoholic extract with petroleum naphtha to effect deoiling, followed by distillation of the alcohol.

The chemical composition of petroleum sulfonates has been studied (12) using the technique of hydrolytic desulfonation (discussed under Sulfonic acids) for the recovery of the parent hydrocarbons. Those from the mahogany sulfonates derived from a heavy distillate typically contained a single aromatic ring with a long aliphatic chain and had an average molecular weight of about 480; no disulfonates were present. The green sulfonates, on the other hand, contained much disulfonate, and yielded hydrocarbons of an average molecular weight of about 360; these comprised polycyclic aromatic ring systems with short aliphatic chains. It will be noted that the mahogany sulfonates are generally similar in structure to the detergent alkylate sulfonates; the sulfonating agents (20% oleum and SO_3) and the process conditions are also similar. Side reactions—notably oxidation, molecular rearrangement, and polysulfonation— are extensive in lubricant sulfonation. The hydrocarbons obtained by hydrolytic desulfonation of the green acids are unstable to oxidation to such an extent that they were given serious commercial consideration at one time as possible synthetic drying oils.

The use of a petroleum oil with a molecular weight of 800 as the base stock, and of SO_3 dissolved in liquid SO_2 as the sulfonating agent, entails no sludge formation and gives a sulfonate with advantages over the conventional type of lower-molecular-weight sulfonate as a motor oil additive (7).

The straight-chain paraffin hydrocarbons isolated from petroleum kerosene fractions can be sulfonated by sulfochlorination, or sulfoxidation, as stated earlier (see p. 289).

Polystyrene. Another noteworthy sulfonation in the benzene hydrocarbon series is that of polystyrene. The two following types of sulfonates are of interest: one is insoluble in water and is produced in bead form from styrene–divinylbenzene copolymer, and used as an ion-exchange resin; the other is water-soluble, produced from styrene homopolymer, and employed as a synthetic gum. In the former case (4) the copolymer beads are heated at 80–100°C with 6–10 parts by weight of 95–98% acid, followed by heating at 130–150°C to complete the reaction. The reaction is exothermic and the temperature must be controlled to avoid cracking of the beads. Reaction is complete when analysis shows the introduction of one sulfonic acid group per benzene ring. The beads are then hydrated and converted to the sodium salt, care being taken in both steps to avoid breakage. The sulfonation rate decreases with increasing bead size and degree of crosslinking, since the rate is determined by the speed of diffusion of the sulfonating agent into the matrix. The sulfonic groups are distributed throughout the entire volume of the resin, rather than merely on the surface. Some years ago it was noted that preswelling of the beads with an organic solvent, such as dichloromethane or 1,2-dichloroethane, allows more rapid penetration of the sulfonating agent with a consequent reduction of the reaction time. This process is used commercially, but it has not supplanted the older method, since the resins made by the two procedures have slightly different properties.

Sulfonation of styrene homopolymer to produce a water-soluble product is conducted with SO_3, used as a complex or in solution in a chlorocarbon solvent. Surprisingly, these reagents, unlike others, do not form sulfones. The presence of more than 0.1% of sulfones leads to an undesirable water-insoluble product by chain cross-linking.

Naphthalene. The naphthalenesulfonic acids (see Naphthalene derivatives) are of major industrial importance as intermediates for dyes, wetting agents, and tanning agents.

Anthraquinone. Anthraquinonesulfonic acids (see Anthraquinone derivatives) are key intermediates for the preparation of important dyes. They are produced by the sulfonation of anthraquinone with oleum, the orientation of the entering group being determined by whether or not mercury is added as catalyst. The preparation of the monosulfonic acids can be effected only by undersulfonating to minimize disulfonation. Isomer mixtures are unavoidable during disulfonation, but the disulfonate isomers can be easily separated by taking advantage of differences in the water solubility of their alkali metal salts. Attempts to introduce more than two sulfonate groups lead only to oxidation.

Miscellaneous Aromatic Compounds. Aniline and its derivatives are sulfonated by two procedures which yield different isomers. (See Vol. 2, p. 424.) Liquid-phase sulfonation at moderate temperatures (eg, 38–80°C) with excess acid or oleum introduces the sulfonic group meta to the amino group, as with o- or p-anisidine, or 5-aminosalicylic acid, or para to it (as with 2,5-dichloroaniline). Aniline forms a mixture of all three isomers, while dimethylaniline gives the meta and para compounds. The "baking process," on the other hand, always yields the para isomer; if the para position is blocked, it gives the ortho compound. This procedure involves heating the amine sulfate at 170–280°C, either in solid form, or as a suspension in a solvent, such as o-dichlorobenzene, or diphenyl sulfone. It has been used with aniline, and with a variety of substituted anilines, naphthylamines, and aminobiphenyls. Direct sulfonation of 1- and 2-naphthylamines leads to several important dye intermediates (see Naphthalene derivatives).

Nitrobenzene, Nitrotoluenes, and Nitrochlorobenzenes. These compounds are sulfonated for use as dye intermediates. The reaction can be conducted at moderate temperatures using oleum. Sulfur trioxide vapor is now the favored reagent for sulfonating nitrobenzene (21). A 5% molar excess of undiluted SO_3 vapor is introduced with agitation and cooling at 25–40°C; the mixture is then heated for 3 hr at 130°C. Sulfone formation is low and there is little unreacted nitrobenzene. Violent explosions can occur during these sulfonations, unless pure reagents are used and precautions are taken to ensure efficient agitation and heat removal.

Phenolic Compounds. These sulfonate with unusual ease. Phenol reacts to the extent of 94% when heated with an equimolar quantity of concentrated sulfuric acid for 2 hr at 100°C. At 20°C phenol forms 39% *ortho*sulfonic acid, the remainder being para. At 120°C little ortho product is obtained, the product comprising 3.7% meta and 96% para isomers. At 209°C 38% meta and 61% para isomers are produced. Phenolic sulfonic acids find application as intermediates for preparing tanning agents and ion-exchange resins (see Phenolsulfonic acids). Chlorinated phenols are sulfonated in the preparation of dye intermediates. Naphtholsulfonic acids are important dye intermediates; several are made by direct sulfonation.

Chlorosulfonation. Aromatic compounds yield sulfonyl chlorides in a two-step process.

$$RH + ClSO_3H \rightarrow RSO_2OH + HCl\uparrow$$

$$RSO_2OH + ClSO_3H \rightleftarrows RSO_2Cl + H_2SO_4$$

The first step goes readily to completion, but the second step is an equilibrium reaction which can be pushed toward completion by the use of excess chlorosulfuric acid, chemical removal of the sulfuric acid as formed, or physical removal of the sulfonyl chloride. The usual industrial process involves gradual addition of the organic compound to 2–6 molar proportions of chlorosulfuric acid in the range of 10 to 60°C; the reaction is completed by a digestion step. Compounds thus converted commercially to their sulfonyl chlorides include acetanilide (an intermediate for nearly all sulfa drugs), benzene and chlorobenzene (for insecticides), salicylic acid, 2-hydroxy-1-naphthoic acid, and chlorinated nitrobenzenes (all as dye intermediates), and toluene (for saccharin). In the case of toluene, a low temperature (about 0°C) is used to promote preferential formation of the desired ortho isomer; in the other cases the range of 10 to 60°C is common. The di(chlorosulfonation) of anilines meta substituted by halogen, methoxy, nitro, amino, trifluoromethyl, or methyl groups is of interest for preparing drug intermediates. The reaction is usually run by heating with excess $ClSO_3H$ for 2–4 hr at 115–180°C; yields are improved by adding NaCl or $SOCl_2$.

Oxidative Procedures. This approach has been of comparatively little commercial interest for the preparation of aromatic sulfonates. Aqueous chlorination of bis-(o-nitrophenyl) disulfide has been employed industrially to prepare o-nitrobenzenesulfonyl chloride, an intermediate in the manufacture of orthanilic acid.

Sulfite Reactions. The direct replacement of an aromatic chlorine atom by the sulfo group is used in special cases for preparing aromatic sulfonates. The procedure involves heating the organic halide with aqueous sodium sulfite under pressure. 2-Chlorobenzaldehyde, 2,4-dichlorobenzaldehyde, and 2-chlorobenzoic acid have been converted to the sulfonates by this method on an industrial scale. This approach has also been employed for the manufacture of anthraquinonesulfonates in special cases where direct sulfonation is not applicable, eg, anthraquinone-1,4-disulfonic acid and 1,4-diaminoanthraquinone-2,3-disulfonic acid.

Condensation and Polymerization. Several aromatic sulfonic acids have been employed as sulfoarylating reagents for preparing more complex sulfonates not accessible by direct sulfonation.

Phenolsulfonic acid, as stated previously, is easily obtained as a mixture of the 2- and 4-isomers by sulfonating phenol. The free acid and its salts have seen industrial application as monomers and comonomers for preparing water-soluble and -insoluble sulfonated phenol–formaldehyde-type resins, used as synthetic tanning agents and ion-exchange resins, respectively. Sulfoarylation is the only practical approach for making these materials, since direct sulfonation of the polymers has not proved satisfactory. Preparation of the tanning agents using numerous variations has been studied at length using empirical methods, as have also the preparation and properties of the ion-exchange resins. In both cases, the most effective products are copolymers of sulfonated and unsulfonated phenols, made from one of several possible aldehydes o ketones. Although the water-insoluble phenol–sulfonate resins have been supplanted in recent years by those based on polystyrene, patents continue to appear on preparative variations for the former, as well as for the water-soluble type. The allyl ether, the acrylate ester, and various carboxyalkyl ethers of phenolsulfonic acid have been used as comonomers to improve the dyeability of vinyl and polyester fibers, respectively.

Sulfanilic and *metanilic acids* (4- and 3-aminobenzenesulfonic acids, respectively) have been employed extensively for sulfoarylation via their reactive amino groups.

The isocyanate derivatives sulfoarylate cellulose, polyamides, and polyamines. The sulfonyl fluorides are of special interest as containing amino groups with normal reactivity, together with the sulfonyl fluoride group which is inert in neutral or acid solutions. This permits the preparation of many derivatives in which the sulfonyl fluoride moiety can be finally hydrolyzed to sulfonate in weakly alkaline solution without disturbing the other groups in the molecule (17).

Other sulfoarylating agents include benzaldehyde-2-sulfonic and -2,4-disulfonic acids, sulfobenzoic acid, sulfoderivatives of the three phthalic acids, and 4-hydrazino-benzenesulfonic acid. As discussed below, 4-sulfophthalic anhydride can be converted to phthalocyanine dyes (see p. 301). The polymerization of 4-styrenesulfonic acid gives polymers of greater purity and uniformity than those made by the direct sulfonation of polystyrene; the two types consequently have different properties. Naphthalene-2-sulfonic acid reacts with formaldehyde, forming water-soluble low-molecular-weight condensation polymers. Such products are widely marketed as tanning and dispersing agents of the Tamol type.

Heterocyclic Sulfonates

Direct Sulfonation. Some heterocyclic compounds (furan, pyrrole, indole, and their derivatives) are best sulfonated with SO_3–pyridine, since more acidic reagents induce extensive decomposition. Yields are generally good (70–90%), the technique is simple (heating in a sealed tube at 80–140°C, preferably with ethylene dichloride as solvent), and the method is widely applicable (55).

On the other hand, many heterocyclic compounds are sulfonated with SO_3 or oleum under more drastic conditions than those ordinarily employed with hydrocarbons, as discussed in the preceding section. Several of these are of industrial interest. 3-Pyridinesulfonic acid, an intermediate in a process for producing nicotinic acid (see Vitamins) can be prepared by heating SO_3–pyridine at 225–235°C in the presence of mercuric sulfate, or by reacting pyridine with 20% oleum at 250–270°C using the same catalyst. Quinoline can be sulfonated in the benzene ring (5 and 8 positions) with oleum at 170–180°C; caustic fusion of the 8-isomer yields 8-hydroxyquinoline, an important analytical reagent and fungicide. Carbazole has been converted commercially to the 1,3,6-trisulfonic acid by heating with 95% acid at 50°C; this sulfonate is then nitrated to yield a tetranitrocarbazole fungicide. The dye Quinoline Yellow Ex. is prepared by heating quinophthalone with oleum at 115°C to yield a mixture of the di- and trisulfonic acids (see also Quinoline dyes). A dye intermediate is prepared by treating dehydrothio-*p*-toluidine (see Thiazole dyes) with 20% oleum to yield mainly the 7-sulfonic acid. The disulfonic acid is formed by further sulfonation using the baking process discussed above (see p. 298). Sulfonated phthalocyanine compounds

Table 4. Sulfonation of Copper Phthalocyanine

Derivative	Temperature, °C		Reaction time, hr	
	40% Oleum	ClSO₃H	40% Oleum	ClSO₃H
mono	>20			
di	51	100	15	5
tri	60	145		5
tetra		150		

(qv) are important dyes because of their fastness to light and attractive shades. As shown in Table 4, from one to all four of the benzene rings in copper phthalocyanine can be sulfonated with oleum or chlorosulfonic acid, the latter forming the sulfonyl chlorides. Reaction temperature is evidently an important factor.

Sulfonated phthalocyanines can also be made by sulfoarylation, ie, heating 4-sulfophthalic anhydride with ammonia. However, these dyes are of a different color from those made by direct sulfonation, which have the sulfonic group mainly in the 3 position.

Oxidative Procedures. Heterocyclic sulfonyl chlorides can be prepared by aqueous chlorination of the corresponding thiols, the same procedure cited above (see p. 287) for the preparation of aliphatic sulfonyl chlorides. This approach appears widely applicable, ie, to imidazoles, triazoles, tetrazoles, thiazoles, pyridines, pyrazines, and others (52).

Lignosulfonates

The production of pulp (qv) by heating wood under pressure with an aqueous solution of metallic bisulfite and sulfur dioxide ("sulfite cooking acid") yields water-soluble lignosulfonates as the major by-product. These materials, available to the extent of millions of tons annually, have found use as dispersing agents, raw materials for producing vanillin, tanning agents, ion-exchange resins, and other purposes (see Lignin).

The structure of lignin is not known, but it appears to comprise a mixture of polymers containing aromatic rings, methoxyl groups, hydroxyl groups (both phenolic and alcoholic), and carbonyl groups. For a possible structural formula of a lignin monomer unit, see Lignin. Correspondingly, the chemical structures of the sulfonates are not known, although they have been under continual intensive investigation for many years and with the application of a variety of techniques. The reaction may proceed stepwise with the formation of at least three types of sulfonates, depending upon the conditions used, especially the pH of the reaction mixture. Treatment of pure chemical compounds of types thought to be present in the lignin molecule with sulfite cooking acid under simulated commercial conditions have shown that a hydroxyl group α to a benzene nucleus is replaced by a sulfonate group as follows:

$$RC(OH)R'R'' + NaHSO_3 \rightarrow RC(SO_2ONa)R'R'' + H_2O$$

where R = substituted phenyl.

This type of reaction occurs with veratryl alcohol (3,4-dimethoxybenzyl alcohol) and related compounds, leading to the conclusion that lignosulfonates may be formed in part by a similar reaction.

Sulfation

Sulfation involves the placement of an $-OSO_2OH$ group on carbon when sulfating an alkene, or of an $-SO_2OH$ group on oxygen when sulfating an alcohol or phenol. Concentrated sulfuric acid is employed for sulfating alkenes. Alcohols are sulfated with SO_3 or its complexes, sulfuric acid, oleum, chlorosulfuric acid, or amidosulfuric acid.

Sulfates have found important uses as intermediates for preparing alcohols (see Ethanol; Propyl alcohols; Butyl alcohols), as alkylating agents, such as dimethyl and diethyl sulfates (see Sulfuric and sulfurous esters), as detergents, eg, sodium lauryl sulfate, and dyes. Sulfation is biologically important, since alkyl, aryl, steroidal, and carbohydrate sulfates are synthesized in living systems. Sulfation is the predominant reaction in the "sulfonation" of fatty oils, as discussed below.

Sulfated Alkenes. Sulfation of the lower alkenes derived from petroleum, in particular ethylene, propylene, and the butylenes, is an operation of established commercial importance for producing the corresponding alcohols. As typified by the preparation of ethanol, the reactions are as follows:

$$CH_2{=}CH_2 + HOSO_2OH \rightarrow CH_3CH_2OSO_2OH$$
$$CH_3CH_2OSO_2OH + H_2O \rightarrow CH_3CH_2OH + HOSO_2OH$$

Diethyl sulfate is formed by a side reaction:

$$CH_3CH_2OSO_2OH + CH_2{=}CH_2 \rightarrow CH_3CH_2OSO_2OCH_2CH_3$$

This sulfation is usually effected with 96–98% acid at 70–80°C under 5–15 atm pressure. Since the rate of reaction is largely contact-controlled, efficient agitation is essential. The commercial success of the process has been made possible by good yields, continuous operation on a large scale, and an efficient procedure for reconcentrating the spent acid from the hydrolysis step to permit its reuse in the sulfation reaction.

The sulfation of alkenes proceeds according to Markownikoff's rule, forming the secondary sulfates from monosubstituted or 1,2-disubstituted ethylenes. 1,1-Disubstituted ethylenes may form the tertiary sulfates, but they have not been isolated as such, even though the corresponding alcohols (eg, *tert*-butyl alcohol) are formed. Propylene and the butylenes are sulfated with weaker acid and under milder conditions than ethylene. Side reactions (other than dialkyl sulfate formation) occurring during alkene sulfation include oxidation, polymerization, and tar formation.

The sulfation of long-chain alkenes (C_{12}–C_{18}) has been practiced commercially in Europe for many years for the production of detergents, such as Teepol (Shell Oil Co.) (35), using hydrocarbons obtained by the cracking of paraffin wax or shale oil. This type of sulfation is carried out at 10–15°C in 90–98% acid with a 5-min contact time at an acid–alkene molar ratio of approx 2:1. Efficient mixing is essential, since the acid and hydrocarbon are immiscible. Working-up involves tar removal (by centrifuging), breakdown of undesired dialkyl sulfates (by holding at 90°C for 8 hr with aqueous sodium carbonate), and removal of unreacted hydrocarbons (by solvent extraction). This type of detergent is not manufactured in the United States.

Pure terminal alkenes of varying chain lengths are now cheaply available from petroleum. In a study (16) of the sulfation of one such compound, it was found that if 96% acid is added to 1-dodecene at 0°C, dialkyl sulfate is formed almost exclusively at first, but that this is converted to an 80% yield of monoalkyl sulfate as more acid is added. The yield of monoalkyl sulfate can be increased to 90% by using 98% acid at −15°C with pentane as solvent. The product obtained by these methods is almost exclusively the 2-isomer. On the other hand, if the olefin is added to the acid, or if higher reaction temperatures are employed, the position of the entering sulfate group is entirely random on the various possible secondary atoms.

Sulfated Fatty Oils. The manufacture of sulfated ("sulfonated") oils from fatty glycerides or acids containing olefinic or hydroxyl groups or both (for example, sperm, tallow, peanut, soybean, castor, olive, and various fish oils, as well as the desired esters, amides, and free acids) has steadily increased since 1875, when "sulfonated" castor oil (Turkey-red oil; see Vol. 4, p. 531) was introduced as the first commercial sulfonate-type chemical, assisting in the processing of textiles.

With all of the oils except castor, sulfation of double bonds is the predominant reaction (40). In the case of castor oil (the triglyceride of 12-hydroxyoleic acid), sulfation under the usual industrial conditions occurs almost exclusively at the hydroxyl group. Reaction conditions used for preparing several commercial sulfonated oils are summarized in Table 5. These usually involve the gradual addition of cold

Table 5. Reaction Conditions for the Preparation of Sulfonated Oils

Oil	Sulfonating agent,[a] lb/lb oil	Time, hr	Temperature, °C
castor	0.25–0.30	3	30
castor	0.21	9	25–30
olive	0.38	3	20
shark	0.20	3	25
sperm	0.09	3	25
neat's foot	0.10	>2	15–25
cod	0.12		7–18
cod	0.28	10	35
oleic acid	0.23	1	52
oleic acid	0.40[b]	1.5	20
oleic esters	0.30–0.50[b]	3	25
oleic N-ethyl anilide	1.0[c]	10–15	0
butyl ricinoleate	1.0	6.5	0

[a] 96% acid used, except as indicated. [b] 98% acid used. [c] 100% acid used.

96% sulfuric acid (often 20–40% of the weight of the oil) to the oil, with efficient agitation and cooling in a batch operation at room temperature or below. The acid is present in excess, since sulfation is an equilibrium reaction and, with the olefinic oils, stops when the acid strength reaches 85%. Reaction solvents are not commonly employed, but chlorinated hydrocarbons and highly refined petroleum oils have been used in isolated instances. The acid removal and neutralization steps are critical ones, since hydrolysis of the sulfate and glyceride linkages occurs easily. The conditions

Table 6. Sulfation of a C_{12}–C_{18} Alcohol Mixture with Various Reagents

Reagent	Acid:alc mole ratio	Reaction temp, °C	Active ingredients, %	Oil,[a] %	Yield,[b] %	Color, RCD[c]
96% acid alone	2.3	55	14.2	3.4	80.6	3
96% acid with CCl₄	2	15	32.8	4.8	87.2	2
20% oleum alone	3	35	9.4	2.0	82.4	
20% oleum in ether	1.2	15	14.7	10.8	57.7	
amidosulfuric acid	1.05	130	19.6	12.0	61.9	
ClSO₃H alone	1.03	35	40.5	1.6	96.2	4
ClSO₃H in ether	1.1	10	38.7	0.3	99.3	1
SO₃ vapor	1.02	35	44.0	3.0	93.6	6
SO₃ in liquid SO₂	1.15	−10	31.2	1.2	96.2	5

[a] On an "as is" basis. [b] Based on alcohol. [c] Relative color density (36a, 41a).

used in these operations determine most of the important characteristics of the sulfonated oils.

Alcohol Sulfates. The sulfation of saturated long-chain (C_{10}–C_{18}) alcohols is of great importance for the production of detergents. Table 6 shows the results of a laboratory study in which the suitability of various reagents is compared for this type of sulfation (66). Two of them (amidosulfuric acid and oleum in ether) were unsatisfactory. Oleum and sulfuric acid gave products of good color, but only fair yields; the content of active ingredient was low and the oil was high. Chlorosulfuric acid in ether gave outstanding yield and color, and this system has long been a preferred laboratory method, although too costly for commercial use. The remaining three procedures ($ClSO_3H$ alone, SO_3 vapor, and SO_3 in SO_2) are employed commercially, especially the first two. Oleum sulfation is also employed commercially (22).

Sulfation with $ClSO_3H$ is usually conducted batchwise, and involves adding the acid to the undiluted alcohol in a glass-lined kettle at about 30°C. The following reaction occurs:

$$ROH + ClSO_3H \rightarrow ROSO_2OH + HCl\uparrow$$

Two factors have hindered large-scale commercialization of this process on a continuous basis. One of these is the exceptionally corrosive nature of hydrogen chloride, which necessitates the use of stainless steel or glass apparatus. The unbalanced patterns of heat and gas evolution also present problems (70). During addition of the first half of the acid, much of the hydrogen chloride formed is retained in the reaction mixture by exothermic formation of the alkoxonium chloride. As the second half is added, most of the hydrogen chloride is endothermically evolved as gas with considerable foaming. Overall, 60% of the total heat is evolved by the time only 20% of the acid has been added. In spite of these objections, continuous processes are in use (22).

Commercial processes for sulfating long-chain alcohols with SO_3 vapor are in general similar to those described for the sulfonation of detergent alkylate. Since the long-chain acid sulfates are exceptionally unstable, the reaction temperature and the stoichiometry must be closely controlled, and neutralization must be effected immediately, to assure good product quality. The Marchon process (24) accomplishes this by using a ten-chamber reactor, in which the SO_3 is in excess only during the last seconds of reaction. The Allied Chemical Corp. (62) and Stepan Chemical Co. (37) procedures employ vertical film-type reactors (34) without moving parts. The Chemithon process (11) entails a scraped-wall reactor; a vertical reactor equipped with six four-bladed turbine rotors has also been described (56). All of these procedures employ dilute SO_3 vapor; the Jergens process (23) effects such dilution by operation in vacuo, rather than by employing a diluent gas. Similar procedures are used to sulfate ethoxylated long-chain alcohols to important commercial detergents.

Alcohols containing reactive groups other than hydroxyl must be sulfated by different procedures if it is desired to limit reaction to the hydroxyl group. Thus, ethoxylated alkylphenols are sulfated by heating with amidosulfuric acid at 125°C:

$$ROH + NH_2SO_2OH \rightarrow ROSO_2\overset{-}{O}N\overset{+}{H_4}$$

Such products are widely used as detergents; ring sulfonation also occurs if SO_3 or $ClSO_3H$ is employed with these compounds (31). Oleyl alcohol is similarly sulfated with amidosulfuric acid, in this case to avoid attack of the double bond. Sterols are best sulfated with amidosulfuric acid in pyridine at 95°C. For some industrial purposes, however, it is actually desirable to effect at least some attack of the double bond in this sulfation, since empirically prepared materials of this kind have been found best for special uses. Oleyl alcohol has thus been sulfated with 98% sulfuric acid at 45°C and 100% acid below 30°C; with ClSO$_3$H–urea without a solvent; and with ClSO$_3$H–urea with formamide in chloroform as solvent.

Dimethyl sulfate is manufactured in excellent yield and purity by the continuous reaction of dimethyl ether with SO$_3$, as shown below:

$$(CH_3)_2O + SO_3 \rightarrow (CH_3)_2SO_4$$

This process involves simple countercurrent mixing of the reactants in an aluminum tower, filled with reaction product, at 40°C, with moderate external cooling. Dimethyl ether is available as a by-product of the synthesis of methanol.

Sulfates of Ring Compounds. Sulfur trioxide–amine complexes are the principal sulfating agents for this category, which includes phenolic compounds, steroids, and the leuco (or dihydroxy) forms of vat dyes. The first two types of sulfates have a biological interest, since phenols and sterols are excreted from the body as sulfates; the third type is manufactured in large quantities.

Phenols are usually sulfated in an anhydrous medium with SO$_3$–pyridine, or in aqueous solution with SO$_3$–trimethylamine. The relative ease of sulfation of phenolic isomers often differs widely, thereby providing a basis for the separation of mixtures, such as o- and p-phenylphenols, and 5- and 8-benzamido-1-naphthols. The phenolic sulfates are stable in neutral or alkaline solution, and are not affected by the oxidation or reduction of other groupings in the molecule. Also, the sulfates are water-soluble, and the sulfate group is easily introduced and removed. Consequently, sulfation has sometimes been used to block phenolic hydroxyl groups before the oxidation of various organic compounds.

Sulfation of the leuco forms of vat dyes, especially those derived from anthraquinone, has been used increasingly in industry since 1924 to achieve water solubility, with consequent easy application to textile fibers. Oxidation of the organic sodium sulfate in acid solution reconverts it on the fiber to the original insoluble keto form of the dye, thereby fixing it firmly. Combined reduction and sulfation of the dye is effected by heating with a metal (copper, iron, or zinc) and SO$_3$–pyridine (or other amine complexes). The reactions involved are as follows:

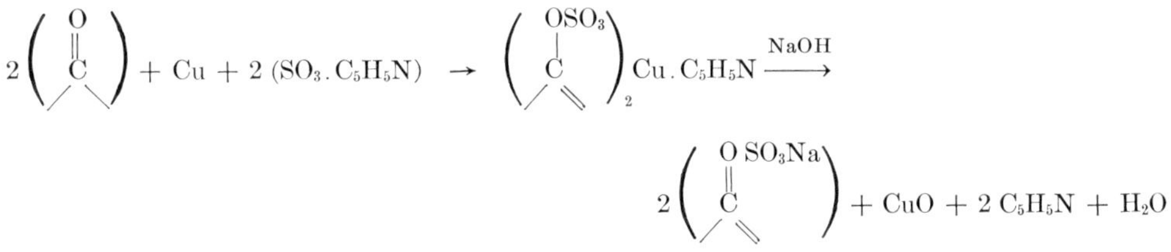

This direct and widely applicable procedure is used to produce over fifty dyes (64). The general procedure involves adding chlorosulfuric acid to excess pyridine at 20°C, and then simultaneously adding the dye and the metal with agitation in the range 40–80°C over several hours. Aqueous sodium hydroxide is added next and the mixture is steamed to recover the pyridine. The yields of leuco sulfate are 80–90%. Pyridine has been the most commonly used base, but picolines are more suitable for certain dyes. Also, the metal and its degree of subdivision, as well as the temperature and time of heating, vary from case to case.

Sulfated Carbohydrates. Water-soluble sulfated derivatives of cellulose and starch have been of industrial interest for many years as possible substitutes for naturally occurring gums. Biological interest has centered on preparing sulfated sugars and compounds related to the naturally occurring anticoagulant heparin. In most cases with such materials the problem involves finding suitable conditions for sulfating a solid of low solubility and high melting point, and of unusual sensitivity to degradation by acidic reagents.

Undegraded water-soluble products containing one sulfate group for every two or three anhydroglucose units have been prepared from cellulose semicommercially by treatment with sulfuric acid at 0–20°C in the presence of an alcohol containing three or more carbon atoms. The parameters of this reaction have been studied in some detail (47). The chain length of the alcohol (from C_2 to C_8), and its structure, straight chained or branched, do not influence the rate of reaction or the degree of substitution; these factors depend upon the acid-to-alcohol molar ratio (between 1:1 and 3:1) and the temperature (between 0 and 10°C). The alcohols form acid sulfates, but sulfate interchange was surprisingly found not to be a factor in forming the cellulose sulfate. Methyl acid sulfate in an unusual way did undergo sulfate interchange, but with excessive degradation of the cellulose. Poly(vinyl alcohol) can be similarly sulfated with a mixture of ethanol and sulfuric acid, but methanol was again found unsatisfactory. Cellulose is also sulfated without degradation by SO_3–dimethylformamide.

It has long been known that a minor degree of sulfation occurs during the usual commercial sulfuric acid-catalyzed acetylation of cellulose. It was later found that water-soluble acetate–sulfates could be made by simply increasing the quantity of sulfuric acid. Commercial interest in this type of product has supplanted the interest in cellulose sulfate made by the alcohol–sulfuric acid process.

Starch can be sulfated with SO_3–triethylamine dissolved in dimethylformamide at 0°C (51) with the introduction of as many as two sulfate groups per monomer unit. These conditions are the ultimate in mildness and are well suited for the sulfation of many acid-sensitive carbohydrates without degradation. Starch is sulfated commercially at room temperature in an aqueous medium with SO_3–trimethylamine (71).

Sulfamation

Sulfamation involves the formation of compounds of the structure R_2NSO_2OH, usually by treatment of an amine with SO_3 or a compound thereof, such as $ClSO_3H$, amidosulfuric acid, or an SO_3–amine adduct (19). Sulfamates are of limited interest in comparison with sulfonates or sulfates. However, the widely developing use of cyclohexylsulfamic acid salts as sweetening agents has prompted the investigation of various alternative methods of synthesis, as well as the preparation of other sulfamates which might have the same property. The discovery that heparin, the naturally occurring blood anticoagulant, contains sulfamate, as well as sulfate groups, has resulted in a notable increase in interest in sulfamates of this type on the part of biochemists and pharmaceutical manufacturers. Sulfamated dyes have also attracted some industrial attention.

Amidosulfuric acid (see Sulfamic acid) is manufactured by heating urea with oleum:

$$NH_2CONH_2 + H_2SO_4 + SO_3 \rightarrow 2\,NH_2SO_2OH + CO_2$$

However, this type of reaction is not of general interest for the preparation of other sulfamates.

A more general sulfamation procedure involves the treatment of an amine with chlorosulfuric acid in the presence of a solvent (6):

$$3 \, RNH_2 + ClSO_3H \rightarrow RNHSO_2\bar{O}H_3^+NR + RNH_3^+Cl^-$$

Neutralization with caustic soda forms the sodium salt and liberates two moles of amine for possible recovery and recycle. This approach, with chloroform as reaction solvent, has been employed in the laboratory for cyclohexyl- and other cycloaliphatic and aliphatic primary amines. It has been used commercially to sulfamate dibutylamine to a textile mercerizing assistant; the solvent in this case was 2-chlorotoluene. The best commercial approach to the preparation of 1-aminoanthraquinone-2-sulfonic acid involves, as the first step, sulfamation with $ClSO_3H$ in o-dichlorobenzene as solvent (39); rearrangement to the desired product occurs upon heating at 150°C.

A second general approach to sulfamation involves heating an amine with amidosulfuric acid:

$$2 \, RNH_2 + NH_2SO_2OH \rightarrow RNHSO_2\bar{O}H_3^+NR + NH_3\uparrow$$

This method is in extensive commercial use to prepare cyclohexylsulfamic acid salts. Excess amine is used under pressure at 160–180°C for about 1–3 hr. Neutralization liberates one mole of amine for recovery and recycle (1).

The direct use of SO_3 has been considered, since it is cheaper than amidosulfuric acid. The reaction is strongly exothermic, and a mixture is formed which contains the desired amine salt as the major constituent:

$$2 \, RNH_2 + SO_3 \rightarrow RNHSO_2\bar{O}H_3^+NR$$

This process is being developed commercially (43). Sulfur trioxide–tertiary amine complexes, on the other hand, react smoothly and in good yield. If the reaction is conducted in the presence of an aqueous base, the desired salt is obtained directly and the tertiary amine is liberated for recovery and recycle, as shown below. This process is also of commercial interest (2).

$$RNH_2 + SO_3 \cdot base \xrightarrow{\text{NaOH}} RNHSO_2ONa + base + H_2O$$

Industrial Equipment and Operation

Most industrial sulfonations are conducted on a batch scale and basically comprise simple mixing of a liquid sulfonating agent with the organic compound in a reaction kettle of standard design varying in capacity from 30 to 2500 gal. Jackets or coils are usually necessary to provide heating or cooling, and efficient agitation is required to facilitate heat transfer, especially since many sulfonation reaction mixtures are viscous. Special ball-mill sulfonators, equipped for operation under vacuum, are used for extremely viscous or solid sulfonations. This type of apparatus is commonly employed in the baking process for sulfonating aromatic amines.

Continuous processing is employed for sulfonating or sulfating a few products made in large quantities, as discussed earlier in each specific case. Sulfur trioxide reacts rapidly and is therefore suitable for the continuous sulfonation of detergent alkylate, petroleum oils, and long-chain alkenes, and for sulfating long-chain alcohols. Benzene is sulfonated continuously with oleum in a cascade system, and the lower olefins are thus sulfated with sulfuric acid for the production of alcohols. Film reactors, which involve no moving parts, are increasingly favored when sulfur trioxide is used.

Specialized equipment is employed for sulfochlorination, since this reaction is catalyzed by light. Steel towers, plastic-coated to resist the corrosive action of hydrogen chloride, are suitable. Illumination is provided by mercury vapor lamps inserted in transverse quartz tubes located in the lower section of the tower. Similar apparatus is used for sulfoxidation. See Photochemical technology.

Many sulfonations are conducted in aqueous solution at temperatures ranging from room temperature to about 100°C. These include sulfite reactions (sulfomethylations, the Strecker reaction, addition to maleic acid esters), which are conducted in standard reaction kettles using aqueous or aqueous–alcoholic sodium sulfite or bisulfite. Sulfomethylations can be run in a brick-lined vat, while the other two reactions can be conducted in lead-lined reactors under slight pressure (about 2 atm) at about 100°C. An aqueous medium is also suitable for many condensation-type sulfonations, including the preparation of ion-exchange resins, tanning agents, and the surface-active agent Igepon T.

Pressure reactors are required in some cases, as in the preparation of o-sulfobenzoic acid from o-chlorobenzoic acid at 150°C and 5 atm pressure. An iron pressure vessel is also used for the sulfoethylation of methylamine at 85°C with sodium 2-chloroethanesulfonate.

Lead- or glass-lined equipment is necessarily employed for sulfonations in which highly corrosive hydrogen chloride is formed. These include the aqueous oxidative chlorination of bis(o-nitrophenyl)disulfide to the sulfonyl chloride, and the preparation of Igepon A. In the latter case, a viscous liquid mixture of solid sodium isethionate and oleoyl chloride is heated and agitated with a heavy-duty mixer. The product is first converted to a crumbly solid, then to waxy flakes which comprise the final product. Hydrogen chloride is also evolved in all sulfations and sulfonations effected with ClSO$_3$H.

Bibliography

"Sulfonation and Sulfation" in *ECT* 1st ed., Vol. 13, pp. 317–337, by E. E. Gilbert, Allied Chemical Corporation.

1. Abbott Laboratories, Brit. Pat. 662,800 (Dec. 12, 1951).
2. Abbott Laboratories, Brit. Pat. 669,200 (March 26, 1952).
3. A. Abrams, E. J. Carlson, E. E. Gilbert, and H. R. Nychka, *J. Am. Oil Chemists' Soc.* **37** (2), 63 (1960).
4. I. M. Abrams and L. Benezra, in N. Bikales, ed., *Encyclopedia of Polymer Science and Technology*, Vol. 7, Interscience Publishers, a div. of John Wiley & Sons, Inc., New York, 1967, p. 702.
5. F. Asinger, *Chemie und Technologie der Paraffin-Kohlenwasserstoffe*, Akademie Verlag, Berlin, 1956, pp. 399 ff.
6. L. F. Audrieth and M. Sveda, *J. Org. Chem.* **9**, 89 (1944).
7. W. N. Axe, J. T. Gragson, and R. S. Logan, *Paper Am. Chem. Soc., Petrol Div. Meet., Detroit, Mich., April, 1965*.
8. M. Ballestra, U.S. Pat. 3,198,849 (Aug. 3, 1965).
9. C. Beermann, *European Chem. News (London)* **10**, 254 (1966). (*Suppl. Proc. Symp. n-Paraffins, Manchester, Nov. 1966*.)

10. F. G. Bordwell, R. D. Chapman, and C. E. Osborne, *J. Am. Chem. Soc.* **81**, 2002 (1959).

11. R. J. Brooks and B. Brooks (to Chemithon Corp.), U.S. Pat. 3,259,645 (July 5, 1966).

12. A. B. Brown and J. O. Knoblock, *ASTM Tech. Bull. No. 224*, American Society for Testing Materials, Philadelphia, 1958, p. 213.

13. T. F. Brown, *Inst. Petrol. Rev.* **9**, 314 (1955).

13a. P. J. Canterino, in reference 4, Vol. 6, 1967, pp. 443 449.

14. W. Carasik and J. R. Hughey, *Soap Chem. Specialties* **40** (6), 49 (1964).

15. N. H. Christensen, *Acta Chem. Scand.* **15**, 1507 (1961).

16. E. Clippinger, *Ind. Eng. Chem. Prod. Res. Develop.* **3** (1), 3 (1964).

17. A. DeCat and R. Van Poucke, *J. Org. Chem.* **28**, 3426 (1963).

18. H. Distler, *Angew. Chem. (Intern. Ed. Engl.)* **4** (4), 300 (1965).

19. A. Dorlars, "Methoden zur Herstellung und Umwandlung von Stickstoff-Schwefel-Verbindungen," in E. Müller, ed., *Methoden der Organischen Chemie (Houben-Weyl)*, 4th ed., Vol. 11/2, Thieme Verlag, Stuttgart, 1958, p. 641 ff.

20. I. B. Douglass and T. B. Johnson, *J. Am. Chem. Soc.* **60**, 1486 (1938).

21. R. L. Drisko and G. F. Hazen (to Allied Chemical Corp.), Belg. Pat. 706,631 (1968).

22. Editorial Staff, *Soap Chem. Specialties* **35** (4), 131 (1959).

23. Editorial Staff, *Sulphur (London)* **57**, 24 (1965).

24. *Ibid.*, **59**, 19 (1965).

25. S. W. Englund, R. S. Aries, and D. F. Othmer, *Ind. Eng. Chem.* **45**, 189 (1953).

26. R. F. Fischer, *Ind. Eng. Chem. Prod. Res. Develop.* **56** (3), 41 (1964).

27. E. E. Gilbert, C. J. McGough, and J. A. Otto, *Ind. Eng. Chem.* **51**, 925 (1959).

28. E. E. Gilbert and C. B. Miller (to Allied Chemical and Dye Corp.), U.S. Pat. 2,793,964 (May 28, 1957).

29. E. E. Gilbert and B. Veldhuis, *Ind. Eng. Chem.* **49**, 31 (1957).

30. *Ibid.*, **50**, 997 (1958).

31. E. E. Gilbert and B. Veldhuis, *J. Am. Oil Chemists' Soc.* **37**, 298 (1960).

32. E. E. Gilbert, B. Veldhuis, E. J. Carlson, and S. L. Giolito, *Ind. Eng. Chem.* **45**, 2065 (1953).

33. S. Holtzman and B. M. Milwidsky, *Soap Chem. Specialties* **41** (10), 64 (1965).

34. R. C. Hurlbert, R. F. Knott, and H. A. Cheney, *Soap Chem. Specialties* **43** (6), 88 (1967).

35. G. D. Inskeep and A. Mussard, *Ind. Eng. Chem.* **47**, 2 (1955).

36. H. Kaye, E. Forsyth, and A. I. Mills, *Proc. 5th World Petrol. Congress, Sect. 3, New York, 1959.*

36a. R. E. Kitson et al., *Ind. Eng. Chem. Anal. Ed.* **16**, 42 (1944).

37. E. A. Knaggs and M. L. Nussbaum (to Stepan Chemical Co.), U.S. Pat. 3,169,142 (Feb. 9, 1965).

38. A. Kutrne and D. S. Breslow, in reference 4, Vol. 6, 1967, p. 455 ff.

39. H. R. Lee and D. X. Klein (to E. I. du Pont de Nemours & Co., Inc.), U.S. Pat. 2,135,346 (Nov. 1, 1938).

40. J. Levy, *J. Am. Oil Chemists' Soc.* **38**, 36 (1961).

41. V. O. Lukashevich, *Dokl. Akad. Nauk SSSR* **112**, 872 (1957); *Chem. Abstr.* **51**, 14591 (1957).

41a. L. Lykken et al., *Ind. Eng. Chem. Anal. Ed.* **21**, 787 (1949).

42. D. M. Marquis, S. H. Sharman, R. House, and R. A. Sweeney, *J. Am. Oil Chemists' Soc.* **43** (11), 607 (1966).

43. M. V. Mhatre (to Abbott Laboratories), U.S. Pat. 3,226,430 (Dec. 28, 1965).

44. H. Mina, M. Razavipour, and D. M. Rejali, *Paper Sixth World Petrol. Congr., Frankfurt, 1963.*

45. K. L. Nelson and H. C. Brown, "Aromatic Substitution—Theory and Mechanism," in B. F. Brooks, ed., *The Chemistry of Petroleum Hydrocarbons*, Vol. 3, Reinhold Publishing Corp., New York, 1955, pp. 537 ff.

46. E. H. Northey, *The Sulfonamides and Allied Compounds*, Reinhold Publishing Corp., New York, 1948.

47. G. A. Petropavlovskii and M. M. Krunchak, *J. Appl. Chem. USSR (English Transl.)* **36**, 2424 (1963); *Chem. Abstr.* **61**, 13517 (1964).

48. M. A. Phillips, *Mfg. Chemist* **34** (12), 575 (1963).

49. W. A. Proell, C. E. Adams, and B. H. Shoemaker, *Ind. Eng. Chem.* **40**, 1129 (1948).

50. F. Pueschel and C. Kaiser, *Chem. Ber.* **98** (3), 735 (1965).

51. H. J. Roberts, in R. L. Whistler and E. F. Paschall, eds., *Starch: Chemistry and Technology*, Vol. 1, Academic Press, Inc., New York, 1965, pp. 451 ff.

52. R. O. Roblin, Jr., and J. W. Clapp, *J. Am. Chem. Soc.* **72**, 4890 (1950).

53. K. Rosenbusch, *Leder* **16** (10), 237 (1967).

54. R. C. Schulz, in reference 4, Vol. 1, 1964, p. 171.

55. J. F. Scully and E. V. Brown, *J. Org. Chem.* **19**, 894 (1954).

56. C. Q. Sheely, Jr., and R. G. Rose, *Ind. Eng. Chem. Prod. Res. Develop.* **4** (1), 24 (1965).

57. J. S. Showell, J. R. Russell, and D. Swern, *J. Org. Chem.* **27**, 2853 (1962).

58. F. D. Smith and A. J. Stirton, *J. Am. Oil Chemists' Soc.* **44** (7), 405 (1967).

59. M. A. Smook, E. T. Pieski, and C. F. Hammer, *Ind. Eng. Chem.* **45**, 2731 (1953).

60. A. J. Stirton, *J. Am. Oil Chemists' Soc.* **39**, 490 (1962).

61. F. J. Stubbs, C. D. Williams, and C. N. Hinshelwood, *J. Chem. Soc.* **1948**, 1065.

62. J. E. Vander Mey (to Allied Chemical Corp), U.S. Pat. 3,328,460 (June 27, 1967).

63. A. A. Vasil'ev, M. B. Gershman, and T. A. Vasil'eva, *J. Appl. Chem. USSR* (*English Transl.*) **35**, 2288 (1962); *Chem. Abstr.* **58**, 6224 (1963).

64. K. Venkataraman, *The Chemistry of Synthetic Dyes*, Vol. II, Academic Press, Inc., New York, 1952, pp. 1046 ff.

65. L. G. Vol'fson and N. H. Mel'nikov, *J. Gen. Chem. USSR* (*English Transl.*) **20**, 2080 (1950); *Chem. Abstr.* **45**, 5608 (1951).

66. R. W. Waddelow and E. L. Hatlelid, *Paper Southwest Regional Meet. Am. Chem. Soc., Oklahoma City, Okla., Dec. 1960*.

67. T. J. Wallace and A. Schriesheim, *Tetrahedron* **21**, 2271 (1965).

68. W. E. Walles (to The Dow Chemical Co.), U.S. Pat. 2,832,696 (April 29, 1958).

69. J. R. Weil, A. J. Stirton, and F. D. Smith, *J. Am. Oil Chemists' Soc.* **42**, 873 (1965).

70. D. D. Whyte, *J. Am. Oil Chemists' Soc.* **32**, 313 (1955).

71. O. B. Wurzburg, M. W. Rutenberg, and L. J. Ross (to National Starch Products, Inc.), U.S. Pat. 2,786,833 (March 26, 1957).

General References

H. Cerfontain, *Mechanistic Aspects in Aromatic Sulfonation and Desulfonation*, Interscience Publishers, a div. of John Wiley & Sons, Inc., New York, 1968.

E. E. Gilbert, *Sulfonation and Related Reactions*, Interscience Publishers, a div. of John Wiley & Sons, Inc., New York, 1965.

E. E. Gilbert and P. H. Groggins, "Sulfonation and Sulfation," in P. H. Groggins, ed., *Unit Processes in Organic Synthesis*, 5th ed., McGraw-Hill Book Co., Inc., New York, 1958, pp. 303 ff.

E. Müller, ed., *Methoden der Organischen Chemie (Houben-Weyl)*, 4th ed., Vol. 9, Thieme Verlag, Stuttgart, 1955, pp. 343 ff., 407 ff., 429 ff.

K. L. Nelson, "Sulfonation," in *Friedel-Crafts and Related Reactions*, G. A. Olah, ed., Vol. III, Pt. II, Interscience Publishers, a div. of John Wiley & Sons, Inc., New York, 1964, pp. 1355 ff.

C. M. Suter, *The Organic Chemistry of Sulfur*, John Wiley & Sons, Inc., New York, 1944.

C. M. Suter and A. W. Weston, "Direct Sulfonation of Aromatic Hydrocarbons and Their Halogen Derivatives," in R. Adams, ed., *Organic Reactions*, Vol. 3, John Wiley & Sons, Inc., New York, 1946, pp. 141 ff.

EVERETT E. GILBERT
Allied Chemical Corp.

SULFONIC ACIDS

Sulfonic acids are characterized by the presence of the sulfo group, —SO₃H (or —SO₂OH), and can be considered derivatives of sulfuric acid with one of the hydroxyl groups replaced by a univalent organic radical.

Inorganic acids with the general-type formula XSO_2OH, where X is Cl, F, or NH_2, have also been commonly designated as sulfonic acids. (See Chlorosulfonic acid; Fluorine compounds, inorganic; Sulfamic acid.) In accordance with the 1957 recommendation of the IUPAC Commission on the Nomenclature of Inorganic Chemistry, however, these compounds are now preferably designated as "sulfuric" acids—ie, chloro- and fluorosulfuric, and amidosulfuric acids. This nomenclature is employed here.

Sulfonic acids have the general-type formula RSO_2OH and are classified as alkane- and cycloalkanesulfonic acids, arenesulfonic acids, and heterocyclic sulfonic acids. The nature of the R group largely determines the physical and chemical properties of the individual acids, but in general they are nonvolatile, water-soluble, and chemically stable acids comparable in strength to sulfuric acid. Careful distinction should be made between the sulfonic acids, RSO_2OH, and the sulfuric esters, $ROSO_2OH$, which are different in physical and chemical properties. (See Sulfuric and sulfurous esters.)

Nomenclature. Sulfonic acids are named by adding this term as a suffix to the name of the parent compound, as shown in the following examples:

CH₃SO₂OH

methanesulfonic
acid

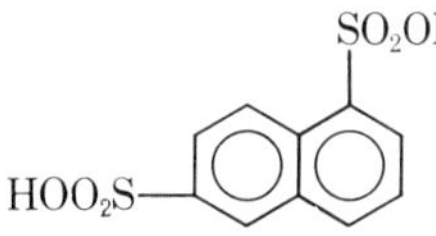

1,6-naphthalenedisulfonic
acid

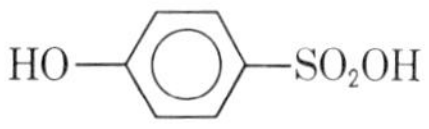

4-hydroxybenzene-
sulfonic acid

Compounds containing sulfonic and carboxylic acid groups are named by using the prefix "sulfo," as shown in the following examples:

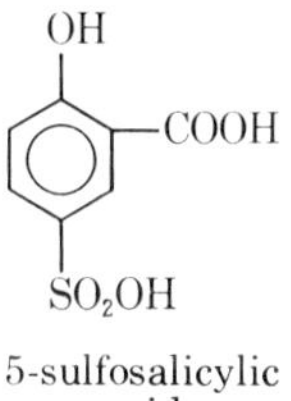

5-sulfosalicylic
acid

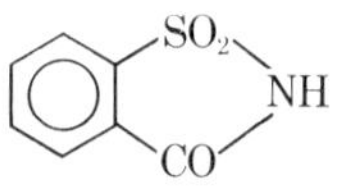

o-sulfobenzoic
imide (saccharin)

HOOCCH₂CH(SO₂OH)COOH

sulfosuccinic acid

Some sulfonic acids, which contain other functional groups, have common or trivial names, such as the examples listed below:

HOCH₂CH₂SO₂OH

isethionic acid
(2-hydroxyethanesulfonic
acid)

H₂NCH₂CH₂SO₂OH

taurine
(2-aminoethanesulfonic
acid)

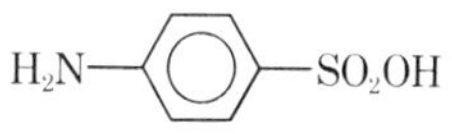

H₂N—⟨ ⟩—SO₂OH

sulfanilic acid
(4-aminobenzenesulfonic acid)

Physical Properties

Like sulfuric acid, the organic sulfonic acids are hygroscopic, highly acidic, and soluble in water and polar solvents. Because of the influence of the organic radical, sulfonic acids differ markedly from sulfuric acid in other physical properties.

Table 1. Physical Properties of Some Alkanesulfonic Acids

Sulfonic acid	Boiling point, at 1 mm Hg, °C	Melting point, °C	Density, d_4^{25}
methane-	122	20	1.4844
ethane-	123	-17	1.3341
propane-	136	7.5	1.2516
butane-	149	-15.2	1.1906
pentane-	163	15.9	1.1226
hexane-	174	16.1	1.1047
hexadecane-		53	
2-aminoethane- (taurine)		305–310 (dec)	

The hydrocarbon-derived alkanesulfonic acids (see Table 1) can be distilled only in high vacuum without decomposition.   All the acids are difficult to obtain in anhydrous form.   The lower members of the series are completely miscible with water at room temperature.   However, as the molecular weight increases, water solubility decreases; n-hexadecanesulfonic acid is only slightly soluble at room temperature.   The density also drops markedly with increasing size of the organic moiety.   Taurine and other aminosulfonic acids have high melting points because of internal salt (zwitterion) formation, ie $^+H_3NCH_2CH_2SO_2O^-$.

Trifluoromethanesulfonic acid, F_3CSO_2OH, differs from the hydrocarbon sulfonic acids cited above, in having a relatively low boiling point (162°C at 760 mm Hg), greater acid strength than sulfuric acid, and high thermal stability, since it is unchanged even at 350°C (2).   It forms a distillable hydrate.   The other perfluoroalkanesulfonic acids have similar properties (2); n-$C_8F_{17}SO_2OH$ boils at 260°C at 760 mm Hg.

Arenesulfonic acids are generally solids at room temperature.   They crystallize from water as hydrates which are often deliquescent.   It is therefore usually difficult to prepare the acids in anhydrous form, and for this reason there is little agreement in the literature on their physical properties.   For example, melting points ranging from 52 to 66°C are reported for the simplest member of the series, benzenesulfonic acid, and the range is even larger for many others.   For this reason, sulfonic acids are generally identified as derivatives which are free of this objection (see below under Identification and analysis).   The arenesulfonic acids usually decompose on attempted distillation even in vacuo.   Benzene- and p-toluenesulfonic acids can be distilled at 0.1 mm Hg, with boiling points of 172 and 187°C, respectively.

Detailed descriptions of the more important acids are given elsewhere.   See Sulfonic acid derivatives under Aniline; Anthraquinone derivatives; Benzenesulfonic acid; Naphthalene derivatives; Phenolsulfonic acids.

The preparation of the various classes of sulfonic acids, as well as of the salts, sulfonyl chlorides, and sulfonic anhydrides, when such are the primary products, is discussed in the article Sulfonation and sulfation.

Chemical Properties

The sulfonic acids are almost completely ionized in aqueous solution and in solutions of many polar organic solvents.   They are comparable in acid strength to sulfuric acid.   The chemical reactions of the sulfonic acids can be divided into four categories on the basis of the structural changes which occur.

Salt Formation. When the hydrogen atom of the sulfonic acid group is replaced by reaction of the acid with metals above hydrogen in the electromotive series, or with inorganic oxides, hydroxides, and carbonates, a salt is formed. Treatment of the sulfonic acid with aqueous sodium chloride often results in precipitation of the sodium salt, a convenient preparative procedure:

$$RSO_2OH + NaCl \rightleftharpoons RSO_2ONa + HCl$$

With ammonia and its derivatives, ammonium and substituted ammonium salts are formed. In most cases, the salts are crystalline solids that are much more water-soluble than the corresponding sulfates (see Table 2). Some amine salts, such as tri-ethylammonium ethanesulfonate, are mobile liquids at room temperature.

Table 2. Water Solubility of Sulfonates and Sulfates, g/100 g H_2O at 20°C

Cation	Methanesulfonate	Ethanesulfonate	Sulfate
NH_4^+	145	252	75
Ba^{2+}	70	73	2×10^{-5}
Ca^{2+}		87	3×10^{-1}
Co^{2+}	75	83	36
Cu^{2+}	68	90	21
Pb^{2+}	143	175	4×10^{-4}
Li^+	142	210	35
Mg^{2+}		40	34
K^+	106	141	11
Na^+	100	105	19
Ag^+	101		8×10^{-1}
Zn^{2+}	76	76	116

The sodium and potassium salts of trifluoromethanesulfonic acid have lower melting points (248 and 230°C, respectively) than the corresponding sulfates (884 and 588°C) or methanesulfonates (345 and >370°C) (2), and are substantially unchanged by heating even at 400°C.

Transformation of the Sulfonic Acid Group. Replacement of the hydroxyl of the sulfonic acid group by chlorine can be accomplished by treating the acid or a salt with phosphorus pentachloride or chlorosulfuric acid. Sulfonyl chlorides are formed, as shown:

$$RSO_2OH + ClSO_3H \rightleftharpoons RSO_2Cl + H_2SO_4$$

$$RSO_2OH + PCl_5 \rightarrow RSO_2Cl + POCl_3 + HCl$$

Alkanesulfonyl chlorides are, however, more often prepared directly by aqueous chlorination of a thiol derivative, while arenesulfonyl chlorides are prepared by the direct treatment of the parent aromatic compound with chlorosulfuric acid. (See Sulfonation and sulfation.) The sulfonyl chlorides are the intermediates usually employed to convert the sulfonic acids to the derived sulfonamides, sulfonate esters, sulfinic acids, and thiols, since (except for the thiols and certain aliphatic esters) these compounds cannot be prepared directly from the sulfonic acids.

Sulfonyl bromides are obtained in a similar manner by the treatment of the sulfonic acid or a salt with phosphorus tribromide and bromine. These compounds are of limited interest in comparison with the chlorides. Sulfonyl fluorides can be made by reacting fluorosulfuric acid with the parent aromatic compound, the sulfonic acid, or a salt thereof:

$$RSO_2OH + FSO_3H \rightleftharpoons RSO_2F + H_2SO_4$$

The extreme stability of the fluorosulfonyl group under acid or neutral conditions allows its retention during various chemical reactions of the organic portion of the molecule.

Sulfonic anhydrides result from treatment of a sulfonic acid with dehydrating agents, such as thionyl chloride or phosphorus pentoxide:

$$2\,RSO_2OH + SOCl_2 \rightarrow (RSO_2)_2O + 2\,HCl + SO_2$$

$$2\,RSO_2OH + P_2O_5 \rightarrow (RSO_2)_2O + 2\,HPO_3$$

Arenesulfonic anhydrides are also formed in some cases by direct treatment of the aromatic compound with sulfur trioxide–nitromethane complex:

$$2\,RH + 3\,SO_3 \rightarrow (RSO_2)_2O + H_2SO_4$$

Mixed anhydrides are powerful acylating agents and can be prepared as shown below (11):

$$RSO_2OH + R'COCl \rightarrow RSO_2OCOR' + HCl$$

Alkane- and arenesulfonic acids form sulfones with aromatic compounds under a variety of dehydrating conditions:

$$RSO_2OH + R'C_6H_5 \xrightarrow{-H_2O} RSO_2C_6H_4R'$$

This reaction is thought to proceed via the formation of the sulfonic anhydride as intermediate.

Methane- and ethanesulfonic acids react at room temperature with propylene, 1-pentene, 2-pentene, and other olefins, forming secondary esters (19):

$$CH_3SO_2OH + RCH{=}CHR' \rightarrow CH_3SO_2OCH(R)CH_2R'$$

Ethylene gives a 25% conversion to the ester at 100°C and 800 psi pressure. Trifluoromethanesulfonic acid, on the other hand, reacts rapidly with ethylene at room temperature, forming the ethyl ester and a low polymer of ethylene (2).

Sulfonic acids are reduced to the corresponding thiols only with difficulty:

$$RSO_2OH + 2\,P \xrightarrow{I_2} RSH + P_2O_3$$

4-Chlorothiophenol has been made commercially by this procedure (16). In the more common laboratory and industrial preparation the sulfonyl chloride is reduced with powdered zinc or iron in the presence of aqueous mineral acids, or with phosphorus and iodine (23):

$$RSO_2Cl \xrightarrow{3\,H_2} RSH + 2\,H_2O + HCl$$

Cleavage of the Carbon–Sulfur Bond. Depending upon the structural environment, an aromatic sulfonic acid group can be replaced by H, OH, CN, NH_2, NH_2NH, OR, COOH, Cl, Br, I, NO_2, aryl-N=N, RS, and SH. Some of these reactions give poor yields and have limited utility, while others proceed easily and are employed commercially. Heterocyclic sulfonates behave similarly in some cases.

The process of steaming an aromatic sulfonic acid to recover the parent aromatic compound by reversal of the sulfonation reaction, known as hydrolytic desulfonation, has proved widely useful in the laboratory and industry (9):

$$RSO_2OH + H_2O \rightarrow RH + H_2SO_4$$

Since each sulfonic acid has a characteristically different desulfonation temperature, this approach can be used in conjunction with selective sulfonation to separate isomers. m-Xylene has been isolated by this method on a commercial scale. The same method has been applied experimentally to the separation of other di- and polyalkylated benzenes and naphthalenes, chlorinated benzenes, and phenols. In the industrial sulfonation of naphthalene in the 2-position (intermediate to the preparation of 2-naphthol), a sulfonic acid mixture of 85% of the 2-isomer and 15% of the 1-isomer is obtained. The 1-sulfonate is removed by steaming at 165°C to effect cleavage, the 2-isomer being stable. In the manufacture of the insecticide DDT, oleum is employed as the condensing agent; as a side reaction sulfonation of some of the raw material chlorobenzene occurs. Passing steam into the spent acid results in hydrolysis of the sulfonic acid, permits recovery of the chlorobenzene, and at the same time partially purifies the acid.

Mixtures of isomers of anthraquinonedisulfonic acid (mainly 1,7-, also some 1,6-, 1,5-, and 1,8-) are recovered by removing all the sulfo groups in the 1-position, yielding anthraquinone and its 2-sulfonate; this is effected by prolonged heating in dilute sulfuric acid at 180–200°C. In the sulfonation of styrene–divinylbenzene copolymers for the preparation of ion-exchange resins, the rate of reaction is controlled by diffusion and therefore depends upon the size of the resin pore. On the other hand, desulfonation of the resin with concentrated HCl is independent of pore size. By appropriate combination of these two techniques, it is possible to prepare resins with sulfonate groups in positions either related, or not related, to pore size. As indicated below, hydrolytic desulfonation has proved an indispensable tool in studying the chemical composition of mixtures of sulfonated hydrocarbons.

Hydrolytic desulfonation is also useful for synthesis. 2-Chlorotoluene has been made commercially as follows (8):

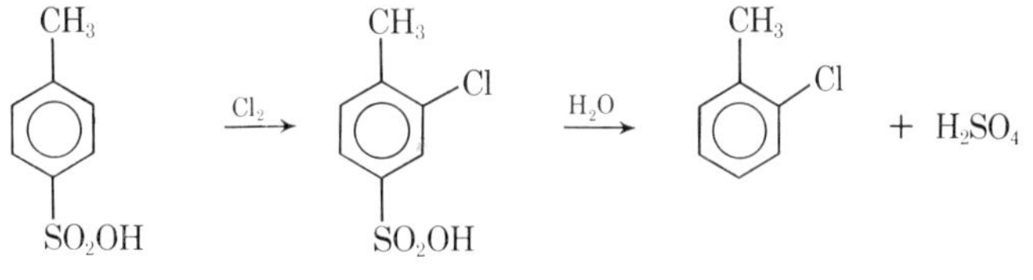

Other compounds prepared by this general scheme include 2,3,5,6-tetrachlorotoluene, 2,6-dichloro- and -dibromoanilines, and 2-bromophenol.

Alkaline fusion of sulfonic acid salts yields phenols:

$$RSO_2ONa + 2\,NaOH \rightarrow RONa + Na_2SO_3 + H_2O$$

Phenolic compounds made commercially by this procedure include phenol (qv), p-cresol (see Cresols), 2-naphthol (see Naphthalene derivatives), resorcinol (see Hydroquinone, resorcinol, pyrocatechol), hydroxyanthraquinones (see Anthraquinone derivatives), 8-hydroxyquinoline, and 4-hydroxybiphenyl.

Labile sulfonic acid groups are replaceable by halogens. This reaction has been used commercially to make chlorinated anthraquinones that are otherwise difficultly accessible (see Anthraquinone derivatives):

$$3 RSO_2ONa + 6 HCl + NaClO_3 \rightarrow 3 RCl + 4 NaCl + 3 H_2SO_4$$

Chlorinated naphthalenes and heterocyclic derivatives have been made similarly.

Stable sulfonic acids can be converted to the aryl halides in good yields by another approach, involving a free-radical reaction activated by heat, light, or a catalyst (4):

$$RSO_2Cl \xrightarrow{130-250°C} RCl + SO_2$$

Arenesulfonate groups can be exchanged for amino groups in some cases by heating with ammonia, and in others by fusion with sodamide. Mono- and dialkylamines can also be used. Replacement by the hydrazino moiety occurs in excellent yield even at a temperature as low as 35°C (6):

$$RSO_2ONa + NaNHNH_2 \rightarrow RNHNH_2 + Na_2SO_3$$

Fusion with metallic cyanides yields nitriles (13):

$$RSO_2ONa + NaCN \rightarrow RCN + Na_2SO_3$$

This reaction is quite widely applicable for the preparation of the mono- and di-cyano derivatives of benzene, naphthalene, biphenyl, and higher condensed-ring systems. It has been employed commercially for making nicotinonitrile and cyano-anthraquinones.

Sulfonated phenols are converted to nitrophenols by treatment with nitric acid, the sulfonic groups being replaced during nitration. Compounds prepared in this way include the 2,4-dinitro derivatives of 2-sec-butylphenol, 2-cyclohexylphenol (18), 1-naphthol (Martius Yellow), and 1-naphthol-7-sulfonic acid (Naphthol Yellow S).

Only a few cases of carbon–sulfur cleavage are known in the aliphatic series. Alkanesulfonyl chlorides are smoothly converted to the corresponding chlorides by heating to 150–250°C (1):

$$RSO_2Cl \rightarrow RCl + SO_2$$

Alkenes are formed by heating sodium alkanesulfonates (17):

$$RCH_2CH_2SO_2ONa \rightarrow RCH{=}CH_2 + NaHSO_3$$

This reaction has been considered for the commercial production of alkenes from by-product water-soluble petroleum sulfonates (24).

Reactions of the Organic Moiety. Methane- and ethanesulfonic acids are notably resistant to chlorination and sulfochlorination because the sulfonic acid group exerts a retarding effect at a distance of two carbon atoms. However, these reactions occur normally with aliphatic sulfonic acids of longer chain lengths. The acids, or their halides (X = Cl or F), can be perfluorinated electrochemically in yields ranging from 87% for C_1 to 25% for C_8 (2):

$$CH_3SO_2X + 4 F_2 \rightarrow CF_3SO_2F + 3 HF + XF$$

The C_8 compound is thus manufactured commercially from n-$C_8H_{17}SO_2Cl$. Functional groups in sulfonic acids, such as hydroxyl, chlorine, amino, and olefinic unsaturation, react normally, and are widely used for making important derivatives via the usual reactions of organic synthesis. For example, the surfactant Igepon T (GAF Corp.) is made by reacting $CH_3NHCH_2CH_2SO_2ONa$ with a long-chain acid chloride to form the amide. This type of procedure, known as *sulfoalkylation*, is discussed in more detail under Sulfonation and sulfation.

Aromatic sulfonic acids undergo the normal types of substitution reactions, such as halogenation, nitration, and further sulfonation, with the original sulfo group functioning in a meta-directing, electron-withdrawing capacity. As stated previously, labile sulfonic acid groups are sometimes replaced during such reactions. The hydroxyl, amino, carboxyl, and other functional groups in aromatic sulfonic acids react normally, and such compounds are employed as *sulfoarylating* agents. Thus, phenolsulfonic acid can be resinified with formaldehyde, yielding water-soluble tanning agents, or water-insoluble ion-exchange resins. Dimethyl 5-sulfoisophthalate is incorporated by ester interchange into polyesters to increase dyeability.

Unusual inertness, rather than reactivity, is sometimes required in the organic moiety. For example, sulfonated polystyrene film components of fuel cells are steadily exposed to heat, moisture, and oxidants. The sulfonated trifluorostyrene (**a**) is extremely stable, since the side chain is fully substituted and the meta sulfonic acid group is difficult to remove hydrolytically (10). In contrast, the benzylic hydrogen atoms in (**b**) are fairly easily oxidized and the *p*-sulfonic acid group can be removed by hydrolytic desulfonation.

(a)   (b)

Uses

The sulfonic acids and their derivatives are important industrial chemicals, useful as catalysts, detergents, emulsifying agents, lubricating oil additives, ion-exchange resins, and for many other purposes. They are intermediates for the preparation of phenolic compounds, dyes, pharmaceuticals, tanning agents, pesticides, and other products. The main use for long-chain alkylbenzenesulfonic acid salts is in household detergents (see Detergency; Surfactants). Solutions of the lower alkylbenzenesulfonic acid salts are hydrotropic, ie they dissolve materials which are relatively insoluble in water (3).

Sulfonamides are important commercially (see Chloramines; Sweeteners (about Saccharin); Sulfonamides); all of the many sulfa drugs are derivatives of *p*-aminobenzenesulfonamide, $H_2NC_6H_4SO_2NH_2$. Sulfonate esters are highly reactive alkylating agents; certain aromatic esters have insecticidal activity.

Although sulfonates are ordinarily employed as salts, some uses require the acid form. The acids are effective catalysts for polymerization, alkylation (19), esterification, ester interchange, etherification, and dehydration. They are often milder and more selective than sulfuric acid or aluminum chloride. The acids most commonly used are methanesulfonic, toluenesulfonic, and the acid form of cation-exchange resins.

Although the first two acids are nearly equivalent for many catalytic reactions, methanesulfonic acid is markedly superior for the acidolysis of esters, and for the preparation of dioctyl phthalate (15). The ion-exchange resins have the advantage of being insoluble in the reaction mixture, and can therefore be recovered for reuse by simple filtration. The acid form of the resins also finds application in fuel cells; the resin in this case can be regarded as a solid electrolyte.

Identification and Analysis

Individual sulfonic acids are suitably characterized by the formation of salts with definite melting points (14). The thallium salts can be prepared from the sulfonic acid and thallium hydroxide, or by treating a sulfonic acid salt with thallium formate. The salts of organic amines, such as p-toluidine, 2-phenylethylamine, phenylhydrazine, S-benzylisothiourea, or guanidine, are also suitable.

The molecular weights of sulfonic acids above approx 300 can be determined by titration with quaternary ammonium halides (22).

The composition of the organic groups in sulfonic acid mixtures is conveniently studied by hydrolytic desulfonation under pressure with 30% phosphoric acid, followed by chromatographic or spectrographic examination of the hydrolyzate (5,12). This approach has been effectively employed with sulfonates derived from petroleum, coaltar, detergent alkylate, and the high-boiling by-product from detergent alkylate production. Dibutylnaphthalenesulfonic acid mixtures have been desulfonated with 50–60% sulfuric acid at 130°C (20).

Toxicity

The sulfo group is in general strongly detoxifying. Even highly toxic compounds, such as aniline, 2-naphthylamine, or various nitro aromatics, become nontoxic when sulfonic acid groups are introduced. The addition of the sulfonic acid group usually changes a lipophilic compound, which easily penetrates the skin, to one which is hydrophilic and therefore rapidly excreted in the urine either as such, or as a conjugate with glycine or glucuronic acid (7).

Sulfonic acids, particularly the lower aliphatic derivatives, such as methanesulfonic acid, can cause typical acid burns on contact with the skin. However, the primary irritant effects of sulfonic acids vary greatly (7), and do not correlate well with ionization constants.

A derivative of taurine, $NH_2CH_2CH_2SO_2OH$, occurs naturally in human bile acids. Sulfonate salts widely used as detergents and wetting agents (ie, those from C_{10-15} alkylbenzene detergent alkylates, isopropylnaphthalene, butylbiphenyl, butylphenylphenol, oleoyl N-methyltauride, dodecyldiphenyl ether, and dioctyl succinate) are nontoxic in both acute and chronic tests (21).

Dioctyl sulfosuccinate salts have been added to pharmaceutical preparations to increase penetration, and salts of alkylnaphthalenesulfonic acids have been used in laxative formulations and as antitussives.

The above remarks apply to the sulfonic acids and their common salts. Other derivatives may be more toxic. For example, p-toluenesulfonic acid is only a skin irritant, but its sulfonyl chloride and its methyl ester are both potent vesicants (7).

Bibliography

"Sulfonic Acids" in *ECT* 1st ed., Vol. 13, pp. 346–353, by A. A. Harban and C. E. Johnson, Standard Oil Company (Indiana).

1. F. Asinger, *Chemie und Technologie der Paraffin—Kohlenwasserstoffe*, Akademie Verlag, Berlin, 1956, p. 428.
2. R. E. Banks and R. N. Haszeldine, "Perfluoroalkyl Derivatives of Sulfur," in N. Kharasch and C. Y. Meyers, eds., *The Chemistry of Organic Sulfur Compounds*, Vol. 2, Pergamon Press, Inc., New York, 1966, pp. 165–176.
3. H. S. Booth and H. E. Everson, *Ind. Eng. Chem.* **42**, 1536 (1950).
4. J. Blum, *Tetrahedron Letters* **26**, 3041 (1966).
5. A. B. Brown and J. O. Knobloch, *ASTM Tech. Bull. No. 224*, American Society for Testing and Materials, Philadelphia, 1958, p. 213.
6. W. Burkhardt and T. Kauffmann, *Angew. Chem. (Intern. Ed. Engl.)* **6** (1), 84 (1967).
7. D. W. Fassett, "Organic Acids, Anhydrides, Lactones, Acid Halides and Amides, Thioacids," in F. A. Patty, ed., *Industrial Hygiene and Toxicology*, 2nd rev. ed., Vol. II, Interscience Publishers, a div. of John Wiley & Sons, Inc., New York, 1963, pp. 1837–1845.
8. H. E. Fierz-David and L. Blangey, *Fundamental Processes of Dye Chemistry*, 5th ed., Interscience Publishers, Inc., New York, 1949.
9. E. E. Gilbert, "Sulfonation and Related Reactions," Interscience Publishers, a div. of John Wiley & Sons, Inc., New York, 1965, pp. 425–442.
10. R. B. Hodgdon, Jr., *J. Polymer Sci.* **A-1** (6), 171 (1968).
11. M. H. Karger and Y. Mazur, *J. Am. Chem. Soc.* **90** (14), 3878 (1968).
12. S. Lee and N. A. Puttnam, *J. Am. Oil Chemists Soc.* **44** (2), 158 (1967).
13. D. T. Mowry, *Chem. Rev.* **42** (2), 189 (1948).
14. F. Muth, "Methoden zur Herstellung und Umwandlung aromatischer Sulfonsäuren," in E. Müller, ed., *Houben-Weyl, Methoden der organischen Chemie*, 4th ed., Vol. IX, Thieme Verlag, Stuttgart, 1955, p. 429.
15. *Bulletin PD-101*, Pennsalt Chemicals Corporation, Product Development, Philadelphia, 1965.
16. U.S. Pat. 2,947,788 (Aug. 2, 1960), H. Pitt (to Stauffer Chemical Co.).
17. J. Pollerberg, *Fette, Seifen, Anstrichmittel* **67** (11), 927 (1965).
18. U.S. Pat. 2,112,543 (March 29, 1938), R. F. Prescott (to Dow Chemical Co.).
19. W. A. Proell and C. E. Adams, *Ind. Eng. Chem.* **41**, 2217 (1949).
20. G. Sonnek and F. Wolf, *Tenside (Munich)* **4** (10), 325 (1967).
21. R. D. Swisher, "Surfactant Effects on Humans and Other Mammals," in *The Soap and Detergent Association Scientific and Technical Report No. 4*, Soap and Detergent Association, New York, Nov. 1966.
22. B. Veldhuis, *Anal. Chem.* **32**, 1681 (1960).
23. A. W. Wagner, *Chem. Ber.* **99**, 375 (1966).
24. U.S. Pat. 3,341,614 (Sept. 12, 1967), M. M. Wirth and J. Habeshaw (to British Hydrocarbon Chemicals Ltd.).

General References

W. A. Proell, "Unsubstituted Aliphatic Sulfonic Acids," in N. Kharasch and C. Y. Meyers, eds., *The Chemistry of Organic Sulfur Compounds*, Pergamon Press, Inc., New York, 1968.

W. A. Proell, C. E. Adams, and B. H. Shoemaker, *Ind. Eng. Chem.* **40**, 1129 (1948).

References 1, 8, 9, and 14 cited above.

EVERETT E. GILBERT
Allied Chemical Corporation

SULFONYL HALIDES. See Sulfur compounds.

SULFOXIDATION. See Sulfonation and sulfation.

SULFOXIDES

Sulfoxides contain the sulfinyl group, >SO, covalently bonded to two carbon atoms at the sulfur. They represent an intermediate oxidation level between the sulfides, RSR, and sulfones, RSO_2R. A number of sulfoxides occur naturally, and the oxidation or reduction reactions of them and other sulfoxides occur in living systems (**1**). Dimethyl sulfoxide is produced commercially in several countries and the bulk of sulfoxide literature deals with this compound.

Although sulfoxides bear a nominal similarity to the ketones, they are more nearly like the phosphine oxides, R_3PO. The sulfoxide oxygen is more basic than the corresponding ketone oxygen, and the activating effect of the sulfinyl group is much less than that of the carbonyl group. The ketones are planar, while the sulfoxides are pyramidal and exhibit optical isomerism when the two groups attached to the sulfinyl group are different.

The sulfur–oxygen bonding in sulfoxides consists of a σ overlap of an oxygen p orbital with one of the sp^3 hybrid orbitals of the sulfur and two π bonds between appropriate d orbitals of the sulfur and p orbitals of the oxygen. The π bonds are weak and the overall bond strength is about that of a double bond (2).

Sulfoxides in which the sulfoxide group is the principal function are named like ethers or sulfides by means of the hydrocarbon groups attached to the sulfur; for example, $(CH_3)_2SO$ is optionally methyl sulfoxide (CA) or dimethyl sulfoxide (IUPAC), and $C_2H_5SOC_6H_5$ is ethyl phenyl sulfoxide. When the molecule contains both the sulfoxide and another function, the compound is usually named as a sulfinyl derivative, the other function being the chief one. Chemical Abstracts uses the following order of precedence: "onium" compounds, peroxide, acid, acid halide, amide, imide, aniline, aldehyde, nitrile, isocyanide, ketone, thione, alcohol, phenol, thiol, amine, imine, organometallic compounds, ether, sulfide, sulfoxide, sulfone. Thus, $CH_3SOCH_2CH_2OH$ is 2-(methylsulfinyl)ethanol and $C_6H_5SOCH_2CH_2SCH_3$ is methyl 2-(phenylsulfinyl)-ethyl sulfide. When identical units containing higher-order groups are attached to the sulfinyl group, the compounds are named using the sulfinyl prefix, ie, $OS(CH_2CH_2OH)_2$ is 2,2′-sulfinyldiethanol. When the sulfinyl group is incorporated in a ring the compound is named as an oxide, ie, thiophene-1-oxide.

Properties

For the most part, sulfoxides are crystalline, colorless substances, although the lower aliphatic sulfoxides melt at relatively low temperatures (see Table 1). The lower aliphatic sulfoxides are water soluble, but as a class the sulfoxides are not soluble in water, although they are soluble in dilute acids, and a few are soluble in alkaline solution. They are soluble to a variable extent in organic solvents, depending upon associated functional groups. Because of the very polar sulfoxide group they generally are high boiling and when distillable, require reduced pressure. Dimethyl sulfoxide (DMSO) is a colorless and nearly odorless liquid (properties shown in Table 2).

Most of the reactions of sulfoxides are either reactions at the highly polar sulfinyl group or reactions involving initial removal of hydrogens from α or β carbon atoms. A moderate activation at the α carbon results from the electron-withdrawing influence of the sulfinyl group and resonance stabilization of the carbanions produced by proton removal. The magnitude of the activating effect is indicated by the autoprotolysis of pure DMSO for which the pK_a is 33.5, suggesting an acidity about one thousandth that of diphenylmethane (20).   On the other hand, the sulfoxide oxygen of DMSO is protonated in aqueous sulfuric acid to approximately the same extent as the lower aliphatic alcohols (21) so that it is a weak base.   DMSO generally shows typical sulfoxide reactions and is used in the following section to illustrate these.

Table 1. Representative Sulfoxide Properties

Name	Formula	Mp, °C	Bp, °C	Ref.
dimethyl sulfoxide	$(CH_3)_2SO$	18.55	189.0	3
diethyl sulfoxide	$(C_2H_5)_2SO$	15	88–90 (15 mm)	4
di-n-propyl sulfoxide	$(n\text{-}C_3H_7)_2SO$	18		4
di-n-butyl sulfoxide	$(n\text{-}C_4H_{10})_2SO$	32		5
2-chloroethyl sulfoxide	$(ClCH_2CH_2)_2SO$	110.2		6
diphenyl sulfoxide	$(C_6H_5)_2SO$	70.5	340 (sl dec)	7
methyl phenyl sulfoxide	$C_6H_5SOCH_3$	30–30.5	139–140	8,9
benzyl phenyl sulfoxide	$C_6H_5SOCH_2C_6H_5$	125.5		10
dibenzyl sulfoxide	$(C_6H_5CH_2)_2SO$	135		11

Table 2. Properties of Dimethyl Sulfoxide

	Value	Ref.
boiling point, 760 mm, °C	189.0	3
conductivity, 20°C, $\Omega^{-1}cm^{-1}$	3×10^{-8}	3
dielectric constant, 25°C, 10 MHz	46.7	12
dipole moment, D	4.3	3
entropy of fusion, cal/(mole)(°C)	11.4	13
free energy of formation (g), kcal/mole (C_{graph}, $S_{2(g)}$), 25°C	27.65	14
freezing point, °C	18.55	3
heat capacity (liq), 25°C, cal/(mole)(°C)	36.4	15
heat capacity (ideal gas), C_p (T °K)	$6.94 + 5.6 \times 10^{-2}T - 0.227 \times 10^{-4}T^2$	14
heat of formation (liq), 18°C, kcal/mole(C_{graph}, S_{rhomb})	-47.7	16
heat of fusion, kcal/mole	3.22	17
heat of vaporization, 70°C, kcal/mole	11.3	18
molal fp constant, °C/(mole)(kg)	4.07	19
pK_a	33.5	20
pK_{BH^+} (aqueous sulfuric acid)	-2.7	21
refractive index, n_D^{25}	1.4768	22
flash point (open cup), °C	95	18
autoignition temp in air, °C	300–302	18
flammability limits in air		
lower (100°C), vol %	3–3.5	18
upper (180°C), vol %	42–63	18

	25°C	*35°C*	*45°C*	*100°C*	
vapor pressure, mm	0.600	1.195	2.27	30	18,23
density, g/ml	1.0955	1.0855	1.0757		24
viscosity, cP	1.996	1.654	1.396	0.68	24

Thermal Stability. DMSO decomposes slowly at 189°C to a mixture of products including methanethiol, formaldehyde, water, bis(methylthio)methane, dimethyl disulfide, dimethyl sulfone, and dimethyl sulfide.

The decomposition is accelerated by acids, glycols, or amides (25). The products obtained suggest a Pummerer reaction accompanied by different redox reactions, ie:

$$(CH_3)_2SO \rightarrow CH_3SCH_2OH \rightleftharpoons CH_3SH + HCHO$$

$$2\ CH_3SH + HCHO \rightleftharpoons CH_3SCH_2SCH_3 + H_2O$$

$$2\ CH_3SH + (CH_3)_2SO \rightarrow CH_3SSCH_3 + CH_3SCH_3 + H_2O$$

$$2\ (CH_3)_2SO \rightarrow CH_3SO_2CH_3 + CH_3SCH_3$$

Oxidation. Sulfoxides oxidize more slowly than the corresponding sulfides but are readily converted to sulfones by a number of strong oxidizing agents (26) such as potassium permanganate, hypochlorites, hydrogen peroxide, ozone, selenium dioxide, or hot nitric acid. The oxidation commonly gives high yields. Side reactions producing sulfonic acids are sometimes encountered during oxidation with nitric acid. Treatment of DMSO under strongly alkaline conditions with either sodium hypochlorite or hypobromite gives oxidation accompanied by halogenation forming the hexahalodimethyl sulfones in good yield (27):

$$CH_3SOCH_3 + NaOCl \rightarrow CCl_3SO_2CCl_3$$
$$\text{bis(trichloromethyl)}$$
$$\text{sulfone}$$

The moderate resistance of DMSO to oxidation permits it to be used as a solvent for some oxidations such as with lead tetracetate (28) or the 2-nitropropane anion (29). Dichromate oxidation (32) and permanganate oxidation (33) have been used for quantitative determination of DMSO.

Reduction. DMSO is reduced to dimethyl sulfide by a number of strong reducing agents (26) including aluminum hydrides, hydriodic acid, diborane, thiols, phosphine derivatives, and zinc in sulfuric acid. Quantitative procedures for determining DMSO have been based on its reduction using stannous chloride in hydrochloric acid (30) or titanium trichloride in dilute hydrochloric acid (31). DMSO is sufficiently resistant to reduction to be used as a solvent for polarography with a useable potential range from $+0.3$ V anode potential to -2.8 V cathode potential (both relative to calomel electrode using ammonium perchlorate electrolyte) (34).

DMSO is reduced by a number of organic functional groups. The reactions appear to involve sulfonium intermediates and offer selective synthetic oxidation procedures (35). Compounds such as phenacyl halides, benzyl halides, alkyl iodides, or alkyl esters of sulfonic acids react with DMSO at 100–120°C to give aldehydes and ketones commonly in 50–85% yields (36). The reaction is considered to involve initial formation of an alkoxydimethylsulfonium salt from which dimethyl sulfide is eliminated to give the product.

$$C_6H_5CH_2Cl + (CH_3)_2SO \longrightarrow (C_6H_5CH_2-O-S(CH_3)_2)^+Cl^- \longrightarrow$$

$$CH_3SCH_3 + HCl + C_6H_5C{=}O$$
$$\overset{|}{H}$$

A number of procedures have been developed for the selective oxidation of primary and secondary alcohols to the carbonyl compounds using DMSO at room temperature. The initiating step is the conversion of DMSO to a reactive intermediate by coordination with an electrophilic agent at the oxygen. In the Pfitzner-Moffatt procedure the reagent is dicyclohexylcarbodiimide. The following sequence was demonstrated for the reaction (37):

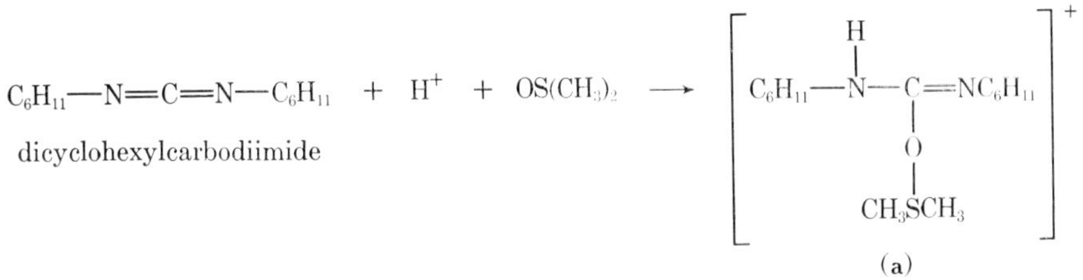

$$C_6H_{11}\!-\!N\!=\!C\!=\!N\!-\!C_6H_{11} \;+\; H^+ \;+\; OS(CH_3)_2 \;\longrightarrow\; \left[\begin{array}{c} H \\ | \\ C_6H_{11}\!-\!N\!-\!C\!=\!NC_6H_{11} \\ | \\ O \\ | \\ CH_3SCH_3 \end{array} \right]^+$$

dicyclohexylcarbodiimide

(a)

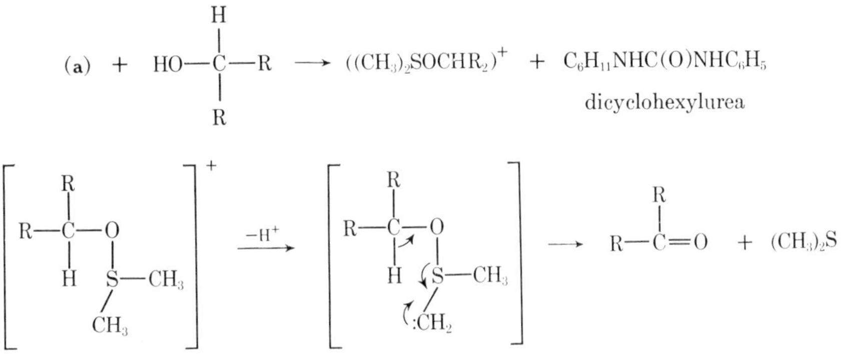

$$\textbf{(a)} \;+\; \begin{array}{c} H \\ | \\ HO\!-\!C\!-\!R \\ | \\ R \end{array} \;\longrightarrow\; ((CH_3)_2SOCHR_2)^+ \;+\; C_6H_{11}NHC(O)NHC_6H_5$$

dicyclohexylurea

$$\left[\begin{array}{c} R \\ | \\ R\!-\!C\!-\!O \\ | \quad | \\ H \quad S\!-\!CH_3 \\ \quad / \\ \quad CH_3 \end{array} \right]^+ \;\xrightarrow{-H^+}\; \left[\begin{array}{c} R \\ | \\ R\!-\!C\!-\!O \\ \nearrow | \\ H \;\;S\!-\!CH_3 \\ \quad :CH_2 \end{array} \right] \;\longrightarrow\; \begin{array}{c} R \\ | \\ R\!-\!C\!=\!O \end{array} \;+\; (CH_3)_2S$$

Because of the reaction path the reaction is selective and the procedure can be used to oxidize hydroxyl groups in molecules containing carbon–carbon double bonds and in sensitive alkaloids. The initial adduct, (a), also undergoes analogous reaction with a number of nucleophiles other than alcohols to displace the dicyclohexylurea (38): Phenols yield *o*- or *p*-thiomethoxymethyl derivatives and other products; active methylene compounds give sulfonium ylides; oximes react at the nitrogen to give thiomethoxymethyl nitrones or at the oxygen to give *O*-thiomethoxymethyl oximes; carboxylic acids give the thiomethoxymethyl esters; and primary carboxylic amides or sulfonamides give the corresponding *S*,*S*-dimethyl sulfilimines (38).

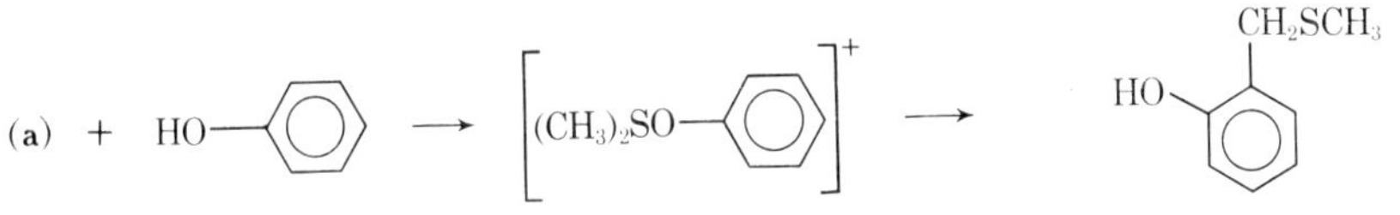

$$\textbf{(a)} \;+\; HO\!-\!\bigcirc \;\longrightarrow\; \left[(CH_3)_2SO\!-\!\bigcirc \right]^+ \;\longrightarrow\; HO\!-\!\bigcirc^{CH_2SCH_3}$$

o-thiomethoxymethylphenol

$$\textbf{(a)} \;+\; HON\!=\!C(C_6H_5)_2 \;\longrightarrow\; CH_3SCH_2N(O)\!=\!C(C_6H_5)_2 \;+\; CH_3SCH_2ON\!=\!C(C_6H_5)_2$$

N-thiomethoxymethyl-
α,α-diphenylnitrone

O-(thiomethoxymethyl)-
benzophenone oxime

$$\textbf{(a)} \;+\; C_6H_5COOH \;\longrightarrow\; C_6H_5COOCH_2SCH_3$$

thiomethoxymethyl benzoate

$$\textbf{(a)} \;+\; C_6H_5CONH_2 \;\longrightarrow\; C_6H_5C(O)NS(CH_3)_2$$

N-benzoyl-*S*,*S*-dimethylsulfilimine

Acetic anhydride (39), phosphorus pentoxide (40), and the pyridine–sulfur trioxide complex (41) also react with DMSO to form labile intermediates which usually react in a pattern similar to that of the dicyclohexylcarbodiimide–DMSO reagent. Anhydrous DMSO containing boron trifluoride will oxide epoxides to hydroxyketones (42). Dry DMSO oxidized 1-aroylaziridines to benzamide derivatives upon sufficient heating (43).

Pummerer-Type Reactions. Sulfoxides containing at least one hydrogen on the α-carbon atom undergo reactions in which the oxygen is removed and an α hydrogen replaced. Pummerer treated ethyl phenylsulfinylacetate with acetic anhydride at 70°C to obtain 70% of the α-acetoxy sulfide (10):

$$C_6H_5SOCH_2COOEt \rightarrow C_6H_5SCH(OAc)COOEt$$

| ethyl phenyl- | ethyl acetoxy- |
| sulfinylacetate | (phenylthio)acetate |

The reaction is quite general and usually gives 75–90% yields (44). The reaction is synthetically useful for preparing the initial α-substituted sulfides and also for obtaining either a carbonyl compound by hydrolysis of the initial hemithioacetal derivative or an unsaturated derivative by elimination of the introduced acid. The ketone synthesis was used in the ninhydrin synthesis of Becker and Russell. Diethyl phthalate was condensed with DMSO and sodium ethoxide to give the indanedione sulfoxide, which was rearranged and hydrolyzed to ninhydrin (2,2-dihydroxy-1,3-indanedione) in high overall yield (45):

| diethyl phthalate | 2-(methylsulfinyl)-1,3-indanedione | 2,2-dihydroxy-1,3-indanedione |

The elimination to produce α,β-unsaturated sulfides often occurs when the initially obtained α-acetoxy compound is heated. Thus heating thiochroman oxide in acetic anhydride gave 77% of 1-benzothiopyran (47,48):

| thiochroman-1-oxide | 1-benzothiopyran |

Present evidence suggests that the Pummerer reactions occur by the initial formation of an acyloxysulfonium salt which further reacts by α-proton abstraction to form an ylide. Such ylides, compounds in which a carbanion is adjacent to a hetero atom carrying positive charge, appear frequently as reaction intermediates or products from sulfoxides. In the Pummerer reaction the ylide undergoes nucleophilic attack at the α carbon to give the substituted derivative (49):

$$RS\overset{O}{\overset{\|}{-}}CH_2R' \xrightarrow{Ac_2O} \left[RS\overset{OAc}{\underset{CH_2R'}{\diagup}} \right]^+ \xrightarrow{OAc^-}$$

$$\left[RS\overset{\diagup OAc}{\underset{+\diagdown CHR}{}} \leftrightarrow RS\overset{=CHR}{\underset{OAc}{\diagdown}} \right] + HOAc \xrightarrow{OAc^-} R\!-\!S\!-\!CH(OAc)R'$$

Other reactions are possible for the intermediate ylide (47,48).

The Pummerer-type reactions are general for the sulfoxides capable of forming ylides as indicated. The initiating step is the formation of a covalent bond to the sulfoxide oxygen which weakens the sulfur–oxygen bond and also enhances proton removal to form the ylide. These sulfoxides react characteristically with organic or inorganic acid chlorides and sometimes even with HCl to give the α-chlorosulfides in good yield (26). However, in the presence of pyridine, nitrosyl chloride produces good yields of α-chlorosulfoxides which result from oxidation of the initially produced α-chlorosulfide (116). The oxidation of alcohols or halides by DMSO (see p. 322) proceeds through an alkoxydimethylsulfonium intermediate which is deprotonated to the ylide. In this oxidation the ylide collapses intramolecularly to give the aldehyde as indicated. However, rapid exchange of alkoxy groups and introduction of α-alkoxy groups have also been demonstrated for this intermediate (50) and can provide the dominant reaction path in some situations. The reactions mentioned above in which the dicyclohexylcarbodiimide adduct of DMSO leads to thiomethoxymethyl derivatives also illustrate this competitive path.

Carbon–Sulfur Cleavage. The carbon–sulfur bond is broken in a number of reactions. Attempts to form the DMSO anion by reacting DMSO with sodium result in cleavage and the gas evolved is methane (51):

$$CH_3\overset{O}{\overset{\|}{S}}CH_3 + 2\,Na \longrightarrow CH_3SONa + CH_3Na$$

$$CH_3Na + CH_3\overset{O}{\overset{\|}{S}}CH_3 \longrightarrow CH_4 + CH_3\overset{O}{\overset{\|}{S}}CH_2Na$$

Sulfoxides containing β-hydrogen atoms react with strongly basic systems such as potassium t-butoxide in DMSO by sulfenic acid elimination to produce olefins (52):

$$((CH_3)_3C)_2SO \xrightarrow[\substack{DMSO\\55°C}]{Bu^tOK} (CH_3)_2C{=}CH_2 + (CH_3)CSO^-$$

It has also been observed that sulfenic acid elimination can involve γ-hydrogen atoms to form cyclopropane derivatives and that γ-elimination was favored when DMSO was used as the reaction solvent (53):

$$C_6H_5CH_2CH(C_2H_5)CH_2SOCH_3 \xrightarrow[\substack{DMSO\\70°C}]{NaCH_2SOCH_3} C_6H_5CH\overset{\diagup CH_2}{\underset{\diagdown CH(C_2H_5)}{\Big|}} + CH_3SO^-$$

methyl 2-ethyl-3-phenylpropyl   1-ethyl-2-phenyl-
         sulfoxide   cyclopropane

Diphenyl sulfoxide is cleaved by carbanions such as the benzhydryl anion to give benzenesulfenate anion (54).

The "Dimsyl" Ion, Methylsulfinyl Carbanion, $(:CH_2SOCH_3)^-$. The activating influence of the sulfinyl group on α hydrogens is considerably less than that of a carbonyl group but still sufficient to give a pK_a of 33.5 for DMSO. Consequently strong bases such as sodium hydride or sodium amide react with DMSO to produce solutions of sodium methylsulfinyl carbanion (dimsyl ion) which have proved to be synthetically useful (55). The solutions also provide a strongly basic reagent for generating other carbanions. The dimsyl ion shows the expected nucleophilicity of carbanions and serves as a source of methylsulfinylmethyl groups (55). Thus, with alkyl halides or sulfonate esters, sulfoxides are obtained, carbonyl compounds yield β-hydroxysulfoxides, and esters give β-ketosulfoxides (55):

$$n\text{-}C_4H_9Br \;+\; (:CH_2SOCH_3)^- \rightarrow n\text{-}C_4H_9CH_2SOCH_3$$
methyl amyl sulfoxide

$$(C_6H_5)_2CO \;+\; (:CH_2SOCH_3)^- \rightarrow (C_6H_5)_2C(OH)CH_2SOCH_3$$
diphenyl methylsulfinyl-
methylmethanol

$$C_6H_5COOEt \;+\; (:CH_2SOCH_3)^- \rightarrow C_6H_5C(O)CH_2SOCH_3$$
phenyl methylsulfinyl-
methyl ketone

The dimsyl ion also adds to carbon–carbon double bonds, and when the mixture is heated for several hours the initial adduct eliminates methanesulfenic acid. The overall result is methylation and with compounds such as quinoline or isoquinoline, yields are nearly quantitative (56). The reaction sequence is as follows:

isoquinoline   H   CH_2SOCH_3   1-methylisoquinoline

Care is required in running these reactions because the decomposition of the intermediate sulfoxide (and also dimsyl sodium) during the heating in the strongly alkaline system is exothermic and also produces a precipitate which can interfere with heat removal. Explosions have been observed (8,57) which were not detonations but were due to a pressure buildup by an uncontrolled exotherm.

Sulfonium Compound Formation. Alkylating agents such as methyl iodide react with DMSO at the oxygen to produce the alkoxysulfonium salts. These are not very stable and upon continued heating either decompose to give carbonyl compounds or rearrange to the more stable trimethyloxosulfonium salt (59). Treatment of trimethyloxosulfonium iodide with dimsyl sodium produces solutions of dimethyloxosulfonium methylide (60). This reagent is an active methylenating agent converting carbonyls to epoxides, some olefins to cyclopropanes, and entering into a number of similar reactions (60).

$$(CH_3)_2SO \;+\; CH_3I \;\rightarrow\; ((CH_3)_2SOCH_3)^+I^- \;\rightarrow\; ((CH_3)_3SO)^+I^-$$
methoxydimethyl-   trimethyloxo-
sulfonium iodide   sulfonium iodide

$$((CH_3)_3SO)^+ I^- + NaCH_2SOCH_3 \longrightarrow (CH_3)_2\overset{\overset{\displaystyle O}{\|}}{S}{=}CH_2 + NaI + (CH_3)_2SO$$

dimethyloxosulfonium
methylide

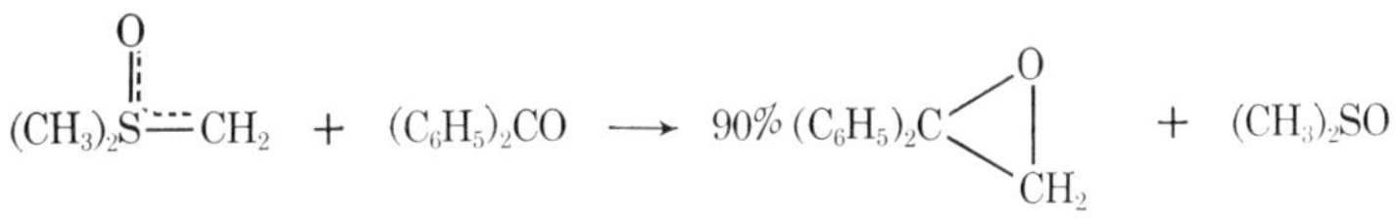

$$(CH_3)_2\overset{\overset{\displaystyle O}{\|}}{S}{=}CH_2 + (C_6H_5)_2CO \longrightarrow 90\% \; (C_6H_5)_2C\overset{O}{\underset{CH_2}{\diagdown}}\!\!\triangleleft + (CH_3)_2SO$$

2,2-diphenyloxirane

$$(CH_3)_2\overset{\overset{\displaystyle O}{\|}}{S}{=}CH_2 + C_6H_5CH{=}CHC(O)C_6H_5 \longrightarrow 95\% \; C_6H_5HC\overset{\overset{\displaystyle CH_2}{\triangle}}{\!-\!\!-\!\!-\!\!}CHC(O)C_6H_5$$

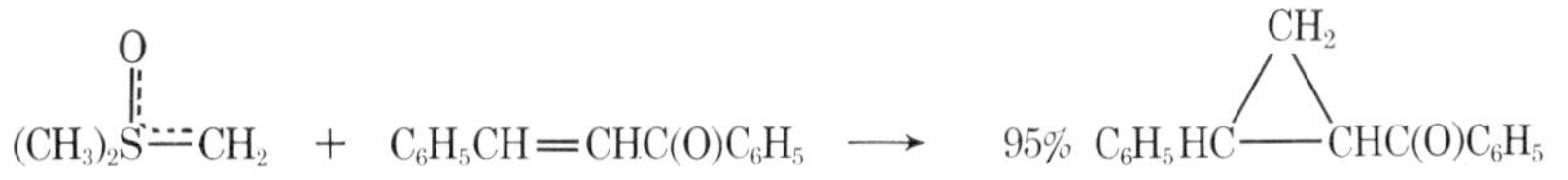

benzalacetophenone   1-phenyl-2-benzoylcyclopropane

Sulfoxides condense with reactive aromatic rings in the presence of catalysts such as thionyl chloride or hydrogen chloride to produce sulfonium salts. With phenol, or *m*- or *o*-cresols, and DMSO the corresponding 4-hydroxyphenyldimethylsulfonium chlorides are readily obtained at room temperature (61):

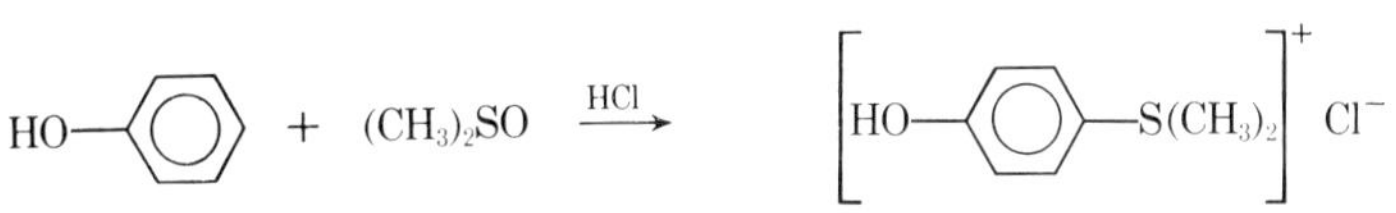

$$HO{-}\!\!\bigcirc\!\!{-} + (CH_3)_2SO \xrightarrow{\;HCl\;} \left[HO{-}\!\!\bigcirc\!\!{-}S(CH_3)_2 \right]^+ Cl^-$$

dimethyl(4-hydroxyphenyl)sulfonium
chloride

Diaryl sulfoxides react similarly to give triarylsulfonium salts. DMSO also reacts with aryl methyl ketones using anhydrous HCl as a catalyst to give sulfonium chlorides of the type: $(ArCOCH_2S(CH_3)_2)^+Cl^-$ (115).

Ylide Formation. In addition to the dimethyloxosulfonium methylide obtained by dehydrohalogenation of trimethyloxosulfonium iodide, DMSO gives stable ylides by condensation with compounds containing active methylene groups. DMSO reacts at room temperature with 5-bromo-2,2-dimethyl-1,3-dioxa-4,6-cyclohexanedione to give 80% of a very stable ylide (62):

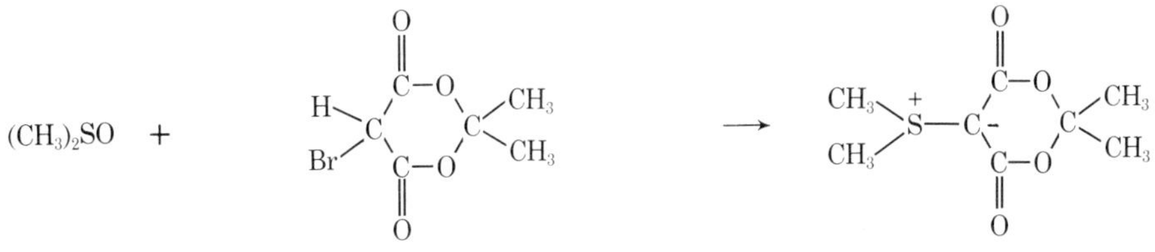

$(CH_3)_2SO$ +

5-bromo-2,2-dimethyl-1,3-dioxa-
4,6-cyclohexanedione

5-dimethylsulfuranylidene-
2,2-dimethyl-1,3-dioxa-
4,6-cyclohexanedione

The bromine is not necessary if a condensing agent such as acetic anhydride (62) or dicyclohexylcarbodiimide (63) is used. Barbituric acid gives 90% of the corresponding ylide upon reacting with acetic anhydride and DMSO at 120°C. Ylide yields of 40–93% result from the reaction of DMSO and dicyclohexylcarbodiimide with a broad spectrum of active methylene compounds including β-diketones, β-ketoesters, β-cyano-esters, β-diesters, α-dinitriles, β-ketoamides, and β-cyanophosphonates (63).

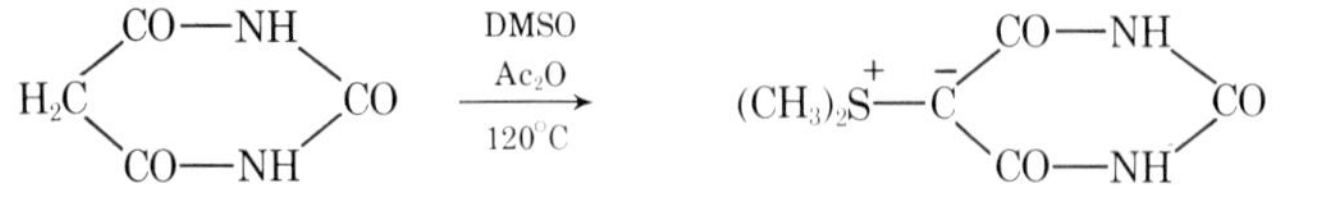

barbituric acid

5-dimethylsulfuranylidene-
2,4,6-trioxohexahydropyrimidine

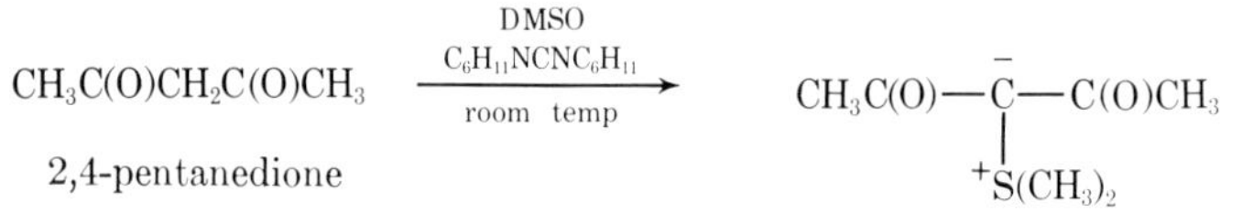

$CH_3C(O)CH_2C(O)CH_3$

2,4-pentanedione

3-dimethylsulfuranylidene-
2,4-pentanedione

The nominally similar reaction of DMSO with aryl sulfonamides using acetic anhydride or phosphorous pentoxide catalysts leads to approximately 65% yields of sulfilimines (64):

$$C_6H_5SO_2NH_2 + (CH_3)_2SO \xrightarrow{Ac_2O} C_6H_5SO_2N{=}S(CH_3)_2$$

benzenesulfonamide

S,S-dimethyl-*N*-
(phenylsulfonyl)sulfilimine

Sulfoxides are also converted to sulfilimines at room temperature in 60–80% yields in the following reaction (65):

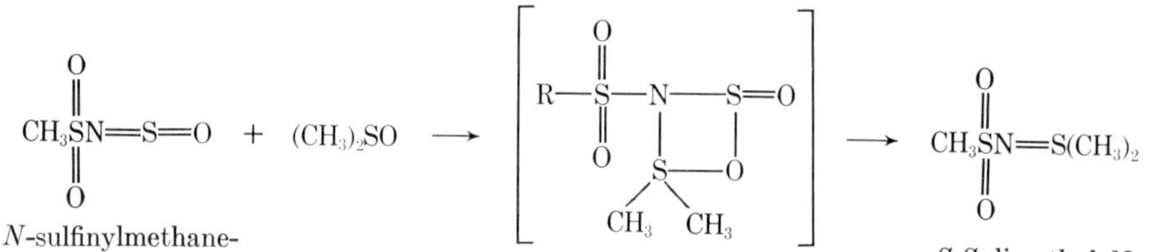

N-sulfinylmethane-
sulfonamide

S,S-dimethyl-*N*-
(methylsulfonyl)
sulfilimine

With hydrazoic acid DMSO gives 20–50% yields of *S,S*-dimethylsulfoximine, which is a distillable, somewhat basic liquid (58):

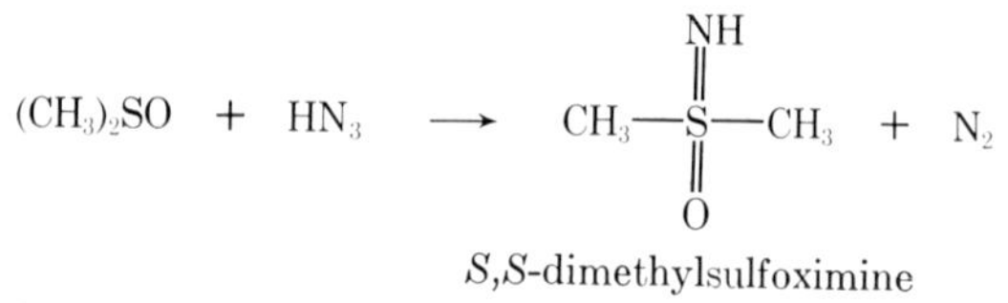

S,S-dimethylsulfoximine

Sulfonyl azides and some acyl azides react similarly, although they require catalysis. With heat or ultraviolet-radiation catalysis, 20–30% yields of the N-sulfonylsulfoximines are obtained (67):

$$C_6H_5SO_2N_3 \quad + \quad (CH_3)_2SO \quad \rightarrow \quad C_6H_5SO_2N{=}S(CH_3)_2{=}O$$
phenylsulfonylazide
S,S-dimethyl-N-(phenyl-
sulfonyl)sulfoximine

Using copper powder catalysis, quantitative yields result (68). Cyanogen chloride reacts at room temperature with a benzene solution of DMSO to give carbon dioxide and a product derived from two DMSO molecules (69).

$$2\,(CH_3)_2SO \quad + \quad ClCN \quad \longrightarrow \quad ((CH_3)_2S{=}\overset{..}{N}{-}\overset{+}{S}(CH_3)_2 \quad \longleftrightarrow \quad (CH_3)_2S{=}\overset{+}{N}{=}S(CH_3)_2)\ Cl^-$$
tetramethyldisulfurnitride chloride

Addition to Multiple Bonds. DMSO adds to very reactive unsaturated systems as a nucleophile through the oxygen. The addition to the methyl ester of acetylene dicarboxylic acid gave 81% of a thetin (**a**) and a smaller amount of a thetin (**b**) which contained two moles of the ester (70). The suggested reaction path involves an initial adduct which can react in either of two ways:

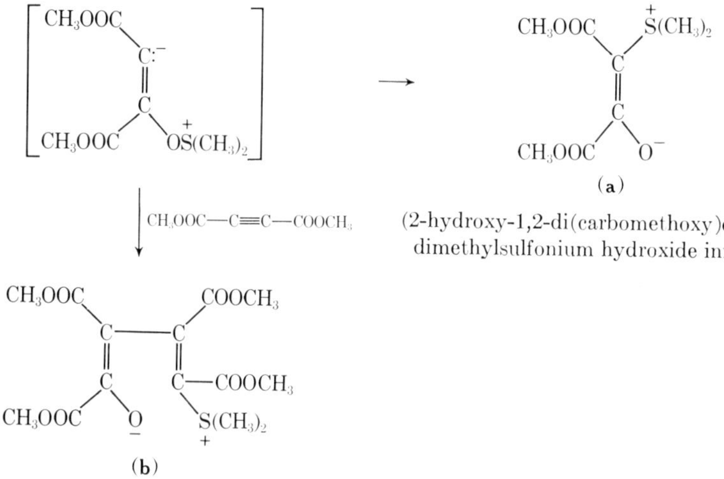

(a)

(2-hydroxy-1,2-di(carbomethoxy)ethenyl)-
dimethylsulfonium hydroxide inner salt

(b)

(4-hydroxy-1,2,3,4-tetra(carbomethoxy)-
1,3-butadienyl)dimethylsulfonium hydroxide
inner salt

Methyl propiolate reacts in the same pattern (71).

Thermal decomposition of benzenediazonium-2-carboxylate in DMSO at 50°C produces a benzyne intermediate which adds DMSO to give a thetin that decomposes to 2-(methylthio)phenol (72). Some salicylic acid is obtained by a different reaction path (72).

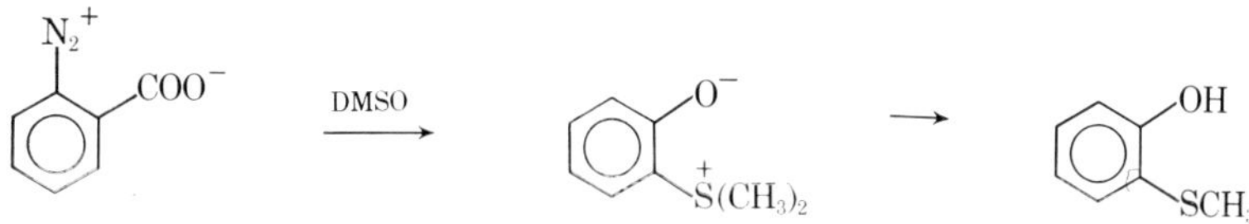

benzenediazonium-
2-carboxylate

2-hydroxyphenyldimethyl
sulfonium hydroxide inner salt

2-(methylthio)phenol

The addition of DMSO to cumulative bond systems occurs with acid catalysis and follows the pattern shown above for the DMSO adduct with dicyclohexylcarbodiimide. Similar reactions which give high yields from diphenylketene and N-(p-tolyl)-diphenylketeneimine also involve the initial addition of DMSO (73):

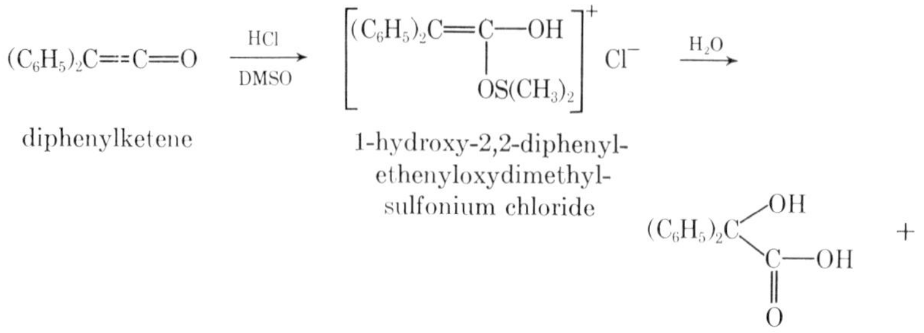

$$(C_6H_5)_2C{=}{=}C{=}O \xrightarrow[\text{DMSO}]{\text{HCl}} \left[\begin{array}{c} (C_6H_5)_2C{=}C{-}OH \\ | \\ OS(CH_3)_2 \end{array} \right]^{+} Cl^{-} \xrightarrow{H_2O}$$

diphenylketene   1-hydroxy-2,2-diphenyl-
ethenyloxydimethyl-
sulfonium chloride

benzilic acid

With the keteneimine the reaction path is similar, giving substituted acetamides in 71–91% yields when water or methanol is the other addend (73). It is interesting that the alcohol attacks the carbon in the ketene intermediates rather than the sulfur as in the dicyclohexylcarbodiimide intermediates.

The usual alkyl or aryl isocyanates are quite unreactive toward DMSO and reactions of these are favorably run in DMSO solution. However, DMSO reacts with isocyanates which have electron-withdrawing groups attached to the nitrogen. Acyl isocyanates react to give the sulfilimines (74):

benzoyl isocyanate

N-benzoyl-S,S-di-
methylsulfilimine

Sulfonyl diisocyanate and chlorosulfonyl isocyanate react rapidly with DMSO in acetonitrile solution to give the sulfilimines (75). p-Toluenesulfonyl isocyanate reacts with DMSO without diluent to give the sulfilimine in 87% yield.

Sulfoxide Complexes. The sulfoxides have a high dipole moment (approx 4) characteristic of the sulfinyl group and a basicity about the same as that of alcohols, and are strong hydrogen-bond acceptors. They would be expected, therefore, to solvate ions having electrophilic character, and a large number of DMSO complexes of metal ions have indeed been reported (76). The bonding to the metal is through the oxygen except for platinum(II), palladium(II), and rhodium(II) complexes where metal–sulfur bonds occur. The strength of the solvates is commonly about the same as that of the corresponding hydrate, and exchange of ligands is readily accomplished.

The strong tendency of the DMSO oxygen to act as a hydrogen-bond acceptor leads to a number of complexes. Chloroform forms both 1:1 and 1:2 complexes (77). Pyrrole (78) and phenol (79) give 1:1 complexes. In solutions of monosaccharides in DMSO the anomer with cis hydroxyls on the first and second carbons is stabilized in DMSO solution (80). Complexes with organic molecules which do not involve hydrogen bonding also occur, such as the 1:1 complex of DMSO and 4-chlorobenzonitrile (81) and other nitriles (82). Strong 1:1 complexes are formed with nitrogen tetroxide

(83) and sulfur trioxide (84). Complexes of the charge transfer type are known for cyanogen iodide (85), tetracyanoethylene (86), and oxygen (87).

Occurrence and Synthesis

A variety of sulfoxides have been isolated from natural sources, such as allyl vinyl sulfoxide from garlic oil (88) and bis-2-hydroxyethyl sulfoxide from adrenal cortex, where it occurs as fatty esters (89). Homologous methylsulfinylalkyl isocyanates, having the formula $CH_3SO(CH_2)_nNCS$, where $n = 3, 4, 5, 8, 9,$ or 10, have been isolated from mustard oils of a number of species, where they occur as glucosides (90). Two methylsulfinyl amino acids have also been reported: methionine sulfoxide from cockroaches (91), and the sulfoxide of S-methylcysteine. The latter is the dominant sulfur-containing amino acid in turnips and may account in part for their characteristic odor (92).

The sulfoxides are most frequently synthesized by oxidation of the sulfides (95). A broad group of oxidizing agents may be used and since the oxidation to the sulfoxide is considerably more rapid than further oxidation to the sulfone a proper choice of reagent quantity and conditions leads to good sulfoxide yields. Hydrogen peroxide in stoichiometric amounts can give 75–90% sulfoxide yields (93). Nitrogen tetroxide in a solvent such as carbon tetrachloride at temperatures below about 0°C selectively gives the sulfoxide in yields of up to 95% (94). Oxidations with sodium metaperiodate in aqueous or water–methanol solutions at ice-bath temperatures give high sulfoxide yields without sulfone formation (96). Oxidation with tertiary amine–bromine complexes in aqueous acetic acid gives yields above 70% and has been suggested as a convenient procedure for preparing ^{18}O-labeled sulfoxides when $H_2^{18}O$–acetic acid is used as the reaction solvent (97). A number of sulfoxide synthesis procedures are known in which the appropriate fragments are joined to give the product as shown in the following equations:

$$ArS\overset{O}{-}Cl \; + \; RMgX \; \longrightarrow \; ArS\overset{O}{-}R \; + \; MgXCl$$

$$ROS\overset{O}{-}OR \; + \; 2R'MgX \; \longrightarrow \; R'S\overset{O}{-}R' \; + \; 2\,ROMgX$$

$$ArS\overset{O}{-}OR \; + \; R'MgX \; \longrightarrow \; ArS\overset{O}{-}R' \; + \; ROMgX$$

$$2\,CH_3OC_6H_5 \; + \; SO_2 \; \xrightarrow{AlCl_3} \; CH_3OC_6H_5\overset{O}{\underset{\parallel}{S}}-C_6H_5OCH_3$$

$$2\,C_6H_6 \; + \; SOCl_2 \; \xrightarrow{AlCl_3} \; C_6H_5\overset{O}{\underset{\parallel}{S}}-C_6H_5$$

The reaction of Grignard reagents with sulfinyl chlorides (98) has the disadvantage of giving sulfides and sulfones as by-products. The reaction with sulfite esters (99) gives 40–70% yields, and with arylsulfinate esters the yields are around 55% (98). Optically active sulfoxides are synthesized in good yield by reacting optically active sulfinate esters with Grignard reagents (100). Sulfoxides are obtained in greater than 50% yield by alkylating sodium sulfenates with alkyl bromides (101). Diaryl sulfoxides are also obtained by Friedel-Crafts syntheses such as the reaction of anisole with sulfur dioxide and aluminum chloride to obtain 40% of bis(4-methoxyphenyl) sulfoxide (102) or the reaction of benzene with thionyl chloride and aluminum chloride to obtain 51% of diphenyl sulfoxide (103).

Manufacture

DMSO is manufactured from dimethyl sulfide (DMS), which is obtained either by processing spent liquors from the kraft pulping process or by the reaction of methanol or dimethyl ether with hydrogen sulfide. In the kraft pulping process the spent liquors are normally concentrated to about 50% solids and burned to recover inorganic chemicals and heat values. The lignin in the liquor contains aromatic methoxyl groups which are cleaved by sulfide ions to produce dimethyl sulfide when the concentrated liquor is processed in a reactor at 200–250°C (47). See Vol. 16, p. 712. The synthesis from methanol is accomplished by a vapor-phase reaction over a catalyst at temperatures above 300°C.

DMS has been oxidized to DMSO by several procedures. In pilot-plant quantities the oxidation has been accomplished with nitric acid, but this route is now supplanted by oxidation using nitrogen dioxide or oxygen containing minor amounts of nitrogen dioxide. The oxidation using nitrogen dioxide is diagrammed in Figure 1 (104). In the process dimethyl sulfide is oxidized with a DMSO solution of nitrogen dioxide in a reactor at 40–50°C. The reactor contents pass into a zone at 100°C, where excess dimethyl sulfide is sparged from the crude DMSO with nitrogen. The crude DMSO is then neutralized and distilled. The flow of nitrogen dioxide into the reactor is kept insufficient to oxidize all of the dimethyl sulfide so that all the nitrogen dioxide is converted to nitric oxide, which is quite insoluble in DMSO and escapes in the exit-gas stream. This gas stream passes through a heat exchanger to condense some of the dimethyl sulfide, which is recycled to the reactor. The gases then are conducted to a second reactor where an excess of nitrogen dioxide converts all of the remaining sulfide

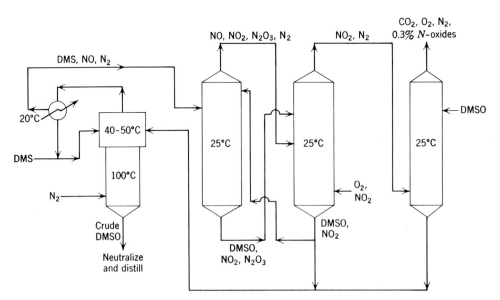

Fig. 1. DMSO manufacture using nitrogen tetroxide.

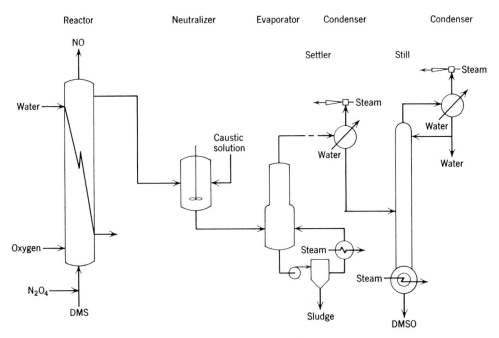

Fig. 2. DMSO manufacture using oxygen.

to the sulfoxide. The gases from this reactor contain substantially no organic matter and are oxidized with oxygen in a third reactor to regenerate the nitrogen dioxide. The gases finally pass through a DMSO scrubber to remove nitrogen dioxide prior to venting to the atmosphere.

Processes using oxygen with nitrogen oxides as catalysts have been operated commercially using either vapor-phase or liquid-phase reactors. The vapor-phase reactors require particularly close control because of the wide explosive limit of dimethyl sulfide in oxygen (1–83.5 vol %); the currently operating plants use liquid-phase reactions.

Table 3. Typical Industrial DMSO Analysis

Property	Analysis
assay, %	99.9
water content, %	0.1
color	water-white
other impurities	negligible
nonvolatiles	negligible

Figure 2 shows a schematic diagram for the liquid-phase process. A small amount of nitric oxide gas is diluted with air and vented. The product stream from the reactor is neutralized with aqueous caustic, vacuum evaporated, and the DMSO finally dried in a distillation column to obtain the product.

DMSO is produced in commercial quantities in the United States by Crown Zellerbach Corporation. The 1969 sales price was $0.33/lb in bulk quantities. Typical properties of industrial DMSO are given in Table 3 (18).

Health and Safety

Dimethyl sulfoxide is a relatively stable solvent of low toxicity. The LD_{50} for single-dose oral administration to rats is about 40,000 mg/kg. DMSO by itself presents less hazard than many chemicals and solvents commonly used in industry. However, DMSO has the ability to penetrate through the skin and may carry with it certain chemicals with which it is combined under certain conditions. Normal protective measures should be followed in the laboratory. In handling larger quantities where splashing and accidental contact may occur, protective clothing is recommended, including suitable gloves and eye protectants. Butyl-rubber gloves have been found to be more suitable than other types of material for resisting penetration by DMSO solutions.

DMSO has received considerable attention as a useful agent in medicine (105). Compositions containing it are marketed in Germany and Austria as prescription items for analgesic uses. In the United States in 1969, the possible efficacy of DMSO as a drug is being examined under jurisdiction of the Food and Drug Administration, but this agency has not released DMSO for drug use other than for approved clinical investigation.

Uses

Polymerization and Spinning Solvent. DMSO is used as a solvent for the polymerization of acrylonitrile. The low incidence of transfer from the growing chain to DMSO leads to high molecular weights. Fibers are spun from the resulting DMSO solution (106). A number of other polymers also can be spun from DMSO solution (107). DMSO is a particularly good solvent for polysaccharides and other polymers having active hydrogens or polar groups.

Extraction Solvent. DMSO is immiscible with alkanes but a good solvent for most unsaturated and polar compounds. It is used in the Institut Français du Pétrole (IFP) process for extracting aromatic hydrocarbons from refinery streams (109). It also is used in the analytical procedure for determining polynuclear hydrocarbons in food additives of petroleum origin (110).

Solvent for Displacement Reactions. DMSO as the most polar of the common aprotic solvents is a favored solvent for displacement reactions because of its high dielectric constant and because anions are less solvated in it (112). Rates for these reactions are sometimes a thousand times faster in DMSO than in alcohols. Suitable nucleophiles include acetylide ion, alkoxide ion, hydroxide ion, azide ion, carbanions, carboxylate ions, cyanide ion, halide ions, mercaptide ions, phenoxide ions, nitrite ions, and thiocyanate ions (26). Rates of displacements by amides or amines are also greater in DMSO than in alcohol or aqueous solutions (26).

Solvent for Base-Catalyzed Reactions. The ability of hydroxide or alkoxide ions to remove protons is enhanced by using DMSO as the solvent instead of water or alcohols (113). The equilibrium change is also accompanied by a rate increase of 10^5 or more (114). Thus, reactions in which proton removal is rate determining are favorably accomplished in DMSO. These include olefin isomerizations, elimination reactions to produce olefins, racemizations, and H–D exchange reactions.

Solvent for Electrolytic Reactions. DMSO has been widely used as a solvent for polarographic studies and permits use of a more negative cathode potential than in water. In DMSO cations can be successfully reduced to form metals that would react with water. Thus, cerium can be electrodeposited from cerium chloride in DMSO (111). Lithium also does not react with DMSO (101).

Pesticide Solvent. The majority of organic fungicides, insecticides, and herbicides are soluble in DMSO, including such difficultly soluble materials as the substituted ureas and carbonyl, 1-naphthyl N-methylcarbamate (108).

Dye Solvent. DMSO is a good solvent for a number of dyes and is used to prepare concentrates of them.

Cleanup Solvent. DMSO is used to remove urethan polymers and other difficultly soluble materials from processing equipment.

Bibliography

"Sulfoxides" in *ECT* 1st ed., Vol. 13, pp. 353–357, by E. G. Rietz, Chicago City Colleges, Wright Branch.

1. D. C. Wood and S. W. Jacob, *Quarterly Reports on Sulfur Chemistry* **3** (2), 159–162 (1967).
2. A. B. Burg in N. Kharasch, ed., *Organic Sulfur Compounds*, Vol. 1, Pergamon Press, Inc., New York, 1961, pp. 30–41.
3. H. L. Schlafer and W. Schaffernicht, *Angew. Chem.* **72**, 618–626 (1960).
4. W. Strecker and R. Spitaler, *Chem. Ber.* **59**, 1754–1775 (1926).
5. N. Grabowsky, *Ann.* **175**, 348, 351 (1875).
6. H. Mohler, *Helv. Chim. Acta* **20**, 1188–1192 (1937).
7. F. Krafft and R. E. Lyons, *Chem. Ber.* **29**, 435–442 (1896).
8. D. Barnard, J. M. Fabian, and H. P. Koch, *J. Chem. Soc.* **1949**, 2442–2454.
9. H. Bohme, H. Fischer, and R. Frank, *Ann.* **563**, 54–72 (1949).
10. R. Pummerer, *Chem. Ber.* **43**, 1401–1412 (1910).
11. H. Rheinboldt and E. Giesbrecht, *J. Am. Chem. Soc.* **68**, 2671–2673 (1946).
12. R. A. Hovermale and P. G. Sears, *J. Phys. Chem.* **60**, 1579–1580 (1956).
13. T. Skerlak and B. Ninkov, *Glasnik Drustva Hemicara Technol. S.R. Bosne Hercegovine* **11**, 43–47 (1962); *Chem. Abstr.* **61**, 2496d, (1964).
14. H. Mackle and P. A. G. O'Hare, *Trans. Faraday Soc.* **58**, 1912–1915 (1962).
15. H. L. Clever and E. F. Westrum, Jr., private communication.
16. T. B. Douglas, *J. Am. Chem. Soc.* **68**, 1072–1076 (1946).
17. E. E. Weaver and W. Keim, *Proc. Indiana Acad. Sci.* **70**, 123–131 (1961).
18. *Dimethyl Sulfoxide*, Tech. Bull., Crown Zellerbach Corp., Chemical Products Division, Camas, Washington, 1966.
19. R. Garnsey and J. E. Prue, *Trans. Faraday Soc.* **64**, 1206–1209 (1968).
20. E. C. Steiner and J. M. Gilbert, *J. Am. Chem. Soc.* **87**, 382–384 (1965).
21. P. Haake, D. A. Tysse, S. R. Alpha, J. Kleckner, and R. D. Cook, *Quart. Rev. Sulfur Chem.* **3** (2), 105–106 (1968).
22. R. G. LeBel and D. A. I. Goring, *J. Chem. Engr. Data* **7**, 100–101 (1962).
23. T. B. Douglas, *J. Am. Chem. Soc.* **70**, 2001–2002 (1948).
24. P. G. Sears, W. D. Siegfried, and D. E. Sands, *J. Chem. Engr. Data* **9**, 261–263 (1964).
25. V. J. Traynelis and W. L. Hergenrother, *J. Org. Chem.* **29**, 221–222 (1964).
26. *Dimethyl Sulfoxide as a Reaction Solvent*, Crown Zellerbach Corp., Chemical Products Division, Camas, Washington, 1968.
27. U.S. Pat. 3,304,331 (Feb. 14,1967), C. Di Santo (to Stauffer Chemical Company).
28. V. Zitko and C. T. Bishop, *Can. J. Chem.* **44**, 1749–1756 (1966).
29. B. H. Klanderman, *J. Org. Chem.* **31**, 2618–2620 (1966).
30. E. Glynn, *Analyst* **72**, 248–250 (1947).
31. R. R. Legault and K. Groves, *Anal. Chem.* **29**, 1495–1496 (1957).
32. K. Stelmach, *Chem. Anal. (Warsaw)* **11**, 627–628 (1966).
33. L. H. Krull and M. Friedman, *J. Chromatog.* **26**, 336–338 (1967).
34. J. L. Jones and H. A. Fritsche, Jr., *J. Electroanal. Chem.* **12**, 334–340 (1966).
35. W. W. Epstein and F. W. Sweat, *Chem. Rev.* **67**, 247–259 (1966).
36. N. Kornblum, W. J. Jones, and G. J. Anderson, *J. Am. Chem. Soc.* **81**, 4113–4114 (1959).
37. M. G. Burdon and J. G. Moffatt, *J. Am. Chem. Soc.* **89**, 4725–4735 (1967).

38. J. G. Moffatt, *Quart. Rept. Sulfur Chem.* **3**(2), 95–98 (1968).

39. N. F. Blau and C. M. Buess, *J. Org. Chem.* **28**, 3349–3351 (1963).

40. K. Onodera, S. Hirano, N. Kashimura, and T. Yajima, *Tetrahedron Letters* **1965,** 4327–4331.

41. J. R. Parikh and W. V. E. Doering, *J. Am. Chem. Soc.* **89**, 5505–5507 (1967).

42. T. Cohen and T. Tsuji, *J. Org. Chem.* **26**, 1681 (1961).

43. H. W. Heine and T. Newton, *Tetrahedron Letters* **1967,** 1859–1860.

44. L. Horner and P. Kaiser, *Ann.* **631**, 198 (1960).

45. H. D. Becker and G. A. Russell, *J. Org. Chem.* **28**, 1896 (1963).

46. W. M. Hearon, W. S. MacGregor, and D. W. Goheen, *Tappi* **45** (1), 28A, 30A, 34A, 36A (1962).

47. W. E. Parham and R. Koncos, *J. Am. Chem. Soc.* **83**, 4034–4038 (1961).

48. M. D. Bharsar and W. E. Parham, *J. Org. Chem.* **28**, 2686–2690 (1963).

49. C. R. Johnson and W. G. Phillips, *Tetrahedron Letters* **1965,** 2101.

50. C. R. Johnson and W. G. Phillips, *J. Org. Chem.* **32**, 1926–1931 (1967).

51. D. E. O'Connor and W. I. Lyness, *J. Org. Chem.* **30**, 1620–1623 (1965).

52. J. E. Hofmann, T. J. Wallace, P. A. Argabright, and A. Shriesheim, *Chem. Ind.* (*London*) **1963,** 1243–1244.

53. R. Baker and M. J. Spillett, *Chem. Commun.* **1966,** 757–758.

54. A. Schonberg and A. Stephenson, *Chem. Ber.* **66**, 250–252 (1933).

55. E. J. Corey and M. Chaykovsky, *J. Am. Chem. Soc.* **87**, 1345–1353 (1965).

56. G. A. Russell and S. A. Wiener, *J. Org. Chem.* **31**, 248–251 (1966).

57. F. A. French, *Chem. Eng. News* **44**, 48 (1966).

58. J. K. Whitehead and H. R. Bentley, *J. Chem. Soc.* **1952,** 1572–1574.

59. S. G. Smith and S. Winstein, *Tetrahedron* **3**, 317, 319 (1958).

60. E. J. Corey and M. Chaykovsky, *J. Am. Chem. Soc.* **87**, 1353–1364 (1965).

61. E. Goethals and P. deRatzitzky, *Bull. Soc. Chim. Belg.* **73**, 546–559 (1964).

62. A. Hochrainer and F. Wessely, *Monatsh. Chem.* **97**, 1–9 (1966).

63. A. F. Cook and J. G. Moffatt, *J. Am. Chem. Soc.* **90**, 740–746 (1968).

64. D. S. Tarbell and C. Weaver, *J. Am. Chem. Soc.* **63**, 2939–2942 (1941).

65. G. Schulz and G. Kresze, *Angew. Chem. Intern. Ed.* **2**, 736 (1963).

66. J. K. Whitehead and H. R. Bentley, *J. Chem. Soc.* **1952,** 1572–1574.

67. L. Horner and A. Christmann, *Chem. Ber.* **96**, 388–398 (1963).

68. H. Kwart and A. A. Khan, *J. Am. Chem. Soc.* **89**, 1951–1953 (1967).

69. P. Y. Blanc, *Experientia* **21**, 308–310 (1965).

70. E. Winterfeldt, *Chem. Ber.* **98**, 1581–1587 (1965).

71. E. Winterfeldt, *Angew. Chem. Intern. Ed.* **5**, 741 (1966).

72. M. Kise, T. Asari, N. Rurudawa, and S. Oae, *Chem. Ind.* (*London*) **1967,** 276–277; H. H. Szmant and S. Vasquez, *Chem. Ind.* (*London*) **1967,** 1000.

73. I. Lillien, *J. Org. Chem.* **29**, 1631–1632 (1964).

74. R. Neidlein and W. Haussmann, *Angew. Chem. Intern. Ed.* **4**, 708–709 (1965).

75. R. Appel and H. Rittersbacher, *Chem. Ber.* **97**, 852–856 (1964).

76. *Dimethyl Sulfoxide: Reaction Medium and Reactant,* Crown Zellerbach Corp., Chemical Products Division, Camas, Washington, 1962.

77. A. L. McClellan, S. W. Nicksic, and J. C. Guffy, *J. Mol. Spectry.* **11**, 340–348 (1963).

78. D. M. Porter and W. S. Brey, Jr., *J. Phys. Chem.* **72**, 650–654 (1968).

79. R. S. Drago, B. Wayland, and R. L. Carlson, *J. Am. Chem. Soc.* **85**, 3125–3128 (1963).

80. V. S. R. Rao and J. F. Foster, *J. Phys. Chem.* **69**, 656–657 (1965).

81. C. D. Ritchie and A. Pratt, *J. Phys. Chem.* **67**, 2498–2499 (1963).

82. C. D. Ritchie and A. Pratt, *J. Am. Chem. Soc.* **86**, 1571–1576 (1964).

83. C. C. Addison and J. C. Sheldon, *J. Chem. Soc.* **1956,** 2705–2708.

84. R. L. Whistler, A. H. King, G. Ruffini, and F. A. Lucas, *Arch. Biochem. Biophys.* **121**, 358–363 (1967).

85. E. Augdahl and P. Klaeboe, *Acta Chem. Scand.* **18**, 18–26 (1964).

86. F. E. Stewart, M. Eisner, and W. R. Carper, *J. Chem. Phys.* **44**, 2866–2872 (1966).

87. T. Sato, H. Inoue, and K. Hata, *Bull. Chem. Soc. Japan* **40**, 1502–1506 (1967).

88. A. Zwergal, *Pharmazie* **7**, 245–256 (1952); *Chem. Abstr.* **47**, 3224d, (1953).

89. T. Reichstein and A. Goldschneidt, *Helv. Chim. Acta* **19**, 401–402 (1936).

90. A. Kjaer, *Fortschr. Chem. Org. Naturstoff.* **18**, 122–176 (1960); *Chem. Abstr.* **55**, 12465b, (1961).

91. S. M. Henry, R. J. Block, and T. W. Cook, *Advan. Chem. Ser.* **44**, 85–95 (1964).

92. C. J. Morris and J. F. Thompson, *J. Am. Chem. Soc.* **78**, 1605–1608 (1955).

93. D. Jerchel, L. Dippelhofer, and D. Renner, *Chem. Ber.* **87**, 947–955 (1954).

94. L. Horner and F. Hubenett, *Ann.* **579**, 193–203 (1953).

95. E. E. Reid, *Organic Chemistry of Bivalent Sulfur*, Vol. 2, Chemical Publishing Co., New York, 1960, pp. 64–66.

96. N. J. Leonard and C. R. Johnson, *J. Org. Chem.* **27**, 282–284 (1962).

97. S. Oae, Y. Ohmishi, S. Kozuka, and W. Tagaki, *Bull. Chem. Soc. Japan* **39**, 364 (1966).

98. H. Hepworth and H. W. Clapham, *J. Chem. Soc.* **119**, 1188–1198 (1921).

99. H. Gilman, J. Robinson, and N. J. Beaber, *J. Am. Chem. Soc.* **48**, 2715–2718 (1926).

100. K. K. Andersen, W. Gaffield, N. E. Papanikolaow, J. W. Foley, and R. I. Perkins, *J. Am. Chem. Soc.* **86**, 5637–5646 (1964).

101. D. E. O'Connor and W. I. Lyness, *J. Org. Chem.* **30**, 1620–1623 (1965).

102. E. Knoevenagel and J. Kenner, *Chem. Ber.* **41**, 3315–3322 (1908).

103. R. L. Shriner, H. C. Struck, and W. J. Jorison, *J. Am. Chem. Soc.* **52**, 2060–2069 (1930).

104. H. Pruckner, *Erdöl und Kohle—Erdgas Petrochemie* **16**, 188–192 (1963).

105. "Biological Actions of Dimethyl Sulfoxide," *Ann. N.Y. Acad. Sci.* **141**, Art. 1, 1–671 (March 15, 1967).

106. E. F. T. White and M. J. Zissell, *J. Polymer Sci.* [A] **1**, 2189–2191 (1963).

107. D. Martin, A. Weise, and H.-J. Niclas, *Angew. Chem. Intern. Ed.* **6**, 318–334 (1967).

108. *DMSO as a Component in Agricultural Chemicals*, Crown Zellerbach Corp., Chemical Products Division, Camas, Washington, 1968.

109. B. Choffe, C. Raimbault, F. P. Navarre, and M. Lucas, *Hydrocarbon Process. Petrol. Refiner* **45**, 188–192 (1966).

110. E. O. Haenni, J. W. Howard, and F. L. Joe, Jr., *J. Assoc. Offic. Agr. Chemists* **45**, 67–70 (1962).

111. J. A. Porter, *AEC Research & Development Rept. DP-389* (July 1959).

112. A. J. Parker, *Advan. Org. Chem.* **5**, 1–46 (1965).

113. R. Stewart, *Quart. Rept. Sulfur Chem.* **3** (2), 99–104 (1968).

114. D. J. Cram and L. Gosser, *J. Am. Chem. Soc.* **86**, 5457–5465 (1964).

115. E. Goethals and P. deRadzitzky, *Bull. Soc. Chim. Belg.* **73**, 579–584 (1964).

116. R. N. Loeppky and D. C. Chang, *Abstracts Papers 155th Natl. ACS Meeting, San Francisco, P16*, April 1–5, 1968.

W. S. MacGregor
Crown Zellerbach Corporation

SULFUR

Sulfur, S, a nonmetallic element, at. wt 32.066, at. no. 16, is in group VI, series 3, of the periodic table. Although the ACS-approved spelling is sulfur, the spelling sulphur is used in England, and is frequently used commercially in the U.S. In massive elemental form it is also sometimes referred to as brimstone. Sulfur, one of the most versatile and essential elements on this planet, is the chemical industry's most widely used raw material. In fact, its applications are so widespread that sulfur consumption is often used as a measure of a nation's economic activity. See also Sulfur compounds; Sulfuric acid; and numerous other articles dealing with sulfur-containing compounds.

Although sulfur has been known and used by man for thousands of years, it was considered a strange (rare) earth until Lavoisier proved that it is an element. Prehistoric man used sulfur to color his cave drawings, and supposedly ate sulfur as a spring tonic to purify his blood. Man discovered that the strange yellow rock would burn with an ethereal blue flame, and give off a sharp, pungent odor. This seemingly supernatural power led him to believe that burning sulfur could be used to ward off evil spirits. Historians report that some twenty centuries before the birth of Christ, high priests used these same qualities of sulfur to add mysticism to temple sacrifices and purification rites. These early practices were probably the origin of the notion that hellfire is fueled by brimstone. About 1600 BC, the Egyptians discovered that sulfur dioxide from the burning of sulfur had more practical value as a bleach for cotton and linen. Egyptian artists at the same time used various sulfur compounds as color additives for paints. In 1000 BC, Homer reports that Odysseus burned sulfur in his home—presumably as a fumigant—after he had slain his wife's suitors. One of the contemporary uses was developed about 500 BC, when the Chinese invented gunpowder, using sulfur as an ingredient. The historian Pliny writes that in AD 50, sulfur possessed fourteen medical virtues. During the Middle Ages, the alchemists were concerned with sulfur, for they believed that its absence, or presence in varying quantities, accounted for the difference between base metals, and the noble metals, silver and gold.

The first commercial sulfur in modern times was produced in Sicily early in the fifteenth century. Competition for control of the Sicilian sulfur deposits was generated in 1735 by commercial development of a process to manufacture sulfuric acid from sulfur. Sulfur production became Sicily's chief industry. A French company, realizing the potential value of sulfur, gained control of the Sicilian deposits in 1839 and subsequently raised the price of sulfur from $25 to $75 per ton. Other countries, particularly England and the United States, undertook the development of their own sources. They soon learned that sulfuric acid could be made from sulfur dioxide derived from the roasting of iron pyrites. As a result, Sicilian sulfur production received a setback from which it never recovered.

The discovery of pyrites as a source of sulfur did not, however, free America from foreign domination in the sulfur market. More than a quarter-century passed before sulfur was discovered in the United States. Oil prospectors drilling in Calcasieu Parish, Louisiana, in 1867 found the first sulfur deposit in the United States; this deposit was associated with a salt dome.

The Calcasieu Parish deposit was buried hundreds of feet beneath successive strata of clay, gravel, and quicksand which contained hydrogen sulfide. During the 1870s and 1880s, various unsuccessful attempts were made to sink mine shafts down to the sulfur formation. This idea was finally abandoned after five men were asphyxiated by hydrogen sulfide. In the 1890s, Dr. Herman Frasch, who had previously developed a process for removing sulfur from crude oil, became interested in the Louisiana sulfur deposit. Dr. Frasch realized that the usual rock-mining processes could not be used to recover the sulfur from this deposit economically enough to compete with Sicilian sulfur. He conceived the idea of melting the sulfur underground by injecting super-heated water into the formation, and then lifting the sulfur to the surface with a sucker-rod pump. Dr. Frasch proceeded with his scheme and, in December 1894, pumped the first flow of molten sulfur from the Calcasieu Parish deposit. Eight years later, after a succession of setbacks, the Frasch process was established as a commercial success.

Later, other salt dome sulfur deposits discovered in the Gulf Coast states were successfully mined by the Frasch process, and this eventually made the U.S. the major producer of sulfur in the world. Sulfur is available from many sources throughout the world. The U.S., Mexico, and Poland are just some of the sources of elemental sulfur produced by the Frasch process. Elemental sulfur recovered from hydrogen sulfide, the by-product from the desulfurization of natural gas, crude petroleum, and coal, has become a very large resource and is growing rapidly. Other sources include metal sulfides (such as pyrites), sulfate minerals (such as gypsum), elemental sulfur in volcanic deposits, and more recently, sulfur compounds in the vast tar sands (qv) of Canada.

Properties

Allotropy. Sulfur appears in a number of different allotropic modifications, that is, in various molecular aggregations which differ in solubility, specific gravity, crystalline form, etc. Like many other substances, sulfur also exhibits dynamic allotropy, ie, the various allotropes exist together in equilibrium in definite proportions, depending on the temperature and pressure. The formulas for the molecules of various allotropes range from S_1 to S_n, where n is a very large but unidentified number ($n > 10^6$). The particular allotropes that may be present in a given sample of sulfur depend to a large extent upon its previous thermal history, the amount and type of foreign substances present, and the length of time that has been allowed for equilibrium to be attained.

In the solid and liquid states the principal allotropes have been designated traditionally as S_λ, S_μ, and S_π. Of these, only S_λ is stable in the solid state. Upon solidification of molten sulfur S_π rapidly changes into S_μ, which in turn is converted into S_λ, although at a much slower rate. The molecular structure of S_π has been determined to be that of an octatomic sulfur chain (1). The symbol S_μ designates longer, polymerized chains of elemental sulfur. S_λ is perhaps the most characteristic molecular form of sulfur, namely that of a crown-shaped octatomic sulfur ring designated in more recent literature as S_8^R (2). The allotropes differ in their solubility in carbon disulfide. S_π and S_λ are soluble in carbon disulfide, while S_μ does not dissolve readily in this solvent.

Sulfur crystallizes in at least two distinct systems, the rhombic and the monoclinic. Rhombic sulfur, S_α, is stable at atmospheric pressures up to 95.5°C, where transition to monoclinic sulfur, S_β, takes place. Monoclinic sulfur is then stable up to its natural melting point of 114.5°C. The basic molecular unit of both of these crystalline forms of sulfur is the octatomic sulfur ring, S_8^R.

Other forms of solid sulfur include hexatomic sulfur, as well as numerous modifications of catenapolysulfur (3).

The molecular constitution of liquid sulfur undergoes significant and reversible changes with temperature variations. These changes are evidenced by the characteristic temperature dependence of the physical properties of sulfur. A wealth of experi-

Table 1. Physical Constants of Sulfur

	Ideal	*Natural*
freezing point of solid phase, °C		
rhombic, S_α	112.8	110.2
monoclinic, S_β	119.3	114.5
boiling point, °C (9)		444.6
density of solid phase, at 20°C, g/ml		
rhombic		2.07
monoclinic		1.96
amorphous		1.92
density of liquid, g/ml		
125°C		1.7988
130°C		1.7947
140°C		1.7865
150°C		1.7784
density of vapor at 444.6°C and 1 atm, g/l		3.64
n_D^{110}		1.929
vapor pressure (p = mm Hg, T = °K)		
rhombic (20–80°C) (10)	$\log p = 11.664 - 5166/T$	
monoclinic (96–116°C) (11)	$\log p = 11.364 - 5082/T$	
liquid (120–325°C) (9)	$\log p = 14.7 - 0.0062238T - 5405.1/T$	
(325–550°C)	$\log p = 7.43287 - 3268.2/T$	
surface tension, dyn/cm (12)		
120°C		60.83
150°C		57.67
critical temperature, °C		1040
critical pressure, atm		116
critical volume, ml/g		2.48
specific heat, cal/(g-mole)(°K)		
rhombic (24.9–95.5°C)	$C_p = 3.58 + 6.24 \times 10^{-3}T$	
monoclinic (-4.5–118.9°C)	$C_p = 3.56 + 6.96 \times 10^{-3}T$	
liquid (S_λ) (118.9–114.9°C)	$C_p = 5.4 + 5 \times 10^{-3}T$	
gas (S) (25–1727°C)	$C_p = 5.43 - 0.26 \times 10^{-3}T - 0.27 \times 10^5 T^{-2}$	
gas (S_2) (25–1727°C)	$C_p = 8.54 + 0.28 \times 10^{-3}T - 0.79 \times 10^5 T^{-2}$	

mental information is available on this subject. In most studies of liquid sulfur some abnormal changes in its physical properties are observed at about 160°C. For example, the viscosity of purified sulfur at 120°C is about 11 cP, drops to a minimum of 6.7 cP at about 157°C, and then begins to rise. Between 159 and 160°C the viscosity of liquid sulfur rises very sharply, increasing to 30 cP at 160°C and reaching a maximum of about 93,000 cP at 187°C. Above this temperature, the viscosity gradually drops off again to about 2000 cP at 306°C. A qualitative explanation of these viscosity changes in terms of the allotropy of sulfur implies that below 159°C sulfur consists mainly of S_8 rings, and a normal viscosity decrease with rising temperature is observed. The sudden increase in the viscosity of sulfur above 159°C is attributed to the formation of polymeric sulfur chain molecules. Then, as the temperature rises further, the concentration of polymeric sulfur continues to increase, but the opposing effect of decreasing chain length due to thermal sulfur–sulfur bond scission causes a gradual decrease in viscosity in the temperature range between 187°C and the boiling point of sulfur. The chemical equilibria between the various molecular forms in molten sulfur have been extensively investigated (2,4,5).

Table 1 (*continued*)

	Ideal	*Natural*
heat of transformation (rhombic to monoclinic) at 95.5°C, cal/g		2.687
heat of fusion, cal/g		
112.8°C (S (rhombic) → S_λ (liquid))		11.9
118.9°C (S (monoclinic) → S_λ (liquid))		9.2
thermal expansion of rhombic sulfur (linear)		
0–13°C		4.567×10^{-5}
13–50°C		7.433×10^{-5}
50–78°C		8.633×10^{-5}
78–97°C		20.67×10^{-5}
97–110°C		103.2×10^{-5}

latent heat of vaporization, cal/g (9)

	L^a	L^b
200°C	73.7	
300°C	69.1	
400°C	68.4	66.4
420°C	68.7	66.0
440°C	69.3	65.6
460°C	70.0	65.2

electrical resistivity, ohm-cm (13)		
20°C		1.9×10^{17}
110°C		4.8×10^{12}
400°C		8.3×10^{6}
magnetic susceptibility, cgs units (13)		
rhombic at 18°C		0.49×10^{6}
monoclinic at 112°C		0.49×10^{6}
liquid at 220°C		0.49×10^{6}
standard electrode potential, S/S^{2-}, approx (13)		0.5

[a] Including heat of dissociation to S_2 present in vapor.
[b] Minus heat of dissociation to S_2 present in vapor.

The molecular composition of sulfur vapor is a complex function of temperature and pressure. Vapor pressure measurements have been interpreted in terms of an equilibrium between several molecular species (6,7). Mass spectrometric data obtained on sulfur vapor indicate the presence of all possible S_n molecules from S_2 to S_8 and of negligible concentrations of S_9 and S_{10} (8). In general, octatomic sulfur is the predominant molecular constituent of sulfur vapor at low temperatures, but the equilibrium shifts toward smaller molecular species with increasing temperature and decreasing pressure.

Physical Constants. The physical constants of sulfur are presented in Table 1. Two freezing points are given for each of the two crystalline modifications. When the liquid phase consists solely of octatomic sulfur rings, the temperatures at which the various modifications are formed are called the "ideal" freezing points. The temperatures at which the crystalline forms are in equilibrium with liquid sulfur containing equilibrium amounts of S_π and S_μ are called "natural" freezing points.

Chemical Properties. There are four stable isotopes of sulfur, ^{32}S, ^{33}S, ^{34}S, and ^{36}S, comprising 95.1, 0.74, 4.2, and 0.016%, respectively. The relative abundance of the various isotopes has been found to vary slightly, depending on the source of the sulfur; the ratio of ^{32}S to ^{34}S ranges from 21.61 to 22.60. Three radioactive isotopes of masses 31, 35, and 37 have been generated artificially. The normal orbital electron structure is of the arrangement (2), (2,6), (2,4) (ref. 14). Sulfur has valences of $2-, 2+, 3+, 4+,$ and $6+$.

Sulfur falls between oxygen and selenium in its group, and resembles oxygen in its chemical reactions with most of the elements. An element closely related to sulfur is selenium, which has a similar group of valences and analogous allotropy. Sulfur is between phosphorus and chlorine horizontally, and its properties are, in general, those to be expected from its position in the periodic table. An exception is that its melting point is higher than would be expected, probably because of its complex molecular structure (14).

Sulfur is insoluble in water, but is soluble to varying degrees in many organic solvents, such as carbon disulfide, benzene, warm aniline, and warm carbon tetrachloride, and also in liquid ammonia. Carbon disulfide is the mostcom monly used solvent for sulfur.

Sulfur combines directly and usually energetically with almost all of the elements; exceptions include gold, platinum, iridium, and the inert gases (15). In the presence of oxygen or dry air, sulfur is very slowly oxidized to form sulfur dioxide. When burned in air, it forms predominantly sulfur dioxide, with small amounts of sulfur trioxide. In the presence of moist air, sulfurous and sulfuric acids are slowly generated.

Hydrochloric acid reacts with sulfur only in the presence of iron, forming hydrogen sulfide. Sulfur dioxide is formed when sulfur is heated with concentrated sulfuric acid at 200°C. Dilute nitric acid up to 40% concentration has little effect, but sulfur is oxidized by concentrated nitric acid in the presence of bromine with a strongly exothermic reaction (15).

Sulfur combines directly with hydrogen at 150–200°C to form hydrogen sulfide. Molten sulfur reacts with hydrogen sulfide to form hydrogen polysulfides. At red heat, sulfur and carbon unite to form carbon disulfide; this is a commercially important reaction. In aqueous solutions of alkali carbonates and alkali and alkaline earth hydroxides, sulfur reacts to form sulfides, polysulfides, thiosulfates, and sulfites.

At normal temperatures, sulfur unites readily with copper, silver, and mercury, and vigorously with sodium, potassium, calcium, strontium, and barium to form sulfides. Iron, chromium, tungsten, nickel, and cobalt react much less readily. In a finely divided state zinc, tin, iron, and aluminum react with sulfur on heating (15).

Various sulfides of the halogens are formed by direct combination of sulfur with fluorine, bromine, and chlorine. No evident reaction occurs with iodine; instead the elements remain as components of a complex mixture. Mixtures of sulfur and potassium chlorate or sulfur and powdered zinc are highly explosive.

Sulfur enters into numerous organic reactions. When dissolved in amines, chemical interaction between sulfur and the solvent is evidenced by the formation of colored species ranging from deep yellow to orange and green. Many organic reactions involving sulfur are commercially significant. Sulfur is important in phases of the processes for the manufacture of lubricants, plastics, pharmaceuticals, dyes, and rubber goods.

Sulfur itself is not considered to be corrosive to the usual construction materials. Dry, molten sulfur is handled satisfactorily in mild steel or cast-iron equipment. Acid-generating impurities, however, which may be introduced in handling and storage, create corrosive conditions. The exposure of sulfur to moisture and air causes the formation of acids which attack a number of metals. To combat such corrosion difficulties, protective coatings of organic compounds, cement, or sprayed resistant metals are often applied to exposed steel surfaces, including pipe and equipment used in handling liquid sulfur, and to structural members which come in contact with solid sulfur. Also practical in some applications is the use of resistant metal alloys, particularly of the aluminum and stainless steel groups. Neutralization of the generated acids by the addition of basic chemicals is sometimes employed.

Analysis

Elemental sulfur in either its ore or its refined state can generally be recognized by its characteristic yellow color or by its generation of sulfur dioxide when it is burned in air. Its presence in an elemental state or in a compound can be detected by heating the material with sodium carbonate and rubbing the resulting fused product on a wet piece of silver metal. A black discoloration of the silver indicates the presence of sulfur. This test is quite sensitive. Several other methods for detecting small amounts of elemental sulfur have been developed (16).

Quantitatively, sulfur in a free or combined state is generally determined by oxidizing it to a soluble sulfate (by fusion with an alkali carbonate if necessary) and precipitating it as insoluble barium sulfate. Oxidation can be effected with such agents as concentrated or fuming nitric acid, bromine, sodium peroxide, potassium nitrate, or potassium chlorate. Free sulfur is normally determined by solution in carbon disulfide, the latter being distilled from the extract.

Generally, crude sulfur contains small percentages of carbonaceous matter. The amount of this impurity is usually determined by combustion, which requires exacting technique. The carbonaceous matter is oxidized to carbon dioxide and water; the carbon dioxide is subsequently absorbed (17). Automated, onstream determination of organic impurities in molten sulfur has been accomplished by continuous infrared photometry (18).

The moisture content of crude sulfur is determined by the differential weight of a known sample before and after drying at approx 110°C. Acid content is determined by volumetric titration with a standard base. Nonvolatile impurities, known as "ash," are determined by burning the sulfur from a known sample, and igniting the residue to remove the residual carbon and other volatiles.

Occurrence and Extraction

It is estimated that sulfur constitutes 0.1% of the earth's crust. The forms in which it is commonly found include elemental sulfur in deposits over salt domes, in volcanic deposits, and in deposits associated with calcite, gypsum, and anhydrite; combined sulfur in metal sulfide ores; combined sulfur in mineral sulfates; hydrogen sulfide contaminant in natural gas; organic contaminants in crude oil; pyritic and organic compounds in coal; and organic compounds in tar sands.

ELEMENTAL SULFUR

Salt Dome Sulfur Deposits. The sulfur deposits associated with the salt domes in the Gulf Coast regions of southern U.S. and Mexico are of primary economic importance because of their known and potential reserves, their productive capacity, and the unequaled purity of the product as mined. In 1968, the output from the salt domes of the U.S. and Mexico exceeded 9 million long tons.

Salt domes of the Gulf Coast are vertical structures, usually circular in outline with steeply dipping flanks, composed of coarsely crystalline halite (NaCl) interspersed with anhydrite ($CaSO_4$). During the late Triassic and early Jurassic periods a thick mother bed of salt, derived from evaporated sea water, was deposited several thousands of feet below the present surface of the Gulf Coast area. In subsequent geological ages the salt bed was covered by sedimentary deposits. In contrast to salt, which is but slightly compressible, the overlying sediment compacted until at lower depths it had a gravity greater than that of salt. The resultant gravity difference caused the salt to flow upward and to intrude the overlying sediment where some deformation existed to initiate the movement. The cap rock which surmounts the salt dome consists of anhydrite lying in contact with the salt, and gypsum ($CaSO_4.2H_2O$) derived from the anhydrite. As the salt plug rose through the overlying sediment, circulating ground water dissolved away salt and left the less soluble anhydrite crystals to be compacted into a dense anhydrite cap over the salt. Limestone in the form of fine-grained gray carbonate interspersed with vugs, seams, fissures, and cavities is frequently associated with the gypsum and anhydrite formations. It may be present as a stratum overlying these formations, as lenticular beds covering part of them, or as disseminated lenses and nodules included in the upper part of the cap rock. Figure 1 is a cross section of a typical salt dome.

The sulfur occurs as well-developed crystal aggregates in veins and vugs, or as disseminated particles in the porous limestone and gypsum section of the cap rock. Several theories are proposed for the occurrence of sulfur in salt domes. One theory suggests the formation of limestone and hydrogen sulfide from anhydrite in the presence of reducing agents. This reaction requires temperatures on the order of 1200°F, and, although oil or other hydrocarbons may be present to act as reducing agents, the temperature actually attained is not sufficient to support this theory of the origin of sulfur. In 1946, the presence of anaerobic, sulfate-reducing bacteria was discovered in cap rock; their ability to promote reaction at normal temperatures is now recognized as the more likely origin of sulfur. Anaerobic bacteria consume hydrocarbons as a source of energy, but combine sulfur (instead of oxygen) with the hydrogen. The hydrocarbon-fueled bacteria reduce anhydrite to hydrogen sulfide, calcium carbonate, and water. The hydrogen sulfide remains dissolved in the formation waters until precipitated as crystalline sulfur through various oxidation reactions, possibly initiated by oxygen and carbon dioxide dissolved in water percolating from the upper sediments.

Prospect drilling has proved the existence of 409 salt dome structures in the coastal and offshore continental shelf area of the Gulf of Mexico. In April 1968 there were twenty salt dome sulfur deposits being commercially mined by the Frasch process, two were being developed for operation, and eight formerly productive domes were no longer being mined. In the mid-1960s the demand for sulfur began to exceed the existing productive capacity. Increased sulfur prices encouraged the prospecting for new deposits and the reopening of six former producing domes considered to be uneconomical at the time they were abandoned. The reopened domes include Bryanmound and Nash in Texas, and Chacahoula in Louisiana, all formerly operated by Freeport Sulphur; Sulphur Dome in Louisiana, formerly operated by Union Sulphur; and Gulf Dome in Texas and Nopalapa Dome in Mexico, formerly operated and reactivated by Texas Gulf Sulphur. In 1968 Texas Gulf Sulphur opened the Bully

Camp Dome in Louisiana and planned to produce the Texistepec Dome in Mexico. Pan American Petroleum Corporation started operating the High Island Dome in Texas. Also in 1968, Jefferson Lake opened the Lake Hermitage Dome in Louisiana. The eight producing domes no longer being mined include Hoskins Mound, Damon, Clemens, and Palangana in Texas; Starks, Jefferson Island, and Bay Ste. Elaine in Louisiana; and San Cristobal in Mexico. The twenty producing domes in April 1968 were these:

In Texas

Bryanmound Dome	Hooker Chemical Co.
Fannett Dome	Texas Gulf Sulphur Co.
Gulf Dome	Texas Gulf Sulphur Co.
Long Point Dome	Jefferson Lake Sulphur Co.
Moss Bluff Dome	Texas Gulf Sulphur Co.
Nash Dome	Phelan Sulphur Co.
Newgulf (Boling Dome)	Texas Gulf Sulphur Co.
Orchard Dome	Duval Sulphur & Potash Co.
Spindletop Dome	Texas Gulf Sulphur Co.

In Louisiana

Caminada Dome	Freeport Sulphur Co.
Chacahoula Dome	John Mecom
Garden Island Bay Dome	Freeport Sulphur Co.
Grande Escaille Dome	Freeport Sulphur Co.
Grand Isle Dome	Freeport Sulphur Co.
Lake Hermitage Dome	Jefferson Lake Sulphur Co.
Lake Pelto Dome	Freeport Sulphur Co.
Sulphur Dome	Allied Chemical Co.

In Mexico

Amezquite Dome	Gulf Sulphur Co.
Jaltipan Dome	Pan American Sulphur Co.
Nopalapa Dome	Texas Gulf Sulphur Co.

Evaporite Basin Sulfur Deposits. Elemental sulfur ore occurs in another type of subsurface deposit which is similar to the salt dome structures in that the sulfur is associated with anhydrite or gypsum. These deposits are sedimentary and occur in huge evaporite basins. It is believed that the sulfur in these deposits, like that found in the Gulf Coast salt domes, was derived by hydrocarbon reduction of the sulfate materials, assisted by anaerobic bacteria to permit the reactions to occur at ordinary temperatures. The sulfur deposits of Sicily, Poland, the U.S.S.R., the western United States, and those more recently discovered in western Texas, fall into this category. Significant deposits of similar type ore exist in Iraq.

Of more significance than the mere existence of the deposits is the fact that mining techniques very similar to the Frasch salt dome mining systems have been applied successfully. These developments, particularly in Poland and in west Texas, have significantly contributed to the world reserves of low-cost sulfur. Hot-water mining of the Polish deposits was first begun in 1966 at Gryzbow. By 1968 the production level at Gryzbow and another deposit at Jeziorko exceeded one million tons/ year; a greater potential was indicated. Production of sulfur from the west Texas de-

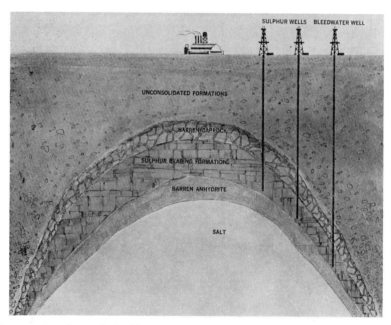

Fig. 1. Cross section of a typical sulfur-bearing salt dome. Courtesy Freeport Sulphur Company.

posits was proved early in 1968, and plans were immediately initiated for a major expansion.

Salt domes and similar structures are known in regions other than the U.S., Mexico, Poland, and the U.S.S.R., but sulfur deposits that are worthy of being developed have not been discovered in any of them.

The Frasch Process. The Frasch process is abundantly described in the literature. Economical operation of a salt dome or a subsurface sulfur deposit by the Frasch process requires a porous, sulfur-bearing limestone, a large and dependable supply of water, and a source of cheap fuel. A primary requisite for use of the process is a power plant where the necessary volume of hot water is produced, together with compressed air for pumping molten sulfur from the wells, and electric power for drilling, lighting, operating maintenance equipment, loading sulfur for shipment, and similar operations.

A typical setting of equipment in a sulfur well and the principles of mining are illustrated schematically in Figure 2. First, a hole is drilled to the bottom layer of salt dome cap rock using equipment of the same type as that used in oil fields. Three concentric pipes within a protective casing are placed in the hole. An 8-in. pipe inside an outer casing is sunk through the cap rock to the bottom of the sulfur deposit. Its lower end is perforated with small holes. Then a 4-in. pipe is lowered to within a short distance of the bottom. Last, and innermost, is a 1-in. pipe which is lowered more than halfway to the bottom of the well.

Water heated under pressure to about 325°F is pumped down the space between the 8-in. and 4-in. pipes and, during the initial heating period, also down the 4-in. pipe. The superheated water flows out the holes at the bottom into the porous sulfur-bearing formation (Fig. 2, picture 1). When the temperature of the sulfur-bearing formation exceeds the melting point of sulfur, the liquid sulfur, being approximately twice as

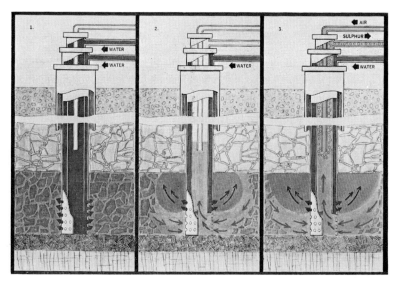

Fig. 2. The Frasch process. Courtesy Freeport Sulphur Company.

heavy as water, percolates downward through the porous limestone to form a pool at the bottom of the well. A heating period of 24 hr or longer is required to accumulate a liquid sulfur pool of sufficient size, and then pumping of hot water down the 4-in. pipe is stopped. Static pressure of the hot water pumped into the formation then forces liquid sulfur several hundred feet up the 4-in. pipe (Fig. 2, picture 2). Compressed air forced down the 1-in. pipe aerates and lightens the liquid sulfur so that it will rise to the surface (Fig. 2, picture 3). Injection of hot water is continued down the 8-in. pipe to maintain the sulfur melting process, and the compressed air volume is adjusted to equalize the sulfur pumping rate with the sulfur melting rate. If the pumping rate exceeds the melting rate, the sulfur pool will become depleted and the well will produce water. At this point the compressed air flow is stopped, and hot water is again injected into the 4-in. pipe until the liquid sulfur pool is re-established.

The sulfur-bearing cap rock, being an enclosed formation, is essentially the equivalent of a pressure vessel. Hot water, pumped into the formation to melt sulfur, must be withdrawn at approximately the same rate as it is put in, otherwise the pressure in the formation would increase to the point where further water injection would be impossible. Bleedwater wells to extract water from the formations usually are located on the flanks of the dome, away from the mining area where the water temperature is lowest.

On the surface, the liquid sulfur moves through steam-heated lines to a separator where the air is removed. Depending on the mine location, the liquid sulfur may be pumped either to storage bins to be solidified, to tanks for storage in the liquid state, to pipelines, or into thermally insulated barges for transport to a central shipping terminal.

Hot water needed for sulfur mining by the Frasch process is produced in power plants with water-heating capacities that range from 1 to 10 million gal/day. Until 1952, all mines used freshwater obtained from wells, rivers, or other surface sources. About one fourth of the volume of water is converted to steam in high-pressure boilers. Some of this steam is used to drive pumps, air compressors, and power generators.

The heat in the steam exhausted from these machines, as well as the heat in the boiler flue gases is used to preheat the mine water. Additional high-pressure steam is used in direct-contact heaters to raise the water temperature to that required for mining. Before being heated, the water is chemically treated to control corrosion and scale in the pipelines.

Not all deposits exist near a source of fresh water. The Bay Ste. Elaine Dome was a small deposit located near the Gulf of Mexico, some 30 miles from the nearest source of fresh water. A portable plant was installed on a large steel barge and used a new seawater heating process, the culmination of a long research program. In this plant, seawater was heated to 325°F for the purpose of mining sulfur. To overcome excessive corrosion, oxygen was removed from the raw sea water by bringing it in direct contact with combustion gases in a packed tower. Then, preheated by these gases, the seawater temperature was raised to 325°F in indirect heat exchangers, using steam furnished by high-pressure boilers. Condensate from the heat exchangers was recycled to the boilers, which limited the freshwater requirements to those lost in leaks and to other small losses in the system. Between November 1952 and December 1959, Bay Ste. Elaine produced over 1 million long tons of sulfur and established the feasibility of using seawater in the Frasch process. Since then, three more sulfur mines have been brought into operation using seawater for mining. The Grand Isle and Caminada mines are operated from mining platforms, both being located approx 7 miles off the Louisiana coast in the Gulf of Mexico. The Lake Pelto mine is producing sulfur with seawater, using the same barge-mounted power plant formerly used at Bay Ste. Elaine.

Sulfur produced from Gulf Coast deposits has an exceedingly low ash content (noncombustibles), and is free of arsenic, selenium, and tellurium. The principal contaminants are low concentrations of hydrocarbons and sulfohydrocarbons.

Volcanic Sulfur Deposits. Native or elemental sulfur is found in other types of surface or underground deposits throughout the world, but seldom in sufficient concentration or tonnage to attain commercial importance.

Sulfur of volcanic origin is found in many parts of the world. These deposits originated from gases emitted from active craters, solfataras, or hot springs which have deposited sulfur in the fractures of rock, by replacement in the rock itself, or in the sediments of lake beds. Volcanic deposits are usually found in tuffs, lava flows, and similar volcanic rocks, but many may also be found in sedimentary and intrusive formations. Scattered deposits of this type are found throughout the mountain ranges bordering the Pacific Ocean, particularly in Japan, the Philippine Islands, and Central and South America. Some volcanic deposits are worked profitably and are of importance to the countries in which they are found. The Japanese sulfur deposits are among this group because of their long productive history and the considerable tonnages that have been produced from them in modern times. Most volcanic deposits, however, are situated in isolated regions and at high elevations where production and transportation costs are prohibitive.

Extraction Methods. Sulfur is recovered from volcanic and other surface deposits by a number of different processes, including distillation, flotation, autoclaving, filtration, and solvent extraction, or a combination of several of these processes.

The Japanese sulfur deposits are reached by tunnel, and mining is done by the room-and-pillar, chamber-and-pillar with filling, and cut-and-fill systems. Sulfur is extracted from the ore by a distillation process, performed in rows of cast-iron pots, each containing about 400 lb of ore. Each row of pots is connected to a condensation chamber outside the furnace. A short length of pipe connects each pot with a condenser. Brick flues conduct combustion gases under the pots. Sulfur vapor flows from the pots to the condensation chamber where the liquid sulfur is collected. Japanese ore contains between 25 and 35% sulfur.

The sulfur deposits of Sicily have been worked since ancient times. Originally the sulfur was recovered by piling the ore in conical heaps, covering it with earth, and then igniting the pile. By this method 30–50% of the sulfur was burned to provide heat for melting the remainder of the sulfur in the ore. Less than 50% of the sulfur originally contained in the ore was recovered. About 1880 the first Gill furnace was installed. The original furnace had two chambers arranged so that the heat from burning ore in one chamber passed through ore in the other chamber to melt a considerable portion of the sulfur. When the sulfur in the first chamber was burned out, it was refilled and the partially extracted ore in the other chamber was then ignited. This method obtained better utilization of the heat of combustion. Later furnaces contained as many as six chambers, and achieved up to 80% sulfur recovery (19).

Extensive experimentation has lead to the granting of numerous patents on various thermal processes for extracting sulfur from ores, either as elemental sulfur or as SO_2, but very few of these processes have ever achieved commercial operation. The proposed processes use shaft furnaces, multiple-hearth furnaces, rotary kilns, and fluidized-bed roasters, in all of which the ground ore is heated with oxygenfree, hot combustion gases to distill elemental sulfur, or the sulfur in the ore is burned with air to yield SO_2 for sulfuric acid production. In 1953 a commercial plant was put into operation at the Yerrington, Nevada, copper mine for recovering the sulfur, as SO_2, from the Leviathan deposit of low-grade sulfur ore in Alpine County, California. The process consisted of four fluid-bed reactors in which the ore was roasted in air to produce SO_2 for a contact sulfuric acid plant (20). When elemental sulfur is the desired product, the use of oxygenfree, hot combustion gases in a fluidized bed has been proposed for distilling sulfur from the ore as a vapor, which is then condensed to liquid sulfur.

Various processes have been proposed and tested to recover sulfur from surface ore by solvent extraction. Carbon disulfide, being the best solvent for sulfur, has often been suggested for extraction of sulfur from ore. Some plants in Italy, Germany, South America, and the U.S. have used carbon disulfide for this purpose, but the cost of solvent, high solvent losses, and the flammability of carbon disulfide are detrimental to low operating costs. Many other solvents have been tried, including hot caustic solution, ammonium sulfide, xylene, kerosene, and various high-boiling oils. The sulfur can be recovered either by volatilizing the solvent, or by crystallization of the sulfur.

Various combinations of autoclaving, flotation, filtration, and centrifuging are used in some processes used to recover sulfur from ore. One such process, incorporating continuous autoclaving, flotation, and filtration, was first used commercially at a plant in Colombia (21). The ore is ground to −28 mesh and suspended in water to form a slurry of about 30% solids, which is pumped continuously to a three-compartment, agitated autoclave. In the autoclave, the slurry is heated and the sulfur melted by steam injection into the bottom of each compartment. Agitation causes the sulfur to coalesce into globules which separate from the gangue. Hot slurry from the autoclave flows into a quench pot to be cooled by water injection, and the sudden cooling solidifies the separated sulfur particles. The cooled slurry is throttled to atmospheric pressure onto a 28-mesh vibrating screen. The oversize material goes directly to a sulfur melter, while the underflow from the screen goes to a flotation circuit for separation of the smaller sulfur particles, yielding a concentrate of 90–95% sulfur, which then goes to the sulfur melter. Melted sulfur is pumped through a pressure filter for removal of gangue.

SULFIDE ORES

Occurrence. The metal sulfides, found scattered throughout most of the world, are an important source of sulfur. Some of the more important metal sulfides are pyrite, FeS_2; chalcopyrite, $CuFeS_2$; pyrrhotite, $Fe_{11}S_{12}$; sphalerite, ZnS; galena, PbS; arsenopyrite, $FeS_2.FeAs_2$; and pentlandite, $(Fe,Ni)_9S_8$. Sulfide deposits often occur in massive lenses, but may occur in tabular shape, in veins, or in a disseminated state. They may be of igneous, metamorphic, or sedimentary origin.

Pyrite (FeS_2) is the most abundant of the metal sulfides and in production presently ranks second to brimstone as a source of sulfur. For many years pyrite was the major source of sulfur, and for much of the first half of this century over 50% of the total world sulfur production was derived from pyrite. In 1967, sulfur recovered in various forms from pyrites represented approx 25% of the free-world total sulfur produced from all sources. Pyrite is usually obtained either as a run-of-mine or beneficiated ore from straight pyrite deposits, or recovered as by-product flotation concentrates in the processing of ores for their base-metal values. Pyrite reserves are distributed throughout the world, and deposits are being mined in approximately thirty countries. Possibly the largest pyrite reserves in the world are located in southern Spain, Portugal, and the U.S.S.R. Major deposits are also located in South America, Canada, Cyprus, Finland, Italy, Japan, Norway, South Africa, Sweden, U.S., and Yugoslavia. In 1966, the principal free-world producers were Japan, Spain, Italy, and Cyprus.

The Orkla Process. A process for producing sulfur from cuprous pyrite was developed by the Orkla Mining Company at Phamshan, Norway (22). The sulfur output, ranging from 80,000 to 100,000 tons annually, furnished an important part of European requirements until 1962, when the smelter was shut down. The process was also used on a much smaller scale by Mason and Barry, Ltd., in Portugal, and by Rio Tinto Co., Ltd., in Huelva, Spain (23). The smelter in Portugal was shut down in 1962, and the one in Spain in 1965. The process is probably being used in the U.S.S.R.

The Orkla process involves recovery of approx 80% of the sulfur content of a pyritic copper ore by direct smelting in the presence of a carbonaceous reducing agent. A charge consisting of ore, flux, and coke is introduced into a shaft furnace. In the upper part of the furnace the charge is heated to 900–1400°F, this temperature being sufficient to drive off one atom of sulfur that is feebly bound in the pyrite. In the bottom zone, the FeS is oxidized to ferrous oxide, and the sulfur dioxide formed in the bottom zone is reduced to sulfur vapor by coke in the middle section of the furnace. Smelting takes place in the bottom section, where the heat from the oxidation of FeS is sufficient to form copper matte and slag.

Other side reactions between carbon, oxygen, and sulfur occur in the furnace, so that the furnace exit gas contains sulfur vapor, sulfur dioxide, carbon dioxide, carbon oxysulfide, hydrogen sulfide, and carbon disulfide. The gas is passed through dust precipitators, and then through catalytic converters where the sulfur dioxide reacts with the other compounds, oxidizing the carbon and hydrogen to form sulfur vapor. The sulfur is condensed in waste-heat boilers and Cottrell precipitators.

This process is only good for pyrites containing copper, since copper is the only metal recovered. The iron is eliminated in the slag.

The Noranda Process. It has long been known that when pyrite is heated to about 1000°F in the absence of oxygen it will evolve about one half of its sulfur in elemental form. Noranda Mines, Ltd., and Battelle Memorial Institute developed a process based upon this property to recover elemental sulfur from pyrite (24). The first commercial plant was built at Welland, Ontario, in 1954. The reactions involved are approximated by

$$8 \, FeS_2 \rightarrow S_8 + 8 \, FeS \quad \text{and} \quad 3 \, FeS + 5 \, O_2 \rightarrow Fe_3O_4 + 3 \, SO_2$$

The heat of reaction of the second equation furnishes the heat necessary for the first. The SO_2-containing gases are used for the production of sulfuric acid.

Fine pyrite concentrates are pelletized with water and charged to the pallets of a Dwight-Lloyd sinter machine (see Vol. 3, p. 887). After ignition of the charge, the pellets pass through the wind boxes of the machine, where a mixture of air and recycle gas is blown down through the pallets. The recycle gas reduces temperature, thus preventing fusion of the iron oxide, and also helps vaporize the sulfur. The combustion, or oxidation zone, proceeds downward through the charge in a distinct wave, distilling elemental sulfur ahead of it. The gases from a pallet just entering the wind box may be at a temperature of about 600°F, whereas those from a pallet just before leaving may be about 1800°F, the average temperature of the gases when leaving the machine being about 1000°F. The gases, which contain SO_2, N_2, and sulfur vapor, are cooled in a waste-heat boiler to condense the sulfur vapors, after which part of them is recycled and part is sent to the sulfuric acid plant. The cinder leaving the machine contains residual sulfur and may be sintered on a separate machine to produce merchantable iron ore. About 40% of the sulfur in the pyrites may be recovered as elemental sulfur, and about 50% as sulfuric acid.

The Outokumpu Process. Outokumpu Oy, Finland's largest mining and metallurgical company, discovered a complex ore body at Pyhasalmi, Finland, containing pyrite, sphalerite, chalcopyrite, barite, and small amounts of pyrrhotite, arsenopyrite, and molybdenite. The ore can be beneficiated by flotation to obtain pyrite concentrate, as well as copper and zinc concentrates. A process was developed to treat the pyrite concentrate in a flash smelter for recovery of elemental sulfur and iron cinder. The commercial smelter located at Kokkola has been in operation since August 1962 (25).

Pyrite concentrate is dried in a rotary kiln, and elevated to the top of the flash smelter where it is blown into the smelter with hot combustion gases. These gases must be oxygenfree in order to prevent sulfur from burning to SO_2. The temperature inside the smelter is 2280°F, which is high enough to drive off one atom of sulfur per molecule of FeS_2, and almost all of the zinc and arsenic, in the form of vapors. The combustion gases, vapors, and molten particles pass downward through the vertical smelter shaft. The FeS, with a small amount of silica slag, collects as a molten pool of matte in a horizontal section below the smelter. The matte is continuously tapped from the furnace into a water bath, in order to produce granular particles suitable for feed to a fluidized-bed roaster. The hot gases and vapors from the smelter pass into a large radiant furnace with water tubes in the walls and collecting hoppers in the bottom.

The vapors are cooled by giving up radiant heat, and solidified zinc and iron sulfide–iron oxide particles drop into the hoppers. The gases, now cooled to 1300°F, pass into a conventional convection boiler where steam at 1000 psig is generated. The gases leave the convection boiler at 660°F and pass through four hot-gas electrostatic precipitators in series, where additional burnt-ore fines are collected.

The gas-stream temperature is raised to 755°F in an oil-fired reheater before the gases are led into a catalytic conversion unit. In the first catalyzer, the reactions involved are approximated by

$$4\,CO + 2\,SO_2 \rightarrow S_2 + 4\,CO_2 \text{ and } COS + H_2O \rightarrow H_2S + CO_2$$

Before entering the second catalyzer, the gases are cooled to 500°F in a waste-heat boiler to produce low-pressure steam. The gases now go into the second conversion unit where elemental sulfur vapor is produced by the catalytic reaction which combines H_2S and SO_2. Some condensation of sulfur occurs in the waste-heat boiler that follows the first catalyzer, but most of the condensed sulfur is recovered by spraying cooled liquid sulfur into the rising gas stream in a tower which follows the second catalyzer. The gas stream is finally cooled in a water-spray tower where a small additional amount of sulfur is separated from the gases. This sulfur is separated from the water in a settling tank and is then charged into the sulfur storage pit for remelting.

The pyrite concentrate contains a small amount of arsenic which is vaporized in the smelter and condenses with the sulfur. In order to remove the arsenic, the liquid sulfur is pumped through an autoclave where it is washed with preheated milk of lime. Sulfur is stored and shipped as liquid or is converted to solid pellets in an air-cooled prilling tower.

The granulated FeS from the flash smelter is fed to fluidized-bed roasters to produce SO_2 and coarse iron oxide calcine. Close control of the furnace temperature is most important for successful operation of the fluid-bed roaster. The FeS will not ignite at temperatures less than 1750°F, but above 1925°F the granular feed will fuse into a solid mass. Steam is generated in cooling coils located in the fluid bed.

The roaster gas, containing 8% SO_2, is cooled in a waste-heat boiler, then freed of dust in cyclones and hot-gas electrostatic precipitators before being piped to an adjacent sulfuric acid plant. Iron oxide calcine from the roaster is cooled in a water-jacketed Redler conveyor, and is sold locally as blast-furnace feed.

Approximately 47% of the sulfur available in the pyrite concentrate is recovered as elemental sulfur, and about 44% as SO_2 for sulfuric acid production.

BY-PRODUCT SULFUR

Occurrence. Sulfur has been recovered as a by-product from various process operations for years. Some old and some yet undeveloped processes will become more important as serious attention is focused on reducing atmospheric pollution caused by sulfur oxides. Sulfur recovered from sour natural gas is presently the largest source of "non-Frasch" elemental sulfur in the world. The major sour gas fields now producing sulfur are in Alberta Province, Canada, the Lacq field in France, and the gas fields of Texas. Very large production facilities for the recovery of sulfur from sour natural gas are in the planning or construction phase in western Canada, France, the U.S., northern Africa, and the Middle East.

Sulfur as a by-product from refining of sour crude oil has received added stimulus from more rigid air-pollution-control laws which have reduced the allowable sulfur

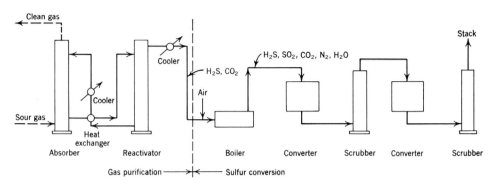

Fig. 3. Preparation of sulfur from hydrogen sulfide (generalized flowsheet).

content for fuel oil. New sulfur recovery plants in conjunction with oil refineries are planned or in construction in the U.S., Middle East, Japan, and Latin America. With existing and planned facilities to recover sulfur from natural gas and refinery gases, production of sulfur in the Middle East could reach one million tons by 1970. Another oil source of sulfur is that from the Athabasca tar sands in northern Alberta Province, Canada. A plant to recover 45,000 bbl/day of synthetic crude oil and 340 long tons/day of sulfur was put into operation in 1967. See Tar sands.

Another large, but as yet uneconomic, source of recovered sulfur is that associated with coal deposits throughout the world. Sulfur occurs in coal both as organic sulfur and pyritic sulfur. Pyritic sulfur is found in small, discrete particles within the coal, and could be removed by mechanical means. The organic sulfur is usually evenly distributed throughout the coal, and cannot be removed without changing the chemical property of the coal. When sulfur is not, or cannot be, economically removed from fuel oil or coal prior to combustion, removal of the sulfur oxides from the combustion flue gases will become necessary for compliance with stricter air-pollution-control laws. Sulfur dioxide emitted into the atmosphere in the U.S. from the combustion of coal and fuel oil is presently estimated at 22 million short tons/yr, or 11 million short tons of sulfur. Smelting of sulfide ores is another source of sulfur; it is usually recovered as sulfur dioxide and converted into sulfuric acid.

Sour Natural Gas and Refinery Gas. In sour natural gas the sulfur occurs as hydrogen sulfide. In petroleum refining, sulfur is reacted with hydrogen to form hydrogen sulfide. In either case, the hydrogen sulfide which is separated from the natural gas or petroleum is then converted to elemental sulfur. The hydrogen sulfide is usually removed in either case by absorption in a solution of an alkanolamine. On being heated, the pregnant amine solution gives up its hydrogen sulfide in concentrated form, along with any carbon dioxide absorbed from the natural gas or refinery stream.

The process for converting hydrogen sulfide into elemental sulfur, known as the Claus process, was developed in Germany about 1880, and through the years improvements in the original process have resulted in smaller and more efficient plants (see Fig. 3). The concentrated hydrogen sulfide is fired in a combustion chamber, and burned in such a manner that one third of the volume of hydrogen sulfide is converted to sulfur dioxide. The products of combustion are cooled, and then passed through a catalyst-packed converter, in which the following hydrogen sulfide and sulfur dioxide reaction occurs:

$$2\,H_2S + SO_2 \rightarrow 3\,S + 2\,H_2O$$

Sulfur vapor is condensed by countercurrent scrubbing with liquid sulfur in a packed tower. One catalytic converter will usually recover only 70–75% of the available sulfur. A second converter and scrubbing tower are normally used. With two converters about 90–93% sulfur recovery is possible. It may become necessary to add a third converter in the future, but only to meet stricter air-pollution-control laws. Production of sulfur by this general process grew from practically nothing in 1940 to approx 5 million tons/year by 1967.

There are other processes, of little importance in the U.S., for recovering hydrogen sulfide from industrial gases. They include the sodium phenolate and Thylox processes. In the U.S., the Thylox process is used primarily for the removal of hydrogen sulfide from coke-oven gas in steel mills. The Thylox process uses a neutral or slightly alkaline solution of sodium or ammonium thioarsenate to absorb hydrogen sulfide, as follows:

$$H_2S + Na_4As_2S_5O_2 \rightarrow Na_4As_2S_6O + H_2O$$

The pregnant solution is oxidized to release the sulfur and regenerate the solution:

$$Na_4As_2S_6O + \tfrac{1}{2} O_2 \rightarrow S + Na_4As_2S_5O_2$$

The sulfur can be recovered as a wet paste, a dry powder, or a cast crude sulfur. For more on these and other processes, see reference 26.

Pyritic Sulfur from Coal. Sulfur occurs in coal as pyritic sulfur, and in organic combinations as part of the coal itself. Pyritic sulfur occurs in varying quantities, and in particle sizes that range from microscopic to large lenses and balls. The coarser particles of pyrite can be removed from coal by gravity separation methods. These methods include heavy media, launders, jigs, upward current classifiers, and pneumatic tables. See Gravity concentration. However, only from 30 to 80% of the total sulfur content of coal is present as pyrite, so that gravity separation can never achieve complete sulfur removal.

Organic Sulfur from Coal. Organic sulfur cannot be removed from coal by mechanical separation. Removal requires decomposition or chemical processes which evolve the sulfur as hydrogen sulfide for conversion to elemental sulfur. Several of these processes are in the research pilot plant stage, but none has yet been used on a commercial scale.

One such extraction process under study for the Office of Coal Research produces a desulfurized coal char, and recovers hydrogen sulfide for conversion into elemental sulfur (27). In the process, coal char and hydrogen sulfide acceptor are contacted with hydrogen at 1600°F in a fluidized-bed reactor. The hydrogen sulfide acceptor is calcined dolomite, which readily reacts with the liberated hydrogen sulfide to maintain a low partial pressure of hydrogen sulfide in the bed, and improves the release of sulfur from the char. The hydrogen sulfide is picked up by the calcined dolomite:

$$(CaO.MgO) + H_2S \rightarrow (CaS.MgO) + H_2O$$

The char and the acceptor are separated, and the sulfur is desorbed from the acceptor at 800°F with steam and carbon dioxide:

$$(CaS.MgO) + CO_2 + H_2O \rightarrow (CaCO_3.MgO) + H_2S$$

The hydrogen sulfide can be recovered as elemental sulfur in a conventional catalytic converter unit, while the solid product is calcined at 1600°F to regenerate the acceptor.

Sulfur recovery from gaseous and liquid fuels is much easier than from a solid fuel, and for this reason most of the research is devoted to gasification or liquefaction of coal. One major oil company proposes a process for solvent extraction of coal followed by hydrogenation, by which it aims to produce a synthetic crude oil suitable as petroleum refinery feedstock (28). The hydrogenation step would convert the sulfur to hydrogen sulfide for recovery as elemental sulfur in a conventional catalytic conversion unit.

Another company is doing development work on a catalytic process to hydrogenate coal directly into liquid and gaseous products (28). The Institute of Gas Technology and the American Gas Association have for years been investigating a direct-hydrogenation process for the gasification of coal. This process would convert the coal into a pipeline quality gas, suitable for use in existing natural gas transmission facilities (28). Sulfur would then be recovered from the hydrogen sulfide formed by hydrogenation.

Sulfur from Flue Gases. The worldwide campaign against sulfur dioxide air pollution has accelerated the search for processes to remove SO_2 from power plant and other industrial stack gases. The chemistry for SO_2 recovery presents a variety of choices, and the 1958 review prepared by the U.S. Bureau of Mines is still a valuable reference (29). Of the many systems under study, four are considered as first-generation processes for cleaning gases: (1) sorption of SO_2 on active metal oxides with regeneration to produce sulfur; (2) catalytic oxidation of SO_2 to produce sulfuric acid; (3) sorption of SO_2 on char with regeneration to produce concentrated SO_2; and (4) reaction of dolomite or limestone with SO_2 by direct injection into the combustion chamber.

Alkalized Alumina Process. This process involves the absorption of sulfur dioxide with "alkalized alumina," a coprecipitate of sodium and aluminum oxides (30). Flue gas is fed to a reactor where SO_2 and SO_3 are absorbed by the alkalized alumina in free fall or in a fluidized bed. The spent absorbent is heated to 1200°F and treated with producer gas. The SO_2 reacts with H_2 and CO to produce H_2S, CO_2, and water vapor. Sulfur is recovered from the H_2S in a conventional catalytic conversion unit.

Catalytic Oxidation Process. This process is actually carried out in a modified contact sulfuric acid plant. The first experimental unit was installed at a power plant in eastern Pennsylvania (30). Flue gas, at 850°F, is passed through an electrostatic precipitator for fly ash removal, and then into a catalytic converter where the SO_2 is converted to SO_3 by a vanadium pentoxide catalyst. The gas stream is cooled to 200°F in an economizer and air preheater. Sulfuric acid is formed by reaction of the SO_3 with moisture in the gas, and begins to condense in the air preheater. The remaining acid is removed in a mist eliminator and is combined with the acid from the air preheater to produce 70% sulfuric acid.

Reinluft Process. This process involves the adsorption of SO_2 by a slowly moving bed of activated char, formed by carbonization of semicoke under vacuum at 1100°F. Flue gas at 300°F enters the bottom of the adsorption tower where all SO_3 is removed. The gas stream is drawn off, cooled to 220°F, and returned to the adsorption tower at a higher level. Here the SO_2 is oxidized to SO_3 and adsorbed with water on the char to form sulfuric acid. The char and adsorbed acid are heated to 750°F in a regenerator section. At this temperature, the sulfuric acid is reduced by the SO_2 and CO_2. The SO_2 is then converted to sulfuric acid in a conventional acid plant (31).

Dolomite Process. Finely ground limestone or dolomite is injected into the boiler furnace in roughly stoichiometric quantities. Part of the SO_2 is removed in the dry state by reaction with the limestone or dolomite to form sulfates. The amount of SO_2 reduction accomplished by this method has been disappointing. A combination of the dry injection of dolomite into the furnace, plus scrubbing of the stack gases with a water slurry of calcined dolomite, is also under investigation. A number of companies are actively engaged in studying these processes (32). For details on other processes being investigated in Europe and Japan, see reference 30.

Athabasca Tar Sands. A project to extract oil from Athabasca tar sands in Alberta, Canada, was begun in 1967. Hydrogen sulfide derived in the refining process is converted to elemental sulfur in a catalytic conversion unit. Several oil companies are interested in developing the huge potential oil reserves in the Athabasca tar sands, with the result that this area could become a major source of sulfur (33). See Tar sands.

SULFATES

Occurrence. The largest untapped source of sulfur is contained in the oceans as dissolved sulfates of magnesium, calcium, and potassium. One cubic mile of seawater contains approx 4 million short tons of elemental sulfur in the form of sulfates. Natural and by-product gypsum, $CaSO_4 \cdot 2H_2O$, and anhydrite, $CaSO_4$, rank second only to the oceans as a potential source of sulfur. Mineral deposits of gypsum and anhydrite are widely distributed in extremely large quantities. Gypsum is a by-product waste material from several manufacturing processes; most notable is the waste gypsum produced in the manufacture of phosphoric acid from phosphate rock and sulfuric acid.

Extraction. Although many processes have been developed to recover the sulfur from gypsum or anhydrite, high capital and operating costs preclude their widespread use in most countries where sulfur is cheap and plentiful. The sulfur-from-gypsum processes acquired renewed interest in the mid-1960s as world sulfur consumption continued to exceed production capacity.

Various processes convert gypsum into elemental sulfur, sulfuric acid, or ammonium sulfate fertilizer. As of early 1969, two plants utilizing gypsum were operating in the U.S. One recovers elemental sulfur from gypsum in a 1000 long ton/day plant located in Culberson County, Texas. The other consists of a 200 ton/day ammonium sulfate-from-gypsum plant at Handford, California.

Sulfuric Acid–Cement Process. One of the older industrial processes converts gypsum or anhydrite into sulfuric acid and cement. The first experimental plant was built during World War I at the Farbenfabriken Bayer works in Leverkusen, Germany. W. S. Muller and H. H. Kuhne both worked on the project, but Kuhne developed the true chemical reactions which made the process workable (34). All of the plants using this process are located in Europe, primarily in England, Germany, Poland, and Austria. Because plants of this type have high capital and operating costs, they have usually been competitive with other sulfur processes only when located near a plentiful, cheap supply of gypsum or anhydrite, and where a demand exists for sulfuric acid and cement within its marketing area.

The process consists of preparing a properly proportioned mixture of anhydrite, coke, and shale to be used as feed to a rotary kiln. In the kiln the dissociation of anhydrite takes place essentially in three stages: (1) Carbon reacts with one fourth of the anhydrite to form calcium sulfide, as follows:

$$CaSO_4 + 2\,C \rightarrow CaS + 2\,CO_2$$

This reaction takes place between 900 and 1100°C. (*2*) The calcium sulfide reacts with the remaining anhydrite, at 1100°C, to form sulfur dioxide,

$$CaS + 3\,CaSO_4 \rightarrow 4\,CaO + 4\,SO_2$$

(*3*) A side reaction can occur in a neutral atmosphere, producing sulfur vapor instead of sulfur dioxide:

$$3\,CaS + CaSO_4 \rightarrow 4\,CaO + 2\,S_2$$

Between 900 and 1000°C reactions (*2*) and (*3*) occur in about the same order, while higher temperatures strongly favor reaction (*2*). The remaining reaction in the kiln takes place at 1400–1450°C, when the lime formed during decomposition reacts with the shale components to form cement clinker. The sulfur dioxide-bearing gas, after dust removal, gas cooling, and moisture removal, is fed into a contact sulfuric acid plant.

Elemental Sulfur from Gypsum. The U.S. Bureau of Mines and others are developing two processes to recover elemental sulfur from gypsum or anhydrite (35). Reduction roasting of gypsum to calcium sulfide in rotary kilns or fluidized-bed reactors is common to both processes, using either coal, natural gas, carbon monoxide, or hydrogen for reduction of the gypsum at 900–950°C. In the first process, the calcium sulfide is ground and slurried with water until the solution formed is 20–40% solids. Carbon dioxide-bearing flue gas, from the reduction kiln, is passed countercurrently through the slurry to precipitate calcium carbonate and evolve hydrogen sulfide. The hydrogen sulfide that evolves is treated in a standard catalytic conversion unit for recovery of elemental sulfur.

A second process proposes to convert gypsum or anhydrite into elemental sulfur, sodium carbonate, and calcium chloride. Calcium sulfide is dissolved in water along with some recycle hydrogen sulfide to produce a $3N$ solution of calcium hydrosulfide. The calcium hydrosulfide solution is passed through an ion-exchange resin which removes the calcium ion, and exchanges it for a sodium ion. The effluent from this operation is an approx $3N$ solution of sodium hydrosulfide. Flue gas from the gypsum reduction kiln is used to carbonate the solution to precipitate sodium bicarbonate and evolve hydrogen sulfide. The sodium bicarbonate is calcined to sodium carbonate. Most of the recovered hydrogen sulfide is converted to elemental sulfur in a catalytic conversion unit, while the remainder is recycled to react with calcium sulfide. The ion-exchange resin is regenerated to the sodium form with sodium chloride solution. Effluent from the regeneration step is a strong solution of calcium chloride that may be evaporated for recovery of solid calcium chloride. Where there is ready access to sulfate-rich brine, the calcium chloride solution may be used to precipitate gypsum for feed to the process. This process will produce more than 3 tons each of by-product sodium carbonate and calcium chloride per ton of sulfur.

Bacteriological Sulfur. The bacteriological origin of sulfur in the Gulf Coast salt domes is discussed earlier in this article. Anaerobic, sulfate-reducing bacteria burn hydrocarbons as a source of energy, but combine sulfur instead of oxygen with the hydrogen to form hydrogen sulfide. Now certain experimenters are trying to develop this idea into a controlled process for producing sulfur from gypsum or anhydrite (36). The process requires a strain of sulfate-reducing bacteria, an organic substrate whose hydrocarbons provide food for the bacteria, and close control of environmental conditions in order to obtain maximum sulfur yields.

Finely ground gypsum is fed into a stirred reaction tank containing the organic substrate and the bacteria. The substrate can be a petroleum fraction, although sewage, spent sulfite liquor, molasses, or brewery waste can also be used. The advantage of a petroleum-based substrate is that its composition can be more closely controlled. Air must be excluded from the system because the bacteria are anaerobic. A hydrogen purging system keeps air out, and at the same time promotes fermentation. Carbon dioxide generated by the fermentation process must be removed to help maintain the pH of the solution between 7.6 and 8.0. Carbon dioxide also inhibits the activity of the bacteria. The oxidation-reduction potential is kept at 150–200 mV. Ideal temperature in the reactor will vary with different strains in bacteria, but will generally be in the range of 75–95°F.

As the reaction proceeds, a part of the mix is continuously withdrawn from the tank and centrifuged. The solids removed by centrifuging are resuspended in the reactor. Filtrate from the centrifuge goes to a stripping tower for removal of dissolved carbon dioxide and hydrogen sulfide, which is combined with the carbon dioxide and hydrogen sulfide gases coming off the top of the reactor. The combined gases are passed through a scrubbing tower for removal of the carbon dioxide and recovery of the hydrogen sulfide which is fed to a conventional recovery unit for conversion to elemental sulfur. There is also the possibility of recovering other organic coproducts, such as vitamins and steroids. The rate at which the bacteria reduce gypsum to hydrogen sulfide is quite slow, necessitating many large reaction tanks. A 300 long ton/day sulfur plant is estimated to need ten 1-million-gal reactor tanks.

Economic Aspects

World production and consumption of sulfur have undergone a series of dramatic changes during this century. In the early 1900s production ranged between $1\frac{1}{2}$ and $2\frac{1}{2}$ million tons annually, primarily from the elemental sulfur deposits of Italy and Sicily and the pyrite deposits of the Iberian peninsula. In contrast, in 1968, free world production exceeded 27 million tons, and over fifty countries produced sulfur in one form or other.

The development of the Frasch process for mining the deposits of the United States Gulf Coast area brought about a rapid change in the world's sources of sulfur after the turn of the century.

Frasch-produced sulfur rapidly began to displace imported material in the United States and to supplement Italian brimstone on the world market. Disruption of shipping during World War I resulted in a major conversion of American sulfuric acid plants from Spanish pyrites to Frasch brimstone. Also, development of the contact acid process which began to replace the chamber process in the 1920s and 1930s favored very pure brimstone over pyrites or less pure sulfur ores. See Sulfuric acid.

The chamber process could operate satisfactorily with dirty, wet sulfur dioxide gases, and pure raw material did not command a significant premium. The contact process requires a clean, dry sulfur dioxide gas which can be produced from brimstone in a simple burner. Contact acid plants based on pyrites or sulfur ores, on the other hand, require much more elaborate and expensive burners and gas purification equipment. Therefore, the sulfur content of pyrites or impure ores is worth less on the market for modern acid processes than the equivalent amount of pure brimstone.

During World War II, production of sulfur materials outside of America was badly disrupted, and recovery of production after cessation of hostilities was slow.

Many foreign consumers turned to brimstone when rehabilitating and expanding their facilities. By 1950, when the Korean crisis developed, exports of U.S. brimstone had almost doubled, as compared with the tonnage exported immediately preceding the outbreak of World War II.

During the time when the foreign consumers were becoming more dependent on U.S. sulfur, the sulfur requirements of the U.S. industry were also expanding. In the decade 1940–1950, brimstone consumption doubled in the United States. The increase was much greater than the growth in the use of minerals in general. The U.S. brimstone industry increased its output by 1950 to about two-and-one-half times the average of the prewar years 1935–1939, but this increase in production was not sufficient to meet the expanded demand for the product. Accordingly, in order to meet the market demand, sales were made from stocks of sulfur above ground, and this drastically reduced the stocks to about a six months' supply.

After the outbreak of the Korean War in 1950, it became evident that the full world demand for brimstone would not be met. During 1951, the United States Government instituted a sulfur allocation system, under which producers were directed to ship specified tonnages. At the beginning of 1952, the Government further restricted the use of sulfur, limiting domestic consumption to a basis of 90% of the amount used in 1950, and adopted the policy of maintaining existing stocks of mined sulfur.

In the meantime, the outlook for sulfur supplies improved greatly. The shortage stimulated exploration and development of new sources. Simultaneously, measures for conservation of sulfur during processing led to improved raw material efficiency in the various consuming industries. Further progress was made in the reuse and regeneration of spent sulfuric acid.

The improvement in the world situation led to decontrol of sulfur in the United States market later in 1952, and international allocation was discontinued in 1953.

By the mid-1950s, U.S. Frasch producers had brought in seven new mines and Frasch mining had commenced in Mexico in 1954. Although these new operations added a substantial quantity of material to the supply, the market absorbed most of the new production, resulting in a relatively modest increase in stocks.

In the late 1950s, economic activity in the United States and some of the other major industrial nations slowed down. This had the effect of retarding the growth in sulfur consumption. During this same period, substantial reserves of sour natural gas were found, particularly in Western Canada and France. Demand for energy was such that the natural gas was committed to pipelines and plants were constructed for cleaning the sulfur from the gas, with less consideration of whether markets were available for the by-product sulfur.

Production of sulfur from natural gas in Canada and France grew from about 100,000 tons in 1957 to almost 2.4 million tons in 1962. This tremendous increase in production outstripped the growth in consumption, and stockpiles built up in almost all producing countries. Some of the smaller U.S. Frasch mines were closed down, and exploration for new deposits came to a virtual halt.

By the early 1960s, there was a worldwide increase in economic activity, especially in the fertilizer production sector. Sulfuric acid had long been used to react with phosphate rock to solubilize the phosphate values, and thus produce a useable fertilizer. Direct reaction of acid with rock produces normal superphosphate, which contains soluble phosphate values, but in relatively low concentration. The trend in the industry was to shift to more concentrated fertilizer materials by leaching the phosphate values out of the rock with acid, and then reacting the resulting phosphoric acid with fresh rock or ammonia to produce triple superphosphate or ammonium phosphates. See Fertilizers.

Ammonium phosphates contain much higher concentrations of plant food values, but require approx 65% more sulfur per unit of phosphate. Therefore, while the growth in production of phosphate fertilizers during the early and mid-1960s was substantial, the growth in consumption of sulfur was even higher. Also, during the early 1960s, a number of sulfuric acid producers around the world based their expansions on brimstone rather than on pyrites or other raw material.

The rate of growth in consumption of brimstone in the free world between 1950 and 1962 was about 4% per year. In sharp contrast, the growth between 1962 and 1967 was greater than 9% per year. Demand outpaced production and the industry was forced to reduce its inventories sharply in order to fully meet the increased demand. Producers' inventories fell from 42 weeks' supply in 1962 to 12 weeks' supply at the end of 1967.

Table 2. U.S. Consumption of Sulfur[a] (1000 long tons (2240 lb) of contained sulfur)

	Brimstone						
Year	U.S. Frasch[b]	U.S. recovered	Imported[c]	Total	Pyrites[d]	Sulfur in gases	Total
1960	3343	775	741	4859	562	441	5862
1961	3259	831	832	4922	533	438	5893
1962	3320	907	1040	5267	524	453	6244
1963	3438	929	1351	5718	437	452	6607
1964	3847	988	1462	6297	474	489	7260
1965	4303	1167	1486	6956	514	527	7997
1966	5314	1258	1514	8086	516	558	9160
1967	5536	1287	1474	8297	520	499	9316

[a] Apparent consumption as reported by the U.S. Bureau of Mines.
[b] Includes native ores.
[c] Primarily Frasch from Mexico and recovered brimstone from Canada.
[d] Includes imported pyrites.

Early in 1966, the Mexican Government established export quotas for the Mexican Frasch producers at tonnage levels below those which had prevailed during the previous year. These quotas were eased somewhat later after the producing companies carried out extensive exploratory drilling programs to prove up additional ore reserves. The major United States producers adopted programs of limiting sales in both the domestic and overseas markets.

Once again, this shortage stimulated a worldwide search for new sources of sulfur. A number of U.S. Frasch mines that had been closed down in earlier years were reworked, and other Frasch deposits that were considered marginal when sulfur was in more plentiful supply have been brought into production.

In addition, a number of projects were launched based on hydrogen sulfide from sour gas fields and from desulfurizing sour crudes in oil refineries, primarily in Canada, the United States, and the Middle East.

Table 3. U.S. Frasch Sulfur Production,
Apparent Sales, and Year-end Inventories[a] (1000 long tons)

Year	Production	Apparent sales			Year-end inventories
		Domestic	Exports	Total	
1960	4943	3298	1786	5084	3668
1961	5385	3227	1596	4823	4691
1962	4985	3281	1554	4835	4841
1963	4882	3438	1613	5051	4594
1964	5228	3847	1928	5775	4124
1965	6116	4303	2635	6938	3302
1966	7001	5314	2373	7687	2616
1967	7014	5536	2193	7729	1901

[a] Reported by the U.S. Bureau of Mines.

After five years in which the world used more sulfur than it had produced, the world returned to a supply-and-demand balance in 1968.

Table 2 shows estimated consumption of sulfur in all forms in the United States for the years 1960 through 1967, while Table 3 shows the production, sales, and producers' year-end inventories of United States Frasch brimstone during the same period.

Specifications and Standards

Specifications and standards for commercial grades of sulfur are given below.

Crude, Run-of-Mine, and Recovered By-Product (Solid or Liquid). "Bright" sulfur is 99.5% pure, while the "dark" variety may contain up to 1% carbon. Both grades are free of arsenic, selenium, and tellurium.

Refined Sulfur. Refined sulfur is elemental sulfur produced by distilling crude sulfur; it has a purity not less than 99.8%, and is generally free burning. The chemical is available in lumps and cast forms, such as cones or cylindrical sticks, and is usually used where sulfur is burned in small quantities to provide sulfur dioxide for fumigation, sugar and starch refining, bleaching of wool and straw, etc.

Sublimed Sulfur, Flowers of Sulfur. This is a powdered form of sulfur produced by the process of sublimation. It contains up to 30% of the amorphous allotrope, which is insoluble in carbon disulfide. Fineness is usually expressed as 97% -80 mesh and 93% -100 mesh. Used in the preparation of medicines, pharmaceuticals, stock feeds, cutting oil, and dusting sulfur.

Flour Sulfur. This variety of the element consists of ground refined or crude sulfurs for industrial and agricultural uses. It is available in various finenesses from 95% -80 mesh to 98% -325 mesh. Flour sulfur is used in manufacture of matches, pyrotechnics, pharmaceuticals, and also for dusting and wettable sulfurs.

Rubbermakers Sulfur. This grade consists of ground sulfurs of various finenesses with special specifications for low acid, ash, and moisture contents.

Insoluble Sulfur. This form of sulfur contains up to 90% of the amorphous allotrope of sulfur and is insoluble in carbon disulfide. It is used for vulcanization of special rubber products, rubber cements, cutting oils, and high-pressure lubricants. See also Sulfurization.

Health and Safety Factors

Solid Sulfur. Solid, elemental sulfur in itself is virtually nontoxic and can be taken internally without injury. Although the inhalation of sulfur dust is not known to cause systemic poisoning, it is capable of irritating the ocular conjunctivae and the mucous membranes of the respiratory passages. Certain predisposed individuals occasionally develop an eczematous reaction to sulfur dust. When sulfur burns in air it forms sulfur dioxide, an irritant gas which readily affects the eyes and respiratory tract. Concentrations of 8–20 ppm will cause eye irritation and coughing. The generally accepted maximum concentration that can be tolerated for several hours without causing physiological symptoms is 10 ppm by volume. Exposure to 50–100 ppm can be tolerated for $\frac{1}{2}$–1 hr, and exposure to 500 ppm or more is instantly dangerous (37). See also Sulfur compounds.

Although sulfur is nontoxic, dust-type respirators and dust-tight goggles are recommended for personnel who handle solid sulfur. Because of the low ignition temperature of sulfur and its tendency to develop static charges, sulfur dust presents a fire and explosion hazard. Additional information on safe practices for handling, storing, and processing of solid sulfur can be found in references 38–40.

Liquid Sulfur. Sulfur becomes a liquid at 246.1°F. The primary hazards to be recognized when handling liquid sulfur include its relatively low ignition point, the possible presence of hydrogen sulfide, and the fact that it is a hot liquid capable of producing severe burns. Hydrogen sulfide is not only toxic, but also has a low explosive limit. The generally accepted maximum allowable concentration of hydrogen sulfide for an 8-hr exposure is 20 ppm by volume. Exposure to 100 ppm for 1 hr will produce symptoms of local irritation of the eyes and respiratory tract. At 500 ppm inhalation for 15–30 min will cause severe irritation of the eyes and respiratory tract with the risk of pneumonia or serious injury to the lungs. Hydrogen sulfide in concentrations of 1000 ppm or higher will cause immediate unconsciousness and will result in death unless artificial respiration is applied immediately (37). See also Sulfur compounds.

At room temperature, the lower explosive limit for hydrogen sulfide in air is 4.3% by volume.

When measured at 270°F, the normal storage temperature for liquid sulfur, the lower explosive limit for hydrogen sulfide in air is about 3.4% by volume. Sulfur storage tanks should be equipped with submerged fill lines to minimize agitation of the sulfur and release of dissolved hydrogen sulfide. Sulfur storage tanks should also have adequate roof vents to provide natural draft ventilation of hydrogen sulfide gas which may be released from liquid sulfur. All sources of ignition should be excluded from the immediate vicinity of liquid sulfur storage tanks. Personnel engaged in liquid sulfur operations should have the body completely protected by clothing, and in addition, should wear safety hats, safety glasses with side shields, and heat-resistant gloves. An additional full-face shield should be worn when disconnecting piping used for transporting liquid sulfur.

Because it is a hot material, liquid sulfur can cause severe burns when it contacts the skin. First-aid treatment should include immediate cooling of the affected area with cool running water, by immersion in water, or by application of cold compresses. The sulfur crust should not be removed because it serves as a sterile dressing. Further treatment should be administered by a doctor.

For additional information on safety practices for the handling and storage of liquid sulfur see references 39–41.

Uses

Sulfur is used directly or indirectly in the manufacture of such a diversity of products that a nation's sulfur consumption is considered to be a barometer of its economic activity.

The largest single use of sulfur is for the production of sulfuric acid, which is then used in many other manufacturing processes. Therefore, the uses for sulfur are usually classified as either sulfuric acid uses or nonacid uses. In 1968, approx 87% of the sulfur consumed in the U.S. was used to make sulfuric acid. Sulfuric acid is used primarily for the manufacture of fertilizers, organic and inorganic chemicals, pigments, steel, rayon, petroleum products, and explosives. See Sulfuric acid. Only 13% of the sulfur was consumed in nonacid uses.

The principal industries using elemental sulfur as such include wood pulp, carbon disulfide, insecticide and fungicide, rubber, sugar, starch, malt, and dyestuffs.

Sulfur is required for the preparation of sulfite cooking liquors in the production of sulfite pulp, and sometimes in the production of pulp by the sulfate process. See Pulp.

Ground crude sulfur, and flowers of sulfur, are constituents of fungicides and insecticides and soil conditioners. See Fungicides; Insecticides.

The rubber industry uses ground sulfur and specially prepared amorphous sulfur for compounding and vulcanizing. Certain organic sulfur compounds act as accelerators to reduce the curing time of sulfur. See Rubber chemicals; Rubber compounding.

Sulfur dioxide, obtained from the combustion of sulfur, is used to decolorize beet sugar juice (see Sugar) and to bleach malt (qv). The gas is absorbed in water to form sulfurous acid in the production of starch from corn (see Dextrose) and in the treatment of boiler and cooling waters (see Water).

Sulfur is used in the manufacture of certain dyes by heating organic compounds with sulfur (see Sulfur dyes); in the manufacture of ultramarine blue by igniting soda ash, kaolin, charcoal, and sulfur; and in the manufacture of chromic oxide pigment by igniting sodium or potassium dichromate with sulfur.

Sulfur is also used in the manufacture of polysulfide elastomers (see Vol. 16, p. 253); in making sulfur cements; in the production of free-machining steels; as a polymerization inhibitor in the manufacture of styrene monomer; and in the manufacture of matches. See also under Special uses.

Bibliography

"Sulfur" in *ECT* 1st ed., Vol. 13, pp. 358–373, by F. L. Jackson, E. H. Thaete, Jr., L. B. Gittinger, Jr., L. A. Nelson, Jr., and H. Blanchet, Freeport Sulphur Company.

1. P. W. Schenk and U. Thummler, *Z. Elektrochem.* **63,** 1002 (1959).
2. T. K. Wiewiorowski and F. J. Touro, *J. Phys. Chem.* **70,** 3528 (1966).
3. B. Meyer, "Solid Allotropes of Sulfurs," *Chem. Rev.* **64,** 429 (1964).
4. A. V. Tobolsky and A. Eisenberg, *J. Am. Chem. Soc.* **81,** 780 (1959).
5. T. K. Wiewiorowski, A. Parthasarathy, and B. L. Slaten, *J. Phys. Chem.* **72,** 1890 (1968).
6. G. Preuner and W. Schupp, *Z. Physik. Chem. (Leipzig)* **68,** 129 (1909).
7. H. Braune, S. Peter, and V. Neveling, *Z. Naturforsch.* **6a,** 32 (1951).
8. J. Berkowitz and J. R. Marquart, *J. Chem. Phys.* **39** (2), 275 (1963).
9. W. A. West and A. W. C. Menzies, *J. Phys. Chem.* **33,** 1880 (1929).
10. G. Fouretier, *Compt. Rend.* **218,** 194 (1944).
11. K. Neumann, *Z. Physik. Chem.* **A171,** 416 (1934).
12. R. Fanelli, *J. Am. Chem. Soc.* **72,** 4016 (1950).
13. *International Critical Tables of the Numerical Data of Physics, Chemistry, and Technology* (ICT), E. W. Washburn, ed., McGraw-Hill Book Co., Inc., New York, Vols. I–VIII, 1926–1930.

14. P. C. L. Thorne and A. M. Ward, *Inorganic Chemistry*, 3rd ed., Nordeman Publishing Co., Inc., New York, 1939, p. 6.
15. J. W. Mellor, *A Comprehensive Theoretical Chemistry*, Vol. X (S, Se), John Wiley & Sons Inc., New York, 1930, pp. 27, 87–95, 651.
16. F. Feigl, *Spot Tests in Inorganic Analysis*, Elsevier Publishing Company, Amsterdam, 1958, pp. 372–375.
17. W. N. Tuller, *The Sulphur Data Book*, McGraw-Hill Book Co., Inc., New York, 1954.
18. R. F. Matson, T. K. Wiewiorowski, and D. E. Schof, Jr., *Chem. Eng. Progr.* **61** (9), 67 (1965).
19. D. B. Mason, *Ind. Eng. Chem.* **30,** 740 (1938).
20. R. B. Thompson and D. MacAskill, *Chem. Eng. Prog.* **51** (8), 369 (1955).
21. T. P. Forbath, *Trans. AIME* **196,** 881 (1953).
22. T. Kiaer, *Eng. and Mining J.* **155** (7), 88 (1954).
23. H. R. Potts and E. G. Lawford, *Trans. AIME,* **58,** 1 (1949).
24. *Eng. and Mining J.* **155** (9), 142 (1954).
25. G. O. Argall, Jr., *World Mining*, March 1967, pp. 18–22.
26. A. L. Kohl and F. C. Riesenfeld, *Gas Purification*, McGraw-Hill Book Co., Inc., New York, 1960.
27. A. M. Squires, *Chem. Eng.* **74** (23), 260 (1967).
28. *Chem. Eng.* **72** (25), 78 (1965).
29. D. Bienstock, L. W. Brunn, E. M. Murphy, and H. E. Benson, *Sulfur Dioxide—Its Chemistry and Removal from Industrial Waste Gases*, U.S. Bureau of Mines Information Circular 7836, U.S. Government Printing Office, Washington, D.C., 1958.
30. A. V. Slack, *Chem. Eng.* **74** (25), 188 (1967).
31. *Chem. Eng.* **74** (22), 94 (1967).
32. A. M. Squires, *Chem. Eng.* **74** (24), 133 (1967).
33. *Chem. Eng.* **74** (24), 66 (1967).
34. W. Q. Hull, F. Schon, and H. Zirngible, *Ind. Eng. Chem.* **49** (8), 1204 (1957).
35. *Eng. and Mining J.* **169** (7), 69 (1968).
36. *Chem. Eng.* **75** (10), 94 (1968).
37. M. B. Jacobs, *The Analytical Chemistry of Industrial Poisons, Hazards, and Solvents*, Vol. 1, 2nd ed., Interscience Publishers, Inc., New York, 1949.
38. National Safety Council, *Handling and Storage of Sulfur*, Data Sheet D-275.
39. Manufacturing Chemists Assoc., *Properties and Essential Information For Safe Handling and Use of Sulfur*, Chem. Safety Data Sheet SD-74 (1959).
40. National Fire Protection Assoc., *Sulfur Fires and Explosions*, National Fire Codes, NFPA No. 655 (1959).

P. T. Comiskey, L. B. Gittinger, Jr.,
L. F. Good, F. L. Jackson, L. A.
Nelson, Jr., and T. K. Wiewiorowski
Freeport Sulphur Company

Special Uses

Sulfur has been employed in various types of chemical uses for many years. Although the element possesses unusual physical properties, these have not been used to any great extent. It is the purpose of this brief article to describe some of the new and potential uses that utilize the unique physical properties of sulfur, sometimes requiring the addition of plasticizers or other modifiers.

Sulfur in Building Construction. The construction of concrete block walls is normally a slow process because of three factors: (*1*) The method of laying bricks is time-consuming. (*2*) When concrete blocks are used in building construction it is desirable to waterproof or decorate such structures after they have been completed. (*3*) A curing time is necessary before the wall achieves its maximum strength. In an improved method of wall construction the mortar is eliminated from concrete block walls by stacking the blocks one upon another and subsequently painting both sides of the wall with a special sulfur formulation, which waterproofs and decorates the wall and gives it an appreciable tensile strength.

The formulation used to paint the walls should consist of 97% sulfur, 1% plasticizer, 1% ¼-in. chopped strand glass fibers, and the remainder decorative material, such as an appropriate dye. These ingredients are heated in an open vessel to a temperature just above the melting point of sulfur and spread with a blunted brush on the surface of the concrete blocks in as thin a layer as is feasible to use. The resulting layer will be approx $\frac{1}{32}$–$\frac{1}{16}$ in. thick. The brushing operation should be carried out quickly, allowing no time for the cooling and setting of the sulfur formulation before it is properly spread. Within 5 min or less after spreading the formulation on the concrete block wall the material has developed its maximum strength and the resulting wall has a substantial tensile strength. When such a wall is destroyed there is no accompanying dusting or scattering of fragments.

The new construction technique appears to be well suited for the construction of buildings designed to be waterproofed and to resist wind stress. It is particularly applicable in areas where damage from earthquakes, tornadoes, and similar disturbances is expected. The method has the advantages of being inexpensive, rapid, and efficient. The sulfur thus applied can be subsequently painted if desired, or left with its natural color. Paint of conventional types adheres very well to a sulfur-coated surface.

Sulfur in Highway Marking. Conventional types of paint, including both lacquers and plastic materials, leave a great deal to be desired in their use for marking traffic lanes and highways. Some of these paints do not adhere well to asphalt, others do not wear well on concrete; many require substantial time for drying. Some plastic materials are very expensive as well as requiring appreciable time between application and use. Sulfur paints have been formulated to overcome several of these difficulties. Sulfur may be appropriately modified with polysulfide-type polymers (see Vol. 16, p. 253) which stabilize and enhance its polymeric characteristics. This formulation for highway marking purposes should also contain an appropriate dye to meet the color standards required of the paint. The mixture of sulfur, dye, and plasticizer is heated to a temperature of approx 150°C, mixed with reflecting beads where desirable, and sprayed on the surface of the highway with a conventional type of paint sprayer modified to spray the paint at a temperature of approx 125–130°C. Under these conditions the sulfur cools rapidly enough so that no subsequent protection is required to keep passing cars from crossing the stripe. The fact that the plastic characteristics of the sulfur are stabilized confers upon the stripe exceptionally good wearing qualities. The paint adheres very well both to asphalt and concrete surfaces without prior preparation or cleaning or priming of the surfaces. The product has been tested in wet, dry, hot, and cold climates on asphalt and on concrete and has shown exceptional wear properties.

Special advantages of sulfur as a highway marking paint are its low cost, its exceptional wear characteristics, and its quick drying. The product can easily be made in appropriate yellow, red, and black formulations, but a truly white sulfur paint has yet to be produced.

Research work at Southwest Research Institute sponsored by a number of government agencies has shown promise of developing practical uses of sulfur as a component of quick-setting sulfur-aggregate mixtures for structural uses, and rigid sulfur foams for various applications.

Sulfur-aggregate concretes were easily prepared by preheating the aggregate to about 400°F and charging it into a paddle mixer with solid sulfur. The heat in the aggregate melted the solid sulfur and the temperature of the mass stabilized at about 280°F. The mass was then poured and solidified comparatively rapidly (30–60 min, depending on the mass of material). The physical compressive strength and other properties of sulfur concrete depend on the type of aggregate, the ratio of fine to coarse aggregate particles, and the percentage of sulfur present (18–26%). Typical compressive strengths ranged from 6000–7000 psi with limestone to about 300 psi with granite. The differences are attributed to variations in the strength of the bonding of sulfur to aggregate.

Foamed Sulfur. Rigid sulfur foams may be produced by reacting elemental sulfur above its melting point with various viscosity improvers, surface-active agents, stabilizers, and blowing agents in such a way that on release from a pressurized vessel a foam is produced which solidifies to a rigid foam on cooling. The foam has a closed cell type structure, and the density can be made to vary from 10 to 50 lb per cubic foot.

A typical formulation for a sulfur foam is:

Component	Parts by weight
sulfur	100.00
phosphorus pentasulfide (P_2S_5)	5.00
1,5-cyclooctadiene	3.00
talc	10.00
tricresyl phosphate (TCP)	0.25
phosphoric acid	5.00

General procedure for foam preparation involves heating sulfur to 290°F, adding P_2S_5, 1,5-cyclooctadiene, and talc, and allowing the mixture to react at this temperature for 5–10 min; phosphoric acid and tricresyl phosphate are then added and agitated for about 5 min. The mass is then expanded through a valve to atmospheric conditions.

Various structural applications of the foam have been reported in publications from Southwest Research Institute.

MARION D. BARNES
Covenant College

SULFURATION.   See Sulfur dyes; Sulfurization of oils.

SULFUR CHLORIDES.   See Sulfur compounds.

SULFUR–CHLORINATION.   See Sulfurization of oils.

SULFUR COMPOUNDS

Introduction

A key feature of the industrial chemistry of sulfur is that sulfur is abundant and inexpensive. It has thus attracted much effort by industrial and academic research workers. In addition, compounds of sulfur are exceedingly numerous and varied and find many relations with natural products and metabolic processes. All of these factors have given impetus to studies of many kinds, and the scope of these is on the increase. The strong interest on the part of industrial investigators has led to extensive practical developments, which in turn have led to a realization of the need for a fundamental understanding of sulfur compounds, and this has promoted many studies of theoretical aspects of the subject.

The industrial utility of sulfur compounds continues to grow apace. The old standbys, sulfuric acid—the "workhorse of industry"—elemental sulfur, carbon disulfide, sulfur dioxide, sulfur trioxide, and many other products, continue to be used for an ever-increasing series of applications. These may include syntheses of polymers, the preparation of a host of manufactured chemicals, the use of elemental sulfur in agriculture, and the synthesis of fungicides, insecticides, dyes, detergents, pharmaceuticals, photographic products, sweetening agents, etc.

Sulfur chemistry has traditionally been considered in terms of inorganic and organic divisions. A knowledge of both the inorganic and organic aspects is essential for understanding the full scope of sulfur chemistry. For example, to understand the reactions of sulfur trioxide with olefins or with alcohols one must know the properties of both sulfur trioxide and the olefins or alcohols. Similarly, the chemistry of sulfur dichloride, ClSCl, has many analogies with that of organic sulfenyl chlorides, RSCl. The artificial separation between the inorganic and organic aspects of sulfur chemistry is not desirable, and maintaining the classification into two groups is only a matter of convenience.

Oxygen Analogs and Extensions Thereof. Many classes of sulfur compounds are formal analogs of oxygen compounds, as may be expected from the relationship between oxygen and sulfur as the first and second members of the sixth main group of the periodic system of the elements. Some of the formally analogous groups of substances are shown in Table 1.

The formal analogy in structure types (Table 1) may be misleading, for the sulfur compounds are generally distinct and quite different in behavior from the formal oxygen analogs. One major difference between sulfur and oxygen is the ability of sulfur to show higher positive covalencies, as well as its capacity to form sulfur chains. These two features allow for the existence of many series of sulfur compounds for which there are no possible oxygen analogs. Table 2 lists some compounds of sulfur which are not formal analogs of oxygen compounds.

Sulfur Compounds in Nature and in Medicinal Chemistry. The broad occurrence of sulfur compounds in nature is noteworthy. Not only does sulfur occur in inorganic species such as the sulfide ores and sulfates, but it also occurs in many organic forms. In insulin and keratin, which are proteins, the peptide chains are held together by disulfide linkages, which are critically important parts of their structures. Amino acids

Table 1. Oxygen Compounds and Their Sulfur Analogs

Oxygen group	Sulfur analog
alcohols, ROH	thioalcohols, RSH
	(also called thiols or mercaptans)
phenols, ArOH	thiophenols, ArSH
peroxides, ROOR	disulfides, RSSR
cyanates, ROCN	thiocyanates, RSCN
isocyanates, $RN{=}C{=}S$	isothiocyanates, $RN{=}C{=}S$
oxonium compounds, $R{-}\overset{+}{\underset{H}{O}}{-}RX^-$	sulfonium compounds, $R{-}\overset{+}{\underset{R}{S}}{-}RX^-$
aldehydes, $R{-}\overset{H}{\underset{}{C}}{=}O$	thioaldehydes, $R{-}\overset{H}{\underset{}{C}}{=}S$
ketones, $R_2C{=}O$	thioketones, $R_2C{=}S$

Table 2. Some Other Sulfur Compounds

Type	Examples
polysulfides, $R(S_n)R$	alkyl trisulfides and alkyl tetrasulfides
thiono compounds	related to thionic acid, $H_2S_2O_6$, and its sulfur homologs, $H_2S_nO_6$
sulfenyl thiocyanates	compounds of general structure RSSCN and showing behavior characteristic of sulfenyl compounds
"sulfanes"	term applied to hydrides of general structure HSSH, HSSSH, etc, with increasing sulfur-chain lengths
organic thiosulfates	compounds of general structure $RSSO_3^-Na^+$, also known as Bunte salts
various sulfur–fluorine compounds	examples include FSSF (sulfur monofluoride), SF_4 (sulfur tetrafluoride), $ArSF_3$ and $ArSF_5$ compounds, and sulfur hexafluoride, SF_6
sulfoxides and sulfones	general structures $R\overset{O}{\overset{\|}{S}}R$ and $R{-}\overset{O}{\overset{\|}{\underset{\|}{\underset{O}{S}}}}{-}R$
sulfonic acids and many derivatives of these	sulfonic acids, $R\overset{O}{\overset{\|}{\underset{\|}{\underset{O}{S}}}}{-}OH$ and derivatives of these, including the sulfonyl chlorides, RSO_2Cl, sulfonate esters, RSO_2OR, and sulfonamides, RSO_2NHR

such as cysteine, methionine, and coenzyme A, among others, contain sulfur. Naturally occurring isothiocyanates are found as glucosidic components in plant species, and biotin, α-lipoic acid, thiamine (vitamin B_1), the polypeptides like vasopressin (the diuretic hormone), oxytocin (the lactating hormone), and glutathione (a peptide of general biochemical importance), are key body components, each of which contains sulfur as a constituent. The odoriferous components of onion, garlic, and other plants are sulfur compounds, and various sulfoxide structures are found also in plant and animal organisms. The penicillins and the cephalosporins contain sulfur. Also, compounds containing the disulfide linkage are basic features of the mitotic apparatus. In addition to these, a number of sulfur compounds are formed in wood processing, eg methanethiol (see Pulp; Thiols), and a series of sulfur compounds are available from petroleum.

All of the above relations to natural products, of which only a few examples have been cited, have fostered a strong interest in the metabolism of sulfur compounds and their relations to body processes. It is therefore not surprising to find that sulfur compounds are of particular interest and value in medicinal chemistry. Among the well-known examples are the bacteriocide Merthiolate (Eli Lilly and Co.), the numerous sulfa drugs, the penicillins, vitamin B_1 (thiamine), and oral agents of simple structure which may be used in certain diabetic conditions in place of insulin, to mention only a few examples. Sugar substitutes, such as saccharin and Sucaryl (Abbott Laboratories), are are simple sulfur compounds which are widely used (see Sweeteners, nonnutritive). Even in radioprotective substances (compounds which protect against radiation) sulfur compounds play a dominant role at this time (1969).

Development of New Uses for Sulfur Compounds and for Elemental Sulfur. The overall view we have been developing shows the multifaceted interests in sulfur chemistry, with a balanced program of basic and applied research. In the latter, new uses for sulfur compounds are vigorously sought and frequently found. The areas of application include (*1*) the utilization of sulfoxides as oxidants and antioxidants (15), (*2*) the use of elemental sulfur for carrying out oxidation processes (note relation to oxygen), (*3*) the continuing succession of new physiologically active substances containing sulfur, (*4*) the use of dimethyl sulfoxide as a broadly useful reagent and as a solvent of unique utility, (*5*) a renewed interest in organic thiosulfates (Bunte salts), including their use in protection against radiation damage, (*6*) continuing development of the chemistry of sulfur–fluorine compounds, with some utilizations being found, (*7*) development of various polymers from sulfur compounds, including the polysulfones and polysulfide polymers, and (*8*) the use of elemental sulfur as a component of structural material, and in paint applications. There are many common materials, such as carbon disulfide, methanesulfonic acid, carbonyl sulfide (COS), thiourea and substituted thioureas, trichloromethanesulfenyl chloride, and many others, which are a continuing challenge to the industrial chemist who would like to develop new uses for them. The plentiful availability of such substances makes them of special interest.

New Research Interests and Studies of the Mechanisms of Reactions of Sulfur Compounds. In the past few years, because of its many relations, sulfur research has moved into new and expanding areas. The most intriguing research is the type that concerns basic aspects and reaction mechanisms, as well as complicated biochemical interrelations. In this sense, one can truly say that sulfur chemistry offers a new frontier, for so little is as yet known about many of the areas of special interest. These may include studies such as the following:

1. *Studies with sulfur isotopes.* Sulfur isotopes of masses 33, 34, and 35 are now being studied for their effects in mass spectral determinations, effects on NMR spectra with ^{33}S, kinetic isotope effects with ^{34}S vs ^{32}S, and radioactive tracer studies with ^{35}S, which is a radioactive isotope.

2. *Research on the nature of atomic and diatomic sulfur species.* In its usual form, sulfur exists as the S_8 molecule. When this form is heated to higher temperatures, lower associated forms occur, including S_6, S_2, and finally monatomic sulfur, S. A relatively new area of study involves research into the nature of the reactions of monatomic sulfur, with olefins for example, to yield olefin sulfides. The spectroscopic character of the various sulfur species is also being studied.

3. *New classes of sulfur compounds, and transient sulfur species.* By the use of electron spin resonance spectroscopy, new data about sulfur radicals, such as $RS\cdot$, and radical anions involving sulfur, are being obtained. The spectra give evidence for the existence of such radicals, and the properties of the radicals can in part be followed by use of the characteristic spectra. Other transient species and reactive intermediates are being studied. Among these are the sulfenes ($R_2C{=}SO_2$), which are sulfur analogs of ketenes, and the sulfines ($R_2C{=}SO$), which can be formed by dehydrohalogenation, respectively, of selected sulfonyl chlorides and the lately discovered aliphatic sulfinyl chlorides, $RCH_2SO(Cl)$. Species such as sulfenium ions, RS^+, continue to be of interest in connection with the mechanisms of reactions of bivalent sulfur compounds, especially the sulfenyl chlorides, RSCl and related substances, as do also other positive sulfur species, such as RSO^+, $RSO_2{}^+$, etc, and the corresponding radicals, $RSO_2\cdot$, $RSO\cdot$, etc. Sulfur ylides, such as $R\overset{+}{S}(O)\overset{-}{C}H_2$, are another reactive species which has been attracting attention in recent studies. The entire chemistry of sulfinic acids, which has never been suitably understood in many basic aspects, is being explored from a mechanistic point of view, as are also sulfonium compounds, sulfoxides, various reactions of sulfenyl compounds, the photochemistry of sulfur compounds, many new heterocyclic series, the thiothiophthenes (so-called no-bond resonance compounds), and many other specific systems. In rubber chemistry, the manner in which sulfur interacts with various olefins is receiving continued attention, and the chemistry of sulfamic acids is also being restudied in some detail. Many of the studies are made by using the techniques of reaction kinetics, spectral studies, and related synthetic conversions. The much needed details of reactions involving sulfur compounds can thus be learned. Related to these studies are systematic studies which have been made on the thermochemistry of various sulfur compounds, which in turn give information about the strengths of individual bonds in various compounds.

Other Research Developments. The total syntheses of molecules like vasopressin, oxytocin, coenzyme A, insulin, vitamin B_1, and penicillin, among others, have laid the groundwork for syntheses of other natural products containing sulfur. Also being studied are synthetic routes to various sulfur-containing amino acids and peptides, to oxidation products of the disulfide linkages in cystine and related compounds, and to unusual types of compounds such as the thiothiophthenes, and thiabenzene (*CA* **67,** 43640j (1967)), thio derivatives of sugars, and many other analogs of natural products.

Biochemical research on sulfur chemistry is intent on studying the metabolic fate of certain sulfur-containing compounds, the precise way in which disulfide linkages are cleaved in the body, the manners in which certain sulfur compounds act to detoxify, for example, ingested aromatic hydrocarbons, and the mode of action of sulfur-containing drugs. One other area of current research is the question of how radiation damage occurs and how certain sulfur compounds act to retard it.

Future Developments. The strong tempo in industrial and academic, as well as medicinal and biochemical research, on sulfur chemistry, is likely to continue in the next years, and new uses for various sulfur compounds will continue to be developed. Problems which may well challenge investigators are briefly mentioned here:

1. The nature of the sulfur–oxygen link in sulfoxides, sulfones, and related systems has long perplexed research investigators. As new spectral data on such substances accumulate, and as bond lengths are measured more accurately and in a greater number of examples, and quantum mechanical calculations on various systems are made, such problems, and related ones pertaining to sulfur valence, may be resolved.

2. The photochemistry of sulfur compounds will surely be strongly developed in the next few years, both in synthetic aspects and in mechanistic features.

3. Metabolic studies of sulfur compounds, using tracer techniques, will be further developed.

4. The syntheses of new types of sulfur compounds will no doubt continue, and studies of the properties of such substances will be made.

5. Selenium chemistry will be studied in greater degree and depth, and the findings will be related to sulfur compounds.

6. The specific properties of particular allotropes and species of sulfur will be developed more fully.

7. Studies of the mechanisms of particular reactions of sulfur compounds will be made, and in greater depth than previously.

8. The roles of sulfur compounds in various enzymic systems will be studied in full detail.

In addition to the following sections in this article, sulfur compounds are discussed in a number of other articles. Inorganic sulfates, sulfides, and sulfites are in general discussed under compounds of the cation involved, organic sulfates and sulfites under Sulfuric and sulfurous esters. Other articles dealing with sulfur compounds are Amino acids; Benzenesulfonic acids; Biotin; Carbon disulfide; Chlorosulfonic acid (chlorosulfuric acid); Fluorine compounds, inorganic (Vol. 9, pp. 664–681); Fluorine compounds, organic (Vol. 9, pp. 802–805); Naphthalene derivatives; Penicillins; Phenolsulfonic acids; Polymers containing sulfur; Proteins; Sulfamates; Sulfolane; Sulfonation and sulfation; Sulfonamides; Sulfonic acids; Sulfur dyes; Sulfurization; Thiamine; Thiazole dyes; Thioglycolic acid; Thiols; Thiophene; Thiosulfates.

Norman Kharasch
Department of Chemistry
University of Southern California

CARBON SULFIDES AND THEIR INORGANIC DERIVATIVES. Sulfur and carbon combine to form a number of compounds, including carbon subsulfide, C_3S_2, carbon monosulfide, CS, and the well-known carbon disulfide, CS_2. Also reported, although of somewhat less certain existence, are C_4S, C_5S_2, and C_2S_3.

Carbon subsulfide, C_3S_2, is a deep-red lacrimatory liquid produced by the action of an electric arc on carbon disulfide. It reacts with bromine to produce a compound of the composition $C_3S_2Br_6$.

Carbon monosulfide, CS, is an unstable gas produced by the reduction of carbon disulfide by either hydrogen or carbon monoxide in the presence of a silent electrical discharge,

$$CS_2 + H_2 \rightarrow CS + H_2S$$

Its life at room temperature is about 10 min, while at 100°C it is only 3 min. It is detected by its absorption spectrum.

Carbon disulfide, CS_2, is treated in Vol. 4, pp. 370–385.

Carbonyl sulfide (carbon oxysulfide), COS, is a colorless and odorless gas, mp, −138.2°C; bp, −50.2°C; crit temp, 105°C; crit pressure, 60.5 atm; density, of solid, 1.52 at −195°C, of liquid, 1.24 at −87°C; heat of fusion, 18.81 cal/g at −138.2°C; heat of vaporization, 73.62 cal/g at −50.2°C; heat of formation, 545.98 cal/g for gas at 25°C; free energy of formation, −673.31 cal/g for gas at 25°C. The specific heat for the gas between 25 and 1500°C is given by the equation

$$C_p \ (\text{cal/mole}) = 12.89 + 0.83 \times 10^{-3} \, T - 3.60 \times 10^5 \, T^{-2}$$

where $T = $ °K. Concentrations between 11.9 and 28.5% of carbonyl sulfide in air are explosive. The vapor pressure of carbonyl sulfide at various temperatures is as follows:

Temperature, °C	−40	−30	−20	−10	0	10	20	30	40	50	60
Vapor pressure, atm	1.5	2.2	3.1	4.4	6.1	8.2	11.4	15	18	22	27

The solubility in water is shown at various temperatures.

Temperature, °C	0	5	10	15	20	25	30
Soly, g/100 ml H_2O per atm partial pressure	0.356	0.281	0.221	0.179	0.147	0.122	0.104

Solubility (at 22°C) of carbonyl sulfide in alcohol is 1.7 g/100 ml and in toluene is 3.2 g/100 ml. Its dipole moment is 0.650×10^{-18} cgs unit.

Carbonyl sulfide is always formed when carbon, oxygen, and sulfur, or their compounds, such as carbon monoxide, carbon disulfide, and sulfur dioxide, are brought together at high temperatures. Hence, carbonyl sulfide is found as an impurity in various types of manufactured gases and as a by-product in the manufacture of carbon disulfide. Carbonyl sulfide in these reactions is made basically by the following reaction:

$$CO + S \rightleftharpoons COS$$

This reaction, when catalyzed with kaolin, for example, proceeds to the right at temperatures up to about 500°C. At higher temperatures the equilibrium tends toward the left, the carbonyl sulfide being 64% dissociated at 900°C.

Table 1. Some Reactions Yielding Carbonyl Sulfide

Reaction	Condition
$CO_2 + CS_2 \rightleftharpoons 2 \ COS$	about 500°C; quartz catalyst
$CS_2 + 3 \ SO_3 \rightarrow COS + 4 \ SO_2$	react in oleum at about 100°C
$ROCSOK + HCl \rightarrow COS + ROH + HCl$	
$COCl_2 + CdS \rightarrow COS + CdCl_2$	270°C
$HCNS + H_2O \rightarrow COS + NH_3$	in concd H_2SO_4 at 20°C
$NH_2COSNH_4 + 2 \ HCl \rightarrow COS + 2 \ NH_4Cl$	

Carbonyl sulfide may also be prepared by a number of other reactions, some of which are listed in Table 1. Because carbonyl sulfide reacts only slowly with aqueous alkali metal hydroxides, such solutions may be used to purify carbonyl sulfide by removing any acidic gases.

Dry carbonyl sulfide is a rather stable compound. At elevated temperatures, however, it decomposes according to the following equations:

$$2 \ COS \rightleftharpoons CO_2 + CS_2$$
$$COS \rightleftharpoons CO + S$$

The first of these reactions predominates at temperatures around 600°C, and the second at temperatures around 900°C.

Carbonyl sulfide provides the best known source of useable atomic sulfur. Sulfur in the excited singlet state and in the triplet ground state is produced in good yield by photolysis of carbonyl sulfide in the gas phase at room temperature, using ultraviolet sources in the range of 2139–2550 Å. Atomic sulfur from the photolysis of carbonyl sulfide has been used in the synthesis of three types of sulfides from olefins, namely episulfides, alkenylthiols, and vinylic thiols (45). Thermal sources are not useful since the sulfur-containing products would be too unstable at the required temperatures (900°C in the case of carbonyl sulfide).

Carbonyl sulfide burns with a blue flame to carbon dioxide and sulfur dioxide. It is slowly hydrolyzed to carbon dioxide and hydrogen sulfide. It reacts slowly with aqueous alkali metal hydroxides to form thiocarbonates. These, however, are unstable, breaking down into carbonates and sulfides.

$$COS + 2 \ NaOH \rightarrow NaSCOONa + H_2O$$
$$\text{sodium}$$
$$\text{thiocarbonate}$$
$$NaSCOONa + 2 \ NaOH \rightarrow Na_2CO_3 + Na_2S + H_2O$$

Carbonyl sulfide reacts with chlorine to form phosgene and sulfur dichloride. With ammonia it forms urea and hydrogen sulfide.

Carbonyl sulfide reacts with alcohols in the presence of alkalis to form monothiocarbonates,

$$C_2H_5OH + COS + KOH \rightarrow C_2H_5COSK + H_2O$$

Its reaction with amines is somewhat similar.

$$2 \ RNH_2 + COS \rightarrow RNHCOSNH_3R$$

Thiophosgene (thiocarbonyl chloride, carbon dichlorosulfide), $CSCl_2$, is a red liquid with a strong unpleasant odor, bp 73.5°C, d_{20}^{15} 1.5085. It is produced by the reduction of trichloromethanesulfenyl chloride (see below), either with hydrogen sulfide or with a metal and an acid,

$$Cl_3CSCl + Fe \rightarrow FeCl_2 + CSCl_2$$

It may also be obtained by treating carbon tetrachloride at high temperatures with sulfur-containing reducing agents,

$$CCl_4 + H_2S \rightarrow CSCl_2 + 2 \ HCl$$

Other reducing agents used include iron sulfide, sulfur, and phosphorus sulfides.

Thiophosgene hydrolyzes to form carbon dioxide, hydrochloric acid, and hydrogen sulfide. It is readily chlorinated to trichloromethanesulfenyl chloride. When heated with sulfur at 130–150°C, it forms CS_2Cl_2.

Trichloromethanesulfenyl chloride (perchloromethanethiol), Cl_3CSCl, is a pale-yellow oily liquid; bp, 149°C at 760 mm, 68°C at 52 mm; d_{20}^{20} 1.700; n_D^{24} 1.538; surface tension, 35.02 dyn/cm at 20°C. It is insoluble in water but soluble in organic liquids.

Perchloromethanethiol is stable at room temperature but begins to decompose at its boiling point, sulfur chloride being among the decomposition products. It is hydrolyzed only slowly at room temperature; thiophosgene and trichloromethanesulfonyl chloride, Cl_3CSO_2Cl, are primary hydrolysis products under these conditions. At 160°C, the hydrolysis is rapid, carbon dioxide, hydrochloric acid, and sulfur being formed. At ordinary temperatures, metallic iron decomposes perchloromethanethiol, with the formation of carbon tetrachloride. Under some circumstances, however, iron may be used to reduce $CSCl_4$ to thiophosgene. Oxidation of perchloromethanethiol with nitric acid yields trichloromethanesulfonyl chloride, a solid that melts at 140–142.5°C and resists hydrolysis. Treatment of $CSCl_4$ with powdered silver yields bis(trichloromethyl) disulfide, $(CCl_3)_2S_2$, a thick yellow oil.

The organic reactions of Cl_3CSCl are characterized by the reactivity of the chlorine on the sulfur atom. In its reaction with primary or secondary amines, amides, or imides, the nitrogen attaches to the sulfur.

$$Cl_3CSCl + RNH_2 \rightarrow Cl_3CSNHR + HCl$$

Dialkylarylamines, when treated with perchloromethanethiol, give p-dialkylaminoaryl trichloromethyl sulfides. Thus with dimethylaniline the following reaction takes place:

$$(CH_3)_2NC_6H_5 + Cl_3CSCl \rightarrow (CH_3)_2NC_6H_4SCCl_3 + HCl$$

With olefins, perchloromethanethiol reacts as follows:

$$RCH{=}CH_2 + ClSCCl_3 \rightarrow RCH(SCCl_3)CH_2Cl$$

In general, the thiol group ($-SH$) is reactive toward perchloromethanethiol,

$$RSH + ClSCCl_3 \rightarrow RSSCCl_3 + HCl$$

Correspondingly, the sodium alkoxides react as follows:

$$RONa + ClSCCl_3 \rightarrow ROSCCl_3 + NaCl$$

An excess of sodium alkoxide produces the tetraalkyl ester of orthocarbonic acid.

Perchloromethanethiol is prepared by the chlorination of carbon disulfide at 20°C in the presence of iodine as a catalyst. The reaction is carried out batchwise in glass-lined jacketed vessels, care being taken to exclude iron or other metals that would catalyze the formation of carbon tetrachloride. The reaction is as follows:

$$CS_2 + 3\,Cl_2 \rightarrow Cl_3CSCl + SCl_2$$

The temperature of reaction is held low to prevent the formation of excess S_2Cl_2. It is difficult to separate S_2Cl_2 by distillation. Chlorination is continued until 3–5% excess chlorine is present. A period of about 45 hr is required for the chlorination. The reaction mixture is then fractionally distilled under a 20-in. vacuum to remove the SCl_2, the excess chlorine, any unreacted carbon disulfide, and any carbon tetrachloride that may have been produced. Any S_2Cl_2 present is difficult to remove by this means. An 85% yield of 97–98% purity is obtained.

The vapors of perchloromethanethiol are extremely toxic, 1 ppm being lethal to test animals during a three-month exposure test. The material is also very corrosive to the skin. Accordingly, appropriate precautions must be taken in its handling, including the use of organic-cartridge gas masks in contaminated areas. If perchloromethanethiol is spilled on the skin, the area should immediately be flushed with water and washed thoroughly with soap and water.

Perchloromethanethiol is an organic intermediate. It is used in the manufacture of the agricultural fungicide captan, N-(trichloromethylthio)-4-cyclohexene-1,2-dicarboximide. See Vol. 10, p. 225.

CHLOROSULFURIC ACID, HSO_3Cl. See Chlorosulfonic acid, Vol. 5, pp. 357–362.

HYDROGEN SULFIDES. Although more than one hydrogen sulfide is known—including hydrogen polysulfides—hydrogen sulfide, H_2S, is by far the best known and most important.

Hydrogen Sulfide

Hydrogen sulfide, H_2S, is a colorless gas having an offensive odor. It occurs widely throughout nature and industry, mostly as an objectionable impurity. From it are produced substantial tonnages of elementary sulfur, sulfuric acid, and a variety of other chemicals.

Although its odor must have been recognized at a very early period, hydrogen sulfide was not described by the ancient Greek writers. The gas was first studied intensively by Scheele, who reported in 1777 that it could be obtained by the action of acids on calcium polysulfide, manganese sulfide, or ferrous sulfide. He also showed that it could be prepared by heating sulfur in hydrogen. Scheele observed the solubility of the gas in water and its oxidation to sulfur by air, nitric acid, or chlorine. He

Table 2. Thermodynamic Properties of Hydrogen Sulfide

Temp, °K	Entropy, $S°$, cal/(°K)(mole)	Free energy, $-(F° - H_0°)/T$, cal/(°K)(mole)	Heat content, $H° - H_0°$, kcal/mole	Heat capacity, C_p, cal/(°K)(mole)
298.16	49.15	41.18	2.38	8.14
400	51.36	43.53	3.13	8.48
500	53.30	45.34	3.99	8.81
600	54.97	46.83	4.89	9.14
700	56.40	48.13	5.82	9.47
800	57.73	49.27	6.78	9.81
900	58.96	50.30	7.78	10.14
1000	59.81	51.24	8.81	10.47

noted that the gas reacts with solutions of numerous metallic salts; however, it was not until it was analyzed by Berthollet in 1796 that the gas was recognized as hydrogen sulfide.

Hydrogen sulfide has the following properties: mp, $-82.9°C$; bp, $-61.80°C$; sp gr of gas (air = 1.00), 1.189, of liquid, d_4^{60} 0.96; C_p, between 25 and 1500°C, 0.236 + 9.74t × 10^{-5} cal/g (t = °C); heat of vaporization at $-61.4°C$, 131.9 cal/g; heat of formation (gas, 18°C), 154 cal/g. The thermodynamic properties of hydrogen sulfide are given in Table 2 (2). See also references 24 and 35. The thermal conductivity is 0.0076 Btu/(hr)(ft^2)($^\circ$F/ft) at 32°F. The vapor pressure of hydrogen sulfide at various temperatures is as follows:

Temperature, $^\circ$C	0	10	20	30	40	50	60	70	80	90	100
Vapor pressure, atm		10.8	14.1	18.5	23.6	29.7	36.5	44.5	53.1	64.0	72.6	88.7

The crit pressure is 88.9 atm; crit temp, 100.4°C. The solubility in water is shown at various temperatures.

Temperature, $^\circ$C	0	10	20	30	40	50	60	70	80	90	100
Soly, g/100 g soln per atm partial pressure	4.95	6.72	8.77	10.93	13.2	15.5	17.8	20.3	22.8	24.1	24.7

For solubility in amine solutions see reference 4; in alkali carbonates, bicarbonates, and hydrosulfides, reference 11; in liquid sulfur, references 15 and 46; in hydrocarbon solvents, reference 29. Liquid hydrogen sulfide is generally a poor solvent for salts. It will, however, dissolve appreciable quantities of anhydrous $AlCl_3$, $ZnCl_2$, $FeCl_3$, $HgCl_2$, PCl_3, $SiCl_4$, and SO_2. Hydrogen sulfide has an ignition temperature of 250°C and an explosive range in air of 4.5–45.5%.

Although H_2S is thermodynamically stable at room temperature, at elevated temperatures it breaks down reversibly into its elements,

$$2\,H_2S \rightleftharpoons 2\,H_2 + S_2$$

The equilibrium constants for this reaction at various temperatures (24) are given in Table 3.

Table 3. Equilibrium Constants for the Decomposition of Hydrogen Sulfide into Hydrogen and Sulfur

Temp, $^\circ$K	$K = [p(H_2)]^2[p(S_2)]/[p(H_2S)]^2$	Temp, $^\circ$K	$K = [p(H_2)]^2[p(S_2)]/[p(H_2S)]^2$
298	1.7×10^{-26}	800	2.2×10^{-6}
300	2.7×10^{-26}	900	4.3×10^{-6}
400	7.6×10^{-19}	1000	4.8×10^{-5}
500	2.6×10^{-14}	1250	3.8×10^{-3}
600	2.9×10^{-11}	1500	7.1×10^{-2}
700	4.6×10^{-9}	1750	0.95

Hydrogen sulfide is readily oxidized by many oxidizing agents. The oxidation products depend upon the oxidizing agent, its concentration, its molal ratio to the hydrogen sulfide, and the conditions of the reaction. Some of the oxidizing agents for hydrogen sulfide, and their products of oxidation, are summarized in Table 4. The reaction

$$H_2S + I_2 \rightarrow 2\,HI + S$$

is used in the analysis of hydrogen sulfide.

Completely dry hydrogen sulfide, whether gaseous or liquid, has no acidic properties. Aqueous solutions, however, are weakly acidic. The dissociation constant for the first hydrogen at 18°C is 9.1×10^{-8}; that for the second hydrogen is 1.2×10^{-15}. A solution of hydrogen sulfide reacts with a wide variety of alkaline substances. Thus, it

Table 4. Oxidation of Hydrogen Sulfide

Oxidizing agent	Conditions	Chief products
O_2 (air)	flame, air in excess	SO_2
	flame, H_2S in excess	sulfur
	aq soln of H_2S	sulfur
SO_2	elevated temp, catalyst	sulfur
	aq soln	sulfur, polythionic acids
H_2SO_4	concd acid	sulfur, SO_2
H_2O_2	neutral soln	sulfur
	alk soln	$S_2O_3^{2-}$, SO_4^{2-}
Na_2O_2	dry system at elevated temp	Na_2S, Na_2S_x
O_3	aq soln	sulfur, H_2SO_4
HNO_3	concd aq soln	H_2SO_4
NO	silica-gel catalyst	sulfur
NO_2^-	pH 5–7	sulfur, NO
	pH 8–9	sulfur, NH_3
Cl_2	gaseous reaction, excess Cl_2	SCl_2
	gaseous reaction, excess H_2S	sulfur
	aq soln, excess Cl_2	H_2SO_4
I_2	aq soln	sulfur
Fe^{3+}	aq soln	sulfur

reacts with alkali-metal hydroxides to form first the normal sulfides and then the hydrosulfides,

$$2\ NaOH + H_2S \rightarrow Na_2S + 2\ H_2O$$
$$Na_2S + H_2S \rightarrow 2\ NaHS$$

With alkali carbonates, however, the reaction proceeds only to the bicarbonate state, hydrogen sulfide being insufficiently acidic to release carbon dioxide from solution.

$$Na_2CO_3 + H_2S \rightarrow NaHCO_3 + NaHS$$

Alkali metals, when heated in hydrogen sulfide, react to form the hydrogen sulfides; but tin and other metals form the normal sulfides,

$$2\ K + 2\ H_2S \rightarrow 2\ KSH + H_2$$
$$Sn + H_2S \rightarrow SnS + H_2$$

Dry hydrogen sulfide does not react with metals such as mercury, silver, or copper, but in the presence of air and moisture the reaction is rapid.

$$4\ Cu + 2\ H_2S + O_2 \rightarrow 2\ Cu_2S + 2\ H_2O$$

Hydrogen sulfide precipitates sulfides from many heavy-metal salt solutions. The solubility constants of these sulfides vary widely. Owing to the very small dissociation constant for the second hydrogen of hydrogen sulfide, the concentration of sulfide ions in hydrogen sulfide solutions may be controlled over a broad range by adjustment of the pH. This control, in turn, permits the selective precipitation of heavy-metal sulfides. Such reactions are useful in the primary separation of the metals in the standard scheme of qualitative analysis.

Hydrogen sulfide forms comparatively few addition compounds. At high pressures and low temperatures, it reacts with water to form the crystalline hydrate, $H_2S \cdot 6H_2O$. Aluminum bromide, either fused or in solution in carbon disulfide, will react with hydrogen sulfide to form the colorless crystalline compound $AlBr_3 \cdot H_2S$, mp 83°C. Correspondingly, boron trichloride reacts with liquid hydrogen sulfide to form the white crystalline compound $BCl_3 \cdot 12H_2S$.

Hydrogen sulfide reacts with liquid sulfur at elevated temperatures to form long-chain hydrogen polysulfides. Recent spectral and thermodynamic studies (46) have established that the polysulfides contain no fewer than six sulfur atoms. The concentration rises rapidly in the range approx 130–180°C, attaining about 0.104% (calculated as H_2S) at 180°C and 760 mm partial pressure of H_2S. The solubility of hydrogen sulfide itself, namely about 0.0405%, decreases with temperature in accordance with the van't Hoff relation, based on a heat of solution of hydrogen sulfide in molten sulfur equal to −818 cal/mole. These polysulfides represent an equilibrium concentration at any given temperature and act to reduce the number-average degree of polymerization, and hence the viscosity, of sulfur very markedly at temperatures around 180°C. This is ordinarily the high-viscosity range of liquid sulfur.

Hydrogen sulfide reacts with olefins at elevated temperatures and pressures and in the presence of a catalyst to form thiols (qv),

$$(CH_3)_2C{=}CH_2 + H_2S \xrightarrow[\substack{\text{pressure;} \\ 100-300°C}]{\text{clay catalyst}} (CH_3)_3CSH$$

Other catalysts that have been used for this reaction include metallic sulfides and sulfur. Since thiols may add to olefins, sulfides are by-products of the reaction. Passage of an alcohol and hydrogen sulfide over thoria at elevated temperatures also yields the thiol.

$$ROH + H_2S \xrightarrow[400°C]{ThO_2} RSH + H_2O$$

On reaction with aldehydes or ketones, hydrogen sulfide yields the corresponding thioaldehydes or thioketones. A catalyst is not always necessary for the reaction with aldehydes, but a mineral acid, or zinc chloride, is necessary to promote the reaction with ketones. The thioketones and thioaldehydes have a stronger tendency to polymerize than the parent aldehydes or ketones.

$$3\ R_2C{=}O + 3\ H_2S \xrightarrow{ZnCl_2} (R_2C{=}S)_3 + 3\ H_2O$$

The reactions of polyfunctional carbonyl compounds with hydrogen sulfide are sometimes different from the simple members of the series; for example, thiophenes have been obtained from 1,4-diketones.

Hexamethylenetetramine reacts with hydrogen sulfide to give the polymer $(CH_2S)_x$.

OCCURRENCE

Hydrogen sulfide and other sulfur compounds occur to some extent in most petroleum and natural-gas deposits. Particularly large and industrially important quantities are found in the natural-gas and petroleum fields of central and north central Wyoming, in western Texas, in southeastern New Mexico, and in Arkansas. Hydrogen sulfide concentrations as high as 42% have been reported (13) in the gas from the Neiber Dome field of central Wyoming. Mineral reserves of hydrogen sulfide in petroleum and natural-gas deposits are large. Those in Wyoming alone are estimated (13) to be about 6,500,000 tons. Substantial tonnages of hydrogen sulfide are also recovered from petroleum-refinery operations.

Hydrogen sulfide is occasionally encountered in coal-mining operations. Very substantial quantities of this gas are liberated in coking operations or in the production of manufactured gases from coal. Inasmuch as the hydrogen sulfide is an objectionable impurity in manufactured gas, it is removed, usually by passage through boxes of iron oxide (see p. 384). Hydrogen sulfide is present in most volcanic gases, probably having been produced by the action of steam on sulfides at high temperatures. Hydrogen sulfide is also found in numerous "sulfur springs." Its origin in these is at least partly in the bacterial reduction of mineral sulfates. Bacterial reduction of sulfates also accounts for the occurrence of hydrogen sulfide in numerous bodies of water, such as the lakes near El Agheila, Libya. Hydrogen sulfide is familiarly formed as a bacterial-decomposition product of protein matter, particularly of animal origin.

Hydrogen sulfide is a by-product of many industrial operations. Its production in the natural-gas, petroleum, and coal-coking operations has already been mentioned. In general, it is formed whenever sulfur or many sulfur compounds are associated with organic materials at high temperatures. Thus, it is a by-product in the manufacture of carbon disulfide. In the recently developed process, in which sulfur reacts with natural gas at elevated temperatures to produce carbon disulfide, half of the sulfur introduced is consumed in the production of hydrogen sulfide. In the older process, in which sulfur is reacted with charcoal, smaller but appreciable quantities of hydrogen sulfide are produced.

Processes for the manufacture of reactive petroleum coke produce as a by-product large quantities of hydrogen sulfide. The process for making thiophene (qv) by the reaction of sulfur with butane at elevated temperatures also yields hydrogen sulfide as a by-product. The refining of sulfur by distillation produces small quantities of hydrogen sulfide. In the coagulation of viscose rayon, some 6–9 tons of hydrogen sulfide are formed per 100 tons of rayon produced. Hydrogen sulfide can also be recovered from sulfite waste liquors in the pulp and paper industry.

PREPARATION AND RECOVERY

Hydrogen sulfide may be prepared by direct synthesis from hydrogen and sulfur vapor according to the following reaction:

$$2 H_2 + S_2 \rightleftharpoons 2 H_2S$$

This reaction proceeds at a satisfactory rate at about 500°C in the presence of a catalyst such as bauxite or aluminum hydrosilicate minerals. Yields of 96% on a sulfur basis are obtained. Manufacture by this means is economical only if hydrogen is a waste product at the location. The hydrogen sulfide so produced is essentially free of carbon dioxide or other acidic gases and is therefore well suited to the preparation of sodium sulfide and sodium hydrosulfide (see Sodium compounds).

For laboratory purposes, hydrogen sulfide is conveniently prepared by the action of an acid on iron sulfide,

$$FeS + H_2SO_4 \rightarrow H_2S + FeSO_4$$

This reaction is usually run in a Kipp generator. The gas so produced contains as impurities traces of hydrogen and arsine. The latter may be removed by passing the gas over alkali polysulfide at 350°C. In place of iron sulfide, which may contain arsenic or free iron, it has been suggested that manganese sulfide, antimony sulfide, zinc sulfide, or sodium hydrosulfide be used for supplying the sulfur for the laboratory H_2S generator. Small laboratory quantities of hydrogen sulfide may be conveniently prepared by heating a mixture of sulfur and a hydrogen-rich organic material such as paraffin, napthhalenes, resins, soaps, etc. To facilitate the smooth evolution of gas asbestos or diatomite is used as a catalyst and suspending agent. Evolution of gas, becomes rapid at temperatures from 280 to 320°C.

Primarily of historical interest, the Claus-Chance process recovered large tonnages of hydrogen sulfide from the waste calcium sulfide of the Leblanc soda process by treatment with carbon dioxide,

$$2 \ CaS + CO_2 + H_2O \rightarrow Ca(HS)_2 + CaCO_3$$
$$Ca(HS)_2 + CO_2 + H_2O \rightarrow CaCO_3 + 2 \ H_2S$$

Lime-kiln gas was first introduced into a slurry of the waste calcium sulfide, forming in the net reaction $Ca(SH)_2$ and calcium carbonate and leaving unreacted nitrogen, which was discarded. The $Ca(SH)_2$ was then further carbonated to calcium carbonate, and the exit gases contained relatively high concentrations of hydrogen sulfide. This hydrogen sulfide was converted to sulfur.

Also of historical interest is the Schaffner and Helbig process for the recovery of hydrogen sulfide from the same waste calcium sulfide. In this process, calcium sulfide slurry was treated at or near the boiling point with a concentrated magnesium chloride solution to yield hydrogen sulfide, calcium chloride, and magnesium hydroxide. The magnesium chloride was recovered by carbonating the slurry of calcium chloride and magnesium hydroxide to yield magnesium chloride and calcium carbonate. The reactions involved were the following:

$$CaS + MgCl_2 + 2 \ H_2O \rightarrow H_2S + CaCl_2 + Mg(OH)_2$$
$$Mg(OH)_2 + CaCl_2 + CO_2 \rightarrow CaCO_3 + MgCl_2 + H_2O$$

Conversion of Sulfur Constituents of Petroleum to Hydrogen Sulfide. The sulfur content of petroleum in the United States varies from a low of 0.04% in Pennsylvania crude to about 5.0% for a heavy Mississippi crude oil. The practice of removing sulfur compounds from petroleum has tripled during the past decade in terms of the amount of sulfur recovered and now amounts to over 1 million metric tons per year worldwide (47).

Over 90% of the sulfur content of crude oils is found in the gas–oil and coke-distillate fractions. All of the sulfur in petroleum consists of divalent sulfur compounds of carbon and hydrogen, chiefly thiols, sulfides, thiophenes, and benzothiophenes. Processes for conversion of these constituents are based on their hydrodesulfurization to hydrogen sulfide, which is then absorbed from the gas stream and subsequently regenerated from the absorbent. The conversion to hydrogen sulfide is accomplished by passing the sulfur-rich gas–oil and coke-distillate fractions through a fixed-bed catalyst in the presence of hydrogen. By-product hydrogen from the catalytic-reforming operations of the refinery is used. The partial pressure of hydrogen in the reaction zone is sufficiently high to cause hydrogen to saturate free carbon bonds and to react with oxygen, nitrogen, sulfur, and molecular fragments containing these elements under the selected reaction conditions. Thus the undesirable constituents are converted to easily removed compounds, while the saturation of the hydrocarbon stocks is improved. Conversion of sulfur content is on the order of 80–90%.

Three leading commercial processes for the conversion of sulfur in petroleum to hydrogen sulfide are described briefly here. See also under Hydroprocesses, Vol. 11, p. 432.

The Unifining process of Union Oil Company of California employs a fixed-bed reactor containing a cobalt molybdate catalyst. The hydrocarbon feedstock is premixed with hydrogen and enters the top of the reactor at about 700°F, exiting at about 800°F. It then goes to a separator. Liquid from the separator is washed with caustic soda to remove dissolved hydrogen sulfide. The separator gas, containing chiefly hydrogen and hydrogen sulfide, is treated in an oil-absorption unit at reactor pressure (about 1150 psig) to separate the two gases. The hydrogen is returned to the reactor. Some ammonia is also recovered along with hydrogen sulfide from the steam-stripping operation on the absorption oil. The catalyst is regenerated periodically at about 900°F by adding air to inert combustion gas which is passed through the reactor at about 25 psig.

The hydrodesulfurization process of Shell Development Company utilizes a reactor packed with a cobalt–molybdenum–aluminum catalyst or a tungsten–nickel sulfide catalyst. Mixed hydrocarbon feed and hydrogen are trickled through the reactor at about 700°F and at 735 psig. The reactor products are separated into recycle hydrogen gas and a liquid phase. The liquid layer is sent to a second, lower-pressure, separator, where it is flashed and then stripped to separate hydrogen sulfide and light ends from the desulfurized oil.

The Gulf HDS process of the Gulf Oil Company resembles the Shell hydrodesulfurization process except that higher temperatures and lower space velocities are employed. This leads to larger amounts of low-boiling hydrocarbons, which are separated by means of a fractionation step in place of the more usual stripping operation.

Other similar processes in use at the present time are the fluidized-bed *H-oil process* of Hydrocarbon Research Inc., and the fixed-bed *Isomax process* of Universal Oil Products Company.

Recovery of By-Product Hydrogen Sulfide. By far the greatest quantities of hydrogen sulfide produced are obtained as by-products of other operations. Frequently, the recovery of the hydrogen sulfide is motivated more by the need to purify the source material than by the value of the recovered gas. This was formerly true in the petroleum, natural-gas, and manufactured-gas operations, from which the bulk of the hydrogen sulfide is recovered. In the case of rich sources, such as sour natural gas and certain oil-refinery gases, the economics of recovery have become favorable since about 1955.

The known methods for removing hydrogen sulfide from industrial gases can be classified (48) as *chemical-absorption* processes in alkaline liquids, namely alkanolamine, ammonia solution, and alkaline salt solutions; as *physical-absorption* or solution processes, namely in water or in an organic solvent such as methanol at low temperatures; as *dry oxidation processes to form sulfur*, namely on activated carbon (49) or on a catalyst with added sulfur dioxide (50,51); as *dry oxidation processes to form oxides;* and, finally, as *liquid oxidation processes to form sulfur*, wherein the oxidant or catalyst is suspended or dissolved in a liquid medium.

Several processes are in use for the recovery of hydrogen sulfide from industrial gases. A number of these are listed in Table 5.

A more recent process, the *Sulfinol process* (Shell Development Co.) (52), which utilizes diisopropanolamine and sulfolane, has also entered commercial use (since 1964) and is described on pp. 383–384.

Table 5. Principal Processes in Use for the Recovery of Hydrogen Sulfide from Industrial Gases

Process	Inventor	Assignee	U.S. patent (year)	Absorbent
Girbotol	R. R. Bottoms	The Girdler Corp.	1,783,901 (1930)	alkanolamines
Shell phosphate	L. Rosenstein and G. A. Kramer	Shell Development Co.	1,945,163 (1934)	K_3PO_4
Alkazid	Hans Baehr	Germany	1,990,217 (1935)	salts of amino acids
phenolate	J. A. Shaw	Koppers Co.	2,028,124 (1936)	sodium phenoxide
vacuum carbonate	A. R. Powell and H. A. Gollmar	Koppers Co.	2,242,323 (1941)	Na_2CO_2
			2,379,076 (1945)	
			2,464,805 (1945)	

All of these processes employ the same basic flow scheme. The gas containing hydrogen sulfide is introduced into the bottom of a contacting tower or absorber, down through which a solution of the absorbing agent flows. As the gas rises through the tower, its hydrogen sulfide is absorbed, and the gas leaving the top of the tower is essentially free of hydrogen sulfide. The hydrogen sulfide-bearing solution leaving the bottom of the tower is sometimes heated by passage through a heat exchanger before being introduced into the top of a reactivating tower. The solution flows down through the reactivating tower counter to a flow of steam generated at the bottom of the tower by boiling the solution. The rising steam strips the hydrogen sulfide from the absorbent, and upon leaving the reactivating tower is condensed, thereby leaving the hydrogen sulfide available for further use. The stripped solution leaving the bottom of the reactivator is run through a heat exchanger (if one is used) to recover part of the heat of the operation, is further cooled, and is then recycled through the absorber. The absorber and reactivator may be either packed towers or bubble-plate towers.

The *Girbotol process* of the Girdler Corporation is the method most widely used process for the removal of hydrogen sulfide from natural and refinery gases (10). The absorbent employed for this purpose is usually an aqueous solution of monoethanolamine or diethanolamine. Triethanolamine, which was used in early installations at a time when it was the only such amine commercially available, has since been largely replaced in the treatment of natural gas by the more reactive monoethanolamine. Diethanolamine, because of its inertness toward carbonyl sulfide, is used largely in the treatment of refinery gases, which often contain this impurity. Monethanolamine reacts with carbonyl sulfide to form the relatively heat-stable compound diethanolurea, $CO(NHCH_2CH_2OH)_2$. See also Ethanolamines.

The relatively high cost of the ethanolamines necessitates special precautions to avoid either physical or chemical losses of the absorbent. Thus, the impurities in manufactured gases (primarily tars, cyanogen, and oxygen) have prevented the use of amine solutions in the commercial purification of such gases. A relatively small amount of steam is required to strip the amine solution down to a few grains of hydrogen sulfide per gallon. This complete removal of hydrogen sulfide from the solution permits equally efficient (negative lead acetate test) removal of hydrogen sulfide from the treated gas in the absorbing cycle. These advantages, in large measure, account for the widespread use of the Girbotol process.

The *Shell phosphate process* of the Shell Development Company is essentially similar to the Girbotol process but uses solutions containing over 40% of tripotassium phosphate as the absorbent. The reaction is

$$K_3PO_4 + H_2S \rightarrow K_2HPO_4 + KHS$$

The low volatility of this material permits the use of live steam for stripping in place of a reboiler, with some saving in investment. The material is also somewhat more stable chemically, thereby reducing losses from this source. Still another advantage of this process is that some degree of selectivity in the absorption of hydrogen sulfide in the presence of carbon dioxide is obtained. This selectivity is based upon the greater rate of solution of hydrogen sulfide over that of carbon dioxide. Against these advantages is the disadvantage that somewhat more steam is required for reactivation than is needed in the Girbotol process.

The *vacuum carbonate process* was developed by Koppers Company as a modification of their Seaboard carbonate process (see p. 384) to permit recovery of the hydrogen sulfide. The absorbent in this process is a 3.0–3.5% solution of sodium carbonate. The reaction involved is

$$Na_2CO_3 + H_2S \rightarrow NaHCO_3 + NaHS$$

In order to reduce the quantity of steam needed for stripping, the reactivation is carried out under a vacuum of about 25 in. Hg. This results in a threefold saving: *(1)* While the volume of steam used for stripping is the same as would have been used at atmospheric pressure, its weight is only about one-fifth as much; *(2)* the stripping can be accomplished at about the same temperature (53°C) as the absorption, thereby reducing the need to transfer sensible heat; *(3)* the low pressure of operation permits the use of low-pressure exhaust steam for reactivation. The low cost of the absorbent solution, and its relative chemical stability, permit the use of this process in the recovery of hydrogen sulfide from manufactured gases.

The *Alkazid and phenolate (phenoxide) processes* are not used in the United States at the present time. The Alkazid process was developed and used in Germany before World War II, where some 1,000,000 ft³ of H_2S was being removed by the process daily. The three absorbents employed are called Alkazid solutions M, Dik, and S. Solution M contains sodium alanine, $H_2NCH(CH_3)COONa$, and is used for removal of either hydrogen sulfide or carbon dioxide or both. Solution Dik contains the potassium salt of dimethylglycine; it is used for the selective removal of hydrogen sulfide in the presence of carbon dioxide. Solution S contains sodium phenoxide. Operation of the process with solutions M or Dik presents severe corrosion problems.

The *phenoxide process* was developed by Koppers Company for removing hydrogen sulfide from manufactured gases. The process employs a solution of sodium phenoxide as the absorbent. Operating difficulties encountered in this process have caused the few plants in which this process was operated to be converted to other processes.

The *Shell Sulfinol process* of Shell Development Company has come into commercial use since 1964 as a replacement for systems using monoethanolamine. "Sulfinol" is the designation for a solvent composed of sulfolane (qv), $CH_2CH_2CH_2CH_2SO_2$, plus an

alkanolamine, preferably diisopropanolamine. This solvent is nearly equivalent to aqueous monoethanolamine in hydrogen sulfide capacity at low partial pressures. Sulfinol is much superior to aqueous monoethanolamine at high partial pressures. In part this is due to the practical loading limit at about 4.5 ft^3/gal imposed on aqueous monoethanolamine because of corrosion and foaming problems. For very sour natural gas, the solvent-circulation requirements for Sulfinol may be as low as one-half those for aqueous monoethanolamine. Since part of the effect of Sulfinol depends on the physical solubility of hydrogen sulfide in sulfolane, in which solvent it is nearly eight times more soluble than in water, the acid gas–solvent equilibria are much more sensitive to temperature. These two features of low solvent circulation and temperature sensitivity combine to give significantly lower stripping steam and heat-exchange requirements. The process also removes thiols and carbonyl sulfide. Sulfinol solvent using diisopropanolamine is relatively insensitive to degradation by carbonyl sulfide. The Sulfinol solvent absorbs more hydrocarbons from the sour gas (especially C_5 compounds (52)) than does aqueous monoethanolamine. Special treatment for the removal of hydrocarbons from the acid gas stream will be necessary prior to the sulfur plant, if the content is too high for feed to a Claus sulfur-recovery operation.

Other Processes. In addition to those described in the previous section, there are a number of other processes for removing hydrogen sulfide from industrial gases. These, however, do not recover the hydrogen sulfide as such, and in some cases are used as the final "cleanup" operation after one of the preceding operations has removed most of the gas.

Of perhaps greatest economic importance is the *"dry-box"* process for removing hydrogen sulfide from coke-oven gases and other industrial gases. In this process, hydrated iron oxide is coated on shavings or other supporting material spread on trays in rectangular boxes. The gas, to which sufficient air has been added to provide an oxygen concentration of 0.6–1.0%, is passed over the iron oxide. The hydrogen sulfide reacts to form ferric sulfide, which, in turn, is reoxidized by the added oxygen to the original iron oxide and sulfur. After some use, it is necessary to remove the iron oxide and allow it to become thoroughly revivified in the air before returning it to the boxes for further use. The iron oxide is finally discarded when the total sulfur content reaches 50 to 60%. When used for final cleanup, the oxide may be discarded with a sulfur content as low as 30%. The advantages of the dry-box process are the completeness of removal of hydrogen sulfide and the simplicity of the process. The dry-box process is one of the most selective methods of removing hydrogen sulfide in the presence of carbon dioxide. A process related to the dry-box process has been used in several plants in Germany. In this process, gas to which the stoichiometric amount of oxygen and 330–500 ppm of ammonia have been added, is passed over activated carbon. The hydrogen sulfide is thereby converted into sulfur, which can then be recovered by extraction with ammonium sulfide solution. The hydrogen sulfide content of the treated gas is reduced to about 1 ppm.

The *Seaboard process*, developed by Koppers Company in 1920, is similar to the more recently developed vacuum carbonate process (see p. 383). However, instead of employing steam under reduced pressure to reactivate the carbonate solution, large volumes of air are employed to strip the hydrogen sulfide from the absorbent. The hydrogen sulfide is not usually recoverable from this process. The air used in the reactivation operation tends to oxidize some of the hydrogen sulfide to thiosulfate; hence, it is necessary to discard some of the absorbent periodically and add fresh solution to maintain the desired composition (3.0–3.5% Na_2CO_3). Removal of hydrogen sulfide from the treated gas by this process is not usually complete.

Somewhat related to the Seaboard process are the procedures for recovering hydrogen sulfide as elementary sulfur. In these the hydrogen sulfide is again absorbed in dilute solutions of sodium carbonate, but instead of being desorbed with air (whereby the solution is reactivated), the hydrogen sulfide, in the presence of a catalyst, is oxidized by air to elementary sulfur. In the *Ferrox process*, a suspension of iron oxide is used as the catalyst, and, in the *nickel process*, nickel sulfate is generally employed. In the *Thylox process*, a neutral solution of sodium thioarsenate is used instead of sodium carbonate, both as the absorbent and as the oxidation catalyst. Because of its larger yield of precipitated sulfur and lower loss of absorbent, the Thylox process has largely replaced the Ferrox and nickel processes.

In these processes, the absorbent is regenerated in tall flooded towers. These vessels are sometimes more than 100 ft high, and in some plants two or more may be used in series. Both compressed air and preheated foul solution are introduced into the bottoms of these vessels. The air bubbles up through the solution and oxidizes the hydrogen sulfide. The precipitated sulfur clings to the air bubbles and rises with them to the surface of the solution, where it gathers as a froth. The froth and the regenerated solution are separated. The froth is filtered and washed on continuous filters to yield a product containing about 50% finely divided sulfur and 50% water plus small quantities of impurities. These impurities, unless removed by further refining of the sulfur, limit the usefulness of the product to agricultural fungicides and other less critical uses.

About 10–15% of the absorbed hydrogen sulfide is oxidized to thiosulfate in the Thylox process, while 30–40% is so oxidized in the Ferrox or the nickel process. It is necessary, therefore, to replace part of the solution continuously to maintain the desired composition of the absorbent. Another disadvantage of the process is the relatively poor removal of hydrogen sulfide from the treated gas, 90–95% removal being usual.

Where complete removal of relatively small quantities of hydrogen sulfide is necessary, it is the practice to use sodium hydroxide solutions. This is normally a batch operation, the solution being replaced when most of the sodium hydroxide has been converted into sodium sulfide. Gas–liquid contacting devices employed to effect this reaction include packed towers, jet scrubbing devices, and simple bubbling of the gas through the solutions. In some cases the removal of hydrogen sulfide is carried out in two stages, the gas being first contacted with a solution of sodium sulfide, which is converted to the hydrosulfide, concentrated, and sold. The gas is then contacted with a solution of sodium hydroxide, which completely removes the remaining traces of hydrogen sulfide from the gas, the solution being converted to sodium sulfide, which is later converted to sodium hydrosulfide.

Calcium hydroxide is a less expensive base, but its insolubility and that of calcium sulfide cause processing difficulties. It is therefore less frequently used than sodium hydroxide.

Where hydrogen sulfide must be removed from acid gases such as carbon dioxide, alkaline absorbents cannot be used. In these cases, oxidizing agents such as potassium permanganate solution or a buffered solution of sodium dichromate and zinc sulfate may be used. These reagents are relatively expensive and hence may be economically employed only where the concentration of hydrogen sulfide is small.

The addition of chlorine has been used to remove hydrogen sulfide from the vent gases of viscose rayon factories. Less than stoichiometric quantities of chlorine are required for complete removal of hydrogen sulfides, the chlorine apparently serving also as a catalyst for the atmospheric oxidation of the hydrogen sulfide. This method, however, presents severe corrosion problems (19). Rayon mills have more often preferred processes such as the Thylox and Ferrox processes. More recently a process using a sodium arsenate–arsenite absorbent solution (49) has gained favor in European viscose plants.

Oxidation of Hydrogen Sulfide to Sulfur. Almost all the hydrogen sulfide recovered from natural-gas and refinery operations is converted to high-quality sulfur which competes in the same market as native or Frasch-process sulfurs. While several of the processes described in the previous section result in sulfur or oxidation products of sulfur, many of them are geared to disposal of sulfur content rather than recovery of sulfur values. The following processes are aimed primarily at volume-economic recovery of sulfur values from gases enriched with regard to hydrogen sulfide content. They are described only briefly here. See Sulfur for a fuller description.

The *modified Claus process* of Stanolind Oil and Gas Company is most commonly used for the conversion of concentrated hydrogen sulfide gas streams to sulfur. One third of the acid gas feed is burned with stoichiometric air to form sulfur dioxide. This is combined with the main part of the acid–gas feed and introduced to a catalytic converter where sulfur is formed at about 540°F in accordance with the overall equation,

$$2 \, H_2S + SO_2 \rightarrow 3 \, S + 2 \, H_2O$$

Conversions up to 80% are obtainable in a single-stage converter and up to 92% in a two-stage converter. The converter gas is passed through a tube condenser where liquid sulfur is separated from the process gas. The combustion to sulfur dioxide is highly exothermic, and the heat is used to generate high-pressure steam.

A variant of the modified Claus process is known as the straight-through, direct-oxidation, partial-oxidation, or *selective-oxidation process*. In this process the hydrogen sulfide in acid feed gas, which contains considerable quantities of saturated hydrocarbons, is selectively oxidized to sulfur over a catalyst at about 425°F. The catalyst must be cooled to prevent undue temperature rise from the exothermic reaction

$$2 \, H_2S + O_2 \rightarrow 2 \, S + 2 \, H_2O$$

Excessive temperatures would lead to oxidation of the contained hydrocarbons. Although stoichiometric quantities of air are used, some sulfur dioxide is formed, so that conversion can be as low as 70%. If a higher degree of conversion is required, the converter gas, following passage through the condenser, is introduced into a Claus reactor with appropriate adjustments in temperature and composition to minimize oxidation of hydrocarbons.

The latter process is applied to gases containing large quantities of carbon dioxide or low concentrations of hydrogen sulfide, about 25% or less for the Stanolind version of this process, and about 10% for the Pan American Petroleum Corporation version. Gases treated by these methods are usually too low in hydrogen sulfide content to support combustion. These processes are unsuited to gases containing unsaturated hydrocarbon since these poison the catalysts and darken the sulfur product.

ECONOMIC ASPECTS OF BY-PRODUCT HYDROGEN SULFIDE RECOVERY

Recovery of by-product hydrogen sulfide has increased rapidly since World War II. This increase has been subject to considerable acceleration in the past decade. Several factors have stimulated this increase in the recovery of hydrogen sulfide. The advancing prices of sulfur since World War II have increased the number of recovery operations which are economically feasible. The need to process petroleum crudes and natural gases of higher sulfur contents has increased the quantities of hydrogen sulfide available for recovery. Also, the need to reduce atmospheric pollution has added further stimulus to the recovery of hydrogen sulfide.

Table 6 gives 1965 estimates on the recovery of hydrogen sulfide in millions of metric tons of elementary sulfur (47).

Table 6. World Recovery of Hydrogen Sulfide, million metric tons

Plant capacities		Amount recovered	
By country		*By source*	
United States	1.95	natural gas	4.0
Canada	2.45	oil refineries	1.0
France	1.52	coal gas and other	0.2
other	0.68	total	5.2
total	6.60		
		By form	
By source		elemental sulfur	4.9
natural gas	4.7	other, chiefly	0.3
oil and coal	2.0	sulfuric acid	
total	6.7	total	5.2

The dominant position of natural gas as a source of hydrogen sulfide for recovery of sulfur has come about only during recent years, which saw a sixteenfold increase from this source in the decade 1955–1965. The recovery activity is centered almost completely in the United States, Canada, and France, and has resulted from a combination of intensive exploitation of pipeline gas and favorable economics for recovery of hydrogen sulfide from this source. The utilization of capacity in such recovery runs over 80%, as against about 70% utilization of recovery capacity in oil-refinery operations. Only about 5% of the sulfur content of current world production of petroleum is extracted and recovered via hydrogen sulfide obtained by hydrorefining.

The value or "cost" of recovered hydrogen sulfide depends upon many factors which vary so widely that each case of recovered hydrogen sulfide utilization must be considered individually. These factors include the quantity and composition of the hydrogen sulfide source, its location with respect to product markets, and the intended use, namely production of sulfur, of sulfuric acid, or other chemical use. For chemical applications, the purity of the recovered hydrogen sulfide and the possible need for further purification and compression are major cost elements. The cost of sulfur is also a factor since it represents both a product and a competing raw material for the manufacture of other products based on recovered hydrogen sulfide. The distance of natural-gas wells from most sulfur-product markets has dictated the recovery of hydrogen sulfide almost completely as elemental sulfur because of the relative ease of storage and shipment in this form.

MATERIALS OF CONSTRUCTION

Anhydrous hydrogen sulfide is relatively noncorrosive to carbon steel, and a wide variety of metals and alloys, including aluminum; Stellite, Co–Cr–W; Inconel, Ni–Cr–Fe; Ni-Resist, cast iron–nickel, and types 304 and 316 stainless steels. However, all hard magnetic steels, if highly stressed, are subject to hydrogen embrittlement by hydrogen sulfide, the hydrogen possibly resulting from slight corrosion of the metal by the hydrogen sulfide. This can be prevented by coating the steel with aluminum or PTFE (polytetrafluoroethylene), or by replacing the steel with an alloy such as age-hardened Inconel or type 316 stainless steel (3).

In the presence of moisture, hydrogen sulfide is much more corrosive, carbon steel being corroded at rates in the vicinity of 0.1 in./yr. The rate of corrosion is a function of local conditions and other materials present. The stainless steels (particularly type 316) will often be found satisfactory. In a Girbotol process, absorbing gas having a 5:1 ratio of carbon dioxide to hydrogen sulfide and using as an absorbent monoethanolamine (15%), diethylene glycol (80%), and water (5%), steels containing either 2.5% chromium and 1% molybdenum or 4–6% chromium and 0.5% molybdenum showed no corrosion. The 2-S or 3-S aluminum alloys and 18–8 chrome–nickel stainless steels were also satisfactory (28).

HEALTH AND SAFETY FACTORS

Hydrogen sulfide is one of the more dangerous materials of industry. In its handling, two types of hazards must be taken into account, its extreme toxicity and its explosive nature when mixed with air or sulfur dioxide.

Of perhaps greatest importance is its toxicity. Its maximum safe concentration is about 13 ppm. Although at first this concentration can be readily recognized by its odor, hydrogen sulfide may partially paralyze the olfactory nerves to the point at which the presence of the gas is no longer sensed. Hence, the odor of the gas, strongly unpleasant though it is, is not a reliable safeguard or warning against its poisonous effects. Hydrogen sulfide, in its toxic action, attacks the nerve centers. Early symptoms of poisoning are slight headache, burning eyes, and clouded vision.

Some precautions against poisoning to be taken in working with hydrogen sulfide are: (1) Closed-in areas should be well ventilated, preferably with a forced draft. (2) Equipment containing hydrogen sulfide should be tightly sealed. Any leaks should be repaired immediately. (3) At seals or stuffing boxes where leaks might occur during normal operation, means should be provided for venting the escaped gas to a safe location. (4) Vessels should be purged of hydrogen sulfide before being opened. (5) Masks furnishing pure air should be worn by personnel who are likely to be exposed to the gas. (6) Personnel who may be exposed to low concentrations of the gas should frequently retire to areas of fresh air. (7) As a good safety measure, personnel should learn to recognize the early symptoms of hydrogen sulfide poisoning.

Hydrogen sulfide is a combustible material, and, when mixed with air or sulfur dioxide, may be explosive. It is essential, therefore, to avoid such mixtures in the processing of hydrogen sulfide. The explosive range of hydrogen sulfide in air is from 4.5–45.5%. The ignition temperature of such mixtures is around 250°C.

USES

The great bulk of the hydrogen sulfide recovered as a by-product is converted into either elementary sulfur or sulfuric acid. When there is a market for sulfuric acid in the vicinity of the source of hydrogen sulfide, it is economical to convert the hydrogen sulfide directly to sulfuric acid without going through the intermediate sulfur step. However, when there is insufficient market for the acid near the site of recovery, hydrogen sulfide is usually converted into elementary sulfur.

Conversion of hydrogen sulfide into sulfur is advantageous because sulfur is a stable, easily stored, easily shipped product for which there is a very broad market. The bulk of the hydrogen sulfide is converted into sulfur by modifications of the Claus process. Smaller quantities are converted into sulfur paste by the Thylox process (see p. 385). Because of the large quantities involved, hydrogen sulfide has become an important source of elemental sulfur.

Hydrogen sulfide finds use in the preparation of various sulfides. Considerable quantities of hydrogen sulfide serve to manufacture sodium sulfide and sodium hydrosulfide. See Sodium compounds.

Hydrogen sulfide is also employed to prepare organic sulfur compounds such as the thiophenes, thiols, sulfides, etc. Sulfur-containing additives for extreme-pressure lubricants and cutting oils are made by the reaction of hydrogen sulfide with various organic reagents. See Sulfurization.

Hydrogen sulfide is sometimes used to remove arsenic from 53°Bé chamberprocess sulfuric acid (qv) produced from pyrites. Inasmuch as this treatment also removes other heavy metallic impurities, acid treated in this manner is relatively pure.

Hydrogen sulfide is a familiar reagent in the chemical laboratory, where it serves as a precipitating agent in the usual scheme of qualitative analysis.

Hydrogen Polysulfides

Hydrogen polysulfides (hydrogen persulfides), H_2S_x, are yellow, oily liquids formed when alkali or alkaline-earth polysulfide solutions are added to mineral acid solutions. They were first observed in 1777 by Scheele, who noted that a yellow, pungent, oily substance resulted from the rapid addition of much acid to a solution of sulfur in an alkali.

The hydrogen polysulfide formed upon addition of an alkali polysulfide solution to acid is generally a mixture of compounds, the following of which have been isolated and characterized: H_2S_2, H_2S_3, H_2S_4, H_2S_5, and H_2S_6, and probably a continuous series beyond S_6.

The polysulfides of hydrogen may be separated by fractional distillation. The higher polysulfides are particularly subject to thermal decomposition, hence an extremely high vacuum is required in their distillation. The separation of H_2S_5 and H_2S_6 is accomplished at 10^{-4} mm Hg. The decomposition of H_2S_x results in hydrogen sulfide and sulfur.

Hydrogen disulfide (hydrogen persulfide), H_2S_2, is an unstable, yellow, flammable liquid with a pungent odor whose vapors attack the eyes and mucous membranes. It has the following properties: mp, $-89.6°C$; bp, $70.7°C$; d_4^{20} 1.3339; heat of fusion, 27.2 cal/g; heat of vaporization, 129.2 cal/g; C_p, 0.334 cal/g; surface tension, 38.1 dyn/cm. It is miscible with carbon disulfide, benzene, and ether. It is a good solvent for sulfur.

Hydrogen disulfide is extremely sensitive to alkalis, and it is necessary to treat the glass or silica vessel in which it is kept with HCl to prevent decomposition. Correspondingly, it is rapidly decomposed by water and by alcohols, and almost explosively if the water is alkaline. It is oxidized by silver oxide,

$$H_2S_2 + Ag_2O \rightarrow Ag_2S + S + H_2O$$

It is also oxidized by concentrated sulfuric acid to sulfur dioxide. Hydrogen disulfide forms addition compounds with aldehydes and ketones.

Hydrogen disulfide may be prepared by the thermal decomposition of crude hydrogen polysulfide or of hydrogen trisulfide at temperatures ranging from 100–150°C and at reduced pressures. Best yields are obtained from a crude prepared from $Na_2S_{2.5}$. The product is purified by fractional distillation.

Hydrogen trisulfide, H_2S_3, is an unstable, pale-yellow, mobile oil with a disagreeable pungent odor suggesting camphor and sulfur chloride. It has the following properties: mp, −52°C; bp, 69°C at 2 mm; sp gr, 1.496. It is slightly less sensitive to the presence of alkalis than is hydrogen disulfide but is more easily decomposed at elevated temperatures. It is soluble in carbon disulfide, benzene, chloroform, ether, and similar solvents, and is itself a solvent for sulfur. It is decomposed by water, alkalis, and alcohols. It forms very unstable addition products with ketones and aldehydes. When distilled at atmospheric pressure, it decomposes, about one-third being converted into hydrogen disulfide. Exposure to light accelerates its decomposition. It slowly reduces concentrated sulfuric acid. It is oxidized by dry silver oxide, cupric oxide, lead dioxide, and mercuric oxide, the metallic sulfides being thereby obtained. Its oxidation by potassium permanganate or dichromate is violent.

Hydrogen tetrasulfide, H_2S_4, **hydrogen pentasulfide,** H_2S_5, and **hydrogen hexasulfide,** H_2S_6, are yellow, oily liquids obtained by fractional distillation of crude hydrogen polysulfide at 10^{-4} mm Hg. They have no definite melting points.

Compound	Formula wt	d_4^{15}
H_2S_4	130.28	1.588
H_2S_5	162.35	1.660
H_2S_6	194.41	1.699

These compounds are very unstable. They are decomposed on contact with powdered quartz and glass, wood, or paper. They are soluble in benzene and similar solvents, and are themselves solvents for sulfur (17).

A crude hydrogen pentasulfide is obtained by treating pure dry ammonium pentasulfide crystals with carefully dried formic acid. The molecular weight of the product so produced is 152.5, as determined by cryoscopic measurement in benzene.

SULFUR HALIDES AND OXYHALIDES. Sulfur combines with halogens to form several series of halides. The compounds so formed generally become less stable as the atomic weights of the halogens increase. Thus several stable fluorides of sulfur exist, but no compounds of sulfur and iodine have ever been isolated. The following halides of sulfur are known: fluorides, SF_6, S_2F_{10}, SF_4, SF_2, S_2F_2; chlorides, SCl_4, SCl_2, S_2Cl_2; bromides, S_2Br_2. For the sulfur fluorides see Vol. 9, p. 664.

Sulfur Monobromide. Sulfur monobromide (disulfur dibromide), S_2Br_2, is the only definite bromide of sulfur. It is a garnet-red, oily liquid; mp, −46°C; bp, 54°C at 0.18 mm; d_4^{20} 2.6355. It is prepared by the reaction of an equiatomic mixture of sulfur and bromine, preferably at 100°C, in a sealed vessel. Sulfur monobromide is soluble in carbon disulfide and similar solvents, and is a solvent for sulfur. It is chemically similar to sulfur monochloride, but is less stable.

Sulfur Chlorides

Chlorine and sulfur react readily to form a series of compounds, including the following well-established members: SCl_4, SCl_2, and S_2Cl_2, as well as S_3Cl_2, S_4Cl_2, ..., S_xCl_2, and S_3Cl_4, whose existences are somewhat less certain.

The initial reaction between sulfur and chlorine yields sulfur monochloride, S_2Cl_2,

$$2\ S + Cl_2 \rightarrow S_2Cl_2$$

Upon further addition of chlorine, sulfur dichloride, SCl_2, is slowly formed,

$$S_2Cl_2 + Cl_2 \rightleftharpoons 2\ SCl_2$$

At low temperatures, S_2Cl_2 and SCl_2 combine to form trisulfur tetrachloride, S_3Cl_4. This compound is, however, largely decomposed at room temperature.

$$S_2Cl_2 + SCl_2 \rightleftharpoons S_3Cl_4$$

When chlorine is added to sulfur monochloride or sulfur dichloride at low temperatures, sulfur tetrachloride is formed.

$$SCl_2 + Cl_2 \rightarrow SCl_4$$

Freezing points of the chlorine–sulfur system lying between S_2Cl_2 and sulfur suggest the existence of S_3Cl_2 and S_4Cl_2. It is probable that "chlorine polysulfides" containing even longer chains of sulfur have at least transient existence.

Sulfur Monochloride. Sulfur monochloride (disulfur dichloride), S_2Cl_2, is a golden-yellow liquid, with a pungent odor; it was first studied in 1810 by Davy and Buchholz. Although most readily formed by the direct combination of chlorine and sulfur, S_2Cl_2 may be obtained by a wide variety of other reactions, including the action of chlorine on numerous sulfides or the action of higher-valence chlorides such as phosphorus pentachloride or mercuric chloride on sulfur.

S_2Cl_2 has the following properties: mp, $-82°C$; bp, $138°C$; sp gr, d_4^{25}, 1.6733; heat of vaporization, 64.6 cal/g; C_p (liquid), 0.220 cal/g; heat of formation, -106 cal/g (liquid at 18°C); surface tension at 22°C, 40.78 dyn/cm; viscosity at 18°C, 2.015 cP. The vapor pressure of sulfur monochloride is given in millimeters by the equation

$$\log p = 7.4550 - 1880.1/T$$

where $T = °K$. The boiling-point-elevation constant is 52.9.

Sulfur monochloride is quite stable at room temperature, but experiments with radioactive sulfur in solution in sulfur monochloride at 100°C demonstrate an appreciable rate of exchange of sulfur between the two materials. This indicates a reversible breakdown of the sulfur monochloride at 100°C. The breakdown does not, however, become important until temperatures in excess of 300°C are reached. At this temperature decomposition occurs as follows:

$$S_2Cl_2 \rightleftharpoons S_2 + Cl_2$$

Sulfur chloride is noncombustible at room temperature, but at elevated temperatures decomposition is sufficiently rapid to permit the liberated sulfur to burn, producing sulfur dioxide, sulfur trioxide, and chlorine.

Many metallic oxides are attacked by sulfur monochloride, yielding the corresponding chlorides,

$$2\ MO + 2\ S_2Cl_2 \rightarrow 2\ MCl_2 + SO_2 + 3\ S$$

Metallic sulfides react similarly.

$$2\ ZnS + 2\ S_2Cl_2 \rightarrow 2\ ZnCl_2 + 6\ S$$

Sulfur trioxide reacts with sulfur monochloride to give pyrosulfuryl chloride, $S_2O_5Cl_2$. Sulfates heated with sulfur monochloride are converted to chlorides, sulfuryl chloride being simultaneously formed.

$$Na_2SO_4 + 2\ S_2Cl_2 \rightarrow SO_2Cl_2 + 2\ NaCl + SO_2 + 3\ S$$

Sulfur monochloride is hydrolyzed with water, slowly at room temperature but rapidly at elevated temperatures. The rate of hydrolysis in the vapor state is rather slow.

$$S_2Cl_2 + 2\ H_2O \rightarrow 2\ HCl + SO_2 + H_2S$$

In solution, hydrogen sulfide and sulfur dioxide react further to form sulfur and polythionic acids. In the presence of additional chlorine, the hydrolysis produces sulfuric acid,

$$S_2Cl_2 + 8\ H_2O + 5\ Cl_2 \rightarrow 2\ H_2SO_4 + 12\ HCl$$

This reaction may occasionally be useful in dehydrations.

With iodides, sulfur monochloride liberates iodine, a reaction useful in its analysis,

$$S_2Cl_2 + 2\ HI \rightarrow I_2 + 2\ HCl + 2\ S$$

When treated with dry ammonia in a suitable solvent, at low temperatures, it yields sulfur nitrides.

$$6\ S_2Cl_2 + 16\ NH_3 \rightarrow S_4N_4 + 12\ NH_4Cl + 8\ S$$

When an excess of S_2Cl_2 is treated with phosphorus, thiophosphoryl chloride ($PSCl_3$), and free sulfur are formed. However, when phosphorus is in excess, then phosphorus trichloride and phosphorus sulfide are formed.

$$3\ S_2Cl_2 + 2\ P \rightarrow 2\ PSCl_3 + 4\ S\ (S_2Cl_2\ in\ excess)$$

$$3\ S_2Cl_2 + 10\ P \rightarrow 2\ PCl_3 + 2\ P_4S_3\ (phosphorus\ in\ excess)$$

In the presence of iodine as a catalyst, sulfur monochloride reacts with phosphorus trichloride to produce phosphorus pentachloride and thiophosphoryl chloride.

$$3\ PCl_3 + S_2Cl_2 \rightarrow PCl_5 + 2\ PSCl_3$$

Antimony pentachloride, boron trichloride, and ferric chloride react with sulfur monochloride and chlorine to form the complexes $SbCl_5.SCl_4$, $BCl_3.SCl_4$, and $FeCl_3.-2SCl_4$. The iron complex reacts with organic acids to form the corresponding acyl chlorides.

With organic reagents, sulfur monochloride reacts to introduce either sulfur, chlorine, or both. Thus, in its well-known reaction with ethylene to produce mustard gas (see Chemical warfare), both sulfur and chlorine are introduced. The reaction is believed to proceed in steps as follows:

$$S_2Cl_2 \rightleftharpoons SCl_2 + S$$
$$SCl_2 + CH_2{=}CH_2 \rightarrow ClCH_2CH_2SCl$$
$$ClCH_2CH_2SCl + CH_2{=}CH_2 \rightarrow (ClCH_2CH_2)_2S$$

When sulfur monochloride is reacted with aromatic hydrocarbons, the corresponding aromatic dithiochlorides are formed,

$$ArH + S_2Cl_2 \rightarrow ArS_2Cl + HCl$$

These compounds in turn react with additional hydrocarbon to produce a variety of sulfides. Thus, the reaction of sulfur monochloride with benzene in the presence of zinc yields benzenethiol, diphenyl sulfide, diphenyl disulfide, and thianthrene,

When reacted with thiols, sulfur monochloride yields tetrasulfides.

$$2\ RSH + S_2Cl_2 \rightarrow RS_4R + 2\ HCl$$

Because of its dehydrating action, sulfur chloride reacts with organic acids to form the corresponding acid anhydrides. With the higher aliphatic acids, the acid chlorides are produced.

Manufacture. The sulfur monochloride of commerce is usually obtained by direct combination of the elements in batch processes carried out in horizontal steel vessels. The process consists of charging refined sulfur to a reactor that contains sufficient sulfur chloride from a previous batch to cover the sparger through which the chlorine is to be introduced. The batch is heated to 50–60°C to facilitate the initiation of the reaction, and chlorine is then metered into the batch until the desired degree of chlorination has been achieved. Since the reaction is exothermic and not very rapid, the rate of chlorine addition must be controlled to prevent excessive loss of this reactant or of the sulfur dichloride that may be formed as an intermediate compound.

The chlorination of sulfur is a progressive reaction that no doubt starts with the chlorination of the free ends of ruptured S_8 rings. The S_8Cl_2 thus formed is unstable and breaks down into smaller fragments, which either reorient themselves to shorter chain chlorides or in turn become further chlorinated, ultimately to SCl_2. The compound S_2Cl_2 appears to be the most stable member of the series, the stability of the other members falling off as the length of the sulfur chain increases (or decreases). Since the reactions in this series are relatively slow, equilibrium among the various products may not be maintained during the chlorination if this operation is carried on rapidly; both SCl_2 and higher sulfur chlorides are present when the average composition reaches that of S_2Cl_2. Commercial batches are produced sufficiently slowly to yield a product which is largely S_2Cl_2 at the end of the chlorination.

Large quantities of sulfur monochloride appear as an intermediate product in the manufacture of carbon tetrachloride from carbon disulfide and chlorine.

$$CS_2 + 3\ Cl_2 \rightarrow CCl_4 + S_2Cl_2$$

The mixture of carbon tetrachloride and sulfur monochloride is separated by fractional distillation to yield a concentrated sulfur monochloride, which is, however, too impure to be marketed as a commercial grade. It contains carbon tetrachloride, sulfur, tars, traces of carbon disulfide, etc. The crude sulfur monochloride is treated with additional carbon disulfide in the presence of a catalyst to yield more carbon tetrachloride and sulfur.

$$2\ S_2Cl_2 + CS_2 \rightarrow CCl_4 + 6\ S$$

Sulfur monochloride vapor is extremely toxic, the threshold limit of toxicity being about 1 ppm. It is very irritating to the eyes and mucous membranes. The liquid is also extremely corrosive to the skin. It is necessary, therefore, to follow the usual precautions for handling toxic and corrosive volatile liquids.

Dry sulfur monochloride is not corrosive to iron or steel at ordinary temperatures; it is very corrosive in the presence of moisture, however, and it is essential to exclude moisture from any equipment in which the compound is stored.

Commercial sulfur monochloride is produced in a variety of grades, depending upon the ratio of sulfur to chlorine. *Yellow sulfur chloride* may contain 0–7% excess sulfur; *red sulfur chloride* is usually a mixture of sulfur mono- and dichlorides in varying proportion. Sulfur monochloride is shipped in 7000- to 8000-gal tank cars containing about 100,000 lb, in 55-gal steel drums containing 700 lb, or in 10-gal drums containing 130 lb. It is shipped as a corrosive liquid under a White label. The price in 55-gal-drum car lots in November 1968 was 7.1¢/lb.

Uses of Sulfur Chlorides. Sulfur monochloride in combination with chlorine is often used as a substitute for sulfur dichloride. Hence, the uses considered here will include those for sulfur dichloride.

Sulfur chlorides are useful as chlorinating agents or for introducing sulfur into organic compounds, or both. For example, sulfur monochloride is treated with ethylene to produce mustard gas. Of more importance commercially, considerable sulfur chloride is used in the treatment of unsaturated fatty acids to produce compounds containing chlorine and sulfur. These materials are useful as additives to cutting oils and extreme-pressure lubricants (see Sulfurization). Phenols and a variety of unsaturated compounds (primarily of petroleum origin), in addition to fatty acids, have been treated with sulfur chlorides for the same purpose and represent the major outlet for sulfur chlorides. Treatments of various vegetable oils, such as corn oil, cottonseed oil, rapeseed oil, and soybean oil, with sulfur chloride yield rubberlike products, known as factice. The largest outlet for this type of product is in the production of Artgum erasers.

Sulfur dichloride is sometimes used in the treatment of drying oils for varnishes. This use somewhat parallels its use as a drying agent for coatings of ink, paint, or varnish. Sulfur monochloride is used to cold-vulcanize articles made of thin rubber sheets. Toy balloons and drug sundries are examples of such products.

Sulfur dichloride, or the combination of sulfur monochloride and added chlorine, when treated with the sodium salts of organic acids, produces the corresponding acid anhydrides. Thus, acetic anhydride has been obtained from the action of sulfur chloride on sodium acetate. With the higher aliphatic acid salts, the acid chlorides can be produced by this process.

Sulfur chlorides are often used as catalysts in the chlorination of organic compounds. Thus sulfur monochloride serves as a catalyst in the chlorination of acetic acid to monochloroacetic acid. The hydrolysis of sulfur monochloride can be made to yield that form of sulfur which is insoluble in carbon disulfide (39). Some uses for sulfur monochloride depend upon its ability to dissolve sulfur. Sulfur dichloride or sulfur monochloride and chlorine are treated with sulfur trioxide to produce thionyl chloride.

$$SCl_2 + SO_3 \rightarrow SOCl_2 + SO_2$$

Sulfur Dichloride. Sulfur dichloride, SCl_2, is a dark-brown or reddish liquid, mp, $-122°C$; bp, about $59°C$ (some decompn); d_4^{15} 1.621; vapor pressure at $-23°C$, 7.6 mm; heat of formation at $25°C$, -116.5 cal/g; heat of vaporization at $59°C$, 67.6 cal/g. It decomposes rapidly $>40°C$.

A development of considerable significance to the chemistry and technology of sulfur dichloride has been the disclosure (53) of a method for stabilizing this compound against dissociation, even at the boiling point, thereby permitting the purification of sulfur dichloride by distillation. This is accomplished by the addition of traces of phosphorus trichloride, pentachloride (54), or pentasulfide. Crude product containing 80% sulfur dichloride to which is added 0.1% phosphorus trichloride can be distilled to yield a 98%–99% pure sulfur dichloride which can be stored for weeks at room temperature without appreciable change. Reference 53 gives data on the vapor pressure of pure stabilized sulfur dichloride in the temperature range -38–$85°C$. The availability of substantially pure stabilized sulfur dichloride has promoted new interest in the synthetic organic chemistry of sulfur dichloride (55).

Chemically, sulfur dichloride behaves very much like a mixture of S_2Cl_2 and chlorine. This follows in part, at least, from the equilibrium,

$$2\ SCl_2 \rightleftharpoons S_2Cl_2 + Cl_2$$

the constant for which is 0.013 at $18°C$.

Sulfur dichloride reacts with sulfur trioxide or with chlorosulfonic acid to produce thionyl chloride and sulfur dioxide,

$$SCl_2 + SO_3 \xrightarrow[100°C]{} SOCl_2 + SO_2$$

$$SCl_2 + ClSO_3H \rightarrow SOCl_2 + SO_2 + HCl$$

Treatment of sulfur dichloride with an excess of sulfur trioxide yields pyrosulfuryl chloride, $S_2O_5Cl_2$.

$$SCl_2 + 3\ SO_3 \rightarrow S_2O_5Cl_2 + 2\ SO_2$$

Sulfur dichloride is the primary product in the gaseous reaction between hydrogen sulfide and chlorine,

$$H_2S + 2\ Cl_2 \rightarrow SCl_2 + 2\ HCl$$

However, it is prepared commercially by the addition of chlorine to sulfur monochloride. The reaction proceeds rather slowly, and particularly at its later stages is limited to temperatures below $40°C$. It is carried out in the same equipment used to produce the monochloride. The commercial product often contains a small percentage of dissolved free chlorine.

The uses of sulfur dichloride have been discussed with those of the monochloride. Handling precautions and packaging are also similar to those for the monochloride. The price of sulfur dichloride, as of November 1968, was 6.7¢/lb in 55-gal car lots.

Sulfur Tetrachloride. Sulfur tetrachloride (trichlorosulfonium chloride), SCl_4, is a yellow solid that melts to a red liquid at about $-30°C$. Even at its melting point, the liquid dissociates into chlorine and sulfur dichloride. It is formed by the addition of chlorine to sulfur dichloride at high pressures and low temperatures. The solid is believed to be the salt, $(SCl_3)^+Cl^-$.

Sulfur tetrachloride reacts rapidly with water to form sulfur dioxide and hydrochloric acid.

$$SCl_4 + 2\ H_2O \rightarrow SO_2 + 4\ HCl$$

It reacts with chlorosulfuric acid to yield a salt (see p. 405).

$$(SCl_3)Cl + ClSO_2OH \rightarrow ClSO_2OSCl_3 + HCl$$

It reacts with anhydrous ammonia to form sulfur nitride.

$$12 \ SCl_4 + 16 \ NH_3 \rightarrow 3 \ S_4N_4 + 48 \ HCl + 2 \ N_2$$

Sulfur tetrachloride forms the following unstable crystalline addition compounds: $SbCl_5 \cdot SCl_4$, mp, $125°C$; $TiCl_4 \cdot SCl_4$, soluble in carbon disulfide and hydrocarbon solvents; $SnCl_4 \cdot 2SCl_4$; $FeCl_3 \cdot SCl_4$, useful in some chlorination reactions; $AlCl_3 \cdot SCl_4$; $2ICl_3 \cdot SCl_4$, soluble in $CHCl_3$, CCl_4, and hydrocarbon solvents; $2AsF_3 \cdot SCl_4$; and $BCl_3 \cdot SCl_4$, mp, $-23°C$.

Oxyhalides

Most of the sulfur oxyhalides may be considered to be the halo derivatives of the sulfur–oxygen acids (oxyacids). The known oxyhalides falling into this category are listed in Table 7. Although sulfur dichloride and difluoride are not oxyhalides, they are included in the table as derivatives of an oxygen acid.

Sulfur oxytetrachloride, $S_2O_3Cl_4$, does not fall into the above classification (see p. 405).

Thionyl Bromide. Thionyl bromide, $SOBr_2$, is an orange-yellow liquid, with d_4^{15}, 2.697; bp, $138°C$ (with decompn); vapor pressure at $45°C$, 22 mm; at $68°C$, 40 mm. It is prepared by the action of HBr on $SOCl_2$ at low temperatures. Its reactions are similar to those of thionyl chloride, but it is less stable, decomposing slowly at room temperature,

$$4 \ SOBr_2 \rightarrow S_2Br_2 + 2 \ SO_2 + 3 \ Br_2$$

It is readily hydrolyzed by water, and reacts with organic acids to form acid bromides.

Table 7. Halogen Derivatives of Sulfur–Oxygen Acids

Halogen derivative	Sulfoxylic HOSOH	Sulfurous $\overset{O}{\underset{\uparrow}{HOSOH}}$	Sulfuric $\overset{O}{\underset{\downarrow}{\overset{\uparrow}{HOSOH}}}\overset{}{_O}$	Pyrosulfuric $HO{-}\overset{\overset{O}{\uparrow}}{\underset{\downarrow}{S}}{-}O{-}\overset{\overset{O}{\uparrow}}{\underset{\downarrow}{S}}{-}OH$
oxyfluoride	sulfur difluoride, SF_2	thionyl fluoride, SOF_2	fluorosulfonic acid, FSO_3H sulfuryl fluoride, SO_2F_2	
oxychloro-fluoride			sulfuryl chlorofluoride, SO_2FCl	
oxychloride	sulfur dichloride, SCl_2	thionyl chloride, $SOCl_2$	chlorosulfonic acid, $ClSO_3H$ sulfuryl chloride, SO_2Cl_2	pyrosulfuryl chloride, $S_2O_5Cl_2$
oxybromide		thionyl bromide, $SOBr_2$		

Sulfur Oxychlorides

Thionyl Chloride. Thionyl chloride (sulfurous oxychloride), $SOCl_2$, is a colorless, fuming liquid which finds its primary use as a chlorinating agent in organic chemistry. It has the following properties: mp, $-104.5°C$; bp, $79°C$; d_4^0, 1.676; n_D^{20}, 1.517; C_p, 0.24 cal/g; latent heat of vaporization, 62.9 cal/g; heat of formation, $-47,200$ cal/g-mole; coefficient of cubical expansion, $0.0010/°C$; viscosity at $0°C$, 0.801 cP, at $38°C$, 0.545 cP; dielectric constant at $20°C$, 9.25; electrical conductivity at $25°C$, 2×10^{-6} $(\Omega^{-1})(cm^{-1})$. The vapor pressure of thionyl chloride at various temperatures is as follows:

Temperature, °C	20	30	40	50	60	70	75
Vapor pressure, mm Hg	96.6	147.9	221.3	321.6	458.1	637.9	746.0

Thionyl chloride is miscible with benzene, chloroform, carbon tetrachloride, etc. It will dissolve the iodides of arsenic, antimony, tin, mercury, cobalt, and tetramethylammonium to give slightly conducting solutions. It forms the addition product $2AlCl_3SOCl_2$. Thionyl chloride may be considered to be the chloro derivative of sulfurous acid. It is characterized by its very strong tendency to replace OH or SH

Table 8. Summary of Inorganic Reactions of Thionyl Chloride

Reactant	Conditions of reaction	Primary reaction products
Reactions characteristic of the thermal decomposition of thionyl chloride		
sulfur	180°C	S_2Cl_2, SO_2
phosphorus	elevated temp	PCl_3, SO_2, S_2Cl_2
	prolonged heating with excess $SOCl_2$	PCl_5, SO_2, S_2Cl_2
PCl_3	high temp	PCl_5, $PSCl_3$, $POCl_3$
selenium	high temp	$SeCl_4$, SO_2, S
SeO_2		$SeCl_4$, SO_2
tellurium	$SOCl_2$ in excess	$TeCl_4$, SO_2, S
	tellurium in excess	$TeCl_2$, SO_2, S
many metals	elevated temp	metal chlorides, S_2Cl_2, SO_2
metal sulfides	150–200°C	metal chlorides, SO_2, S_2Cl_2
metal oxides	200°C	metal chlorides, SO_2
Reactions characteristic of thionyl chloride itself		
water	low temp, rapid reaction	H_2SO_3, HCl
BaO_2	$SOCl_2$ in excess	$BaCl_2$, SO_2, SO_2Cl_2
	BaO_2 in excess	$BaCl_2$, $BaSO_4$, SO_2Cl_2
Hg or HgO	150°C, excess $SOCl_2$	$HgCl_2$, SO_2Cl_2, S_2Cl_2
Hg	150°C, excess Hg	$HgCl_2$, SO_2, S_2Cl_2
H_2S	$AlCl_3$ catalyst (reaction slow without $AlCl_3$)	HCl, SO_2, S
H_2SO_4		$ClSO_3H$ or $S_2O_5Cl_2$, SO_2, HCl
SO_3	100°C	$S_2O_5Cl_2$
HNO_3		H_2SO_4, NO_2Cl, NOCl
$AgNO_3$	dry reaction	NO_2SO_2Cl, AgCl
N_2O_4		NOCl, SO_3
HBr	$-80°C$	$SOBr_2$, HCl
HI		I_2, HCl, SO_2, S
NH_3	vapor-phase reaction	HCl + HNSO (bp, $-85°C$) (61)

groups with chlorine atoms. It will also, under some circumstances, replace SO_2, H, or O with chlorine. Thionyl chloride begins to decompose at about 150°C, decomposition being largely complete at about 500°C,

$$4 \, SOCl_2 \rightarrow 3 \, Cl_2 + 2 \, SO_2 + S_2Cl_2$$

The ease of decomposition of thionyl chloride accounts for many of its reactions, particularly those at elevated temperatures.

Table 8 summarizes the inorganic reactions of thionyl chloride.

Thionyl chloride reacts with organic compounds containing hydroxyl groups to form the corresponding chlorides. Thus its reaction with alcohols or phenols produces the corresponding chloro compounds. With organic acids, either acid chlorides or acid anhydrides are formed, depending upon the ratio of acid to thionyl chloride. Equimolal quantities of acid and thionyl chloride yield the acid chloride, but when the ratio of acid to thionyl chloride is $2:1$ the acid anhydride is obtained. Reactions with sulfonic acids yield sulfonyl chlorides.

The reaction of thionyl chloride with a Grignard reagent yields the corresponding sulfoxide.

$$2 \, RMgX + SOCl_2 \rightarrow R\overset{\overset{\displaystyle O}{\uparrow}}{S}R + MgX_2 + MgCl_2$$

Ionic reactions with thionyl chloride as a solvent have been studied (62).

Manufacture. Thionyl chloride was first obtained by Persoz and Bloch in 1849 by the interaction of sulfur dioxide and phosphorus pentachloride,

$$SO_2 + PCl_5 \rightarrow POCl_3 + SOCl_2$$

The thionyl chloride may be obtained with some difficulty from the reaction mass by fractional distillation.

Most commercial methods of preparation, however, are based upon the oxidation of sulfur dichloride with either sulfur trioxide or sulfuryl chloride,

$$SCl_2 + SO_3 \rightarrow SOCl_2 + SO_2$$
$$SCl_2 + SO_2Cl_2 \rightleftharpoons 2 \, SOCl_2$$

A variety of starting materials may be used for these reactions. The sulfur dichloride is usually produced directly in the reactor by reaction of chlorine with either sulfur or sulfur monochloride. The sulfuryl chloride results from the chlorination either of sulfur dioxide or of sulfuric acid with part of the thionyl chloride produced.

$$HOSO_2OH + SOCl_2 \rightarrow HOSO_2Cl + HCl + SO_2$$
$$HOSO_2Cl + SOCl_2 \rightarrow SO_2Cl_2 + HCl + SO_2$$
$$SO_2 + Cl_2 \rightleftharpoons SO_2Cl_2$$

The sulfur trioxide may either be introduced (as oleum) into the reactor as such, or be derived from the sulfuric acid,

$$HOSO_2OH + SOCl_2 \rightarrow HOSO_2Cl + SO_2 + HCl$$
$$HOSO_2Cl \rightleftharpoons SO_3 + HCl$$

It will be seen that these reactions permit a fairly wide variety of raw materials to be used in the manufacture of thionyl chloride, with the result that several related processes have been developed for the manufacture of this chemical.

In the process patented by Hooker Electrochemical Company (40), the reaction is carried out in a glass-lined, jacketed, iron vessel, fitted with an agitator, and with a condenser arranged either for reflux or for distillation. The vessel may be charged with either sulfur monochloride or sulfur dichloride and about 1% of antimony trichloride as a catalyst. Chlorine is introduced into the reactor near its bottom. Liquid oleum of as high a free SO_3 concentration as is practical (usually around 70% free SO_3) is added to the reactor at such a rate that the temperature of the reaction mass is held at around 25°C. The use of cooling water in the jacket of the reactor helps to speed the reaction by cooling the mass. When the batch has been completed, a slight excess of oleum and chlorine is added to reduce to a minimum the residual SCl_2. The reaction can be written as a combination of the following equations:

$$S_2Cl_2 + Cl_2 + 2 SO_3 \rightarrow 2 SOCl_2 + 2 SO_2$$

$$2 S_2Cl_2 + 4 Cl_2 + 2 H_2SO_4 \rightarrow 4 SOCl_2 + 4 HCl + 2 SO_2$$

Inasmuch as thionyl chloride combines readily with sulfur trioxide to form the relatively stable pyrosulfuryl chloride, it is essential to maintain the concentration of sulfur trioxide in the reaction mass at a low level—hence, the addition of oleum to sulfur chloride rather than the reverse operation. Correspondingly, low temperatures are employed to minimize formation of the higher oxides. When all of the reactants have been added, heat is applied to the jacket of the reactor, and the batch is refluxed until most of the sulfur dioxide, hydrogen chloride, chlorine, etc, have been eliminated. The thionyl chloride is then distilled from the reactor (leaving the high-boiling oxides and other impurities) and further purified if necessary. A batch requires 45–50 hr of processing time.

In the process as patented by E. I. du Pont de Nemours & Company, Inc. (41), the reaction is operated on a continuous basis at a temperature between 105 and 110°C. The reactor contains a heel of sulfur monochloride with about 1% of antimony trichloride as catalyst. A mixture of sulfur trioxide vapor and an excess of chlorine are introduced into the reactor near its bottom. The thionyl chloride and sulfur dioxide which are formed by the reaction, together with the excess chlorine, any unreacted sulfur trioxide, and a substantial quantity of vaporized sulfur monochloride, rise from the reactor. The excess chlorine is recovered in a sulfur–sulfur chloride scrubber and is returned to the reactor. The thionyl chloride is separated from the sulfur monochloride in a fractionating column. The sulfur monochloride is returned to the reactor. By maintaining a low (3–15%) concentration of thionyl chloride in the reactor, as well as a low concentration of sulfur trioxide, the formation of pyrosulfuryl chloride is minimized, and a continuous operation is achieved. Yields of thionyl chloride by this process are around 92%, based on the chlorine and sulfur. Reaction rates of between 5 and 6 lb of thionyl chloride per gallon of reaction heel volume per hour are experienced.

In the process patented by Pittsburgh Plate Glass Company (42) sulfur monochloride, sulfur dioxide, and chlorine are reacted at around 200°C in the presence of an activated carbon catalyst to produce thionyl chloride,

$$S_2Cl_2 + 2 SO_2 + 3 Cl_2 \rightleftharpoons 4 SOCl_2$$

Using a 0–10% excess of chlorine and about 100% excess of sulfur dioxide, conversions of around 50% are obtained. The liquids in the reaction product are condensed and separated, the sulfur mono- and dichloride being returned for further reaction. The excess gases are likewise recycled. This process has the advantage that it produces an ultimate yield of near 100% on all of the reactants.

The process patented by Allied Chemical & Dye Corporation (43) is based upon the reaction

$$COCl_2 + SO_2 \rightarrow SOCl_2 + CO_2$$

In this process, sulfur dioxide, chlorine, and carbon monoxide are brought together in the presence of activated wood charcoal at carefully controlled temperatures (170°C in the first stage and 200°C in the second stage) in such a manner as to minimize the formation of either sulfur chlorides or sulfuryl chloride. The reaction is

$$2\ CO + 2\ Cl_2 + SO_2 \rightarrow COCl_2 + SOCl_2 + CO_2$$

The thionyl chloride condensed out of the reaction gases from these stages is of high purity, containing only a trace of either sulfur chloride or sulfuryl chloride. To the phosgene remaining in the noncondensable fraction is added an excess of sulfur dioxide, and the mixture is passed through a third reaction chamber maintained at 310°C. The reaction taking place in this reactor is

$$COCl_2 + SO_2 \rightarrow SOCl_2 + CO_2$$

The products from the third reactor are condensed at $-30°C$ to remove all but the carbon dioxide. A technical grade of thionyl chloride is obtained upon fractionation of this condensate.

Thionyl chloride is a hazardous chemical. Its vapors are irritating to the eyes and mucous membranes. The liquid is corrosive to the skin. In handling thionyl chloride, the care usual in the handling of volatile, corrosive, and toxic materials must be exercised; one part of water reacts with about seven parts of thionyl chloride, so contact with water or moist air must be avoided in storage and handling. Storage tanks should be furnished with vents modified to contain drying agents to prevent suckback of moist air. Drums of thionyl chloride should be tightly sealed but vented periodically to relieve any pressure which may develop. Lead, nickel, or glass equipment may be used in handling thionyl chloride; iron can be used, but it is not completely free from attack.

Thionyl chloride is produced in the technical and refined grades. Typical analyses and boiling ranges of these are given in Table 9.

Table 9. Analysis of Technical and Refined Thionyl Chloride

Analysis	Technical grade	Refined grade
$SOCl_2$, %	93+	97.5
SO_2, %	0.7	0.5
S_2Cl_2, %	1.5	0.5
SO_2Cl_2, %	4.5	1.5
Fe, ppm		20
boiling range, °C	72–79	75–78

Uses. Thionyl chloride is used extensively in organic synthesis to replace various groups, particularly hydroxy groups, with chlorine. It is used in the preparation of fatty acid chlorides, which in turn are reacted to form a variety of surface-active agents. It also finds use in the preparation of pharmaceuticals and of dyes. The following are some of the end products prepared through the use of thionyl chloride:

isoamyl chloride, synthetic pyrethrum, synthetic vitamin A palmitate, and antihistamines.

Because of its extreme reactivity with water, and because the products of its hydrolysis are gases, thionyl chloride has been suggested as a dehydrating agent for removing the last traces of water of hydration from difficultly dehydratable salts, such as $MgCl_2 \cdot 6H_2O$, $FeCl_3 \cdot 4H_2O$, $AlCl_3 \cdot 6H_2O$, $TiCl_3$, etc.

Sulfuryl Chloride. Sulfuryl chloride (sulfuric oxychloride), SO_2Cl_2, is a colorless liquid with an extremely pungent odor. It has the following properties: mp, $-46°C$; bp, $69.1°C$; d_4^{20} 1.6674; n_D^{20}, 1.443; sp heat, 0.233 cal/g; latent heat of vaporization, 49.5 cal/g; heat of formation, 89.540 cal/g-mole; ebullioscopic constant, 45; coefficient of cubical expansion, $0.0012/°C$; viscosity, 0.918 cP at $0°C$, 0.1596 at $38°C$; vapor pressure, 40.9 mm at $0°C$, 95.2 mm at $18°C$, 745 mm at $68.7°C$; dielectric constant at $22°C$, 9.15; electrical conductivity at $25°C$, 3×10^{-8} $(\Omega^{-1})(cm^{-1})$.

Sulfuryl chloride is a solvent for many substances, including sulfur dioxide, iodine, bromine, iron chloride, iodides of mercury, cadmium, arsenic, tin, and the substituted ammonium radicals. Solutions of most salts in sulfuryl chloride are only slightly conductive, but solutions of tertiary or quaternary ammonium salts are considerably dissociated and conduct well. Sulfuryl chloride is miscible with organic solvents, including acetic acid and ether.

Sulfuryl chloride is stable at room temperature but decomposes at elevated temperatures,

$$SO_2Cl_2 \rightleftharpoons SO_2 + Cl_2$$

The equilibrium constant for the reaction in the vapor phase, $K = [p(SO_2)][p(Cl_2)]/[p(SO_2Cl_2)]$, is given below for various temperatures.

Temperature, °C	30	40	50	102	159	191
Equilibrium constant	0.0288	0.0506	0.0837	2.37	8.9	13.1

The decomposition of sulfuryl chloride is photochemically accelerated. It is also catalyzed by a variety of materials, including aluminum chloride, activated charcoal, glass, etc.

The ease with which sulfuryl chloride decomposes into sulfur dioxide and chlorine, particularly in the presence of catalysts, explains at least partially many of its reactions. Thus, it reacts with sulfur at $200°C$, or at room temperature in the presence of aluminum chloride, to form sulfur monochloride and sulfur dioxide,

$$SO_2Cl_2 + 2 S \rightarrow S_2Cl_2 + SO_2$$

With hydrogen sulfide, it forms a variety of products, including hydrogen chloride, sulfur monochloride, sulfur, sulfur dioxide, etc. Sulfuryl chloride liberates bromine or iodine from bromides or iodides, and breaks down into the corresponding chloride and sulfur dioxide.

Sulfuryl chloride is hydrolyzed very slowly by cold water,

$$SO_2Cl_2 + 2 H_2O \rightarrow H_2SO_4 + 2 HCl$$

With controlled quantities of water, or with sulfuric acid directly, it is converted to chlorosulfuric acid,

$$SO_2Cl_2 + H_2SO_4 \rightleftharpoons 2 ClSO_2OH$$

This reaction, however, is reversed at boiling temperatures. In the presence of a mercuric salt (probably a catalyst) it is possible to fractionate sulfuryl chloride from boiling chlorosulfuric acid.

Iodine reacts with sulfuryl chloride in the presence of aluminum chloride to form iodine chlorides,

$$I_2 + SO_2Cl_2 \rightarrow 2\ ICl + SO_2$$
$$ICl + SO_2Cl_2 \rightarrow ICl_3 + SO_2$$

Phosphorus chlorides react with sulfuryl chloride,

$$PCl_5 + SO_2Cl_2 \rightarrow POCl_3 + SOCl_2 + Cl_2$$
$$PCl_3 + SO_2Cl_2 \rightarrow POCl_3 + SOCl_2$$

Zinc reacts with sulfuryl chloride in ether solution to yield the chloride and sulfoxylate.

$$2\ Zn + SO_2Cl_2 \rightarrow ZnCl_2 + ZnSO_2$$

Metal oxides react to form the chlorides and sulfates. Metal sulfides may be chloridized with sulfuryl chloride.

Sulfuryl chloride reacts with anhydrous ammonia to yield a variety of sulfamides having the general formula $NH_2SO_2(NHSO_2)_nNH_2$ where n may vary from zero up. Cyclic compounds of the formula $(SO_2NH)_3$ are also produced.

In organic chemistry, sulfuryl chloride is a chlorinating agent and a sulfonating agent. As a chlorinating agent, it in many cases parallels the action of elementary chlorine. However, by careful selection of the reaction conditions and the catalyst, it is often possible to obtain more selective chlorination with sulfuryl chloride than with chlorine itself. Thus, m-cresol is chlorinated in the para position with sulfuryl chloride to yield a disinfectant. Similarly thymol is selectively chlorinated in a commercial operation. A variety of aromatics may be chlorinated in a stepwise manner with sulfuryl chloride. In these reactions, aluminum chloride is sometimes used as a catalyst.

Sulfuryl chloride reacts with sodium salts of organic acids to form the corresponding acid chlorides. Acetyl chloride may be prepared in this manner:

$$2\ CH_3COONa + SO_2Cl_2 \rightarrow 2\ CH_3COCl + Na_2SO_4$$

By varying the conditions of the reaction, the acid anhydride may be formed. The by-product sulfuric acid or sodium sulfate tends to introduce oxidation reactions which reduce the yield.

Sulfuryl chloride reacts with ethyl alcohol to yield ethyl chlorosulfurate.

$$SO_2Cl_2 + C_2H_5OH \rightarrow C_2H_5OSO_2Cl + HCl$$

The use of organic peroxides as catalysts permits the chlorination of aliphatic hydrocarbons and their derivatives. Thus toluene is chlorinated in the side chain, first to benzyl chloride and then to benzal chloride. Alkenes are chlorinated to saturated dichlorides with sulfuryl chloride in the presence of organic peroxides as catalysts. Correspondingly, organic acids and acid chlorides may be chlorinated in various positions. Benzaldehyde under these conditions is chlorinated to benzoyl chloride.

The use of pyridine as a catalyst causes the formation of sulfonyl chlorides. Thus, with alkenes,

$$RCH{=}CH_2 + SO_2Cl_2 \xrightarrow{\text{pyridine}} RHCClCH_2SO_2Cl$$

With saturated hydrocarbons,

$$RCH_3 + SO_2Cl_2 \xrightarrow{pyridine} RCH_2SO_2Cl + HCl$$

Besides pyridine, a number of other compounds catalyze this reaction. Thus triethanolamine or benzonitrile may under certain circumstances be used to catalyze the chlorosulfonation of saturated hydrocarbons. This reaction is useful in the preparation of surfactants from petroleum products, and in the preparation of some types of tanning agents.

When sulfuryl chloride is reacted with alkenes, using sulfur monochloride as the catalyst, chlorosulfites are formed.

$$RCH{=}CH_2 + SO_2Cl_2 \xrightarrow{S_2Cl_2} RHCClCH_2OSOCl$$

Sulfuryl chloride is prepared by the reaction of dry sulfur dioxide with chlorine in the presence of an active carbon catalyst. The reaction is carried out in a steel vessel with water-cooled walls, so arranged that the catalyst is wetted with the sulfuryl chloride being formed. The product is condensed in a steel condenser.

A number of organic compounds may replace the active carbon as a catalyst. Thus, camphor may be dissolved in liquid sulfur dioxide, and chlorine then passed through the resulting clear solution at about 0°C. The sulfuryl chloride so formed may be distilled from the reaction mass. Terpene hydrocarbons, certain ethers, phenols, and esters are also effective catalysts.

Sulfuryl chloride is a hazardous chemical. Its vapor is highly toxic, and the liquid is corrosive to the skin. It is therefore essential to follow the usual precautions in handling a volatile liquid of this type, avoiding contact of the liquid with the skin or clothing. In case of contact with the skin or eyes, immediately flush with plenty of water for at least 15 min. Medical attention is required if the liquid touches the eyes.

Sulfuryl chloride, if completely dry, does not corrode aluminum, magnesium, or nickel, at room temperature. It slightly corrodes chrome steel, iron, cast iron, lead, zinc, aluminum, bronze, and German silver, and rapidly corrodes copper and brass. Moisture considerably increases corrosion, but the increased attack on lead is less than with other metals. Dry sulfuryl chloride may be handled in iron or steel equipment, but lead, glass, or nickel equipment is preferred because of its greater resistance to corrosion.

Since moisture in contact with sulfuryl chloride causes the liberation of hydrogen chloride, it is necessary to vent storage containers at frequent intervals to prevent undue buildup of pressure. Correspondingly, it is essential to protect the sulfuryl chloride from attack by atmospheric moisture. It follows also that empty drums must not be washed out with water or used for other purposes. The use of pressure to empty a drum of sulfuryl chloride is hazardous. Since light catalyzes decomposition, carboys or other glass containers of sulfuryl chloride should be kept out of the sun and away from heat.

The commercial material is a pale-yellow liquid with a distillation range of 2 deg Celsius (including 69.5°C). It contains at least 99% sulfuryl chloride.

Sulfuryl chloride is primarily a chlorinating or chlorosulfurating agent. It is used to convert organic acids to the corresponding acid chlorides and acid anhydrides. It is employed as a selective chlorinating agent, particularly in the production of chlorophenol and chlorothymol, which are used as disinfectants. Sulfuryl chloride is also used in the syntheses of various pharmaceuticals, dyes, and surfactants.

Pyrosulfuryl Chloride.   Pyrosulfuryl chloride (disulfuryl chloride), $S_2O_5Cl_2$, is a colorless, dense, somewhat viscous liquid.   It has the following properties: mp, $-37°C$; d_4^{20} 1.837; n_D^{19}, 1.449; heat of vaporization, 35.1 cal/g; bp, $152°C$.   At room temperature, pyrosulfuryl chloride is fairly stable.   However, at temperatures over $180°C$ it decomposes into sulfur dioxide, sulfur trioxide, and chlorine.   At $360°C$, its decomposition is virtually complete.   Pyrosulfuryl chloride is slowly attacked by water, sulfuric and hydrochloric acids resulting.   If the pyrosulfuryl chloride is in excess, some chlorine and sulfur dioxide are also formed.   Pyrosulfuryl chloride reacts with chromates to form chromyl chloride.

$$K_2CrO_4 + S_2O_5Cl_2 \rightarrow CrO_2Cl_2 + K_2S_2O_7$$

Pyrosulfuryl chloride may be prepared by the chlorination of sulfur trioxide with a wide range of chlorides. S_2Cl_2, $SOCl_2$, PCl_5, $POCl_3$, $SiCl_4$, Si_2OCl_6, NaCl, and CCl_4 have all been reported to have converted sulfur trioxide to pyrosulfuryl chloride.   Strangely enough, however, pyrosulfuryl chloride cannot be prepared by refluxing together sulfuryl chloride and sulfur trioxide.   Pyrosulfuryl chloride may also be obtained by dehydrating chlorosulfuric acid with phosphorus pentoxide or pentachloride.

The usual method for preparing pyrosulfuryl chloride is to add oleum to hot carbon tetrachloride,

$$H_2SO_4 + SO_3 + CCl_4 \rightarrow 2\ ClSO_2OH + COCl_2$$

This reaction is immediately followed by

$$2\ HOSO_2Cl + CCl_4 \rightarrow S_2O_5Cl_2 + 2\ HCl + COCl_2$$

The reaction mass is treated with dry sodium chloride to remove any unreacted chlorosulfuric acid (as sodium chlorosulfurate) and is then fractionally distilled to obtain a refined pyrosulfuryl chloride.   This process has the disadvantage that extremely poisonous phosgene is produced as a by-product.

Another process used for the production of pyrosulfuryl chloride involves the reaction between sulfur monochloride and sulfur trioxide.   In this process, which is operated on a batch basis, sulfur monochloride is added slowly to liquid sulfur trioxide at a temperature of $35°C$ until 85–95% of the sulfur trioxide has been reacted. The batch is then fractionally distilled to remove sulfur dioxide, unreacted sulfur trioxide, and traces of sulfur chlorides.   The net reaction is as follows:

$$S_2Cl_2 + 5\ SO_3 \rightarrow S_2O_5Cl_2 + 5\ SO_2$$

A third process (44) involves the reaction of sulfur trioxide vapor with sulfur dichloride in a heel of pyrosulfuryl chloride held at around $110°C$.   The reactor is fitted with a reflux condenser to return any reactants or intermediates which may have vaporized from the reaction mass.   The pyrosulfuryl chloride produced is collected in the reactor.   The crude product is fractionally distilled to remove sulfur dioxide, sulfur trioxide, sulfur dichloride, and thionyl chloride.   A product purity of 99% is obtained. The reactions are

$$SCl_2 + SO_3 \rightarrow SOCl_2 + SO_2$$
$$SOCl_2 + 2\ SO_3 \rightarrow S_2O_5Cl_2 + SO_2$$

Any sulfuric acid introduced into the reactor forms chlorosulfuric acid.   This material forms an azeotrope with the pyrosulfuryl chloride, which is difficult to separate.   Hence it is essential to minimize the sulfuric acid carry-over if the sulfur trioxide is obtained from oleum.

Pyrosulfuryl chloride is useful as a chlorinating agent in organic chemistry.

Sulfur Oxytetrachloride. Sulfur oxytetrachloride ("trichlorosulfonium chlorosulfonate," $(SCl_3)^+(ClSO_2O)^-$), $S_2O_3Cl_4$, is a pungent, colorless, crystalline solid that melts at about 57°C, with decomposition. It is formed by the action of sulfur tetrachloride on chlorosulfuric acid at -15°C or lower.

$$SCl_4 + ClSO_2OH \rightarrow ClSO_2OSCl_3 + HCl$$

It slowly decomposes at room temperature to thionyl chloride and sulfuryl chloride. Sulfur oxytetrachloride hydrolyzes to sulfurous acid, sulfuric acid, and hydrochloric acid. It is believed to be the trichlorosulfonium salt of chlorosulfuric acid.

SULFUR NITRIDES. Nitrogen combines with sulfur to form several sulfur nitrides of which the most important and most extensively studied is tetrasulfur tetranitride, S_4N_4. Among the many sulfur nitrides which have been reported, several have been identified with the aid of more recent chemical and physical evidence. These are tetrasulfur dinitride, S_4N_2, disulfur dinitride, S_2N_2, polymeric sulfur nitride, $(SN)_x$, and $S_{15}N_2$ and $S_{16}N_2$. The latter are believed to be the mono- and disulfides, respectively, of heptasulfur imide, S_7NH, with the hydrogens on two of the imide molecules replaced by one or two sulfurs respectively to form the appropriate mono- or disulfide. The family of derivatives of the sulfur nitrides is very large. Although many of them have been further studied in recent years, the structural chemistry of these derivatives contains many anomalies and is not yet fully systemized (56). The outstanding work in this field has been that of M. Becke-Goehring. A summary of recent developments in the inorganic chemistry of compounds containing the sulfur–nitrogen bond will be found in reference 58.

Tetrasulfur tetranitride (tetranitrogen tetrasulfide, nitrogen sulfide), S_4N_4, is an orange, crystalline solid, mp, 178°C (with sublimation at about the same temperature), d_{20}^{15}, 2.22. The solid is explosive at elevated temperatures and will detonate when struck, even at room temperature (see Vol. 8, p. 593). It is slowly decomposed by water but is soluble in organic solvents. Its solubility in several of these solvents is listed in Table 10. Other solvents are carbon tetrachloride, chloroform, methylene chloride, and tetrahydrofuran.

Table 10. Solubility of Tetrasulfur Tetranitride in Organic Solvents

Temperature, °C	Solubility, g/l soln		
	CS_2	C_6H_6	C_2H_5OH
0	3.705	2.266	0.645
10	6.845	4.260	0.830
20	9.391	6.301	1.050
30	13.188	8.692	1.271
40	16.887	11.107	1.478
50		13.721	1.640
60		17.100	

Tetrasulfur tetranitride is formed by the reaction of sulfur with dry ammonia through a rather complex series of reversible reactions. The overall reaction is given by the following equation:

$$10\ S + 16\ NH_3 \rightleftharpoons S_4N_4 + 6\ (NH_4)_2S$$

The equilibrium for this reaction appears to be predominantly toward the left of this equation. In order to recover tetrasulfur tetranitride, it is therefore necessary to remove the ammonium sulfide as it is formed. This may be accomplished by oxidation (with chlorine or other reagents) or by precipitation with silver ion or some other sulfide-insoluble cation. Since the tetrasulfur tetranitride is readily hydrolyzed by water, the reaction must be carried out in an anhydrous medium. The reactions most frequently used to prepare tetrasulfur tetranitride are

1. The reaction of dry ammonia gas (usually diluted with air) with an ice-cold 10–12% solution of SCl_2 in benzene,

$$6\ SCl_2 + 16\ NH_3 \rightarrow S_4N_4 + 12\ NH_4Cl + 2\ S$$

The products of reaction are largely insoluble in benzene, and the tetrasulfur tetranitride is recovered from the precipitate by fractional crystallization. The mother liquor contains, in addition to some dissolved tetrasulfur tetranitride and sulfur, a variety of other by-products, including $N_4H_4SCl_2$ and $N_4H_4Cl_4$.

2. The reaction of sulfur with an excess of liquid ammonia in the presence of silver iodide,

$$10\ S + 16\ NH_3 + 12\ AgI \rightarrow S_4N_4 + 6\ Ag_2S + 12\ NH_4I$$

The tetrasulfur tetranitride, which is soluble in ammonia, is obtained by evaporation of the filtrate from the reaction mass. Again, the progress of the reaction is complex,

Table 11. Some Reactions of Tetrasulfur Tetranitride

Reactant	Conditions	Product	Product properties
CS_2 and sulfur	heat and pressure, 100–120°C	S_4N_2, tetrasulfur dinitride	dark-red, oily liquid, mp 23°, with penetrating iodine-like odor; decomposes explosively into sulfur and nitrogen at 100°C
Cl_2	in organic solvent	$(NSCl)_3$, trithiazyl chloride	yellow cryst solid; hydrolyzes rapidly to NH_4Cl and sulfite
S_2Cl_2	in CCl_4	S_4N_3Cl, thiotrithiazyl chloride	yellow cryst solid, slightly sol in thionyl chloride; decomposed by water to $(NH_4)_2S_3O_6$, NH_4Cl, and S; the chloride may be replaced by other anions such as NO_3^-, HSO_4^-, I^-, Br^-, CNS^-, etc
Br_2		$(SNBr)_x$, nitrogen bromosulfide	bronze-colored crystals
S_2Br_2	CS_2 soln	S_4N_3Br, thiotrithiazyl bromide	yellow, needlelike crystals
PbI_2	in liquid NH_3	$PbN_2S_2.NH_3$	olive-green prisms

and numerous intermediates are formed. Among these, $S(NH_3)_3$ and $S(NH_3)_6$ have been reported.

Tetrasulfur tetranitride is not wetted with water, hence it hydrolyzes rather slowly in cold water. The hydrolysis reaction is as follows:

$$2 S_4N_4 + 15 H_2O \rightarrow (NH_4)_2S_2O_3 + 2 (NH_4)_2S_3O_6 + 2 NH_3$$

In the presence of alkalis,

$$S_4N_4 + 6 KOH + 3 H_2O \rightarrow 2 K_2SO_3 + K_2S_2O_3 + 4 NH_3$$

Dry hydrogen chloride reacts with tetrasulfur tetranitride to produce as primary products ammonia, sulfur, and chlorine. Hydrogen sulfide reduces tetrasulfur tetranitride in benzene solution to ammonium polysulfide. Some of the reactions of tetrasulfur tetranitride are listed in Table 11.

Tetrasulfur tetranitride forms addition compounds with many chemicals, $S_4N_4TiCl_4$, $S_4N_4SbCl_5$, $2S_4N_4SnCl_4$, $S_4N_4 \cdot SeCl_2$, $S_4N_4 \cdot WCl_4$, $S_4N_4 \cdot SCl_2$, $S_4N_4 \cdot 4SO_3$, $S_4N_4 \cdot BF_3$, and $S_4N_4 \cdot BCl_3$ having been reported.

Structural investigations on sulfur nitrides and other derivatives have shown S_4N_4 to have an eight-membered ring structure in a cagelike conformation. S_4N_3Cl is a salt, $(S_4N_3)^+(Cl)^-$, with the cation forming a nearly planar ring. $(NSCl)_3$ is a six-membered planar ring of alternating S and N atoms, with Cl attached to the sulfur atoms, and in a plane parallel to the S–N ring.

SULFUR OXIDES. A large number of oxides of sulfur have been reported, described, or prepared (30,33). These include S_2O, SO, S_2O_2, S_2O_3, SO_2, SO_3, S_2O_7, SO_4, and S_2O_8, as well as various polymers of SO_3. Of these, only the dioxide, SO_2, and the trioxide, SO_3 (see Sulfuric acid), are commercial and well known. S_2O is doubtful, as is S_2O_7. S_2O_2 and S_2O_8 are doubtful dimers of SO and SO_4 (7).

Sulfur Monoxide, SO. Sulfur monoxide is known largely through the work of F. W. Schenk (62). It is known only as a gas which is stable for several days at room temperatures. Sulfur monoxide can be prepared by several methods, the best of which is passing sulfur vapor and sulfur dioxide through an electric discharge at low pressures and at about 175°C. It can also be formed in small yields by the action of silver on thionyl chloride or bromide at about 150°C. Upon compressing or cooling, the gas polymerizes irreversibly to an orange-red solid, which decomposes on heating to the monoxide, the dioxide, and sulfur. Sulfur monoxide can be detected by its characteristic absorption bands, extending from 3130 Å to the shorter wavelengths. It has the same spectral ground state as oxygen and S_2 and hence is probably paramagnetic like oxygen and gaseous sulfur. Its dissociation energy is also intermediate between diatomic sulfur and oxygen. Upon hydrolysis, both sulfur and dithionite ion, $S_2O_4{}^{2-}$, are obtained.

Disulfur Trioxide (sulfur sesquioxide), S_2O_3. Disulfur trioxide is a blue-green solid prepared by the addition of powdered sulfur to liquid sulfur trioxide at 15°C. The product is undoubtedly a polymer of S_2O_3 and slowly decomposes on standing in air to the trioxide, the dioxide, and sulfur.

Sulfur Tetroxide, SO_4. Sulfur tetroxide is a white solid formed by subjecting a mixture of dry sulfur dioxide and oxygen to a silent electric discharge. It is a powerful oxidizing agent that melts at about 3°C with some decomposition. Its structure is unknown.

Sulfur Dioxide, Owing to the wide occurrence and peculiar properties of sulfur and sulfides, sulfur dioxide fumes have been known and ultilized since earliest recorded history. Homer refers to their use as a disinfectant, and the bleaching of linen with the fumes of burning sulfur was known and practiced as early as 2000 BC in Egypt. With the development of modern industrial civilization and its demand for metals, sulfuric acid, and wood pulp, sulfur dioxide achieved great technical importance far exceeding its minor and more recent development as a pure commercial chemical.

Sulfur dioxide is one of the very minor and variable constituents of the atmosphere. Volcanic and other terrigenous gases contain on the order of 10% of sulfur-containing gases, largely sulfur dioxide and hydrogen sulfide. In some areas the amount of sulfur dioxide in the atmosphere is increasing and reaches measurable concentrations as the result of heavy and widespread industrial activity (22). It has been estimated that, during World War II, about 75 million tons of sulfur dioxide were released to the atmosphere annually in the United States in the form of waste gases from various sources (23).

The sources and disposition of sulfur dioxide are quite varied. The most economic and important source is elemental sulfur. Most of the Frasch-process sulfur produced in this country is burned to make sulfur dioxide. Practically all of this is consumed immediately in the manufacture of sulfuric acid, sulfite pulp, and other captive uses. Most of the liquid sulfur dioxide made originates from this source. Smelter gases are a large and relatively concentrated source of sulfur dioxide, which was once largely wasted to the atmosphere, although a substantial and increasing percentage is now being recovered as sulfuric acid and liquid sulfur dioxide. Another source of sulfur dioxide is the combustion of hydrogen sulfide from oil refining, coke-oven operation, and the refining of natural and manufactured gas. Most of it is wasted to the atmosphere, but in recent years the recovery of the sulfur content of these wastes, as either sulfuric acid or elemental sulfur, has grown rapidly. The widespread combustion of fuels, such as petroleum oil, natural and manufactured gases, and coal, particularly the latter, produces enormous quantities of sulfur dioxide in the form of dilute flue gases, which are vented to the atmosphere. In some very large power plants in some communities, notably in English urban districts (23), removal of sulfur dioxide from gases at levels as low as 0.02–0.05% initial sulfur dioxide content has proved necessary, and in more recent years the recovery of over 90% of the sulfur values in these dilute gases has been studied on a pilot-plant scale. See the discussion of sulfur dioxide recovery on pp. 409 and 415.

Air Pollution Aspects. While normal emissions during the past two decades have been well below those of the war years, when many new plants were erected rapidly, with little concern for pollution, they have continued to rise at an accelerated rate in more recent years in densely populated temperate-zone areas of the world. In the United States alone, emissions of sulfur dioxide to the atmosphere were estimated (57) to be nearly 29 million tons/yr in 1966. About 75% of this arises from the combustion of coal and oil, mostly in plants for the generation of electric power.

Most concentrated emissions are found in the densely populated industrial areas. Despite many uncertainties as to the exact effects on animal and vegetable life, as well as the economics of controlling such emissions, the practical effects of air pollution have resulted in the adoption of air-pollution regulation in most of the industrial countries of the world. In others, regulations are in the process of being worked out. Typically, as of 1966–1968 in the United States, a series of Federal, State and local legislations, as well as voluntarily adopted criteria, are leading to the adoption of several types of control measures:

1. Maximum sulfur dioxide concentrations in ambient air are limited according to an average-time-period basis as follows:

$$0.10\text{--}0.50 \text{ ppm for 5 min}$$

$$0.12\text{--}0.20 \text{ ppm for 1 hr}$$

$$0.05\text{--}0.08 \text{ ppm for 24 hr}$$

2. Maximum sulfur concentrations in fuel oils burned in various localities are currently being set at 1%, notably in New York City. The tendency throughout the country is to still lower levels, probably closer to 0.5%.

3. Recommended flue gas stack heights at 600–1000 ft, in place of the more common 200–400-ft stacks, to give significantly lower ground-level concentration of sulfur dioxide and other pollutants.

The economics of sulfur dioxide recovery from dilute flue gases are unfavorable from the point of view of the value of the products recovered. The pressure of government regulations, the development of improved recovery processes, and a substantial increase in the prices of sulfur, sulfuric acid, and sulfur dioxide, along with a growing demand for these products, have greatly narrowed the gap between recovery cost and product-value credit.

Coal, which accounts for at least half the problem, is the most difficult of all the fuel sources to control in regard to sulfur dioxide emissions. This is due to the organic nature of the bulk of the sulfur in coal, and the difficulty, if not the practical impossibility, of its removal by chemical means. The removal of sulfur dioxide from flue gases thus appears to be the most likely means for controlling the problem, at least as far as the major area of power-plant burning of coal is concerned. The difficulty can be seen from the fact that an average coal, containing about 3.4% sulfur, yields stack gas containing about 3000 ppm of sulfur oxides, of which 90% is sulfur dioxide and 10% is sulfur trioxide. This is too low a yield for economic recovery of sulfur dioxide yet too high to meet new lower ground-level maximums being suggested by public-health agencies. The tendency is toward ground-level maximums of 0.1 ppm in place of present levels of about 0.3 ppm. This would require coal with less than 1% sulfur. About 90% of the coals now being burned for power generation in the United States have a sulfur content greater than 1%.

Sulfur dioxide in the atmosphere is oxidized to sulfuric acid at a rate which depends on such factors as humidity, sulfur trioxide content, and particulate-matter concentration. Studies on the exhaust plumes from the stacks of coal-burning power plants and of smelters have shown oxidation rates for sulfur dioxide ranging from 0.1–2%/min, depending principally on whether the humidity was low or high (34).

Properties. Sulfur dioxide is a colorless gas with a characteristic pungent choking odor. It condenses at $-10°C$ at atmospheric pressure to a colorless liquid that freezes at $-75.5°C$. The molecular formula is SO_2, corresponding to a molecular weight of 64.06 in all its states. The critical temperature is $157.12°C$, and the critical pressure is 77.65 atm. At $0°C$ and 1 atm pressure, the gas has a specific gravity of 2.2636 relative to air, occupies 5.47 ft^3/lb, has a specific heat of 0.15 cal/g, and a dielectric constant of 1.0095. It has discontinuous absorption bands in the ultraviolet region.

The liquid at 20°C has the following properties: $d_{15.6}^{20}$, 1.4542; C_p, 0.327 cal/g; dielectric constant, 12.8; n_D^{20}, 1.410; surface tension, 22.73 dyn/cm; latent heat of vaporization, 149 Btu/lb; viscosity, 0.28 cP.

Liquid sulfur dioxide expands about 10% in volume in going from 20 to 60°C. The pure liquid is a poor conductor of electricity, although solutions of a limited number of salts that are soluble in sulfur dioxide exhibit high conductivity. Liquid sulfur dioxide is only slightly miscible with water, is a nonsolvent for sulfur, and is miscible in all proportions with sulfur monochloride. The gas is soluble to the extent of 36 vols in water at 20°C, but is very much more soluble, several hundred to one by vol, in a number of organic solvents, such as camphor, acetone, and formic acid.

Sulfur dioxide is a relatively inert and stable gas that can be heated to about 2000°C without appreciable decomposition. It does not form flammable or explosive mixtures with air. Its stability is indicated by its high heat and free energy of formation, which are 70.9 and −69.7 kcal/mole, respectively. Sulfur dioxide gas undergoes addition reactions with gaseous or solid halogens,

$$SO_2 + X_2 \rightarrow SO_2X_2$$

Reduction of the gas to sulfur and water or carbon dioxide, as the case may be, can be carried out with reducing agents such as hydrogen, hydrogen sulfide, carbon monoxide, and carbon at temperatures up to 1000°C. Reaction takes place at a much lower temperature if a catalyst, such as bauxite, is used. The oxidation of sulfur dioxide to the trioxide has been the subject of a very large amount of study (see Sulfuric acid). It is generally carried out in the presence of a catalyst at temperatures in the range of 400–700°C.

Sulfur dioxide is readily formed by the air oxidation of sulfur and many sulfides, by the pyrolysis in air of sulfites and thiosulfates, by the reduction of sulfur trioxide and sulfuric acid by metals, carbon, sulfur, and sulfides with heating, and by the decomposition of sulfite and bisulfite solutions with strong acids.

Liquid sulfur dioxide, or the gas at low temperatures, forms solid complex salts with solid iodides and thiocyanates and other salts. The addition compounds contain from 0.5–4 moles of sulfur dioxide and form conducting solutions in liquid sulfur dioxide. Reactions in liquid sulfur dioxide are considered (21) to depend on its ionization,

$$2\ SO_2 \rightarrow SO^{2+} + SO_3^{2-}$$

corresponding to

$$2\ H_2O \rightarrow H_3O^+ + OH^-$$

in water. Thus, in liquid sulfur dioxide, thionyl chloride can be considered to be an acid,

$$SOCl_2 \rightarrow SO^{2+} + 2\ Cl^-$$

and sodium sulfite,

$$Na_2SO_3 \rightarrow 2\ Na^+ + SO_3^{2-}$$

a base, which react to form a salt,

$$Na_2SO_3 + SOCl_2 \rightarrow 2\ NaCl + 2\ SO_2$$

See also Acid–base systems.

Sulfurous Acid. Sulfur dioxide dissolves in water to form the weak acid, sulfurous acid, H_2SO_3. At a partial pressure for sulfur dioxide gas of 1 atm, solutions containing 18.5% SO_2 by weight are formed at 0°C, and 5.1% strength at 40°C. Under practical conditions, where solutions are formed most often at 1 atm total pressure with air or other diluent gases present, concentrations of from only one third to one half of these values are obtained. At 25°C the first and second ionization constants of sulfurous acid in water are 1.72×10^{-2} and 1.1×10^{-9}, respectively. Free sulfurous acid has not been prepared, although a hydrate, $SO_2 \cdot 7H_2O$, has been isolated from concentrated solutions at low temperatures.

Sulfites are first formed by the absorption of sulfur dioxide in alkaline solutions, followed by the formation of even more soluble bisulfites as absorption of sulfur dioxide continues. In addition to these simple salts, M_2SO_3 and $MHSO_3$, a series of alkali-metal "pyro" salts, $M_2S_2O_5$, also exists. These may be considered anhydrides of the bisulfites and are formed by heating the bisulfites or their solutions. These pyrosulfites (metabisulfites) are nonhygroscopic and more stable than the corresponding sulfites and bisulfites.

The alkali-metal sulfites and bisulfites exist in the solid state as well as in solution. Sulfites of many of the other metals exist in the solid state and are sparingly soluble, while their more soluble bisulfites exist only in solution. Sulfites form complexes with many of the heavy-metal salts, the sulfite radical occupying one or more of the available coordination positions. Aqueous solutions of formaldehyde react with sodium bisulfite to form sodium formaldehyde bisulfite (see Formaldehyde). Sodium sulfite, Na_2SO_3, is produced and used in large quantities. Although production capacity in the United States is believed to be about 750,000 tons/yr, over two thirds of this is captive capacity in pulp and paper mills. Thus actual production, sales, and consumption are difficult to determine. About 80% is consumed in pulp production, and the remainder divides about equally between boiler-water treatment, where it functions as an oxygen scavenger, photographic-chemical use as a reducing agent, and miscellaneous uses. Sodium sulfite anhydrous technical grade, is priced at $4.00 per cwt (hundredweight, equals 100 lb) (Oct. 1968) works, in bulk car lots; photographic grade is priced at $8.35 per cwt works, in car-lot bags.

Many of the uses of sulfur dioxide depend on the fact that sulfurous acid and its salts are excellent low-cost reducing agents. Oxidation to sulfate is rapid and quantitative with halogens. The action with oxygen is slow and is accelerated in the presence of certain reducing agents such as ferrous or arsenite ions, while many organic substances and stannous chloride inhibit the action. Many common oxidizing agents, such as peroxide, permanganate, ferric ion, and manganese dioxide, lead to the formation of dithionate, $S_2O_6^{2-}$, as well as sulfate. In acid solutions, sulfurous acid will act as an oxidizing agent in the presence of many reducing agents, such as hydrogen sulfide, hydrogen iodide, reduced metal salts, and zinc. The reactions are complex. Sulfur is usually stated to be a product of these reductions, although there is reason to believe that higher polythionic acids are actually formed. Depending on the reducing agents used, hydrogen sulfides, hydrogen polysulfides, dithionic acid, sulfate, and thiosulfate may also be formed, indicating simultaneous oxidation and reduction of sulfurous acid in some cases (37).

Analysis. The most common methods of analysis of sulfur dioxide in various materials are based on its reducing action in aqueous solution, either as sulfurous acid or in the form of bisulfites, sulfites, and other related compounds. Titration with iodine,

$$SO_2 + I_2 + 2 H_2O \rightarrow H_2SO_4 + 2 HI$$

is most frequently employed, although other oxidizing agents are used in some methods. A common method is to add a fixed amount of standard iodine and then titrate the excess iodine with standard sodium thiosulfate and a starch indicator. Where colored solutions are involved, or certain interfering substances present, distillation methods are employed. The most widely used method of this type is the AOAC (Association of Official Analytical (formerly Agricultural) Chemists) version of the Monier-Williams procedure (1). This method involves distilling sulfur dioxide into hydrogen peroxide and titrating the sulfuric acid formed with standard alkali, using bromophenol blue as indicator. Sulfur dioxide in gas mixtures can be determined by bubbling the gas through standard iodine solution to the point of discharge of the iodine–starch color. Sulfurous acid and bisulfites may also be determined by titration as acids with standard alkali solution. Gas-chromatography methods (59) are also available for the analysis of sulfur dioxide at low concentrations (0.2–0.4%) in the presence of sulfur trioxide.

Manufacture. In most chemical-process applications requiring sulfur dioxide gas or sulfurous acid, sulfur dioxide is prepared by the burning in air of sulfur or of pyrite, FeS_2, usually sulfur. A large number of sulfur and pyrite burners have been developed for the sulfuric acid (qv) and wood-pulp (see Pulp) industries (14,32), which produce and immediately consume about 90% of some 27 million tons of captive sulfur dioxide annually in the United States.

The production of sulfur dioxide gas by the combustion of Frasch-process sulfur is relatively simple and is the preferred method, except in cases in which economic considerations favor the use of pyrite. For most applications, with the exception of sulfuric acid manufacture, as high a sulfur dioxide content as possible is desired. For sulfur burners, the theoretical maximum is 21% SO_2 by vol, and under satisfactory conditions from 14% to as high as 20% may be achieved. The various sulfur burners commercially available are rated by their manufacturers as capable of producing gas in the range of 5–18% sulfur dioxide. In the upper range of sulfur dioxide concentration, theoretical flame temperatures for the combustion of sulfur in air range from 1200–1600°C. The temperature of the gas leaving the combustion chamber in continuous sulfur burners ranges from 700 to 1000°C. One pound of sulfur requires 1 lb of oxygen for its complete combustion. This is the amount contained in 53.8 ft³ of air. The reaction produces 1942 Btu/lb of sulfur dioxide produced (from rhombic sulfur at 25°C).

The selection or design of sulfur burners is determined by several factors. These are primarily the rate and concentration of sulfur dioxide to be produced and the quality of sulfur to be burned. The continuity of operation and the degree of operator and maintenance attention are important secondary considerations. The two principal types of sulfur burners in use at the present time, namely the rotary and spray types, can be used with most qualities of sulfur and also cover a wide range of sulfur dioxide concentrations and rates. In general, the rotary burners are less sensitive to the sulfur feed rate and require less operating attention than spray burners. Spray burners, on the other hand, can be operated intermittently and can handle higher rates than rotary burners. Carbonaceous matter in dark sulfurs poses no problem for spray burners and is readily handled in rotary burners which are properly designed to burn off or remove the resulting scum. The ash content of sulfurs can be a problem in sulfur dioxide from high-rate spray burners, since ash can be carried into the product gas stream. Pan and cascade burners are generally more limited in flexibility and are useful only where low sulfur dioxide concentrations are desired. The principal types of sulfur burners in use, and their operating features, are discussed in reference 60. Gases from sulfur burners also contain small amounts of sulfur trioxide, hence the moisture content of the air used can be an important factor in corrosionfree operation. Continuous operation at temperatures above the dewpoint is indicated where exposure to steel surfaces is involved.

The rotary and spray burners used today have to a large extent replaced the earlier pan or retort type, which had several disadvantages: irregular gas strength and temperatures, along with higher losses and difficulty in handling the organic scum formed on the burning surfaces. Best known and most widely used of the modern rotary burners is the Glens Falls rotary sulfur burner, manufactured by Glens Falls Machine Works, Inc. The burner consists of a horizontal steel cylinder that slowly rotates to keep the interior surfaces wet with molten sulfur, which is maintained at close to overflow level, either by mechanical solid feed or preferably by liquid feed from an external sulfur melter. Air is drawn through the burner by a draft of 0.25–2 in. applied to the discharge end. At all but the lowest drafts and capacities, the cylinder is followed by a brick-lined afterburner or combustion chamber into which further air may be admitted through dampers. Rated capacities range from 10–2000 lb of sulfur/hr, although capacities as high as 6000 lb of sulfur/hr have been reported for brick-lined burners. Several improvements have been proposed for the rotary burner to permit the use of sulfurs of high bituminous content (25). These include tilting of the burner cylinder for a continuous overflow of carbonaceous scum into the combustion chamber, fins within the burner to increase surface, insulation to increase the temperature for increased capacity, and better ashing of bituminous matter. Regulation of the air supply is the most important factor in the burning of sulfur to form sulfur dioxide. Excess air, particularly if it is moist and if operating temperatures are too low, will lead to formation of sulfur trioxide, and about 2 or 3% of the sulfur is usually lost in this way. A lesser difficulty is the formation of sublimed sulfur if the burner is overheated (25) or too little air is used once the burner has come to temperature. A properly operated afterburner can practically eliminate this source of loss.

Several other types of sulfur burners are available to meet various needs, each offering particular advantages of its own. A pan type of continuous sulfur burner, with capacities from 25–1350 lb/hr, offered by Acme Process Equipment Company, can operate either under pressure or under vacuum. A successful sulfur spray burner that is particularly suitable when high capacities are needed has been offered by Chemical Construction Corporation in recent years. Molten sulfur is pumped through a spray gun into a brick-lined combustion chamber, and air is supplied under pressure by a blower. A waste-heat boiler utilizes the heat of combustion to make steam for melting and pumping the sulfur. Capacities range from 100 to 40,000 lb of sulfur/hr. Quick starting and stopping, and ease of regulation, are among the advantages claimed for spray burners.

The burning of pyrite is considerably more difficult to control than the burning of sulfur, although many of the difficulties have been overcome in modern mechanical pyrite burners, of which the Herreshoff and wedge burners are well-known types (see also Sulfuric acid). The pyrite is burned on multiple trays which are subject to mechanical raking. The theoretical maximum SO_2 content is 16.2%, and levels of 10–14% are generally attained. As much as 13% of the sulfur in pyrite may be converted to sulfur trioxide in pyrite burners. The spent pyrite may contain up to 4% of sulfur. In most applications, the separation of dust is necessary when sulfur dioxide is made from pyrite. Several methods may be employed for this (see Gas cleaning), but for many purposes the use of water-spray towers is most satisfactory. This also serves to remove some of the sulfur trioxide and to cool the gas. For most applications, burner gases need no further treatment, other than cooling to permit their absorption either by water or by alkaline solutions or slurries. Lead pipes in flowing water are generally used, about 15 ft² of cooling surface/(ton/day) of SO_2 being sufficient to cool the gas to near ambient temperatures.

There are about ten manufacturers of liquid sulfur dioxide in the United States and Canada at the present time. Sulfur dioxide is obtained from one of two sources—from the burning of sulfur and from waste gases, usually smelter gases, although at least one manufacturer uses waste from phenol production (see Vol. 15, p. 153). Most plants in the United States utilize sulfur as their starting material and employ water as the absorbent in various modifications of the old Hanisch-Schroder process (20) first described in 1884. The cooled sulfur-burner gas is blown into the bottom of packed towers down which water flows. The exit gas contains from 0.02–0.1% sulfur dioxide, while the rich absorbent contains 1–2%. The cool rich liquor is stripped by heating with low-pressure steam. The stripped liquor contains about 0.01% SO_2 and is discharged. The gaseous mixture of sulfur dioxide and water vapor leaving the stripper is then dried with sulfuric acid and finally compressed and liquefied. From 50–100 tons of water are required per ton of sulfur dioxide produced. Because of the large volume of water required, and the heavy heat losses in stripping, this process is relatively expensive and unsuited for the recovery of sulfur dioxide from waste gases.

At least two plants in the United States manufacture liquid sulfur dioxide from lead- and copper-smelter gases at about 5% strength by a process based on absorption in dimethylaniline (18). This process has important advantages over other alkaline-absorption methods, principally because of its economies in materials, space, and equipment. Losses due to oxidation of sulfite to sulfate are also minimized. The flue gas containing sulfur dioxide coming from the smelter is first cleaned by passage in turn through a hot Cottrell precipitator for removal of dust and fumes, a water scrubber for removal of residual fume and for cooling and conditioning the gas, a Cottrell mist precipitator for removing water droplets and sulfuric acid mist, and finally a coke filter to remove the last trace of water droplets. The clean gas is then cooled and passed through a bubble-cap tower, where it is absorbed in cool anhydrous dimethylaniline. The tail gas which is vented to the atmosphere contains about 0.05% SO_2. The rich absorbent is passed through a heat exchanger to a second bubble-cap tower, where it is stripped with steam. The mixture of sulfur dioxide and water vapor is cooled and scrubbed with water to remove any residual dimethylaniline. The purified gas is dried with sulfuric acid and is then compressed, cooled, and liquefied to the final product, containing less than 50 ppm of water. Efficient recovery of the absorbent from both gas and liquid phases is an important feature of the process, and the consumption of dimethylaniline is only about 1 lb/ton of sulfur dioxide produced.

Many other alkaline absorbents have been utilized or studied for the recovery of sulfur dioxide from dilute gases (23). These include ammonia, basic aluminum sulfate, and various aromatic and aliphatic amines. At Copper Cliff, Ontario, liquid sulfur dioxide is produced by direct compression, without the use of an absorption process, from nickel-smelter gases. This is made possible by a sulfur dioxide content on the order of 75% in the gases resulting from a flash roasting process using pure oxygen instead of air (38). Direct compression with cooling has also been employed in the Bayer plant at Leverkusen, Germany, using smelter gas at 6.5–7.0% sulfur dioxide concentration by vol.

Recovery of Sulfur Dioxide from Dilute Flue Gases. At the present time (1969) a number of processes for the removal of sulfur dioxide from dilute flue gases are in various stages of pilot-scale or initial commercial operation. These processes, unlike earlier processes based on treatment with lime or chalk slurries, are aimed at treating the hot flue gases with a minimum of cooling so that effective stack dispersal of residual gas can still be accomplished. This involves processing flue gases in the range from 100 to 500°C. They also aim at treatment of dilute gases which result from the burning of coals and oils containing 2 to 4% sulfur. Such gases contain sulfur dioxide in concentrations ranging from 0.1 to 0.4%, along with appreciable amounts of sulfur trioxide and fly ash. Many of the earlier developed absorption processes, such as the aromatic amine or the aqueous ammonia processes, are economically suited only for gas streams some 3–30 times richer in sulfur dioxide, namely smelter gases which run typically from 1 to 7% in sulfur dioxide concentration in the more usual roasting processes. Ash is generally removed from the flue gases as an initial step in the recovery process.

Most of the newer processes are dry processes aimed at the removal of 90% or more of the sulfur dioxide content and the recovery of the sulfur content in some saleable product form. Usually this is sulfuric acid or elemental sulfur. If sulfur-value credits can be obtained without shipping to distant markets, some of these processes promise to be economically advantageous in larger power plants burning high-sulfur fuels (57).

A number of dilute sulfur dioxide recovery processes are listed in Table 12.

Table 12. Processes for Recovery of Sulfur Dioxide from Dilute Flue Gases

Process	Primary product	End product(s)	Developer
alkalized alumina	H_2S	H_2SO_4 or S	U.S. Bureau of Mines
sodium aluminate	H_2S	H_2SO_4 or S	SW Research Institute
activated charcoal	SO_3	H_2SO_4	Reinluft
catalytic oxidation	SO_3	H_2SO_4	Monsanto Co.
catalytic oxidation plus ammonia		$(NH_4)_2SO_4$	Kiyoura-T.I.T.
molten carbonate	H_2S	H_2SO_4 or S	North American Rockwell
chemical absorption, stripping	SO_2	H_2SO_4, S, or SO_2	Wellman-Lord Ltd.
nitrogen dioxide		HNO_3 and H_2SO_4	Tyco Laboratories
manganese oxide		H_2SO_4	Mitsubishi

At least one process based on addition of reactants to the furnace in which coal is burned is currently under development and demonstration. This is the dolomite process of Combustion Engineering, Inc., and it is believed to be competitive with recovery processes at 90% sulfur dioxide removal, even though there are no marketable by-products in the dolomite process (57).

Materials of Construction (26). Almost all common materials of construction are resistant to commercial dry liquid sulfur dioxide, dry sulfur dioxide gas, and hot sulfur dioxide gas containing water above the dewpoint. These include cast iron, carbon steel, copper, brass, and aluminum. Where hot gases or hot solutions are involved, the temperature resistance, particularly for plastics and resins, and the resistance to thermal shock, particularly for ceramic, glass, and stone, should be taken into account. The latter materials are inert to the wet gas, sulfurous acid, and sulfite solutions. Carbon, graphite, and impregnated carbon are suitable for practically all types of sulfur dioxide service. Lead is also resistant to sulfur dioxide and sulfites under most conditions, except those ruled out by its mechanical and physical limitations. Aluminum is resistant under a variety of conditions and is favored in some food-industry applications involving wet sulfur dioxide. Organic coatings are generally resistant but may fail where gas diffusion through the film is appreciable. Among the organic materials, hard rubber has been found satisfactory in sulfurous acid at moderate temperatures, and butyl rubber may be expected to perform similarly.

Iron, steel, Monel Cu–Ni, nickel, and Inconel Ni–Cr–Fe are common materials satisfactory for dry or hot sulfur dioxide, but they are readily corroded below the dewpoint or by wet sulfur dioxide gas, sulfurous acid, and sulfites. Inconel is especially resistant to very hot sulfur dioxide gas. Metals best suited to a wide variety of wet, dry, and hot sulfur dioxide, sulfurous acid, and sulfite service are Worthite, Ni–Cr; Durimet, 20 Ni–Cr; and several of the common stainless steels. Liquid sulfur dioxide will discolor iron, copper, and brass at about 300 ppm of moisture and will produce light scale at about 0.1% moisture and serious corrosion at about 0.2% or higher moisture content. Copper and brass can be used in a wide variety of light sulfur dioxide wet service. Wooden tanks are widely used for sulfurous acid preparation, handling, and storage. Sulfite pulp digestors are made of steel lined with acid-resisting brick. Thermosetting phenolic and furan resins and various inorganic acid-resistant cements have been used for digestor mortar joints resistant to the hot bisulfite liquors.

Grades and Specifications. The major grade of liquid sulfur dioxide sold is variously known as the technical, industrial, or commercial grade. This grade contains a minimum of 99.98% of sulfur dioxide and is a water-white liquid free of sulfur trioxide and sulfuric acid; it shows only a trace at most of nonvolatile residue. Its most important specification is the moisture content, which is generally set at 100 ppm maximum. The only other grade sold is the refrigeration grade of liquid sulfur dioxide, which is a premium grade having the same purity and specifications as the industrial grade, except for the moisture content, specified as 50 ppm maximum (8). At least one manufacturer sells a single grade for which specifications have been established as follows: color, APHA 25 max; nonvolatile residue, 25 ppm max; moisture, 50 ppm max.

Shipping, Storage, and Handling. Liquid sulfur dioxide is shipped in tank cars, ton drums, and cylinders. All shipping containers are governed by regulations of the Department of Transportation (DOT) (6), which classifies sulfur dioxide as a nonflammable gas. The various containers are made of specified steel, must pass hydrostatic-pressure tests, and are protected by safety devices. Single-unit tank cars are available in 32,000-, 40,000-, or 60,000-lb capacities. Sulfur dioxide tank cars are lagged and provided with a spring-loaded pressure-relief valve. Purchasers of tank-car quantities of sulfur dioxide are required to have adequate storage facilities for prompt transfer from tank cars.

Ton drums containing 2000 lb of sulfur dioxide are shipped on multiunit railroad cars holding 15 drums. These drums are provided with fusible safety plugs which melt at 165°F. Since the purchaser ordinarily retains the drums until they are empty, they serve as their own storage containers. The common cylinder size for sulfur dioxide is the 150-lb container, although other cylinder sizes are available for refrigeration-grade material. Cylinders are also provided with 165°F fusible safety plugs and carry the Green label for nonflammable gases.

All shipping containers for liquid sulfur dioxide are arranged so that withdrawal or transfer of the contents may be effected either as a gas or as a liquid. In general, the pressure of the sulfur dioxide itself in its container is utilized to effect the transfer. The most convenient method of attaining the required pressure differential in the case of cylinders and drums is heating. Since these containers are equipped with fusible plugs, it is recommended that the temperature never be allowed to exceed 125°F, either in storage or during heating for transfer (8). In order to minimize the danger that a container of sulfur dioxide will become full of liquid and fail, due to the development of hydrostatic pressure with rising temperature, the maximum allowable sulfur dioxide capacity, in pounds, of any container has been set by DOT at 1.25 times the water capacity, in pounds. To allow for safety under all possible conditions, it is common practice to fill containers to only 1.15 times the water capacity.

Health and Safety Factors. Sulfur dioxide presents two potential hazards. One is its physiological action as an irritating, asphyxiant gas; the other is its freezing action when in contact with the skin or other tissues in the form of a liquefied low-boiling gas. Cases of severe exposure to sulfur dioxide gas are rare, because the gas is so strongly irritating that it serves as its own warning agent at very low concentrations. Exposure to high concentrations for even short periods may be dangerous in that suffocation may result from involuntary shutting of the glottis to keep out the gas. Fortunately, the irritation caused by sulfur dioxide is so severe that a person will not remain in a contaminated atmosphere unless trapped. There is no evidence that continued exposure to sulfur dioxide in allowable concentrations produces a cumulative effect.

The physiological effects of various concentrations of sulfur dioxide gas are shown in Table 13, which has been assembled from various sources (8).

Table 13. Physiological Effects of Sulfur Dioxide Gas

Quantity	Concn, ppm
least amount causing detectable odor	3–5
least amount causing immediate eye irritation	20
least amount causing immediate throat irritation	8–12
least amount causing coughing	20
max concn allowable for prolonged exposure	10
max concn allowable for short (30 min) exposure	50–100
amount dangerous for even short exposure	400–500

Green plant life is far more sensitive to sulfur dioxide gas than are men and animals. Injury to vegetation may occur at ground-level concentrations under 1 ppm. The damaging effects of sulfur dioxide on plants and animals, particularly in the vicinity of smelters and other industrial process and power plants, has led to regulations designed to limit the amount of atmospheric contamination in many countries, cities, and areas of the world (23). The increasing necessity of limiting atmospheric pollution by sulfur dioxide and other sulfur compounds has been one of the important factors in the growing practice of removing sulfur compounds from waste-process gases and recovering their sulfur values in many cases.

Sulfur dioxide does not form explosive or combustible mixtures with air and does not offer any fire hazards. A Chemical Safety Data Sheet, SD-52, on sulfur dioxide, adopted July 1953, is available from Manufacturing Chemists' Association, Inc, Washington, D.C.

Economic Aspects. About 50 million metric tons of sulfur dioxide was produced and consumed annually as of 1966 for various purposes throughout the free world. About 85% of this production goes into making sulfuric acid, and another 8% goes into pulp and paper manufacture. Almost all of this is captive production. The production of liquid sulfur dioxide during 1966 amounted to about 328,000 metric tons. About 75% of this is derived from brimstone (massive elemental sulfur), the rest from pyrites, smelter gases, and recovered sulfur sources. About half of the liquid sulfur dioxide produced goes into the manufacture of pulp and paper.

United States production of liquid sulfur dioxide in 1966 amounted to nearly 120,000 metric tons. Unlike the worldwide consumption pattern, only about 27% of this amount goes into pulp and paper manufacture. The largest portion, 48%, goes into the manufacture of hydrosulfites and other chemicals. The balance is used in preservative, oil-refining, and metal-refining applications. In the fifteen years from 1951 to 1966, the production of liquid sulfur dioxide has increased about two and one-half fold. The price per short ton has declined during the same period from $90 to $75, in tanks at works.

The economic and marketing picture for liquid sulfur dioxide is complicated and even obscured by the widespread use of captive sulfur dioxide in many applications. Liquid sulfur dioxide, because of purity, pricing, and relative ease of handling, would ordinarily be an attractive outlet for recovery of sulfur values from individual process gases. The growth of applications is tied, however, to the growth of the pulp and paper industries and the refining and textile industries, and not to the availability or price of liquid sulfur dioxide. The local or captive generation and use of sulfur dioxide and of sulfur dioxide derivatives, such as the hydrosulfites and other reducing salts, is a changing but ever-present factor. In addition to the large amount of sulfur dioxide gas consumed captively, at least 10% of the liquid sulfur dioxide produced is used in captive outlets. This is reflected partly in the fact that merchant sales of liquid sulfur dioxide have been estimated to run from 70 to 80% of total production in the United States in most years. U.S. capacity for production of liquid sulfur dioxide was estimated to be 133,000 short tons/yr in 1967.

Uses. Aside from the enormous consumption of sulfur dioxide in the manufacture of sulfuric acid and sulfite pulp, well over 1 million tons of sulfur dioxide is consumed each year in a wide variety of industrial and agricultural applications. In sulfite pulp production, about 80% of the sulfur dioxide consumed goes into the pulping process, and about 20% into the bleaching operation, namely in the generation of chlorine dioxide. With improvements in sulfite pulping, principally in the recent adoptions of soluble-base pulping, the efficiency of sulfur dioxide utilization has improved greatly, dropping from 25% sulfur dioxide consumption to more nearly 10% of the sulfite-pulp tonnage produced. The other uses for sulfur dioxide stem from its several aspects as a reducing agent (bleach, antichlor), a preservative and fumigant, a liquid solvent (extractant), an easily compressible condensable gas (refrigerant), a stable gas (inert atmosphere), and a low-cost reagent for the manufacture of chemicals (36). Many of the important applications of sulfur dioxide are to be found in the food industries and in the related fields of agricultural, animal, and vegetable products, where one or more of its functions as a fumigant, preservative, or bleach are utilized. Certain fruits that are subject to rapid spoilage, such as grapes, can more safely be shipped and stored prior to processing if fumigated with sulfur dioxide. Stored grains and cereals are fumigated with sulfur dioxide to overcome infestation by insects and rodents. In the manufacture of wine, a small amount of sulfur dioxide is added to the must to destroy bacteria, molds, and wild yeasts, without harming the yeasts that produce the desired fermentation. Sulfur dioxide is used as a bleaching agent in the refining of sugar, in the processing of fruits and grains, and in the prevention of browning in apple slices. It is also useful as a preservative in the sun drying and artificial drying of various fruits. Sulfur dioxide also serves as a preservative and bleach in the brining of cherries. It is widely used as an extractant, precipitant, bleach, and preservative in the manufacture of various industrial and food proteins, such as soybean protein, casein, gelatin, and glue. Sulfur dioxide also finds some use as a preservative for silage.

Many uses have been proposed for liquid sulfur dioxide as a reaction medium and an extractant. These include Friedel-Crafts condensations, isomerization, and sulfonation reactions. Among various extraction processes, one, the Edeleanu petroleum-refining process, has found commercial application (see Vol. 15, p. 57). It is based on the fact that aromatics, unsaturates, and sulfur compounds are readily miscible with it, saturated hydrocarbons having only limited solubility.

Sulfur dioxide finds many uses as a raw material in the manufacture of chemicals, such as its uses in the manufacture of sulfites, bisulfites, metabisulfites, and hydrosulfites. Liquid sulfur dioxide has been used in the manufacture of sulfuryl and thionyl chlorides and a variety of organic sulfonates, sulfones, and sulfonyl chlorides. The reactions of sulfur dioxide with anthracite to produce carbon disulfide (31), and with olefins to produce thiophene (9), have been studied.

Miscellaneous uses for sulfur dioxide include adjustment of chlorine in water supplies, treatment of boiler waters, bleaching of various fiber and mineral products, cleaning of filter beds and wells, as an inert atmosphere in magnesium metallurgy, as a

Table 14. Reducing Salt Derivatives of Sulfur Dioxide

Commercial name	Formula	Parent acid	Page reference
sodium sulfite	Na_2SO_3	sulfurous	83
sodium metabisulfite	$Na_2S_2O_5$	pyrosulfurous	105
sodium thiosulfate	$Na_2S_2O_3$	thiosulfuric	see Thiosulfates
sodium hydrosulfite	$Na_2S_2O_4$	dithionous	102
zinc hydrosulfite	ZnS_2O_4	dithionous	102
sodium formaldehyde sulfoxylate	$NaSO_2CH_2OH\cdot2H_2O$	sulfoxylic	105
zinc formaldehyde sulfoxylate	$Zn(SO_2CH_2OH)_2$	sulfoxylic	105
basic zinc formaldehyde sulfoxylate	$Zn(OH)SO_2CH_2OH$	sulfoxylic	105

surface alkali neutralizer in glass manufacture, in the preparation of chrome liquor for leather tanning, as a refrigerant in mechanical refrigerators, as an antichlor in textile processing, in ore flotation, and in many other minor uses. An extensive discussion of food and pharmaceutical applications for sulfur dioxide will be found in reference 34.

Sulfur Dioxide Derivatives. The reducing salts of the various oxyacids based on sulfur dioxide comprise the most important group of inorganic derivatives of sulfur dioxide. These salts are closely related to each other and to sulfur dioxide in their chemistry and applications as reducing agents. Their principal differences, from a practical viewpoint, lie in their relative stabilities with regard to the temperature and pH in their applications as reducing agents. These salts, which also provide a variety of forms with regard to purity, concentration, reducing power, storage stability, and handling convenience, are listed in Table 14.

Metabisulfites are known more accurately as pyrosulfites and inaccurately as bisulfites or acid sulfites. The latter salts exist but are too unstable for successful commercial handling. Thus most, if not all, material sold as bisulfite is actually the pyrosulfite. Thiosulfates (qv) are also known as hyposulfites, eg the "hypo" of commerce. Hydrosulfites are also known properly as dithionites. As indicated in Table 14, the anhydrous forms of the reducing salts are most commonly marketed, usually because they are the most stable, but sometimes for economy in shipment, as in the case of the thiosulfate.

SULFUR–OXYGEN ACIDS AND THEIR SALTS. See also under Introduction.

Dithionous Acid (hydrosulfurous acid). This acid, $H_2S_2O_4$, is formed by passing aqueous sulfurous acid through a column containing zinc amalgam granules (Jones reductor). The acid is very unstable and breaks down rapidly into thiosulfate, bisulfate, or, if the reaction medium is sufficiently acid, into sulfurous acid and sulfur. The free acid has never been isolated, but its salts, particularly the sodium and zinc salts, have been prepared and are well-known articles of commerce. The salts were originally termed hydrosulfites, as a consequence of the composition first assigned to them following their initial preparation in 1869; this designation has persisted to the present day as the exclusive commercial name. After the present formula was established, the names hyposulfurous acid and hyposulfite were widely used in the literature. In more recent years the names dithionous acid and dithionites have been proposed and widely adopted in the literature to avoid confusion with the "hypo" of commerce, which is sodium thiosulfate.

Sodium dithionite (hydrosulfite), $Na_2S_2O_4$, crystallizes from solution as a dihydrate that oxidizes rapidly in air to sodium metabisulfite. The anhydrous salt is much more stable and is the form more commonly manufactured. In 1967, when production was estimated to be about 74 million lb/yr, the compound was priced at about 26.5¢/lb in car-lot drums. The commercial material is marketed as a dry white crystalline powder of about 94% purity. Some large textile users manufacture the salt at their own plants in the form of solutions.

Zinc hydrosulfite is also produced commercially, to the extent of perhaps 12 million lb/yr, and is marketed as a fine white powder containing about 80% of zinc dithionite. Zinc hydrosulfite is less active and more stable at a given temperature and pH than is sodium hydrosulfite; hence, it is used only in applications requiring higher temperatures or lower pH values than sodium hydrosulfite.

Dithionites are prepared by the reduction of sulfites, bisulfites, and sulfur dioxide with reductants such as iron or zinc powder, sodium or zinc amalgam, or sodium suspension. The electrolytic reduction of sodium bisulfite to sodium dithionite in a hydrogen atmosphere has also been studied (27). Although few particulars are available on the methods of manufacturing hydrosulfites in the United States, considerable information on German practice has been made available since the close of World War II. One process that has been described in detail (12) involves as a first step the reduction of liquid sulfur dioxide in a continuous reactor with zinc dust slurried in water. The reaction mixture is circulated through a tubular cooler at 35°C, and zinc hydrosulfite is continually bled off. The filtered liquor is converted in a large vessel to the sodium salt by means of 25°Bé caustic soda. The resultant slurry of zinc hydroxide and sodium hydrosulfite is filtered and washed several times after being treated with sodium sulfide to remove heavy metals. The ensuing 20% solution is then salted out with the aid of salt and alcohol. The resulting crystals are partially decanted and dehydrated by means of direct steam at about 65°C, and after further removal of mother liquor, the crystals are washed with alcohol and finally vacuum-dried at 80–90°C. Almost all of the equipment involved is stainless steel, rubber-covered, or enameled. Solutions of zinc or sodium hydrosulfite can be economically manufactured on location by large users by methods that have been developed over a number of years by Virginia Smelting Company, using liquid sulfur dioxide. One simple method produces 3 lb of zinc hydrosulfite per gallon of solution by the introduction of liquid sulfur dioxide into a well-agitated, water-cooled tank containing a water suspension of zinc dust.

The commercial utilization of the dithionites is based on their powerful reducing action on many materials. They readily reduce a large number of metal ions to the metal, as well as disulfide linkages in wool and hair, and a large number of nitro compounds and many dyes. Principal applications are in various textile operations (5), such as dyeing, printing, and stripping. The vat dyeing of textiles, principally cotton, represents the largest outlet by far for the hydrosulfites. Other important uses include bleaching of ground wood pulp, soap, sugar, molasses, and glue.

Metabisulfites. See Pyrosulfurous acid.

Peroxysulfuric Acids, Persulfuric Acids. See Peroxides.

Pyrosulfuric Acid. Sulfur trioxide forms hydrates with water, one of which corresponds to the composition $H_2S_2O_7$, or pyrosulfuric acid, melting at 36°C. The acid is very unstable, and upon dissolving in water, or on heating, it behaves like a mixture of sulfuric acid and sulfur trioxide. A series of pyrosulfates exists, the best known of which are the alkali-metal pyrosulfates, formed by strongly heating the appropriate bisulfate. Although these salts give definite x-ray diffraction patterns and contain a definite S–O–S linkage, they hydrolyze readily in water to yield bisulfate and sulfate ions. The alkali-metal pyrosulfates melt more readily than the corresponding sulfates and give up sulfur trioxide upon calcining, to form the sulfate. Trisulfates, $M_2S_3O_{10}$, having structures and properties similar to those of the pyrosulfates are known. They are formed by reacting the alkali-metal sulfate with excess sulfur trioxide. The trisulfates hydrolyze readily in water to yield bisulfates (30).

Pyrosulfurous Acid, $H_2S_2O_5$, is known only through its salts, the pyrosulfites, or, as they are known commercially, the metabisulfites, $M_2S_2O_5$, formed by heating the bisulfites, with which they are closely associated. Most of the sodium bisulfite sold commercially is in the form of its anhydride, *sodium metabisulfite*, since the latter is less hygroscopic and more stable in storage and shipment. The production of sodium bisulfite and metabisulfite in the United States is estimated to be about 60 million lb/yr. Anhydrous sodium metabisulfite is priced at $5.85 per cwt works in car-lot bags (Feb. 1969). It finds use in reducing and preservative applications, where a solid source of sulfur dioxide is preferred.

Sulfoxylic Acid. Free sulfoxylic acid, H_2SO_2, is unknown. Reports of its sodium and zinc salts may be due to an analytical error. The structure $S(OH)_2$, sulfur(II) hydroxide, is known only as esters, ROSOR, and amides, R_2NSNR_2. Derivatives of a sulfinic acid form (HSO_2H), eg, ester salts, $HOCH_2SO_2M$, and a cobalt complex, $Co(SO_2)$, are known.

The ester salts are prepared (5,12) by the addition of formaldehyde to the appropriate dithionite salt and have the structure exemplified by sodium formaldehydesulfoxylate, $NaSO_2CH_2OH$. Three commercial salts are produced to the extent of perhaps 15 million lb/yr in the United States. These are *sodium sulfoxylate*, in the form of a white granular dihydrate of about 100% purity, *zinc sulfoxylate*, $Zn(SO_2CH_2OH)_2$, which is a white crystalline powder of at least 95% purity, and a *basic zinc sulfoxylate*, $Zn(OH)SO_2CH_2OH$, which is a light gray powder of about 89% purity. In general, the formaldehydesulfoxylates find the same applications as the hydrosulfites (dithionites), except that they are somewhat less active and more stable. They are therefore used in many bleaching and reducing applications at higher temperatures and lower pH values than the corresponding hydrosulfites. The sulfoxylates are best applied at a pH of about 3.4, as against an optimum pH of about 6 for zinc hydrosulfite, and about 9.5 for sodium hydrosulfite. The basic zinc formaldehydesulfoxylate, the most stable of the series, can be used at temperatures around 100°C, as against a preferred temperature of about 50°C for sodium hydrosulfite. An important application of sodium formaldehydesulfoxylate is as a means of directly introducing the group $-CH_2SO_2Na$ upon nitrogen, as in the preparation of the medicinal neoarsphenamine (see Vol. 2, p. 730). The principal function of the sulfinate group in this and in related cases is to increase the water solubility of the compound; it is readily split off in vivo. The sulfoxylates have been marketed under a number of trade names, Formopon, Rongalite, Dekrolin, and Sulfoxite being among the better-known ones.

Bibliography

"Sulfur Compound—Structures" and "Sulfur Compounds, Inorganic" in *ECT* 1st ed., Vol. 13, pp. 374–430, by Pat Macaluso, Stauffer Chemical Co.

1. Association of Official Agricultural Chemists (since changed to Association of Official Analytical Chemists), *Method of Analysis*, 7th ed., Washington, D. C., 1950.
2. Barrow, G. M., and K. S. Pitzer, *Ind. Eng. Chem.* **41**, 2737 (1949).
3. Bice, W. O., F. Prange, and R. E. Weis, *Ind. Eng. Chem.* **44**, 2497 (1952).
4. Bottoms, R. R., *Ind. Eng. Chem.* **23**, 501 (1931).
5. Brearley, G., and J. Starkie, *J. Soc. Dyers Colourists* **64**, 278 (1948).
6. *Campbell's Freight Tariff No. 4 and Motor Carrier Tariff No. 7*, Association of American Railroads, Bureau of Explosives, New York.
7. *Chem. Abstr.* **46**, 7451c (1952); **47**, 2076d, 5838c (1953).
8. *Sulfur Dioxide*, Pamphlet G-3, Compressed Gas Association, Inc., New York, adopted 1949.
9. Conary, R. F., et al., *Ind. Eng. Chem.* **42**, 467 (1950).
10. Estep, J. W., and E. W. Plum, "Economics at the Sour Gas Industry," *Sulphur*, No. 74, Jan./Feb. 1968, pp. 30–36.
11. Dryden, I. G. C., *J. Soc. Chem. Ind. (London)* **66**, 59 (1947).

12. Edwards, W. A. M., and J. H. Clayton, *Sodium Hydrosulfite and Related Compounds*, I. G. Ludwigshafen, *BIOS (British Intelligence Objectives Subcommittee) Rept. 422 (PB 34027)* and *271 (PB 22409)*; U.S. Dept. of Commerce, Office of Technical Services.
13. Espach, R. H., *Ind. Eng. Chem.* **42**, 2235 (1950).
14. Fairlie, A. M., *Sulfuric Acid Manufacture*, Reinhold Publishing Corp., New York, 1936.
15. Fanelli, R., *Ind. Eng. Chem.* **41**, 2031 (1949).
16. Baudler, M. and F. Feher, *Z. Anorg. Chem.* **253**, 170 (1947).
17. Ibid., **258**, 132 (1949).
18. Fleming, E. P., and T. C. Fitt, *Ind. Eng. Chem.* **42**, 2253 (1950).
19. Freitag, R., *Zucker* **3**, 16 (1950).
20. Hitchcock, L. B., and A. K. Scribner, *Ind. Eng. Chem.* **23**, 743 (1931).
21. Jander, G., and K. Wickert, *Z. Physik. Chem.* **178**, 57 (1936).
22. Katz, M., *Ind. Eng. Chem.* **41**, 2450 (1949).
23. Katz, M., and R. J. Cole, *Ind. Eng. Chem.* **42**, 2258 (1950).
24. Kelley, K. K., "The Thermodynamic Properties of Sulfur and Its Inorganic Compounds," *Contributions to the Data on Theoretical Metallurgy, VII*, Bull. 406, U.S. Dept. of the Interior, Bureau of Mines, 1936, pp. 18–24.
25. Lippman, A., Jr., *Ind. Eng. Chem.* **42**, 2215 (1950).
26. "Materials of Construction Report (14th)," *Chem. Eng.* **57**, 136 (1950).
27. Patel, C. C., and M. R. A. Rao, *Proc. Natl. Inst. Sci. India* **15**, 131 (1949).
28. Riesenfeld, F. C., and C. L. Blohm, *Petroleum Refiner* **29** (4), 141 (1950).
29. Rorschach, R. L., and F. T. Gardner, *Ind. Eng. Chem.* **41**, 1380 (1949).
30. Sidgwick, N. V., *Chemical Elements and Their Compounds*, Vol. 2, Oxford University Press, Inc., New York, 1950.
31. Siller, C. W., *Ind. Eng. Chem.* **40**, 1227 (1948).
32. Sutermeister, E., *Chemistry of Pulp and Paper Making*, 3rd ed., John Wiley & Sons, Inc., New York, 1948.
33. Thorne, P. C. L., and E. R. Rogerts, *Ephraim's Inorganic Chemistry*, 4th ed., revised, Nordeman, New York, 1943.
34. Schroeter, L. C., *Sulfur Dioxide*, Pergamon Press, Inc., New York, 1966, 342 pp.
35. West, J. R., *Chem. Eng. Progr.* **44**, 287 (1948).
36. Willson, C. S., et al., *Chem. Inds.* **53**, 178 (1943).
37. Yost, D. M., and H. Russell, *Systematic Inorganic Chemistry*, Prentice-Hall Inc., New York, 1944.
38. Zabel, H. W., *Chem. Ind.* **63**, 960 (1948).
39. Brit. Pat. 633,469 (March 18, 1950), R. Darlington, V. Oakes, and K. C. Roberts (to Anchor Chemical Co., Ltd.).
40. U.S. Pat. 2,362,057 (Nov. 7, 1944), J. P. Edwards (to Hooker Electrochemical Co.).
41. U.S. Pat. 2,420,623 (May 13, 1947), W. H. Salzenberg and M. Sveda (to E. I. du Pont de Nemours & Co., Inc.).
42. U.S. Pat. 2,431,823 (Dec. 2, 1947), A. Pechukas (to Pittsburgh Plate Glass Co.).
43. U.S. Pat. 2,471,946 (May 31, 1949), E. F. Fricke (to Allied Chemical & Dye Corp.).
44. U.S. Pat. 2,530,410 (Nov. 21, 1950), M. Sveda (to Du Pont).
45. Strausz, O. P., and H. E. Gunning, "Synthesis of Sulfur Compounds by Singlet and Triplet Sulfur Atoms," in A. V. Tobolsky, ed., *The Chemistry of Sulfides*, Interscience Publishers, a division of John Wiley & Sons, Inc., New York, 1968, pp. 23–43.
46. Wiewiorowski, T. K., and F. J. Touro, "The Sulfur–Hydrogen Sulfide System," pp. 9–21 of reference 45.
47. *World Survey of Sulphur Resources*, The British Sulphur Corp. Ltd., London, 1966.
48. Kohl, A. L., and F. C. Riesenfeld, *Gas Purification*, McGraw-Hill Book Co., Inc., New York, 1960, 556 pp.
49. Kraus, H., F. Fischer and L. Klöckner, "Purification of Exhaust Air from Viscose Rayon Mills," *Sulphur*, No. 60, The British Sulphur Corp. Ltd., London, Oct. 1965, pp. 19–27.
50. U.S. Pat. 3,144,307 (Aug. 11, 1964), H. W. Haines, Jr., (to Sulphur Recovery, Inc.).
51. U.S. Pat. 3,149,920 (Sept. 22, 1964), P. Urban (to Universal Oil Products Co.).
52. *Sulphur*, No. 62, The British Sulphur Corp. Ltd., London, Feb./March 1966, pp. 18, 29–32.
53. Rosser, R. J., and F. R. Whitt, *J. Appl. Chem.* **10**, 229–237 (1960).

54. U.S. Pats. 3,071,441 and 3,071,442 (Jan. 1, 1963), V. H. Schmadebeck (to Hooker Chemical Co.).
55. Lautenschlaeger, F., "The Synthesis of Novel Bicyclic Sulfides from Sulfur Dichloride and Cyclic Diolefins," pp. 73–81 of reference 45.
56. Jolly, W. L., "Recent Studies of Sulfur-Nitrogen Compounds," pp. 3–7 of reference 45.
57. *Sulphur*, No. 73, The British Sulphur Corp. Ltd., London, Nov./Dec. 1967, pp. 20–27.
58. Becke-Goehring, M., and E. Fluck, "Developments in the Inorganic Chemistry of Compounds Containing the Sulphur–Nitrogen Bond," in C. B. Colburn, ed., *Developments in Inorganic Nitrogen Chemistry*, Vol. 1, American Elsevier Publishing Co., New York, 1966, pp. 150–240.
59. Bond, R. L., W. J. Mallin, and F. J. Pinchin, *Chem. Ind.* **1963**, 1902–1903.
60. *Sulfur Manual*, Section VII, Texas Gulf Sulphur Co., Inc., New York, 1963.
61. Schenk, P. W., *Ber.* **75**, 94 (1942).
62. Schenk, P. W., *Z. Anorg. Chem.* **211**, 150 (1933); *Z. Physik. Chem.* [B]**51**, 113 (1942).
62a. Spandau, H., and E. Brunneck, *Z. Anorg. Allgem. Chem.* **270**, 201 (1952).

PAT MACALUSO
Stauffer Chemical Co.

SULFUR DIOXIDE, SO$_2$.   See Sulfur compounds.

SULFUR DYES

The early sulfur dyes were made from quite simple intermediates by sulfurization or "thionation" with either sulfur or sodium polysulfide. They were insoluble in water but dissolved in sodium sulfide solutions, from which they dyed cotton directly. Thus, they formed a "chemical class" having a common chemical origin and a "dyeing class" having a common method of application (see Vol. 7, p. 551). This simple picture was soon complicated by the appearance of new dyes which were made by a thionation procedure, but were dyed from an alkaline dithionite vat. From the chemist's viewpoint these were sulfur dyes, but to the dyer, vat dyes (see Vol. 2, p. 529; Vol. 7, p. 554). More recently, entirely synthetic dyes of the anthraquinone and phthalocyanine classes have appeared which are sulfur dyes according to their method of application. There is therefore disagreement as to what defines a sulfur dye. This confused situation is exemplified in the *Colour Index*, which lists amongst the sulfur dye chemical class CI Vat Blue 42, and in the sulfur dye application class CI Sulfur Green 14, which is a synthetic dye of the phthalocyanine class. (See also Anthraquinone dyes; Phthalocyanine compounds; Dyes—application and evaluation.)

It is no longer logical to attempt a definition of sulfur dyes which encompasses both their manufacture and use. Sulfur dyes are best defined as those dyes which are applied in a reduced state from solutions containing sodium sulfide, hydrosulfide, or polysulfide, and which are subsequently oxidized on the fiber. This definition is to be preferred over one based on chemical class, since the sulfur dyes include a wide variety of chromophores. Furthermore, a definition based on formation by a thionation procedure would include a number of dyes made in this way which are properly defined as vat dyes. However, since the manufacture of the "sulfurized vat dyes" resembles that of sulfur dyes, they will also be described herein.   (See also Sulfur compounds.)

Preparation and Chemical Properties

Intermediates. Most sulfur dyes are still made by the thionation of fairly simple intermediates by reaction with sulfur or sodium polysulfide. The intermediates are thereby converted to highly colored bodies which dissolve in solutions of sodium sulfide as a reduced or "leuco" form. The leuco form of the dye has good affinity for cotton and other cellulosic fibers and, when reoxidized in the fiber, forms an insoluble coloring matter of high molecular weight. There are two principal methods of thionation. In the reflux method, sodium polysulfide is used in an aqueous or solvent

Table 1. Indophenol Dyes

Intermediate	Shade	CI number	CI name
phenyl–NH–C$_6$H$_4$–OH	red-brown, bordeau	53228	Sulfur Red 10
naphthyl–NH–C$_6$H$_4$–OH	black	53290	Sulfur Black 11
(CH$_3$)$_2$N–C$_6$H$_4$–NH–C$_6$H$_4$–OH	blue	53430	Sulfur Blue 9
H$_2$N–C$_6$H$_3$(CH$_3$)–NH–C$_6$H$_4$–OH	reddish-blue, navy	53440	Sulfur Blue 7
O$_2$N–C$_6$H$_3$(NO$_2$)–NH–C$_6$H$_4$–OH	navy, black	53235	Sulfur Blues 1, 3, 4, 5, 11
H$_2$N–C$_6$H$_2$(NH$_2$)(CH$_3$CONH)–NH–C$_6$H$_4$–OH	violet	53410	Sulfur Violet 1
H$_2$N–naphthyl(SO$_3$H)–NH–C$_6$H$_4$–OH	green-blue	53540	Sulfur Blue 15
phenyl–NH–naphthyl(HO$_3$S)–NH–C$_6$H$_4$–OH	green bluish-green	53570 53571	Sulfur Green 3 Sulfur Green 2
carbazole(N–H)–NH–C$_6$H$_4$–OH	blue	53630	Vat Blue 43
carbazole(N–C$_2$H$_5$)–NH–C$_6$H$_4$–OH	blue	53640	Vat Blue 42

medium; in the bake process, the intermediates are heated with elementary sulfur or with sodium polysulfide at temperatures up to 330°C.

The reflux method is employed for the manufacture of sulfur black from 2,4-dinitrophenol, and for the large and important group of colors made from indophenols of general formula (**1**), or from the corresponding diarylamines (**2**). (See also Dyes and dye intermediates; Aminophenols; Naphthalene derivatives; Nitrophenols; Phenylenediamines.) They comprise red-brown, violet, blue, green, and black dyes

(**1**)   (**2**)

characterized by high light- and washfastness. The indophenol dyes are reduced to straw-colored leuco compounds which have good affinity for cellulose. Table 1 lists the more important indophenol sulfur dyes and sulfurized vat dyes.

Sulfur bake colors are derived from a wide variety of intermediates, including hydrocarbons, simple primary aromatic amines, phenols, and anthraquinone derivatives. (See also Amines; Aminophenols; Anthraquinone derivatives; Benzidine; Nitrophenols; Thiazole dyes.) Some of the more important bake dyes are listed in Table 2.

Whereas most dyes of other classes are clearly defined compounds of known structure, with few exceptions the sulfur dyes are mixtures of variable and unknown constitution. Their mode of formation gives little indication of structure, and their peculiar properties have hindered analysis. They are mixtures of polymeric compounds of high molecular weight, and, as commercially prepared, contain both organic and inorganic impurities. However, the main structural elements of some dyes are well known.

Indophenol Dyes. CI Sulfur Blue 9, made from the indophenol having structure (**3**), was an early dye of this class which has been studied in some detail. Gnehm and Kauffler (1) brominated the dye and obtained from it a tetrabromo compound identical

(**3**)   (**4**)

with the bromination product of Methylene Violet (**4**). That they incorrectly assigned positions to the bromine atoms does not invalidate their conclusion that a phenothiazinone group is present in the dye. This grouping would account for the strong color of the dye, as in Methylene Violet itself, and its ready reduction to a pale leuco compound corresponding to (**5**).

(**5**)

Subsequent work has confirmed that this structural element occurs throughout the indophenol dyes. Thus, thionation of 4-hydroxydiphenylamine (**6**) and the trichloro-phenothiazinone (**7**) gives practically indistinguishable dyes. Evidently the three chlorine atoms of (**7**) are replaced by sulfur, and so presumably are the corresponding hydrogen atoms of (**6**). Von Weinberg (2) has shown that the blue dyes made from the

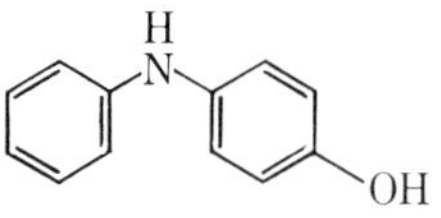

(6)

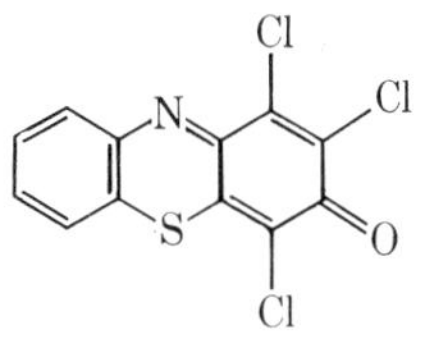

(7)

indophenol (**8**) and the trichlorophenothiazinone (**9**) are essentially identical. Likewise, CI Vat Blue 43 may be made from either carbazole indophenol, 3-*p*-hydroxyani-

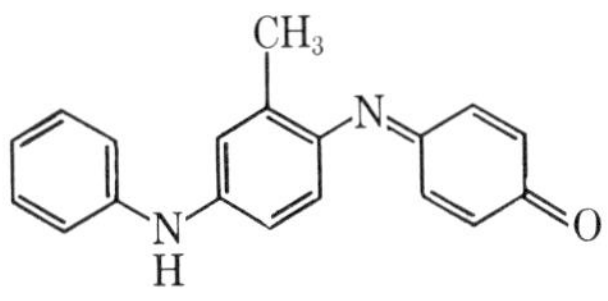

(8)

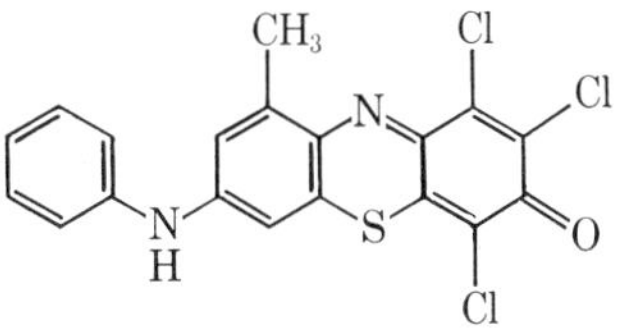

(9)

linocarbazole (**10**), or the related phenothiazine compound (**11**). (For other uses of many phenothiazine derivatives see Vol. 2, pp. 148–152; see also Psychopharmacological agents.)

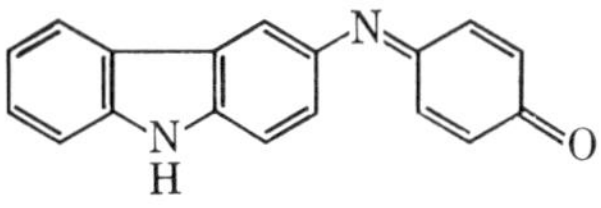

(10)

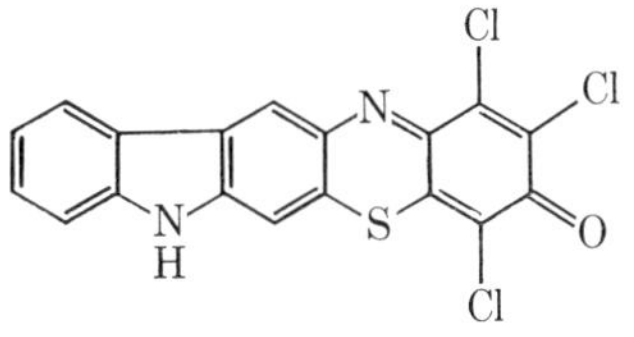

(11)

Similarly, Zerweck, Ritter, and Schubert (3) showed that CI Sulfur Black 11, from *N*-*p*-hydroxyphenyl-2-naphthylamine (**12**), is identical with the thionation product of (**13**).

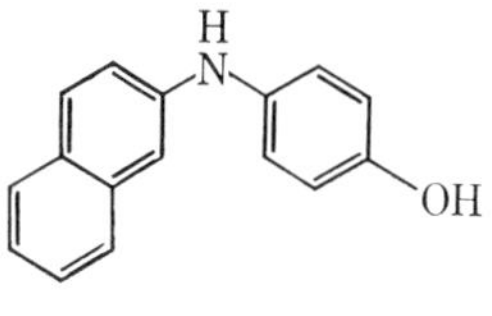

(12)

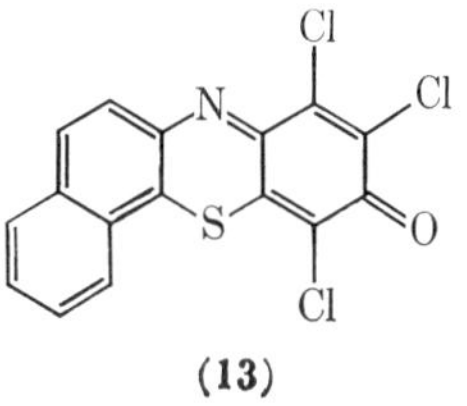

(13)

These workers demonstrated conclusively that formation of a sulfur dye involves substitution of all the free hydrogen atoms on the quinoneimine ring. Thus they prepared phenothiazinones with various blocking groups in the quinoneimine ring and thionated them. Condensation of the thiosulfate (**14**) with 1-naphthol and with *o*-xylenol gave the phenothiazinones (**15**) and (**16**). Their thionation products were very weak compared to CI Sulfur Blue 9. The trimethylphenothiazinone (**17**) was

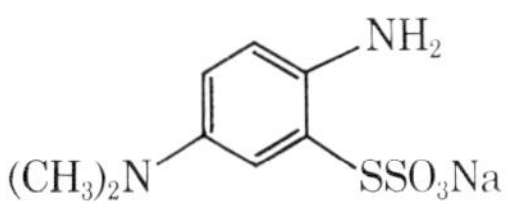

(14)

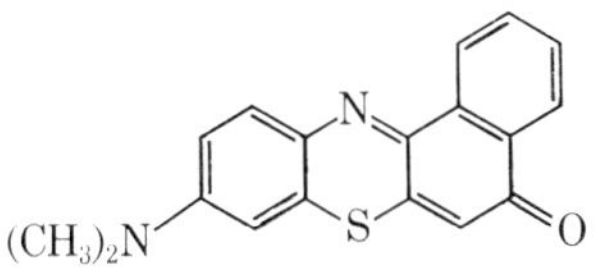

(15)

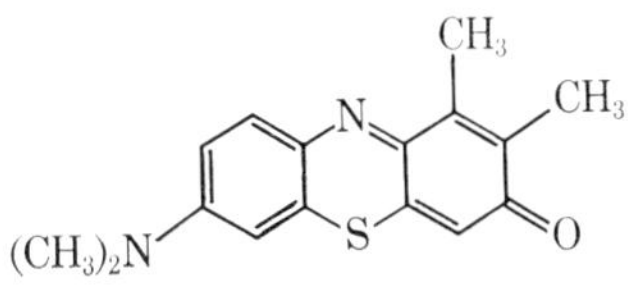

(16)

Table 2. Bake Dyes

Intermediates	Bake	Shade	CI number	CI name
decacyclene[a]	sulfur	reddish-orange, brown	53320	Sulfur Brown 52
H_2N—, NH_2, CH_3 (toluenediamine)	sulfur	orange	53050	Sulfur Orange 1
O_2N—, NO_2, CH_3 (dinitrotoluene)	poly-sulfide	brown	53020	Sulfur Brown 8
H_2N—, NH_2, CH_3 (toluenediamine)	sulfur	reddish-yellow	53105	Sulfur Yellow 6
H_2N——NH_2 (benzidine)		yellowish-orange		Sulfur Orange 3
O_2N—, NO_2, CH_3 (dinitrotoluene) and H_2N——NH_2 (benzidine)	poly-sulfide	yellowish-brown	53025	Sulfur Brown 24
CH_3, NH_2, NH_2, H_2N—, NH_2, NO_2, NH_2	sulfur	yellow-brown	53075	Sulfur Brown 23
phthalic anhydride and NO_2, NO_2, $NHCOCH_3$ substituted ring	poly-sulfide	yellow	53010	Sulfur Yellow 9
$HOCN(H)$—, $NCOH(H)$, CH_3 and H_2N——NH_2 (benzidine)	sulfur	yellow	53120	Sulfur Yellow 2

Table 2 (*continued*)

Intermediates	Bake	Shade	CI number	CI name
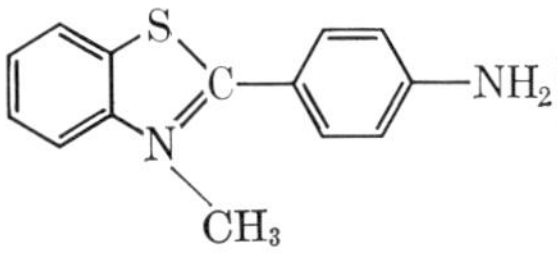 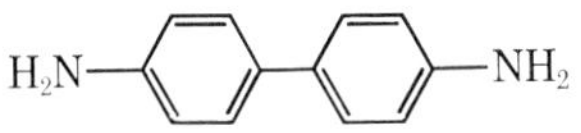	sulfur	yellow	53160	Sulfur Yellow 4
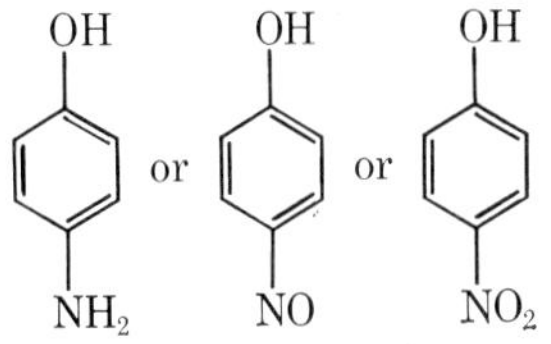	poly-sulfide[c]	olive green	53165	Sulfur Green 11
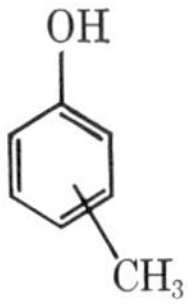	poly-sulfide	brown	53210	Sulfur Brown 4
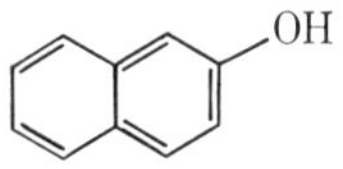	poly-sulfide	brown	53280	Sulfur Brown 31
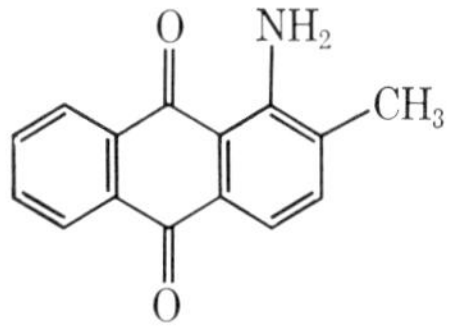 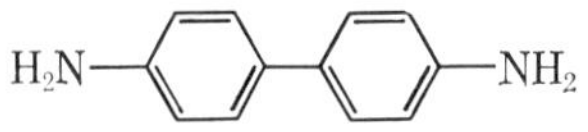	sulfur	red-violet	66515	vat dye
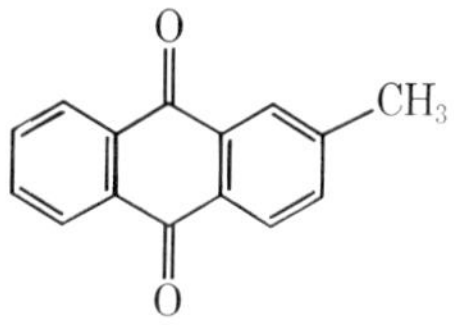	sulfur	yellow	69700	Vat Orange 21
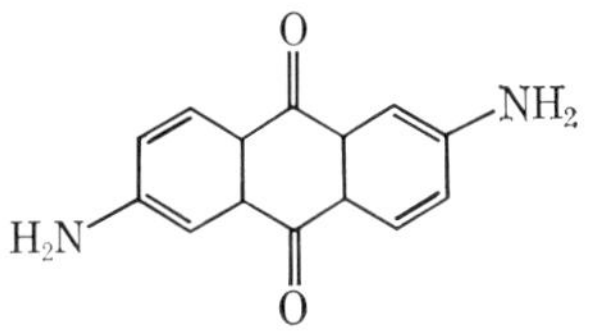 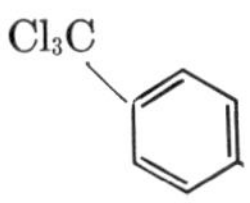	sulfur	yellow	67300	Vat Yellow 2

(*continued*)

Table 2 (*continued*)

Intermediates	Bake	Shade	CI number	CI name
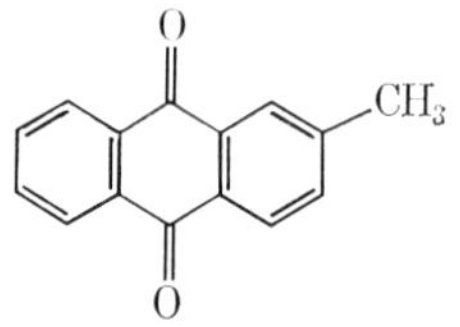 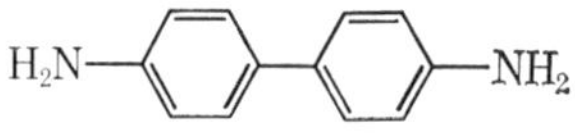	sulfur	yellow	66510	Vat Yellow 9
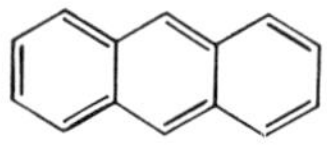	sulfur	olive	58825	Vat Green 7

a CA: diacenaphtho[1,2-*j*;1′,2′-*l*]fluoranthene.
b CA: 2-*p*-aminophenyl-6-methylbenzothiazole.
c Bake or reflux.

recovered unchanged after prolonged thionation, which indicates that sulfur does not enter the benzenoid ring. This is hardly surprising, since the benzenoid ring is not

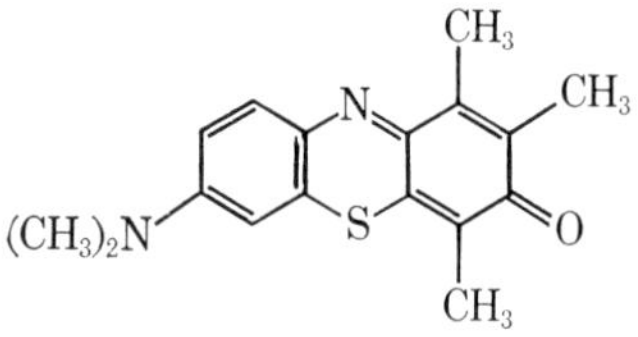

(**17**)

activated toward nucleophilic reagents, whereas the quinonoid ring is activated by the carbonyl and ketonimine groups.

The same authors also showed that the entering sulfur atoms do not form merely disulfide bridges with adjacent units, as had been proposed by von Weinberg. The compound (**19**) was prepared by condensing sodium trithiocarbonate with the trichlorophenothiazinone (**18**). This was reduced to the trimercapto compound (**20**), which was found to be of much lower strength and affinity than CI Sulfur Blue 9.

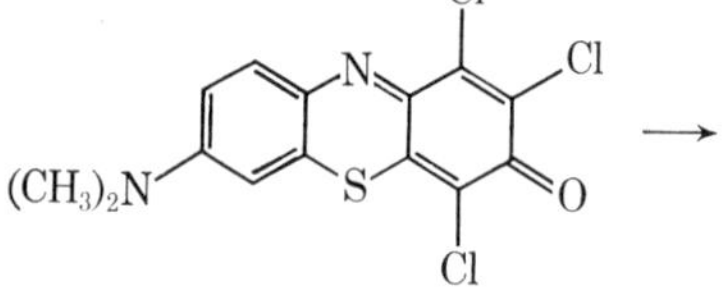

(**18**)

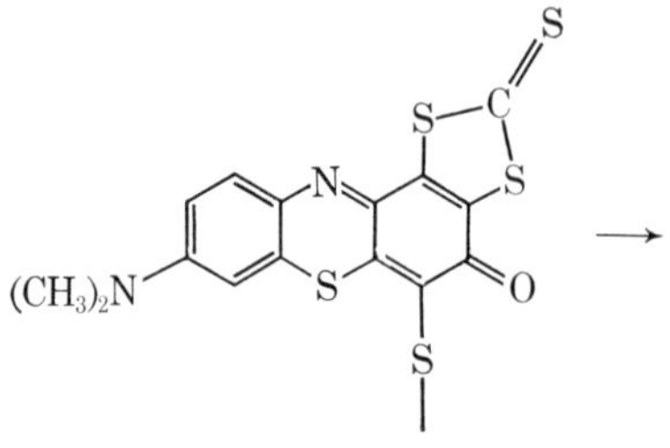

(**19**)

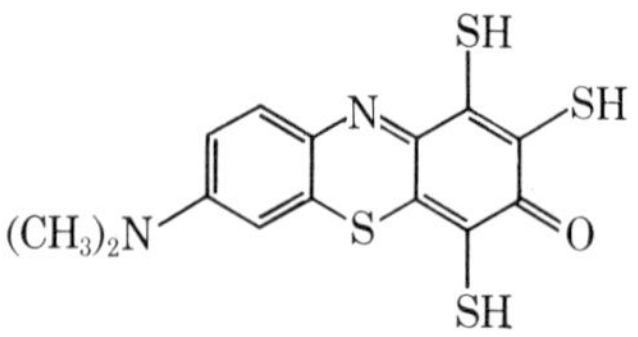

(**20**)

Zerweck and co-workers postulated that two phenothiazinone units are joined by a thianthrene ring and showed that reaction of (**21**) with one mole of sodium sulfide gives first a mercapto derivative (**22**), which condenses with itself to form (**23**).

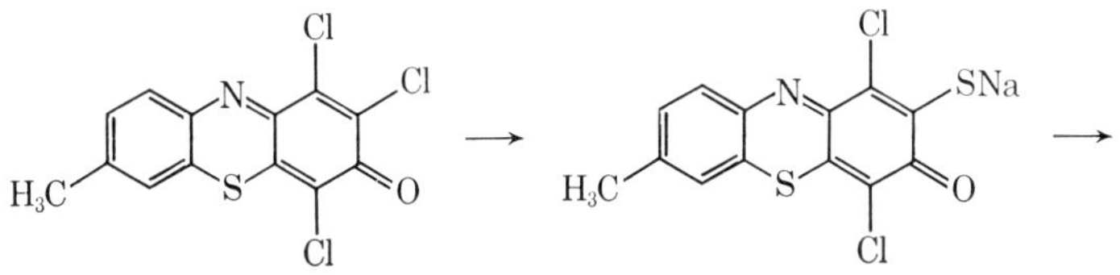

(**21**)   (**22**)

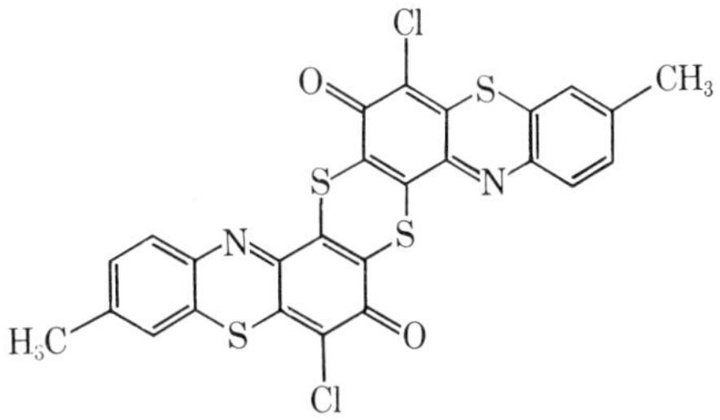

(23)

This crystalline compound already had the essential properties of an indophenol sulfur dye, being highly colored and readily reduced to a pale-colored leuco. The leuco had good affinity for cellulose and was reoxidized on the fiber, regenerating the original color. Further thionation of (**23**) in polysulfide replaced the two remaining chlorine atoms with thiol groups, forming a dye (**24**) indistinguishable from the thionation product of the indophenol (**25**). That (**23**) and (**24**) have affinity for cellulose is not surprising in view of their close steric resemblance to the vat dye indanthrone (**26**) (see also Vol. 2, p. 522).

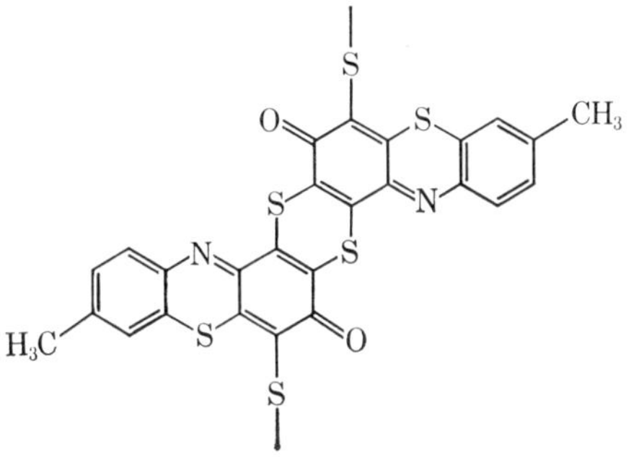

(**24**) 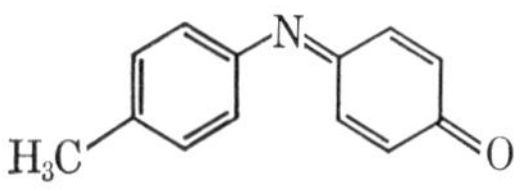   (25)

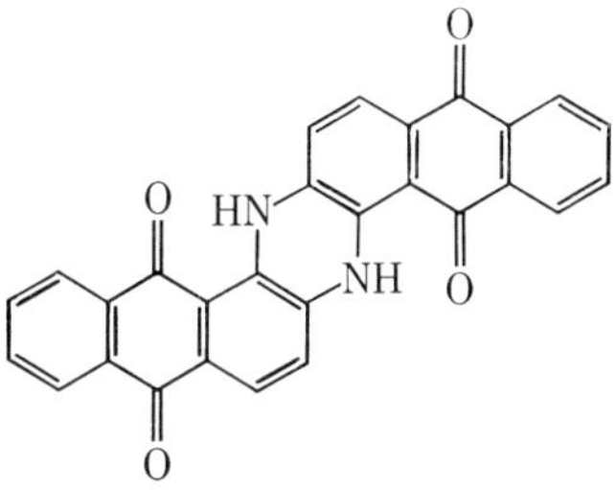

(26)

Thus indophenol sulfur dyes may be represented by the general formula (**27**), and their leuco forms by (**28**).

(**27**)   (**28**)

This formula, however, is at best only an approximation, since it takes no account of the considerable shade variations obtained by varying the thionation conditions.

Azine and Oxazine Dyes. Closely related to the indophenol dyes are the bordeaux and violet dyes derived from such phenazines as (**30**), which is made from 2,4-toluene-diamine and p-aminophenol by way of the indamine (**29**). Dyes based on the oxazine

(**29**)   (**30**)

intermediates (**31**) and (**32**) were developed by I. G. Farbenindustrie and bear a close structural resemblance to the indophenol dyes.

(**31**)   (**32**)

Both the azine and oxazine dyes resemble the indophenol dyes in reducing to a straw-colored leuco compound having good affinity for cellulose. (See also Azine dyes; Azines.)

Sulfur Black. On account of its low cost and excellent fastness properties, CI Sulfur Black 1, derived from 2,4-dinitrophenol, is the most important sulfur dye, a position it has maintained for over half a century. Yet its chemistry is perhaps less well understood than that of any other sulfur dye. A considerable variety of structures have been postulated, involving thiazine and sometimes azine groups (4–6). However, no single formula has yet been proposed which can account for all the properties of sulfur black. It is known that the first stage in the thionation is the rapid reduction of dinitrophenol to 2-amino-4-nitrophenol. The suggestion (5) that 2,4-diaminophenol is formed does not withstand scrutiny, since there is not enough poly-sulfide in the thionation to reduce both nitro groups, and in any case 2,4-diaminophenol does not give sulfur black on thionation. Immediately following the reduction to 2-amino-4-nitrophenol, the evolution of ammonia begins, which may indicate the formation of a diphenylamine. At this point fact gives way to speculation.

Benzothiazole Dyes. The benzothiazole chromophore has been postulated for a number of sulfur bake dyes and in some cases has been proved to be present. It was known that sulfur fusion of p-toluidine gave dehydrothio-p-toluidine (**33**) and Primuline Base (**34**). (See also Thiazole dyes.)

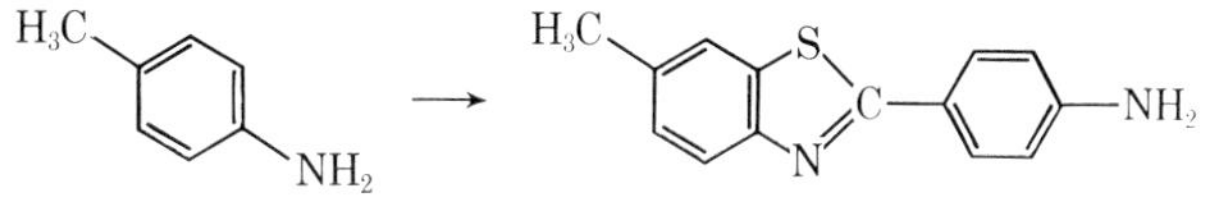

(**33**)

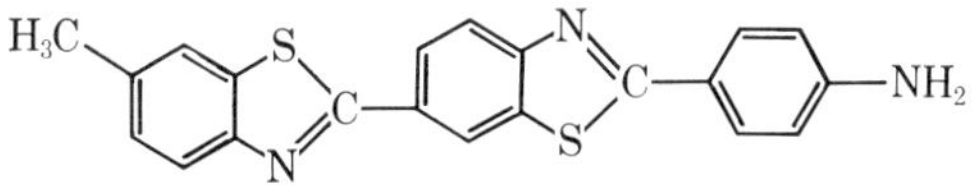

(**34**)

Zerweck, Ritter, and Schubert (3) investigated CI Sulfur Yellow 4, made by the sulfur fusion of benzidine and dehydrothio-p-toluidine. Alkali fusion degraded the dye to p-aminobenzoic acid and a number of o-aminobenzene thiols, which were condensed with chloroacetic acid and characterized as the lactams (**35**), (**36**), and (**37**).

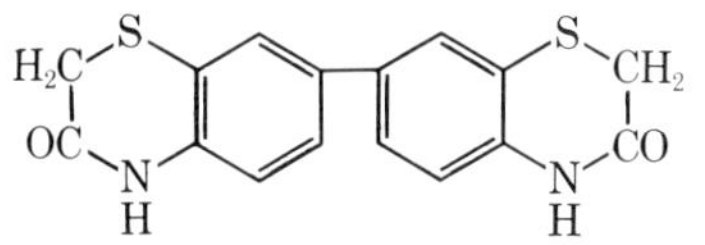

(**35**)

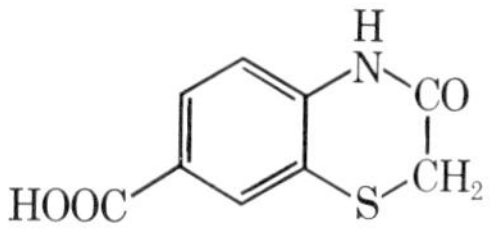

(**36**)

From the relative proportions of the degradation products, these researchers deduced that the main component of the dye was (**38**), the other components being (**39**), (**40**), and (**41**) (3).

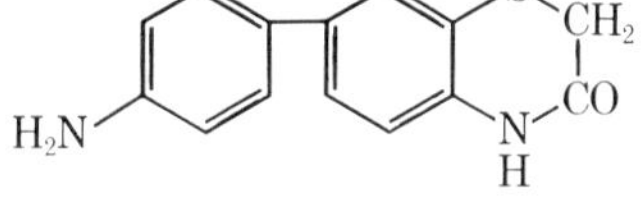

(**37**)

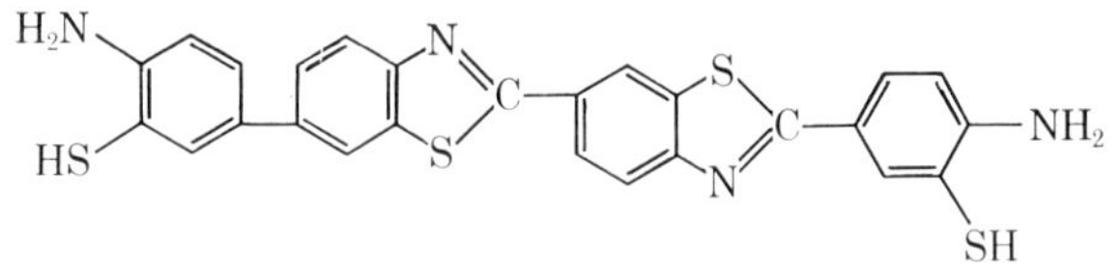

(**38**)

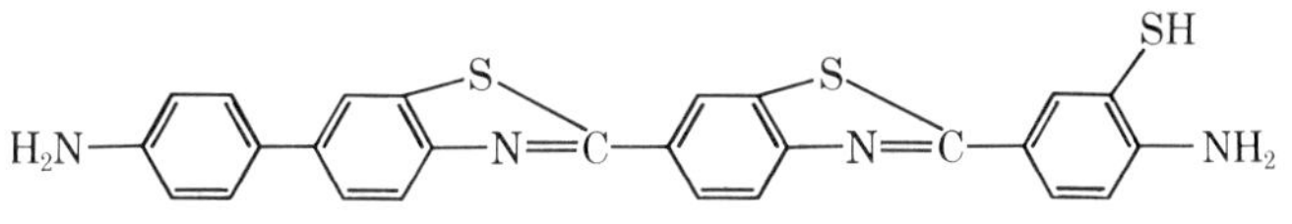

(**39**)

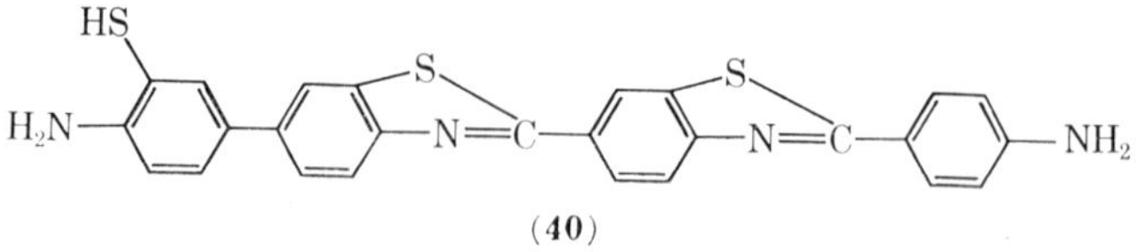

(40)

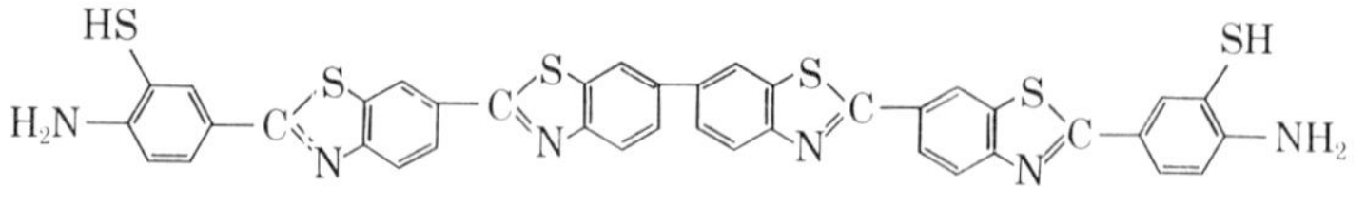

(41)

The four components were synthesized, and a mixture in the calculated proportions closely resembled CI Sulfur Yellow 4 in its dyeing and fastness properties. In the same way, Zerweck et al. (3) investigated CI Sulfur Orange 1, the thionation product of 2,4-diaminotoluene. Although the structure was not proved rigorously, it was shown that the benzothiazole chromophore is present, and that sulfide solubility is derived from mercapto groups.

CI Vat Yellow 9, made by a sulfur bake of 2-methylanthraquinone and benzidine, was investigated by Fierz-David and Koch (7), who arrived at the structure (42). The same workers studied CI Vat Yellow 1, made by thionating 2,6-diaminoanthraquinone with benzotrichloride. They determined the structure (43).

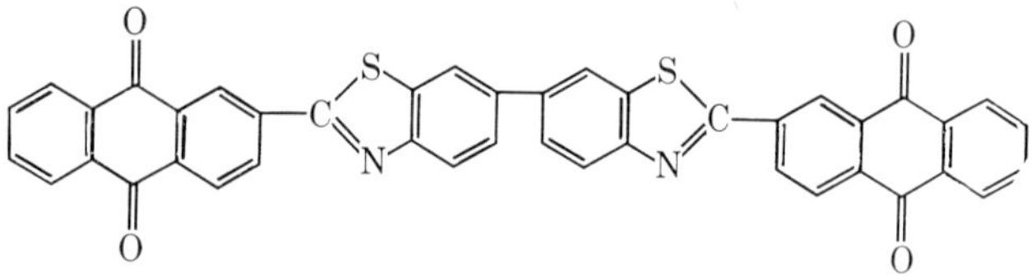

(42)

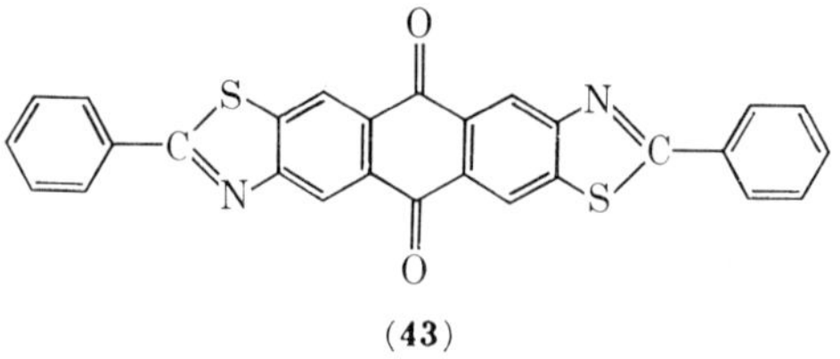

(43)

Synthetic Sulfur Dyes. When it became understood that a large group of the sulfur dyes derive their sulfide solubility from mercapto groups, there were numerous attempts to introduce this group into other chromophores and thus make new sulfur dyes of brighter shades and improved properties. Various mercapto-substituted dyes of the azo, phthalocyanine, anthraquinone, and dioxazine series have been made. The bright-green sulfur dye (44) is made either by chlorosulfonation of copper phthalocyanine and subsequent reduction to the tetramercaptan (8), or from tetraamino copper phthalocyanine by the Sandmeyer reaction to the thiocyanate (9). Imperial

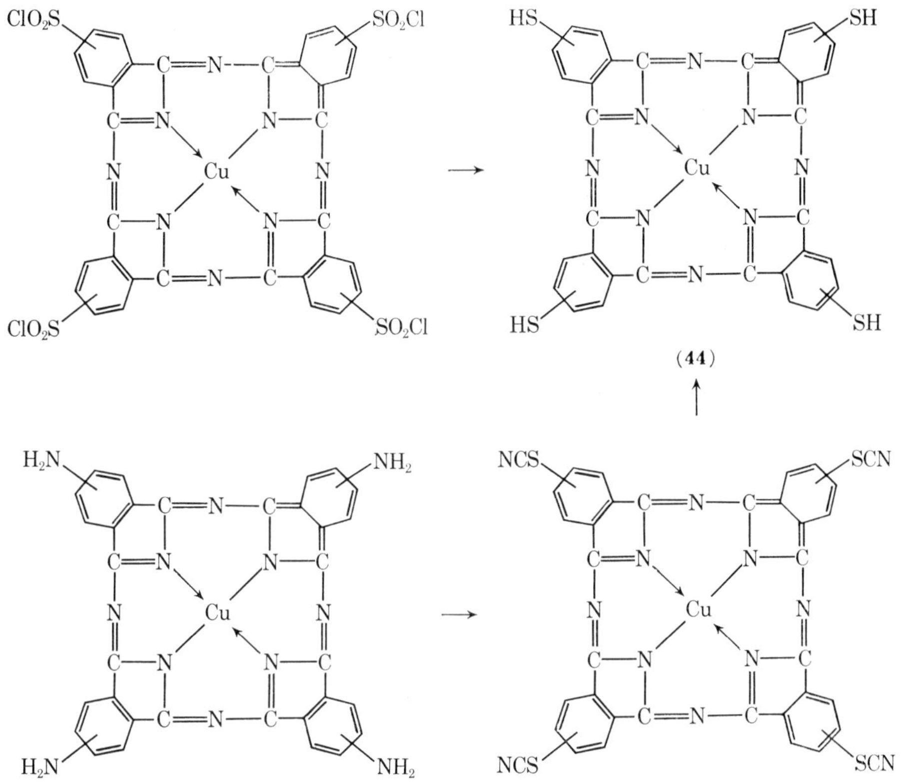

(44)

Chemical Industries, Ltd. (ICI) (10) prepared the first true red sulfur dye by condensing m-phenylenediamine with perylene-3,4,9,10-tetracarboxylic dianhydride (45) and converting the diamine (46) to the bisthiocyanate (47).

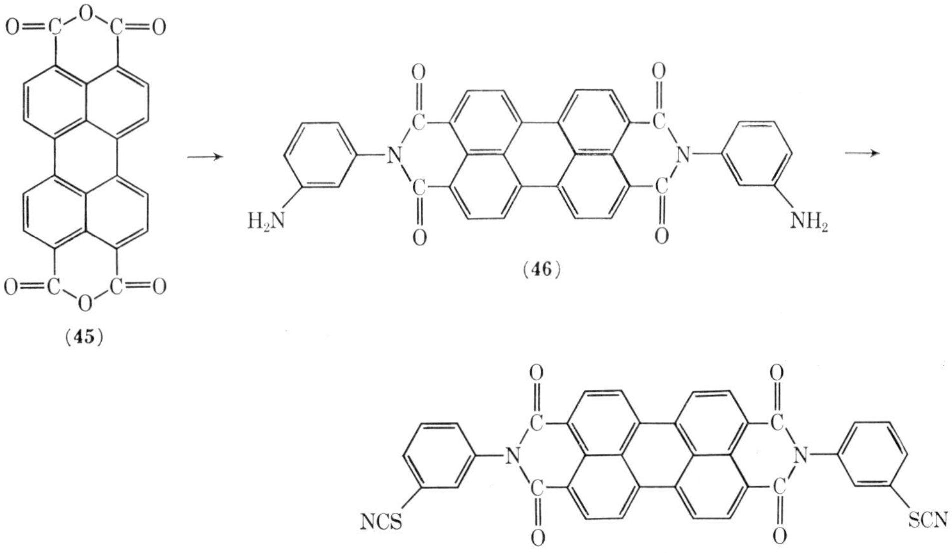

(45)

(46)

(47)

Manufacture

The early sulfur dye processes were developed empirically, since the nature of the chemical reactions involved was quite unknown. Manufacturing processes have been gradually improved, and many of the former disadvantages of sulfur dyes have now been overcome. Modern sulfur dyes are sold in the form of prereduced solutions, clarified to remove any insolubles, and containing the necessary alkali and reducing agent to confer storage stability and optimum dyeing properties.

The shade and properties of a sulfur dye depend on the nature of the organic intermediates and any metals used, the thionation conditions, and any aftertreatments given to the thionation product. The dyes obtained from the principal intermediates are described in Tables 1 and 2. Further examples may be found in the *Colour Index* (11). In certain cases the addition of copper, manganese, or molybdenum compounds has a marked effect. The most important example is CI Sulfur Greens 2 and 3, made from phenylperi acid indophenol, 8-anilino-5-*p*-hydroxyanilinonaphthalene-1-sulfonic acid. When copper salts are added to the thionation, CI Sulfur Green 3 is obtained, which is much yellower than the copperfree product CI Sulfur Green 2, and slightly inferior in fastness to light and washing. The copper is complexed into the dye molecule, and does not merely act as a thionation catalyst, as has been proposed. Differences in thionation conditions cause quite wide variations in shade, strength, and other properties. The optimum conditions have to be determined empirically, and once adopted must be followed closely to ensure reproducibility from batch to batch.

The actual thionation conditions used by dye manufacturers are closely guarded secrets. However, typical examples may be found in the patent literature (11) and the PB reports listed under General references.

Applications

Like many classes of dye, the sulfur dyes do not cover the entire shade range. There are greenish-yellows, reddish-yellows, and oranges, and a full range of blues, greens, browns, and blacks. Washfastness is generally between that of the developed direct dyes and of the vats. Lightfastness is variable, the blues, greens, browns, and blacks being particularly good. The yellows are less fast to light, especially in pale shades. With one or two exceptions, the sulfur dyes are not fast to hypochlorite. The high color value of the sulfur dyes, together with their ease of application, makes them especially suitable for dyeing heavy shades on cotton rawstock, yarn, and piece goods, and on blends of cotton with synthetic fibers. More recently, sulfur dyes have begun to find uses in the dyeing of nylons and blends of nylons with cellulosic fibers. In particular, CI Sulfur Black 11, which has a considerable degree of chlorine fastness, is used on automobile carpeting.

For many years sulfur dyes were sold as insoluble amorphous powders, which had to be pasted with water and dissolved with sodium sulfide. In addition to this inconvenience, the powders were unstable to storage, particularly on exposure to air, while some brands tended to heat up spontaneously and even ignite. The introduction of ready-reduced solutions of dyes in 1936 was followed closely by the development of pad-steam methods in the United States, and the use of prereduced liquids increased rapidly to where they now comprise probably 90% of the U.S. sulfur dye market. Liquid sulfur dyes are highly concentrated and contain the optimum amounts of alkali and reducing agent for continuous piece goods dyeing. They are stable to storage, since the reducing agent protects them from atmospheric oxidation. The amount of alkali present is much lower than when a powder dye is dissolved with sodium sulfide, and this improves penetration. Since the liquids are clarified and contain no insoluble matter, there is no chance of specky dyeings, which may arise with powder brands imperfectly dissolved.

Batch Dyeing. Sulfur dyes were formerly used in very large amounts for raw-stock dyeing, but this trade has declined considerably. However, batch methods are still important for the dyeing of yarn, knitted goods, and socks. Yarn in packages accounts for a large proportion of this trade. The use of clarified liquid dyes, together with a considerable body of technical experience, now makes it possible to dye knitting and fine weaving yarns in packages as a matter of routine. The principal requirements for successful package dyeing are (1) consistent winding, (2) soft water, (3) adequate yarn scouring, (4) thorough washing before oxidation, (5) controlled oxidation, and (6) yarn finishing.

Sulfur dyes are precipitated by calcium and magnesium salts, and so these must be removed from the dyehouse water supply. Owing to the widespread use of defoliants and ground water in the cotton fields, the cotton fiber itself often contains appreciable amounts of metal salts. These are best removed by a hot scour with acetic acid and detergent, with the optional addition of an organic chelating agent.

At one time it was the practice to give a minimal wash before oxidation in order to avoid color loss. It is now known that very thorough washing removes only unfixed dye, and allows a milder and more controlled oxidation procedure to be used. This gives better crocking fastness, softer hand, and improved winding properties.

The development of softening agents applicable in circulating-liquor machines facilitates subsequent winding and knitting.

Thus a satisfactory procedure for package dyeing is the following:

1. Scour 30 min at 200°F with 2% acetic acid and 2% of a compatible wetting agent.
2. Drop, refill, and wash until clean.
3. Adjust temperature to 120°F, add 2–3% Sodyefide B (Southern Dyestuff Co.), a low-alkalinity reducing agent, and run for 10 min.
4. Dilute liquid dye with water and add at 120°F over 20 min.
5. Raise slowly to 140–160°F (200°F for blacks).
6. Add calciumfree salt over 20 min.
7. Run 20–30 min at dyeing temperature.
8. Give running wash outside-in for 10–15 min without dropping bath.
9. Give running wash inside-out until clear, then for 10–15 min longer.
10. Oxidize and wash out oxidant.
11. Soap at 160°F with synthetic detergent plus soda ash or tetrasodium pyrophosphate.
12. Drop, refill, and give running washes until clear.
13. Give hot circulating wash.
14. Soften. For blacks, do not use a cationic softener, and add 1–2% soda ash or 0.5% caustic to the last bath.

Over the last decade, the beck dyeing of knit goods has increased considerably. Sulfur dyes have the advantage over vats that the sulfide used for reduction is relatively stable to atmospheric oxidation. However, additional amounts of **reducing** agent are required. In addition to heavyweight tubular knit raised goods and lightweight jersey fabrics, automotive carpeting is now dyed successfully with sulfur dyes on the beck. By proper selection of dyes, and temperature regulation, solid shades are obtained on both all-rayon and rayon/nylon blends.

Continuous Dyeing. This accounts for the greater part of present-day sulfur dye usage. The simplest and most widely used technique is to pad-steam-wash-oxidize-wash. A typical procedure would be the following: (*1*) Pad liquid dye at 120°F, (*2*) steam at 220°F with water seal overflowing, (*3*) wash box no. 1, 100°F; box no. 2, 120°F; box no. 3, 140°F; box no. 4, 160°F; box no. 5, 160°F, (*4*) oxidize, box no. 6 at 140°F, containing 1 oz/gal sodium dichromate and 1 oz/gal acetic acid (56%), and (*5*) wash boxes nos. 7–10 at 180°F.

This procedure may give rise to an unsatisfactory surface appearance on tightly woven hard-surfaced fabrics, and a much superior result is obtained by the two-bath method. A typical procedure is as follows: (*1*) pad liquid dye at 100°F, (*2*) dry, (*3*) chemical pad, 6.4 oz/gal Sodyefide B, cold, (*4*) steam, and (*5*) wash and oxidize as in the previous example.

Where surface appearance is a particular problem, the sulfur dye pastes may be substituted for the reduced liquid dyes in the two-bath method. The water-soluble sulfur dyes are also applicable by this method but offer no advantage to offset their higher cost.

Blends of cotton with polyester fibers are dyed successfully with a combination of disperse and sulfur dyes. The most common procedure is the following: (*1*) Pad disperse dye, (*2*) dry, (*3*) bake at 415°F, (*4*) pad liquid sulfur dye, (*5*) steam, (*6*) wash, (*7*) oxidize, (*8*) hot-wash, and (*9*) soap and rinse. An alternative method is to (*1*) pad disperse dye with sulfur dye paste, (*2*) dry, (*3*) bake, (*4*) pad through 3–5 oz/gal Sodyefide B, and (*5*) steam, wash, and oxidize as before. (See also Vol. 7, p. 566.)

Oxidation of Sulfur Dyes. Various oxidation systems are employed for sulfur dyeings. On continuous ranges, bichromate and acetic acid is the most popular, since it is easy to control and gives reproducible, stable shades. However, the resulting dyeings do show decreased absorbency and a somewhat harsher hand. The main alternative is peroxide. This gives good absorbency and a soft hand, and brighter shades are possible. It does require control, however, since overoxidation may cause decreased color value and lower washfastness.

Sulfur Black Tendering. It is well known that under high temperature and humidity, dyeings of sulfur black may lose tensile strength on storage. This possibility is minimized by including an alkaline rinse after the chroming operation. That millions of yards of sulfur black are dyed annually reflects the low incidence of this problem.

Economic Aspects

Sulfur dyes are important dyes for cellulosic fibers on account of their low cost (see Table 3), ease of application, and good fastness properties. The major manufacturing countries are the United States, Germany, and Japan, with some production in China, India, U.S.S.R., Mexico, Brazil, and certain European countries.

Table 3 lists the total U.S. production and sales figures for sulfur dyes during 1964–1966, and details of individual dyes where such data are available. For purposes of comparison, data are included for all dyes, and for all cotton dyes, ie, azoic, direct, fiber-reactive, sulfur, and vat dyes. The sulfur dye production and sales figures are also expressed as a percentage of the total dye market, and as a percentage of the

Table 3. U.S. Production and Sales of Sulfur Dyes and Comparisons with Other Dyes for the Years 1964–1966

Dye (CI name)	1964				1965				1966			
	Production	Sales, 1000 lb	Sales, 1000 $	Price, $/lb	Production	Sales, 1000 lb	Sales, 1000 $	Price, $/lb	Production	Sales, 1000 lb	Sales, 1000 $	Price, $/lb
Sulfur Red 6	121	123	103	0.84	120	130	92	0.71	141	16	28	1.75
Sulfur Blue 7	639									122	106	0.87
Leuco Sulfur Blue 7	21	16	19	1.19						10	15	1.50
Sulfur Blue 11						26	26	1.00				
Sulfur Blue 15						6	13	2.17				
Sulfur Brown 10	47	50	35	0.70	47	50	34	0.68				
Sulfur Black 1	1,076	1,188	407	0.34	1,419	1,160	404	0.35	1,638	1,585	547	0.35
Sulfur Black 1					5,827	5,871	2,154	0.37				
Sulfur Black 2	2,776	2,452	974	0.40	2,207	2,030	800	0.39				
Leuco Sulfur Black 2	13,096	13,439	8,260	0.61	9,028	8,198	6,437	0.79				
all other sulfur dyes									18,180	17,503	10,338	0.59
total sulfur dyes	17,776	17,268	9,798	0.57	18,648	17,471	9,960	0.57	19,959	19,236	11,034	0.57
total all dyes	184,387	178,273	264,023	1.48	207,193	189,965	292,284	1.54	219,194	204,135	331,453	1.62
all sulfur dyes as % of total	9.7	9.7	3.7		9.0	9.2	3.4		9.1	9.4	3.3	
total cotton dyes	112,211	109,831	121,177	1.10	123,490	113,559	129,779	1.15	126,051	120,716	148,047	1.22
all sulfur dyes as % dyes for cellulosic fibers	15.8	15.7	8.1		14.3	15.3	7.7		15.8	15.9	7.4	

cotton dye market (12–14). The various brands currently offered in the United States are listed in Table 4.

Table 4. List of Manufacturers

Brand name	Form	Manufacturer[a]
Accosul	reduced liquid	Synalloy, a division of Blackman-Uhler Chemical Co.
Calcogene	reduced liquid, unreduced powder	American Cyanamid Co.
Cassulfon	reduced liquid	Sou-Tex Chemical Co.
Dykosol	thiosulfate half ester as a liquid	Southern Dyestuff Co., a division of Martin Marietta Corp.
Hydrosol	thiosulfate half ester as a liquid	Sou-Tex Chemical Co.
Sodyesul	reduced liquid, unreduced powder	Southern Dyestuff Co., a division of Martin Marietta Corp.
Indocarbon	unreduced liquid, unreduced powder	GAF Corp.[b]
Katigen	reduced liquid, unreduced powder	GAF Corp.[b]

[a] Unless otherwise indicated.   [b] Distributor.

Bibliography

"Sulfur Dyes" in *ECT* 1st ed., Vol. 13, pp. 445–458, by J. J. Ayo, Jr. and Ernest Kuhn, General Aniline & Film Corporation.

1. R. Gnehm and F. Kauffler, *Ber.* **37,** 2619, 3032 (1904).
2. A. von Weinberg, *Ber.* [A]**33, **122 (1930).
3. W. Zerweck, H. Ritter, and M. Schubert, *Angew. Chem.* **60**(6), 141–168 (1948).
4. I. Chmelnitzkaya and V. Werchowsaya, *Anilinokrasochnaya Prom.* **5,** 67–75 (1935); (through) *Chem. Abstr.* **29,** 4943 (1935).
5. H. Hiyama, *J. Chem. Soc. Japan, Ind. Chem. Sect.* **51,** 97–98 (1948).
6. T. Kubota, *J. Chem. Soc. Japan* **55,** 565 (1934).
7. H. E. Fierz-David and J. Koch, *J. Soc. Dyers and Colourists* **51,** 61 (1935).
8. Brit. Pat. 541,146 (Nov. 14, 1941), N. H. Haddock (to ICI).
9. Brit. Pat. 544,953 (May 5, 1942), N. H. Haddock (to ICI).
10. Brit. Pat. 547,853 (1942), N. H. Haddock (to ICI).
11. U.S. Pat. 2,657,112 (1953), E. D. Robinson and D. F. Mason (to Southern Dyestuff Corp.).
12. *Synthetic Organic Chemicals, U.S. Production and Sales, 1964,* TC Publication 167, U.S. Government Printing Office, Washington, D.C., 1965.
13. *Synthetic Organic Chemicals, U.S. Production and Sales, 1965,* TC Publication 206, U.S. Government Printing Office, Washington, D.C., 1967.
14. *Synthetic Organic Chemicals, U.S. Production and Sales, 1966,* TC Publication 248, U.S. Government Printing Office, Washington, D.C., 1968.

General References

Otto Lange, *Die Schwefelfarbstoffe, Ihre Herstellung und Verwendung,* 2nd ed., Spamer, Leipzig, 1925.
H. A. Lubs, *The Chemistry of Synthetic Dyes and Pigments,* Reinhold Publishing Corp., New York, 1955, Chap. 6.
K. Venkataraman, *The Chemistry of Synthetic Dyes and Pigments,* Vol. 2, Academic Press, Inc., New York, 1952, Chap. 35.

J. F. Thorpe and M. A. Whiteley, eds., *Thorpe's Dictionary of Applied Chemistry*, Vol. 2, 4th ed., Longmans, Green & Co., London, 1954.

BIOS (British Intelligence Objectives Committee) Misc. 55 (PB 91711), 1946.

BIOS 983 (PB 79226), 1946.

BIOS 1155 (PB 79309), 1947.

FIAT Microfilm 764, Reels 82CC *(PB 74026)*, 92AA *(PB 70276)*, and 186C *(PB 25626)*, 1946.

FIAT 1313, Vols. 1 and 2 *(PB 85172)*, 1948.

Micro BIOS FDX 885, 1946.

L. Tigler, *Am. Dyestuff Reptr.* **57**, 333 (1968).

H. Tobin, *Am. Dyestuff Reptr.* **55**, 451 (1966).

Ibid., **57**, 37 (1968).

J. M. Youngblood, *Am. Dyestuff Reptr.* **52**, 760 (1963).

W. B. Amos, G. L. Dozier, G. C. Jones, C. J. Horne, R. E. Rupp, J. H. Stradley, and W. C. Wilcoxson, *Am. Dyestuff Reptr.* **52**, 761 (1963).

Denis G. Orton
Southern Dyestuff Company,
a division of Martin
Marietta Corporation

SULFURIC ACID AND SULFUR TRIOXIDE

Sulfuric acid, H_2SO_4, is a colorless, corrosive, oily liquid, d_4^{15}, 1.8357; bp, 270°C. It has always been considered the foundation of the inorganic chemical industry. Although some of its historic uses, such as the first step of the Leblanc process for manufacture of alkalis, have been superseded in whole, or in part, by development of other processes, it is being consumed in increasing volume in many new uses, such as the rayon industry, the titanium-pigment industry, and the petroleum industry, with the result that consumption of sulfuric acid in the U.S. has risen from about 13,000,000 net tons (that is, tons of 2000 lb of 100% sulfuric acid) in 1950 to approx 28,200,000 net tons in 1967. It is the widespread use of sulfuric acid throughout industry rather than tonnage that has caused consumption of sulfuric acid to be considered as a dependable barometer of general business conditions.

History

Chamber Process. There is considerable doubt as to the date of discovery of sulfuric acid. Basil Valentine in the latter part of the fifteenth century described its preparation from calcined copperas ($FeSO_4.7H_2O$) and silica and also by burning sulfur with saltpeter (1); but there are indications that it had been produced at a much earlier date, perhaps as early as 1000 AD. It was produced on a small laboratory scale by apothecaries during the early part of the seventeenth century by burning sulfur in moist air, and about a century later, on a somewhat larger scale, by burning a mixture of sulfur and saltpeter and condensing the acid formed in large glass vessels. In 1746 a lead chamber about 6 ft square was built in Birmingham by Dr. Roebuck for burning a mixture of sulfur and saltpeter, thus forming the basis for the chamber process which, with various modifications and on an ever-increasing scale, was employed exclusively for the manufacture of sulfuric acid until the latter part of the nineteenth century when the contact process was developed.

Steam was first employed in the chamber process in 1774, but it was about twenty years later before it was demonstrated that the saltpeter served only as an intermediary in the oxidation of the sulfur dioxide and that much niter could be saved by supplying the chambers with a continuous flow of air. All niter supplied to the chambers was lost in the exit gases until 1827 when the Gay-Lussac tower was first employed to recover the nitrogen oxides as "nitrous vitriol" (2). This was followed in 1859 by the invention of the Glover tower for denitrification of the nitrous vitriol, resulting in a great saving of niter. It will be noted that the development of the chamber process in its completed form took somewhat more than 110 years.

Contact Process. The contact process had its origin in the filing of a patent in 1831 by Peregrine Phillips, who recorded his discovery that sulfur dioxide could be caused to react directly with atmospheric oxygen by passage at strong yellow heat over platinum wire or finely divided platina. Many investigators followed up the method, but with no practical success, probably because their efforts were directed primarily toward development of a more economical substitute for the chamber process since there was no great demand for fuming acid (oleum) for which the contact process was particularly adapted. This situation changed with the synthetic production of alizarin about 1870 and the realization that the future of the synthetic-dye industry was dependent upon the availability of a cheap and plentiful supply of fuming acid. Up to that time, the relatively small demand for oleum had been met by the firm of Starck of Bohemia, which enjoyed a monopoly in distilling it from ferrous sulfate extracted from the Pilsen shales. With the publication of a paper by Clemens Winkler in 1875, great interest was awakened in the possibilities of the contact process. However, most investigators were misled by the faulty conclusions arrived at by Winkler, who insisted that the reaction could only be carried out by providing a stoichiometric mixture of two volumes of sulfur dioxide and one volume of oxygen. He prepared oleum by decomposing ordinary sulfuric acid by heat, and, after the removal of the water vapor by condensation, passing the resultant dry sulfur dioxide and oxygen over platinized asbestos maintained at low red heat.

Winkler's process was employed by a number of firms; the earliest commercial production was by Emil Jacob at the Kreuznack works, where the decomposition process was later replaced by production of sulfur dioxide from sulfur. Meanwhile, other German firms had returned to using pyrite burner gas as a source of sulfur dioxide, and a tremendous amount of time and money were expended in research, mostly directed toward purification of the roaster gas to prevent contamination and poisoning of the catalyst. This culminated in Knietsch's classic lecture before the German Chemical Society in 1901 (3) revealing, in part, some of the many investigations that had been carried out by the Badische Anilin- und Soda-Fabrik during the years in which that firm's production at Ludwigshafen had increased from 18,500 tons in 1880 to 116,000 tons in 1900. In addition to Badische, patents were also taken out between 1898 and 1902 on the Mannheim process, which employed a first stage of conversion utilizing a shaft filled with ferric oxide, followed by a final stage employing platinum; the Schröder-Grillo process, employing platinum-impregnated magnesium sulfate as catalyst; and the Tentelew Chemical Company process, which employed the principle of filtration and final washing with a dilute alkaline solution, thus utilizing a chemical purification process as contrasted with the Badische mechanical and physical procedures. Tentelew also introduced many novel features of apparatus design (4).

Properties

Sulfuric Acid 0–100%. The *density* of sulfuric acid solutions is given in Table 1 (5). The density of sulfuric acid is often reported in degrees Baumé, according to the formula °Bé = 145 − (145/sp gr). Baumé and specific gravity values are given in Table 2.

Table 1. Density of Sulfuric Acid Solutions

H_2SO_4, wt %	Sp gr$_4^{15}$	H_2SO_4, wt %	Sp gr$_4^{15}$	H_2SO_4, wt %	Sp gr$_4^{15}$
5.0	1.0332	40.0	1.3065	75.0	1.6740
10.0	1.0681	45.0	1.3515	80.0	1.7323
15.0	1.1045	50.0	1.3990	85.0	1.7841
20.0	1.1424	55.0	1.4494	90.0	1.8198
25.0	1.1860	60.0	1.5024	95.0	1.8388
30.0	1.2220	65.0	1.5578	100.0	1.8357
35.0	1.2636	70.0	1.6151		

Table 2. Baumé and Specific Gravity Values of Sulfuric Acid Solutions

°Bé	Sp gr$_{60°F}^{60}$	H_2SO_4, %	°Bé	Sp gr$_{60°F}^{60}$	H_2SO_4, %
50	1.5263	62.18	58	1.6667	74.36
51	1.5426	63.66	59	1.6860	75.99
52	1.5591	65.13	60	1.7059	77.67
53	1.5761	66.63	61	1.7262	79.43
54	1.5934	68.13	62	1.7470	81.30
55	1.6111	69.65	63	1.7683	83.34
56	1.6292	71.17	64	1.7901	85.66
57	1.6477	72.75	65	1.8125	88.65
			66	1.8354	93.19

In Germany and France the Baumé scale is calculated using a modulus of 144.3 instead of 145, giving slightly different figures, which are, for the most frequently used values:

U.S. Bé	German Bé	H_2SO_4, %
50	49.76	62.18
60	59.71	77.67
66	65.68	93.19

The total *vapor pressure* of aqueous solutions of sulfuric acid at 100°C and the partial pressures of sulfuric acid and water over sulfuric acid solutions at varying temperatures are given in Table 3 and Table 4 (6), respectively.

In the system H_2SO_4–H_2O there is a constant-boiling mixture at 98.3% sulfuric acid.

Many determinations of the *specific heat* of sulfuric acid solutions have been made, and it is believed that the most accurate are those given in Perry (6) and in reference (7), which are shown as Figure 1. The *boiling point* curve of Figure 2 is that presented by Zeisberg (8) and the *freezing point* curve of Figure 2, the *viscosity curve* of Figure 3, and the *index of refraction* curve of Figure 3 are derived from data presented in Mellor

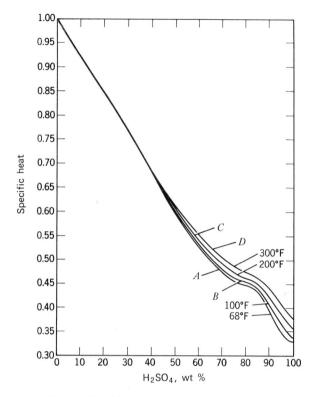

Fig. 1. Specific heat of sulfuric acid solutions.

(9). The *electrical conductivity* curve of Figure 4 is plotted from data of Kohlrausch and the *heat of dilution* curve of Figure 4 from National Bureau of Standards data.

Oleum. Fuming sulfuric acid or oleum consists of a solution of sulfur trioxide in 100% sulfuric acid (which is often referred to as monohydrate, since it comprises SO_3 combined with one molecule of water). The strength of oleum is designated as wt %

Table 3. Total Vapor Pressure of Sulfuric Acid Solutions at 100°C

H_2SO_4, %	95	90	85	80	75	70	65	60	50	40	30	20	10
mm Hg	0.237	1.49	5.39	13.9	32	67	114	178	326	474	590	678	720

Table 4. Partial Pressures of Sulfuric Acid and Water over Sulfuric Acid Solutions

H_2SO_4, 89.25%			H_2SO_4, 95.06%			H_2SO_4, 98.06%			H_2SO_4, 99.23%		
°C	$p_{H_2SO_4}$	p_{H_2O}	°C	$p_{H_2SO_4}$	p_{H_2O}	°C	$p_{H_2SO_4}$	p_{H_2O}	°C	$p_{H_2SO_4}$	p_{H_2O}
183.0	0.5	78.8	180.0	2.1	10.1	204.0	5.9	0.0	211	32.2	
197.5	1.3	116.9	200.0	4.8	21.2	218.5	9.8	1.5	225	49.9	
216.5	2.1	233.1	215.5	8.5	46.5	234.5	14.7	3.2	227	55.4	
230.0	3.6	306.3	232.0	13.4	91.9	249.0	28.5	2.6	244	84.1	<0.1
241.5	5.3	414.8	244.5	19.9	120.1	261.0	38.8	5.0	261	163.8	
			261.0	27.9	180.7	273.0	61.9	5.3	270	229.8	
			270.0	39.9	254.9	285.0	91.6	11.8	281	272.3	
			282.0	52.6	350.2	295.0	132.3	14.7	290	381.5	

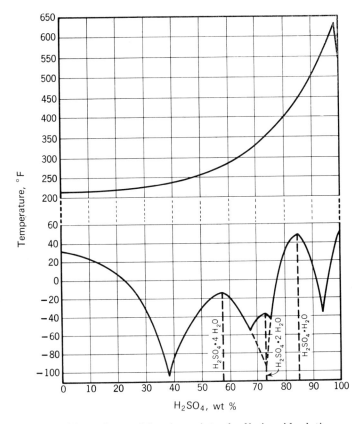

Fig. 2. Boiling points and freezing points of sulfuric acid solutions.

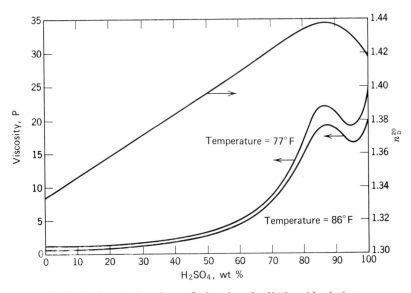

Fig. 3. Index of refraction and viscosity of sulfuric acid solutions.

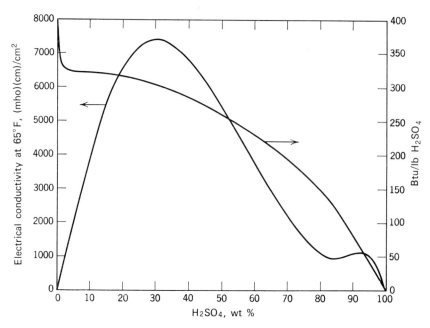

Fig. 4. Electrical conductivity of sulfuric acid solutions, and heat evolved on adding water to 1 lb H₂SO₄ (wt % of resulting solution, at 77°C, read on abscissa).

of free sulfur trioxide: thus 20% oleum contains 20% SO_3 and 80% H_2SO_4 by weight. Since the physical properties of oleum are quite different from those of sulfuric acid, they are presented independently. Some of the values most in dispute are those covering specific heat, vapor pressure, and freezing point.

Table 5 presents density data of the Industrial Chemicals Division, Allied Chemical Corporation.

The most accurate data on the *vapor pressure* of oleum are given by Miles, Niblock, and Wilson (10), from whose data Figure 5 was made, showing the equilibrium partial pressure of sulfur trioxide over oleum of various strengths at various temperatures.

The *boiling point* curve of Figure 6 was calculated from the same data (10) and is compared with prior data from Knietsch (3) with which it is in reasonably close agreement. The lower curve of Figure 6, which has been adopted by the Manufacturing Chemists' Association of the U.S., is believed to represent the best available data on *freezing points*. The *specific heat* curve of Figure 7 represents a portion of a curve pre-

Table 5. Density of Oleum

	Wt %		Equivalent	Density
SO_3	H_2SO_4	Total SO_3	H_2SO_4, %	(15°C)
10	90	83.47	102.25	1.8716
20	80	85.31	104.50	1.9056
30	70	87.14	106.75	1.9412
40	60	88.98	109.00	1.9737
50	50	90.82	111.25	1.9900
60	40	92.65	113.50	1.9919
65	35	93.57	114.63	1.9842

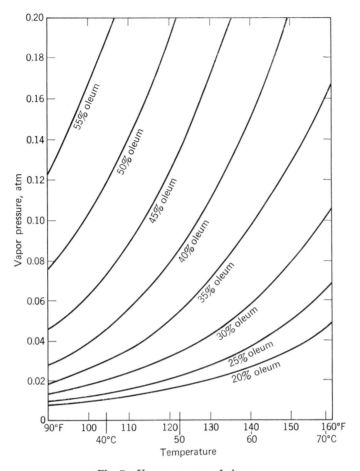

Fig. 5. Vapor pressure of oleum.

sented by Miles, Niblock, and Smith (11), recalculated from total sulfur trioxide as presented by the authors to % oleum or free sulfur trioxide. The *viscosity* curve of Figure 7 is obtained from Mellor (9). The *electrical conductivity* curve of Figure 8 is from the data presented by Kohlrausch and the *heat of solution* of gaseous sulfur trioxide in oleum (Fig. 8) is plotted from data from several sources. It is of interest to note here that the peaks on the density, freezing point, and viscosity curves correspond approximately with the composition of *pyrosulfuric acid*, $H_2S_2O_7$.

Manufacture of Sulfur Dioxide

RAW MATERIALS

The more important raw materials are sulfur (qv) and various metal sulfides. The important metal sulfides are those of iron (pyrite, FeS_2, and pyrrhotite, approx FeS) and zinc, ZnS. Spain was originally the chief source of supply of pyrite, but there are large deposits in almost every country, although few are worked owing to economic considerations. A large percentage of present U.S. consumption is imported from Canada, where it is a by-product of the selective flotation of ores that are mined for

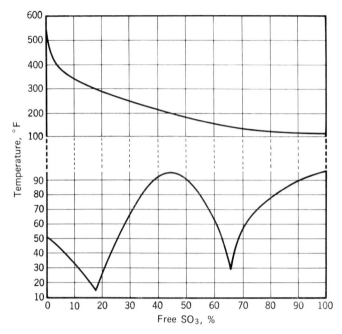

Fig. 6. Boiling points and freezing points of oleum.

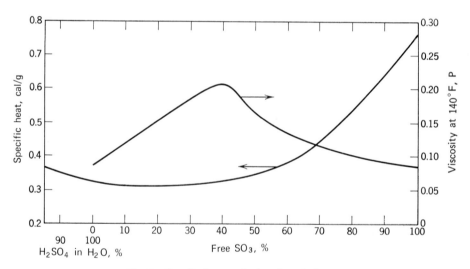

Fig. 7. Specific heat and viscosity of oleum.

their nonferrous values. Pyrite also occurs as veins in coal deposits, but these "coal brasses" contain so much carbon that they are not favorable for acid manufacture unless the carbon content is materially reduced, and the cost of the beneficiation is excessive. Large deposits of pyrrhotite exist in the eastern part of the United States and some of these deposits are worked for acid manufacture, although the sulfur content of pyrrhotite is only about 70% that of pyrite. Zinc sulfide, sphalerite, ZnS, is roasted to convert it to zinc oxide, and the by-product sulfur dioxide gas is used for manufacture of acid. Large tonnages of sulfuric acid are now being produced from the

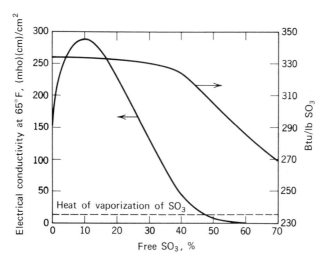

Fig. 8. Electrical conductivity of oleum, and heat evolved on adding sulfuric acid to gaseous sulfur dioxide (% free sulfur dioxide of resulting oleum, at 86°F, read on abscissa).

sulfur dioxide resulting from smelter operation when processing sulfur-bearing copper. lead, nickel, and other ores. Of the several metals sulfides, only pyrite and pyrrhotite are mined expressly for acid manufacture. Since about 1936, hydrogen sulfide (see Sulfur compounds) recovered from sour natural gas and oil-refinery still gases has been used in production of sulfuric acid in ever-increasing amounts at a number of locations. As in the case of the smelter gas, this was initiated as a means of avoiding damage to vegetation and atmospheric pollution.

Calcium sulfate in the form of anhydrite, gypsum, $CaSO_4 \cdot 2H_2O$, or by-product gypsum, is used to produce sulfuric acid and cement. Approx 1 ton of Portland cement is produced for each ton of sulfuric acid. The capital costs of a cement–acid plant complex will be approx two to three times the capital cost of a pyrite plant complex and six to eight times the cost of an elemental-sulfur burning plant. The cement-acid plant has not found favor in North America due to the high capital cost and the lower costs of elemental sulfur. Cement–acid plants are operating in Great Britain, Poland, East Germany, and Austria (12) (see Sulfur, p.356).

SULFUR BURNERS

Masonry Burner. The earliest sulfur burners employed in conjunction with the lead chamber process consisted of a brick chamber with brick arch, containing a horizontal cast-iron pan with a low upstand on which the sulfur was charged intermittently. Impurities in the sulfur formed a scum on the surface of the molten sulfur that required occasional raking to secure relatively uniform gas. The ash was periodically scraped over the front upstand, which was set at an angle of 30–45°. Niter "hogs" (cast-iron pots used to react sulfuric acid and sodium nitrate) used in conjunction with the chamber process were installed in an extension of the brick chamber in which combustion of any vaporized sulfur was completed. Frequently the top arch supported pans in which some concentration of the chamber acid was accomplished.

Glens Falls Burner. Although many improved burners were employed in subsequent years, the most popular developed was the Tromblee and Paull, commonly known as the Glens Falls burner, and a few are still in use. It consists of an unlined, horizontal, cylindrical steel shell with conical ends mounted on trunnions and revolved at about 2 rpm. Angle irons are sometimes attached to the shell to increase the rate of burning and to break up dirt accumulations. Sulfur is fed to one end through a helicoid conveyor, and the cone at the opposite end terminates in a flange that is spaced relatively close to a similar flange on the nozzle of a combustion chamber. The burner operates under a negative gage pressure.

Vesuvius Burner. Another burner that has been used to some extent in the past, that of Hinzke, is commonly known as the Vesuvius burner. This is a vertical, cylindrical steel shell lined with firebrick, the arch of which supports a sulfur-melting kettle; the molten sulfur drops through the burner over a series of superimposed cast-iron shelves. The gas, which contains both sulfur dioxide and sulfur vapor, is passed through a separate combustion chamber to which additional air is admitted to complete combustion.

Sublimer. All of the above burners are, in fact, part sublimers and part burners with the relative proportion depending on radiation characteristics. Another unit employed is known as a sublimer, since in operation the combustion occurring is only that necessary to maintain an operating temperature of about 700°F. This unit can be regulated to provide a gas of very uniform sulfur dioxide concentration by controlling the volume of air that is bubbled through the molten sulfur. Less than 10% of the sulfur is burned to sulfur dioxide, the remainder passing over as vapor to the combustion chamber, where additional air is admitted. This unit is suitable for operation at positive gage and can be supplied with dry (solid) sulfur, although the preferred practice is to melt the sulfur and either filter it or allow impurities to settle.

Molten-Sulfur Spray. The most recent practice involves spraying the settled or filtered molten sulfur directly into the combustion chamber, where the necessary air is admitted. This method is also applicable to plus-pressure operation. In any procedure involving the handling of molten sulfur, the lines and spray nozzles must be steam-jacketed and a pressure employed that will hold the molten sulfur within approx 275–310°F, where its viscosity is at a minimum. Above 320°F the viscosity rises sharply, and at 390°F, for example, it is 3000 times that at 300°F.

ORE BURNERS

Lump Burners. The earliest pyrite burners were known as lump burners because the ore was charged into burners in lumps 2.5–3 in. in size. Jaw crushers were employed to some extent, but the preferred method was hand breaking of the coarse ore because much less fines were produced. These burners, 24–30 ft² in area, were built in sets of 36–48 burners, erected in a double row, back to back. Ore was charged by hand onto the bed, supported on grate bars. The ore charge approximated 15 lb/ft² of grate area per 12 hr, and charging time on individual burners was staggered so that fresh ore was being charged to some burner about every 15–20 min in order to secure uniform gas for the acid plant. It is extremely doubtful whether any lump burners are in operation today. The cinder usually contained from 3 to 5% sulfur.

McDougall Burner. The earliest mechanical burner was the McDougall, which consisted of cast-iron flanged rings, 6 ft in diameter, bolted together in a vertical pile to provide seven superimposed firebrick hearths, each of which was supported from a bearing ring at the flange. This burner never attained commercial importance, but the basic principle was employed in the highly successful Herreshoff and Wedge burners.

Herreshoff Furnace. The Herreshoff furnace, in its improved form, consists of a steel cylindrical vessel of varying diameter, lined with firebrick and containing five or more internal brick hearths, plus the bottom hearth, and the top hearth which is employed as an ore dryer. Arms, which may be either steel or cast iron, are connected to an air-cooled central cast-iron shaft containing passages whereby the cooling air is circulated through the arms as well as shaft. The shaft is supported on a button bearing at the base and revolved at approx $\frac{1}{2}$ rpm. The arms, which are oriented 90° at adjacent shelves, are fitted with cast-iron rabbles that move the ore inward on one hearth and outward on the next hearth. The rabble blades are bent so that the burning ore is turned over as well as advanced. Hot air leaving the shaft is passed through a horizontal duct to an annular bustle pipe by which the air can be delivered to a series of small vertical cast-iron flues of rectangular shape that are set flush with the interior of the brick lining. These temperature-control flues serve the double purpose of transferring heat from the very hot hearths (second and third from the top) to the lower hearths and delivering the heated air to the bottom hearth, thereby assisting in the desulfurization of the cinder. A seven-hearth, $15\frac{3}{4}$ ft in diameter burner of this type is capable of roasting 10 net tons per day of ordinary pyrite containing 48–50% sulfur, provided the ore is crushed to $\frac{3}{8}$-in. size. The cinder ranges from 1 to 4% sulfur, depending on the character of the ore. Particles larger than $\frac{3}{8}$ in. are likely to have an unburned core of green ore. The operating condition in the Herreshoff furnace gives good arsenic removal from arsenical pyrites, leaving the resulting cinder suitable as raw material for steel production.

Zieren-Chemiebau Furnace. The Herreshoff-type furnace has been increased in size and modified by the addition of a waste-heat boiler to cool the sulfur dioxide gas and control the temperature of the several hearths. A portion of the cooled and dedusted gas is recycled to the intermediate hearths for temperature control in the roasting zones. These units have been built up to approx 22 ft in diameter and with thirteen roasting hearths. With a roaster of this size recycle cooled gas is introduced into the fourth, fifth, sixth, seventh, eighth, and tenth hearths. One roaster will treat 100 metric tons of 48% sulfur pyrites ore per day (13). The recovery of steam on this unit will be approx 1 lb of steam at 60 atm pressure per 1 lb of 48% sulfur pyrites ore. This type of roaster has found considerable favor in roasting high-arsenic pyrite ores from Spain and Portugal.

Wedge Furnace. The Wedge furnace follows the same general principle as the Herreshoff, but it is somewhat larger and is characterized by the use of a large 5-ft-diameter steel central shaft, open at the top and bottom, and protected from the furnace gases by a firebrick facing which eliminates the need of cooling. The arms are water-cooled, with a separate control to each arm, and are keyed in place from inside the shaft, so that, owing to the large shaft diameter and the insulation, workmen can enter the shaft to replace arms or carry out other repairs without shutting down and cooling off the furnace. The large Wedge furnaces are stated to have a capacity of 20 net tons per day of normal pyrite. They have reportedly been used with good success in the roasting of lead matte containing about 25% sulfur.

Hegeler Furnace. The Hegeler furnace was installed for roasting zinc blende. This mechanical furnace, which is 75 ft long, is constructed of brick and divided by a central wall into two compartments, each containing seven shelves; the lower two are built with muffles to permit use of fuel to assist in desulfurization of the ore. Agitation of the bed is accomplished by dragging a rake fitted with rabbles through a hearth by means of a rod. The rake is then removed through a large door, permitted to cool off, and then started back over the adjacent shelf. Such a furnace can handle only about 40 tons of blende per 24 hr and the cost of operating labor and fuel is very high. Since the rabbling is of an intermittent nature, desulfurization is not very good and the gas produced is only about 4–5% sulfur dioxide, which imposes quite a penalty on the associated acid plant.

Flash Roaster. Application of selective flotation procedures for recovery of values from ores necessitated very fine grinding, the particle size in many cases being reduced to 300 mesh and even finer, and as the tailings consisted of a mixture of pyrite and gangue, a final flotation permitted recovery of the pyrite at relatively low cost. Although this material created problems in operation of the mechanical roasters due to more rapid combustion, it was particularly well suited for flash roasting. This resulted in the development of an entirely new type of roaster in which the ore was burned while in gaseous suspension, as contrasted with the predominantly bed roasting carried out in the mechanical burners.

From an initial plant installation in 1926 of such a burner of approx 900 ft^3 capacity, successive installations of increasing size have been made; recent installations have approx 24,000 ft^3 of combustion space. The burner is a vertical steel vessel lined with refractory and fitted with a dome top and a conical or pyramidal base for discharge of cinder, but containing no moving parts. The principle has been employed in several different ways: The ore and combustion air may be admitted through the top arch with cinder discharged at the base and gas discharged through a side opening adjacent to the base; the ore may be fed to the burner through side injectors located just above the base with the remainder of the combustion air admitted to the base, and the gas outlet through a side opening just below the top arch; and a combination coflow–counterflow arrangement may be made in which the ore is admitted with part of the combustion air through the top arch and the remainder of the combustion air admitted at the base, and the cinder discharged at the base, the side gas outlet port being just below the top arch.

When bottom injectors are employed, they must be mounted at an angle and the air pressure kept below the point where particles would strike either the top arch or the side wall, and when ore is introduced at the top, a nozzle design must be employed that will provide good dispersion over the cross-sectional area of the burner, securing rapid ignition, yet avoiding impingement on side walls. As desulfurization of the ore proceeds, a mixture of iron sulfide and oxide is reached that has a much lower fusion point than either, and, while the burning ore is in this sticky stage, impingement on any portion of the interior must be prevented to avoid the building up of a clinker.

The flash roaster possesses many advantages over the mechanical roaster from the point of view of sulfuric acid manufacture (apart from metallurgical considerations); the sole disadvantage is the cost of grinding the ore in the event that flotation concentrates are not available and a heavier carry over of fine cinder to the dust collectors. The advantages are (*1*) combustion space of only about 10% of a Herreshoff or Wedge; (*2*) minimum repairs, since the burner contains no shaft, arms, or rabbles, resulting in substantially continuous operation; (*3*) high gas concentration, 11.5–12.0% on pyrite and 10% on pyrrhotite, permitting about 25% reduction in gas-purification equipment; (*4*) increased credit for by-product steam when the gases from the burner are passed through a waste-heat boiler, and approx 1.2 lb of steam at 30–35 atm pressure per 1 lb of 48% sulfur pyrites ore will be produced; and (*5*) reduced formation of sulfur trioxide due to the high concentration and temperature of the gas and the rapid cooling of the gas through the conversion range when a waste-heat boiler is employed. Sulfur trioxide would form a mist which would cause serious corrosion (sulfation), and it must be removed as a weak impure acid which is difficult to dispose of.

The theoretical temperature produced by the combustion of sulfur and iron sulfides is shown in Figure 9. The gas leaving the Herreshoff burner is at somewhat less than 1000°F because of radiation loss and because the shaft and arms are air-cooled, and the cost of recovering heat in a waste-heat boiler is difficult to justify, except in the case of the high-capacity Zieren-Chemiebau furnace. In the suspension roaster, the gas leaving is between 1750 and 1800°F. Moreover, this temperature is maintained by the recycling of gas from the outlet of the boiler to prevent a temperature rise that

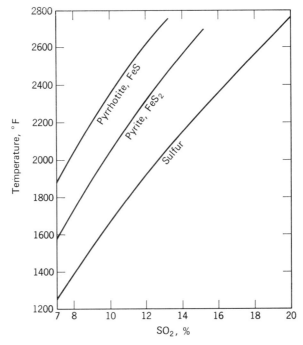

Fig. 9. Temperature of sulfur dioxide gases from sulfur and iron sulfides. Assumptions: combustion air, 95°F (sulfur); 60°F, and 75% rh (sulfides); all sulfur burned to sulfur dioxide, all cinder burned to Fe_3O_4 at combustion temp. *Pyrite,* 48% sulfur, cinder-to-ore ratio 68%; *pyrrhotite,* 32.5% sulfur, cinder-to-ore ratio 87.3%.

would result in fusion of the cinder. On large well-insulated burners this recycled gas will range from 40% up to 50% with pyrrhotite ore, where a higher temperature is reached due to oxidation of the larger quantity of iron. The temperatures referred to above are those of the gases produced as the ore particles on flashing are raised to incandescence, thus tending to form ferrites; the cinder will be found under the microscope to consist of minute hollow spheres that have obviously been raised above the melting point. The interior of a burner operating on pyrite or pyrrhotite will be filled with luminous particles shooting about in all directions, but, where this type of roasting has been applied to zinc concentrates, no incandescent particles can be observed. The cinder from pyrite, pyrrhotite, or zinc blende contains 1.0–3.5% sulfur.

Fluid Flash. The flash burner is often modified by a small fluid bed. The flash burners when operating on wet flotation concentrates require that the ore be either dried in a gastight rotary dryer, using hot low-oxygen process gas as the heat source, or the installation of a small fluid-bed unit or dryer. All of the wet concentrates ore is fed into the dryer at a uniform rate. A controlled portion of the combustion air is forced through the bed of the dryer, and partial burning occurs. The partially desulfurized ore is injected into the base of the flash roaster. The balance of the air required for combustion is introduced into the base of the roaster (14).

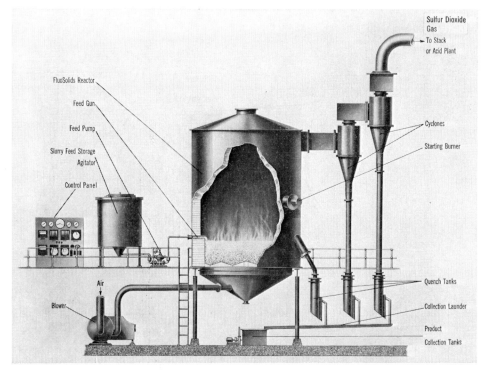

Fig. 10 FluoSolids roaster with slurry feeding.   Courtesy Dorr-Oliver Inc.

In addition to burners specifically designed fors uspension roasting, many Herreshoff and Wedge burners have been converted to suspension roasting by removal of shaft, arms, and internal shelves; this has resulted in satisfactory operation, with the consequence that the mechanical burner, as such, is becoming obsolete in operations specifically intended for sulfuric acid manufacture, although it still has metallurgical uses. All of the burners described above are of such design that they must be operated under negative pressure.

Fluidized Roasters. Several roasters have been developed using the fluid-bed principle to roast various sulfide ores (see Fluidization). The two roasters which have had widespread utilization are the Badische whirling-layer type and the Dorr Fluo-Solids type (see Fig. 10). Both types operate on the same principle, differing only in methods of feeding the ore and of controlling the temperature in the bed. Ore ranging in size from flotation concentrates to 8 mesh is fed either dry or in a slurry form to the roaster bed. The bed is maintained at a predetermined level which is usually 20–40 in. when the bed is at rest. The combustion air under pressure is fed to the plenum chamber underneath a perforated plate or grate. This grate is usually refractory-lined. The air is uniformly distributed through the grate and flows upward through the bed, giving a boiling or heavy aeration to the bed. The roaster can be either a rectangular or round steel vessel lined with firebrick. The roasters are equipped with either an overflow standpipe or a pneumatically controlled gate to maintain the bed depth and to discharge the cinders. In the handling of flotation concentrates, a large portion of the cinders is carried overhead and recovered in the cyclones and waste-heat boilers. Air pressure may have to be reduced to maintain the desired depth of bed. Lack of agitation will cause the formation of fused material or clinker, causing failure of the bed. It is essential that the temperature of the bed be carefully controlled and that the entire bed be kept in motion to avoid fusion. The temperature of the bed is controlled by vaporization of water which is added directly to the bed with the ore when feeding a slurry or by spraying water into and through the combustion zone and onto the bed. Where heat recovery is important, the bed temperature is controlled by inserting specially designed pipes or coils in the bed through which treated water is circulated prior to its use in the waste-heat boiler system. The fluid bed has the following advantages over other modern units: better sulfur removal on the larger ore sizes, high capacities per roaster unit, lower capital costs than the multihearth type of roaster, and where heat is recovered in the bed by means of coils preheating feedwater, good heat recovery in the form of high-pressure steam. The main disadvantages are higher power costs, slightly higher capital costs than has the flash roaster, and the fact that, on roasting of arsenical pyrites, the arsenic is fixed in the form of arsenic pentoxide (As_2O_5) dissolved in the solid phase of the iron oxide (Fe_2O_3). This arsenic cannot readily be removed in subsequent cinder treatment. Modifications have been made by installing two fluid beds in series; with proper controls, high-quality cinders result. Another modification which has successfully been demonstrated is careful control of the combustion air going to the roaster, resulting in the production of Fe_3O_4 cinder, removing the dust from the gas stream, and installing a secondary combustion chamber (15). This results in a low-arsenic cinder, but this type of oxide cannot readily be treated subsequently to remove metals other than iron.

Rotary Burners and Spray Burners. These types of burners are used extensively abroad, and in producing sulfur dioxide for purposes other than the manufacture of sulfuric acid, as well as in some special plants (p. 474). See under Sulfur dioxide in Sulfur compounds.

By-Product Iron Oxide. The iron oxide by-product resulting from the roasting of pyrite and pyrrhotite is marketable to blast furnace operators and provides a substantial credit against cost of manufacturing acid. To be acceptable, however, the roasted cinder must be subjected to a further processing to reduce sulfur content below 0.10% and effect agglomeration of the small particles. This can be accomplished in a rotary "nodulizing" kiln or in a sintering machine of standard design. Cinder containing zinc is unacceptable, but most other nonferrous constituents are not present in sufficient amount to be objectionable.

Manufacture of Sulfuric Acid—Chamber Process

Originally the chamber process employed sulfur dioxide gas produced from sulfur, but roaster gas or smelter gas was substituted later. As finally developed, the process employs the following principal units to which must be added the necessary accessories

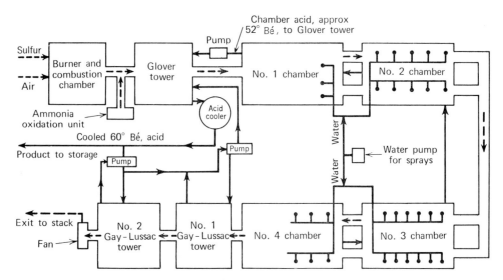

Fig. 11. Original chamber process.

such as conveyors and pumps (see Fig. 11): (*1*) The Glover tower receives the hot burner gas, and is fed at the top with the nitrous vitriol from the Gay-Lussac tower, and with 52°Bé (65%) acid from the chambers. Its functions are to denitrify the Gay-Lussac acid, thus reducing niter requirements to a small makeup for process loss; to evaporate water from the chamber acid, thus concentrating it to about 60°Bé (78%); cooling the gas to the point at which it can be safely introduced into the lead chambers; and supplying water vapor, equivalent to about one-third of the water requirement of the set (when producing acid of 52°Bé). (*2*) A series of large lead chambers, usually comprising from three to as many as ten, in which the reactions between sulfur dioxide, oxygen from the air, oxides of nitrogen, and water are carried out with resultant production of chamber acid. (*3*) Usually two Gay-Lussac towers in series, in which the oxides of nitrogen leaving the final chamber are absorbed in sulfuric acid of about 60°Bé, forming nitrous vitriol. (*4*) An ejector or fan to provide the necessary flow of air through the system. The ejector may be located in the exit stack from the Gay-Lussac tower; a fan is usually placed between the final chamber and Gay-Lussac tower. Occasionally the fan is placed between the Glover tower and first chamber, although this location is not preferred owing to the higher temperature at that point.

Chamber Reactions. Although the various reactions that may take place in the chambers have been the subject of endless arguments, the primary reactions are the formation of an intermediate compound, nitrososulfuric acid, from sulfur dioxide, nitrogen oxides, and oxygen, followed by its decomposition by water into sulfuric acid with liberation of nitrogen trioxide for continuation of the cyclic reaction according to the following equations:

$$2\,SO_2 + 2\,NOOH + O_2 \rightarrow 2\,SO_2(OH)ONO$$
$$2\,SO_2(OH)ONO + H_2O \rightarrow 2\,H_2SO_4 + N_2O_3$$
$$N_2O_3 + H_2O \rightarrow 2\,NOOH$$

In the conventional chamber set as described, it was the practice to provide about 16 ft³ of chamber space per 1 lb of sulfur burned per 24 hr, and although this space requirement could be somewhat reduced by more intensive working, this was generally considered uneconomical due to the additional loss of niter caused thereby.

For proper working of the process, it is essential that the gases leaving the final chamber be substantially free of sulfur dioxide, but contain not less than 5% free oxygen. A large glass bell jar, usually located in the flue at the exit of the final chamber, permits visual observation of the completeness of the reaction. Under normal conditions this glass would be filled with a characteristic clear ruddy or orange-red vapor, whereas if, through deficiency of niter, oxygen, or excess water, the oxidation of the sulfur dioxide is incomplete, this glass takes on a cloudy yellow cast. In the presence of sulfur dioxide, the nitrogen oxides cannot be recovered in the Gay-Lussac tower. When this occurs, it is necessary to increase sharply the niter charge to restore proper conditions in the chambers.

Glover Tower. The Glover tower, as originally introduced, was a square lead vessel about 25 ft high and of sufficient cross section to provide about 0.25 ft^3/lb of sulfur per 24 hr, or roughly 1.5% of the cubic contents of the entire chamber set. The bottom and the lower half of the sides were constructed of very heavy lead, about 35 lb/ft^2, with the upper half of the sides about half this weight. The bottom and lower sides were lined with a temperature- and acid-resisting material, such as chemical stoneware 10–12 in. in thickness; the thickness was reduced to about half for the upper sides. The tower was erected within a frame consisting of vertical steel corner angles with horizontal members to support the sides. The top was of lighter lead (8–10 lb/ft^2, supported from above. The tower was packed with material similar to the lining, and acid distribution was secured by providing a central leaden box with overflow lips or pipes feeding from thirty to forty separate compartments, each of which was connected by pipes to the top of the tower to effect a relatively uniform distribution of acid over the tower cross section. Later, round towers came into use, and acidproof stoneware in many manufactured forms was employed as packing.

The niter loss is frequently made up by supplying the Glover tower with spent nitric acid from other operations, or by potting sodium nitrate with sulfuric acid in a cast-iron niter "hog" located at the back end of the sulfur burner, or in more modern practice, by inclusion of a small ammonia-oxidation unit.

Lead Chambers. These vary in number, and in length from 50 to 200 ft, but they are usually restricted to a width of about 25 ft and height of 20 ft. It is customary to erect the chambers some 10–12 ft above grade to provide good air circulation. Each chamber consists of a bottom or pan of about 12 lb/ft^2 lead, bent up at the edges, like a tray, to a height of about 2 ft. The chamber sides are 6–8 lb/ft^2 lead, supported from a steel or wood skeleton. Lead straps burned to the sheets are attached to this frame, and the lower ends of the sheets hang down in the 10–12 in. pool of acid carried in the pan, thus providing a gas-tight lute. The chamber top, also of light lead, is supported by lead straps burned to the horizontal top and attached to wood joists or steel members spanning the chamber width. Small lead trays are placed inside the chambers to provide a continuous sample of the acid being produced. Thermometers are placed at one or more locations in each chamber, and the temperature and strength of the drip are used by the operator to control the working of the set, and to regulate the water supply to the chamber sprays.

The total water requirement of the chambers when producing 60°Bé acid is approx 1.50 lb water/1 lb of sulfur burned. This water must be provided through the use of either atomizing nozzles or steam.

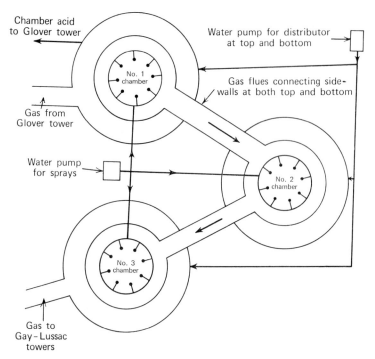

Fig. 12. Mills-Packard water-cooled chambers (three truncated cones, 25 ft in diameter at the top; 30 ft in diameter at the bottom; 40–50 ft in height).

Gay-Lussac Towers.   These usually consist of two in series and are generally cylindrical, of about 8 lb/ft² lead, lined with acidproof masonry of about 12 in. wall thickness for the bottom third, 8 in. for the intermediate third, and 4 in. for the top third.   Such towers were formerly packed with coke, but later, stoneware in various molded forms was substituted, thus permitting some reduction in tower area.   Also, plate columns were used with considerable success for the first tower.   The amount of tower space provided was about 2% of the cubic capacity of the chamber set.

Process Developments.   Critical study of the process disclosed that from 20 to 25% of the acid produced in the chamber operation was being formed in the Glover tower; indeed, the velocity of reaction in the denitration zone of the Glover tower was some 100–150 times that in the actual chamber space.   The front part of the first chamber was also very active, but the reaction became sluggish in the back part.   From 50 to 60% of the total acid was formed in the first chamber.   Activity picked up a trifle in the front part of the second chamber, but then became sluggish again, and this performance was repeated on a constantly decreasing scale of activity through the remainder of the set.   This reduced activity could be accounted for in part by the constantly decreasing sulfur dioxide content of the gas, but it was argued that the major reason was lack of adequate cooling and mixing of the gases.   This led to numerous proposals looking toward a more intensive working of the chamber process which included installation of open, packed, or plate towers irrigated by weak acid, or towers containing cooling pipes, which were placed between chambers, and use of steam jets or fans to promote mixing of gases within the chambers.   When the conventional lead chambers are eliminated, the process is often referred to as the *nitration process*.

A process most extensively employed both here and abroad is the *Mills-Packard* water-cooled chambers, which are built in the shape of a truncated cone ranging in size from 35 ft in base diameter by 40 ft in height to 35 ft in base diameter by 50 ft in height, supported from a steel framework and built in the open (Fig. 12). Radiating capacity of the lead walls is increased by flowing a film of water down the outside, and this also materially increases the life of the chambers. In some instances such chambers were installed in combination with the old rectangular chambers, but more generally the plant consists of such chambers exclusively, interposed between Glover and Gay-Lussac towers. With the smaller chambers, which provide about a 1:40 ratio of ft^2 of surface area to ft^3 of chamber space, a capacity as high as 2 ft^3/lb of sulfur burned per day has been realized, but with the larger chambers where the ratio of surface to cubic contents has risen to about 1:7, the space requirement rises to from 4 to 5 ft^3 chamber space per lb of sulfur burned per day. The capacity of the large chambers has been increased by providing an alleyway about 4 ft wide down the center with vertical water-cooled side walls, thus converting the horizontal section from the original circle into two semicircles, thereby increasing the ratio of surface to cubic contents to about 1:4.3, virtually duplicating the advantage of the smaller chambers.

A detailed discussion of the chamber process will be found in Fairlie (16), including a complete description of modern practice modification. Although these modern systems constitute a substantial advance beyond the original horizontal chamber sets, the fact remains that the chamber or nitration process accounted for less than 5% of the total production of sulfuric acid in the U.S. in 1967 as compared with 75% of the total production in 1921. Moreover, the contact process is gradually replacing the nitration even in the fertilizer industry, where acid above 60°Bé strength is not required and where the nitration process is consequently in the best competitive position.

The sulfuric acid produced directly in the lead chambers approximates 65% sulfuric acid (52°Bé) which can be concentrated to about 78% (60°Bé) in the Glover tower. The acid flows through the chamber set countercurrent to gas and is taken off the first chamber where it is lower in niter content and of highest concentration. The 60°Bé Glover-tower product is suitable for many industrial purposes, particularly for acidulation of phosphate rock. Most of the present production of approx 900,000 tons of chamber acid is used for this purpose.

Purification. The quality of the acid produced in the process is, of course, dependent on the impurity content of the raw material employed. Acid produced from sulfur contains chiefly a small amount of nitric acid, which for many uses is not objectionable. When the acid is produced from smelter gases or sulfide ores, however, impurities will vary considerably. Many sulfide ores are arsenical and, although this is not of geat importance for fertilizer, acid containing arsenic is unsuitable for many industrial uses, particularly for manufacture of food products and for pickling of steel that is to be painted, tinned, galvanized, or enameled. This impurity may be removed by passing hydrogen chloride, which converts the arsenic to arsenic trichloride which can be volatilized below the boiling point of the acid, or by precipitation of the arsenic with hydrogen sulfide added as gas, or generated by addition of sodium sulfide. The hydrogen sulfide method also removes traces of nitric acid and also selenium, which imparts a red-to-pinkish color to the acid. Since hydrogen sulfide is extremely toxic, it must be employed with the greatest care.

Concentration. Where acid stronger than 78% (Glover tower product) is required, it can be secured by concentration, but above 80% sulfuric acid corresponding to 390°F at atmospheric pressure, sulfuric acid is vaporized in ever-increasing amounts until the constant boiling point is reached at 98.3% sulfuric acid when the composition of the vapor is identical with that of the liquid. A concentrator, therefore, must include means for recovery of the vaporized acid. Originally this concentration was carried out in platinum pans arranged in cascade form over a firebrick flue through which the hot gases passed to the stack. The pans were fitted with lead covers through which gases were carried to a condenser before evacuation to the atmosphere. Later, vitreous silica basins were used, and occasionally cast-iron pans when the concentration was to be carried above 92% sulfuric acid (17). Subsequently, the Gaillard tower was introduced (17). This is an unpacked tower into which acid is

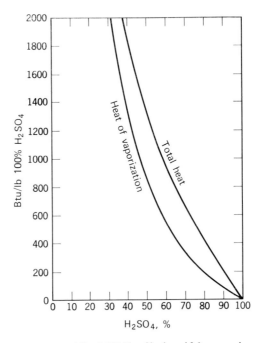

Fig. 13. Heat required to concentrate 1 lb of 100% sulfuric acid from various strengths up to 98.5%.

sprayed at the top, and passes counter current to furnace gases. More recently, the concentration has been effected in apparatus such as the Simonson-Mantius vacuum evaporator, the Du Pont falling film concentrator, or the Chemical Construction drum concentrator. In the latest design of the latter, the high-temperature products of combustion are forced below the acid level in the drum, which is a steel vessel lined with acidproof brick. The stack gases are passed through an electrical precipitator before admission to the atmosphere. Thermal requirements for concentration as presented by Zeisberg (8) appear as Figure 13.

Manufacture of Sulfuric Acid–Contact Process

Platinum was the catalyst originally discovered by Phillips in 1831 and was employed in all the early commercial applications around 1900. Although use of other materials, such as the salts of vanadium and silver, ferric oxide, chromium oxide, and some of the rare earths had been proposed, none of these substitutes possessed the

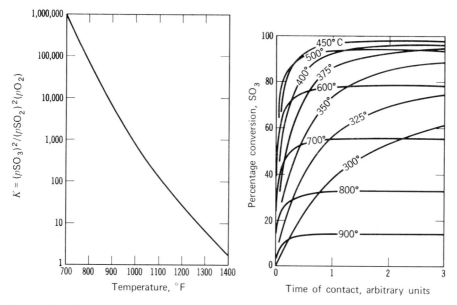

Fig. 14. Equilibrium constant for 2 SO₂ + O₂ → 2 SO₃.

Fig. 15. Relation between conversion and time of reaction at various temperatures.

activity of platinum or were capable of carrying the reaction so nearly to completion, and consequently platinum alone was found capable of providing satisfactory yields.

Values of the equilibrium constant for the reaction $2\,SO_2 + O_2 \to 2\,SO_3$ are shown in Figure 14. Substantially 100% conversion is obtainable at 715–750°F, provided the catalyst is sufficiently active and the time of contact is sufficient. Figure 15 reproduces curves presented by Knietsch (3) that show the effect of time of contact with a platinum catalyst. Taking both equilibrium and time of contact into consideration, it will be evident that although optimum conversion will be obtained at 715–750°F, maintenance of that temperature throughout the reaction would require excessively long contact. From a practical point of view, a great saving in contact mass can be secured by doing the major part of the work at a higher temperature, where a much higher reaction velocity is obtained, and then completing the reaction in the lower temperature range to secure optimum overall conversion.

In contrast to the chamber process, the contact process from the start was based on the use of sulfide ores, rather than sulfur, and the tremendous effort that was expended in the development of the process between 1875 and 1900 was due to the fact that the catalyst was subject to rapid impairment. Painstaking research on the causes of catalyst deterioration and development of methods to prevent it finally resulted in an elaborate procedure for purification of gas prior to conversion. Platinum is extremely sensitive to poisoning; for example, the amount of arsenic in the gases supplied to the platinized asbestos catalyst should not exceed about 0.3×10^{-6} g arsenic/ft³ to avoid gradual loss of catalytic activity.

Production methods have followed the general trend of American industry to units of larger size. Starting with the earliest contact units of 20 tons sulfuric daily capacity, a modern sulfur-burning plant may provide upward of 1500 tons daily capacity in a single unit. An ore-burning wet purification system for the larger capacities will usually include several ore burners and purification units in parallel. This paralleling may continue through the entire plant to permit flexibility.

In addition to effecting a material saving in fixed-capital requirements, the large unit also effects a corresponding reduction in process control, and this has been even further reduced by instrumentation. The instrument panel, in a central control room, shows plus, minus, and differential pressures at various points through the system, boiler pressure and boiler-water-level indicator, sulfur dioxide concentration, etc, and high- and low-level alarms are provided for the various pump tanks, or to call attention to any irregularity in distribution of acid over towers. One multipoint recorder will provide interrupted lines for a continuous record of all pertinent temperatures throughout one conversion unit, and another recorder can be used to provide a record of other gas and acid temperatures through the system. Strength of acid in circulation over the various towers is shown by a pointer on large clocklike dials, and an attached pen makes a continuous record on the chart. The same instrument can be arranged to regulate diluent automatically to maintain strength at the desired point.

WET–GAS PURIFICATION

The objective in gas purification is to provide a mixture of sulfur dioxide, oxygen, and nitrogen virtually free of all solid, liquid, and gaseous impurities. This is effected in a series of steps comprising: (1) dust removal; (2) cooling and scrubbing; (3) mist removal; and (4) drying (see Fig. 16).

Dust Removal. Solids must be removed from the gas as a first step, since the packed towers, filters, etc, employed in subsequent steps would otherwise rapidly become plugged. The magnitude of this problem is primarily determined by the physical character of the raw material and particularly by the type of apparatus employed in roasting the ore. The lump-ore burners employed in the earliest plant installations produced very little dust. Even with the mechanical burners, such as the Herreshoff and Wedge, operating on fines passing through a ⅜-in. screen, the dust leaving the burner rarely amounted to more than about 4.5% of the total cinder, but this was

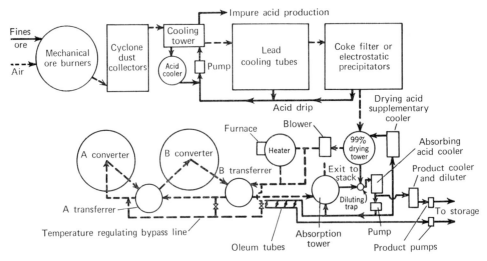

Fig. 16. American-type Badische contact unit.

more than could be tolerated in scrubbing towers and resulted in the application of dust-removal equipment in the form of large-volume baffled chambers (Howard dust chambers), hot electrostatic precipitators, or tangential dust collectors (cyclones). The temperature of the gas is maintained in the 650–1000°F range to minimize condensation and sulfation.

Today tangential dust collectors (cyclone) or improved electrostatic precipitators are used. The efficiency of the cyclone collector depends on radial acceleration of the dust particle and particle size. Since particle size controls the optimum diameter of the individual unit, it is advisable, when dealing with very fine dust, to employ a unit comprising a number of small tubes in parallel. This will give satisfactory efficiency at reasonable tangential velocity, which is the determining factor in power requirements. The efficiency of the electrostatic precipitator is not affected by particle size. Electrostatic precipitators, although considerably higher in capital costs, are normally used when the dust has nonferrous value, due to their high efficiency. (See also Gas cleaning; Electrostatic precipitation.)

Cooling and Scrubbing. Gas leaving the suspension roaster at about 1800°F is rapidly reduced to about 700°F in the waste-heat boiler, permitting employment of ordinary steel cyclone dust collectors to remove the dust; the gas is now admitted to a brick-lined scrubbing tower where, as a result of evaporation of water from the scrubbing acid, the gas temperature is further reduced to about 250°F, and the major part of the remaining dust is removed. The scrubbing acid is cooled prior to recirculation, and is recovered as an off-grade product, which has a limited outlet for certain industrial uses, as in fertilizers. Cooling of the gas is then continued to approximately atmospheric temperature in vertical unlined lead tubes, cooled by a film of water on the outside. The tubes are arranged both in parallel and series, the distribution being determined by the volume and water content of the gas. When ores either of high arsenic content or containing fluorides are roasted, the major portion of the arsenic or fluoride is deposited in these tubes. The headers are fitted with removable covers at the ends so that the cooler can be flushed out periodically. The number of tubes in parallel in successive passes should be gradually reduced in direct ratio to the contraction of the gas through cooling and condensation. A properly designed installation of 8-in.-diameter vertical tubes will provide a heat transfer coefficient of 8 Btu/(hr)(ft²)-(deg F). The quantity of water that can be supplied to such a cooler is naturally limited by the thickness of film that will remain in contact with the lead tube.

As an alternative to such indirect cooling, the gas may be cooled by direct contact with water or weak sulfuric acid, achieved through the use of sprays and packed towers. The weak acid is circulated through and cooled by the use of shell and tube coolers. The coolers are built of acid-resisting materials, normally baked carbon. The acid from the indirect coolers or the excess acid from the direct-cooling method is usually pumped to the scrubbing tower where a major portion of the dissolved sulfur dioxide is removed by the higher operating temperature. This off-grade acid has limited use and large quantities must be neutralized.

A decided advantage of direct cooling arises from the fact that the condensate from successive passes varies considerably in acidity, and when operating on a tight water balance, segregation of drips permits discard of the maximum amount of water with the minimum loss of acid. Similarly, when gases contain impurities such as fluorine, as much as 95% of the fluorine content can be eliminated with loss of no more than about 15% of the sulfuric acid content of the total cooler drip.

Mist Removal. The gas at this point can be assumed to be free of impurities other than water vapor, sulfuric acid, and those carried in the sulfuric acid mist. This mist is a carrier for arsenic, and would in any case cause corrosion. It can be removed by either filtration or electrical precipitation. While many materials such as quartz, sand, rock wool, coal, pumice, asbestos, saw dust, wood shavings, and coke have been employed from time to time, none have equaled the efficiency of coke. This should be 72-hr hard-burned beehive oven coke, free of soft and tarry knots, broken down and screened to five size ranges.

The filter is usually constructed as a rectangular lead-lined wooden box of approx 1000-ft² area, fitted with a grid tile carried on brick or tile supports about 1 ft above the bottom of the box. The largest size coke is spread over the tile and carefully leveled off before placing the next size in position, continuing in this manner with the smaller sizes until the packing reaches a total depth of about 8 ft. It is important from the standpoint of both efficiency and resistance that mixing of sizes be avoided.

Should the gas entering the filter contain any solids, or should the ores contain lead, it is advisable, if not necessary, to protect the main filter by a preliminary or scalper filter, which may be packed with an intermediate-size coke carried on slotted lead sheets. Even if the gases contain no impurities other than sulfuric acid and water, the preliminary filter is still advisable as it will relieve the main filter of much of the condensation of weak acid, thus freeing it for the more important work of mist removal. The main filter can be satisfactorily operated at rates between 3 and 6 cfm/ft² box area, and the primary or scalper can be operated at somewhat higher rates. Pine "excelsior" (wood shavings) placed on a wooden grid has also been used successfully in the primary filter, though it does not equal the efficiency of coke. If the gas entering the main filter is free of solids as it should be, such filters can be operated for 20 years or longer without washing or repacking. The preliminary or scalper filter, however, will require cleaning or repacking, where a material like excelsior is employed, as frequently as monthly to semiannually, depending on the impurity content of the entering gas.

The filter is very efficient and low in maintenance, but it requires considerable space and is being replaced with electrostatic precipitators, constructed of acid-resisting materials. The electrostatic precipitator can be designed for efficiencies of 99%, but normally it does not remove the mist to the same degree as the filter box. Two precipitators are often used in series if the inlet gas has a high mist loading.

Drying. As a final step in the wet purification train, the moisture content of the gas should be reduced to a figure between 0.005 and 0.010 grams of water/ft³ and certainly not higher than 0.015 grams of water, as anything above that value will not only increase corrosion of subsequent apparatus, but in addition will most likely cause formation of sulfuric acid mist that will result in a visible absorber exit.

This drying is accomplished in packed towers irrigated by drying acid which may be either 99%, 66°Bé (93%), or 80–85%. Use of 99% acid has the advantage of combining the drying system with the absorbing system, thus eliminating a separate acid-circulating system. A portion of the absorbing acid is subjected to supplemental cooling in a cast-iron cooler and is then sent to the drying tower. Acid leaving the drying tower is combined with that from the absorber. The drying tower is of steel, lined with acid brick, and set in acidproof cement.

Another extensively employed system utilizes 66°Bé acid for drying. This avoids the use of lead or lead-lined equipment, the drying tower being of steel lined with acid brick, and the acid cooling and circulating system of cast iron. Corrosion of the cast-iron equipment, however, is more severe than when employed for 99% acid, and this system does not lend itself readily to production of low-iron acid.

A very extensively employed drying system uses acid ranging from 80 to 85%, depending on temperature. This method requires an independent acid-circulating system comprising a steel tower, lead-lined and preferably also brick-lined, in conjunction with all-lead acid-circulating lines, pump, tank, and coolers. The latter should be adequate to deliver acid to the tower cooled to no higher than 100°F. Acid is maintained at the desired strength by continuous interchange with absorbing acid.

Gas dried in this manner is free of the fume that is associated with 99% drying and that results in increased maintenance because of the corrosion of blowers and flues and the plugging of converters with the deposited sulfate. Although the weaker acid does not have the avidity for water of 99% acid, there is no difficulty in reaching equilibrium in a properly packed tower, taking care that the proper strength of acid is used, according to the temperature and the amount of water to be left in the gas. Before leaving the tower the gas can be passed through a basket containing steel wool or glass wool to remove any mechanically carried spray.

Blowers. In the wet purification process, the blower is placed between the drying tower and the conversion unit, since it is handling a purified and dried gas at approximately atmospheric pressure. On a sulfur-burning unit, the blower is usually placed before the drying tower as it is handling undried atmospheric air which has no acid-mist contamination. Modern practice is to use one or two centrifugal blowers sized for the total capacity on the large units. The Roots-type positive displacement blower (see Rotary screw compressor, Vol. 16, p. 748) is still preferred when the required capacity can be obtained with one or two blowers.

HOT–GAS PURIFICATION

After World War I, a changeover was made from pyrite to Frasch sulfur. In many ore-burning plants, sulfur was burned in the lump-ore burners and mechanical roasters, and the gas was subjected to the customary wet purification procedures, but it was found that this gas contained such a low content of impurities exerting a poisoning effect on platinized asbestos, that the wet purification procedure could be dispensed with. The gas was treated by hot-gas purification (Merriam process) (18), in which at no point in the process subsequent to combustion of the sulfur is the gas permitted to drop below the temperature at which condensation would occur. Purification was actually limited to the use of a filter placed before the first converter to remove solids suspended in the gas stream. The first large unit of this type, with an annual capacity of 50,000 tons, was erected in the winter of 1925–1926. The blower or fan was placed at the front end of the system handling air which was passed first through a drying tower to dry it to about 0.005 g of water/ft³. If the air were not dried, then if at any later point in the process the gas should fall below the condensation temperature, there would be danger of severe corrosion in the coolers (see below under Conversion) and of the formation of a mist in the absorbing system which would pass out the exit stack. After the dryer, the following apparatus was arranged in series: sublimer and combustion chamber, cast-iron pipe radiator, and filter, after which the gas was handled in the standard conversion and absorption system. The sulfur was melted and impurities settled out or filtered, and the sublimer was supplied with the molten purified sulfur.

The hot-gas purification system reduced the cooling requirement of the drying system to from 20 to 60% of that of the wet-gas system, depending on the geographic location of the plant, and reduced the fixed-capital expenditure for a contact acid plant

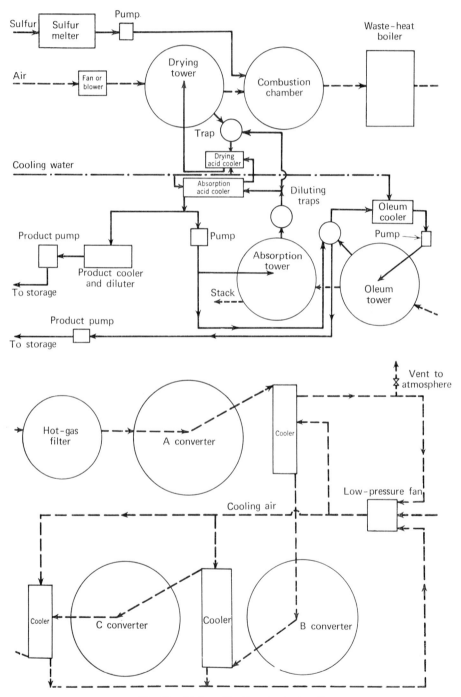

Fig. 17. Hot purification contact unit.

to about 40% of that required for an ore-burning plant with complete wet purification system (see Fig. 17).

This process was modified by the use of the molten-sulfur spray burner, the use of a portion of the air for cooling between conversion stages, the use of interstage waste-heat boilers for temperature control, and boiler feedwater heaters (economizers) for the final gas cooling. This results in the modern sulfur-burning acid plant.

CONVERSION

Platinum Catalysts. The contact process has always used either platinum or vanadium catalysts, as they are the only materials providing commercially acceptable conversion rates. The Mannheim process had a first stage utilizing ferric oxide, but conversion rarely exceeded 40% and it was necessary to employ platinum in subsequent stages. Of the many materials employed as supports or carriers for platinum, only magnesium sulfate (Grillo mass), silica gel, and asbestos have stood the test of time, the latter being by far the most frequently employed, and incidentally the original Badische catalyst.

Long-fiber asbestos (chrysotile), after a preliminary washing, is dried and carded and then immersed in a solution of chloroplatinic acid (hexachloroplatinic(IV) acid), H_2PtCl_6. After draining and drying, it is repeatedly fluffed in a carding machine until matted material is pulled apart, and finally fluffed by hand by means of tweezers. The finished material may contain from 5 to 10 wt % platinum and is customarily employed in an amount approximating 0.015 troy oz (0.461 g) of platinum per ton of annual capacity. When the catalyst mass is first put on stream, the chloroplatinic acid is decomposed to platinum black.

Magnesium sulfate is subjected to a double calcination to produce a hard mass which is crushed and screened to approx $3/8$–$1/2$ in. in size. The cold mass is then sprayed with a solution of chloroplatinic acid in such amount that the platinized mass will contain about 0.25 wt % platinum, with the same platinum requirement per ton of acid as platinized asbestos.

Silica gel, prepared as a hard granular material, is sprayed with a compound such as ammonium chloroplatinate in an amount sufficient to provide from 0.075 to 0.125 wt % platinum, and the platinized gel, after drying, is ready for use in the converters. Platinum provided per ton of acid produced is lower than in the case of the other platinum catalysts but, as the silica gel is quite expensive, the overall cost of the prepared catalyst is substantially higher.

Contaminated Grillo mass can be reactivated several times by spraying with aqua regia and recalcining, but platinized asbestos is too fragile to stand removal from the converter. If blanketed by a deposit of iron sulfate, the resistance can be largely removed by reverse blowing with a current of air, but if poisoned by arsenic, there is no known procedure by which activity can be restored. Silica gel is claimed to be immune to arsenic poisoning and is only temporarily poisoned by chlorine, but it is disintegrated by fluorine compounds. This particular catalyst appears to have found wider use abroad than in the U.S.

Up to about 90% of the original platinum can be recovered from any of the above catalysts whenever loss of activity necessitates replacement.

Vanadium Catalysts. The use of vanadium as a catalyst for the oxidation of sulfur dioxide to sulfur trioxide was first discovered by DeHaen, who took out a patent in Germany in 1900, but the activity of his catalyst was too low to be of commercial importance. It remained for Slama and Wolf (19) to develop a commercially successful vanadium mass which was employed in large commercial units by Badische Anilin-und Soda-Fabrik beginning in 1915; by 1928 it had completely replaced platinum in all converters of that company. It was not until 1927 that vanadium catalyst was employed commercially in the United States. The Slama-Wolf patent disclosed and claimed a catalyst consisting of a carrier, such as powdered pumice or kieselguhr, with particle size less than 60 μ, with which the catalytic agent of vanadium pentoxide and potash was combined. The mass was prepared with a consistency which permitted compression into tablet or pellet form and later was formed into worms by extrusion.

Although the particle size of the carrier has been emphasized, it appears that the combination with vanadium of an alkali, which has been variously referred to as a stabilizer or promoter, is of great importance. Under converter operating conditions the alkali with which the vanadium is combined appears to be in the form of bisulfate and when this is so, the vanadium is capable of migration. This can readily be demonstrated by preparing worms or pellets identical in every respect, except that half the mass would contain no vanadium. After a relatively short period of operation, it will be found that all pellets have about the same vanadium content.

Vanadium catalysts are complex compositions containing vanadium in the oxidation state corresponding to vanadium pentoxide (V_2O_5). Before being put on stream, they must be heated in a low concentration of sulfur dioxide, since the conversion of the alkalis present to sulfates or bisulfates is strongly exothermic.

Vanadium vs Platinum. Many conflicting statements have been published with respect to the relative merits of platinum and vanadium catalysts in the contact process. Aside from the admitted sensitivity of platinum to poisoning, it has been stated by some that the conversion efficiency of vanadium catalyst exceeded that of platinum and was cheaper, whereas others contended that vanadium required a larger excess of oxygen than platinum and gave lower conversion on gases of equal concentration.

Platinum possesses much greater catalytic activity than vanadium and is active over a much wider temperature range. The ignition temperature (lowest temperature at which a vigorous reaction will take place) of an average vanadium mass may approximate 800–805°F, whereas a good platinized-asbestos catalyst will have an ignition temperature at least 70–90 deg F lower; this affects the conversion in two ways, as follows:

In a large well-insulated unit, each 1 vol % of sulfur dioxide converted will produce a temperature rise of about 50 deg F, from which it follows that 1.5–2 vol % of sulfur dioxide can be converted in the first platinum converter by the time the temperature has reached the point at which the gas would have been admitted to the vanadium converter. The reaction will be halted at the equilibrium curve, and a vanadium catalyst, on a 10% sulfur dioxide gas from sulfur, will give 60% conversion in the first converter, but a platinum catalyst, with the extra 2% of sulfur dioxide converted, will give 80% conversion. Thus the vanadium catalyst will necessitate the use of an additional stage.

The top range of the conversion is affected in the same way. An overall conversion of 98.25% can readily be secured in the final platinum converter on an 11% sulfur dioxide gas from sulfur, which would contain only 4.5% free oxygen after conversion. The reaction, however, would have to be completed within the range of 780–790°F, at

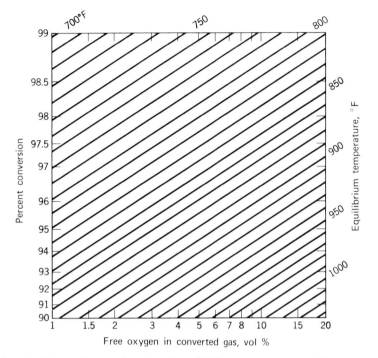

Fig. 18. Conversion as a function of equilibrium temperature and free oxygen.

which platinum possesses good activity. Under these conditions, vanadium catalyst would be so sluggish as to make the operation impracticable. On raising the temperature to about 830°F, at which vanadium would have satisfactory activity, the maximum conversion obtainable would drop to 97.25%.

On the other hand, if the 11% gas is diluted with air to a 7% sulfur dioxide basis, which would provide 10.6% free oxygen after conversion, then the vanadium mass at the same 830°F temperature will provide the desired 98.25% conversion.

Conversion equilibrium is determined by the temperature and free-oxygen content of the converted gas and is independent of the catalyst. The influence of these factors is shown in Figure 18 which covers the range of 90–99% conversion. It will be obvious that to secure the desired conversion at higher gas concentrations implies use of a catalyst that is active at the necessary reaction temperature. The alternative is to raise the oxygen content the necessary amount to permit use of the desired catalyst at a temperature at which it is active.

The susceptibility of platinum to poisoning is overemphasized, since, even if the sulfur dioxide originates with a sulfur-bearing ore rather than sulfur, the gas will in any case have to be purified and the mist removed to protect subsequent apparatus. One disadvantage of vanadium is that it cannot be economically recovered from discarded mass. However, the preparation of a good vanadium mass is relatively simple as compared with the preparation of platinized asbestos; because of this fact and the high cost of platinum, all of the modern acid plants use vanadium catalyst.

Converters. The early Badische converter consisted of a brick or steel vessel containing a bundle of parallel steel tubes, the platinized asbestos being supported on perforated plates placed within the tubes and separated by spacers. The Tentelew converter followed the same general design. As modified by American practice, the converter was a cast-iron or steel vessel about 7 ft in diameter, and the catalyst was carried on perforated steel plates separated by 1-in. pipe spacers.

Operating on a pyrite gas of about 8.5% sulfur dioxide content, some units are provided with three converters in series and other units with only two; the latter, with active catalyst, give approximately 96% overall conversion. With a total provision of 70 to 80 plates, of which about 25 are in the first converter, about 80% conversion is obtainable from about 10 plates, where reaction is stopped by the temperature rise. (The remaining 15 plates in the first converter are a factor of safety so that, with gradual deterioration of the catalyst, the converter will have a long life.) It is then necessary to cool the gas to about 750–780°F before it enters the second converter. This cooling is effected by heat exchange with incoming cold gas, utilizing boilerlike tubular vessels called "transferrers"—one placed between each converter and one following the final converter.

Used in conjunction with a wet purification system, the gas from the blower at about 95–100°F is passed through the transferrers in series before entering the first converter. Temperature regulation is secured by valves located in bypass lines installed across the transferrers. The transferrers are fitted with baffles, and it is customary to pass the converted gas through the tubes since they can be readily cleaned.

When a sulfur gas is employed in a hot purification unit, the gas is cooled (against air) before entering the first converter, and again between converters. More converters are required in series to obtain the desired overall conversion if it is desired to take advantage of the higher sulfur dioxide concentration possible when burning sulfur.

For use with platinized magnesium sulfate, two converters, each containing 5–6 trays on which the catalyst was spread to a depth of 9–12 in., were employed in series.

Vanadium mass is employed in solid beds that may vary from 20 to about 50 in. in depth, supported on a screen placed over a cast-iron or steel grille. The vessels may be cast iron but are usually steel, the size being determined by the capacity of the unit. It is customary to provide 1 ft² of converter area per 75–100 cfm (NTP) gas volume.

Converter systems are of two general types: One employs internal heat exchange by means of cooling tubes embedded in the catalyst, the other, more common, system utilizes external coolers installed between converters.

Since the reaction velocity increases with temperature, maximum utilization of catalyst would be achieved by raising the gas temperature initially to about 1000°F, and then continuously removing heat produced by the reaction plus additional cooling so as to maintain the temperature at that required for a favorable equilibrium. In practice, however, this theoretical advantage cannot be realized since it requires continuous maintenance of preestablished conditions of gas concentration, volume loading, oxygen ratio, and catalyst activity. Greater flexibility is secured through external cooling, so that changes in these factors can be compensated for by adjustment of valves in bypass lines across the coolers. In such a system, however, if overall conversion on the order of 98% is desired, the sulfur dioxide content of the gas entering the final converter should not be appreciably in excess of 0.80%.

Converters and transferrers are always well insulated, not only to conserve heat, which is quite important in the wet purification unit, but also to prevent the condensation and corrosion that would result on contact of the converted gas with a cool metal surface. Preheaters are employed for restarting the unit after a shutdown. The heater is a steel tubular vessel in a fuel-fired furnace.

The double catalysis (20) or interstage absorption process was originally patented in 1931 (21) and further developed by Farbenfabriken Bayer and others to abate atmospheric pollution. The conversion is increased from approx 98% to approx 99.5%. A conventional conversion system is used for the first two or three converters, where at least 90% of the sulfur dioxide is converted to sulfur trioxide. The partially converted gas is passed through a tubular gas-to-gas heat exchanger, cooled, and the sulfur trioxide removed in an absorbing tower. The sulfur trioxide-free gas exiting from the absorbing tower is reheated to conversion temperature by passing through the gas-to-gas heat exchanger. The remaining sulfur dioxide is converted to sulfur trioxide in a final converter and the sulfur trioxide removed in a second absorbing tower. This process, although more expensive, has the advantage of not only giving a low sulfur dioxide content in the exit gas, but also permitting the use of stronger sulfur dioxide gas in the conversion system.

ABSORPTION

Absorbing Towers. The converted gas is absorbed in strong sulfuric acid which, for best results with respect to absorption and low iron content, should approximate 99.0–99.2% sulfuric acid in its final contact with the gas. Absorption is usually carried out in a packed tower, and the absorbing acid is recirculated by means of a cast-iron or alloy-steel pump at a rate that will permit a strength rise in the tower of not over 0.6% sulfuric acid. The acid leaving the tower is diluted back to its original concentration with water or weak acid. The electrical conductivity of the acid (Fig. 4) is utilized to determine and continuously record the strength of the acid in circulation and, if desired, maintain strength automatically by mechanical regulation of diluent.

In the conventional wet purification unit, the converted gas leaving the final transferrer will not exceed about 680°F and can be admitted directly into the absorber. In the hot purification unit, gas leaving the final converter at perhaps 825°F should be partially cooled prior to absorption; otherwise a visible exit gas will result. This cooling should be effected in an air-cooled tubular vessel or by an economizer which preheats the boiler feedwater, and not by radiator pipes installed in the open where they would be wetted by rain, as this will overcool the gas. Overcooling of the gas in turn will result in formation of sulfuric mist that will create a visible exit gas.

Towers in which the absorption is carried out are frequently steel, lined with acid brick set in an acidproof cement. Since it is very difficult to provide a lining that will remain tight over a long period of service, many smaller towers consist of flanged cast-iron sections bolted together. Such towers are unlined and are virtually unattacked by acid of proper strength and temperature. The towers are packed with quartz pebbles or one or more of the many forms of ceramic packing that are available.

In some instances, several towers were employed in series, but this is unnecessary if packing, gas loading, and acid circulation and distribution are such as to permit reaching equilibrium between exit gas and inlet acid. Uniform distribution of acid over the tower area is most important, and is most easily secured by providing numerous points of distribution such as distributor tubes or pipes at uniform spacing. An effective method used on the smaller towers is to set the tubes in acidproof cement in a cast-iron distributor plate on which acid is maintained at a depth of 6–10 in. The tubes should be high-silicon iron.

Absorbing towers are sometimes followed by electrostatic precipitators or mist filters to remove the entrained sulfuric acid and mist. These, however, although they do remove the visibility, do not remove any of the objectionable sulfur dioxide content of the exit gases. Several processes have been developed to decrease the sulfur dioxide content to acceptable levels. In addition to the interstage absorption system, other processes which have been used include absorption of the sulfur dioxide by using an alkaline solution over packed towers and absorption of the sulfur dioxide in a wetted coke bed (22).

Acid Coolers. The heat produced in the absorber is continuously removed by a cast-iron cooler incorporated in the acid-circulating system. To obtain a good heat-transfer coefficient, the cooler design should provide for frequent and abrupt changes in direction of flow of the acid. Better results will be secured by covering the cooler surface with a film of water supplied from a distributor box, or by spray nozzles, rather than immersing the cooler in a tank of water.

The demand for 99% acid is limited by its high freezing point, 40°F. The major demand is for 66°Bé acid (93.19%). The absorbing acid is, therefore, diluted with water or weak acid and the heat of dilution removed in a product cooler. A cooler of the type employed on the absorbing acid is generally used, with due allowance for the fact that the output of the unit is ordinarily not more than 1.5% of the circulating load on the absorber.

OLEUM PRODUCTION

Oleum is obtained by maintaining the absorbing acid in contact with the sulfur trioxide-containing converted gas until the desired concentration is built up. In modern practice the acid is recirculated over packed towers of relatively large diameter, and the heat of absorption is removed in external coolers, as in the production of 99% acid. The towers are of steel, usually unlined. Oleum systems may include from one to three towers placed ahead of, and in series with, the final absorber, depending on the strength of oleum desired, and the sulfur trioxide content of the gas available.

As in the case of 99% acid, the electrical conductivity of the oleum (Fig. 8) is utilized to determine, record, and if desired, automatically regulate the diluent to maintain the desired strength of product.

As will be noted from Figures 5 and 6, the vapor pressure of oleum rises rapidly with strength and temperature.

Since in the production of 40% oleum the recirculated acid has a freezing point of 99°F, it is not practical to cool it below 105°F and, in practice, the gas leaving the 40% tower will contain about 5.25% sulfur trioxide by volume; only the sulfur trioxide in excess of this figure can be absorbed. It is, therefore, the practice to follow the 40% tower with an intermediate tower having an independent acid-circulating system, the product from this tower providing the diluent for the 40% system. The strength maintained on this intermediate system will approximate 25% oleum, and the residual gas sent to the final 99% absorber may vary from about 2.5 to 3.5% sulfur trioxide.

When 40% oleum must be produced in a plant in which the maximum concentration of sulfur trioxide after conversion is about 7.0%, no more than 25% of the total sulfur trioxide content of gas can be absorbed in the 40% tower, and it may be necessary to increase the sulfur trioxide content.

The sulfur trioxide content of the gas leaving the contact converters can be more than doubled by installing, ahead of the strong oleum tower, a stripping tower in which the sensible heat of the gas leaving the final converter or transferrer is utilized to vaporize sulfur trioxide from 20–30% oleum fed to the stripper. The residue from the stripper, usually about 5% oleum, is returned to the intermediate oleum tower. By this procedure (2), sulfur trioxide can be absorbed in the 40% tower in excess of the amount present in the original converted gas. It also makes possible the production of oleum as strong as 60% by direct absorption, although, when utilizing a 7.0% gas, this would require an absorption train comprising a stripper, 60% tower, 50% tower, 30% tower, and final 99% absorber.

Higher-strength oleum is produced by heating strong oleum and absorbing the vaporized sulfur trioxide in an additional body of strong oleum with concurrent cooling, the weak oleum residual from the boiler being returned to the oleum tower for fortification. The higher the strength of the oleum employed for absorption of the vaporized sulfur trioxide, the lower the cost of production. Sulfuric anhydride (sulfur trioxide) is produced in a similar manner by cooling and condensing the sulfur trioxide vaporized in the boiler.

Sulfuric anhydride (sulfur trioxide) is 100% oleum and is produced by heating 20% or stronger oleum to the boiling point, in either an indirect-fired vessel or a high-pressure steam-heated vessel, and distilling off the sulfur trioxide. The gaseous sulfur trioxide contains small quantities of sulfuric mist which is removed by a mesh filter or other similar means. The gas is cooled and the sulfur trioxide condensed out. Extreme care must be taken to keep the liquid sulfur trioxide above the freezing point, $94°F$, but below the boiling point, $112°F$. The liquid sulfur trioxide is not stable and will convert on standing to a solid form. To prevent this polymerization, a stabilizer must be added. Several stabilizers have been used; a more important one is a mixture of one of several boron compounds and dimethyl sulfate (23). The quantity of stabilizer used is very small, with a resulting boron content of between 0.005 and 0.1 wt % expressed as boron oxide (B_2O_3). Sulfuric anhydride is shipped in insulated tank trucks and cars or in steel drums. The sulfuric anhydride in storage must be kept about $95°F$ to prevent it from freezing.

Since production of oleum necessitates bringing gas from the final converter or transferrer into contact with acid much below the condensation point, the result is the chilling of the gas with formation of sulfuric mist which will cause a visible exit from the final absorber. The higher the strength of the oleum being produced, the lower the temperature of the circulating acid, and the worse the exit. When the stripper is included in the oleum system, the weak oleum at the base of the stripper at its first contact with the entering gas is raised to as high as $275°F$, with the result that gas is gradually cooled through the major portion of the condensation range. This materially reduces formation of mist with corresponding reduction in visible exit from the absorber stack.

The oleum coolers incorporated in the acid-circulation system are steel, and the same principle applies as in the case of absorbing tower coolers. Pumps and circulating lines must also be steel.

Nitrification of Oleum. Due to the high freezing point of oleum of the higher strengths, particularly 40% oleum employed so extensively in production of high explosives, it is customary to use nitric acid as an antifreeze. Addition of 6 wt % of 96% nitric acid to 40% oleum will depress the freezing point from 75 to $-11°F$. The nitric acid is added continuously to the product leaving the 40% system, and as the addition produces considerable temperature rise, this provides a means of effecting automatic regulation of the nitric acid content. Where end use prohibits the use of nitric acid, a hot shed must be provided to thaw oleum frozen in transit.

SPECIAL–PURPOSE PLANTS

Acid-Sludge Decomposition.   Acid sludges produced in treating petroleum distillates with sulfuric acid vary widely in composition and are broadly classed as nonlube and lube sludges.   Some refineries hydrolyze the light nonlube sludges, effecting an incomplete separation of acid tars from the weak impure acid.   The acid is then concentrated to about 80% sulfuric acid and mixed with strong acid, or fortified with sulfur trioxide for reuse, but it has a high organic content which may run to 8–10% expressed as carbon.   The refineries may return the nonlube sludge to the acid producer for thermal decomposition.

Where clean acid is desired, it is necessary to decompose the sludge.   This can be effected in limited quantities in the ore roaster when burning sulfide ores or in several specially designed burners, but if handled in any volume, the oxygen consumed in the formation of water and carbon dioxide results in a very dilute sulfur dioxide gas that imposes a heavy penalty on the associated acid plant.

Several plants were built to partially decompose the higher-carbon-content acid sludges using brick-lined rotary kilns, equipped at the discharge end with one or more heavy iron bars to granulate the residual coke which will be approximately the same quantity by weight as the carbon content charged.   The decomposition is effected by supplying the kiln with hot products of combustion of low-oxygen content from a fuel-fired furnace.   Other processes use, as the source of heat, preheated coke, which may be obtained by burning a portion of the by-product coke in a separate furnace.   These types of processes give a gas with a high sulfur dioxide content contaminated with volatile hydrocarbon.   The gas is diluted with air and raised to about 1500°F to decompose the hydrocarbons.   This results in a gas containing about 7% sulfur dioxide and up to 7% carbon dioxide.   The gas is now cooled, with the excess moisture being removed by conventional methods as noted earlier, and converted to sulfuric acid.

A modified Mannheim furnace equipped with a double muffle has also been employed.   This avoids the dilution of the gas with carbon dioxide and nitrogen, but the evolved sulfur dioxide gas must be freed of hydrocarbons by combustion as before.   The acid sludges are often used as a source of fuel for the thermal decomposition of other spent acids.

Where sulfuric acid is used as the catalyst in the alkylation process, the 99% acid is diluted by absorption of hydrocarbons and various by-products.   In practice, the acid in circulation is maintained at from 88 to 92% titratable acidity by continuous addition of fresh 99% acid, with discard of an equivalent volume of contaminated acid.   This alkylate discard, which usually averages from 5 to 8% organic content, expressed as carbon, is decomposed by spraying into a combustion chamber in which the heat deficiency is made up by use of other fuel, or acid sludges; or, if additional production is required, hydrogen sulfide or molten or vaporized sulfur can be substituted in whole or in part.   Since the decomposition is effected at about 1800°F in the presence of an excess of oxygen, all organic matter is completely burned and the gas can be handled in a standard wet purification acid unit, or cooled by direct contact with water, passed through an electrostatic precipitator for removal of mist, and dried prior to admission to a contact unit containing heat-exchange equipment.   The impure acid recovered by hydrolysis of nonlube sludges can, after concentration, be similarly decomposed.

The acid recovered in the production of explosives, which contains up to about 0.25% nitrobodies, can be decomposed at about 1800°F in a low-oxygen atmosphere by hot products of combustion from a fuel-fired furnace. The decomposition can also be effected by combustion of sulfur.

Sulfate Conversion Unit. Several plants have also been built for processing the waste liquors from the titanium-pigment industry, which contain from 9 to 15% sulfuric acid and from 4 to 10% ferrous sulfate ($FeSO_4$). The acid liquors are fed into a fuel-fired, brick-lined rotary kiln together with a portion of the iron oxide by-product for neutralization of the free acid. As the material progresses through the kiln, it passes through a pasty stage into a solid, which is granulated by tumbling irons and is eventually discharged in the form of $FeSO_4 \cdot H_2O$; the waste gases being discharged to the atmosphere. The ferrous sulfate monohydrate is then charged into a second similar fuel-fired kiln, after admixture with powdered coal, or a mixture of coal and pyrite ore. Here the sulfate is decomposed and the pyrite oxidized, resulting in by-product ferric oxide, part of which is recycled to the first kiln. Gas leaving the decomposing kiln is passed through a hot electrostatic precipitator in order to remove dust, and is then cooled and scrubbed. The gas, containing about 7% sulfur dioxide, is then sent to a contact unit equipped with heat exchangers.

The waste titanium liquors have also been subjected to vacuum concentration for recovery of the free acid for reuse in the process; the ferrous sulfate is either crystallized out as the heptahydrate or salted out as the monohydrate by regulating the acid concentration.

A similar type of plant has been proposed for processing the huge volumes of pickle liquor discarded by the steel mills. These liquors also contain free sulfuric acid and ferrous sulfate in varying amounts, but are generally more dilute than the titanium waste liquors, and the economics are consequently less favorable. The ferrous sulfate can be decomposed by heat alone, or by feeding together with sulfide ore into an ore burner in which the temperature is maintained above the dissociation point of sulfur trioxide.

The selection and use of such special-type plants is not, in most instances, approached from the standpoint of producing acid under commercially competitive conditions. Rather, they are intended to solve a waste-disposal problem, thereby avoiding air and stream pollution.

Economic Aspects

The U.S. production of sulfuric acid in all strengths, including fortified acid, increased from 10,780,000 net tons in 1947 to 28,197,000 net tons in 1967, an increase of 161% in the 20-yr period. This increase is illustrated graphically in Figure 19, which shows a breakdown between acid produced by the chamber process and total production, the difference being contact production.

It is of interest to note that the increase in production and capacity has been entirely with the contact process. There was an actual decrease in the number of the operating chamber plants from seventy in 1961 to fifty-four in 1965. Fortified-acid production represented 677,000 tons of the totals in 1947 and 1,019,000 tons of the totals in 1967.

The world production of sulfuric acid increased from 50,900,000 metric tons in 1960 to 80,370,000 metric tons in 1967, with the production divided as shown in Tables 6 and 7.

The raw material for the production of sulfuric acid is principally from elemental sulfur, pyrites, and the smelting of nonferrous sulfide ores. Approx 53½% of the

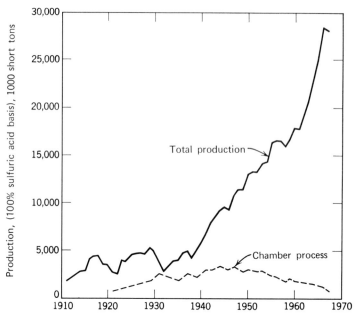

Fig. 19. U.S. production of sulfuric acid.

Table 6. Sulfuric Acid Production, % of World Total

Area	1960	1967
North America	33.4	33.8
Western Europe	30.2	26.5
Asia	10.2	10.0
balance of Free World	7.7	8.3
Communist Block	18.5	21.4

Table 7. Production of 100% Sulfuric Acid by Countries in 1967, 1000 metric tons (2204 lb)

North America	27,149
Latin America	1,941
Africa	2,284
Asia	8,038
Oceania[a]	2,456
Belgium	1,542
Finland	558
France	3,143
West Germany	3,772
Italy	3,515
Netherlands	1,248
Spain	1,783
Sweden	604
United Kingdom	3,234
Communist Block	17,213
others	1,890
total	*80,370*

[a] Including Australia and New Zealand.

Table 8. U.S. Production of Virgin Sulfuric Acid by Divisions and States,
1000 short tons of 100% acid

Region	1951	1966	Installed capacity 1967
New England	210	205	229
Middle Atlantic			
Pennsylvania	808	966	1,040
New York and New Jersey	1,348	1,755	2,243
total	*2,157*	*2,721*	*3,283*
North Central			
Illinois	1,073	1,763	1,835
Ohio	654	689	865
other	1,263	2,023	2,541
total	*2,990*	*4,475*	*5,241*
South			
Alabama	298	415	509
Florida	536	7,444	10,137
Georgia	247	581	468
North Carolina	160	217	1,250
South Carolina	207	159	186
Virginia	550	630	786
Texas	948	2,968	3,206
Delaware and Maryland	1,340	1,049	1,150
Louisiana	435	1,303	1,256
other	1,325	1,982	2,460
total	*7,031*	*16,749*	*21,409*
West			
Arizona		227	412
California		1,423	1,803
Idaho		737	
other		970	
total	*984*	*3,357*	*4,501*

world production is from elemental sulfur, 27½% from pyrites, 10% from smelter gas, and 9% from other sources. In North America, approx 77% is produced from elemental sulfur, 7% from pyrites, 10% from smelter gas, and 6% from other sources.

Distribution of virgin-acid production for 1966 by states and divisions as reported by the Bureau of Census is given in Table 8. Table 8 also shows production in the same areas for 1951 and the installed capacity as of January 1, 1967.

Analysis and Specifications

For 60 and 66°Bé strengths, determination of the specific gravity by means of a Baumé hydrometer is generally employed. Such hydrometers should be graduated at 60°F. For extreme accuracy the 66°Bé hydrometer can be obtained with a 6-in. stem graduated over the range of 63.0–66.5°Bé. The acid should always be tested at about room temperature and a temperature correction applied of 0.026°Bé/deg F on 60°Bé acid, and 0.0235°Bé/deg F on 66°Bé acid. The U.S. Bureau of Standards will check instruments and supply a chart noting corrections to be applied, and these standardized instruments can then be employed to standardize the working instruments.

Table 9. Product Specifications—Commercial Grades

Maximum impurity	60°Bé, 66°Bé, 99% sulfuric acid	Oleum, %		
		20	40	65
hydrochloric acid, %	0.0005	0.0005		
nitric acid, %	0.0005	0.0005		
sulfur dioxide, %	0.015	0.015, 0.015, 0.07		
ammonia, %	0.001			
arsenic trioxide, %	0.00005	0.00005		
iron, %	0.015	0.02		
lead, %	0.005	0.005		
nonvolatile, %	0.05			
color	very slight yellow tint	gray		
turbidity	slightly cloudy	cloudy		

For acid stronger than 66°Bé, the strength is determined by titration of a weighed sample with standard alkali. Since oleum reacts violently with water, the sample should be weighed in a "snake" tube of Pyrex glass with a capillary point. After weighing, while holding the index finger over the open end of the tube, the point is immersed in a casserole of water and the oleum permitted to run slowly into the water, and the empty tube is finally flushed with distilled water. For extreme accuracy, a water-jacketed buret should be employed to avoid temperature changes.

Methods for determination of the impurities in sulfuric acid are fully covered in a Federal Specification, No. 05-801 (24) established by the General Service Administration for all agencies. Although applying specifically to electrolyte acid, it covers all impurities except lead, which is determined colorimetrically by using sodium sulfide to produce a brown coloration.

Standard commercial strengths of sulfuric acid are 60°Bé (77.67%), 66°Bé (93.19%), 99% sulfuric acid, and 20, 40, and 65% oleum. Electrolyte acid for storage batteries is supplied at any strength between sp gr 1.200 (27.24%) and sp gr 1.835 (93.19% or 66°Bé) to meet customer specification. Chemically pure acid is supplied at a strength of 95–96% sulfuric acid to meet ACS specification.

No product specifications have been established other than the purchase specifications issued by the Armed Services and other governmental agencies, covering a few impurities. However, as a result of competitive conditions within the industry, the specifications as given in Table 9 are generally applicable to commercial grades.

Many rayon producers specify an iron content of 0.005% iron for commercial 66°Bé and, for electrolyte acid of 1.835 sp gr, the iron specification is reduced to 0.0042% iron with the following added maximum permissible impurities: platinum, 0.00001%; manganese, 0.00002%; antimony, 0.0001%, nickel, 0.0001%; selenium, 0.002%; zinc, 0.004%; copper, 0.005%; acid colorless and clear.

The commercial grades of sulfuric acid and oleum are shipped in steel drums (returnable), tank trucks, tank cars, and tank barges. In addition, acid below the monohydrate (ie 100% sulfuric acid) is shipped in glass carboys (returnable). Electrolyte quality, 1.835 sp gr, is shipped in specially prepared steel tank trucks, tank cars, and glass carboys. Weaker grades of electrolyte acid and cp sulfuric are shipped in glass containers only.

All shipments must be protected by the DOT white label for corrosive liquids. The labels must be removed from returning empties. All containers must comply with the respective specifications of the Department of Transportation (DOT) and must be marked to show such compliance. The large producers own their own fleets of tank trucks, tank cars, and tank barges and there are several tank-car operating companies from which cars can be leased.

Materials of Construction and Safety

Lines for handling 60°Bé, or less, acid should be of lead. For handling 66°Bé and 99% acid, cast-iron lines are less subject to corrosion than steel, but are not suited to withstand shock. It is, therefore, customary to employ heavy cast-iron flanged pipes and fittings for circulating lines and steel lines for delivery to storage. Steel lines are employed for all strengths of oleum. Steel tanks are used for storage and transportation of all strengths of acid 60°Bé and above, although corrosion is materially greater from 60°Bé acid than at higher strengths, particularly at higher temperatures. Lead must be used for acid weaker than 60°Bé.

Health and Safety

Sulfuric acid is injurious to the skin, mucosa, and eyes. Dangerous quantities of hydrogen may develop in reactions between weakened acid and metals. Sulfuric acid reacts vigorously with organics and reducing agents. It is a strong dehydrating agent.

Those engaged in handling sulfuric acid should obtain information on safe handling and use. Suggested literature, available from Manufacturing Chemists' Association, Inc. (MCA), 1825 Connecticut Avenue, N.W., Washington, D.C., 20009, includes data sheets and the following safety pamphlets:

C- 3	carboy bottle, 13 gal (DOT Spec 1A)
D-31	steel drums (DOT Spec 5A)
SD-20	sulfuric acid
TC- 1	tank cars (DOT Spec 103A)

Much help in promulgating a program for safe handling of acid may be obtained from manufacturers and safety engineers familiar with chemical operations. Containers as received should be carefully inspected and set aside for special handling if defects are found. Manufacturers' recommendations for storage and unloading should be strictly followed. To prevent accumulation of hydrogen in drums, they should be periodically vented. Special precautions are necessary if a tank is to be entered for repair or cleaning. Workers responsible for handling sulfuric acid should wear protective clothing and equipment as described in MCA SD-20. Safety showers, protected against freezing and with deluge heads, should be readily available.

Sulfuric acid has the peculiar property of plugging up lines due to formation of iron or lead sulfates. In dismantling lines and equipment, the assumption should always be made that a spray of acid may occur, and necessary precautions should be taken.

As a general rule, acid should never be diluted by addition of water. The acid should always be poured into the water and this is particularly important in the case of strong acid. Since the dilution is accompanied by a considerable evolution of heat, it should never be carried out in a heavy glass vessel unable to withstand sudden temperature changes.

Table 10. Sulfuric Acid Distribution by End Use

Use	1951		1965[a]		Estimated 1968[b]	
	1000 short tons	% of total	1000 short tons	% of total	1000 short tons	% of total
industrial water treatment			170	0.7	202	0.7
aluminum sulfate, commercial and iron free	413	2.8	580	2.3	643	2.2
chlorine dioxide			120	0.5	211	0.8
tall oil	46	0.3	125	0.5	93	0.3
cellophane (includes cellulose film, sheets or products)			200	0.8	177	0.6
rayon	722	4.9	695	2.7	595	2.1
synthetic detergents and sodium phosphates	214	1.5	510	2.0	427	1.5
superphosphate and phosphatic-type fertilizers	3,850	26.2	9,275	36.1	12,676	44.0
ammonium sulfate, synthetic and chemical by-product	1,218	8.3	1,430	5.6	1,180	4.1
ammonium sulfate, coke oven			537	2.1	635	2.2
benzol (coke oven, light-oil refining only)	75	0.5	47	0.2	40	0.1
iron and steel pickling	975	6.6	1,075	4.2	794	2.8
nonferrous metallurgical purposes, including pickling	205	1.4	275	1.1	316	1.1
copper leaching			345	1.3	345	1.2
uranium leaching and processing			222	0.9	578	2.0
chromium chemicals, including bichromates and chromic acid	87	0.6	85	0.3	89	0.3
titanium dioxide	1,280	8.7	1,900	7.4	1,230	4.3
other inorganic pigments			60	0.2		
explosives, industrial and military (mixed acid included below in other chemicals)	122	0.8	100	0.4	900	3.1
chlorine drying			100	0.4	123	0.4
storage batteries	80	0.6	140	0.5	128	0.4
petroleum catalyst, including clay treatment	148	1.0	300	1.2	350	1.2
aviation and high-test gasoline, petroleum alkylate	952	6.5	1,400	5.4	1,332	4.6
petroleum sulfonates (lube-oil additives)	153	1.0	270	1.0	350	1.3
other petroleum products, excluding sulfonated hydrocarbons and detergents	673	4.6	690	2.7	c	c
rubber, including synthetic	138	0.9	55	0.2	20	0.1
alcohols			665	2.6	706	2.4
dyes and intermediates	309	2.1	330	1.3	392	1.4
pesticides	137	0.9	190	0.7	75	0.3
hydrochloric acid	170	1.2	103	0.4	188	0.6
hydrofluoric acid	131	0.9	710	2.7	675	2.3
boric acids and borates	34	0.3	81	0.3	71	0.2
medicinals	33	0.2	83	0.3	21[c]	0.1[c]
other chemicals	2,002	13.7	2,050	8.0	1,131	3.9
other uses	519	3.5	775	3.0	2,100	7.3
exports			7		12	0.1
total	*14,689*	*100.0*	*25,700*	*100.0*	*28,805*	*100.0*

[a] 1965 data estimated by Business and Defense Services Administration, U.S. Department of Commerce, based on reports from producers for 1963 and 1964 on Form BDSAF-705b.

[b] Estimated from private sources.   [c] Part of consumption included in other uses.

The plant should be provided with a well-equipped hospital room, or first-aid station, under the supervision of a trained nurse. Where the nurse is not provided, selected members of the office or laboratory force should be adequately trained to render first aid while awaiting arrival of doctor or ambulance. A continuing program to teach and enforce safe work habits is essential to safe handling of sulfuric acid.

Uses

Table 10 gives the uses of sulfuric acid.

The fertilizer industry is the largest consumer of sulfuric acid; production of superphosphates accounts for about 36% of the total acid consumption, chiefly from captive plants, and to this must be added another 8% consumed in the production of ammonium sulfate. The chemical industry is the second largest consumer, accounting for approx 21% of total acid consumption. Some of the more important uses are the production of phosphoric acid by the wet process, aluminum sulfate used extensively for water purification and in manufacture of paper, and the rapidly growing petro-chemical industry.

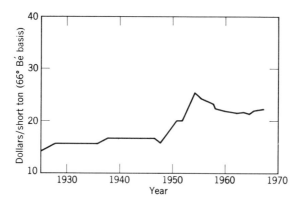

Fig. 20. Price of sulfuric acid.

The petroleum industry is the third-largest consumer, accounting for about 10% of total acid production, of which approx 55% is used in the alkylation process for production of alkylate of high-octane blending power. Sulfuric acid is also used in refining of petroleum distillates for removal of sulfur and gum-forming compounds. Acid used for these purposes is recoverable as a waste acid or acid sludge that may be separated by hydrolysis into an impure acid, or decomposed and converted into clean fresh acid as noted under Special-purpose plants (see p. 474).

Among other important industries consuming large tonnages of sulfuric acid are titanium pigments, steel pickling, rayon, dyes and intermediates, and detergents.

The average yearly wholesale prices, basis 66°Bé, are shown in Figure 20; this illustrates the price stability which in recent years has reflected only increased raw-material costs. The other increased costs have been offset by increased plant capacities, more efficient types of equipment, and automation of operations.

Bibliography

"Sulfuric Acid and Sulfur Trioxide" in *ECT* 1st ed., Vol. 13, pp. 458–506, by B. M. Carter and Gregory Flint (Sulfur Trioxide), General Chemical Division, Allied Chemical & Dye Corporation.

1. W. Wyld, *Raw Materials for the Manufacture of Sulphuric Acid, and the Manufacture of Sulphur Dioxide*, Vol. 1 of A. C. Cumming, ed., *Lunge Series on the Manufacture of Acids and Alkalis*, D. Van Nostrand Co., Inc., New York, 1923, pp. 3, 379.
2. W. Wyld, *Manufacture of Sulphuric Acid (Chamber Process)*, Vol. 2 of A. C. Cumming, ed., *Lunge Series on the Manufacture of Acids and Alkalis*, Gurney and Jackson, London, 1924, p. 144.
3. K. Knietsch, *Ber.* **34**, 4069 (1902).
4. F. D. Miles, *Manufacture of Sulphuric Acid (Contact Process)*, Vol. 4 of A. C. Cumming, ed., *Lunge Series on the Manufacture of Acids and Alkalis*, D. Van Nostrand Co., Inc., New York, 1925, p. 348.
5. E. W. Washburn, ed., *International Critical Tables of Physics, Chemistry and Technology*, Vol. III, McGraw-Hill Book Co., Inc., New York, 1928, p. 56.
6. J. H. Perry, *Chemical Engineers Handbook*, 3rd ed., McGraw-Hill Book Co., Inc., New York, 1950, pp. 168, 169, 234.
7. A. S. Socolik, *Z. Physik. Chem.* **158A**, 305 (1932).
8. F. C. Zeisberg, *Chem. Met. Eng.* **27**, 22 (1922); *Trans. Am. Inst. Chem. Engrs.* **14**, 1 (1922).
9. J. W. Mellor, *Comprehensive Treatise on Inorganic and Theoretical Chemistry*, Vol. X, Longmans, Green & Co., New York, 1930, pp. 353, 391, 410.
10. F. D. Miles, H. Niblock, and G. L. Wilson, *Trans. Faraday Soc.* **36**, 350 (1940).
11. F. D. Miles, H. Niblock, and D. Smith, *Trans. Faraday Soc.* **40**, 287 (1944).
12. *Sulphur* **77**, 36 (1968); **74**, 27 (1968).
13. *Sulphur* **66**, 32 (1966); **58**, 17 (1965).
14. U.S. Pat. 2,785,050 (March 12, 1957), J. W. Swaine et al. (to Allied Chemical Corp.).
15. *Sulphur* **75**, 34 (1968).
16. A. M. Fairlie, *Sulfuric Acid Manufacture*, Reinhold Publishing Corp., New York, 1936.
17. J. W. Parker, *Concentration of Sulphuric Acid*, Vol. 3 of A. C. Cumming, ed., *Lunge Series on the Manufacture of Acids and Alkalis*, D. Van Nostrand Co., Inc., New York, 1924.
18. U.S. Pat. 1,384,566 (July 12, 1921), H. F. Merriam (to General Chemical Co.).
19. U.S. Pat. 1,371,004 (March 8, 1921), F. Slama and H. Wolf (to General Chemical Co.) (Reissue 19,282, Aug. 21, 1934).
20. *Sulphur* **54**, 30 (1964); **75**, 36 (1968).
21. U.S. Pat. 1,789,460 (Jun. 20, 1931), C. B. Clark (to General Chemical Co.)
22. C. F. Scheidel, *Sulphur Dioxide Removal from Tail Gas by Sulfacid Process*, Preprint 6E, Am. Inst. Chem. Engrs., Dec. 1–5, 1968.
23. U.S. Pat. 3,160,474 (Dec. 8, 1964), W. G. Schnoor et al. (to Allied Chemical Corp.).
24. *Federal Specification No. 05-801*, U.S. Govt. Printing Office, Washington, D.C., Aug. 1952.

T. S. HARRER
Allied Chemical Corporation

SULFURIC AND SULFUROUS ESTERS

The esters of sulfuric and sulfurous acids, particularly the former, are familiar reagents employed in organic chemistry. Since both of these acids are dibasic, a variety of esters are possible and known. Replacement of one hydrogen leads to acid esters; both hydrogens can be replaced by the same, dissimilar, or bifunctional aliphatic groups to give dialkyl esters or cyclic esters. Furthermore, the related alkyl acid halides, in which one hydroxyl group is replaced by a halogen atom, are well known. Table 1 illustrates the variety of compounds available. CA nomenclature is not followed here consistently, because it is rather cumbersome.

Table 1. Various Types of Sulfuric and Sulfurous Esters

CH_3OSO_2OH	H_2NOSO_3H	$CH_3OSO_2OCH_3$	CH_3OSO_2Cl
methyl hydrogen sulfate	hydroxylamine-O-sulfonic acid	dimethyl-sulfate	methyl chloro-sulfate
CH_3OSOOH	$CH_3OSOOCH_3$		CH_3OSOCl
methyl hydrogen sulfite	dimethyl sulfite		methyl chlorosulfinate

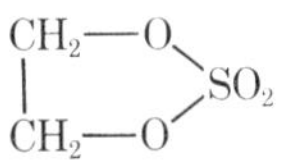

ethylene sulfate

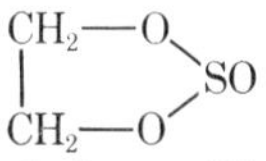

ethylene sulfite

glyoxal sulfate

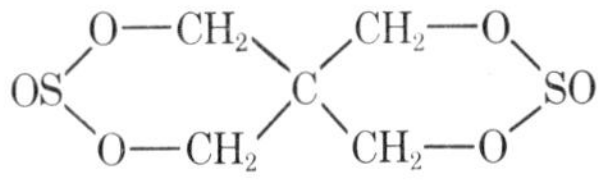

pentaerythritol sulfite

Physical Properties

The lower **alkyl hydrogen sulfates** are oily, low-melting liquids; higher alkyl hydrogen sulfates are hygroscopic, low-melting solids. Their melting points are listed in Table 2. Stability on storage depends apparently on the purity of the individual compound; purer materials have longer shelf-life (1).

Table 2. Melting Points of Alkyl Hydrogen Sulfates

Alkyl group	Melting point, °C	Alkyl group	Melting point, °C
n-decyl	oil	n-hexadecyl	40–42
n-dodecyl	25–27	n-octadecyl	51–52
n-tetradecyl	37–39		

The anhydrous compounds are soluble in ether, the monohydrates are insoluble. Solutions in water are strongly ionized.

The lower **alkyl sulfates** are liquids with pleasant odors; n-nonyl and higher normal aliphatic and cyclic sulfates are solids. Boiling and melting points are listed in Tables 3 and 3a, respectively. The sulfates dissolve readily in the common organic solvents and, for the most part, can be considered insoluble in water. Dimethyl sulfate has a water solubility of 2.8 g/100 ml at 18°C (2).

The alkyl hydrogen sulfites are quite unstable and very little is known of their reactions or properties.

The **alkyl sulfites** have been studied far less than the sulfates. Most are liquids of slightly lower boiling points (see Table 4) than the corresponding sulfates. Aromatic polysulfites are reported to have low intrinsic viscosities and low melting points and are not crystalline (3).

Table 3. Boiling Points of Alkyl Sulfates

Alkyl group	Formula	Boiling point, $^\circ C_{mm\,Hg}$
dimethyl	$(CH_3O)_2SO_2$	190.5_{760}
		$69-70_{10}$
diethyl	$(C_2H_5O)_2SO_2$	208_{760}
		89_9
di-*n*-propyl	$(CH_3(CH_2)_2O)_2SO_2$	95_5
diisopropyl	$((CH_3)CHO)_2SO_2$	80_4
di-*n*-butyl	$(CH_3(CH_2)_3O)_2SO_2$	$103_{1.5}$
methyl ethyl	$CH_3OSO_2OC_2H_5$	85_{15}
ethyl *n*-propyl	$C_2H_5OSO_2O(CH_2)_2CH_3$	107_{18}
ethyl *n*-butyl	$C_2H_5OSO_2O(CH_2)_3CH_3$	117_{20}
bischloromethyl	$(ClCH_2O)_2SO_2$	97_{14}
bis(2-chloroethyl)	$(Cl(CH_2)_2O)_2SO_2$	150_7
methyl chloromethyl	$ClCH_2OSO_2OCH_3$	92_{18}

Table 3a. Melting Points of Alkyl Sulfates

Alkyl group	Formula	Melting point, $^\circ C$
didecyl	$(CH_3(CH_2)_9O)_2SO_2$	37.7
ditetradecyl	$(CH_3(CH_2)_{13}O)_2SO_2$	58.0
methylene		155
ethylene		99
1,3-propylene		63
glyoxal		176

Because of the pyramidal arrangement of the oxygen atoms about the sulfur and because the sulfite group does not execute a thermal vibration causing inversion of its configuration, isomers are possible. This was demonstrated with the aid of proton magnetic resonance and by the isolation of the cis and trans forms of 2-chloro-1,3-propylene sulfite ((**1**) and (**2**), respectively) by fractional distillation and by the separation of *cis*- and *trans*-1,2 propylene sulfite ((**3**) and (**4**), respectively) by vapor-phase chromatography (4,5).

Cis forms   *Trans forms*

(**1**)   (**2**)

(**3**)   (**4**)

A large number of **alkyl halosulfurates** and **halosulfinates** are known. Some of them and their boiling points are listed in Table 5. The lower members are high-

Table 4. Boiling Points of Alkyl Sulfites

Alkyl group	Formula	Boiling point, $°C_{mm Hg}$
dimethyl	$(CH_3O)_2SO$	$126–127_{760}$
diethyl	$(C_2H_5O)_2SO$	$159–160_{760}$
di-*n*-propyl	$(CH_3(CH_2)_2O)_2SO$	82_{15}
diisopropyl	$((CH_3)_2CHO)_2SO$	78_{20}
di-*n*-butyl	$(CH_3(CH_2)_3O)_2SO$	110_{13}
methyl ethyl	$CH_3OSOOC_2H_5$	$140–142_{760}$
n-butyl *n*-propyl	$CH_3(CH_2)_2OSOO(CH_2)_3CH_3$	104_{15}
bis(3-chloro-*n*-propyl)	$(Cl(CH_2)_3CHO)_2SO$	162_{13}
bis(2-chloroethyl)	$(ClCH_2CH_2O)_2SO$	148_{45}
ethylene		80_{28}
1,2-propylene		84_{28}
2,3-butylene		72_{12}
pentaerythritol, di-		154^a

a Melting point.

boiling liquids and have a penetrating odor and a strong lacrymatory action. The alkyl halosulfurates appear to be much more stable to storage and moisture than the alkyl halosulfinates.

Table 5. Alkyl Halosulfurates and Sulfinates

Alkyl halo group	Formula	Boiling point, °C$_{mm\,Hg}$
sulfurates		
methyl chloro	CH_3OSO_2Cl	42_{16}; $134-135_{760}$
methyl fluoro	CH_3OSO_2F	45_{160}; 92_{760}
ethyl chloro	$C_2H_5OSO_2Cl$	58_{20}; 72_{117}
ethyl fluoro	$C_2H_5OSO_2F$	24_{12}; 113_{752}
n-propyl chloro	$CH_3(CH_2)_2OSO_2Cl$	53_{10}
isopropyl chloro	$(CH_3)_2CHOSO_2Cl$	50_5 (dec)
sulfinates		
methyl chloro	CH_3OSOCl	35_{60}
ethyl chloro	C_2H_5OSOCl	$50-53_{60}$
n-propyl chloro	$CH_3(CH_2)_2OSOCl$	42_{12}; 78_{75}
isopropyl chloro	$(CH_3)_2CHOSOCl$	55_{40}; $71-73_{75}$
isobutyl chloro	$(CH_3)_2CHCH_2OSOCl$	48.5_9

Chemical Properties

Commercially, the most important reaction of **alkyl hydrogen sulfates** is hydrolysis to alcohols, particularly ethanol, isopropyl alcohol, and *sec*-butyl alcohol.

Heating alkyl hydrogen sulfates generally yields unsaturated hydrocarbons; however, the methyl ester is converted at 130–140°C to dimethyl sulfate and sulfuric acid.

Alkali salts of alkyl hydrogen sulfates have been used as alkylating agents as illustrated below:

$$ROSO_2ONa + NaNO_2 \rightarrow RNO_2 + RONO \text{ (in low yields)} \tag{6}$$

$$ROSO_2OK + KCN \rightarrow RNC + RCN \text{ (in low yields)} \tag{7}$$

$$ROSO_2ONa + NaSH \rightarrow RSH + RSR \tag{8}$$

$$ROSO_2ONa + R'COOH \rightarrow R'COOR \tag{9}$$

2-Aminoethyl hydrogen sulfate gives an intramolecular alkylation at 120–140°C under pressure to ethylenimine (10). (See Imines.)

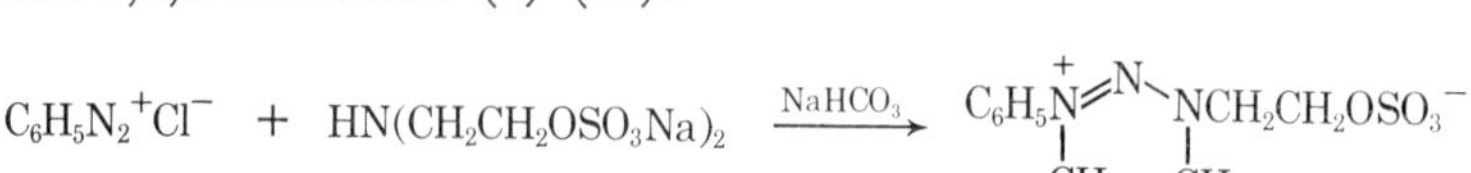

$$H_2NCH_2CH_2OSO_3H + 2\,NaOH \longrightarrow \underset{NH}{CH_2—CH_2} + Na_2SO_4 + 2\,H_2O$$

The reaction of 2-carbamoylethyl hydrogen sulfate, $H_2NCOCH_2CH_2OSO_3H$, with aliphatic and heterocyclic amines leads to carbamoylethyl alkylation with the formation of 2-carbamoylethylamines (11).

The bis(hydrogen sulfate) of diethanolamine couples in basic medium with diazoamino compounds of aromatic diazonium salts with the formation of 1,3-disubstituted 1,2,3-triazolines (5) (12).

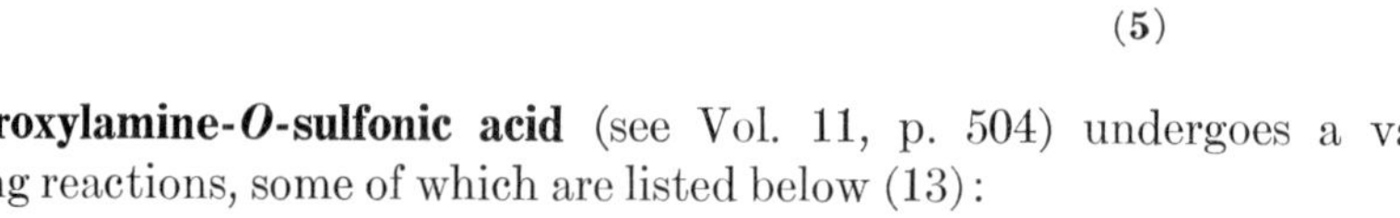

$$C_6H_5N_2{}^+Cl^- + HN(CH_2CH_2OSO_3Na)_2 \xrightarrow{NaHCO_3} C_6H_5\overset{+}{N}{=}N\text{-}NCH_2CH_2OSO_3{}^-$$
$$\underset{CH_2—CH_2}{|\qquad|}$$
$$(5)$$

Hydroxylamine-*O*-sulfonic acid (see Vol. 11, p. 504) undergoes a variety of interesting reactions, some of which are listed below (13):

$$(CH_2)_5CO + H_2NOSO_3H + NaOH \rightarrow (CH_2)_5C \begin{matrix} NH \\ | \\ O \end{matrix}$$

cyclohexanone   3,3-pentamethylene-
                                       oxazirane

$$(CH_2)_5CO + H_2NOSO_3H + NH_3 \rightarrow (CH_2)_5C \begin{matrix} NH \\ | \\ NH \end{matrix}$$

3,3-pentamethylene-
diaziridine

$$(CH_2)_5CO + H_2NOSO_3H + CH_3NH_2 \rightarrow$$
$$(CH_2)_5CO + CH_3NHOSO_3H + NH_3 \rightarrow \quad (CH_2)_5C \begin{matrix} NCH_3 \\ | \\ NH \end{matrix}$$

1-methyl-3,3-pentamethylene-
diaziridine

Of the many **alkyl sulfates** known, only dimethyl and diethyl sulfate are of commercial importance. They are used as alkylating agents for the preparation of methyl- and ethyl-substituted oxygen, nitrogen, and sulfur compounds.

The reaction of dimethyl sulfate with phenol proceeds slowly at 100–120°C with the evolution of methyl ether and the formation of anisole, $C_6H_5OCH_3$, and sulfonation products (14). The alkylation, however, is much cleaner in basic medium. The best results are obtained in the presence of very little water, by adding the dimethyl sulfate to a mixture of molten phenol and sodium hydroxide at 45–60°C. Under these condition one methyl group reacts. Continued heating at 100°C causes the second methyl group to react and a 95% yield of anisole is consistently obtained (15). A large number of phenols have been alkylated either in aqueous or alcoholic alkaline solutions. Alkylation with diethyl sulfate generally requires higher temperatures. The first ethyl group is removed at 50–55°C, while 145°C is necessary for the second ethyl group to react. Thiophenols are also very readily alkylated in alkaline solutions with dialkyl sulfates (16).

One methyl group is utilized for the *C*-alkylation of the sodium salt of ethyl acetoacetate, or of ethyl malonate (17), but refluxing molar quantities of ethyl acetoacetate with dimethyl sulfate produces a 36% yield of ethyl 3-methoxycrotonate besides a 30% yield of the *C*-methylated product of the acetoacetate (18).

Aliphatic and aromatic amines are readily alkylated, but usually only one of the alkyl groups of the sulfate is utilized. A large number of quarternary ammonium compounds have been prepared from tertiary amines and nitrogen heterocyclics with dialkyl sulfates.

The first alkyl group of dimethyl and diethyl sulfate reacts with organic acids at 120°C to give esters in high yield. The second alkyl group reacts at 200°C. This method of esterification, especially when catalyzed by tertiary amines, is simple, rapid, and useful when the preparation of diazomethane is not feasible or when strongly acid conditions must be avoided (19).

Alkali salts of carboxylic acids are readily converted in aqueous solutions (20) or in an organic solvent (21) with dimethyl sulfate to the corresponding esters. Even methyl esters of sulfonic acids can be made by heating their salts with dimethyl sulfate (22).

Dimethyl sulfate alkylates *N,N*-dialkylamides at the oxygen to give complexes of the type (**6**), which react with alcoholates to give *O,N*-acetals (**7**) and with secondary amines to give tetralkylamidinium methylsulfates (8). The latter are transformed with sodium hydride into ketene aminals (9) (23).

$$\left[RCH_2C \begin{array}{c} OCH_3 \\ N(CH_3)_2 \end{array} \right]^+ \quad CH_3OSO_3^-$$

(6)

$$\underset{R'ONa}{\swarrow} \qquad \underset{R_2'NH}{\downarrow}$$

$$RCH = C \begin{array}{c} OR' \\ N(CH_3)_2 \end{array} \qquad \left[RCH_2C \begin{array}{c} NR_2' \\ N(CH_3)_2 \end{array} \right]^+ CH_3OSO_3^- \xrightarrow{\text{NaH}} RCH = C \begin{array}{c} NR_2' \\ N(CH_3)_2 \end{array}$$

(7)　　　　　　　　　　　(8)　　　　　　　　　　　　　　　(9)

Aromatic hydrocarbons, such as benzene or biphenyl, react with alkyl sulfates in the presence of aluminum chloride to form the alkylated hydrocarbons (24). The higher esters, such as di-n-butyl sulfate, behave like the alkyl halides, and a mixture of isomeric alkylated hydrocarbons results.

Phenyllithium (25) and the sodium naphthalene complex (see Sodium) (26) are alkylated with alkyl and cyclic sulfates. Aromatic Grignard reagents behave similarly, but require two moles of dimethyl sulfate for complete reaction (27). Sodium acetylide, when treated with alkyl sulfates, gives the corresponding substituted acetylene, as shown in the following equation:

$$(n\text{-}C_3H_7O)_2SO_2 + NaC\equiv CH \rightarrow n\text{-}C_3H_7C\equiv CH + n\text{-}C_3H_7OSO_2ONa$$

The alkali salts of inorganic acids, when treated with alkyl sulfates, yield the expected products. Dimethyl sulfate and sodium iodide give methyl iodide, and ethyl isocyanate is obtained in 95% yield by heating diethyl sulfate with dry potassium cyanate (28).

Several highly colored organoxy–titanium methyl sulfates are obtained by treating dimethyl sulfate with an organoxy–titanium dichloride (29).

By employing ^{18}O-enriched water, it was shown that the first stage-hydrolysis of dialkyl sulfates occurs under acidic and alkaline conditions almost completely at the alkyl–oxygen linkage (30). Ethylene sulfate, trimethylene sulfate, and dimethyl sulfate undergo first-order solvolysis to the corresponding monoesters in aqueous solution from pH 2 to 9 with the relative rates of 12:1:6 (31); the cyclic catechol sulfate hydrolyzes in alkali 2×10^7 times faster than the linear diphenyl sulfate (32).

The literature concerning the **dialkyl sulfites** is not as extensive as that of the sulfates, but similar reactions are reported (33). Phenols and amines are alkylated by sulfites in excellent yield, much like the sulfates. Quarternary salts of corresponding types are obtained with ease (34).

Ethylene sulfite in many instances can be substituted for ethylene oxide as a reagent for replacing the hydrogen of phenolic or amine groups with the 2-hydroxyethyl group, as shown in the reaction with 2-naphthol:

$$C_{10}H_7OH + OCH_2CH_2OSO \xrightarrow{90-100°C} C_{10}H_7OCH_2CH_2OH + SO_2$$

Two adjacent hydroxyl groups can react to give a cyclic compound in the following manner:

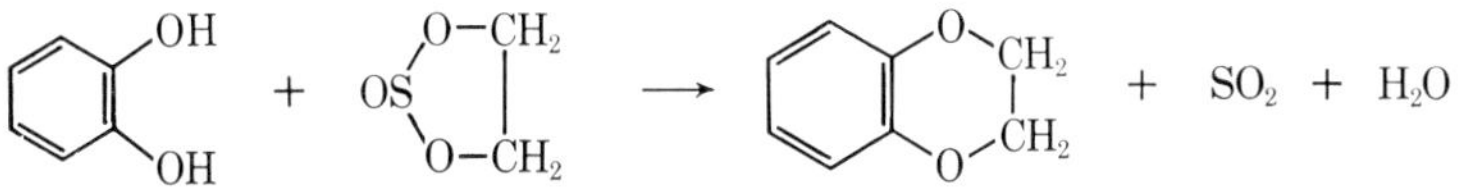

p-Nitrophenyl esters of various organic acids are prepared by the use of a base and p-nitrophenyl sulfite. Unsymmetrical sulfites, $RR'SO_3$, react at R, where R is p-nitrophenyl and R' is ethyl or phenyl (35). The p-toluenesulfonates of methyl and benzyl esters of certain amino acids can be obtained in high yields by the action of methyl and benzyl sulfites on the amino acid in the presence of p-toluenesulfonic acid (36).

Dialkyl sulfites hydrolyze under acidic and alkaline conditions solely by S–O fission as determined by mass spectrometric analysis of the alcohol produced in ${}^{18}O$-enriched water (37). The rate of hydrolysis is generally faster for cyclic and aryl sulfites than for dialkyl sulfites (38).

Pyrolysis of 2,3-butylene sulfite gives some 2,3-butene oxide (39), but other sulfites of 1,2-glycols produce ketones from the cis isomers (10) and aldehydes from the trans isomers (11) (40), as shown below:

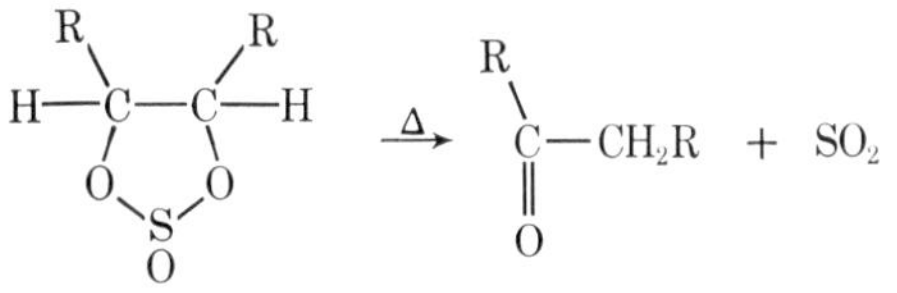

(10)

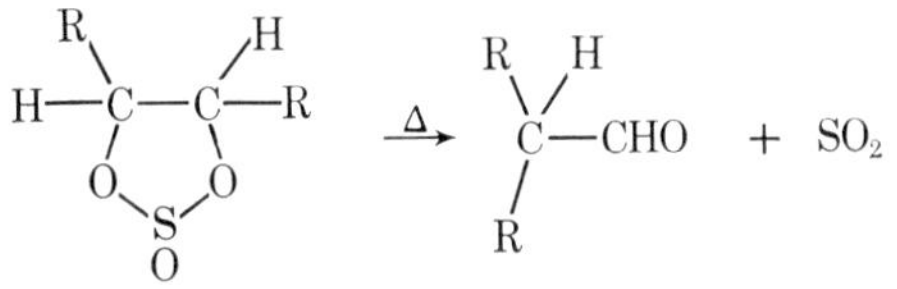

(11)

Various sulfites of 1,3-glycols give mainly tarry materials upon pyrolysis; however, an oxetane (12) is obtained in small yield from pentaerythritol disulfite (41).

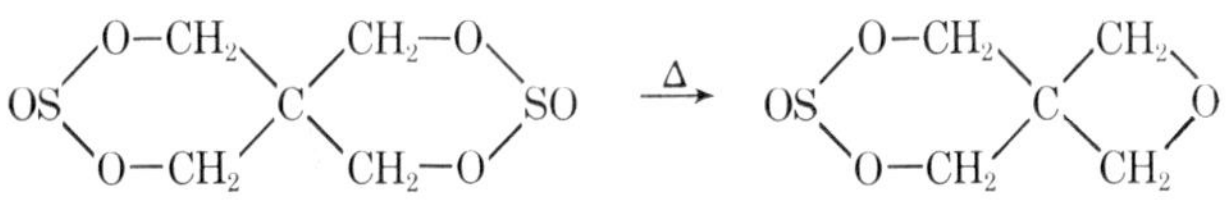

(12)

The reaction of dialkyl and cyclic sulfites with boron trichloride gives alkyl halosulfinates (42).

$$(C_4H_9O)_2SO + BCl_3 \rightarrow C_4H_9OSOCl + C_4H_9OBCl_2$$

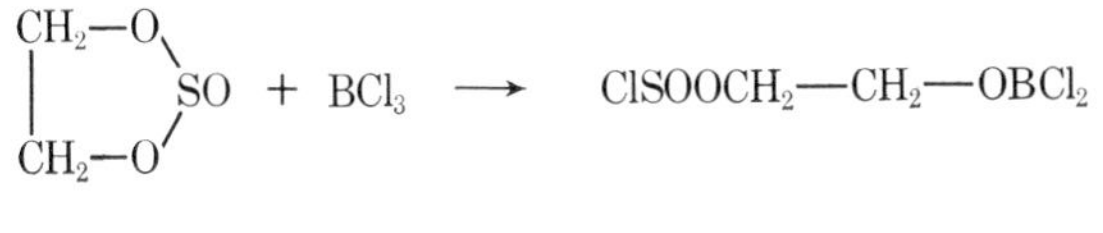

Mixed alkyl sulfites are decomposed to symmetrical sulfites, alkenes, sulfur dioxide, and some chlorine-containing compounds when saturated with dry HCl at room temperature (43).

Cyclic sulfites, such as ethylene sulfite, are also decomposed by triphenylphosphine into olefin, sulfur dioxide, and triphenylphosphine oxide (44).

Di-n-alkyl sulfites, whose combined alkyl residue contains at least eight carbon atoms, form urea adducts usable for the preparation of the pure sulfites (45).

Halosulfurates and **halosulfinates** are mainly employed for the synthesis of symmetrical or unsymmetrical esters, as discussed below.

Tertiary bases, such as pyridine or dimethylaniline, react with halosulfonates, even at $-80°C$, as follows:

$$ROSO_2Cl + base \rightarrow RCl + base.SO_3$$

Therefore such bases cannot be used in the preparation of ordinary halosulfurates from the alcohol and sulfuryl chloride. Only where the carbon attached to the oxygen atom has low susceptibility to nucleophilic attack, such as in $R = CF_3CH_2—$, $CCl_3CH_2—$, $C_6H_5—$, or p-$CH_3C_6H_4—$, can a tertiary base be employed (46).

Manufacture

The **hydrogen sulfates** are prepared by the action of a sulfating agent on the corresponding alcohol or phenol. The following reagents are used for sulfation: sulfur trioxide, sulfuric acid, chlorosulfuric acid, sulfur trioxide–amine complexes, and amidosulfuric acid (see Sulfamates). The latter two produce the amine salts of the sulfate ester directly. The reaction of sulfuric acid with olefins gives hydrogen sulfates. These reactions are commercially important for the preparation of ethyl, 2-propyl, 2-butyl, and longer-chain sodium alkyl sulfates, which are useful as detergents. With the exception of ethylene, the olefins give esters of secondary alcohols.

Methyl hydrogen sulfate may be obtained in yields of 98–99% by treating sulfur trioxide with methanol below $0°C$ (47).

The sulfation of ethylene with sulfuric acid to the hydrogen sulfate, followed by the addition of water to the reaction mixture and hydrolysis, is usually carried out with 96–98% sulfuric acid at 70–80°C under 5–15 atm pressure. The kinetics of this reaction have been thoroughly investigated (48). However, operating at 150°C and higher pressures with only 70% acid, followed by addition of just enough water for hydrolysis, eliminates the otherwise necessary reconcentration of the spent sulfuric acid (49). Because of the severe corrosion under these conditions, tantalum equipment is necessary. Ethyl hydrogen sulfate can be prepared in 87% yield by heating sodium hydrogen sulfate with ethanol (50); a 74–86% yield is obtained by reacting ethanol with sulfur trioxide in liquid sulfur dioxide solution (51), or by treating diethyl sulfate with ethanol and distilling off the ether in vacuo.

$$(C_2H_5O)_2SO_2 + C_2H_5OH \rightarrow (C_2H_5)_2O + C_2H_5OSO_3H$$

Propylene and butylene require much milder conditions for their sulfation with sulfuric acid (49). Butylene is sulfated at 30–50°C and 3–6 atm with 30–60% sulfuric acid, propylene at 10–30°C and 5 atm with 65–85% sulfuric acid. The rate of sulfation of propylene increases sharply with increasing pressure (52). It can also be increased by the addition of kerosene, which raises the concentration of olefin in the liquid phase (53).

Detergents have been manufactured from long-chain alkenes and sulfuric acid, especially those obtained from shale oil or by cracking of petroleum wax. These are sulfated with 90–98% acid at 10–15°C, a 5-min contact time, and an acid/alkene molar ratio of 2:1 (54). Dialkyl sulfate is initially formed when 96% acid is added to 1-dodecene at 0°C, but it is subsequently converted to the hydrogen sulfate in 80% yield upon the further addition of sulfuric acid. The yield can be increased to 90% by using 98% sulfuric acid and pentane as solvent at −15°C (55).

Long-chain alcohols, such as are obtained by the hydrogenation of coconut oil, by polymerization of ethylene, or by the oxo process, are sulfated on a large scale with sulfur trioxide or chlorosulfonic acid to acid sulfates, the alkali salts of which are commercially important as surface-active agents. (See Surfactants; Sulfonation and sulfation.)

Poly(vinyl alcohol) can be sulfated in pyridine with chlorosulfuric acid to the hydrogen sulfate (56).

Some substituted alkyl hydrogen sulfates are readily prepared. For example, 2-chloroethyl hydrogen sulfate is obtained by treating ethylene chlorohydrin with sulfuric acid or amidosulfuric acid. Heating hydrosulfates of amino alcohols produces the corresponding sulfuric monoester (57).

Since phenolic compounds are easily sulfonated, their sulfation must be accomplished with milder sulfating agents, such as complexes of sulfur trioxide with trimethylamine (58), dimethylformamide (59), pyridine (60), or dimethylaniline (61), in anhydrous or aqueous medium below 100°C.

Salts of alkyl hydrogen sulfates, free of sulfuric acid, may be prepared from crude hydrogen sulfates (containing $ROSO_3H$ and sulfuric acid) in a two-step reaction: First, the crude product is reacted in aqueous solution with the hydroxide or carbonate of a metal whose sulfate is insoluble in water. After filtration of the insoluble metal sulfate, the necessary amount of a water-soluble metal sulfate is added to the filtrate, which precipitates the insoluble metal sulfate, leaving the desired salt of the alkyl hydrogen sulfate in solution.

Dialkyl sulfates up to octadecyl can be made from the alcohols by a general method employing the following reactions (62):

$$ROH + SO_2Cl_2 \rightarrow ROSO_2Cl + HCl$$

$$2\ ROH + SOCl_2 \rightarrow (RO)_2SO + 2\ HCl$$

$$ROSO_2Cl + (RO)_2SO \rightarrow (RO)_2SO_2 + RCl + SO_2$$

Another method uses the reaction of dialkyl sulfites with sulfuryl chloride (63).

$$2\ (RO)_2SO + SO_2Cl_2 \rightarrow (RO)_2SO_2 + 2\ ROSOCl$$

Mixed esters are synthesized by the reaction of one alkyl hydrogen sulfate with a different sodium alkoxide or a different dialkyl sulfite (64), as follows:

$$ROSO_2Cl + NaOR' \rightarrow ROSO_2OR' + NaCl$$

$$ROSO_2Cl + (R'O)_2SO \rightarrow ROSO_2OR' + R'Cl + SO_2$$

The only dialkyl sulfates of commercial importance are dimethyl sulfate and diethyl sulfate. *Dimethyl sulfate* was initially made by vacuum pyrolysis of methyl hydrogen sulfate.

$$2\ CH_3OSO_3H \rightarrow (CH_3O)_2SO_2 + H_2SO_4$$

Table 6. Properties of Commercial Dimethyl Sulfate

Property	Value
acidity as H_2SO_4, %	0.07
boiling range, °C at 760 mm Hg	
95%	190.5
96%	192.0
1–97%	4.0
color[a]	passes $0.0001N$ iodine, max
sp gr 15.65/15.65°C	1.334

[a]This test is a visual comparison of the color of dimethyl sulfate witht hat of a $0.0001N$ iodine solution. Commercial dimethyl sulfate should be lighter in color.

Later it was synthesized in a batch process from dimethyl ether and sulfur trioxide (65). It is now made by this process, adapted for continuous operation (66). Gaseous dimethyl ether (33.6 lb/hr) is bubbled into the bottom of an aluminum tower (8 in. diam, 12 ft high), filled with the reaction product dimethyl sulfate. Liquid sulfur trioxide (58.4 lb/hr) is introduced at the top of the tower. The mildly exo-thermic reaction is controlled at 45–47°C. The reaction product (96–97% dimethyl sulfate, sulfuric acid, and methyl hydrogen sulfate) is continuously withdrawn and purified by vacuum distillation over sodium sulfate. The yield is almost quantitative and the product is a clear, colorless, mobile liquid. Properties are listed in Table 6.

Diethyl sulfate can be prepared by a variety of methods. When ethyl hydrogen sulfate is heated with sodium chloride to 80°C, hydrogen chloride is liberated. The resulting reaction mixture is then distilled at 10–15 mm pressure at a maximum kettle temperature of 190°C to give diethyl sulfate in 90% yield (67).

$$2 \, C_2H_5OSO_3H + NaCl \rightarrow C_2H_5OSO_3H + C_2H_5OSO_3Na + HCl\uparrow \rightarrow (C_2H_5O)_2SO_2 + NaHSO_4$$

By passing a stream of nitrogen at 95–100°C through a reaction mixture of ethyl ether and 30% oleum, prepared at 15°C, diethyl sulfate can be entrained. Continu-ous operation gives over 50% yield (68). The most economical process for the manu-facture of diethyl sulfate starts with ethylene and 96% sulfuric acid, heated at 60°C. The resulting mixture of 43% diethyl sulfate, 45% ethyl hydrogen sulfate, and 12% sulfuric acid is heated with anhydrous sodium sulfate under vacuum and diethyl sulfate is obtained in a yield of 86% (69). The purity of the commercial product is over 99%.

Dimethyl and diethyl sulfate are available in a variety of containers from glass bottles of 1-lb capacity to tank cars. The price of dimethyl and diethyl sulfate in tank-car quantities in December 1968 was 15 and 18.5¢/lb, respectively.

Diethyl sulfate has relatively low toxicity and is considered noncorrosive, but dimethyl sulfate is classified as a corrosive liquid and ICC regulations, no exemptions, must be observed. Dimethyl sulfate is manufactured by E. I. du Pont de Nemours & Co., Inc., and diethyl sulfate by Union Carbide Corp.

Cyclic sulfates can be prepared by a variety of methods. Ethylene sulfate is obtained in low yield from ethylene oxide and sulfur trioxide (70). "Methylene sulfate" is produced from formaldehyde and sulfur trioxide (71), as follows:

$$2 \, CH_2O \;+\; 2 \, SO_3 \;\longrightarrow\; \begin{array}{c} O—SO_2—O \\ CH_2 \qquad\qquad CH_2 \\ O—SO_2—O \end{array}$$

Oxidation of cyclic sulfites with permanganate in acetic acid solution gives cyclic sulfates (72). Heating monohydroxyalkyl hydrogen sulfates with thionyl chloride causes ring closure (73), as shown below:

$$HOCH_2CH_2OSO_3H \ + \ SOCl_2 \ \longrightarrow \ \overline{OCH_2CH_2OSO_2}$$

Acidolysis of cyclic sulfites with sulfuric acid (74) and ester interchange with dimethyl sulfate (75) produce cyclic sulfates.

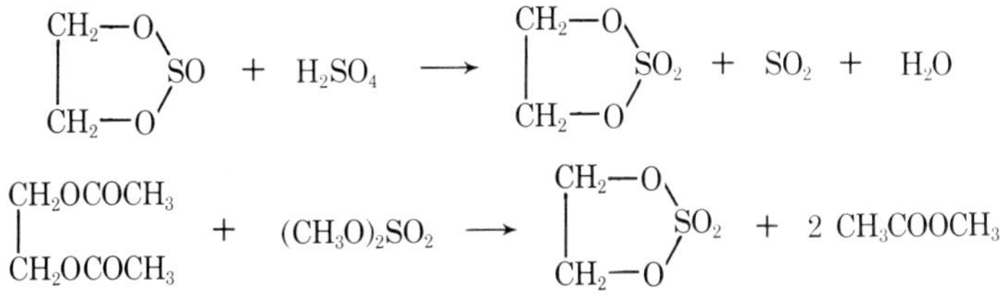

$$\begin{array}{c} CH_2{-}O \\ | \qquad\quad SO \\ CH_2{-}O \end{array} + \ H_2SO_4 \ \longrightarrow \ \begin{array}{c} CH_2{-}O \\ | \qquad\quad SO_2 \\ CH_2{-}O \end{array} + \ SO_2 \ + \ H_2O$$

$$\begin{array}{c} CH_2OCOCH_3 \\ | \\ CH_2OCOCH_3 \end{array} + \ (CH_3O)_2SO_2 \ \longrightarrow \ \begin{array}{c} CH_2{-}O \\ | \qquad\quad SO_2 \\ CH_2{-}O \end{array} + \ 2 \ CH_3COOCH_3$$

Symmetrical or mixed **dialkyl sulfites** are prepared by the stepwise reaction of thionyl chloride either with two molecules of an alcohol or with molar quantities of two alcohols in pyridine (76).

$$ROH + SOCl_2 + C_6H_5N \rightarrow ROSOCl + C_6H_5.HCl$$

$$R'OH + ROSOCl + C_6H_5N \rightarrow R'OSOOR + C_6H_5.HCl$$

Heating the adduct of ethylene oxide and sulfur dioxide with primary alcohols in the presence of alkali hydrides or a transition metal halide (77) yields dialkyl sulfites. Another method for the preparation of methyl alkyl sulfites consists of the reaction of diazomethane with alcoholic solutions of sulfur dioxide (78).

$$ROH + CH_2N_2 + SO_2 \rightarrow ROSOOCH_3 + N_2$$

Cyclic sulfites can be prepared from the glycols and thionyl chloride in the presence of pyridine, analogous to the preparation of dialkyl sulfites (79). Cyclic sulfites are also obtained when the polymerization product of alkylene oxides with sulfur dioxide is decomposed by heating (80).

Aromatic polysulfites can be produced when bisphenols, such as 2,2-(4,4'-dihydroxydiphenyl)propane, are heated with diphenyl sulfite in the presence of lithium hydride (81).

$$(CH_3)_2C(C_6H_4OH)_2 + (C_6H_5O)_2 SO \rightarrow (-SOOC_6H_4C(CH_3)_2C_6H_4O-)_x + C_6H_5OH$$

A general method for the preparation of alkyl **halosulfurates** and **halosulfinates** is the treatment of the alcohol with sulfuryl or thionyl chloride at low temperature, while passing an inert gas through the mixture to remove hydrogen chloride (82).

$$ROH + SO_2Cl_2 \rightarrow ROSO_2Cl + HCl$$

$$ROH + SOCl_2 \rightarrow ROSOCl + HCl$$

This method is also used with alcohols of the structure $Cl(CH_2)_nOH$ (83). Haloalkyl chlorosulfurates are likewise obtained by the reaction of halogenated alkanes with sulfur trioxide (84), or by the chlorination of cyclic sulfites (85).

$$ClCH_2CH_2Cl \ + \ SO_3 \ \longrightarrow \ ClCH_2CH_2OSO_2Cl$$

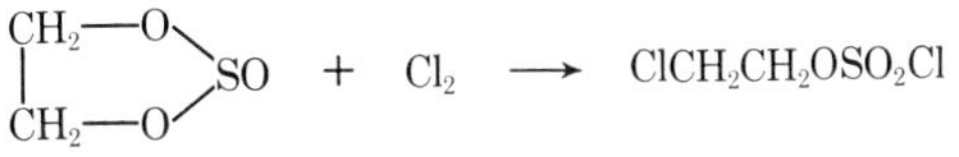

$$\begin{array}{c} CH_2{-}O \\ | \qquad\quad SO \\ CH_2{-}O \end{array} + \ Cl_2 \ \longrightarrow \ ClCH_2CH_2OSO_2Cl$$

Chlorosilanes form chlorosulfurate esters when treated with sulfur trioxide or chlorosulfuric acid (86).

$$(CH_3)_2SiCl_2 \xrightarrow{SO_3} (CH_3)_2Si(Cl)OSO_2Cl \xrightarrow{SO_3} (CH_3)_2Si(OSO_2Cl)_2$$

Another approach to halosulfurates is based on the addition of chlorosulfuric or fluorosulfuric acid to alkenes (87) in nonpolar solvents.

Health and Safety Factors

The alkyl sulfates are generally liquids which constitute only moderate fire hazards. But dimethyl sulfate, the best-known of these esters, is an exceedingly dangerous poison (88). The maximum allowable concentration of its vapors in air for an 8-hr exposure is 1 ppm. Exposure to 97 ppm for 10 min can be fatal. The vapors cause severe inflammation of the eyes, mouth, and respiratory system. Ingestion causes convulsions and paralysis, with later damage to the kidneys, liver, and heart. Contact with the skin, through which it can be absorbed, causes severe blistering. The fact that the symptoms of dimethyl sulfate poisoning are often delayed permits unnoticed exposure to lethal doses. There is no record of chronic poisoning.

In view of the foregoing, the precautions to be observed in handling these materials, especially dimethyl sulfate, are obvious. Impermeable gloves should be worn when opening the containers or transferring the esters from vessel to vessel, and these operations should always be performed in a hood or with other good ventilation. Only mechanical pipeting of such materials should be permitted. If the liquid should come in contact with the skin, the exposed areas should be flushed immediately with copious quantities of water, then soaped and rinsed thoroughly.

Concentrated aqueous ammonia should never be used for the disposal of dimethyl sulfate, because they react explosively on mixing (89). Methods for safe handling, first aid procedures, and disposal procedures should follow the instructions given in the *Chemical Safety Data Sheet* (88).

Uses

The uses of the several types of esters of sulfuric and sulfurous acid range from solvents to pesticides, but chemical reactions, such as alkylation or use as intermediates in the preparation of alcohols, consume the largest tonnage.

Methyl hydrogen sulfate has been used as a solvent in the bromination of indigo dyes on a large scale (47), and other hydrogen sulfates have served as intermediates in the commercial production of various alcohols from unsaturated hydrocarbons. The reaction of sulfur trioxide with ethyl hydrogen sulfate at 50°C is employed commercially for the preparation of ethionic acid, which can be converted with caustic to sodium ethylenesulfonate in 80% yield (90).

$$CH_3CH_2OSO_2OH \xrightarrow{SO_3} HOSO_2CH_2CH_2OSO_3H \xrightarrow{NaOH} NaOSO_2CH = CH_2$$

Salts, esters, and amides of ethylenesulfonic acid can be polymerized and copolymerized with various other monomers to give water-soluble and water-insoluble polymers. For a review of this field, see reference 91. Sodium ethylenesulfonate is also patented for the sulfoethylation of cellulose (92).

2-Aminoethyl hydrogen sulfate has been proposed for introducing aminoalkyl groups into cotton, hereby conferring increased absorption of direct dyes, as well as affinity for acid wool colors (93). It has also been used in basic medium for the preparation of ethyleneimine (10). (See Imines.)

Alkyl sulfates, particularly dimethyl and diethyl sulfate, find their largest use as alkylating agents for phenols and amines, which are important intermediates in the manufacture of dyes and pharmaceuticals. The use of dimethyl sulfate instead of methyl iodide is often advantageous when alkylations are carried out in dimethylformamide (94). Dimethyl sulfate is used in combination with boron compounds for the stabilization of liquid sulfur trioxide (95), and for the preparation of 4,4′-dichlorodiphenyl sulfone from chlorobenzene and sulfur trioxide (96). Diethyl sulfate has been proposed as a curing catalyst for acrolein–pentaerythritol resins (97). The amine salts of ethylene glycol monosulfate have been claimed as flameproofing agents in paper manufacture (98), and glyoxal sulfate was used on a commercial scale in the manufacture of vat dyes (47).

A number of mixed alkyl and aryl sulfites have been patented as insecticides and fungicides (99). Other possible uses of sulfites include a polysulfite (—OSOOCH$_2$-CH$_2$—)$_x$ as sensitizer in photographic emulsions (100), diethyl sulfite for the removal of catalyst fragments in polypropylene (101), and ethylene sulfite as an accelerator for aminoplastic molding compositions (102). A mixed, cyclic sulfite–carbonate ester of pentaerythritol has been polymerized to high-molecular-weight solids, which can be used in preparing laminates (103).

Bibliography

"Sulfuric and Sulfurous Esters" in *ECT* 1st ed., Vol. 13, pp. 506–513, by James M. Straley, Eastman Kodak Co.

1. E. W. Maurer, A. J. Stirton, and J. K. Weil, *J. Am. Oil Chemists' Soc.* **37**, 34 (1960). U.S. Pat. 3,133,946 (1964), E. W. Maurer, A. J. Stirton, and J. K. Weil (to U.S. Dept. of Agriculture).
2. *Dimethyl Sulfate*, Product Data Sheet, E. I. du Pont de Nemours & Co., Inc., Wilmington, Del.
3. Y. Shuto and S. Higashimori, *Kogyo Kagaku Zasshi* **67** (2), 371 (1964); *Chem. Abstr.* **61**, 8419 (1964).
4. P. B. D. de la Mare et al., *J. Chem. Soc.* **1956**, 1813.
5. J. G. Pritchard and P. C. Lauterbur, *J. Am. Chem. Soc.* **83**, 2105 (1961).
6. P. C. Rây and P. Neogi, *J. Chem. Soc.* **89**, 1900 (1906).
7. J. Wade, *J. Chem. Soc.* **81**, 1598 (1902).
8. H. LeB. Gray and G. O. Gutehunst, *J. Am. Chem. Soc.* **42**, 856 (1920).
9. Fr. Pat. 718,672 (1931) (to I. G. Farben); *Chem. Abstr.* **26**, 3261 (1932).
10. H. Wenker, *J. Am. Chem. Soc.* **57**, 2328 (1935). U.S. Pat. 3,326,897 (1967), R. G. Dunning (to Chemirad Corp.).
11. A. A. Michurin and E. N. Zil'berman, *Zh. Organ. Khim.* **1** (4), 711 (1965); *Chem. Abstr.* **63**, 5461 (1965).
12. R. Mohr and H. Hertel, *Chem. Ber.* **96**, 114 (1963).
13. E. Schmitz et al., *Angew. Chem.* **73**, 708 (1961); *Chem. Ber.* **94**, 2166 (1961); *Chem. Ber.* **95**, 2714 (1962).
14. L.-J. Simon and M. Frèjaqcous, *Compt. Rend.* **176**, 900 (1923).
15. H. F. Lewis et al., *Ind. Eng. Chem.* **22**, 34 (1930). E. Y. Wolford, *Ind. Eng. Chem.* **22**, 397 (1930).
16. C. M. Suter and H. L. Hanson, *J. Am. Chem. Soc.* **54**, 4100 (1932).
17. J. U. Nef, *Ann.* **309**, 187 (1899).
18. P. S. Clezy, *Tetrahedron Letters* **1966** (7), 741; *Chem. Abstr.* **64**, 14086 (1966).
19. L.-J. Simon, *Compt. Rend.* **176**, 583 (1923). F. H. Stodola, *J. Org. Chem.* **29**, 2490 (1964).
20. A. Werner and W. Seybold, *Chem. Ber.* **37**, 3658 (1904).

21. U.S. Pat. 1,924,615 (1933), S. R. Merley (to Doherty Research Co.).
22. A. Werner, *Ann.* **321**, 269 (1902).
23. H. Bredereck et al., *Chem. Ber.* **97**, 3081 (1964); *ibid.*, **98**, 1078 (1965).
24. H. L. Kane and A. Lowy, *J. Am. Chem. Soc.* **58**, 2605 (1936).   J. Epelberg and A. Lowy, *J. Am. Chem. Soc.* **63**, 101 (1941).
25. K. K. Anderson and S. W. Fenton, *J. Org. Chem.* **29**, 3270 (1964).
26. D. Lipkin, E. E. Jones, and F. Galiano, *Am. Chem. Soc., Div. Petrol. Chem. Reprints* **4** (4) B11-B15 (1959); *Chem. Abstr.* **55**, 23403 (1961).
27. C. M. Suter and H. L. Gerhart, *J. Am. Chem. Soc.* **57**, 107 (1935).
28. K. H. Slotta and L. Lorenz, *Chem. Ber.* **58B**, 1320 (1925).
29. C. Gopinathan and J. Gupta, *Indian J. Chem.* **3** (5), 231 (1965); *Chem. Abstr.* **63**, 9844 (1965).
30. I. Lauder, I. R. Wilson, and B. Zerner, *Australian J. Chem.* **14**, 41 (1961); *Chem. Abstr.* **55**, 19757 (1961).
31. E. T. Kaiser, M. Panar, and F. H. Westheimer, *J. Am. Chem. Soc.* **85**, 602 (1963).
32. E. T. Kaiser, I. R. Katz, and T. F. Wulfers, *J. Am. Chem. Soc.* **87**, 3781 (1965).
33. W. W. Carlson and L. H. Cretcher, *J. Am. Chem. Soc.* **69**, 1952 (1947).
34. U.S. Pat. 3,168,546 (1965), A. Ballauf et al. (to Farbenfabriken Bayer A.G.).
35. U.S. Pat. 2,917,502 (1959), S. R. Schwyzer (to Ciba Pharmaceutical Prod., Inc.).
36. J. M. Theobald, M. W. Williams, and G. T. Young, *J. Chem. Soc.* **1963**, 1927.
37. D. Kerr and I. Lauder, *Australian J. Chem.* **15**, 561 (1962); *Chem. Abstr.* **58**, 4149 (1963).
38. R. E. Davis, *J. Am. Chem. Soc.* **84**, 599 (1962).   P. B. D. De La Mare, J. G. Tillett, and H. F. Van Woerden, *J. Chem. Soc.* **1962**, 4888.
39. L. Denivelle, *Compt. Rend.* **208**, 1024 (1939).
40. C. C. Price and G. Berti, *J. Am. Chem. Soc.* **76**, 1211 (1954).
41. S. Wawzonek and J. T. Loft, *J. Org. Chem.* **24**, 641 (1959).
42. J. Charalambous, H. J. Davies, M. J. Frazer, and W. Gerrard, *J. Chem. Soc.* **1962**, 1505.
43. C. Libermann, *Compt. Rend.* **250**, 2223 (1960); *Chem. Abstr.* **56**, 5822 (1962).   *Compt. Rend.* **252**, 1483 (1961); *Chem. Abstr.* **55**, 15377 (1961).
44. M. A. Shaw, J. C. Tebby, R. S. Ward, and D. H. Williams, *J. Chem. Soc.* **1968**, 2795.
45. Ger. Pat. 1,207,380 (1965), K. Stuerzer (to Th. Goldschmidt A.G.); *Chem. Abstr.* **64**, 12549 (1966).
46. J. Charalambous, M. J. Frazer, and W. Gerrard, *J. Chem. Soc.* **1964**, 5480.
47. K. A. J. Chamberlain et al., *BIOS Final Report, No. 1482*, 6 (1946).
48. H. G. Harris and D. M. Himmelblau, *J. Phys. Chem.* **67**, 802 (1963); *Chem. Abstr.* **58**, 10770 (1963).   H. G. Harris, Jr. and D. M. Himmelblau, *J. Chem. Eng. Data* **9** (1), 61 (1964); *Chem. Abstr.* **60**, 7500 (1964).
49. Ger. Pat. 1,035,632 (1958), H. G. Van Raay (to Farbwerke Hoechst A.G.); *Chem. Abstr.* **54**, 19482 (1960).
50. U.S. Pat. 3,024,263 (1962), M. Letherman (to Dept. of the Navy).
51. D. S. Breslow, R. R. Hough, and J. T. Fairclough, *J. Am. Chem. Soc.* **76**, 5361 (1954).
52. M. S. Nemtsov, *Khim. Prom.* **1960**, 633; *Chem. Abstr.* **55**, 15070 (1961).
53. G. R. Schultze, J. Moos, and K. D. Ledwoch, *Erdoel Kohle* **11**, 12 (1958); *Chem. Abstr.* **52**, 7677 (1958).
54. G. D. Inskeep and A. Mussard, *Ind. Eng. Chem.* **47**, 2 (1955).   D. Stewart and E. McNeill, *Chem. Age* (*London*) **63**, 48 (1950).   S. F. Birch, *J. Inst. Petrol.* **38**, 69 (1952).   K. L. Butcher and G. M. Nickson, *Trans. Faraday Soc.* **54**, 1195 (1958).
55. E. Clippinger, *Ind. Eng. Chem. Prod. Res. Develop.* **3**, 3 (1964).
56. Ger. Pat. 1,086,434 (1960), J. Szita (to Farbenfabriken Bayer A.G.); *Chem. Abstr.* **55**, 19331 (1961).
57. E. Cherbuliez, Sl. Colak-Antic, et al., *Helv. Chim. Acta* **48**, 830 (1965).   U.S. Pat. 3,194,826 (1965), A. Goldstein et al. (to Chemirad Corp.).
58. J. Parrod and L. Robert, *Compt. Rend.* **230**, 450 (1950).
59. A. Butenandt et al., *Z. Physiol. Chem.* **321**, 258 (1960).
60. G. N. Burkhart and A. Lapworth, *J. Chem. Soc.* **1926**, 684.
61. E. J. Fendler and J. H. Fendler, *J. Org. Chem.* **33**, 3852 (1968).
62. C. Barkenbus and J. J. Owen, *J. Am. Chem. Soc.* **56**, 1204 (1934); R. Levaillant, *Compt. Rend.* **200**, 940 (1935).

63. Ger. (East) Pat. 32,780 (1965), W. Lugenheim, E. Carstens, and H. Fuerst; *Chem. Abstr.* **63,** 6862 (1965).

64. G. A. Sokol'skii, *Zh. Org. Khim.* **2** (6), 951 (1966); *Chem. Abstr.* **65,** 16848 (1966).

65. J. Avery et al., *BIOS Final Rept.*, No. *986*, 175, 227.

66. *U.S. Dept. Comm. Office Tech. Serv. PB Rept. 75,463* (1947).

67. Brit. Pat. 774,384 (1957), E. Roberts (to Ministry of Supply); *Chem. Abstr.* **51,** 15549 (1957).

68. U.S. Pat. 2,816,126 (1957), R. Evans and L. T. Hogarth (to United States of America).

69. Fr. Pat. 1,006,211 (1952), Société Anon. des Manufactures des Glaces et Produits Chimiques de Saint-Gobain, Chauny et Cirey; *Chem. Abstr.* **51,** 12128 (1957).

70. U.S. Pat. 3,100,780 (1963), D. L. Klass (to Pure Oil Co.).

71. U.S. Pat. 2,805,228 (1957), J. L. Smith (to Eastman Kodak Co.).

72. J. Lichtenberger and J. Hincky, *Bull. Soc. Chim. France* **1961,** 1495. W. Baker and B. F. Burrows, *J. Chem. Soc.* **1961,** 2257. Brit. Pat. 944,406 (1963), L. F. Wiggins, C. C. Beard, and J. W. James (to Aspro-Nicholas Ltd.); *Chem. Abstr.* **60,** 5397 (1964).

73. Ger. Pat. 1,049,870 (1959), J. Brunken and E. J. Poppe (to VEB Filmfabrik Agfa Wolfen); *Chem. Abstr.* **55,** 2488 (1961).

74. Ger. (East) Pat. 18,485 (1960), J. Brunken and E. J. Poppe (to VEB Filmfabrik Agfa Wolfen); *Chem. Abstr.* **55,** 8296 (1961).

75. Ger. (East) Pat. 15,024 (1958), J. Brunken and G. Gloeckner; *Chem. Abstr.* **54,** 3201 (1960).

76. W. Gerrard, *J. Chem. Soc.* **1939,** 99. L. Denivelle, *Compt. Rend.* **208,** 1024 (1939). Ger. Pat. 1,133,367 (1962), H. F. Wilson (to Rohm & Haas Co.).

77. Ger. Pat. 1,200,807 (1965), K. Stuerzer (to Th. Goldschmid A.G.); *Chem. Abstr.* **63,** 14704 (1965). Ger. Pat. 1,212,072 (1966), K. Stuerzer (to Th. Goldschmidt A.G.); *Chem. Abstr.* **64,** 15744 (1966).

78. G. Hesse and S. Majumdar, *Chem. Ber.* **93,** 1129 (1960).

79. S. Hauptmann and K. Dietrich, *J. Prakt. Chem.* **19,** 174 (1963); *Chem. Abstr.* **59,** 7506 (1963).

80. U.S. Pat. 3,022,315 (1962), W. A. Rogers, Jr., J. E. Woekst, and R. M. Smith (to Dow Chem. Co.). Ger. Pat. 1,217,970 (1966), H. Distler and G. Dittus (to Badische Anilin- und Soda-Fabrik A.G.); *Chem. Abstr.* **65,** 7189 (1966). Ger. Pat. 1,188,610 (1965), H. Hoefermann and H. Springmann (to Chemische Werke Huels A.G.); *Chem. Abstr.* **62,** 16057 (1965).

81. Ger. Pat. 1,213,612 (1966), K. Stuerzer (to Th. Goldschmidt A.G.); *Chem. Abstr.* **65,** 2375 (1966).

82. R. Lavaillant, *Ann. Chim.* **6,** 459 (1936). W. Voss and E. Blanke, *Ann.* **485,** 258 (1930).

83. Fr. Pat. 965,161 (1950), Société Anon. d'Innovations Chimiques dite: Sinnova ou Sadic; *Chem. Abstr.* **46,** 6137 (1952).

84. F. G. Bordwell and G. W. Crosby, *J. Am. Chem. Soc.* **78,** 5367 (1956). U.S. Pat. 2,860,123 (1958), R. V. Jones (to Phillips Petroleum Co.).

85. U.S. Pat. 2,684,977 (1954), M. J. Viard (to Société Anon. des Manufactures de Glaces et Produits Chimiques de Saint-Gobain, Chauny et Cirey); *Chem. Abstr.* **49,** 11005 (1955).

86. M. Schmidt and H. Schmidbauer, *Chem. Ber.* **95,** 47 (1962).

87. U.S. Pat. 1,510,425 (1925), W. Traube; *Chem. Abstr.* **19,** 76 (1925). W. Traube and R. Justh, *Brennstoff-Chem.* **4,** 150 (1923); *Chem. Abstr.* **17,** 3858 (1923).

88. N. I. Sax, *Handbook of Dangerous Materials*, Reinhold Publishing Corp., New York, 1951, p. 147. *Chemical Safety Data Sheet SD-19*, Manufacturing Chemist's Association, Washington, D.C., 1947.

89. H. Lindlar, *Angew. Chem.* **75,** 297 (1963).

90. D. S. Breslow, R. R. Hough, and J. T. Fairclough, *J. Am. Chem. Soc.* **76,** 5361 (1954).

91. W. Kern and R. C. Schulz, in *Houben-Weyl, Methoden der Organischen Chemie*, Vol. 14/1, 4th ed., Thieme Verlag, Stuttgart, 1961.

92. U.S. Pats. 2,580,351 and 2,580,352 (1951), V. R. Grassie (to Hercules Powder Co.).

93. U. A. Reeves and J. D. Guthrie, *Textile Res. J.* **23,** 522 (1953).

94. R. Kuhn and H. Trischmann, *Chem. Ber.* **96,** 284 (1963).

95. U.S. Pat. 3,160,474 (1964), W. G. Schnoor and A. W. Yodis (to Allied Chemical Corp.).

96. U.S. Pat. 3,355,497 (1967), E. G. Budnick (to Plains Chemical Development Co.).

97. U.S. Pat. 2,970,985 (1961), H. R. Guest, J. T. Adams, and B. W. Kiff (to Union Carbide Corp.).

98. U.S. Pat. 2,511,911 (1950), W. M. Fuchs and E. Gavatin.

99. Japan. Pat. 8345 (1963), M. Nagasawa and F. Yamamato (to Ihara Agricultural Chemical Co.); *Chem. Abstr.* **60**, 4060 (1964). U.S. Pat. 3,179,682 (1965), A. Covey, A. E. Smith, and W. L. Hubbard (to United States Rubber Co.).

100. Belg. Pat. 615,408 (1962), P. P. Chiesa, J. R. Dann, and J. W. Gates, Jr. (to Kodak Soc. Anon.); *Chem. Abstr.* **58**, 1086 (1963).

101. Brit. Pat. 903,077 (1962), "Montecatini" Società Generale per l'Industria Mineraria e Chimica; *Chem. Abstr.* **57**, 11396 (1962).

102. Brit. Pat. 866,440 (1961), C. P. Vale, S. Gutter, and W. Wilson (to British Industrial Plastics Ltd.); *Chem. Abstr.* **55**, 24105 (1961).

103. U.S. Pat. 3,251,857 (1966), F. Hostettler and E. F. Cox (to Union Carbide Corp.).

Julius Fuchs

E. I. du Pont de Nemours & Co., Inc.

SULFURIZATION AND SULFUR-CHLORINATION

This article discusses sulfurized (sulfurated) and sulfur-chlorinated (chlorosulfurized) unsaturated oils that are used mainly as additives to lubricants, as metal cutting oils, and as greases. In 1966, 23 million lb of sulfurized sperm oil were produced in the U.S. (1).

History. It is not possible to determine the exact date when sulfur and fatty material were first combined for use as lubricants. One can conjecture that sulfur was first added in small amounts to oils used for various types of lubrication without any attempt to react it with the substrate. Later it was heated with the oils to get more into solution, and thus the reaction of sulfur with unsaturated oils was discovered.

The first mention of the reaction between sulfur and a fatty oil appeared in a publication by Th. Anderson in 1847 (2). The reaction product was used for surface coatings. In 1918 a British patent was issued to G. W. Pressell (3) claiming the preparation and use of a fat treated with sulfur as a cutting oil compound. M. Gregory was granted a patent in 1917 (4) covering the reaction between sulfur and fish oils at 175°C and after heating to a final temperature of 220°C. This product was also claimed as a cutting oil additive. Other early patents in this field were issued to A. E. Becker (5) in 1926 for use in railway car or roller-mill bearings, and to W. H. Kobbe (6) in 1932, claiming the reaction products between sulfur and terpenes as cutting oil additives.

The description of the reaction between sulfur monochloride and fatty oils appeared first in two different publications (7,8). In 1855 A. Parkes was granted a patent claiming the reaction between sulfur monochloride and fats (9). All of these products were solid resinous materials used in protective coatings. They were given the general name *factice* (see Sulfur compounds), and were considered rubber substitutes and adjuvants.

The first mention of the use of chlorosulfurized oil as a lubricant additive appears in a patent issued to John F. Werder (10) in 1934. The compound was prepared by mixing 10 parts of sulfur monochloride with 90 parts of cottonseed oil at 10°F. The reaction mixture was then heated at 150°F for 6 hr. This product was used in hydrocarbon lubricating oils at a concentration of 6%.

Reactions

To quote Bateman and Moore (11) on the mechanisms of sulfur–olefin interaction: "As the scope for postulating reaction mechanisms varies inversely with the number of facts that have to be correlated, it could be anticipated that sulfur–olefin reactions, where both structural and kinetic features are complex and where so much of the experimental work has lacked critical design and assessment, would provide a fertile field for speculation (and misinterpretation) in this respect. This is particularly so for vulcanization and allied reactions, where the impression might be gained that far more effort has been expended on mental agility in developing wide generalizations than on acquiring definitive data which would bear critically on fundamental principles." (See also refs. 12–15.)

Manufacture

Sulfurized Oils. These products are manufactured in the U.S. by Carlisle Chemical Works, Inc.; The Elco Corp.; Fiske Brothers Refining Co.; E. F. Houghton and Co.; Keil Chemical Co.; Macco Chemical Div. (Glidden Co.); Werner G. Smith, Inc.; Smith-Weihmann Co., Inc.; and D. A. Stuart Oil Co., Ltd.

A typical method for producing a noncorrosive sulfurized sperm oil is the direct addition of molten sulfur to sperm oil, heating the mixture to around 320°F, and thereafter controlling the rate of addition so that the temperature is not allowed to go over 390°F. The reaction is exothermic; therefore heating is discontinued as the sulfur is charged. Alternatively, use of a catalyst such as zinc oxide or a high-molecular-weight amine permits a lower-temperature operation. A caustic scrubber system is required to remove by-product hydrogen sulfide.

Following the initial reaction stage, the temperature is maintained around 390°F for periods up to around 6 hr without a catalyst, and for about 2–4 hr in the presence of a catalyst. During this period the polysulfides formed in the initial stages are converted principally to disulfides, with about 10–12% of the sulfur lost as by-product hydrogen sulfide.

The temperature of the material is allowed to drop to around 340°F while it is being transferred to a second vessel equipped with a sparging ring; air is forced through the ring to convert the product to its final form. Air-blowing not only purges the dissolved by-product hydrogen sulfide but also results in converting most of the residual thiols to disulfides. The temperature during the first 3-hr blowing period is slowly dropped to 300°F, over the 2-hr blowing to 250°F, and during the final hour to 200°F. As might be expected, the viscosity of the product increases during the air-blowing.

Sulfur-Chlorinated Sperm Oil. Sulfur monochloride, S_2Cl_2, reacts with sperm oil in a highly exothermic manner and, up to about 16% total weight, addition is nearly quantitative at temperatures below 150°F. In a typical production method, sulfur monochloride is charged at a controlled rate to sperm oil contained in a steel vessel equipped with a sparging ring and cooling coils or a cooling jacket. The temperature is allowed to rise to 120°F, after which cooling is applied to control the reaction temperature at 135–140°F. After addition of all the sulfur monochloride, the kettle temperature is raised to 145–150°F and air-blowing is conducted for a period of 4 hr or longer until the product is "bland," ie, free of a sharp odor of any residual sulfur monochloride or possible traces of hydrogen chloride and hydrogen sulfide. A water scrubber system is attached to the reactor exhaust system to remove evolved fumes.

After the air-blowing operation the product is cooled to 130°F and an inhibitor is added to protect the material from any moisture attack during storage and shipping and also during subsequent use.

Types of Uses

Sulfurized and sulfur-chlorinated products are extreme-pressure (EP) lubricant additives used in three major application areas: *lubricating oils, cutting oils,* and *greases.* An extreme-pressure lubricant is necessary between moving metal surfaces whenever the fluid boundary film cannot otherwise be maintained under the prevailing temperature and pressure conditions, to prevent metal-to-metal contact.

Under the initial conditions of extreme pressure, suitable *lubricant* additives adhere tenaciously to metal surfaces in thin films, possibly monomolecular films, to maintain separation of the metal surfaces. As conditions become more severe, the extreme-pressure additives form a solid lubricant by chemical action with the surfaces which is not forced out between the interfaces. This solid film prevents welding and has a low shear strength to minimize friction. See also Lubrication.

Metal-cutting operations encounter conditions of extremely high pressures and temperatures between the sliding chip and the tool face. The mechanism of chip formation is common to all metal-cutting operations, and consequently extreme-pressure additives are used in cutting oils and soluble oils to reduce friction (and the attendant heat) during typical operations such as broaching, drilling, milling, turning, planing, reaming, hobbing, and grinding. Reduction of friction and temperature between the chip and tool face extends the tool life and improves the surface finish. Extreme-pressure lubrication is used in machining low and high carbon steels, high alloy steels, brass, bronze, copper, aluminum, and titanium. See also Tool materials.

Three factors for the most part contribute to the wearing out of the tool, namely heat, welding, and chemical erosion. Heat buildup at the tool surface results in the annealing of the metal, with subsequent reduction in hardness and excessive wear. Welding not only shortens tool life but also mars the surface finish. Use of an excessive amount of an "active type" additive can result in chemical erosion of the tool face. An "active type" additive may be characterized as corrosive to copper at temperatures below 150°F in the concentrations required for the machining operation.

Extreme-pressure additives function in *greases* in the same manner as in lubricating oils. Greases are used normally between slow-moving parts where no "reservoirs" or leakproof containers can be employed and where the thickening agent of the grease is relied upon to retain the lubricant on the moving surfaces.

Types of Products

Sulfurized and sulfur-chlorinated products are manufactured principally from two types of raw materials, lard oil and pigskin grease, and sperm oil. Lard oil, derived from pork products, is primarily a glyceride of oleic acid. Sperm oil (obtained by processing the fat of sperm whales) is unique among the usual animal fats in that it consists of a mixture of glycerides of monounsaturated fatty acids (about 35%) and esters of fatty acids and fatty alcohols, also having no more than a single unsaturation in either the alcohol or the acid moiety. These esters are randomly distributed and consist partly of saturated alcohols and acids. This characteristic makes sperm oil nondrying and not subject to gum formation and rancidity. The viscosity of sperm oil changes very little with temperature. This property extends in some degree to sulfurized sperm oil. In addition, sulfurized sperm oils have a higher solubility than sulfurized glycerides, such as lard oil, particularly in paraffinic oils, and consequently are used where these properties are most beneficial. For example, they control the vis-

Table 1. Machining Operations

Group 1	Group 2	Group 3
boring	chasing	broaching
cutting off	forming	form grinding
drilling	grinding	gear cutting
milling	reaming	hobbing
turning	tapping	thread grinding

Table 2. Metal Classifications[a]

Class 1

boiler plate
railroad rail
straight low-carbon steels
   SAE 1010–1050
malleable iron
  ferritic
  pearlitic
stainless iron (free cutting)

Class 2

| carbon steels | SAE 11XX |
| Cr steels | SAE 50XX–51XX |

Class 3

Ni–Cr alloys	SAE 31XX
	SAE 33XX
Mo alloys	SAE 40XX
Cr–Mo alloys	SAE 41XX
Ni–Cr–Mo alloys	SAE 43XX
	SAE 86XX
	SAE 87XX
	SAE 98XX
Cr-V alloys	SAE 61XX
	SAE 81XX
Cr alloys	SAE 50XX
	SAE 51XX

stainless 18-8
cast iron
ingot iron
wrought iron

Class 4

Ampco[d] bronze
drill rod
Monel[c] metal
stainless steel 18-8, austenitic
tool steels

Class 5

magnesium alloys
aluminum
brass
  leaded FC
  CD red
  leaded
bronze, phosphor, leaded
zinc

Class 6

aluminum bronze, cast
brass
  yellow
  red
bronze
  manganese
  phosphor
copper
  cast
  rolled
Everdur[b]
gun metal, cast
nickel, hot rolled
nickel, cold drawn
Monel[c] metal
  regular
  as cast H
  as cast S
  rolled
  K
Inconel,[c] Temper B, cold drawn

[a] Based on machinability rating of various metals noted in Norman E. Weldman and Robert C. Gibbons, *Machinability and Machining of Metals*, McGraw-Hill Book Co., Inc., New York, 1951, pp. 3–5.

[b] Anaconda American Brass Co.

[c] Huntington Alloy Products Div., The International Nickel Co., Inc.

[d] Philadelphia Bronze & Brass Corp.

cosity and extreme-pressure properties of gear lubricants, dual-purpose oils, and auto-motive automatic transmission fluids. A specialty product for water-based coolants used in metal cutting is made from mixed glycerides and esters which enhance the ease of emulsion formation.

The applications of sulfurized fats and oils are determined primarily on the basis of sulfur content. Processing conditions affect the stability and corrosive properties of the product, and consequently end use dictates to some degree the manufacturing procedures. Products containing above 12% sulfur are corrosive to copper in the standard ASTM-130 test and are used in heavy-duty machining operations.

Sulfurized products having less than 12% sulfur, especially those under 10%, when the sulfur is fully reacted, are generally nonstaining toward copper in the ASTM D-130 test. The requirement for this can be well understood, since so many bearing surfaces are copper alloys. Thus the lower sulfurized sperm oils perform in dual applications in metal working as well as in greases and gear lubricants.

Table 3. Typical Sulfurized Products

Products	Number	Base	S, %
glycerides			
based on lard oil	1	100	10
	2	140	11
	3	180	17
based on pigskin grease	1	100 PG	10
	2	180 PG	15
based on choice white	1	100 L	10
grease	2	180 L	14
based on mixed glycerides and esters		120 CLE	12
sperm oil		100 S	10
		140 S	11.5
		180 S	17

Table 3a. Sulfur-Chlorinated Products

Designation	Composition
Sulchlor[a] 55	5.2% S–5.5% Cl
Sulchlor 66	8.0% S–8.0% Cl
Sulchlor 105	10.5% S–10.5% Cl
Sulchlor 1717	17% S–17% Cl
Sulchlor 1717 M	9% S–9% Cl

[a] Lubricant additive (Carlisle Chemical Works, Inc.).

Sulfur-chlorinated sperm oil products are more active extreme-pressure additives on a total weight basis (sulfur plus chlorine) than the sulfurized products. They are also more staining toward copper, and the chlorine is hydrolytically unstable. This necessitates the use of an inhibitor or stabilizer to prevent hydrolysis, which leads to corrosion by hydrochloric acid. As the sulfur and chlorine contents are increased, these products become much more viscous than the corresponding sulfurized sperm oil. For example, a sulfur-chlorinated sperm oil containing 5.2% sulfur and 5.5% chlorine has a viscosity at 210°F of 150 Saybolt Universal Seconds (SUs), and a product containing 10% sulfur has a viscosity of 200 SUs. When the sulfur-chlorination is raised to 8.0% sulfur and 8.0% chlorine, however, the viscosity is increased to 1000 SUs, while sulfurized sperm oil with 17% sulfur has a viscosity of only 365 SUs.

In heavy machining operations, chlorine combined in the EP additive molecule reduces heat buildup on the tool face more than sulfur alone. This has been learned

Table 4. Cutting Oil Recommendations[a]

| | | Uses[b] | |
Number	Recommended composition	Operations	Metals
	Active type (used on ferrous metals)		
1.	1% Sulchlor 105 in 100–150 SUs mineral oil		
	or		
	0.75% Sulchlor 1717 in 100–150 SUs mineral oil	group 1	class 1
2.	2.5% Sulchlor 105 in 100–150 SUs mineral oil	group 2	class 1
	or	group 1	class 2
	0.75% Sulchlor 1717 + 2% Sulchlor 66 in 100–150 SUs mineral oil		
	or		
	3–5% Base 180-S in 100–150 SUs mineral oil		
3.	5% Sulchlor 105 in 100–150 SUs mineral oil	group 3	class 1
	or	group 2	class 2
	0.75% Sulchlor 1717 + 4% Sulchlor 66 in 100–150 SUs mineral oil	group 1	class 3
	or		
	5–10% Base 180-S in 100/100 SUs mineral oil		
4.	8% Sulchlor 105 in 250 SUs mineral oil	group 3	class 2, 3
	or	group 2	class 3, 4
	1.5% Sulchlor 1717 + 8% Sulchlor 66 in 250 SUs mineral oil	group 1	class 4
	or		nickel, Monel, and Inconel types
	25% Base 180-S, 25% cylinder stock, 50% 200/100 SUs mineral oil		
	Inactive type (used on nonferrous metals)		
5.	0.75% Sulchlor 1717 in 100–150 SUs mineral oil	any operation	class 5
	or		
	2% Sulfur Base 140-S in 100–150 SUs mineral oil		
6.	0.75% Sulchlor 1717 + 4% Sulfur Base 140-S in 100–150 SUs mineral oil	any operation	class 6

[a] Blending may be done at room temperature, if the agitation is sufficient. It is considered good practice, however, to blend at a temperature of 120–130°F.

In general, oils containing Base 180-S, more than 1.5% S-1717 or more than 6% S-55, are corrosive to copper at temperatures below 150°F, and should not be used on either copper or brass. Base 140-S is noncorrosive to copper in concentrations up to 50%, and may be used safely on any metal.

[b] All of the uses indicated opposite a number of recommended compositions are intended to apply to each of the alternative compositions.

from experience and has been the guide to selection of the most useful additives for the purpose. This experience, much of which contains feedback from industrial use, is the basis of the following recommendations for cutting oils and specialty oils, Tables 1–5. Data on the other uses of the sulfurized and sulfur-chlorinated oils are limited due to the reluctance of the users to disclose their formulations.

Table 5.   Specialty Oils

Num-ber	Oils	Composition	Uses
		Active type (used on ferrous metals)	
7.	grinding oils (thread and form grinding)		
	(a) "hard oil"	12% Sulchlor 66, 0.5% Ambidex-O,[a] 0.5% antifoam agent,[b] 200/100 SUs mineral oil	on medium to low hardness metals; soft and tough alloys, up to Brinnell 235
	(b) "medium oil"	60% (a) "hard oil," 40% 200/100 SUs mineral oil	for medium hardness metals, Brinell 235/400
	(c) "soft oil"	1.5% Sulchlor 1717 plus 5% methyl lardate	Brinell 400 and up
8.	lapping and honing oils	12% Sulchlor 66, 87% mineral seal, or 65/100 SUs mineral oil, 0.5% Ambidex-O[a]	

[a] Ionic wetting agent (Carlisle Chemical Works, Inc.).

[b] Antifoam agent—2% solution of Dow Corning fluid, 200 series, 350 viscosity, in kerosene; 0.5% of this solution is used as the antifoam agent.

Bibliography

1. *U.S. Tariff Comm. Rept., 50th Ann. Ed.*, No. 248, U.S. Govt. Printing Office, Washington, D.C., 1968.
2. Th. Anderson, *Am. Chem. Pharm.* **63,** 370 (1847).
3. Brit. Pat. 129,132 (1918), G. W. Pressell.
4. Brit. Pat. 123,114 (1917), M. Gregory.
5. U.S. Pat. 1,590,800 (1926), A. E. Becker.
6. U.S. Pat. 1,844,400 (1932), W. H. Kobbe.
7. G. A. Quesneville, *Revue Scientif. et Industr.* (1849); Gunther Schiemann and Fritz Vohwinkel, "Hundert Jahre geschwefelte Öle," *Farbe Lack* **64,** 485 (1958).
8. F. Rochleder, *Dinglers Polytech. J.* **111,** 159 (1849).
9. Brit. Pat. 2359 (1855), A. Parkes.
10. U.S. Pat. 1,971,243 (1934), J. F. Werder.
11. L. Bateman and C. G. Moore, "Reactions of Sulfur with Olefins," in N. Kharasch, ed., *Organic Sulfur Compounds*, Vol. 1, Pergamon Press, Inc., New York, 1961, Chap. 20, pp. 210–228.
12. E. H. Farmer and F. W. Shipley, *J. Chem. Soc. London,* **1947,** 1519.
13. E. H. Farmer and F. W. Shipley, *J. Polymer Sci.* **1,** 293 (1946).
14. G. F. Bloomfield and R. F. Naylor, *Eleventh Intern. Congr. Pure Appl. Chem.* **2,** 7 (1947).
15. L. Bateman et al., *J. Chem. Soc. London,* **1958,** 2838.

Patent and Literature Survey

1. "Sulfurized unsaturated oils and resins. Linseed oil and soybean oil," U.S. Pat. 2,425,597 (1947), John W. Church (to Falk and Co.).
2. "Sulfurized jojoba oil," U.S. Pat. 2,450,403 (1948), Franklin B. Wells (to Ellis-Foster Co.).
3. "Sulfurized fatty or mineral oils," U.S. Pat. 2,454,034 (1948), Dayton P. Clark, Jr. (to Gulf Research and Development Co.).
4. "Sulfurized cutting oils. Sperm oil," U.S. Pat. 2,467,137 (1949), Hollis L. Leland (to Standard Oil Development Co.).

5. "Sulfurized lard oil for cutting oils and gear lubricants," U.S. Pat. 2,577,636 (1951), Elmer H. Sperry (to Sun Oil Co.).

6. "Sulfurized tall oil as corrosion inhibitor," U.S. Pat. 2,646,349 (1953), Don A. Wagner (to Sinclair Refining Co.).

7. "Sulfurizing and leading unsaponifiable portions of degras (wool grease)," U.S. Pat. 2,710,836 (1955), Conrad J. Sunde (to N. J. Malmstrom and Co.).

8. "Sulfurized sperm oil as lubricant EP additive," U.S. Pats. 2,773,035 and 2,773,036 (1956), Stanley P. Waugh (to Tidewater Oil Co.).

9. "Lubricating oil compositions containing sulfurized sperm oil," U.S. Pat. 2,824,063 (1958), Guy M. Verley (to Sinclair Refining Co.).

10. "Sulfurization of hydrogenated oils for lubricant improvement," U.S. Pat. 2,824,067 (1958), John E. Farbak and Paul Gibson (to Swift & Co.).

11. "Hydraulic fluids containing antioxidant antisquawking agents. Sulfurized wool grease, sulfurized sperm oil, sulfurized terpene," U.S. Pat. 2,851,421 (1958), Allan Manteuffel and William D. Gilson (to Pure Oil Co.).

12. S. R. Sprague and R. G. Cunningham, "Frictional Characteristics of Lubricants. Sulfurized Whale Sperm Oil," *Ind. Eng. Chem.* **51** (9), 1047–1050 (1959).

13. "Influence of Lubricant Composition on the Friction of Steel on Steel. Sulfurized Sperm Oil and Sulfurized Terpene Oil," Fred G. Rounds, *Am. Chem. Soc. Div. Petrol. Chem. Preprints,* No. 4A, 129–151 (1958).

14. "Sulfurized sperm oil as lubricant corrosion inhibitor. Crank case oils," U.S. Pat. 2,993,856 (1961), Theodore C. Heisig and Brian Corrigan (to Texaco Inc.).

15. F. T. Barcroft, "A Technique for Investigating Reactions between EP Additives and Metal Surfaces at High Temperatures. Reaction of Sulfurized Sperm Oil with Metals," *Wear* **3,** 440–453 (1960).

16. "Extreme pressure lubricating oil containing molybdate ester and a sulfurized fatty oil or sulfurized olefin," U.S. Pat. 2,987,478 (1961), Howard J. Matson (to Sinclair Refining Co.).

17. "Metal working lubricants. Sulfurized lard, sperm oil, and mineral oil," U.S. Pat. 2,993,857 (1961), Louis H. Sudholz (to Socony Mobil Oil Co., Inc.).

18. "Extreme pressure steel-mill lithium-base lubricating grease containing sulfurized sperm oil and lead naphthenate," U.S. Pat. 3,003,962 (Appl. Dec. 22, 1958), Terence B. Jordan and John P. Dilworth (to Texaco Inc.).

19. "High-phosphorus, EP lubricant additives. Sulfurized sperm oil," U.S. Pat. 3,043,773 (1962), Warren W. Cortiss et al. (to Pure Oil Co.).

20. G. Schiemann, H. Duering, and H. Koerner, "Sulfurized Oils. IV. Comparison with Sulfur Monochloride-Sulfurized Vegetable Oils," *Deut. Farben-Z.* **17,** 408–417 (1963).

21. Fred G. Rounds, "Sulfurized Sperm Oil and Sulfurized Terpene Oil as EP Additives. Effects of Additives on the Friction of Steel on Steel," *Am. Soc. Lubrication Engrs. Trans.* **7** (1), 11 (1964).

22. "Emulsifiable sulfurized cutting oil," Brit. Pat. 1,043,392 (1966), Paul B. Robinson (trading as Meteor Oil Co.).

23. "Improvement in the load carrying capacity of sulfur-phosphorized extreme pressure additives," U.S. Pat. 3,280,028 (1966), Howard J. Matson (to Sinclair Research, Inc.).

24. G. I. Kichkin, "Improving the viscosity-temperature characteristics of transmission oils. Sulfurized mineral oil," *Neftepererabot. Neftekhim. Akad. Nauk Ukr.-SSR, Respub. Mezhvedom Sb.* **1966** (9), 5–8; *Chem. Abstr.* **66,** 4625h (1967).

25. "Drilling muds. Sulfurized tall oil," U.S. Pat. 3,318,396 (1967), Rodolfo J. Tailleur (to Gulf Oil Corp.).

26. Ferdinand L. Ewald, "Sulfurized and Chlorinated Oils for Machining Operations," *Metal Progr.* **90** (4), 133–134,139 (1966).

27. G. W. Rowe and E. F. Smart, "Experiments on Lubrication Breakdown in Friction Tests and in Cutting of Metal on a Lathe. Sulfurized Oil Continues to Lubricate in Friction Tests up to Very High Speeds and Also Give the Best Overall Cutting Performance," *Proc. Inst. Mech. Eng. (London) Pt. 3J* **179,** 229–241 (1965) (published 1966).

28. "Screw cutting compound comprising sulfurized mineral oil," U.S. Pat. 1,401,760 (1921), H. C. Claflin.

29. Carleton Ellis, "Various Sulphur-Treated (Vulcanized) Products," in *The Chemistry of Synthetic Resins,* Vol. 2, Reinhold Publishing Corp., New York, 1935, Chap. 60, pp. 1199–1214.

30. C. Falconer Flint, "Factice: Relation of Structure to Properties," *Proc. Inst. Rubber Ind.* **2,** 151–162 (1955).

31. H. E. Gunning and O. P. Strausz, "Reactions of Sulfur Atoms with Olefins," *Advan. Photochem.* **4,** 143–194 (1966); *Chem. Abstr.* **66,** 2093d (1967).

32. J. B. Harrison, "Factice: Its Use and Function in Rubber Technology," *Trans. Inst. Rubber Ind.* **28,** 117–135 (1952).

33. E. A. Hauser and M. C. Sze, "Chemical Reactions During Vulcanization. III," *J. Phys. Chem.* **46,** 118–131 (1942).

34. F. Lautenschlaeger, "The Reaction of Sulfur Dichloride with Linear Diolefins. Stereochemical Aspect in the Formation of Cyclic Sulfides," *Quart. Rept. Sulfur Chem.* **2** (4), 331 (1967).

35. Michal Hebda, "Surface-Active Substances and Boundary Friction," *Biul. Wojskowej Akad. Tech.* **15** (12), 99; *Chem. Abstr.* **67,** 45742t (1967).

36. "Poly(vinyl chloride) of decreased cold flow. Reaction product of castor oil and S_2Cl_2 as plasticizer," Ger. Pat. 1,067,588 (1959), Rudolph Kern and Rudolf Punessen; *Chem. Abstr.* **55,** P9961b (1961).

37. E. N. Klemgard, *Lubricating Greases: Their Manufacture and Use,* Reinhold Publishing Corp., New York, 1937, pp. 725–757.

38. E. M. Lown et al., "The Reactions of Sulfur Atoms. VIII. Further Investigation of the Reactions with Olefins. Relative Rates of Addition of Sulfur (^{3}P) and (^{1}D) Atoms," *J. Am. Chem. Soc.* **89** (5), 1056 (1967).

39. J. S. Long et al., "The Boiling of Linseed Oil," *Ind. Eng. Chem.* **19** (1), 62 (1927).

40. Noel Lozac'h and Jean Vialle, "The Chemistry of the 1,2-Dithiole Ring," in N. Kharasch and C. Meyers, eds., *Organic Sulfur Compounds,* Vol. 2, Pergamon Press, Inc., New York, 1966, Chap. 10, pp. 257–285.

41. J. R. Nooi and G. J. Huijben, "Preparation of the Oleic Acid/Sulphur Dichloride Adduct and Some Derivatives," *J. Appl. Chem.* **18,** 84 (1968).

42. "Polyolefin shortstopping with sulfur compounds," U.S. Pat. 3,278,498 (1966), Bernard Rudner and George S. Achorn (to Koppers Co., Inc.).

43. Takeshiro Sato et al., "The Sulfur Compound of α-Pinene, "*J. Chem. Soc. Japan Pure Chem. Sect.* **73,** 135 (1952); *Chem. Abstr.* **47,** 9943i (1953).

44. Gunther Schiemann and Fritz Vohwinkel, "Hundert Jahre geschwefelte Öle," *Farbe Lack* **64,** 485–487 (1958).

45. Douglas B. Smith and Herbert E. Schweyer, "Certain Chemical Aspects of Processing Asphalt," *Am. Chem. Soc. Div. Petrol. Chem. Preprints* **12** (2), A-35 (1967); "S Reacts with Asphalt to Form Product Similar to Air-blown Asphalt," *Chem. Abstr.* **67,** 55908r (1967).

46. Harry E. Westlake, Jr., "The Sulfurization of Unsaturated Compounds," *Chem. Rev.* **39,** 219–239 (1946).

RAYMOND S. DALTER AND
INGENUIN HECHENBLEIKNER
Carlisle Chemical Works, Inc.

SULFUR NITRIDE, S_4N_4.   See Explosives, Vol. 8, p. 593.

SULFUROUS ACID, H_2SO_3.   See Sulfur dioxide under Sulfur compounds.

SULFUR TRIOXIDE, SO_3.   See Sulfuric acid.

SULFURYL HALIDES, SO_2X_2.   See Sulfur compounds.

SUNFLOWERSEED OIL.   See Fats and fatty oils.

SUNN.   See Fibers, vegetable, Vol. 9, p. 184.

SUNTAN–SUNSCREEN PRODUCTS.   See Cosmetics, Vol. 6, p. 355.

SUPERALLOYS. See High-temperature alloys.

SUPEROXIDES. See Peroxides and peroxy compounds, Vol. 14, p. 762.

SUPERPHOSPHATE. See Fertilizers.

SUPPOSITORIES. See Pharmaceuticals, Vol. 15, p. 120.

SURFACTANTS

The word *surfactant* is of relatively recent origin and is a condensation of the descriptive phrase *surface-active agent*. The new term was coined by the staff at GAF Corporation as a trademark (1) and shortly thereafter, in 1950, the word was dedicated to the public domain. The phrase "surface-active agent" was awkward to use repetitively and was too extensive in its meaning. The new word overcame these disadvantages but unfortunately was never precisely defined. Six fundamental characteristics of surfactants, representative of current usage, were taken as the basis for selection of the substances considered in this article.

1. *Solubility.* A substance must be soluble in at least one phase of a liquid system in order to be classified as a surfactant. Bentonitic clays, for example, were excluded by this constraint even though they exhibit some of the fundamental properties of surfactants (2).

2. *Amphipathic Structure.* Surfactant molecules are composed of groups with opposing solubility tendencies.

3. *Orientation at Interfaces.* Surfactant molecules or ions form oriented monolayers at phase interfaces.

4. *Adsorption at Interfaces.* The equilibrium concentration of a surfactant solute at a phase interface is greater than its concentration in the bulk of the solution. (Consequently, surfactants cause a greater lowering of the surface tension than would be expected from their gross concentration.)

5. *Micelle Formation.* Surfactants form aggregates of molecules or ions called micelles when the concentration of the solute in the bulk of the solution exceeds a limiting value that is a fundamental characteristic of each solute–solvent system.

6. *Functional Properties.* Solutions of surfactants exhibit some combination of the following functional properties: detergency, foaming, wetting, emulsifying, solubilizing, dispersing.

Surfactant phenomenology deals with di-, tri-, or polyphase systems of which at least one phase is a surfactant solution. In many practical applications the role of the surfactant may simply be to enhance the performance of a "pure" liquid.

Organic Chemistry

A surfactant is an organic compound that encompasses in the same molecule two dissimilar structural groups, eg a water-soluble and a water-insoluble moiety. The composition, solubility properties, location, and relative sizes of these dissimilar groups in relation to the overall molecular configuration determine the surface activity of a compound. The term *amphipathy* was proposed by Hartley to denote the molecular structure of surfactants and his description of its meaning is "the occurrence in a single molecule or ion, with a suitable degree of separation, of one or more groups which have an affinity ("sympathy") for the phase in which the molecule or ion is dissolved, together with one or more groups which are antipathetic to the medium (ie which tend to be expelled by it)" (3).

A variety of pairs of names have been used to designate and describe the opposing tendencies of the moieties or groups that make up a surfactant molecule, viz: *hydro phobic*, water disliking; *hydrophilic*, water liking; *lipophobic*, fat disliking; *lipophilic*, fat liking; *oleophobic*, fat disliking; *oleophilic*, fat liking. The terms *polar* and *non-polar* can also be used to refer to the groups that are soluble or insoluble, respectively, in water.

Amphipathic structures are found in so many classes of organic substances that hundreds of thousands of surfactants are theoretically possible and thousands of individual compounds have been described in the literature. Most of the commercially or theoretically interesting classes of substances have probably been explored to some extent. By reference to this backlog of data, the gross properties of new surfactant compounds are usually predictable from their chemical structures. However, the summaries of structures and properties of commercial surfactants in the following parts of this article are necessarily so generalized that these relationships are obscured.

The definitions of surfactant and amphipathic compound do not limit or specify the compositions of the phases in surfactant systems, and all of the theoretically possible combinations of aqueous and nonaqueous phases are known to occur. Even though the general applicability of these definitions has been established, water is present as a discrete phase or solute in such a large proportion of the commercially important surfactant systems that its presence is assumed in much of the common terminology of the industry, eg the water-soluble type of amphipathic group is referred to as the "solubilizing group."

Hydrophilic and Hydrophobic Groups. Surfactants are classified on the basis of their hydrophilic or "solubilizing groups" into four categories: anionics, nonionics, cationics, and amphoterics. The anionic solubilizing groups are carboxylates, sulfonates, sulfates, and phosphates. Nonionics are solubilized by hydroxyl groups and polyoxyethylene chains. Primary, secondary, and tertiary amines and quaternary ammonium groups are the cationic solubilizers. Amphoteric surfactants are solubilized by some combination of anionic and cationic moieties; nonionic solubilizing groups may also be part of amphoteric molecules. In addition to the primary solubilizing groups, other structural units contribute to the hydrophilic tendencies of molecules, eg ester linkages and amide linkages. The hydrophobic, ie lipophilic, moieties are almost invariably hydrocarbon or halogen-substituted hydrocarbon groups. Olefin linkages are less hydrophobic than carbon-to-carbon single bonds. Products based on silicon-containing hydrophobes are just beginning to be offered in commercial quantities.

Molecular Weight. The molecular weight of surfactants ranges from a low of around 200 or slightly below, eg sodium hexylsulfate, to a high that is well up in the thousands for hydrophilic polymers. Nevertheless, a linear C_{12} hydrophobe solubilized by an anionic, cationic, nonionic or amphoteric group is an effective surfactant for a large proportion of surfactant applications involving dilute aqueous solutions. Extending the range of compositions to include C_{12} to C_{18} compounds and permitting branching of the hydrophobe provides substances that exhibit the full gamut of surfactant properties.

Solubility and Surface Activity. A surfactant solute usually displays maximum surface activity and functional effectiveness when it is near the threshold of insolubility. Moreover, the solubility of surfactants is markedly affected by temperature and electrolyte concentrations. Thus for each set of conditions there is usually an optimum solubility balance for each type of surfactant. Relatively small changes in the composition of a surfactant are often sufficient to change its solubility, and hence its surface activity. There are many ways to effect such changes; for example the average molecular weight of the raw-material mixture, ie hydrophobe, can be increased slightly or the degree of sulfation, sulfonation, or ethoxylation can be increased or decreased. Empirical solubility tests rank with charge weights and chemical analyses as control techniques for surfactant manufacturing processes. They make it possible to produce to tight specifications by compensating for variations in successive lots of raw materials or to adjust a process to obtain a range of optimum performance conditions for essentially the same product but are pointed to different uses. This last practice causes apparent duplications in vendors' product lists since the same nominal composition is often offered under different trade names for different uses.

Nomenclature and Chemical Composition. Practical surfactant technology deals with mixtures of precisely specified properties but incompletely defined compositions. Many surfactant products are *polydisperse* in the meaning of this term proposed by Gibbons (4), "a preparation containing molecules which are all the same type, but which vary only in chain length or in some other structural detail... (as) distinguished from a mixture of two different molecular species." Ethoxylated alkylphenols are typical polydisperse compositions. The properties of the components in heterogeneous surfactant mixtures may be similar even though their structures are different, as for example the sorbitan esters of fatty acids, or they may be dissimilar as illustrated by the "2/1 alkanolamides." The nomenclature recommended by the committees of IUPAC and the practice of Chemical Abstracts are excellent for naming pure compounds, but guidance has not been provided for naming the mixtures that are encountered in surfactant chemistry. As a further complication, IUPAC discourages the use of "lauryl," "myristyl," "palmityl," and "stearyl" as trivial names, preferring systematic expressions such as dodecyl alcohol (or 1-dodecanol), tetradecyl alcohol, etc. However, the American Oil Chemists' Society considers the older nomenclature as precise (5), but in a different way. In surfactant chemistry the trivial names are used with a special denotation, eg "lauryl alcohol" is not a synonym for dodecyl alcohol but rather designates a commercial product which contains dodecyl alcohol as its main constituent but which varies in actual composition from a fairly narrow distillation cut to a broad fraction containing substantial proportions of lower and higher alcohols. It is the same with the terms myristyl, cetyl, etc.

Sometimes expressions are used which are even less systematic, but are descriptive of the origin of a product; for example, "coco acids" refers to the mixed fatty acids obtained from coconut oil; the acyl radical derived from these acids is conveniently referred to as "cocoyl."

Alkyl substituents on aromatic nuclei pose another problem in nomenclature. For example, before 1965 commercial "dodecene," a propylene tetramer, was widely used to alkylate benzene, which was then sulfonated to obtain a surface-active agent. Not only was the propylene tetramer a mixture of isomers (see Propylene), but alkylation catalysts also catalyzed rearrangements as well as depolymerization of the olefin and alkylation by lower-molecular-weight fragments. Even with the newer linear feedstocks, alkylation of benzene leads to a mixture of isomers in which the benzene may be attached to any except the terminal carbons of the aliphatic chain. To add to the confusion, very few data have been published on the distribution of ortho-, meta-, and para-isomers in commercial alkylbenzenesulfonates or ethoxylated alkylphenols.

The complex mixtures that comprise commercial surfactants are noncrystalline substances that are exceedingly difficult to separate into homogeneous isomers and equally difficult to assay in situ (6,7). Furthermore there is little justification for the cost of the research to define precisely the composition of surfactant products since the performance properties of the mixtures that have been resolved were found to approximate so closely the properties of the compound represented by the average composition of the mixture.

All of these factors (ie the complex composition of surfactants, the difficulty of resolving mixtures of surfactants, and the lack of economic significance of these data) tend to minimize the importance of precise product descriptions in practical surfactant technology. Also, the IUPAC-recommended names for the components of these mixtures are usually long and repetitively similar, which does not encourage their widespread use.

The observation that commercial surfactant products are usually mixtures of incompletely specified composition should not be construed to mean that the properties of pure surfactants have not been studied extensively. Homogeneous compounds representative of many surfactant product types have been prepared and their properties studied as such and in comparison to commercial mixtures. Syntheses designed to yield pure compounds from purified starting materials have usually been the preferred approach rather than isolation of the components of commercial products.

It must be admitted, then, that the terminology used in describing commercial surfactants is often ambiguous except for products that are also economic poisons or food additives, where fairly precise disclosure of the composition is required by Federal laws. However, there have been occasions when the ownership of a strong patent has encouraged more precise disclosure of individual surfactant product compositions; an example is sodium di(2-ethylhexyl) sulfosuccinate.

The descriptions of surfactants in the organic chemistry section are followed by tables that list trade names, compositions, properties, and manufacturers of representative products. The compositions shown in these tables are usually not precise but they represent the full disclosure by the manufacturer. As a typical ambiguity, the degree of esterification of polybasic acids and polyols is almost invariably not stated. Whenever the composition of a product is precisely known the information is included, but the incompleteness of the available data is not cited repeatedly.

Wetting and Detergent Structures. Correlations of functional properties with molecular structures have been sought by numerous investigators (8–12). One result has been the identification of *strong wetting* and *strong detergent* structures. The hydrophilic group of strong wetting agents is located at the middle of the hydrophobic chain or at the central branching point if the molecule contains two or more chains. Conversely, the hydrophilic group in strong detergents is located at the end of the hydrophobic chain. This may be illustrated by comparing two isomers, sodium 1-(n-butyl)octylsulfate and sodium n-dodecylsulfate:

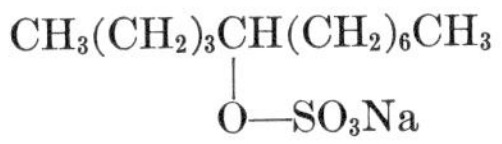

$$CH_3(CH_2)_3CH(CH_2)_6CH_3$$
$$| $$
$$O—SO_3Na$$

strong wetting

$$CH_3(CH_2)_{10}CH_2—O—SO_3Na$$

strong detergent

Although the wetting and detersive properties of unformulated anionic and nonionic compounds follow this structural pattern, usefulness of the generalization is limited to the selection of surfactants for a few specialized applications, eg textile wetting agents. This limitation is due to the pronounced superiority of formulated or "built" products over pure compounds for detergency, emulsification, etc. In formulations, detergency and wetting strength of individual components lose much of their significance. Textile wetting efficiency is not simply related to surface-tension lowering, but dilute aqueous solutions of strong wetting agents characteristically have low surface tensions.

Properties and Abbreviations. Abbreviations used in listing the utilitarian properties of the various classes of commercial surfactants are shown in Table 1.

The list of properties was compiled from the vendors' recommendations which frequently cited a combination of surfactant with nonsurfactant properties. Both were

Table 1. Abbreviations Used in Listing the Properties of Commercial Surfactants

Property	Abbreviation
antistatic protection	A
biodegradable	B
corrosion inhibition	C
demulsification	dE
defoaming	dF
detergency[a]	D
dispersing[a]	Di
emolliency	Es
emulsification[a]	E
flotation assistant	Fl
foaming[a]	F
foam building or foam stabilization	Fs
germicidal or algaecidal activity	G
hair conditioning	H
intermediate for further synthesis	I
opacification and emulsification	O
penetration	P
rewetting (eg paper, textiles)	rW
solubilization[a]	S
stabilization (of dispersed systems)	St
suspending action	Su
textile dyeing and/or processing aid	Ta
textile fabric, fiber or yarn softening	Ts
textile fiber lubrication	Tl
viscosity building	V
wetting[a]	W

[a] Key functional properties of surfactants.

included because very often it is this combination of properties that renders the product useful and saleable. Most of the terms in the table are either self-explanatory or are discussed in later sections. A few need explanation. An *emollient* imparts to a surfactant solution a lubricating or softening feel on contact with human skin. A *flotation assistant* is used in the separation of ore from gangue. The effect of the assistant may be to promote foaming or preferential wetting or adhesion between the bubbles and the particles to be floated. A *hair conditioner* is usually substantive and applied to the hair from an aqueous solution to impart an antistatic and/or lubricating effect. *Opacifiers* are used principally in cosmetic preparations to make solutions appear opalescent and/or more concentrated. *Viscosity builders* are used to thicken cosmetic and detergent formulations, usually to give the appearance of a high concentration of active ingredient but sometimes to retard drainage.

Production. Total production of surfactants in the United States in 1966 was divided among the major categories of products as shown in Table 2.

Table 2. U.S. Production of Surfactants, 1966

Product	Production, 1000 lb
anionic surfactants	2,050,915
nonionic surfactants	685,693
cationic surfactants	161,843
amphoteric surfactants	5,052
total	2,903,503

The economic value of the various product classes was more evenly distributed than the production volumes (cf Table 43).

ANIONIC SURFACTANTS

The hydrophilic moiety in anionic surfactants is a polar group that is negatively charged in aqueous solutions or dispersions. In commercial products it is either a carboxylate, sulfonate, sulfate, or phosphate group. In dilute alkaline solutions in soft water the solubilizing power of the sodium salts of the four anionic radicals is approximately equal and strong enough to balance the hydrophobic tendency of a 12-carbon saturated hydrocarbon group; the sulfate is actually a somewhat stronger solubilizer than the sulfonate. In neutral or acidic media or in the presence of heavy-metal ions, the solubilizing power of the carboxylate is markedly less than that of the other groups.

The ionic environment associated with anionic surfactants influences the properties of their solutions. Sodium and potassium salts are generally more soluble in water and less soluble in hydrocarbons. Conversely, the calcium, barium, and magnesium salts are more compatible with hydrocarbon solvents and less so with water. Ammonium and amine salts, eg triethanolamine, improve the compatibility of anionics with water and hydrocarbons and are widely used in emulsification and detergent applications. Higher total ionic strengths are usually associated with lower solubilities of anionic surfactants. To offset this effect, the molecular weight of the hydrophobe is lower in products designed for use at high electrolyte concentrations. Micellar solubilization by anionics is markedly affected by total ionic strength and also by the identity of the associated cations.

Table 3. U.S. Production of Anionic Surfactants, 1966

Product type	Production, 1000 lb
carboxylic acids and salts	962,222
sulfonic acids and salts	963,812
sulfuric acid esters and salts	111,925
phosphate esters and salts	12,956
total	2,050,915

Production of anionic surfactants in the U.S.A. aggregated 2,050,915,000 lb in 1966, which was 70.6% of total production for all types of surfactants. As shown in Table 3, carboxylates and sulfonates were almost equal in volume and together accounted for 96% of the production of anionics.

Carboxylates. Soaps and a small volume of aminocarboxylates are the only commercial product types in the carboxylate class of surfactants. Soap has the general composition $(RCOO)^-(M)^+$ where R is an alkyl group, usually in the C_9 to C_{21} range and M is a metallic or amine ion. Although most soaps have surfactant properties, the term actually denotes the chemical composition rather than the use, and an appreciable volume of these products, particularly salts of polyvalent metals, go to nonsurfactant uses such as paint driers and gelling agents for kerosene. See Soap; Driers and metallic soaps. The surfactant properties of soaps are excellent in soft water, but the heavy metal and polyvalent metal salts of soap, eg Mg^{2+}, Ca^{2+}, Ba^{2+}, Fe^{3+}, and Al^{3+}, are insoluble in water and form "curds" or "lime-soap" precipitates that reduce the effective concentration and adversely affect performance. If the hardness of the water is not too great, an excess of soap can be used to disperse the curd and render it innocuous. Other types of surfactants are also used as lime-soap dispersants and their relative effectiveness for this purpose can be compared by the method of Borghetty and Bergman (13). Organic sequestering agents such as ethylenediaminetetraacetic acid and nitrilotriacetic acid (see Complexing agents) tie up heavy-metal ions in nonionizing complexes and prevent the formation of soap curds. This makes it possible to use soap as a surfactant in hard water. The relatively high cost of softening water with organic sequestering agents limits their application to specialty uses. This economic limitation is not necessarily permanent since the cost of organic sequestering agents is still decreasing and their annual usage is increasing. Other considerations besides economics are involved that could stabilize or increase the usage of soap. For one, soap is more easily biodegradable in waste-water treatment plants than even linear alkylbenzenesulfonates. For another, the residues from the polyphosphate builders that must be used with alkylbenzene sulfonates in household detergent products are suspected of contributing to excessive growth of algae in lakes and rivers. Public pressure for "purer" water could favor increased usage of soap if the economics of its use became less unfavorable. For many years soap was the only surfactant produced commercially. Then other types of surfactants were introduced to industrial markets as specialties, but this did not significantly reduce the consumption of soap. Introduction of "built" heavy-duty household laundry detergents (comprised of alkylbenzenesulfonates plus alkanolamides, polyphosphates, and carboxymethylcellulose) led to almost complete replacement of soap in this market, which is the largest single use of surfactants. The combinations of synthetic detergents with builders came to be known as "syndets," a term suggested by Foster D. Snell. Despite the inroads of the syndets, production of soap for surfactant uses accounted for one-third of the production of surfactants of all types in 1966.

In order to set a perspective for the description of more recently developed surfactant types, some of the desirable properties of soaps are noted briefly.

1. The sodium and potassium coco fatty acid soaps are unexcelled as lathering and cleansing agents in bar detergents for personal use in soft to medium-hard water.

2. The C_{14} to C_{18} fatty acid sodium soaps are effective laundry and industrial detergents in soft to medium-hard hot water.

3. Soaps, especially amine salts, are excellent emulsifiers, dispersants, and solubilizing agents with a wide range of industrial uses.

4. Soaps have an emollient action in contact with the skin and leave a soft feel on textile fabrics.

5. Soaps have a wide miscellany of well-established industrial surfactant uses, eg ore flotation, wetting of asphalt, fulling of woolens, and emulsifying agents for polymerizations.

Two types of *aminocarboxylate* surfactants, N-acylsarcosinates and acylated protein hydrolysates, are produced in small quantities as specialties. Both series of products are fatty acyl derivatives of aminocarboxylates. As compared to the corresponding soaps, the hydrophilic tendency of the amide linkages in these molecules is strong enough to significantly lessen inactivation of the carboxylate ions by the calcium and magnesium ions that are present in hard water.

N-Acylsarcosinates. Sodium N-lauroylsarcosinate and the sodium N-acylsarcosinate derived from coconut fatty acids are soaplike detergents with good lathering properties. They are principally used in dentifrices where it is claimed they also inactivate the enzymes that convert glucose to lactic acid in the mouth (14). N-Oleoylsarcosinate is used as a textile auxiliary and detergent. The N-acylsarcosinates are prepared by the condensation of a fatty acid chloride with sarcosine (ie N-methylglycine obtained from the reaction of methylamine, formaldehyde, and sodium cyanide) in alkaline aqueous solution.

$$RCOCl + CH_3NHCH_2COONa + NaOH \rightarrow RCON(CH_3)CH_2COONa + NaCl + H_2O$$

Table 4 lists the composition and uses of representative commercial products.

Table 4. N-Acylsarcosinates

Product name	$RCOO^-$	Cation	Concn, wt %	Biodegrad- ability	Functions[a]	Manufac- turer[b]
Hamposyl C	cocoyl	H	100	B	D, E, Fs, C	HMP
Hamposyl C-30	cocoyl	Na	30	B	D, E, Fs, C	HMP
Hamposyl L	lauroyl	H	100	B	D, E, Fs, C	HMP
Hamposyl L-30	lauroyl	Na	30	B	D, E, Fs, C	HMP
Hamposyl O	oleoyl	H	100	B	D, E, Fs, C	HMP
Maprosyl 30	lauroyl	Na	30	B	D, F, C	OXR
Sarkosyl NL-97	lauroyl	Na	97		D, Fs, E, C	GGY
Sarkosyl LC	cocoyl	H	100		D, Fs, E, C	GGY
Sarkosyl L	lauroyl	H	100		D, Fs, E, C	GGY
Sarkosyl S	stearoyl	H	100		D, Fs, E, C	GGY
Sarkosyl O	oleoyl	H	100		D, Fs, E, C	GGY
Sarkosyl T	tall oil acyl	H	100		D, Fs, E, C	GGY

[a] See Table 1.   [b] See Table 44.

Acylated Protein Hydrolysates. Fatty acyl aminocarboxylates are prepared from protein hydrolysates by acylation with fatty acid chlorides or by direct condensation with fatty acids. The commercial products are mixtures that vary in composition from acyl derivatives of polypeptides from incompletely hydrolyzed protein to mixtures of acylated amino acids derived from completely hydrolyzed protein. Collagen from leather scraps and low-grade-hide glues is used as a source of protein. Derivatives of the incompletely hydrolyzed peptides have a greater tolerance for hard water but their effectiveness as surfactants is lower. Table 5 lists trade names and properties for typical acylated protein hydrolysates.

Table 5. Aminocarboxylates, (Fatty Acid/Peptide Condensate)⁻(M)⁺

Product name	Fatty acid	M	Concn, wt %	Biodegrad-ability	Functions[a]	Manufac-turer[b]
Crestopon	fatty acid		100		D, E, Ta	CRT
Lamepon	fatty acid		42	B	D, W, E	PRO
Maypon 4C	coco	K	36	B	D	MYW
Maypon K	oleic	Na	44	B	D, E	MYW
Maypon SK	coco	Na	45	B	W, D	MYW
Maypon UD	undecylenic	K	36	B	D	MYW
Veripon	fatty acid		42	B	D, W	PRO

[a] See Table 1.   [b] See Table 44.

Sulfonates. The most effective structure for an anionic surfactant is a sulfonate of the general formula RSO_3Na where R is a biodegradable hydrocarbon group in the surfactant molecular-weight range. The R group can be alkyl or alkylarylene and the product can be a random mixture of isomers as long as it does not contain chain branching that interferes with biodegradability. The surface activity of the SO_3^- group is not oversensitive to variations in the pH or to heavy metal ions and the C–S linkage is not susceptible to hydrolysis or oxidation under normal conditions of use. The minimum cost for satisfactory performance determines the composition of the principal surfactant ingredient in household laundry detergents, the largest single use of surfactants. Other surfactant users adapt their products or processes to the large-volume product because of its cost advantage. The major research and development programs of the industry have been concentrated on the search for low-cost raw materials for sulfonation and low-cost sulfonation processes. The product of choice has changed more than once. In 1965, linear alkylbenzenesulfonates replaced the branched alkylbenzenesulfonates which had displaced soap from many uses. Earlier, branched alkylbenzenesulfonates had replaced alkanesulfonates prepared by the Reed process (15, 15a). In this process, a saturated hydrocarbon is reacted with SO_2 and Cl_2 to yield an alkylsulfonyl chloride which is then hydrolyzed to the corresponding sulfonic acid.

$$RH + SO_2 + Cl_2 \xrightarrow[\text{light}]{\text{uv}} RSO_2Cl \xrightarrow[\text{water}]{\text{NaOH}} RSO_2ONa$$

High processing costs to obtain sulfonates with acceptable color and odor offset the advantages of the inexpensive raw materials. Several years ago, Du Pont withdrew from the market MP 189, the domestically manufactured Reed-type sulfonate. New developments could again displace the leading surfactant. Breakthroughs in lowering the manufacturing cost of the alkanesulfonates or of the newly introduced olefinsulfonates are possibilities. See Sulfonation and sulfation.

Sulfonation processes on surfactant raw materials can usually be adjusted to increase or decrease slightly the degree of substitution of the solubilizing group on the hydrophobe. The average molecular weight of the hydrophobic bases can also be increased or decreased slightly. Minor adjustments in these two variables can lead to significant differences in performance. Sulfonates are usually obtained in the production process as free acids that can be neutralized to form alkali metal salts, alkaline earth metal salts, or amine salts; thus neutralization is another parameter for modification of properties. Manipulation of these variables leads to products with a multiplicity of combinations of properties from the same raw materials and production equipment.

The *lignosulfonates* (see Lignin), a by-product of the kraft-paper industry, are frequently classified with surfactants; this is plausible since the products do perform some surfactant functions. However, they have not been considered in this article because, as Browning pointed out (16), they do not form an oriented layer in phase interfaces; do not form micelles; and they do not at low concentrations reduce surface tensions to the levels attained by surfactants.

Production of sulfonates in the U.S.A. in 1966 was divided among the product classes as shown in Table 6.

Table 6. U.S. Production of Sulfonates, 1966

Product classes	Production, 1000 lb
alkylbenzenesulfonates	596,416
petroleum sulfonates	246,912
sulfosuccinates	9,450
naphthalenesulfonates	8,277
N-acyl-N-alkyltaurates	2,797
β-sulfoesters of fatty acids	a
α-olefin sulfonates	a
all other sulfonates	99,960
total	963,812

a Data not available.

Alkylbenzenesulfonates. Linear dodecylbenzenesulfonates rank next to soaps in total usage. The sodium salt of linear dodecylbenzenesulfonate is commonly referred to as "LAS." Linear dodecylbenzenesulfonic acid is called LAS acid, and salts other than sodium are named in an analogous manner, eg LAS ammonium salt. LAS was introduced in 1965 as a replacement for "ABS," a branched alkylbenzenesulfonate, because the linear alkyl group is more readily biodegradable than the branched-chain substituent. Commercial dodecylbenzenesulfonic acid is a light-colored, viscous liquid that is used almost entirely as an intermediate for the manufacture of alkali metal, alkaline earth metal, and amine salts. LAS is marketed as a light-colored flake, granule, or bead at 90+% assay and as a viscous liquid, paste, or slurry at lower concentrations. The other salts of LAS acid are usually offered as viscous liquids or pastes at 40–90 wt % active ingredient. Although dodecylbenzenesulfonate salts are by far the largest-volume products in the group, usage of tridecylbenzenesulfonate is substantial. The physical properties of these homologs are similar to those of LAS acid salts.

In comparisons of the performance of alkylbenzenesulfonates to that of aliphatic sulfonates, the effect of the benzene ring is often considered as approximately equivalent to three carbon atoms in an aliphatic chain. Alkylbenzenesulfonic acids are strong organic acids and form essentially neutral alkali metal salts that have a good solubility in aqueous solutions at use concentrations over the entire pH range. These acids are not sensitive to precipitation by the natural hardness of surface waters, but the alkaline earth metal salts are less water soluble than the alkali metal and amine salts. The calcium salts are sufficiently soluble in hydrocarbons for use in these media. The alkylbenzenesulfonates are one of the most chemically stable types of surfactants. The sulfonic group is not susceptible to acidic or alkaline hydrolysis under normal conditions of storage or use. The compounds are stable to strong oxidizing agents in aqueous solutions at use concentrations and are stable in carefully formulated products containing oxidizing agents. Representative pure alkylbenzenesulfonates have been prepared by noncommercial syntheses and properties of the products have been studied (17–18).

The surface activity of unformulated, unbuilt dodecylbenzenesulfonates is sufficiently strong for the salts to be useful for their detersive, wetting, emulsifying, dispersing, and foaming properties, but they are not outstanding surfactants. The widespread usage of LAS stems from other factors which include their low cost, reproducible quality, adequate supply, light color, low odor, and excellent response to formulation and builders. For example, LAS solutions are only average foamers, but mixtures of LAS with alkanolamine or alkylamine oxide foam boosters have excellent foaming properties. Similarly, LAS performs well in built heavy-duty cleaning products where the wetting, foaming, emulsifying, and dispersing properties of the surfactant component are as important as the detergent power. Amine salts of LAS and ABS acids are used in blends with other emulsifiers, particularly the nonionic types, in emulsifiable concentrates of pesticides. Sweeney and Olson (20) compared the performance of LAS and ABS in built formulations and Rubinfeld, Emery, and Cross (7) investigated the relations of structure of LAS (ie isomer distribution) to performance properties.

Starting with the alkylation of benzene, production of LAS and its homologs is a three-step synthesis:

$$R-\underset{\underset{H}{|}}{\overset{\overset{R'}{|}}{C}}-Cl + C_6H_6 \xrightarrow{\text{catalyst}} R-\overset{\overset{R'}{|}}{C}HC_6H_5 + HCl \tag{1a}$$

or

$$R'-CH{:}CH-R + C_6H_6 \xrightarrow{\text{catalyst}} R'-\underset{}{\overset{\overset{CH_2-R}{|}}{C}}-C_6H_5 \tag{1b}$$

$$R-\overset{\overset{R'}{|}}{C}HC_6H_5 \xrightarrow[\text{reactant}]{\text{sulfonating}} R-\overset{\overset{R'}{|}}{C}HC_6H_4SO_3H \tag{2}$$

$$R-\overset{\overset{R'}{|}}{C}HC_6H_4SO_3H + NaOH \rightarrow R-\overset{\overset{R'}{|}}{C}HC_6H_4SO_3Na + H_2O \tag{3}$$

The product of step 1a or 1b is a secondary alkylbenzene with the point of attachment distributed randomly along the carbon chain of the alkyl group. See Alkylation;

Sulfonation and sulfation. Neutralization of the washed free acid may be carried out either by the manufacturer or by a formulator.

Production of alkylbenzenesulfonates aggregated 596,416,000 lb in the U.S.A. in 1966. Linear dodecylbenzenesulfonate free acid and salts accounted for 85% of this quantity. Tridecylbenzenesulfonates, which are very similar in properties, were next in volume. A representative list of commercially available alkylbenzenesulfonic acids and salts is shown in Table 7. Only one concentration of one physical form of a prod-

Table 7. Alkylbenzenesulfonates, $RC_6H_4SO_3M$

Product name	R^a	M	Concn, wt %	Biodegrad-ability	Functions[b]	Manufac-turer[c]
Ardet AB-40	dodecyl	Na	40	B	D	ARD
Conco AAS-50S	dodecyl	NH$_4$	50	B	D	CTL
Conco AAS-60S	dodecyl	TEA[d]	60	B	D	CTL
Conco AAS-90S	dodecyl	Na	90	B	D	CTL
Conco AAS-98S	dodecyl	H	98	B	D	CTL
Conco ATR-98S	tridecyl	H	98	B	D	CTL
Conoco C-550	lin. dodecyl		47	B	D	CO
Conoco C-650	lin. tridecyl		47	B	D	CO
Conoco SA-597	lin. dodecyl	H	97	B	D	CO
Conoco SA-697	lin. tridecyl	H	97	B	D	CO
Emkal NOBS	nonyl	Na	40		D	EMK
Nyapon W	lin. dodecyl	Na	45	B	D, W	CMG
Lanitol F	lin. alkyl	Na	40	B	D, F	AKS
Richonate A	dodecyl	NH$_4$	40	B	D	RCD
Richonate 40 B	dodecyl	Na	40	B	D	RCD
Retzannate SD-35	dodecyl	Na	35	B	D	RTF
Santomerse 85-b	lin. dodecyl	Na	85	B	D, W	MON
Sulfotex DBL-100	lin. alkyl	H	88	B	D, W, E	TXT
Sulfotex LAS-90	lin. alkyl	Na	90	B	D, W	TXT
Sul-Fon-Ate 10	dodecyl	Na	96		W, D	TNN
Solvadine G	lin. alkyl	Na		B	D, W, Di, E	CIB
Sole-Fonate 101 E	dodecyl	Amine	95		E	HDG
Sole-Fonate 102	dodecyl	Ca	70		E	HDG
Siponate LDS-10	dodecyl	Na	98	B	E, D	AAC
Sulframin 90 Flake	alkyl	Na	91	B	D, W	WTC
Sulframin 1298	dodecyl	H	98	B	D, W, E	WTC

[a] An expression such as "dodecyl" here refers to a branched radical $C_{12}H_{25}-$, "lin. dodecyl" to a linear $C_{12}H_{25}-$, with the attachment at any one of the ten internal carbon atoms.
[b] See Table 1.   [c] See Table 44.   [d] TEA = triethanolamine.

uct is included for each manufacturer—there may in fact be several. The functional properties are those listed by the vendor but the description of the composition has been shortened and restated in a more consistent form.

Petroleum Sulfonates. The petroleum sulfonates are the only large-volume class of surfactants that are used predominantly in nonaqueous systems. They are available as co-products of the refining of certain petroleum fractions. See Sulfonation and sulfation. They are usually grouped into two broad classes: (*1*) water-soluble types called *green soaps;* and (*2*) oil-soluble types called *mahogany soaps* (which may also be soluble in water).

The green soaps are of little use. The mahogany soaps are valuable for their properties of solubilization, detergency, dispersion, emulsification, and corrosion inhibition.

Their principal use is in lubricating oils for sludge dispersion, detergency, micellar solubilization of water, and corrosion inhibition. They are also widely used in other products for corrosion inhibition and emulsification. The chemistry, properties, and uses of the petroleum sulfonates have been described by Leslie (21) and Brown (21a). Alkylaromatic hydrocarbon sulfonates are the surfactant components in both product types. The green soaps contain a higher proportion of disulfonates than the mahogany sulfonates, which are principally monosulfonates.

Out of the 246,912,000 lb of petroleum sulfonate salts produced in the U.S.A. in 1966, almost 80% was used by the producer: 132,256,000 lb as the calcium salt, 73,177,000 lb as the sodium salt, and 41,479,000 lb as the barium salt. Producers of the products included Amoco, Humble, Mineral Oil and Refining, Chevron, Pennsylvania, and Witco.

Dialkyl Sulfosuccinates. In 1939, American Cyanamid Co. introduced the dialkyl sulfosuccinate surfactants under the Aerosol trademark and in 1941 Caryl reported on the properties of a series of compounds of this structure (11). Sodium di(2-ethylhexyl) sulfosuccinate, the largest volume product of the group, is now a widely used specialty surfactant. These sulfosuccinate esters are available as the sodium salt from several manufacturers. They are offered as white, waxy, odorless solids or as concentrated colorless solutions. The di-C_8 esters have the optimum solubility balance for use in tap water or aqueous solutions with a low inorganic-salt content; lower alkyl esters are more effective in saline solutions. Sodium dialkyl sulfosuccinates are highly surface active but the susceptibility of the ester linkage to acidic or alkaline hydrolysis limits their usefulness. The products have strong wetting, rewetting, penetration, and solubilization properties.

The symmetrical diesters are produced by esterification of maleic anhydride using conventional technology followed by addition of sodium bisulfite across the olefin linkage:

$$\begin{array}{ccc} \text{ROOCCH} & & \text{ROOCCHSO}_3\text{Na} \\ \| & + \text{ NaHSO}_3 \rightarrow & | \\ \text{ROOCCH} & & \text{ROOCCH}_2 \end{array}$$

See also Succinic acid.

Table 8 lists representative commercial dialkyl sulfosuccinate surfactant products by chemical composition and summarizes the manufacturers' recommendations of their use properties.

Naphthalenesulfonates. Four series of specialty surfactants make up the widely used but relatively low-volume group of naphthalenesulfonate products, viz: salts of alkylnaphthalenesulfonates; salts of sulfonated formaldehyde–naphthalene condensates; salts of naphthalenesulfonates; and salts of tetrahydronaphthalenesulfonates.

In the concentrated dry form, most of the salts are almost odorless light-gray solids. They are readily and highly soluble in water. In fact, except for the nonyl derivatives, the naphthalenesulfonates are generally too soluble to be strongly surface active in soft water. The naphthalenesulfonates are stable to hydrolysis in acidic or alkaline media and are not sensitive to oxidation by strong oxidizing agents under use conditions.

The naphthalenesulfonates are used in many different applications as wetting and dispersing agents. Several members of the series are effective as stabilizing and suspending agents in disperse systems. Some of the products are useful for their solubiliz-

Table 8. Sodium Dialkyl Sulfosuccinates

Product name	Alkyl group	Concn, wt %	Biodegrad-ability	Functions[b]	Manufac-turer[c]
Aerosol AY-100%	diamyl	100	B	W, E	ACY
Aerosol MA	dihexyl	80		W, E	ACY
Aerosol OT-100%	di(2-ethylhexyl)	100	B	W, E	ACY
Aerosol TR-100%	ditridecyl	100	B	E, Di	ACY
Alrowet D-65	dioctyl[a]	65		W	GGY
Crestopen	dioctyl	60		W	CRT
Dianol F-50	dioctyl	50		W	QCP
Duowet	dioctyl	50		W	GAF
Estranol RW 150	dioctyl	75		W	CRC
Monowet MB-70	diisobutyl	70	B	Di	MOA
Monowet MM-80	dihexyl	80	B	W, E	MOA
Monowet MO-75 W	dioctyl	75	B	W	MOA
Monowet MT-70	ditridecyl	70	B	E, Di, W	MOA
Nekal WT-27	dioctyl	70		W, rW	GAF
Pene-Tri-A-Nol O	dioctyl	60	B	W, rW, E	SCO
Rokyl DOS-75	dioctyl	75	B	W, E	ROZ
Shercowet DOS	dioctyl	75	B	W, E	SBC
Shercowet DHS	dihexyl	80	B	W, E	SBC
Tanasol 203	di(2-ethylhexyl)	60		W	CST
Tex-Wet 1001	dioctyl	75		W, rW	TCI

[a] It is noteworthy that this name is being used perfectly correctly to denote $CH_3(CH_2)_6CH_2-$.
[b] See Table 1.   [c] See Table 44.

ing properties. Hard water does not adversely affect the surface activity of typical members of the series.

Numerous processes for manufacture and purification of the various types of naphthalenesulfonates are described in the patent literature and BIOS Reports. The composition and properties of typical products are listed in Table 9.

Table 9. Naphthalenesulfonates, $RC_{10}H_6SO_3^-$

Product name	R or description	Cation	Concn, wt %	Functions[a]	Manufac-turer[b]
Aerosol OS	isopropyl	Na	75	W, Di	ACY
Alkanol S Flakes	tetrahydro	Na		Di, E, St	DUP
Blancol N	CH_2O condensed	Na	86	Di, Ta	GAF
Darvan No. 1	CH_2O condensed	Na	100	Di	VNC
Emkal BNX Powder	butyl	Na	80	W, Di, E	EMK
Emkal BNS Acid	butyl	H	90	W, Di, E	EMK
Emkal NNS	nonyl	Na	35	W, Di, E, D	EMK
Emkal NNS Acid	nonyl	H	90	W, Di, E, D	EMK
Immersol TX Paste		Na	68	W, D	CMG
Nekal BA-75	isopropyl	Na	65	W, Di, St	GAF
Nekal BX-78	butyl	Na	30	W, Di, St	GAF
Petro 250	complex dimethyl	Na	98	Di	PET
Stablex B	none	Na	100	Di	FIR
Syntan NNC	CH_2O condensed	Na	90	Di	BKS
Tamol N	CH_2O condensed	Na	100	Di	RH

[a] See Table 1.   [b] See Table 44.

N-Acyl-N-alkyltaurates (taurine is $H_2NCH_2CH_2SO_3H$, 2-aminoethanesulfonic acid). Relatively high raw material costs have held usage of the presently available N-acyl-N-alkyltaurates in the specialty category and have precluded the introduction of additional products with markedly different properties. The taurates are technically interesting as the only class of anionic surfactants with the combination of advantages: (*1*) They are stable against hydrolysis by acidic or alkaline media at use concentrations; (*2*) they show no loss of performance in hard water; (*3*) they have soaplike biodegradability and residual feel on washed fabrics; and (*4*) they have a molecular structure capable of yielding either strong wetting or strong detergent configurations (22). For example, the products $RCON(R')CH_2CH_2SO_3Na$ are strong detergents when $R = C_{11}–C_{17}$ and $R' = CH_3$ or C_2H_5, but are strong wetters when $R = R' = C_6–C_9$.

Sodium N-oleoyl-N-methyltaurate is available from several manufacturers as a light-yellow solid at about 70% assay or at lower concentrations in water as a light-colored slurry, solution, or gel. One producer, GAF, offers a wider range of taurine derivatives. The products are principally used in detergent applications without builders. Foaming of the N-methyl derivatives is only moderate and is not readily improved by the usual foam builders; the N-cyclohexyl derivatives are low-foaming detergents with good wetting power.

Yields average 95% or higher for each of the three chemical steps in the production of sodium N-oleoyl-N-methyltaurate:

$$H_2C\text{---}CH_2 + NaHSO_3 \rightarrow HOCH_2CH_2SO_3Na$$
$$\text{ethylene oxide}$$

$$CH_3NH_2 + HOCH_2CH_2SO_3Na \rightarrow CH_3NHCH_2CH_2SO_3Na + H_2O$$
$$\text{methylamine}$$

$$C_{17}H_{33}COCl + HN(CH)_3CH_2CH_2Na \xrightarrow{\text{pH 9+}} C_{17}H_{33}CON(CH_3)CH_2CH_2SO_3Na + NaCl$$
$$\text{oleoyl chloride}$$

Representative commercial products are listed in Table 10.

Table 10. Sodium N-acyl-N-alkyltaurates, $RR'NCH_2CH_2SO_3Na$, where R is acyl, R' is alkyl

Product name	R	R'	Concn, wt %	Biodegrad-ability	Functions[a]	Manufacturer[b]
Alkagel	oleoyl	methyl	40	B	D	AML
Amaterg T	oleoyl	methyl	65	B	W, D	AAP
Celopon	oleoyl	methyl	10	B	D, W	AKS
Concogel	oleoyl	methyl	14	B	D, W, Di	CTL
Cresterge L	oleoyl	methyl	32		D, W	CRT
Depcogel 3X	oleoyl	methyl	33	B	D, W	DEP
Igepon TC-42	coco acyl	methyl	24	B	D, F, Di	GAF
Igepon TN-74	palmitoyl	methyl	44	B	D, Di	GAF
Igepon TK-42	tall oil	methyl	20	B	D, Di	GAF
Igepon TE-42	tallow	methyl	24	B	D, Di	GAF
Igepon T-77	oleoyl	methyl	67	B	D, W, Di	GAF
Igepon CN-42	palmitoyl	cyclohexyl	23	B	D, Di	GAF
Tergenol S Liq	oleoyl	methyl	32		D	HRT
Textrapon	oleoyl	methyl			D	TXC
Wooncopon	oleoyl	methyl			D	WON

[a] See Table 1.   [b] See Table 44.

2-Sulfoethyl Esters of Fatty Acids.   These products, known commercially as β-sulfoesters, resemble closely in properties the fatty acids from which they are derived, but they have the advantage that hard water does not impair their performance.   Only the sensitivity of the ester linkage to hydrolysis has prevented their widespread usage in consumer detergents.   Hydrolysis is not a problem with detergents for personal use and the sodium salt of the 2-sulfoethyl ester of lauric acid, or the similar coconut acid mixture, has found acceptance as the foaming and cleansing ingredient in synthetic detergent bars.   The oleic acid analog is less foaming but is a good detergent with specialty uses in neutral or mildly alkaline systems.

The esters can be produced commercially from sodium isethionate (obtained by the reaction of ethylene oxide with a concentrated solution of sodium bisulfite) and the fatty acid or acyl chloride.   The reaction between the acyl chloride which is a viscous liquid and the powdered, anhydrous sodium isethionate is carried out in the absence of water or solvent under vacuum in a heavy-duty mixer.   After the total charge is added to the reactor and brought to temperature, HCl is rapidly evolved, leaving the finely divided, light-colored product as the sodium salt.

$$\text{RCOCl} + \text{HOCH}_2\text{CH}_2\text{SO}_3\text{Na} \rightarrow \text{RCOOCH}_2\text{CH}_2\text{SO}_3\text{Na} + \text{HCl}$$
$$\text{sodium isethionate}$$

At the present time, GAF is the only domestic vendor of the sodium 2-sulfoesters of fatty acids and production statistics are not available.

Olefin Sulfonates.   The increasing availability of relatively low cost linear 1-olefins in the C_{14} to C_{18} range has spurred research and commercial development of their sulfonate derivatives.   Sulfonation of a C_{15-18} 1-olefin is a complex reaction that leads to a mixture of sulfonates, of which the main components after hydrolysis of the intermediate sultones are $R'\text{CH}:\text{CH}(\text{CH}_2)_x\text{SO}_3\text{Na}$ where x has any value from 0 to 11, plus $\text{RCH}_2\text{CHOHCH}_2\text{CH}_2\text{SO}_3\text{Na}$ and $\text{RCHOHCH}_2\text{CH}_2\text{SO}_3\text{Na}$ (23).   The 3- and 4-hydroxysulfonates which may amount to as much as half of the yield of sulfonated products are not very water-soluble but they are solubilized in the presence of the more soluble olefin sulfonate.   The sulfonation mixture which is referred to as α-olefin sulfonate or AOS has detergency and foaming properties similar to C_{11-14} LAS.   It is superior in performance to similar products made from internal straight-chain olefins.   Biodegradability of the AOS is slightly better than LAS; toxicity and skin irritation are slightly less. Bioterge AS 40B, a product of Stephan Chemical Co., is believed to be used in light-duty detergent and specialty applications.   Interest in this type of product is widespread among potential users and suppliers (23a).   The ultimate cost and usage pattern of the 1-olefin sulfonates are yet to be determined.

Sulfates and Sulfated Products.   The hydrophilic group, $-\text{OSO}_3{}^-$, of the half sulfate ester surfactants is $-\text{SO}_3{}^-$ attached through an oxygen atom to a carbon atom in the hydrophobic moiety.   The additional oxygen makes the sulfate a stronger solubilizing group than the sulfonate but the C–O–S linkage of the sulfates is more easily hydrolysed than the C–S linkage of the sulfonates.   This susceptibility to hydrolysis, especially in acidic media, limits the utility of the sulfates.   Solubilization of hydrophobes through the combination of ethoxylation and sulfation is frequently used to obtain the optimum solubility balance and also to utilize less expensive raw materials that cannot be solubilized sufficiently by sulfation alone, eg derived from tallow alcohols.   The shift of the detergent industry to more biodegradable products in 1965 started a trend away from ethoxylated and sulfated alkylphenols and toward ethoxyl-

Table 11. U.S. Production of Sulfates and Sulfated Products, 1966

Product	Production, 1000 lb
sulfated alcohols	41,371
sulfated natural fats and oils	30,421
sulfated acids, amides, and esters	21,504
alkylphenols, ethoxylated and sulfated	9,601
alcohols, ethoxylated and sulfated	9,028
other sulfated esters[a]	120,673
total	232,598

[a] Presumably not detailed to avoid disclosing confidential data.

ated and sulfated aliphatic alcohols. The full effect of this replacement is not reflected in the U.S. production statistics for 1966 shown in Table 11. Within this group of sulfates and sulfated products there are numerous subdivisions.

Alkyl Sulfates (Sulfated Alcohols). Commercial production of alkyl sulfates started about 1930 and the products are well established in specialty markets. The hydrophobes are obtained by reduction of fatty acids or esters and the relatively high cost of the preferred C_{12} and C_{14} bases has held back growth of the products but this condition could change as less expensive synthetic primary alcohols are developed. Secondary alcohol sulfates prepared by the addition of sulfuric acid to an olefin have never been widely used in the U.S.A. although their usage in England at one time exceeded that of the alkylbenzene sulfonates. These products were marketed under the Teepol trademark of Shell Oil Company. Sulfates obtained from the normal primary alcohols are similar in performance properties and in feel or emollient characteristics to the soaps of corresponding molecular weight. The branched-chain alkyl sulfates are strong wetters. As the carbon-chain length increases, the temperature needed to attain maximum detergent and wetting effects also increases. The solubility, surface tension, foaming power, wetting power, and detergency of a series of purified sodium alkyl sulfates were reported by Dreger and others (9). The alkyl sulfates are usually sold as light-colored pastes or almost colorless solutions at concentrations in the range from 25 to 40 wt % of active ingredient. Purified sodium lauryl sulfates are offered by several manufacturers as light-colored powders or crystalline materials at activities of 90–99 wt %. Products with a low content of inorganic salts are almost odorless and tasteless.

The stability of the alkyl sulfates to hard water is excellent. In fact, magnesium lauryl sulfate forms voluminous foams with a low water content that are useful in rug shampoos where the soil is removed by vacuum pickup of the foam that is generated by vigorous brushing with a minimum volume of detergent solution. Sensitivity to hydrolysis in hot alkaline or acidic media is one of the principal disadvantages of the alkyl sulfates. As shown in Table 12 the alkyl sulfate series of products includes high-foaming detergents and strong wetters as well as effective emulsifiers and dispersants. Some of the products are used as lathering and cleansing agents in shampoos and dentifrices. Others are detergents and wetting agents for textile processing. Another use of the alkyl sulfates is as emulsifiers and dispersants in emulsion polymerization. Lauryl sulfates are offered by several manufacturers as the ammonium, sodium, potassium, magnesium, diethanolamine, and triethanolamine salts which is indicative of the marked influence of the cations on the performance properties of this series of anionic surfactants.

Table 12. Alkyl Sulfates, ROSO₃M

Product name	R	M	Concn, wt %	Biodegrad-ability	Functions[a]	Manufac-turer[b]
Avirol 101	lauryl	Na	30	B	D, W, Di	SCP
Avirol 106	2-ethylhexyl	Na	40	B	W, Di	SCP
Avirol 200	lauryl	NH₄	28	B	D, W, Di	SCP
Conco Sulfate WR	lauryl	Na	99	B	D	CTL
Conco Sulfate A	lauryl	NH₄	30	B	D, W	CTL
Conco Sulfate P	lauryl	K	30	B	D	CTL
Conco Sulfate EP	lauryl	DEA[c]	37	B	D, W	CTL
Conco Sulfate M	lauryl	Mg	30	B	D	CTL
Conco Sulfate TL	lauryl	TEA[d]	42	B	D, W	CTL
Conco Sulfate A	cetyl	Na	30	B	D	CTL
Conco Sulfate O	oleyl	Na	30	B	D	CTL
Conco Sulfate T	tallow	Na	30	B	D	CTL
Culverol ALS	lauryl	NH₄	30	B	D, F	CUL
Culverol DLS	lauryl	DEA[c]	40	B	D, E	CUL
Culverol KLS	lauryl	K	30	B	D, F	CUL
Culverol MgLS	lauryl	Mg	30	B	D, F, E	CUL
Culverol SLS	lauryl	Na	30	B	D	CUL
Culverol TAS	lauryl	TEA[d]	40	B	D, F	CUL
Duponol 80	octyl	Na		B	W, Di, E	DUP
Duponol AM	lauryl	NH₄		B	D	DUP
Duponol WA Dry	lauryl	Na		B	D	DUP
Emcol D5-10	2-ethylhexyl	Na		B	W	EMK
Maprofix NHL	lauryl	NH₄	30	B	D, F	OXR
Maprofix WA Paste	lauryl	Na	30	B	D, F	OXR
Maprofix 2109	lauryl	DEA[c]	75	B	D, F	OXR
Maprofix TLS-65	lauryl	TEA[d]	65	B	D, F	OXR
Maprofix TAS	tallow	Na	30	B	D, Di	OXR
Maprofix MG	lauryl	Mg	30	B	W, D	OXR

Natural Fats and Oils, Sulfated. The first commercial surfactant other than soap was a sulfated olive oil that was introduced a little before 1850 as a textile processing auxiliary. In the intervening years the sulfates of almost every potentially available animal, vegetable, and fish oil have been investigated. Ricinoleic acid, ie 12-hydroxy-9,10-octadecenoic acid, which contains one hydroxyl group and one double bond, is a desirable constituent of an oil for sulfation. Oleic acid is also satisfactory. Esters of these acids can usually be sulfated with a minimum of hydrolysis. Polyunsaturated fatty acid moieties are undesirable components of glycerides for sulfation since the resulting surfactants are usually dark in color and sensitive to oxidation. The reaction of sulfuric acid with either —CH=CH— or —OH groups in natural fats and oils yields sulfate half-esters which are neutralized in a later processing step, usually with caustic soda:

$$\text{R'CH=CH} + \text{H}_2\text{SO}_4 \rightarrow \text{R'CH}_2\overset{\text{R}}{\underset{|}{\text{CH}}}\text{—O—SO}_3\text{H} \tag{1}$$

$$\text{R'CH}_2\overset{\text{R}}{\underset{|}{\text{CH}}}\text{—OH} + \text{H}_2\text{SO}_4 \rightarrow \text{R'CH}_2\overset{\text{R}}{\underset{|}{\text{CH}}}\text{—O—SO}_3\text{H} \tag{2}$$

$$\text{R'CH}_2\overset{\text{R}}{\underset{|}{\text{CH}}}\text{—O—SO}_3\text{H} + \text{NaOH} \rightarrow \text{R'CH}_2\overset{\text{R}}{\underset{|}{\text{CH}}}\text{—O—SO}_3\text{Na} \tag{3}$$

Table 12 (*continued*)

Product name	R	M	Concn, wt %	Biodegrad-ability	Functions[a]	Manufac-turer[b]
Maprofix MSP90	myristyl	Na	90	B	E, Di, D	OXR
Richanol WA	lauryl	Na	90	B	D, W	RCD
Richanol AM	lauryl	NH₄	30	B	D, W	RCD
Richanol T	lauryl	TEA[c]	40	B	D, W	RCD
Sipex BOS	2-ethylhexyl	Na	40		W, E	AAC
Sipex OLS	octyl	Na	33	B	E	AAC
Sipex SD	lauryl	Na	90	B	D, Di, E	AAC
Sipex TDS	tridecyl	Na	25	B	E, W	AAC
Sipon L-22	lauryl	NH₄	28	B	D, F	AAC
Sipon LM	lauryl	Mg	27	B	D, F	AAC
Sipon WD Cry.	lauryl	Na	98	B	D, F	AAC
Sipon LT6	lauryl	TEA[c]	40	B	D, F	AAC
Sipon GW	cetyl	Na	25	B	D, F	AAC
Solasol FFA	lauryl	Na	95	B	D	ACI
Sole Terge TS-2-S	2-ethylhexyl	Na	35	B	W, P	HDG
Standapol A	lauryl	NH₄	28	B	D, F	SCP
Standapol WA	lauryl	Na	30	B	D, F	SCP
Standapol DEA	lauryl	DEA[c]	36	B	D, F	SCP
Standapol T	lauryl	TEA[d]	40	B	D, F	SCP
Stepanol WA-100	lauryl	Na	99	B	D	STP
Stepanol DEA	lauryl	DEA[c]	35	B	D	STP
Stepanol TEA	lauryl	TEA[d]	40	B	D	STP
Surco AM	lauryl	NH₄	30	B	D	SUR
Surco DEA-LS	lauryl	DEA	35	B	D	SUR
Surco MG	lauryl	Mg	30	B	D	SUR
Surco SLS	lauryl	Na	30	B	D	SUR
Surco TEA-LS	lauryl	TEA[d]	40	B	D	SUR
Tergitol 4	C₁₄H₂₉[e]	Na	28		W, P, E	UCC
Tergitol 08	2-ethylhexyl	Na	40		W, E	UCC
Tergitol 7	C₁₇H₃₅[f]	Na	27		W, E	UCC
Trisco VS	cetyl		41		Di, P	SCO

[a] See Table 1.	[b] See Table 44.	[c] DEA = diethanolamine.
[d] TEA = triethanolamine.	[e] 7-Ethyl-2-methyl-4-undecyl.	[f] 3,9-Diethyl-6-tridecyl.

Reaction 1 is more important commercially than 2 since the hydrophobes used for sulfation always contain unsaturation but only a few of them contain an appreciable quantity of hydroxyl groups. Solubility in water increases with the degree of sulfation but forcing the reaction to obtain greater water solubility usually causes undesirable side reactions such as hydrolysis of glyceride linkages. Solvent extraction is used to attain higher degrees of sulfation by the removal of unsulfated organic compounds.

The sulfated fats and oils are widely used as emulsifying agents, wetting agents, detergents, penetrants, dispersants, textile softeners, and textile lubricants. The highly sulfated products are more effective as surfactants for aqueous processing, but for use as lubricants and softeners the less completely sulfated derivatives are often more effective.

The 1966 production in the U.S.A. of 31,421,000 lb of sulfated natural fats and oils was fairly evenly distributed among derivatives of tallow, castor oil, sperm oil, coconut oil, cod oil, and neat's-foot oil; lesser quantities of peanut oil, soybean oil, and rice-bran oil were converted. These products are the half sulfate esters and were neutralized to form the sodium salts. The products are usually sold under a generic description rather than a trade name, eg 75% sulfated castor oil or sulfated peanut oil, 50%. Compositions and properties of a few trade-named products are shown in Table 13. There are over thirty producers of sulfated natural oils in the United States.

Table 13. Natural Fats and Oils, Sulfated

Product name[a]	Fat or oil	Concn, wt %	Biodegrad- ability	Functions[b]	Manufac- turers[c]
Laurel Textile Oil	castor	75	B	D, W, Ts, E	LUR
Modicol P	sperm	75	B	W, Di	NOP
Monopol Oil 48	castor	48	B	W, Ti, Ts	GAF
Monopole Oil	castor	80		E, Di	NOP
Monosulph	castor[a]	68	B	P, E	NOP
Nopco 1408	castor	47	B	E	NOP

[a] Highly sulfated.   [b] See Table 1.   [c] See Table 44.

Sulfated Oleic Acid. U.S. production of the disodium salt of sulfated oleic acid amounted to 8,699,000 lb in 1966. This product, which is the largest volume item of the sulfated fatty acids, is used as a textile processing assistant. It is a good dispersing agent for lime soap.

Sulfated Alkanolamides. A typical product of this class would be the sodium salt of the half sulfate ester of lauric ethanolamide, ie $C_{11}H_{23}CONHCH_2CH_2OSO_3Na$. Variations in the product type include mono- and diethanolamides of all of the fatty acids in the range C_{12} to C_{18}. The degree of sulfation is adjusted to obtain the desired solubility in water. See also Alkanolamines. The alkanolamide sulfates are somewhat more stable toward hydrolysis at high temperatures, in alkaline or acidic media, and in hard water than the sulfates of fatty acid esters or glycerides. The products are effective detergents with good foaming and lathering properties. They add viscosity or "body" to aqueous solutions and are widely used in the formulation of janitorial cleaners and textile auxiliaries. Statistics on the production of sulfated alkanolamides in the U.S.A. are not definitive but the indication is that the products do not exceed 5,000,000 lb in annual volume.

Sulfated Esters. Oleic acid and ricinoleic acid esterified with low-molecular-weight alcohols and then sulfated yield useful surfactants. A typical product of this type would be $CH_3(CH_2)_7CH_2CH(OSO_3Na)CH_2(CH_2)_5CH_2COOR$ from the sulfation of an oleic acid ester in which the R represents an ethyl, propyl, butyl, or amyl group. Products of this type are marketed as clear yellow to brown viscous solutions with an active-ingredient content as high as 85 wt %. The balance is water and sometimes as much as 10% of pine oil or terpineol. See Terpenes. The sulfated esters have strong wetting and rewetting power combined with a lubricant effect on textile fibers. They also have good foaming, emulsifying, and detergent properties. The products are stable enough in hot solutions of dilute caustic soda for use as wetting agents in kier boiling and continuous bleaching processes.

Production of the sulfated oleic acid esters does not require elaborate or expensive equipment and even though the total volume is small there are several manufacturers in the U.S.A. including Houghton, Onyx, Arkansas, Nopco, Dexter, and others. U.S.

production of the sodium salts of the half sulfuric acid esters of oleic acid totaled 6,597,000 lb in 1966.

Alkylphenols, Ethoxylated and Sulfated. Sulfated polyoxyethylene alkylphenols were introduced to the U.S. market about 1950. By 1966, the ammonium and sodium salts of the sulfate esters of nonylphenoxytri(ethyleneoxy)ethanols were widely used in retail and industrial detergent products. The salts of the sulfate ester of dodecylphenoxypenta(ethyleneoxy)ethanol were also consumed in substantial volume. The nonyl and dodecyl substituents were from highly branched propylene trimer and tetramer respectively and the alkylated phenol was primarily an ortho, para mixture of monoalkylated products containing some di- and trialkylated derivatives. These products were replaced during 1965 with more easily biodegradable surfactants for applications in which the waste surfactant solution is discarded as effluent into treatment systems. Alkylphenols derived from linear olefins, ethoxylated and sulfated, were introduced as replacements. The data of Table 14 suggest that biodegradability

Table 14. Alkylphenols, Ethoxylated and Sulfated, $RC_6H_4(OCH_2CH_2)_nOSO_3M$

Product name	R	n	M	Concn, wt %	Biodegrad-ability	Functions[a]	Manufac-turer[b]
Alipal CO-433	nonyl	4	Na	28		D, F, W, Di, E	GAF
Alipal CO-436	nonyl	4	NH_4	58		D, F, W, Di, E	GAF
Cellopal 40	alkyl		Na	40		D, F, E, W, Di	TCC
Cellopal 100	alkyl		TEA	100		D, F, E, W, Di	TCC
Concopal AS	linear alkyl		NH_4	60	B	D, F, W, E	CTL
Cocopal SS	linear alkyl		Na	30	B	D, F, W, E	CTL
Neutronyx S-60	alkyl		NH_4	60		D, F	OXR
Neutronyx S-30	alkyl		Na	30		D, F	OXR
Sulfotex BTS	linear alkyl			60	B	D, F	TXT
Triton W-30	alkyl		Na	27		W, E, P	RH
Triton X-200	alkyl		Na	28		D, W, E, Di	RH

[a] See Table 1.   [b] See Table 44.

and performance properties of the new products are satisfactory. It is reported that a high proportion of the *o*-phenyl isomer is necessary to obtain a satisfactory level of biodegradability, but all of the alkylphenol hydrophobes contain para- as well as ortho-isomers and frequently have an appreciable dialkyl content.

The sulfated polyoxyethylenealkylphenols are marketed as colorless, odorless, aqueous solutions at concentrations from 30 to 60 wt % of active ingredient. The more concentrated products often contain 12–15% of ethanol to reduce the viscosity and facilitate handling. These surfactants are high-foaming detergents, strong wetters, and efficient emulsifiers and dispersants that perform effectively in hard as well as soft water. They are mild to the skin, particularly in well-formulated retail detergent products. The largest use of the ethoxylated alkylphenol sulfates is in high-foaming liquid dishwashing detergents. Significant quantities are also consumed in emulsion polymerizations and textile processing. The polyoxyethylene in the molecules in this product series improves their performance over the unethoxylated analogs by decreasing the sensitivity to hard water and by decreasing the skin irritation. It also makes the products more water soluble. Approximately 30–40 wt % of polyoxyethylene is the optimum proportion for most uses.

Amidosulfuric acid (see Sulfamic acid) is uniquely effective as the sulfating agent for alkylphenoxypolyoxyethyleneethanol, giving conversions as high as 99% with no side reactions, eg:

$$C_9H_{19}C_6H_4(OCH_2CH_2)_4OH + H_2NSO_3H \rightarrow C_9H_{19}C_6H_4(OCH_2CH_2)_4OSO_3NH_4$$

This sulfation technique is only applicable directly to the formation of the ammonium salt. Sodium salts can be prepared commercially by adding caustic soda and driving off the ammonia with heat. Sulfation processes using sulfur trioxide, chlorosulfuric acid, or oleum, lead to small percentages of ring sulfonations and thus cause a significant loss in surfactant effectiveness. See Sulfonation and sulfation.

Alcohols, Ethoxylated and Sulfated. The alkylpolyoxyethylene sulfates have been on the market about as long as the analogous alkylphenoxypolyoxyethylene sulfates but the higher cost of the fatty alcohol starting material held back growth of their derivatives in the cost-conscious, larger-volume markets. The efforts of the surfactant industry to provide more biodegradable products have made available petroleum-derived straight-chain primary and secondary alcohols in larger volume and at a lower cost than is attainable from vegetable or animal sources. See Alcohols, higher, synthetic.

In addition to the immediate replacement of branched-chain nonyl- and dodecyl-phenoxypolyoxyethyleneethyl sulfates in consumer detergents, a long-term shift to alcohol-based polyoxyethylene sulfates is expected as industrial products are reformulated.

The advantages of the ethoxylated and sulfated alcohols over the plain sulfated alcohols are (*1*) improved foaming, particularly in hard water, (*2*) decreased irritation of eyes and skin, (*3*) increased solubility in water, and (*4*) lower raw-material cost as

Table 15. Alcohols, Ethoxylated and Sulfated, $R(OCH_2CH_2)_nOSO_3M$

Product name	R	n	M	Concn, wt %	Biodegradability	Functions[a]	Manufacturer[b]
Alipal AB-436	linear		NH₄	58	B	D, E, Di, W	GAF
Avirol 100-E	lauryl		Na	28	B	D, W, Di	SCP
Avirol 113-E	tridecyl			30		W, E, Di	SCP
Calfoam S-30	lauryl		Na	30	B	D, F, E	PIL
Maprofix MB	lauryl	3.5	NH₄	30	B	D, E, Di, W	OXR
Maprofix MBO	lauryl	1.0	NH₄	30	B	F, D, E	OXR
Maprofix ES	lauryl		Na	30	B	F, Di	OXR
Maprofix OX	tridecyl		Na	30	B	E	OXR
Neodol 23-3A	C_{12-13} linear	3.0	NH₄	58	B	D	SHC
Richonol S-1285	lauryl		Na	55	B	D, F	RCD
Richonol S-1300	lauryl		NH₄	60	B	D, F	RCD
Richonol S-5465	lauryl		TEA	40	B	D, F	RCD
Sipex EST-60	tridecyl		Na	57		E	AAC
Sipon EA	lauryl		NH₄	27	B	D, F	AAC
Sipon ES	lauryl		Na	27	B	D, F, E	AAC
Standapol EA-1	lauryl		NH₄	27	B	D, F	SCP
Standapol ES-3	lauryl		Na	28	B	D, F	SCP
Standapol EA-40	myristyl		NH₄	60	B	D, F	SCP
Standapol ES-40	myristyl		Na	60	B	D	SCP
Steol CS-460	coco		Na	60	B	D, E	STP
Sulfotex EL	lauryl		Na	30	B	D, F	TXT

[a] See Table 1.   [b] See Table 44.

long as ethylene oxide is cheaper than the alcohols used for sulfation. The polyoxy-ethylene content is adjusted to obtain optimum performance for the intended use but usually its variation is within the range of 10–40% of the molecular weight calculated as the sodium salt. The polyoxyethylene alkyl sulfates are offered as essentially color-less, odorless liquids at concentrations from approx 25 to 60 wt % of active ingredient. The viscosity of the solutions increases with the concentration unless alcohol is used as a diluent. The products are stable and compatible with builders in liquid and solid alkaline formulations. The sulfate linkage is susceptible to hydrolysis by hot acidic solutions and is more slowly cleaved by hot alkaline media. The sulfated polyoxy-ethylene alcohols are high-foaming detergents, emulsifiers, dispersants, and wetting agents. They are widely used in hand dishwashing detergents, shampoos, emulsion polymerization, and textile processing. Table 15 lists the compositions and properties of typical commercial products. The properties of well-characterized alcohol ether sulfates have been described by Weil et al. (24–26).

High conversions can be obtained in the sulfation of the alkylpolyoxyethylenes with chlorosulfuric acid, oleum, amidosulfuric acid, and sulfur trioxide. The long-run economics favor sulfur trioxide, particularly as the technology of the process is still being improved.

$$R(OCH_2CH_2)_nOH + SO_3 \rightarrow R(OCH_2CH_2)_nOSO_3H$$

The free acid from the sulfation can be neutralized to form any desired salt.

Phosphate Esters. Alkyl orthophosphate and alkyl polyphosphate surfactants have been known and produced in small volumes for over twenty years. Di(2-ethyl-hexyl) phosphate is typical of the orthophosphate esters. It is insoluble in acidic media but stable and soluble in alkaline solutions, where it is useful as a wetting, emulsifying, and solubilizing agent. A typical polyphosphate is $(2\text{-ethylhexyl})_5Na_5$-$(P_3O_{10})_2$, a wetting, emulsifying, and dispersing agent that is used as an assistant in textile processing and metal fabrication. See also Phosphoric acids. Total production of all alkyl phosphates and polyphosphates, free acids and salts, was 5,090,000 lb in the U.S.A. in 1966. Ethoxylated phosphate esters have never been used extensively al-though one product, $(CH_3CH(C_2H_5)CH_2CH_2CH_2CH_2O)_2P(O)(OCH_2CH_2)_nOH$, has been available in semicommercial quantities for almost as long as the alkyl phosphates.

The partial phosphate esters of nonionics were introduced about ten years ago and their usage has grown steadily at a moderate rate in diverse specialty applications. These products are such complex mixtures that a list of reactants and conditions is the most revealing description of their composition, eg 1 mole of lauryltri(ethyleneoxy)-ethanol phosphorylated with $\frac{1}{3}$ mole of P_2O_5 at 50°C for 5 hr and neutralized with 50% aqueous NaOH. After hydrolysis of the P–O–P linkages, such a product would be a mixture of the following components:

$C_{12}H_{25}(OCH_2CH_2)_4OPO_3HNa$	monoester, major fraction
$(C_{12}H_{25}(OCH_2CH_2)_4)_2PO_2Na$	diester, large fraction
$(C_{12}H_{25}(OCH_2CH_2)_4)_3PO$	triester, minor fraction

$$O\!-\!\overset{|}{\underset{|}{P}}\!-\!(OCH_2CH_2)_nO\!-\!\overset{|}{\underset{|}{P}}\!\rightarrow\!O \qquad \text{esters}$$

$$H(OCH_2CH_2)_m\!-\!O\!-\!\overset{|}{\underset{|}{P}}\!\rightarrow\!O \qquad \text{esters}$$

$$NaH_2PO_3 \qquad \text{trace}$$

The two esters are derivatives of the polyethylene glycol that is present in ethoxylated aliphatic alcohols.

The $C_{12}H_{25}(OCH_2CH_2)_{"4"}O-$ group is also a mixture in which the "4" is an average of an actual distribution in which all of the integral values from 0 to 10 inclusive are represented by appreciable fractions. The lauryl group, $C_{12}H_{25}-$, also represents an average composition of a mixture containing C_{10}, C_{12}, and C_{14} components.

The example given above cited P_2O_5, but polyphosphoric acid and $POCl_3$ can also be used as phosphorylating reactants.

Nonionic bases for phosphorylation include ethoxylated alcohols, ethoxylated alkylphenols, and polyoxypropylene–polyoxyethylene copolymers.

Synthetic approaches to the various types of phosphate ester surfactants have been reported by Nusslein (27). The undiluted products are light-colored, almost odorless, viscous liquids or soft waxes. They are stable in alkaline solutions and are available in a wide range of electrolyte compatibilities. Foaming power varies with composition from values intermediate between the nonionic sulfates and nonionics downward to about nonionic levels. Functional properties also vary with composition and are usually balanced to optimize some combination of detergency, wetting, emulsification, solubilization, dispersion, corrosion inhibition, textile lubrication, and antistatic protection of textiles. Some of the compositions are characterized by solubility balances that are fairly strong in both lipophilic and hydrophilic tendencies, which is an unusual and desirable combination. The products are used as additives to electroplating baths; drycleaning detergents; hard-surface detergents; gelling agents and detergents in waterless hand cleaners and cosmetic products; dedusting agents for

Table 16. Phosphate Ester Surfactants (28)

Component	Cation	Manufacturer[b]
2-ethylhexyl phosphate	H, Na	SEY, UCC, UVC, WAY
octyl phosphate	H, K, M[a]	DUP, SFA
decyl phosphate	M[a]	DUP
dodecyl phosphate	M[a]	DUP
octadecyl phosphate	TEA	RCD
9-octadecenyl phosphate	H	DUP
mixed alkyl phosphate	H	BCN, CST, DUP
hexyl polyphosphate	K	CST, DEX
2-ethylhexyl polyphosphate	H	UVC
octyl polyphosphate	H, Na, K	DEX, TXT, SFA
decyl polyphosphate	TEA	MOA, RCD
2-ethylhexanol, ethoxylated and phosphated	H	TCI, WAY
"iso-octyl" alcohol, ethoxylated and phosphated	H	GAF
dodecyl alcohol, ethoxylated and phosphated	H, Ba	GAF
tridecyl alcohol, ethoxylated and phosphated	H	GAF, LUR, NLC, WAY
9-octadecen-1-ol, ethoxylated and phosphated	H	GAF
mixed linear alcohols, ethoxylated and phosphated	H	CRT, CST, GAF, SEY
phenol, ethoxylated and phosphated	H	GAF
octylphenol, ethoxylated and phosphated	H, Mg	RH
dodecylphenol, ethoxylated and phosphated	H, Ba	TCI
dinonylphenol, ethoxylated and phosphated	H	GAF
nonylphenol, ethoxylated and phosphated	H, Ba	GAF, NLC, RTF, SEY, TCC

[a] M = morpholine.   [b] See Table 44.

powdered alkaline detergent formulations; polymerization emulsifiers; and components of metal cutting or lubricating fluids.

The gross compositions of commercial phosphate esters of nonionics that are shown in Table 16, although not precise, include all of the available data on compositions. Production of these products in the U.S.A. reached 7,866,000 lb in 1966.

NONIONIC SURFACTANTS

A nonionic surfactant, as the name implies, bears essentially no charge when dissolved or dispersed in aqueous media. The hydrophilic tendency in a nonionic is due primarily to oxygen in the molecule which hydrates by hydrogen bonding to water molecules (29). The strongest hydrophilic moieties in nonionics are ether linkages and hydroxyl groups, but ester and amide linkages, which are also hydrophilic, are present in many nonionics. The contribution of each oxygen to solubilization is weak and nonionic molecules must contain a multiplicity of them in order to be water soluble. Nearly all of the unmodified polyol surfactants are lipophilic and they are frequently used as coemulsifiers in combinations with more hydrophilic surfactants. One advantage of the nonionics is that they are compatible with ionic and amphoteric surfactants. Polyoxyethylene solubilization is the key to the substantial and continuing growth of the nonionics. Since the polyoxyethylene group can be introduced into almost any organic compound that has a reactive hydrogen, a wide range of organic substances can be solubilized by ethoxylation. Subdivision of the nonionics into classes in accordance with the composition of the solubilizing groups is not as straightforward as with the ionic surfactants.

Polyoxyethylene Surfactants. The polyoxyethylene-solubilized nonionics were introduced in the U.S. as textile auxiliaries a little before 1940. The solubility of these products depends on recurring ether linkages in a polyoxyethylene chain, eg $-CH_2CH_2-O-CH_2CH_2-O-CH_2CH_2-O-$. A solubilized molecule may contain more than one such polymer chain. The hydrophilic tendency increases with the polyoxyethylene content of the molecule and 60–75% by wt is required on most surfactant hydrophobes for complete miscibility with water at room temperature. Another rule of thumb is that the hydrophilic strength of one ethylene oxide unit, $-CH_2CH_2-O-$, is approximately equal to the hydrophobic strength of one methylene unit, $-CH_2-$. The water solubility of polyoxyethylene compounds decreases as the temperature increases, which is attributed to a decrease in the degree of hydration or to an increase in the size of the micelles (30,31). The temperature at which a second phase appears is called the *cloud point*, a practical solubility test that is not sensitive to concentration differences in the range between 0.5 and 10 wt % (32). A minor proportion of anionic mixed with a nonionic will often raise the cloud point several degrees. Surface activity and performance efficiency of polyoxyethylene nonionics are usually greatest at temperatures just below the cloud point. As would be expected from their composition, the surface activity of polyoxyethylene nonionics is not adversely affected by hard water. High electrolyte concentrations in which sodium ions are the predominant component decrease the solubility of polyoxyethylene compounds by a salting-out effect, whereas hydrochloric acid and calcium ions increase their solubility. Nonionic surfactants solubilize iodine in aqueous solutions and lessen its toxicity to humans, but do not weaken its biocidal activity to the lower forms of life (33). The polyoxyethylene surfactants are moderate foamers and do not respond to the conventional foam boosters. Fineman, Brown, and Meyers showed that nonionics exhibit a foam maximum as a function of polyoxyethylene content (34). Low-foaming nonionics are prepared by terminating the polyoxy-ethylene chain with a less soluble group, eg polypropylene oxide. A significant advantage of solubilization by means of polyoxyethylene is the capability of attaining almost any hydrophilic/hydrophobic balance. A shortcoming is that the polyoxyethylene nonionics tend to be liquids or low-melting waxes that are difficult to incorporate into dry, free-flowing powders. Flaked-solid products containing a high ratio of polyoxy-ethylene are manufactured but their surface activity is low because they are too hydrophilic.

Ethoxylation. The conversion of an aliphatic alcohol, alkylphenol, or fatty acid into a polyoxyethylene derivative can be divided into two steps: (*1*) addition of ethylene oxide to the hydrophobe to form a monoadduct, followed by (*2*) subsequent addition(s) of ethylene oxide in a polymerization reaction. Ethoxylations of these hydrophobes are catalysed by bases. The sequence of reactions is shown in equations 4, 5, and 6.

$$RO^- + H_2C\overset{O}{\overset{\triangle}{-}}CH_2 \xrightarrow{\text{slow}} ROCH_2CH_2O^- \tag{4}$$

$$ROH + ROCH_2CH_2O^- \xrightarrow{\text{fast}} RO^- + ROCH_2CH_2OH \tag{5}$$

$$ROCH_2CH_2O^- + H_2C\overset{O}{\overset{\triangle}{-}}CH_2 \xrightarrow{\text{fast}} ROCH_2CH_2OCH_2CH_2O^- \tag{6}$$

Equation 4 represents the rate-controlling step; the reaction rate of the hydrophobes decreases in the order primary alcohols > phenols > carboxylic acids (35). Buildup of polymer chains on carboxylates and alkylphenols does not start until all of the base has been converted to the monoadduct. Polymerization continues until all of the ethylene oxide has reacted. After the first step, the reactivity is essentially independent of the chain length. The effectiveness of ethoxylation catalysts increases with their basicity. Ratios of 0.005 to 0.05 mole of NaOH, NaOCH$_3$, or KOH per mole of hydrophobe are frequently used. Reaction temperatures range from 100 to 200°C, depending on the hydrophobe and the properties desired. Polyoxyethylene-solubilized nonionics are polydisperse mixtures of compounds that differ principally in the distribution of the polymer chain lengths. Their properties usually approximate those of the pure isomer represented by their average composition.

Ethoxylation is normally carried out as a batch reaction although continuous reactors have been designed and operated. The hydrophobe and a solution of catalyst are charged into a reactor. Air and solvent for the catalyst are removed by agitating and heating under a vacuum, or purging with nitrogen, or both. When the hydrophobe is at the reaction temperature, addition of ethylene oxide is started. The polymerization is exothermic (20 kcal/mole of ethylene oxide reacted) and the rate of ethylene oxide addition should not exceed the cooling capacity of the reactor since careful maintenance of the reaction temperature is essential for reproducible manufacture of products to specifications. The end point of ethylene oxide addition is often determined by testing the solubility of a sample for its cloud point in water, a salt solution, or a water–solvent mixture. After the reaction is complete, the catalyst is neutralized and the product is discharged to storage or packaged.

Nonionic Product Groups. The U.S. production of nonionic surfactants in 1966 was divided fairly evenly among the product classes shown in Table 17.

Table 17. U.S. Production of Nonionic Surfactants, 1966

Product class	Production, 1000 lb
ethoxylated alkylphenols	234,032
ethoxylated aliphatic alcohols	209,839
carboxylic esters	146,370
carboxylic amides	93,020
polyoxyalkylene oxide block copolymers[a]	
miscellaneous nonionics	2,432
total	685,693

[a] Production statistics not released; only one manufacturer.

Ethoxylated Alkylphenols. Nonylphenoxypoly(ethyleneoxy)ethanols were, until 1966, the most widely used nonionic surfactants; the combined usage of dodecyl and octylphenols ran somewhat lower. Historically the alkyl substituents on these phenols have been propylene dimers, trimers, or tetramers and therefore highly branched. Both ortho- and para-isomers plus an appreciable dialkyl fraction were present in the commercial products. Surfactant manufacturers started replacing these hydrophobes with the more easily biodegradable linear alkyl substituted phenols in 1965. The differences between linear substituted alkylphenols and branched-chain substituted alkylphenols of the same molecular weight are no greater than the differences between branched-chain alkylphenols from different sources. This is fortunate since much fundamental data have been published on the physical properties, chemical properties, uses, and production of branched-chain alkylphenoxypoly(ethyleneoxy)ethanols.

Undiluted polyoxyethylated C_8 to C_{12} alkylphenols have a slight aromatic odor and vary from pale yellow to almost colorless. Products with low polyoxyethylene content are liquids and their viscosity increases with the content of combined ethylene oxide. High ratios of polyoxyethylene to hydrophobe are waxes. The specific gravity at room temperature increases with polyoxyethylene content from <1 until it levels off at about 1.2. Physical properties of the polyoxyethylated higher alkylphenols, eg dinonylphenol and hexadecylphenol, are similar to those of the C_8 to C_{12} derivatives with the same wt % of combined ethylene oxide.

The solubility in water of the ethoxylated alkylphenols increases with the polyoxyethylene content. About 60 wt % of polyoxyethylene is required for complete miscibility in cold water, and above 75% of polyoxyethylene the products do not cloud out at the boiling point. Water hardness does not adversely affect the surface activity of the products. The solubility of polyoxyethylene alkylphenols in highly aliphatic mineral oils decreases faster with increasing polyoxyethylene content than the water solubility increases. Solubility in aromatic solvents and unsaturated triglycerides persists at higher mole ratios of combined ethylene oxide to hydrophobe. The excellent stability of the polyoxyethylene alkylphenols against decomposition is demonstrated by their uses: in formulations for acid cleaning of metals; in hot alkaline detergent systems; and in oil-well drilling fluids for use at high bottom-hole temperatures.

The maximum surface activity of the unformulated polyoxyethylene alkylphenols in water hardnesses of 0–300 ppm is associated with polyoxyethylene proportions in the range of 50–75 wt %. The optimum composition varies somewhat within this range depending on the property. For example, maximum wetting efficiency in the Draves test (36) usually occurs at a lower polyoxyethylene percentage in a product series than maximum foaming in the Ross Miles test (37). Typical commercial products of poly-

Table 18. Alkylphenoxypoly(ethyleneoxy)ethanols (Ethoxylated Alkylphenols)

Product name	Alkyl group	MR[a]	Concn, wt %	Biodegrad-ability	Functions[b]	Manufac-turer[c]
Adsee 50			80		W, E	RTF
Advawet			100		W, E	CCA
Agrimul 70A			100		E	NOP
Atkaflo-E			100		E	NTL
Brites EOC-10	nonyl		100		W, D	BRI
Carboxane DO			100		D, E	TXT
Carboxane NW			100		S, E	TXT
Conco NI-21	nonyl		100		D, W, E	CTL
Depcopal			100		D, E	DEP
Dergon			88		D	AKS
Dispersant NI-O			100		E, D	ORO
Dispersant NI-W			100		D, W	ORO
Estronon NI Conc			100		D, W	CRC
Examide-G			90	B	D, E, W	SLC
Hipochem AR-100			100	B	D	HPP
Hyonic PE-100					D	NOP
Iberscour W Conc			100		D, W	HAR
Iberwet W-100			100		D, W	HAR
Igepal CA-630	octyl		100		E, D, Di	GAF
Igepal CA-730	octyl		100		D, W, E	GAF
Igepal CO-210	nonyl	1.5	100		D, Di, Fs, I	GAF
Igepal CO-430	nonyl	4	100		E, D, Di, I	GAF
Igepal CO-530	nonyl	6	100		E, D, Di	GAF
Igepal CO-630	nonyl	9.5	100		D, rW, W	GAF
Igepal CO-710	nonyl	10.5	100		D, W	GAF
Igepal CO-730	nonyl	15	100		D, Di, E, W, P	GAF
Igepal CO-850	nonyl	20	100		D, W, E, S	GAF
Igepal CO-880	nonyl	30	100		D, Di, S, E, W	GAF
Igepal DM-530	dialkyl		100		E	GAF
Igepal DM-730	dialkyl		100		E, S, D	GAF
Igepal LO-430	linear alkyl		100	B	E	GAF
Igepal LO-520	linear alkyl		100	B	E	GAF
Igepal LO-630	linear alkyl		100	B	D, E, W	GAF
Igepal LO-730	linear alkyl		100	B	D, E, W	GAF
Immersol NF Supra			60	B	W, D	CMG
Intexon NP-3	nonyl		100		D, W	WSN
Levelene	nonyl		100		W, P, Ta	AAP
Lipal 9N	nonyl		100		D, E	DRW
Makon 4		4	100		D, E	STP
Makon 10		10	100		D, E	STP
Makon 20		20	100		D, E	STP
Makon 30		30	100		D, E	STP
Neopon NP-10						WTC
Neutronyx 600	nonyl	9.5	100		D, W, E, Di	OXR
Neutronyx 605	isooctyl	9.5	100		W, E, D, Di	OXR
Neutronyx 622	nonyl	4	100		E	OXR
Neutronyx 640	nonyl	15	100		E, D, W, Di	OXR
Neutronyx 676	nonyl	30	100		E, D, W, Di	OXR
Ninox BDO			100		E	STP
Ninox BFO			100		E	STP
Nonionic E-4	linear alkyl		100	B	D, W, E	HDG
Nonionic E-10	linear alkyl		100	B	D, W, E	HDG
Nonionic E-15	linear alkyl		100	B	D, W, E	HDG
Nutrosan TS Conc	nonyl		90		D, W	CMG
Polytergent B-300	nonyl		99		D, E, W, Di	OMC

Table 18 (*continued*)

Product name	Alkyl group	MR[a]	Concn, wt %	Biodegrad-ability	Functions[b]	Manufac-turer[c]
Polytergent B-350	nonyl		99		D, E, W, Di	OMC
Polytergent G-300	octyl		99		D, E, W, Di	OMC
Polytergent G-400	octyl		99		D, E, W, Di	OMC
Renex 648	nonyl	5	100		D, E	APD
Renex 650	nonyl	30	100		D, E	APD
Renex 678	nonyl	15	100		D, E	APD
Renex 690	nonyl	10	100		D, E	APD
Retzanol NP-40			100		E, Di, W	RTF
Retzanol NP-80			100		E, Di, W	RTF
Retzanol NP-120			100		E, D, W	RTF
Retzanol NP-200			100		E, D, W	RTF
Retzanol NP-500			100		E, D, W	RTF
Solar 4 Liquid Conc.	nonyl		100		D, E, Di	SWT
Solar 12	nonyl		100		D, E, W	SWT
Solar 53	nonyl		100		D, E, W	SWT
Solar NP 100	octyl		100		D, E, W	SWT
Solar NP Liquid Conc.	nonyl		100		D, E	SWT
Solar NPO	nonyl		100		D, E, W	SWT
Sponto 200			100		E	RTF
Standopon			100		D, rW	SCP
Surfonic N-40	nonyl	4	100		E, D, W, Di	JCC
Surfonic N-60	nonyl	6	100		E, D, W, Di	JCC
Surfonic N-95	nonyl	9.5	100		D, E, W, Di	JCC
Surfonic N-120	nonyl	12	100		D, W, E	JCC
Surfonic N-200	nonyl	20	100		D, W	JCC
Surfonic N-30	nonyl	30	100		D, W	JCC
Synthonon 100	nonyl		100		D, E, W	SYN
T-DET N-4	nonyl	4	100		E, D	TMH
T-DET N-6	nonyl	6	100		D, E, W, Di	TMH
T-DET N-9.5	nonyl	9.5	100		D, E, W, Di	TMH
T-DET N-12.5	nonyl	12.5	100		D, E, W, Di	TMH
T-DET N-15	nonyl	15	100		D, E, W, Di	TMH
T-DET N-20	nonyl	20	100		D, E, W, Di	TMH
Tergitol L2-P-6	dodecyl		100		E, D	UCC
Tergitol 12-P-9	dodecyl		100		E, D	UCC
Tergitol 12-P-12	dodecyl		100		E, D, W	UCC
Tergitol NP-14	nonyl		100		E, D	UCC
Tergitol NP-27	nonyl		100		E, D, W, Di	UCC
Tergitol NP-33	nonyl		100		D, W, E	UCC
Tergitol NP-35	nonyl		100		D, W	UCC
Tergitol NP-44	nonyl		100		D, W	UCC
Triton N-57	nonyl	7–8	100		D, E	RH
Triton N-101	nonyl	9–10	100		W, D, E, Di	RH
Triton N-111	nonyl	12–13	100	B	W, D, E, Di	RH
Triton X-35	octyl	3	100		E	RH
Triton X-45	octyl	5	100	B	E, W, Di	RH
Triton X-100	t-octyl	9–10	100	B	W, D, E, Di	RH
Triton X-102	t-octyl	12–13	100	B	D, W	RH
Triton X-114	t-octyl	7–8	100	B	D, W	RH
Triton X-165	octyl	16	100		D, W	RH
Triton X-205	octyl	20	100		D, W	RH
Triton X-305	octyl	30	100		D, W, E	RH
Valdet	nonyl		100		E, D	VAL

[a] MR = moles of ethylene oxide per mole of hydrophobe.

[b] See Table 1.

[c] See Table 44.

oxyethylene alkylphenols are listed in Table 18. Uses of polyoxyethylene alkylphenols as a function of polyoxyethylene content can be summarized as follows:

1. Alkylphenols containing 20–40% polyoxyethylene are used as defoamers in surfactant solutions; detergent and/or dispersing agents in petroleum oils; coemulsifiers; intermediates for sulfation.

2. Alkylphenols containing 40–60% polyoxyethylene are used for oil-soluble detergents, dispersants, and emulsifiers; emulsifiers in emulsifiable condensates of insecticides and herbicides; intermediates for sulfation.

3. Alkylphenols containing 60–70% polyoxyethylene are used for textile detergents and processing auxiliaries; pitch control in manufacture of paper pulp; rewetting agents in paper towels; processing assistants in leather manufacture; detergents in industrial and consumer cleaning products; wetting agents in acid and alkaline cleaners; emulsifiers in emulsifiable concentrates of insecticides and herbicides.

4. Alkylphenols containing 70–80% polyoxyethylene are used for detergents and wetters at high temperature and/or electrolyte concentrations; emulsifiers for fats, oils, and waxes; stabilizers for synthetic latexes; wetting and penetrating agents in caustic solutions.

5. Alkylphenols containing 80–95% polyoxyethylene are used for stabilizers for synthetic latexes; emulsifiers for vinyl acetate and acrylate emulsion polymerizations; dyeing and leveling assistants; lime-soap dispersants.

Commercial ethoxylations of alkylphenols are almost always alkali-catalyzed but the reaction conditions, catalyst, and catalyst concentration are chosen to obtain optimum properties for the intended use. All of the alkylphenol combines with one molecule of ethylene oxide to form the monoadduct before the buildup of linear polyoxyethylene chains starts, but by relatively minor variations in reaction conditions it is possible to obtain either a broad or narrow distribution of isomers at the same percentage content of polyoxyethylene. These differences are reflected in the properties of the products, particularly the solubilities. Another variant at constant gross composition is the percentage of polyglycol in the product, ie ethylene oxide polymer not combined with the alkylphenol. The distribution of isomers with respect to the number of oxyethylene units in polyoxyethylene alkylphenols has been studied extensively: sometimes it approaches a Poisson distribution (38); more often it comes closer to fitting a Weibull and Nycander distribution (39).

Ethoxylated Aliphatic Alcohols. The alkylpoly(ethyleneoxy)ethanols, like the alkylphenoxypoly(ethyleneoxy)ethanols, were introduced in the U.S.A. before 1940 but the higher cost of alcohol hydrophobes as compared to alkylphenols held back their growth until the changeover of the industry to more biodegradable products made less expensive alcohols available. In the ensuing reformulation of industrial and consumer products, a shift in nonionic types appears to be taking place with polyoxyethylene alcohols instead of polyoxyethylene linear alkylphenols replacing the branched-chain alkylphenol derivatives in a significant fraction of the newer formulations. Table 19 lists the compositions and performance properties of typical alkylpoly(ethyleneoxy)-ethanols. These data indicate that the hydrophobes are generally mixtures of straight-chain alcohols in the range from C_{12} to C_{18} and that the mole ratios of combined ethylene oxide to hydrophobe vary from 1 to 50. The undiluted products vary in physical form from liquids to waxy solids. Viscosity in each homologous series increases as the polyoxyethylene content increases. The products have a slight odor characteristic of the hydrophobe that decreases as the polyethylene content increases. The liquids vary from pale yellow to almost colorless and the solids from yellow to white waxes; the products become lighter colored as the polyoxyethylene content increases. Within each homologous series, the specific gravity at room temperature increases with the polyoxyethylene content from slightly less than 1 until it levels off a little under 1.2. Solubility of the alkylpoly(ethyleneoxy)ethanols in water increases with the ethylene oxide content; about 65–70 wt % of polyoxyethylene is required for complete miscibility at room temperature. The solubility of the polyoxyethylene derivatives of straight-chain alcohols in aliphatic solvents is slightly greater than for the alkylphenols of comparable polyoxyethylene content. The water hardness does not impair the surface activity of the alkylpoly(ethyleneoxy)ethanols.

The functional properties and uses of the polyoxyethylene alcohols parallel very closely those of the polyoxyethylene alkylphenols. The usage of alkylpoly(ethyleneoxy)ethanols is divided more evenly among the available hydrophobes than with alkylphenols. This makes available a wider range of solubilities in water-insoluble liquids and contributes to the widespread use of the products as special-purpose emulsifiers. The alkylpoly(ethyleneoxy)ethanols have certain uses, such as textile-fiber lubrication, that are due to the properties of the hydrophobe and for which the comparable polyoxyethylene alkylphenols are not applicable.

Ethoxylation processes and equipment for manufacture of the alkylpoly(ethyleneoxy)ethanols are similar to those described for the alkylphenols. However, the rate of reaction of primary alcohols with ethylene oxide is much faster than it is with alkylphenols; it is much closer to the rate at which the polyoxyethylene chain grows. Thus the build-up of polyoxyethylene polymer chains starts before all of the hydrophobe has reacted with one unit of ethylene oxide. This means that the distribution of isomers in polyoxyethylene derivatives of primary alcohols does not conform to a Poisson distribution; a Weibull and Nycander distribution is a closer fit. The reactivity of alcohols with ethylene oxide varies in the order primary > secondary > tertiary (41). It is difficult to prepare polyoxyethylene derivatives of tertiary alcohols by direct reaction of the alcohol with ethylene oxide. The synthesis of alcohols for use as surfactant raw materials has been researched for many years and the diversity in origins of the alcohol hydrophobes of Table 19 are an indication of the successful results of the different approaches to this problem.

McFarland and Kinkel (40) have described the composition and properties of nonionic surfactants from linear secondary alcohols and Union Carbide offers products of this type commercially, but they are not known to be a major factor in the market at this time.

Carboxylic Esters. The carboxylic acid ester series of surfactants are polyol-solubilized, polyoxyethylene-solubilized, or both, and are based on several different types of hydrophobes. Each product type is described briefly in the order in which U.S. production for 1966 is listed in Table 20.

Glycerol Esters. The partial fatty acid esters that comprise this product group are either mono- or diglycerides of fatty acids. Their production exceeds the aggregate for all other polyol-solubilized surfactants. The glycerol esters of commerce are usually named according to the most abundant isomer even though the products are almost invariably mixtures of mono- and diglycerides that also differ in respect to the positions of the hydroxyl groups that are esterified. Trade names and compositions of typical commercial products are listed in Table 21. The chemistry of the glycerides has been reviewed by Malkin and Bevan (42).

Table 19. Alkylpoly(ethyleneoxy)ethanols (Ethoxylated Aliphatic Alcohols)

Product name	Alcohol	MR	Concn, wt %	Biodegrad-ability	Functions[c]	Manufac-turer[d]
Alfonic 1218-60	primary, linear[a]			B	D	CO
Alfonic 1012-60	primary, linear[a]			B	D	CO
Alfonic 1014-60	primary, linear[a]			B	D	CO
Alfonic 1480-60	primary, linear[a]			B	D	CO
Allo Scour RB			90	B	D, W, E	SCO
Antarox BL-330			95	B	W, D	GAF
Antarox LF-330			95		D	GAF
Arosurf JL-457	oleyl	5	100	B	D	ASC
Arosurf JL-758	oleyl	20	100	B	D	ASC
Azocrest			35	B		CRT
Bio Soft EA-10			100	B	D, E	STP
Brij 30	lauryl	4	100		E	APD
Brij 35	lauryl	23	100		E	APD
Brij 52	cetyl	2	100		E	APD
Brij 56	cetyl	10	100		E, S	APD
Brij 58	cetyl	20	100		E, S	APD
Brij 72	stearyl	2	100		E	APD
Brij 76	stearyl	10	100		E	APD
Brij 78	stearyl	20	100		E	APD
Brij 92	oleyl	2	100		E	APD
Brij 96	oleyl	10	100		E	APD
Brij 98	oleyl	20	100		E	APD
Carboxane TW-85			85	B	E, F, D, S	TXT
Cerfak			85		D, W	EFH
Crestomul L			100	B	E, D	CRT
Depconol 111			65		E, Di	DEP
Dergopen RN			40		D, W	AKS
Drupene VO-250			50		D	DRW
Emnon 6954			100	B	W, F	PCS
Emulphogéne BC-420	tridecyl[b]		100		E	GAF
Emulphogene BC-610	tridecyl[b]		100		D, Fs	GAF
Emulphogene BC-840	tridecyl[b]		100		D, Fs	GAF
Emulphor ON-870	oleyl	23	100	B	E, Di, St, S	GAF
Ethosperse LA-4	lauryl	4	100	B	E	GLY
Ethosperse LA-12	lauryl	12	100	B	E	GLY
Ethosperse LA-23	lauryl	23	100	B	E	GLY
Ethosperse OA-9	oleyl	9	100	B	E	GLY
Ethosperse TDA-6	tridecyl	6	100	B	E	GLY
Ethosperse TDA-12	tridecyl	12	100	B	E	GLY
Examide-DA			100	B	D, E, W	SLC
Foryl 100			100	B	D	SCP
Hyonic KO-620			100	B	D, W	NOP
Igepal A	linear alc.		100	B	D, W, E	GAF
Kyro EOB			100	B	W, D, Di	PG
Lipal 610	tridecyl		85		E	DRW
Lipal 2 CA	cetyl	2	100		E	DRW
Lipal 9 LA	lauryl	9	100	B	E, Di, D	DRW
Lipal 4 LA	lauryl	4	100		E, S, Di	DRW
Lipal 12 LA	lauryl	12	100		E, S, Di	DRW
Lipal 23 LA	lauryl	23	100		E, S, Di	DRW
Lipal 4 MA	myristyl	4	100		E, W/O	DRW
Lipal 8 MA	myristyl	8	100		E, W/O	DRW
Lipal 2 OA	oleyl	2	100	B	E, W/O	DRW
Lipal 5 OA	oleyl	5	100		E, W/O	DRW
Lipal 10 OA	oleyl	10	100		D	DRW
Lipal 20 OA	oleyl	20	100		D, E	DRW
Lipal 50 OA	oleyl	50	100			DRW
Lipal 20 SA	stearyl	20	100	B	S	DRW

Table 19 (*continued*)

Product name	Alcohol	MR	Concn, wt %	Biodegrad-ability	Functions[c]	Manufac-turer[d]
Lipal 30 SA	stearyl	30	100	B	E, S	DRW
Lipal 3 TD	tridecyl	3	100		E, W/O	DRW
Lipal 6 TD	tridecyl	6	100		E	DRW
Lipal 10 TD	tridecyl	10	100		E	DRW
Neodol 23-3	C_{12-13} prim.-lin.[e]	3	100	B	Di, I	SHC
Neodol 23-6.5	C_{12-13} prim.-lin.[e]	6.5	100	B	D	SHC
Neodol 25-3	C_{12-15} prim.-lin.[e]	3	100	B	Di, I	SHC
Neodol 25-7	C_{12-15} prim.-lin.[e]	7	100	B	D, W	SHC
Neodol 25-9	C_{12-15} prim.-lin.[e]	9	100	B	D, W	SHC
Neodol 25-12	C_{12-15} prim.-lin.[e]	12	100	B	D, W, E	SHC
Nutrosan U-9			100	B	D, W	CMG
Plurafac A-38			100	B	D, E, W	WYN
Poly Tergent J-200	tridecyl[b]		99		D, E, S, Di	OMC
Poly Tergent J-500	tridecyl[b]		99		D, E, S, Di	OMC
Promulgen 1703			100		E	RW
Renex 30	tridecyl[b]	12	100		W, Di, D	APD
Retzanol SN			100	B	D, W	RTF
Siponic E-3	tallow	6	100	B	E	AAC
Siponic E-7	tallow	14	100	B	E	AAC
Siponic E-10	tallow	20	100	B	E	AAC
Siponic E-15	tallow	30	100	B	E	AAC
Siponic L-4	lauryl	4	100	B	E	AAC
Siponic L-12	lauryl	12	100	B	E	AAC
Siponic L-16	lauryl	16	100	B	E	AAC
Siponic L-25	lauryl	25	100	B	E	AAC
Standamul 18			100	B	D, E, W, Di	SCP
Standapon 209			100	B	D, W	SCP
Surfonic JN-70	*n*-alkyl	7	100	B	D	JCC
Surfonic NY-30	primary-linear	3	100	B	E	JCC
Surfonic NY-66	primary-linear	6.6	100	B	E, W	JCC
Surfonic NY-150	primary-linear	15	100	B	D	JCC
Surfonic NY-300	primary-linear	30	100	B	D	JCC
Telkanite M					Di	DEX
Tergitol 3-A-6	tridecyl	6	100		E, I	UCC
Tergitol 15-S-5	secondary, C_{11-15}	5	100	B	D, E, W	UCC
Tergitol 15-S-9	secondary, C_{11-15}	9	100	B	D, E, W	UCC
Tergitol 15-S-12	secondary, C_{11-15}	12	100	B	D, E, W	UCC
Tergitol 15-S-15	secondary, C_{11-15}	15	100		D, W	UCC
Tergitol 45-S-9		9	100	B	D, W, E	UCC
Tergitol 44-S-10		10	100	B	D, W, E	UCC
Tergitol TWN	trimethylnonyl		90		W, rW, P	UCC
Triton X-67			100		D, E	RH
Volpo 3	oleyl	3	100		E, S	CRO
Volpo 10	oleyl	10	100		E, S	CRO
Volpo 20	oleyl	20	100		E, S	CRO
Trycol LAL-4	lauryl	4	100	B	E, Tl	TCH
Trycol LAL-8	lauryl	8	100	B	D, E, W, Tl	TCH
Trycol LAL-12	lauryl	12	100	B	S, E, D, Tl	TCH
Trycol LAL-23	lauryl	23	100	B	E, S	TCH
Trycol TDA-6	tridecyl	6	100		W, Di, D, E	TCH
Trycol TDA-9	tridecyl	9	100		W, rW, D, E	TCH
Trycol TDA-15	tridecyl	15	100		E, D, Ta	TCH
Trycol TDA-18	tridecyl	18	100		E, Di, S, D, Ta	TCH
Trycol OAL-23	oleyl	23	100		E, Di, S, D, Ta	TCH
Sterox AJ-100	tridecyl[b]	9.5	100		D, E, rW, Ta	MON
Steros AP-100	tridecyl[b]	15	100		D, E	MON

[a] Obtained by the Alfol process, Vol. 1, p. 560.

[b] Obtained by the oxo process (qv).

[c] See Table 1.

[d] See Table 44.

[e] prim.-lin. = primary-linear.

Mono- and diglycerol esters of the saturated fatty acids are light-colored solids with melting points between 25 and 85°C. The 1-monoglycerides are higher melting than the corresponding 2-monoglycerides. The glycerides of the unsaturated fatty

Table 20. U.S. Production of Carboxylic Esters, 1966

Product type	Production, 1000 lb
glycerol esters	71,460
polyethylene glycol esters	24,436
anhydrosorbitol esters	13,787
ethoxylated anhydrosorbitol esters	12,349
ethylene and diethylene glycol esters	4,291
propanediol esters	3,534
natural fats and oils, ethoxylated	4,181
other carboxylic acid esters	12,332
total	146,370

Table 21. Glycerol Esters of Fatty Acids

Product name	Glycerol ester	Concn, wt %	Biodegrad-ability	Functions[a]	Manufac-turer[b]
Aldo MC	monococoate	100	B	E	GLY
Aldo ML	monolaurate	100	B	E	GLY
Aldo MR	monoricinoleate	100	B	E	GLY
Aldo MS, Nat. For.	monostearate	100	B	E	GLY
Arlacel 165	monostearate	100		E	APD
Atmos 150	mono and di fatty acid	100		E	APD
Atmul 80	mono and di fatty acid	100		E	APD
Atmul 124	mono and di fatty acid	100		E	APD
Atmul 500	mono and di fatty acid	100		E	APD
Cerasynt O	monostearate	100		E	VND
Drewmulse CNO #70	monococoate	100	B	E	DRW
Drewmulse GMO	monooleate	45		E	DRW
Drewmulse HM-100	monostearate	99	B	E	DRW
Emcol MSC	monostearate	100	B	E	WTC
Emerest 2400	monostearate	100	B	E	EMR
Emerest 2421	monooleate	100	B	E	EMR
Flexricin 13	monoricinoleate	100		E	BAC
Hallco CPH-34-N	monolaurate	100		E	HAL
Hallco CPH-35-N	monoricinoleate	100		E	HAL
Hodag GML	monolaurate	100	B	E	HDG
Hodag GMO	monooleate	100	B	E	HDG
Hodag GMR	monoricinoleate	100	B	E	HDG
Hodag GMS	monostearate	100	B	E	HDG
Kessco Ester	dioleate		B	E, O	ARC
Kessco Ester	monooleate		B	E, O	ARC
Kessco Ester	monostearate, pure		B	E, O	ARC
Monoflake	monostearate	100	B	E	CCW
Myverol Type 18-30	tallow, mono	100		E	EK
Myverol Type 18-40	lard, mono	100		E	EK
Myverol Type 18-45	cottonseed, mono	100		E	EK
Myverol Type 18-98	safflower oil, mono	100		E	EK
Surfactol 13	monoricinoleate	100		E	BAC
Uniwax-GMS	monostearate	100	B	E, Ts	UVC

[a] See Table 1.   [b] See Table 44.

acids are liquids at room temperature. The partial glycerol fatty esters have the characteristic odor of the fats from which they were derived. The polyol group of a monoglyceride is not strong enough as a hydrophilic moiety to carry even an easily solubilized acid like oleic into aqueous solution. Despite their lack of water solubility the partial glycerol esters have commercially important and technically interesting surfactant uses.

The uses of the mono- and diglycerides center around applications involving emulsification, dispersion, suspension, solubilization, and lubrication. One important use is as additives to foods and pharmaceuticals. Products intended for ingestion are prepared from edible fats. Mono- and diglycerides are widely used in bread, cakes, and other bakery products for their emulsifying, dispersing, and lubricating properties. They are also used in candies, ice cream, yeast, butter, whipped toppings, and icings. Flavor oils for carbonated beverages as well as bakery products are emulsified or solubilized by surfactant mixtures that include blends of mono- and diglycerides. Glycerol monostearate is used as an emulsifier and opacifier in cosmetic formulations. The partial glycerol esters are used as components of textile-mill processing oils and in lubricant and softener formulations. The products also find application as emulsifiers, lubricants, and corrosion inhibitors in cutting, drawing, and finishing of metal products. In the manufacture of paints and polymers, the mono- and diglycerides are used as emulsifiers, dispersants, suspending agents, and grinding aids.

Alcoholysis of fats with glycerol is the most important industrial method for the preparation of the partial fatty acid esters of glycerol. In this reaction, the fatty acid groups are redistributed between the original combined glycerol and the added glycerol without weight loss by heating at 180–250°C in the presence of an alkaline catalyst.

Polyethylene Glycol Esters. The polyoxyethylene esters of fatty acids and of alicyclic carboxylic acids related to abietic acid (see Vol. 17, p. 483) comprise the polyethylene glycol series of surfactants. Properties and uses of these two groups of products differ markedly. The compositions and properties of typical polyethylene glycol esters of both groups are listed in Table 22.

Commercial *polyoxyethylene fatty acid esters* are mixtures that contain varying proportions of the following components: monoesters, $RCOO(OCH_2CH_2)_nOH$; diesters, $RCOO(OCH_2CH_2)_nOOCR$; and polyglycol, $H(OCH_2CH_2)_nOH$. The composition of the mixture can be forced toward the mono- or diester by the ratio of reactants and process of manufacture. The descriptions of commercial products usually specify the acid esterified, whether it is predominantly a mono- or diester, and either the mole ratio of polyoxyethylene to fatty acid or the molecular weight of the polyglycol esterified with the acid. Wrigley, Smith, and Stirton have investigated the surface activity of a series of ethoxylated fatty acids (43).

The polyoxyethylene esters of fatty acids range in consistency from free-flowing liquids to slurries to firm waxes. Within a homologous series the products change from liquids to waxes as the polyethylene content increases. Only low mole ratios of polyoxyethylene to unsaturated fatty acids or lower molecular weight acids yield liquid products. The odor of the products is characteristic of the fatty acid hydrophobe and decreases as the polyoxyethylene content increases. Odor and odor stability are important characteristics of these products because of their use in textile finishing. Color stability is also important for the same reason. The oleates, for example, have good softening and lubricating properties but are precluded from some uses because of yellowing on exposure to air and heat.

Table 22. Polyoxyethylene Esters of Fatty, Rosin, and Tall Oil Acids

Product name	Degree of esteri-fication	Composition			Concn, wt %	Bio-degrad-ability	Functions[c]	Manufac-turer[d]
		Acid	PEG[a]	POE[b]				
Aldosperse ML-14	mono	lauric	600		100		E, dF, A	GLY
Aldosperse O-9	mono	oleic		9	100		E, dF, A	GLY
Aldosperse S-9	mono	stearic		9	100		E, dF, A	GLY
Aldosperse S-40	mono	stearic		40	100		E, dF, A	GLY
Arosurf HFL-418	mono	lauric		5	100	B	E, D, W	ASC
Arosurf HFL-714	mono	lauric		14	100	B	E, D, W	ASC
Arosurf HFS-546	mono	stearic		8	100	B	E, D, W	ASC
Arosurf HFS-748	mono	stearic		23	100	B	E, D, W	ASC
Arosurf HFS-846	mono	stearic		40	100	B	E, D, W	ASC
Arosurf HFT-453	mono	tall oil		5	100	B	E	ASC
Arosurf HFT-650	mono	tall oil		10	100	B	E, D, W	ASC
Arosurf HFT-755	mono	tall oil		20	100	B	E, D, W	ASC
Carboxane 863	mono	fatty			100	B	E, Di, Tl	TXT
Emcol H-31A	mono	oleic	400		100		E	WTC
Emerest 2620	mono	lauric	200		100	B	E	EMR
Emerest 2622	di	lauric	200		100	B	E	EMR
Emerest 2640	mono	stearic	400		100	B	E	EMR
Emerest 2642	di	stearic	400		100	B	E	EMR
Emerest 2646	mono	oleic	400		100	B	E	EMR
Emerest 2647	sesqui	oleic	400		100	B	E	EMR
Emerest 2650	mono	lauric	400		100	B	E	EMR
Emerest 2652	di	lauric	400		100	B	E	EMR
Emerest 2660	mono	oleic	600		100	B	E	EMR
Emulphor VN-430	mono	fatty			100	B	E, Tl	GAF
Emulsynt 600	di	oleic	400		100		Di	VND
Estex P4-0	mono	oleic			100	B	E	SWT
Estex P4-S	mono	stearic			100	B	E	SWT
Estex SE 750	mono	lauric			100	B	W, E	SWT
Ethofat C/15	mono	coconut	5		100	B	E, D, Di	ARC
Ethofat C/25	mono	coconut	15		100	B	E, D, Di	ARC
Ethofat 142/20	mono	tall oil	10		100	B	E, D, Di	ARC
Ethofat 242/25	mono	tall oil	15		100	B	E, D, Di	ARC
Ethofat 0/15	mono	oleic	5		100	B	E, D, Di	ARC
Ethofat 0/20	mono	oleic	10		100	B	E, D, Di	ARC
Ethofat 60/15	mono	stearic	5		100	B	E, D, Di	ARC
Ethofat 60/20	mono	stearic		10	100	B	E, D, Di	ARC
Ethofat 60/25	mono	stearic		15	100	B	E, D, Di	ARC
Hodag 20-L	mono	lauric	200		100	B	E, Ts, W	HDG
Hodag 40-L	mono	lauric	400		100	B	E Ts W	HDG
Hodag 40-O	mono	oleic	400		100	B	E, Ts, W	HDG
Hodag 40-S	mono	stearic	400		100	B	E, Ts, W	HDG
Hodag 40-R	mono	ricinoleic	400		100	B	E, Ts, W	HDG
Hodag 42-L	di	lauric	400		100	B	E, Ts, W	HDG
Hodag 42-S	di	stearic	400		100	B	E, Ts, W	HDG
Hodag 60-L	mono	lauric	600		100	B	E, Ts, W	HDG
Hodag 60-S	mono	stearic	600		100	B	E, Ts, W	HDG
Hodag 62-O	di	oleic	600		100	B	E, Ts, W	HDG
Hodag 62-S	di	stearic	600		100	B	E, Ts, W	HDG
Hodag 150-S	mono	stearic	1500		100	B	E, Ts, W	HDG
Hodag 150-O	di	oleic	1500		100	B	E, Ts, W	HDG
Keripon NC	mono	fatty	–		150	B	W, rW, A	AKS
Kessco Ester	mono	lauric	200			B	E	ARC
Kessco Ester	di	lauric	400			B	E	ARC

Table 22 (*continued*)

Product name	Degree of esteri- fication	Composition			Concn, wt %	Bio- degrad- ability	Functions[c]	Manufac- turer[d]
		Acid	PEG[a]	POE[b]				
Kessco Ester	mono	lauric	400			B	E	ARC
Kessco Ester	di	oleic	400			B	E	ARC
Kessco Ester	mono	oleic	400			B	E	ARC
Kessco Ester	di	stearic	400			B	E	ARC
Kessco	mono	stearic	400			B	E	ARC
Kessco Ester	mono	lauric	600			B	E	ARC
Lipal 300DL	di	lauric	300		100		E	DRW
Lipal 400DL	di	lauric	400		100		E	DRW
Lipal 400DS	di	stearic	400		100		E	DRW
Lipal 5S	mono	stearic			100		E, Di, Tl	DRW
Lipal 300S	mono	stearic	300		100		E	DRW
Morosol 120	mono	stearic			100		E, Ts, Tl	MTX
Morosol 3F	mono	oleic			100		W, E	MTX
Morosol 3F	mono	oleic			100		W, E	MTX
Morosol 4L	mono	lauric			100		E, Ta, A	MTX
Myrj 45	mono	stearic		8	100		E	APD
Myrj 52	mono	stearic		40	100		E	APD
Neutronyx 268	di	stearic	300		98		E, O	OXR
Neutronyx 330	mono	soybean	600		98		E, D, W	OXR
Neutronyx 332	mono	stearic	1000		98		E, O	OXR
Neutronyx 834	mono	oleic	300		100		E	OXR
Nonisol 100	mono	lauric	400		100		E, W, D	GGY
Nonisol 200	mono	oleic	400		100		W, E	GGY
Nonisol 300	mono	stearic	400		100		E, W	GGY
Nopalcol 6-L	mono	lauric			100	B	E, Ta	NOP
Nopalcol 6-O	mono	oleic			100	B	E, W	NOP
Pegosperse 400-DL	di	lauric	400		100	B	E, Di	GLY
Pegosperse 400-DO	di	oleic	400		100	B	E, Di	GLY
Pegosperse 1500-DO	di	oleic	1500		100	B	E, Di	GLY
Pegosperse 400-DS	di	stearic	400		10	B	E, Di	GLY
Pegosperse 400-MOT	mono	tallic	400		100	B	E, Di	GLY
Pegosperse 200-ML	mono	lauric	200		100	B	E, Di	GLY
Pegosperse 100-MR	mono	ricinoleic	100		100	B	E, Di	GLY
Pegosperse 100-MS	mono	stearic	100		100	B	E, Di	GLY
Pegosperse 600-MS	mono	stearic	600		100	B	E, Di	GLY
Pegosperse 1000-MS	mono	stearic	1000		100	B	E, Di	GLY
Pegosperse 4000-MS	mono	stearic	4000		100	B	E, Di	GLY
Pegosperse 100-O	mono	oleic	100		100	B	E, Di	GLY
Renex 20	mono	fatty and rosin	16		100		D, W	APD
RJT Base	mono	fatty			100		E	CRT
Soltex 3835	mono	fatty			100		Di	SYC
Stearox CD	mono	tall oil			100		D	MON
Surfactant AR150	mono	rosin			100		D, E	HPC
Teox	mono	tall oil			100		D	OMC
Trydet SA-8	mono	stearic		8	100	B	E, Tl, Ts	TCH
Trydet SA-40	mono	stearic		40	100	B	E, S, Tl, A	TCH
Trydet 20	mono	tall oil			100		E, D, Ta	TCH
Varconic Q 510	mono	oleic			100		E	VAC
Visco L-1117	mono	stearic			100		E	NLC

[a] Mol wt of esterified polyethylene glycol.
[b] Moles of esterified polyoxyethylene.
[c] See Table 1.
[d] See Table 44.

The ester linkage is slightly hydrophilic and only about 60 wt % of polyoxyethylene is required to solubilize the saturated fatty acids in water at room temperature. The surface activity of the fatty acid polyglycol esters, eg wetting and surface-tension lowering, is in the useful range but less than for ethoxylated alkylphenols or aliphatic alcohols. The products are low foamers in aqueous solutions, which is advantageous for certain uses. Emulsification is a key property of this series of compounds and its importance is reflected in the wide range of lipophilic solubilities that are available in commercial products. Susceptibility to hydrolysis in hot acidic or alkaline solutions is their principal limitation. The fatty acid that is formed by acidic hydrolysis either separates as an oil or forms an insoluble precipitate with the heavy-metal ions in hard water.

The polyoxyethylene fatty acids are used extensively in the textile industry as emulsifiers for processing oils, antistatic agents, softeners, fiber lubricants, and de-

Table 23. Fatty Acids Esters of Sorbitan

Product name	Sorbitan ester	Concn, wt %	Biodegrad-ability	Functions[a]	Manufac-turer[b]
Armotan ML	monolaurate	100	B	E, S	ARC
Armotan MO	monooleate	100	B	E, S	ARC
Armotan MS	monostearate	100	B	E, S	ARC
Drewmulse SML	monolaurate	100	B	E	DRW
Drewmulse SMO	monooleate	100	B	E	DRW
Drewmulse SMP	monopalmitate	100		E	DRW
Drewmulse SMS	monostearate	100	B	E	DRW
Emsorb 2500	monooleate	100	B	E	EMR
Emsorb 2505	monostearate	100	B	E	EMR
Emsorb 2510	monopalmitate	100	B	E	EMR
Emsorb 2503	trioleate	100	B	E	EMR
Emsorb 2507	tristearate	100	B	E	EMR
Estasorb L	monolaurate	100	B	E	TCH
Estasorb P	monopalmitate	100	B	E, Tl	TCH
Estasorb S	monostearate	100	B	E, Tl	TCH
Estasorb O	monooleate	100	B	E	TCH
Estasorb TS	tristearate	100	B	E	TCH
Estasorb TO	trioleate	100	B	E	TCH
Glycomul L	monolaurate	100	B	E	GLY
Glycomul O	monooleate	100	B	E	GLY
Glycomul P	monopalmitate	100	B	E	GLY
Glycomul S	monostearate	100	B	E	GLY
Hodag SML	monolaurate	100	B	E	GLY
Hodag SMP	monopalmitate	100	B	E	HDG
Hodag SMS	monostearate	100	B	E	HDG
Hodag STS	tristearate	100	B	E	HDG
Hodag SMO	monooleate	100	B	E	HDG
Hodag STO	trioleate	100	B	E	HDG
Span 20	monolaurate	100		E, V	APD
Span 40	monopalmitate	100		E, V	APD
Span 60	monostearate	100		E, V	APD
Span 65	tristearate	100		E, V	APD
Span 80	monooleate	100		E, V	APD
Span 85	trioleate	100		E, V	APD

[a] See Table 1.   [b] See Table 44.

tergents for neutral scouring operations. The products are also used as emulsifiers in cosmetic preparations, pesticide formulations, etc.

Two methods are used commercially for manufacture of the polyoxyethylene acids. One is the alkali-catalyzed reaction of a fatty acid with ethylene oxide. The other is esterification of a fatty acid with a preformed polyethylene glycol in the presence of an acid catalyst. Some manufacturers claim that the properties are different for products of the same gross composition as prepared by the two methods. However, the ethoxylation catalysts also catalyze transesterification and the products of direct ethoxylation approach closely those obtained by esterification if the manufacturing process is directed to this end. Deodorization and decolorization treatments are commonly incorporated in manufacturing processes.

Abietic acid and related acids are a major constituent of rosin (qv). Tall oil (qv) is a mixture of unsaturated fatty acids with alicyclic acids of the abietic family. Refined tall oil may be high in rosin acids or in unsaturated fatty acids, depending on the purification process. The *polyoxyethylene derivatives of the rosin acids* (eg dehydroabietic acid) are generally similar to the corresponding polyoxyethylene fatty acids in surfactant properties and processes of manufacture except that they are surprisingly stable toward hydrolysis. No noticeable decomposition occurred when an ester of this type was boiled for 15 min in 10% sulfuric acid or 25% sodium hydroxide (44). The stability of these products has been attributed to steric hindrance of the carboxylate group.

The chemical stability of the polyoxyethylene tallates together with their characteristic low-foam generation at use concentrations makes them useful as components of consumer detergents for automatic clothes-washing machines and for continuous high-speed, industrial-cleaning processes. The fused-ring system of rosin acids does not impart softening and lubricating properties comparable to the fatty acid ethoxylates. The differences in properties of the two series are apparent from the functions of the products as shown in Table 22.

Anhydrosorbitol Esters. Fatty acid esters of anhydrosorbitol (see Alcohols, polyhydric) are the second largest class of polyol-solubilized surfactants. The important commercial products in the group are mono-, di- or triesters of sorbitan and fatty acids. Sorbitan is a mixture of anhydrosorbitols. The isomers shown below are the principal components of the mixture:

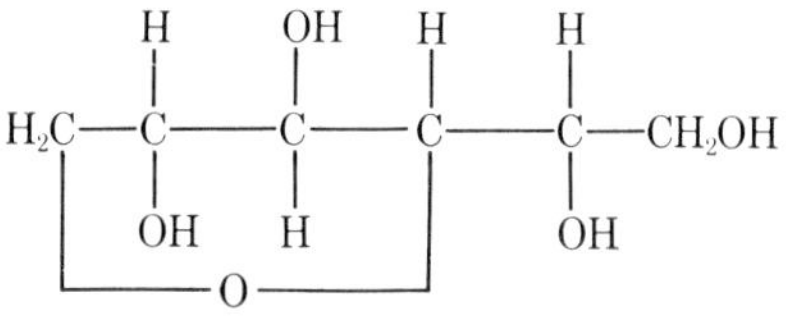

1,4-sorbitan 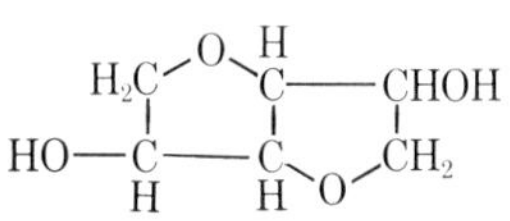   isosorbide

The sorbitan oleates and the monolaurate are pale-yellow liquids. The palmitates and stearates are light-tan solids. Sorbitan is not a strong hydrophilic group and its derivatives are not water soluble but they are soluble in a wide range of mineral and vegetable oils. The sorbitan esters are lipophilic emulsifiers, solubilizers, softeners, and fiber lubricants. Many of the products have been approved for human ingestion and are widely used as emulsifiers and solubilizers in foods, beverages, and pharmaceuticals. Another important application is in synthetic fiber manufacture and textile processing as antistats, fiber lubricants, softeners, and emulsifiers of textile-mill processing oils. The sorbitan esters are also widely used as emulsifiers in cosmetic products.

The anhydrosorbitol esters are prepared commercially by direct esterification of sorbitol with a fatty acid in the presence of an acidic catalyst at temperatures in the range 225–250°C. Internal ether formation as well as esterification takes place under these conditions. Table 23 lists the composition and properties of typical anhydrosorbitan esters.

Ethoxylated Anhydrosorbitol Esters. Ethoxylation of the sorbitan fatty acid esters leads to a series of more hydrophilic surfactants. The structure of a representa-

Table 24. Polyoxyethylene Derivatives of Sorbitan Fatty Acid Esters

Product name	Sorbitan ester	POE[a]	Concn, wt %	Biodegrad-ability	Functions[b]	Manufac-turer[c]
Armotan PML-20	monolaurate	20	100	B	E, S, Tl, Ts, A	ARC
Armotan PMO-20	monooleate	20	100	B	E, S, Tl, Ts, A	ARC
Armotan PMS-20	monostearate	20	100	B	E, S, Tl, Ts, A	ARC
Drewmulse POE-SMO	monooleate	20	100	B	E	DRW
Drewmulse POE-SML	monolaurate	20	100	B	E	DRW
Drewmulse POE-SMP	monopalmitate	20	100	B	E	DRW
Drewmulse POE-SMS	monostearate	20	100	B	E	DRW
Drewmulse POE-STS	tristearate	20	100	B	E	DRW
Emrite 6120	monooleate	20	100	B	E	EMR
Emrite 6125	monostearate	20	100	B	E	EMR
Emrite 6127	tristearate	20	100	B	E	EMR
Glycosperse L-20	monolaurate	20	100	B	E	GLY
Glycosperse O-20	monooleate	20	100	B	E	GLY
Glycosperse O-5	monooleate	5	100	B	E	GLY
Glycosperse P-20	monopalmitate	20	100	B	E	GLY
Glycosperse S-4	monostearate	4	100	B	E	GLY
Glycosperse S-20	monostearate	20	100	B	E	GLY
Glycosperse TO-20	trioleate	20	100	B	E	GLY
Glycosperse TS-20	tristearate	20	100	B	E	GLY
Hodag PSML-20	monolaurate	20	100	B	E	HDG
Hodag PSMO-20	monooleate	20	100	B	E	HDG
Hodag PSMP-20	monopalmitate	20	100	B	E	HDG
Hodag PSMS-20	monostearate	20	100	B	E	HDG
Hodag PSTS-20	tristearate	20	100	B	E	HDG
Hodag PSTO-20	trioleate	20	100	B	E	HDG
Sorbinox L-20	monolaurate	20	97	B	E, S, Tl, A	TCH
Sorbinox O-5	monooleate	5	100	B	E, Tl, Ts, A	TCH
Sorbinox O-20	monooleate	20	100	B	E, Tl, S	TCH
Sorbinox P-20	monopalmitate	20	100	B	E, Tl	TCH
Sorbinox S-20	monostearate	20	100	B	E, Di, S, Tl	TCH
Sorbinox TO-20	trioleate	20	100	B	E, Tl, Ts	TCH
Sorbinox TS-20	tristearate	20	100	B	E, Tl, Ts	TCH
Tween 21	monolaurate	4	100		E, W	APD
Tween 20	monolaurate	20	100		E, Tl, S	APD
Tween 40	monopalmitate	20	100		E, Tl, S	APD
Tween 61	monostearate	4	100		E	APD
Tween 60	monostearate	20	100		E	APD
Tween 65	tristearate	20	100		E	APD
Tween 81	monooleate	5	100		E	APD
Tween 80	monooleate	20	100		E, S, Tl	APD
Tween 85	trioleate	20	100		E, Tl	APD

[a] Oxyethylene units per mole of ester.   [b] See Table 1.   [c] See Table 44.

tive component of polyoxyethylene (20) sorbitan monostearate illustrates the composition of these products:

$$w + x + y + z = 20$$

Table 25. Glycol Esters of Fatty Acids

Product name	Glycol ester[a]	Concn, wt %	Biodegradability	Functions[b]	Manufacturer[c]
Cerasynt M	EG stearate	100		E	VND
Drewmulse EGMS	EG monostearate	100		E	DRW
Drewmulse EGDS	EG distearate	100		E	DRW
Emerest 2350	EG monostearate	100	B	E, O	EMR
Hallco 37-N	EG monostearate	100		E, O	HAL
Hodag EGS	EG monostearate	100	B	E	HDG
Kessco Ester	EG distearate			E, O	ARC
Kessco Ester	EG monostearate			E, O	ARC
EG monostearate		100		E	CCW
EG monostearate		100	B	E, O	PCS
Cerasynt W	DEG monostearate	100		E	VND
Emcol CAD	DEG stearate	100	B	E	WTC
Emcol DOS	DEG oleate	100	B	E	WTC
Emcol RDCD	DEG cocoate	100	B	E	WTC
Emerest 2360	DEG monostearate	100	B	E	EMR
Hodag DGL	DEG monolaurate	100	B	E	HDG
Hodag DGO	DEG monooleate	100	B	E, Tl	HDG
Hodag DGS	DEG monostearate	100	B	E, Tl	HDG
Kessco Ester	DEG monostearate			E, O	ARC
DEG monolaurate		100		E	HAL
DEG monooleate		100		E	HAL
DEG monostearate		100		E	HAL
DEG monolaurate		100		E	SBC
DEG monooleate		100		E	SBC
DEG monostearate		100		E	SBC
Cerasynt PA	PG monostearate	100		E	VND
Drewlene 10	PG monostearate	100	B	E	DRW
Drewmulse PGML	PG monolaurate	100		E	DRW
Drewmulse PGMS	PG monostearate	100		E	DRW
Emerest 2381	PG monostearate	100	B	E	EMR
Emerest 2386	PG distearate	100	B	E	EMR
Hallco CPH-32	PG monostearate	100		E	HAL
Hodag PGML	PG monolaurate	100	B	E	HDG
Hodag PGMS	PG monostearate	100	B	E	HDG
Pegosperse PS	PG stearate	100	B	E	GLY
PG monostearate, distilled		100		E	EK
PG monococoate		100		E	HAL
PG monostearate		100		E	SBC
PG monolaurate		100	B	E, St, Fs	SBC
PG monostearate		100		E	CCW

[a] EG = ethylene glycol; DEG = diethylene glycol; PG = propylene glycol.
[b] See Table 1.   [c] See Table 44.

Table 24 lists the compositions and properties of typical commercially available poly-oxyethylene sorbitan fatty acid esters. All of these products are yellow liquids except the 4- and 5-mole ethylene oxide adducts and the tristearates, which are light tan solids. The 4- and 5-mole adducts of the monoesters and the 20-mole adducts of the triesters are dispersible but insoluble in water. The 20-mole adducts of the monoesters are water soluble. The polyoxyethylene sorbitan fatty acid esters are widely used as emulsifiers, antistats, softeners, fiber lubricants, and solubilizers. The ethoxylated sorbitan esters are often used as coemulsifiers with the unethoxylated sorbitan fatty acid esters or the glycerol partial fatty acid esters. Sorbitan fatty acid esters can be reacted with ethylene oxide in the presence of an alkaline catalyst at temperatures from 130 to 170°C to produce the ethoxylated derivatives.

Glycol Esters of Fatty Acids. The ethylene glycol, diethylene glycol, and 1,2-propanediol esters of fatty acids are widely used surfactants. The commercial products are mixtures of mono- and diesters even though the stated composition usually refers only to the principal component. Table 25 lists compositions and properties of commercially available glycol esters. The mono- and dilaurates and oleates of ethylene glycol, diethylene glycol, and propylene glycol are liquids. Stearates of these glycols are solids. The glycol esters are strongly lipophilic emulsifiers, opacifiers, and plasticizers that are normally formulated in combination with hydrophilic emulsifiers. They are used as components of cosmetic preparations. The monoesters of glycols can be manufactured by the alkali-catalyzed reaction of ethylene or propylene oxide with fatty acids. Mono- and diesters are also prepared by esterification of a fatty acid with a glycol.

Natural Fats, Oils, and Waxes, Ethoxylated. Ethoxylated castor oil accounted for over 85% of the U.S. production of this group of nonionics in 1966. The only other products with significant volume were ethoxylated lanolin derivatives.

Castor oil is a triglyceride with a high content of esterified ricinoleic acid. Ethoxylation of it in the presence of an alkaline catalyst to a polyoxyethylene content of 60–70 wt % yields water-soluble surfactants. The composition of the ethoxylated derivatives is more complex than might be expected. Some of the ethylene oxide is probably reacted with the secondary hydroxyls in the ricinoleic acid moieties or with secondary hydroxyls from cleavage of glycerol esters but much of it is combined with $RCOO^-$ radicals that are formed because the ethoxylation catalyst is also a transesterification catalyst. It is even conceivable that the combination of ethoxylation and transesterification reactions could lead to glycerides of the types illustrated below in which poly-oxyethylene chains are, in effect, inserted between the carboxyl and glyceryl moieties.

$$
\begin{array}{ccc}
RCO(OCH_2CH_2)_a{-}OCH_2 & & RCO(OCH_2CH_2)_b{-}OCH_2 \\
| & & | \\
HOCH & \text{or} & HOCH \\
| & & | \\
HOCH_2 & & RCO(OCH_2CH_2)_c{-}OCH_2
\end{array}
$$

Some unchanged glycerol linkages with fatty acids may be present in the final product even at relatively high mole ratios of ethylene oxide to hydrophobe. (Glycerides of fatty acids that do not contain hydroxyl groups react with ethylene oxide under similar conditions and at comparable rates to castor oil. The products are surfactants with properties similar to the castor oil derivatives.) The ethoxylates are yellow-to-amber viscous liquids with specific gravities slightly greater than 1.0 at room temperature. Ethoxylated castor oils are hydrophilic emulsifiers, dispersants, and lubricants.

Table 26. Ethoxylated Castor Oils

Product name	Ratio, POE to oil	Concn, wt %	Biodegrad-ability	Functions[a]	Manufac-turer[b]
Aldosperse CO-25	POE 25	100	B	E	GLY
Aldosperse CO-200	POE 200	100		E, A	GLY
Castor Oil Ethoxylate		100	B	E	PSC
Emulphor EL-620		100	B	E, Di, Tl	GAF
Lipal 9C		100		E, Di	DRW
Lipal 25C		100		E, S	DRW
Lipal 52C		100		D, W	DRW
Siponic H-35		100	B	E	AAC
Surfactol-318		100		E, Tl, dF	BAC
Surfactol-380		100		E, St, Tl	BAC
T-DET C-30		100	B	E, Di, Tl	TMH
Trylox CO-20	POE 20	100		E, Tl, Ts	TCH
Trylox CO-30	POE 30	100		E, S, Di, Tl, Ts	TCH
Trylox CO-40	POE 40	100		E, S, Di, rW, Tl	TCH
Trylox CO-80	POE 80	100		E, Di, S, Tl	TCH

[a] See Table 1.   [b] See Table 44.

They are used as processing assistants and finishing agents in the manufacture of paper, leather, and textile products. Other uses are in emulsion polymerizations, paints, polishes, and cosmetic products. Skin irritation and phytotoxicity are unusually low. Table 26 lists and describes representative products.

Lanolin alcohols are derived from the fat that is stripped from raw wool. They are a mixture of cholesterol, isocholesterol, and other higher alcohols. Lanolin alcohols purified by bleaching, solvent extraction, crystallization, or molecular distillation are ethoxylated to yield nonionic emulsifiers. The mole ratios of ethylene oxide to alcohols that are offered commercially represent a full series of lipophilic and hydrophilic products. Their largest use is as emulsifiers in cosmetic preparations. Manufacturers

Table 27. U.S. Production of Carboxylic Amides, 1966

Product type	Production, 1000 lb
diethanolamine condensates, amine/acid = 1/1	37,380
diethanolamine condensates, amine/acid = 2/1	25,555
ethanolamine condensates, various ratios	10,310
isopropanolamine condensates	5,842
all other amine condensates, nonionic	13,933
total	93,020

Table 28. Physical Form and Solubility of Fatty Diethanolamides

Fatty acid	Amine/acid	Physical form	Water solubility
coco	2/1	liquid	soluble
coco	1/1	paste	limited solubility
lauric	2/1	soft paste	soluble
lauric	1/1	paste	limited solubility
oleic	2/1	liquid	dispersible
stearic	2/1	paste	dispersible

Table 29. Diethanolamides of Fatty Acids

Product name	Fatty acid	Type[a]	Concn, wt %	Bio-degrad-ability	Functions[b]	Manufac-turer[c]
Aminol COR-2	coco	R	100	B	D, Fs	FET
Aminol CO-S	coco	S	86	B	Fs, V	FET
Ardet DC	coco	R	100	B	D, Fs, E, V	ARD
Ardet LDA 9095	lauric	R	92	B	Fs	ARD
Calamide C	coco	R	100	B	D, Fs	PIL
Calamide L	lauric	R	100	B	D, Fs	PIL
Cardene	oleic	R	100		E	CCW
Clindrol 200 CGN	coco	R	100	B	D, E, Fs	CLI
Clindrol 200 L	lauric	R	100	B	Fs, E	CLI
Clindrol 200 O	oleic	R	100	B	E	CLI
Clindrol 100 L	lauric	S	100	B	Fs, V	CLI
Clindrol 100 CG	coco	S	100	B	Fs, S	CLI
Condensate PO	coco	R	100	B	D, E	CTL
Condensate PE	lauric	R	100	B	Fs	CTL
Condensate PM	myristic	R	100	B	Fs	CTL
Culveride SAL-9	lauric	R	90	B	Fs, D	CUL
Diethanolamine Coconut Superamide	coco	S	100	B	D, Fs	EMR
Diethanolamine Lauric Superamide	lauric	S	100	B	D, Fs	EMR
Emid 6510	lauric	S	100	B	D, Fs	PCS
Emid 6514	coco	S	100	B	E	PCS
Emid 6530	coco	R	100	B	D	PCS
Emid 6540	lauric	R	100	B	D, Fs	PCS
Emid 6544	capric	R	100	B	D, W	PCS
Gafamide CDD-518	coco	S	100	B	D, Fs, V, W	GAF
Hartamide C	coco	S	100		D, Fs	HRT
Hartamide K	coco	R	100		D, Fs	HRT
Hartamide LX	lauric	R	100		D, Fs	HRT
Hartamide L	lauric	S	100		D, Fs	HRT
Marsamid 40	coco	R	100	B	D, V, Fs	MRS

include American Alcoholac, Atlas Chemical Industries, Croda, Malmstrom, and Robinson Wagner.

Carboxylic Amides. Production of the carboxylic amide nonionics is listed in Table 27 by product type in the order of their discussion.

Diethanolamine Condensates. The usage of fatty diethanolamides is fairly evenly divided between "regular" (2/1, amine/acid) and "super" (1/1) amides. See Alkanol-amines. The 2/1 or regular fatty dialkanolamides were the subject of a patent granted to Kritchevsky (45) in 1937. The gross composition of these products is repre-sented by the formula $RCON(CH_2CH_2OH)_2 \cdot HN(CH_2CH_2OH)_2$ as indicated by the ratio of amine to acid. The components in a regular fatty dialkanolamide were reported on a wt % basis (46) as: $RCON(CH_2CH_2OH)_2$, 50%; $KN(CH_2CH_2OH)_2$, 25%; $RCON(CH_2CH_2OH)CH_2CH_2OOCR$, 10%; $RCOOCH_2CH_2NHCH_2CH_2OH$, 10%; $(RCOO)^-H_2N(CH_2CH_2OH)_2^+$, 5%. The 2/1 fatty dialkanolamides behave more like a compound than a mixture. The effect of the excess diethanolamine and its derivatives on the properties of the products is to increase their water solubility as compared to the super amides. A typical 1/1 super amide would contain 90% of the

Table 29 (*continued*)

Product name	Fatty acid	Type[a]	Concn, wt %	Bio-degrad-ability	Functions[b]	Manufac-turer[c]
Marsamid 50	coco	S	100	B	D, V, Fs	MRS
Marsamid 80	lauric	R	100	B	D, V, Fs	MRS
Marsamid 90	lauric	S	100	B	D, V, Fs	MRS
Onyxol 42	stearic	R	97	B	O, V	OXR
Onyxol 336	lauric	R	97	B	D, F, Di, W	OXR
P&G Amide No. 22	lauric	R	100	B	Fs, St, V	PG
P&G Amide No. 23	C_{12-14} acid	R	100	B	Fs, St, V	PG
P&G Amide No. 72	coco	R	100	B	D, Fs	PG
Retzamide LA	lauric	R	100	B	D, Fs	RTF
Retzamide LAX	lauric	S	100	B	D, Fs	RTF
Schercomid 1212	lauric	R	60	B	D, Fs, V	SBC
Schercomid 1821-A	stearic	R	70	B	E, O	SBC
Schercomid CDA	coco	R	60	B	D, Fs, Di	SBC
Schercomid CDA-H	hydrogenated coco	R	60	B	D, Fs, V	SBC
Schercomid MD	myristic	R	70	B	D, Fs, V	SBC
Schercomid RDO	ricinoleic	R	70	B	E	SBC
Schercomid ST	stearic	R	90	B	E, V	SBC
Schercomid TO-1	tall oil	R	100	B	E, V	SBC
Super-Amide B-5	coco	S	90	B	Fs, V	OXR
Super-Amide L-9	lauric	S	90	B	Fs, E, V	OXR
Synotol CN-90	coco	R	100	B	D	DRW
Synotol L-90	lauric	R	90	B	D	DRW
Synotol LO-80	linoleic	R	100		E	DRW
Synotol S-80	stearic	R	100		E	DRW
Synotol M-90	myristic	R	100	B	D	DRW
Tanasol 51	coco	R	100	B	D, W, F	CST
Texol 237	lauric	R	100	B	D, W	GAF
Ultrapole LDA 9005	lauric	R	99	B	Fs	WTC
Ultrapole S	coco	R	99	B	D, E	WTC
Varamide A-1	coco	R	100	B	D	VAC
Varamide L-1	lauric	R	100	B	D, Fs	VAC

[a] R = "regular" (amine/acid, 2/1); S = "super" (amine/acid, 1/1).
[b] See Table 1.   [c] See Table 44.

amide of the fatty acid, 7% unreacted diethanolamine, 2.5% amino esters and ester amides. The physical form and the water solubility of the fatty dialkanolamides are shown in Table 28. Although the regular diethanolamides of the higher fatty acids and the super diethanolamides of lauric and coco acids are insoluble in water, they are readily solubilized in combinations with more hydrophilic surfactants.

Foam stabilization and detergency are the most important functional properties of the fatty diethanolamides. They also increase the viscosity of detergent solutions and act as emollients. The products also have the properties of rust protection, corrosion inhibition, wetting, emulsification, and lime-soap dispersion. The coco and lauric diethanolamides are widely used as foam stabilizers and detergents in liquid dishwashing formulations and shampoos. In janitorial scrub soaps, they are used as the only or principal cleansing agent. The products are also used in textile processing as detergents and dyeing assistants. Other uses are in lubricating oils, slushing oils, and drycleaning detergents.

Regular fatty diethanolamides are prepared by heating 1 mole of fatty acid with 2 moles of diethanolamine at 160–180°C for 2–4 hr. Superamides are prepared by heating a fatty acid methyl ester with an equimolar quantity of diethanolamine at 100–110°C for 2–4 hr and distilling off the methanol that is formed. Representative commercial products are listed and described in Table 29.

Monoalkanolamine Condensates. Coco, lauric, oleic, and stearic monethanolamides and monisopropanolamides with amine ratios in the range from 2/1 to 1/2 are the principal surfactants in the monoalkanolamide group. They are generally water-insoluble solids that are easily solubilized by hydrophilic surfactants. Except for solubility, their properties and uses are similar to the fatty diethanolamides. Manufacturing processes and product yields, which are also similar to the fatty diethanolamides, have been reviewed (47). Composition and properties of typical products are listed in Table 30.

Polyoxyethylene Fatty Acid Amides. The mono- and diadducts obtained by ethoxylation of a fatty acid amide are equivalent in gross composition to the mono and diethanolamide condensates of the corresponding fatty acid, but the condensates are more widely used than the adducts because they have better properties for most uses. Fatty acid mono- and diethanolamide condensates, as well as fatty acid amides, can be ethoxylated by conventional technology. Ethoxylates of fatty acid amides are predominately secondary amides since the second hydrogen on the amide is less reactive than the first toward ethylene oxide. Table 31 lists typical commercial products in this series.

Table 30. Monoalkanolamides of Fatty Acids

Product name	Fatty acid	Amine	Concn, wt %	Biodegradability	Functions[a]	Manufacturer[b]
Ardet LIPA	lauric	isopropanol	93	B	Fs	ARD
Cerasynt 303	stearic	ethanol	100		E, W, Di	VND
Clindrol 101L1	lauric	isopropanol	100	B	Fs	CLI
Emcol 61	oleic	isopropanol		B	E	WTC
Emid 6500	coco	ethanol	100	B	Fs	PCS
Emid 6506	lauric	isopropanol	100	B	Fs, D, V	PCS
Monamid CIPA	coco	isopropanol	100	B	Fs, V	MOA
Monamid LIPA	lauric	isopropanol	100	B	Fs, V	MOA
Monamid CMA	coco	ethanol	100	B	Fs, V	MOA
Monamid LMA	lauric	ethanol	100	B	Fs, V	MOA
Onyxol 368	lauric	isopropanol	97	B	Fs	OXR
P & G Amide No. 27	coco	ethanol	100	B	Fs, St, V	PG
Schercomid CME	coco	ethanol	95	B	D, Fs	SBC
Schercomid EA-100	stearic	ethanol	100	B	O	SBC
Schercomid LME	lauric	ethanol	95	B	Fs	SBC
Schercomid LMI	lauric	isopropanol	90	B	Fs	SBC
Schercomid OMI	oleic	isopropanol	85	B	E, D	SBC
Sole-Onic MEAC	coco	ethanol	100	B	Fs	HDG
Sole-Onic MEAS	stearic	ethanol	100	B	O	HDG
Sole-Onic MIO	oleic	isopropanol	100	B	A, H	HDG
Stepan LIPA	lauric	isopropanol	100		Fs, D	STP
Textamide PL	lauric	isopropanol	100	B	Fs	TXT
Ultrapole H	lauric	ethanol	99	B	Fs	WTC
Ultrapole L	lauric	isopropanol	99	B	Fs	WTC

[a] See Table 1.   [b] See Table 44.

Table 31. Polyoxyethylene Fatty Acid Amides

Product name	Fatty acid	POE[a]	Concn, wt %	Biodegradability	Functions[b]	Manufacturers[c]
Amidox C2	coco	2	100	B	E, D	STP
Amidox C5	coco	5	100	B	E, D	STP
Amidox L2	lauric	2	100	B	E, D	STP
Amidox L5	lauric	5	100	B	E, D	STP
Ethomid HT/15	hydrogenated tallow	5	100	B	E, Di, D	ARC
Ethomid HT/60	hydrogenated tallow	50	100	B	E, Di, D	ARC
Ethomid 0/5	oleic	5	100	B	E, Di, D	ARC

[a] Mole ratio of polyoxyethylene to fatty acid amide.   [b] See Table 1.   [c] See Table 44.

Polyalkylene Oxide Block Copolymers. Propylene oxide, butylene oxide, styrene oxide, and cyclohexene oxide react with compounds containing an active hydrogen in a manner analogous to the reaction of ethylene oxide with an active hydrogen. In contrast to the effect of the added ethylene oxide units, $-CH_2CH_2O-$, the higher alkylene oxide units are more hydrophobic than hydrophilic. This hydrophobic tendency of propylene oxide units, $-CH(CH_3)CH_2O-$, is used in several ways in the manufacture of surfactants. The other hydrophobic alkylene oxides are not known to be used commercially as surfactant raw materials except for minor quantities as chain terminators on polyoxyethylene compounds to lower the foaming tendency. Manufacture, properties, and uses of polyalkylene oxide block copolymers are described by Schmolka (48).

Polyoxypropylene–Polyoxyethylene Nonionics. Propylene oxide (1,2-epoxypropane) is reacted with propylene glycol (1,2-propanediol) to form a series of polyoxypropylene hydrophobes with mol wts of 950–3250. The mol wt of the polyoxypropylene glycol must be at least 900 in order for it to function as a hydrophobe. These polyoxypropylene glycols are then solubilized by ethoxylation to polyoxyethylene contents that range from 20 to 90% of the total weight, ie $HO(CH_2CH_2O)_a(C_3H_6O)_b$-$(CH_2CH_2O)_cH$, where b is at least 15 and a and c are such that the polyoxyethylene amounts to 20–90% of the total weight. A series of twenty-five to thirty products of this general composition is marketed by Wyandotte Chemical Corp. under their Pluronic trademark.

The 100% active Pluronic surfactants vary in physical form from mobile liquids to pastes to flakeable solids. Specific gravities of the liquids at 25/25°C lie between 1.016 and 1.06. The solubility in water ranges from slightly soluble at room temperatures to completely miscible at the boil. The solubility decreases as the temperature increases but a few of the members exhibit a double cloud point, there being a temperature below which, as well as one above which, cloudiness is formed. In general, the products are soluble in aromatic and chlorinated solvents but insoluble in kerosene and mineral oils. They are almost tasteless, and they are nonirritating to the skin and low in toxicity. Their chemical stability is comparable to that of polyoxyethylene-solubilized fatty alcohols and alkylphenols. Phenol and substituted phenols form insoluble complexes with these nonionics but the precipitates are solubilized at higher concentrations of the surfactants.

The polyoxypropylene–polyoxyethylene nonionics are not strongly surface active but they do exhibit commercially useful surfactant properties. Aqueous solutions are characteristically lower foaming than other types of surfactants, and defoaming is an important property of the products. Commercial applications involve wetting, detergency, emulsification, dispersion, and solubilization properties, particularly in uses where their foaming and/or low toxicity are also advantageous. These diols are used as defoamers in papermaking, steam-generating systems, coating compositions, etc. Another important application is demulsification of crude petroleum. The products are used to solubilize and detoxify iodine in detergent/sanitizers and germicides, eg dairy cleaners. Other uses include wetting or rinsing aids for etching, plating, or pickling of metals; for processing photographic films; and for automatic dishwashing machines. They are also used as emulsifiers, detergents, and dispersants in applications where foam would interfere with the surfactant performance. A variety of cosmetic and pharmaceutical preparations take advantage of the low foaming and low toxicity of the materials.

A polyalkylene oxide block copolymer derived from glycerol as the initiator by sequential propoxylation and ethoxylation is marketed by Dow Chemical Co. as Polyglycol 112. The product has limited solubility in water and is useful as an anti-foaming agent and petroleum demulsifier.

Other block copolymers of propylene and ethylene oxides, initiated by glycerol or other triols, and containing 10% or less of polyoxyethylene, are produced as urethan intermediates rather than surfactants.

The Tergitol nonionics XH and XD of Union Carbide Corp. are reported to be the product of a two-step reaction: (1) preparation of a hydrophobe by reacting a mixture of propylene and ethylene oxide with a monohydric alcohol containing eight or less carbon atoms and (2) solubilization by ethoxylation to a polyoxyethylene content of about 50% by wt (48). The products are recommended as emulsifiers for insecticides, chlorinated solvent or emulsion polymerization and as detergents for use at elevated temperatures. Similar mixed nonionics, in the sense that they contain both oxyethylene and oxypropylene units, surfactants have recently been introduced, eg Pluradot HA 430 from Wyandotte Chemical Corp.

Miscellaneous Nonionics. Organosilicones are converted by oxyalkylation to polysiloxane–polyoxyalkylene copolymers (49) with surfactant properties. Manufacturers include Dow Corning Corp., General Electric Co., and Union Carbide Corp. A typical product, eg L-520 of Union Carbide Corp., has the structure $C_2H_3Si(O(Si-(CH_3)_2O)_z(CH_2CH_2O)_x(C_3H_6O)_yC_4H_9)_3$, where the organic portion is a mixed copolymer containing equal weights of propylene and ethylene oxides and terminated with a butoxy group, the silicon base and each of the three organic branch chains has a mol wt of approx 1500, ie total mol wt approx 6000. Products in this series, which includes both water-soluble and solvent-soluble types, are used as emulsifying and foam-control agents in the manufacture of urethan foams.

CATIONIC SURFACTANTS

The hydrophilic moieties in cationic surfactants are amino or quaternary nitrogens. As the name implies, these hydrophobic moieties bear a positive charge when dissolved in aqueous media. The hydrophilic tendency of one amino nitrogen is approximately strong enough to solubilize a lipophilic group in the surfactant molecular-weight range in dilute acidic solution; eg lauryl amine is soluble in dilute hydrochloric acid. To increase the water solubility, additional primary, secondary, or tertiary amino groups can be introduced or the amino group can be quaternized with a low-molecular-weight alkyl group, eg CH_3- or $HOCH_2CH_2-$. Quaternary nitrogen compounds are strong bases that form essentially neutral salts with hydrochloric and sulfuric acid. Most quaternary surfactants are soluble even in alkaline aqueous solutions. Polyoxyethylated cationics behave like nonionics in alkaline solutions and like cationics in acidic solutions.

Cationic surfactants are widely used in acidic aqueous and nonaqueous systems (50) as dispersants, emulsifiers, wetting agents, sanitizers, dye fixing agents, textile lubricants, textile softeners, foam stabilizers, and corrosion inhibitors. This usage pattern parallels somewhat the widespread use of anionics in neutral and alkaline solutions. The negatively charged cationics are more strongly adsorbed than anionic or nonionic surfactants on a diverse group of substrates including metals, glass, textile fibers, plastics, minerals, and animal or human tissues. This substantivity is the key to many applications for which the cationics are uniquely effective. For example, the substantivity of cationics is used to deposit an emulsified oil or dispersed solid on a solid substrate and hold it there. Many of the quaternary cationics have germicidal, fungicidal, or algicidal activity and solutions of the products are widely used for these purposes. The quaternaries are also combined with nonionics to form detergent-sanitizers. Biocidal products are classified as economic poisons and their labeling is regulated by the U.S. Department of Agriculture. The nonethoxylated cationics are generally incompatible with anionics because the salt formed in the reaction of the two oppositely charged heavy ions is insoluble in water.

Although the production of cationics in the U.S. amounted to only 5% of total surfactant production for 1966, the number of products represented in the total was proportionately much larger. The lower average poundage of the cationics is partly offset by their higher unit prices; see Table 43. The usage of cationic surfactants is less than the listed production because many of the simpler products are also used as intermediates for conversion into more highly substituted derivatives (50).

The biocidal activity of quaternaries is a distinctive phenomenon that is not necessarily related to their surface activity. Deducting these two groups would show that the quantity of cationics used as surfactants is substantially below the U.S. production of 161,843,000 lb reported for 1966. Table 32 gives a breakdown of this total by cationic product types.

Table 32. U.S. Production of Cationic Surfactants, 1966

Product type	Production, 1000 lb
amines not containing oxygen	59,636
oxygen-containing amines, except amides	38,518
amines having amide linkages	17,451
quaternary salts	46,238
total	161,843

Amines Not Containing Oxygen. Aliphatic mono-, di-, and polyamines, and rosin-derived amines are the important surfactant compounds in this class. The products are marketed as acetates, naphthenates, and oleates. The principal uses are as ore-flotation agents, corrosion inhibitors, and dispersing agents. The structures of typical products other than mono- and dialkylamines are shown below:

$$RNHCH_2CH_2CH_2NH_2$$

N-alkyltrimethylenediamine

where R is coco alkyl, tallow alkyl, soya alkyl, or 9-octadecenyl,

$$R—C\overset{N—CH_2}{\underset{N—CH_2}{\diagdown}} \\ | \\ CH_2CH_2—NH_2$$

1-(2-aminoethyl)-2-alkyl-2-imidazoline

where R is heptadecyl, 8-heptadecenyl, or mixed alkyl,

$$R—C\overset{N—CH_2}{\underset{N—CH_2}{\diagdown}} \\ | \\ H$$

2-alkyl-2-imidazoline

where R is 8-heptadecenyl, heptadecyl, nonyl, or mixed alkyl.

Surfactant usages of chemically unmodified amines probably consumed only a minor portion of the 59,636,000 lb of amines not containing oxygen that were produced in 1966. Much the larger portion of this quantity was used for the production of more highly substituted nitrogen-containing surfactants. A breakdown of total production between these uses was not reported.

Oxygen-Containing Amines, Except Amides. The oxygen-containing amines encompass several diverse and technically interesting groups of materials that are steadily increasing in economic importance, viz: amine oxides, polyoxyethylene alkylamines, 1-(2-hydroxyethyl)-2-alkyl-2-imidazolines, and N,N,N',N'-tetrakis-substituted ethylenediamine derivatives. Published statistics do not provide an accurate breakdown of the production of these product groups.

Amine Oxides. The first patent on tertiary amine oxides as surfactants was issued in Germany in 1939 and the first amine oxide was introduced to the American market in 1956. The products did not attract widespread interest until 1961, almost coincident with the issuance of several patents describing their surfactant uses (51,52).

Compositions and suggested uses of typical commercial products are listed in Table 33. These materials are offered as pale-yellow aqueous solutions or light-yellow pastes at concentrations of 30–50 wt % of active ingredient. The amine oxide group is polar, with the greatest electron density at the oxygen atom. The compounds exhibit strong hydrogen bonding tendencies and are hygroscopic. The fatty amine oxides act as cationics in acidic solutions and in neutral or alkaline solutions behave as nonionics (53):

$$R(CH_3)_2N \rightarrow O + H^+ \rightleftharpoons R(CH_3)_2NOH^+$$
oxide   hydroxyammonium ion

In acidic media the tertiary amine oxides react metathetically with anionic surfactants to form precipitates. The critical micelle concentration (CMC) is much lower in neutral or alkaline solutions than it is in strongly acidic systems. This change in CMC parallels the change of the surfactants from the ionic to the nonionic form. The products are not active as oxidizing agents and are stable in formulated surfactant products. See Amine oxides in the Supplement Volume.

Table 33. Amine Oxides

$$R-\underset{\underset{CH_3}{|}}{\overset{\overset{CH_3}{|}}{C}}\to O \quad \text{or} \quad R-\underset{\underset{CH_2CH_2OH}{|}}{\overset{\overset{CH_2CH_2OH}{|}}{C}}\to O$$

Product name	R	Me^a or EO^b	Concn, wt %	Biodegrad-ability	Functions^c	Manufac-turer^d
Ammonyx CO	cetyl	diMe	30	B	D, Fs	ONX
Ammonyx LO	lauryl	diMe	30	B	D, Fs, W	ONX
Ammonyx MO	myristyl	diMe	30	B	D, Fs	ONX
Ammonyx SO	stearyl	diMe	30	B	Fs	ONX
Aromax C/12	coco	diEO	50	B	Fs, E	ARC
Aromax DMCD	coco	diMe	40	B	Fs, D	ARC
Aromax DMHTD	hydrogenated tallow	diMe	40	B	Fs	ARC
Aromax DM16D	hexadecyl	diMe	40	B	Fs	ARC
Aromax T/12	tallow	diEO	50	B	Fs, E	ARC
Aromax 18/12	octadecyl	diEO	50	B	Fs, E	ARC
Bairstat 14 E	$C_{12-14-16}$	diEO			A	BRD
Barlox 10S	decyl	diMe	30	B	D, Fs, V	BRD
Barlox 12S	lauryl	diMe	30	B	D, Fs, V	BRD
Barlox 14S	myristyl	diMe	30	B	D, Fs, V	BRD
Barlox 16S	cetyl	diMe	30	B	D, Fs, V	BRD
Barlox 18S	stearyl	diMe	30	B	D	BRD
Barlox E-12C	coco	diEO	30	B	D, Fs	BRD
Conco XA-C	cetyl	diMe	20	B	W, E	CTL
Conco XA-L	lauryl	diMe	30	B	D, E	CTL
Conco XA-M	myristyl	diMe	30	B	W, D	CTL
Conco XA-O	oleyl	diMe	30	B	W, F, D	CTL
Conco XA-2S	stearyl	diMe	30	B	W, Di	CTL
Conco XA-T	tallow	diMe	30	B	W, Di	CTL
Culveroz BHCO	coco	diEO	50	B	Fs, E, W	CUL
Culverox SDMO	stearyl	diMe	40	B	Fs, E	CUL
Culverox TDMO	tallow	diMe	40	B	Fs, E	CUL
Romine FLS-30	lauryl	diMe	30	B	Fs, V	ROZ
Romine FST-30	oleyl	diMe	30	B	Fs, V	ROZ
Schercamox DMC	coco	diMe	30	B	Fs, V, E	SBC
Schercamox DML	lauryl	diMe	30	B	Fs, V, E	SBC
Schercamox DMM	myristyl	diMe	30	B	Fs, V, E	SBC
Schercamox DMS	octadecyl	diMe	30	B	Fs, V, E	SBC

^{a} Me = CH_3. ^{b} EO = $-CH_2CH_2OH$. ^{c} See Table 1. ^{d} See Table 44.

The amine oxides first attracted widespread interest as replacements for the alkanolamides as foam builders in liquid hand-dishwashing formulations. To compete in this application at a comparable cost the amine oxides had to be equally effective at about one-third the concentration of the alkanolamides. In addition to foam boosting, the amine oxides are effective shampoo detergents, cotton detergents, wetting agents in concentrated electrolytes, and emulsifiers. They impart softness to fabrics and body or viscosity to aqueous solutions. The amine oxides are used in household-detergent products, industrial detergents, detergent-sanitizers, plating-bath additives, and textile-mill processing formulations. The amine oxides are prepared by oxidation of tertiary amines with hydrogen peroxide (54), ie:

$$R_3N + H_2O_2 \to R_3N \cdot H_2O_2 \to R_3N \to O + H_2O$$

Table 34. Polyoxyethylene Aliphatic and Rosin Monoamines

$$R{-}N{<}^{(CH_2CH_2O)_mH}_{(CH_2CH_2O)_nH}$$

Product name	Amine	POE[a]	Concn, wt %	Bio-degradability	Functions[b]	Manufacturer[c]
Barlol 12C-2	coco	2	100		E, I	BRD
Barlol 12-C15	coco	15	100		A, Tl	BRD
Ethomeen C/12	coco	2	100	B	E, Di, Ts, A	ARC
Ethomeen C/15	coco	5	100	B	E, Di, Ts, A	ARC
Ethomeen C/20	coco	10	100	B	E, Di, Ts, A	ARC
Ethomeen C/25	coco	15	100	B	E, Di, Ts, A	ARC
Ethomeen S/12	soybean	2	100	B	E, Di, Ts, A	ARC
Ethomeen S/15	soybean	5	100	B	E, Di, Ts, A	ARC
Ethomeen S/20	soybean	10	100	B	E, Di, Ts, A	ARC
Ethomeen S/25	soybean	15	100	B	E, Di, Ts, A	ARC
Ethomeen T/12	tallow	2	100	B	E, Di, Ts, A	ARC
Ethomeen T/15	tallow	5	100	B	E, Di, Ts, A	ARC
Ethomeen T/25	tallow	15	100	B	E, Di, Ts, A	ARC
Ethomeen 18/12	stearyl	2	100	B	E, Di, Ts, A	ARC
Ethomeen 18/15	stearyl	5	100	B	E, Di, Ts, A	ARC
Ethomeen 18/20	stearyl	10	100	B	E, Di, Ts, A	ARC
Polyrad 0100	rosin	1	100		C	HPC
Polyrad 0200	rosin	2	100		C	HPC
Polyrad 0500	rosin	5	100		C, W	HPC
Polyrad 1100	rosin	11	100		C, W	HPC
Polyrad 2000	rosin	20	100		W, C	HPC
Polyrad 4500	rosin	45	100		W, C	HPC
Priminox R-5	t-C_{12-14}	5	100		E	RH
Priminox R-15	t-C_{12-14}	15	100		E, St, Tl, A, Ta	RH
Priminox T-5	t-C_{18-22}	5	100		E	RH
Priminox T-15	t-C_{18-22}	15	100		E, A, St	RH
Priminox T-25	t-C_{18-22}	25	100		E, A, St	RH
Sipenol 1C2	coco	2	100		E	AAC
Sipenol 1C5	coco	5	100		E	AAC
Sipenol 1C15	coco	15	100		E	AAC
Sipenol 1SO2	soya	2	100		E	AAC
Sipenol 1SO5	soya	5	100		E	AAC
Sipenol 1S5	stearyl	5	100		Ta	AAC
Sipenol 1S15	stearyl	15	100		Ta	AAC
Sipenol 1S50	stearyl	50	100		Ta	AAC
Trymeen CAM-10	coco	10	100		A	TCH
Trymeen CAM-15	coco	15	100		S, Di, A, Ts, E	TCH
Trymeen TAM-2	tallow	2	100		E, Tl, Ts, A	TCH
Trymeen TAM-6	tallow	6	100		E, Ts, Tl, Di	TCH
Trymeen TAM-8	tallow	8	100		E, W, A, Ts, Tl	TCH
Trymeen TAM-20	tallow	20	100		E, A	TCH
Trymeen TAM-50	tallow	50	100		E, Di, S, Tl, A	TCH
Trymeen HTA-15	hydrogenated tallow	15	100		E, Tl, Ts, A	TCH
Trymeen SAM-2	stearyl	2	100		E, C, Tl, Ts	TCH

[a] POE = $m + n$.   [b] See Table 1.   [c] See Table 44.

Table 35. Polyoxyethylene Fatty Alkyl-1,3-propanediamines

$$RNCH_2CH_2CH_2N{\overset{\displaystyle (CH_2CH_2O)_aH}{\underset{\displaystyle (CH_2CH_2O)_bH}{\bigg\langle}}}$$
$$\overset{|}{(CH_2CH_2O)_cH}$$

Product name	R	$a+b+c$	Concn, wt %	Biodegrad- ability	Functions[a]	Manufac- turer[b]
Ethoduomeen C/12	coco	2	100	B	E	ARC
Ethoduomeen T/12	tallow	2	100	B	E, Di	ARC
Ethoduomeen T/13	tallow	3	100	B	E, Di	ARC
Ethoduomeen T/20	tallow	10	100	B	E, Di, W	ARC
Ethoduomeen T25	tallow	15	100	B	E, Di, W	ARC

[a] See Table 1.   [b] See Table 44.

Yields vary from 85% with commercial-grade undistilled amines to 99% with freshly distilled amines.

Polyoxyethylene Alkyl and Alicyclic Amines. Ethoxylation is an economic route to the multiplicity of properties required by the numerous and sometimes smalls volume industrial uses of cationic surface-active agents. The chemical composition- and structural formulas of typical polyoxyethylene derivatives of alkyl and alicyclic amines are shown in Tables 34 and 35. Three series of products are represented: polyoxyethylene linear alkyl amines, polyoxyethylene aliphatic *t*-alkylamines, and polyoxyethylene dehydroabietylamines. Despite the wide range of chemical composi- tions, the polyoxyamines tend to have similar physical properties. They are generally yellow or amber liquids or yellow solids with low melting points. Specific gravities at room temperature range from approx 0.9 to 1.15. The ethoxylated amines have the characteristically greater solubility of cationics in acidic solutions as compared to neutral or alkaline solutions, but the difference decreases as the polyoxyethylene content increases. Amines with low mole ratios of polyoxyethylene to hydrophobe form insoluble salts in metathetical reactions with fatty acids and other anionic sur- factants, but the similar salts of the higher mole ratios are soluble surfactants with quite different properties. The N–C linkage of the polyoxyethylene chain to the nitrogen is strongly resistant to hydrolysis by acids or alkalis. Oil solubility of the amines decreases as the polyoxyethylene content increases but many products with a fairly even lipophilic/hydrophilic balance have appreciable solubility in hydrocarbons and are used as solutes in the oil phase.

The polyoxyethylene amines are used as emulsifiers, dispersants, and wetting agents in neutral and acid solutions. As corrosion inhibitors they are used in both oil- and water-based systems. Other uses are as textile softeners, lubricants and anti- stats. The products are used as corrosion inhibitors and dispersants in refined pe- troleum products and in corrosion inhibition and demulsification formulations for use in the production and refining of petroleum products. Other uses are as components of mill-processing formulations for fabrication of metal and textile products, wetting agents for asphalt (see Vol. 2, p. 798), and frothing agents for ore flotation.

Equipment and processes for ethoxylation of the amines are similar to those de- scribed earlier for reaction of ethylene oxide with alkylphenols and aliphatic alcohols. If there is no steric hindrance, ethylene oxide reacts with both hydrogens of a primary amine at a relatively low temperature (90–120°C) in the absence of an added catalyst (54a). Only one hydrogen on the nitrogen of sterically hindered amines reacts with

Table 36. 2-Alkyl-1-(hydroxyethyl)-2-imidazolines

$$R-C \underset{\displaystyle \underset{CH_2CH_2OH}{\overset{|}{N}}-CH_2}{\overset{N-CH_2}{\diagdown}}$$

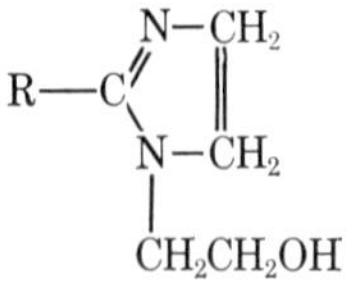

Product name	R	Concn, wt %	Biodegrad-ability	Functions[a]	Manufac-turer[b]
Fatchemco-O	8-heptadecenyl	100	B	A, C, E	UVC
Fatchemco-S	heptadecyl	100	B	A, Ts, C	UVC
Fatchemco-T	heptadecadienyl	100	B	E, C	UVC
Fatchemco-C	undecyl	100	B	A, D, W	UVC
Hodag Amine C-100-O	8-heptadecenyl	100	B	D, E, C	HDG
Hodag Amine C-100-S	8-heptadecyl	100	B	D, E, C	HDG
Hodag C-100-L	undecyl	100	B	D, E, C	HDG
Romine BTQ	8-heptadecenyl	100		D, G	ROZ
Varamine O	8-heptadecenyl	100	B	E, C	VAC

[a] See Table 1.   [b] See Table 44.

ethylene oxide; the t-amine bases of the Priminox surfactants listed in Table 34 are of this type. After the capacity of the amino nitrogens for direct reaction with ethylene oxide is exhausted, a basic catalyst is added and ethoxylation is continued by essentially the same procedure used for nonionics. All three amino hydrogens on the N-alkyl-1,3-propanediamines are available for reaction with ethylene oxide. The 1,3-propanediamines bases for this reaction are prepared by the addition of acrylonitrile to fatty monoamines followed by reduction of the resultant β-cyanoethylalkylamine.

2-Alkyl-1-(hydroxyethyl)-2-imidazolines. Table 36 shows the structural formulas as well as the compositions and properties of typical commercial products in this series. These materials are used in hydrocarbon and acidic aqueous media as wetting agents, dispersants, emulsifiers, corrosion inhibitors, and detergents. They are also useful antistats for application to textile fibers. The 1-(2-hydroxyethyl)-2-alkyl-2-imidazolines are prepared by heating the salt of a carboxylic acid with hydroxyethylenediamine to obtain a substituted amide; raising the temperature to 200–250°C then causes elimination of another mole of water to form the substituted imidazoline. In addition to their use as surfactants per se, these amines are further converted to yield three additional series of cationic surfactants. They are (1) ethoxylated to yield more hydrophilic products, (2) reacted with dimethyl sulfate or benzyl chloride to form quaternaries, and (3) treated with hydrogen peroxide to yield amine oxides. The second and third reactions involve substitutions on the 1-position in the imidazoline ring and the first reaction extends the oxyethylene chain that is already a monoadduct on the nitrogen in the 1-position.

N,N,N',N'-Tetrakis-substituted Ethylenediamines. The reaction of a 1,2-alkylene oxide with ethylenediamine forms the basis of an ether and an ester series of surfactants. The ethers, which are more important commercially, are weakly cationic products that have the structure shown below, where x and y each varies from about 4 to

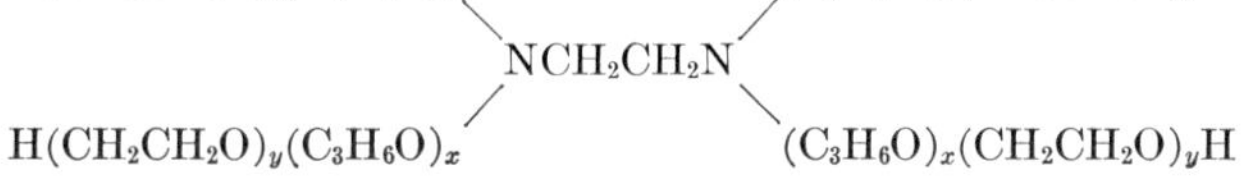

$$\begin{array}{cc} H(CH_2CH_2O)_y(C_3H_6O)_x & (C_3H_6O)_x(CH_2CH_2O)_yH \\ \diagdown & \diagup \\ & NCH_2CH_2N \\ \diagup & \diagdown \\ H(CH_2CH_2O)_y(C_3H_6O)_x & (C_3H_6O)_x(CH_2CH_2O)_yH \end{array}$$

100. The polyoxypropylene groups comprise the hydrophobic moieties in this series of block copolymer surfactants and polyoxyethylene groups the hydrophilic constituents. The two tertiary nitrogen atoms contribute cationic properties to the lower mol wt polymers but are so shielded in the higher mol wt range that the products behave essentially as nonionics.

Ten out of the large number of possible derivatives are offered commercially by Wyandotte Chemical Corp., ie Tetronic 304, 501, 504, 701, 702, 704, 707, 901, and 908. Compositions range from a hydrophobe weight of 900–1000 combined with 40–50 wt % of polyoxyethylene to a hydrophobe weight of 4000 in combination with about 80–90% of polyoxyethylene. Seven of the products are almost colorless, viscous liquids with sp gr slightly greater than 1.0 at room temperature. The high polymers with a balanced ratio of polyoxypropylene to polyoxyethylene are flakeable solids. The products vary in water solubility from relatively insoluble to highly soluble. They are insoluble in kerosene and mineral oils. In general the compounds can be used as detergents, emulsifiers, demulsifiers, defoamers, and lime-soap dispersants but they are not strongly surface active. Uses are claimed in demulsification of crude petroleum, inhibition of clay hydration in drilling fluids, lime-soap dispersion in detergent bars, and antistatic additives to polyethylene. The products are used as processing assistants in the manufacture of polyurethan foams and as thickening agents in water-based hydraulic fluids.

The ester class of a surfactants is represented by N,N,N',N'-tetrakis(2-hydroxyethyl)ethylenediamine dioleate, methyl sulfate, and the tetrakis-2-hydroxypropyl homolog.

Amines Having Amide Linkages. The important products in this category are amide-linked amines prepared by the condensation of a carboxylic acid with a di- or polyamine. The type represents one approach in the search for a less expensive aliphatic amine in the surfactant molecular-weight range. Formulas for typical amide-linked amines are listed below:

$$RCONHCH_2CH_2NHCH_2CH_2NH_2 \ and/or \ RCON\begin{matrix} CH_2CH_2NH_2 \\ CH_2CH_2NH_2 \end{matrix}$$

where R is derived from coconut, oleic, stearic, and tall oil acids;

$$RCONHCH_2CH_2CH_2N(CH_3)_2$$

where R is from stearic acid;

$$RCONHCH_2CH_2CH_2NHCH_2CH_2CH_2NH_2 \ and/or \ RCON\begin{matrix} CH_2CH_2CH_2NH_2 \\ CH_2CH_2CH_2NH_2 \end{matrix}$$

where R is from stearic acid; and

$$RCONHCH_2CH_2NHCH_2CH_2NHCH_2CH_2NHCH_2CH_2NH_2$$

where R is from stearic acid.

More water-soluble polyoxyethylene derivatives are produced from most of the amide-linked di- and polyamines that contain one or more amino hydrogens. Production in 1966 was about equally divided between the amide-linked amines and their

Table 37. Dialkyldimethylammonium Salts

$$\left[\begin{array}{c} R' \\ | \\ R\!-\!N\!-\!CH_3 \\ | \\ CH_3 \end{array} \right]^{+} \; A^{-}$$

Product name	R and R'	A⁻	Concn, wt %	Biodegrad-ability	Functions[a]	Manufac-turer[b]
Adogen 442	hydrogenated tallow	Cl	75		Ts	ASC
Adogen 462	coco	Cl	75		E, Di, C	ASC
Ammonyx 2194	tallow	CH₃SO₄	75		Ts	ONX
Arquad 2C-75	coco	Cl	75	B	E, C	ARC
Arquad 2S-75	soya	Cl	75	B	E, C	ARC
Arquad 2HT-75	stearyl	Cl	75	B	Ts	ARC
Formonyte 1701	coco	Cl	75		E, Ts	FOR
Formonyte 1703	hydrogenated tallow	Cl	75		E, Ts	FOR
Variquat K300	coco	Cl			E, C	VAC
Varisoft 100	stearyl	Cl	75		Ts	VAC

a See Table 1.   *b* See Table 44.

ethoxylated derivatives. Both of these product types are dark-colored liquids that are useful as components of corrosion inhibitors, petroleum demulsifiers, and metal-processing formulations.

Quaternary Ammonium Salts. The quaternary ammonium ion is a much stronger hydrophilic moiety than a primary, secondary, or tertiary amino group. The strong basicity or cationic activity of the quaternary ion will carry compounds in the surfactant mol wt range into solution even in alkaline media. The quaternaries also differ from other cationic types by being more strongly adsorbed on negatively charged substrates and by being less susceptible to yellowing on aging in the presence of air. It is difficult to estimate accurately the usage of quaternaries as surfactants because several key commercial applications of the products do not depend on their surface activity but rather on other characteristics, eg biocidal activity and textile-softening properties. Tables 37–40 show the chemical structures and functional properties for typical commercial quaternary surfactants. In the aggregate these product types accounted for a major proportion of the U.S. production of 46,238,000 lb of quaternaries in 1966. U.S. production of dialkyldimethylammonium halides alone exceeded 20,000,000 lb.

A technically interesting and commercially important quaternary nitrogen compound that apparently is not included in surfactant production statistics warrants comment because of the unusual manner of its use. Stearamidomethylpyridinium chloride is the emulsifier and also an active ingredient in permanent water repellents, eg Du Pont's Zelan. The water-repellent composition which may also contain methylene distearamide, $(C_{17}H_{35}CONH)_2CH_2$, is padded on the fabric that is to be rendered water-repellent. The fabric is then dried and heat treated in an oven where the emulsifier is decomposed, viz:

$$(C_{17}H_{35}CONHCH_2N\!\!\bigcirc)^+ \; Cl^- \longrightarrow C_5H_5N.HCl\uparrow + C_{17}H_{35}CONHCH_2^{-*}$$

*The fate of the hydrophobe is not clearly defined except that it stays on the fabric either by bonding to it or as the insoluble methylene distearamide.

Many of the simple cationics cited earlier as surfactants are also quaternized to form more highly substituted products, eg:

$$R{-}N\begin{array}{c}CH_2CH_2OH\\|\\|\\CH_2CH_2OH\end{array}\xrightarrow{R'X}\left[R{-}N{-}R'\begin{array}{c}CH_2CH_2OH\\|\\|\\CH_2CH_2OH\end{array}\right]^+ X^-$$

$$R{-}C\begin{array}{c}N{-}CH_2\\{\diagdown}\ |\\{N{-}CH_2}\\|\\CH_2CH_2OH\end{array}\xrightarrow{R'X}\left[R{-}C\begin{array}{c}N{-}CH_2\\{\diagdown}\ |\\{N{-}CH_2}\\{\diagup}\ {\diagdown}\\R'\ \ CH_2CH_2OH\end{array}\right]^+ X^-$$

Table 38. Alkylbenzyldimethylammonium Chlorides (Benzalkonium Chlorides)

$$\left[R{-}N\begin{array}{c}CH_3\\|\\|\\CH_3\end{array}{-}CH_2C_6H_5\right]^+ Cl^-$$

Product name	R	Concn, wt %	Functions[b]	Manufacturer[c]
Alacasan SAC-25	stearyl	25	H	AAC
Ammonyx 856	tallow	75	Di, dE	ONX
Ammonyx 4002	stearyl	100	H, A, Es	ONX
Ammonyx T	cetyl	25	E, W, G	ONX
Barquat LB-50	lauryl	50	G	BRD
Barquat MB-50	myristyl	50	G	BRD
Bionol RO-50	alkyl	50	G	GAF
BTC-50	alkyl	50	G	ONX
BTC-824 P100	myristyl	100	G	ONX
Cetol	cetyl	100	G	ONX
Culversan 50-LC	alkyl	50	G	CUL
Culversan SDC-25	stearyl	25	G	CUL
Dibactol	alkyl, $C_{12-14-16}$	100	G	FIN
Germ-i-tol	C_{8-18}	50	G	FIN
Hyamine 3500	$C_{12-14-16}$	50	G	RH
Intexan LB-50	alkyl	50	G	WSN
Intexan SB-85	stearyl	25	H	WSN
Marquat MB-50	alkyl, $C_{12-14-16}$	50	G	MRS
Neo-Germitol	alkyl, $C_{12-14-16-18}$	50	G	FIN
Quaternary # 34	alkyl	50	G	PG
Retzaquat 47	alkyl	85	G	RTF
Roccal 90%	alkyl, C_{8-18}	90	G	SDW
Stedbac	stearyl	100	H	FIN
Surco SDM BAC[a]	stearyl	21	H, A	SUR
Triton X-400	stearyl	22	H, E	RH
Variquat 415	alkyl, high C_{14}	50	G	VAC
Warcocide 1450	tetradecyl	50	G	SNW
Zephiran Chloride	alkyl	17	G	SDW

[a] Biodegradability.   [b] See Table 1.   [c] See Table 44.

Table 39. Alkyltrimethylammonium Salts

$$\left[\begin{array}{c} CH_3 \\ | \\ R-N-CH_3 \\ | \\ CH_3 \end{array} \right]^+ A^-$$

Product name	R	A^{-a}	Concn, wt %	Functions[b]	Manufacturer[c]
Acetoquat CTAB	cetyl	Br	95	G	ACI
Alacsan DBC-50	dodecylbenzyl	Br	50	G	AAC
Ammonyx 23	lauryl	Cl	50	A, Tl	ONX
Ammonyx 27	tallow	Cl	50	G, dE	ONX
Barquat BT-60	benzyl	Cl	60	G	BRD
Barquat TC-50	dodecylphenyl	Cl	50	G	BRD
Bromat	cetyl	Br	100	G	FIN
CETA Stearate	C_{14}, C_{16}, $C_1{}^b$	Cl	100	G	FIN
Culversan DMC	dodecylphenyl	Cl	50	G	CUL
Emicol E-12	alkylphenyl	Cl	50	G	WTC
Intexsan ABM-50	dodecylphenyl	Cl	50	G	WSN
Intexsan CTB	cetyl	Br	100	G	WSN
Intexsan LTC	lauryl	Cl	50	G, A, Ts, C	WSN
Quatroil	"isohexadecyl"	T		C	FIN
Risosan	stearyl	T		G	FIN

[a] T = *p*-toluenesulfonate.　　[b] See Table 1.　　[c] See Table 44.

Table 40. Alkylpyridinium Halides

$$\left[R-N \bigcirc \right]^+ X^-$$

Product name	R	X^-	Concn, wt %	Functions[a]	Manufacturer[b]
Acetoquat CPC	cetyl	Cl	100	G	ACI
Acetoquat CPB	cetyl	Br	95	G	ACI
Intexsan CPB	cetyl	Br	70	G	WSN
Intexsan CPC	cetyl	Cl	100	G	WSN
Intexsan LPB	lauryl	Br	75	G	WSN
Cetyl pyridinium bromide			100	E, G	FIN
Cetyl pyridinium chloride			100	G	FIN
Lauryl pyridinium bromide			100	G	FIN
Lauryl pyridinium chloride			100	G	FIN
Lauryl pyridinium chloride			90	Di, W, G	HK

[a] See Table 1.　　[b] See Table 44.

AMPHOTERIC SURFACTANTS

Amphoteric surfactants (55) contain both an acidic and a basic hydrophilic moiety in their structure. These ionic functions may be any of the anionic or cationic groups that have been described in the preceding sections, and the molecule may contain several ionic functions. Many amphoterics also contain ether oxygens or hydroxyls that strengthen their hydrophilic tendency. In addition to the wholly synthetic

Table 41. Amphoteric Surfactants

Structure	Name
RNHCH₂CH₂COOH	N-coco-3-aminopropionic acid
	N-coco-3-aminopropionic acid, sodium salt
CH₂CH₂COONa | R—N | CH₂CH₂COONa	N-tallow-3-iminodipropionate, disodium salt N-lauryl-3-iminodipropionate, disodium salt

CH₃⁺
|
R—N—CH₂COO⁻
|
CH₃
	N-carboxymethyl-N-cocoalkyl-N-dimethylammonium
	   hydroxide
	N-carboxymethyl-N-dimethyl-N-(9-octadecenyl)ammonium
	   hydroxide

COO⁻ | R—CH—N(CH₃)₃⁺	(1-carboxyheptadecyl)trimethylammonium hydroxide (1-carboxyundecyl)trimethylammonium hydroxide
CH₂CH₂OH | R—CO—N | CH₂COONa	N-cocoamidoethyl-N-hydroxyethylglycine, sodium salt N-hydroxyethyl-N-stearamidoglycine, sodium salt
CH₂CH₂OH | R—CO—N— CH₂CH₂COONa	N-hydroxyethyl-N-lauramido-β-alanine, sodium salt N-cocoamido-N-hydroxyethyl-β-alanine, sodium salt
(CH₂CH₂OH)ₐ | R—N(CH₂CH₂O)ᵦSO₃Na	mixed alicyclic amines, ethoxylated and sulfated, sodium salt
H₂C———CH₂ CH₂CH₂OH | | / N≋C—N—CH₂COOM | \ OH R	2-alkyl-1-carboxymethyl-1-hydroxyethyl-2-imidazolinium hydroxide, sodium salt or free acid R = nonyl, undecyl, heptadecyl M = H or Na
C₂———CH₂ | | /(CH₂COONa)₂ N≋C—N | \ OH C₁₁H₂₃	1,1-bis(carboxymethyl)-2-undecyl-2-imidazolinium hydroxide, disodium salt

(C₃H₆O)ₐH
| (C₃H₆O)ᵦH
C₁₇H₃₃CONCH₂CH₂N<
         (C₃H₆O)ᵪSO₃Na
	Oleic acid–ethylenediamine condensate, propoxylated and
	   sulfated, sodium salt

products, amphoteric derivatives of polypeptides are marketed as surfactants. Total U.S. production of the amphoterics, 5,052,000 lb in 1966, was so small that statistics on the relative volumes of individual product types were not published, but the compositions of twenty-seven products were reported by fourteen manufacturers (55a). The chemical structures of representative compounds are shown in Table 41.

Amphoteric surfactants are frequently marketed as proprietary products with ambiguous descriptions of their chemical compositions. As a result it is difficult to relate the properties and uses to molecular structures. General information on properties and uses of amphoterics was obtained by selecting eighty-four amphoterics from a list of surfactant products that was published in 1968 (56) and analyzing the data quoted from the vendors' brochures. On the basis of this information, the functional properties in order of decreasing importance were: detergency, emulsification, wetting, hair conditioning, textile softening, antistatic protection, and foaming. Uses of the products by industry or application in order of decreasing importance were cosmetics, textiles, industrial- and institutional-cleaning products, metal-processing auxiliaries, polymerization emulsifiers, and pigment-grinding aids. One of the substituted imidazolines is used as an ingredient of shampoos, not only for its surfactant properties but also because it reduces the eye irritation caused by the sulfonate or sulfate surfactant that is used as the primary detergent.   Several of the amphoteric structures of Table 41 would be expected to have good solubility in concentrated electrolyte solutions, which agrees with the vendors' claims of uses in metal-plating baths. Simple amphoteric molecules are least soluble in water at the pH where inner salt formation is at a maximum and this property can be used to help exhaust them on a substrate, eg application of textile softeners.

The 2-alkyl-1-carboxymethyl-1-(2-hydroxyethyl)-2-imidazolinium salts are widely distributed by Miranol Chemical Company, Inc. These products can be prepared by the reaction of a chloroacetate salt with N-2-alkyl-N-1-(2-hydroxyethyl)-2-imidazolines. Alkyl-2-aminopropionates and alkyl-3-iminodipropionates are offered under the Deriphat trademark by General Mills, Inc. These products can be prepared by condensing a primary fatty amine with one or two molecules respectively of an acrylic monomer.

Physical Chemistry

The useful properties of surfactants stem from the effects that they exert on the surface, interfacial, and bulk properties of their solutions. The elementary behavior of pure liquids at phase boundaries will be described and then the effects of surfactants on these interactions discussed.

Elementary Phenomenology at Liquid Interfaces. The area of contact between two phases is called the *interface*. Three phases can have only a line of contact, and only a point of mutual contact is possible between four or more phases. Combinations of phases encountered in surfactant systems are listed below:

L–G	L–L–G	L–S–G	L–S–S–G
L–L	L–L–L	L–S–S	L–L–S–S–G
L–S	L–L–S	L–L–S–G	

where G = gas, L = liquid, and S = solid. An example of an L–L–S–G system would be an aqueous surfactant solution containing an emulsified oil, a suspended solid, and entrained air. The illustration embodies several conditions that are common to practical surfactant systems. First, since the surface area of a phase increases as particle size decreases, the emulsion, suspension, and entrained gas would each have large areas of contact with the surfactant solution. Next, since interfaces can only exist between two phases, analysis of phenomena in the L–L–S–G system breaks down into a series of analyses, ie surfactant solution to the emulsion, to the solid, and to the gas. It is also apparent that the surfactant must be stabilizing the system by pre-

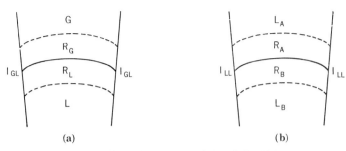

Fig. 1. (**a**) Gas–liquid interface; (**b**) liquid–liquid interface.

venting contact between the emulsified oil and the dispersed solid. Finally, the dispersed phases are in equilibrium with each other through their common equilibrium with the surfactant solution. This example is not discussed further as such but the physical chemical phenomena associated with equilibrium conditions in surfactant systems are described.

Let Figures 1a and 1b schematically represent typical gas–liquid and liquid–liquid interfaces at equilibrium. Referring to Figure 1a and assuming that the gas, G, consists of air and vapor of the liquid, L, at equilibrium, it is obvious that there will be a continuous movement of "liquid" molecules through the gaseous interfacial region, R_G, since the rates of evaporation and condensation at the interface, I_{GL}, are equal. Liquid molecules will also be moving continuously into and out of I_{GL} through the liquid interfacial region, R_L. R_G and R_L represent nonhomogeneous transitional regions between the homogeneous phases G and L. Systems are known in which R_G and R_L have thicknesses equivalent to two or more layers of molecules but for most analyses the interface, I_{GL}, can be considered as consisting of a single layer of molecules.

For thermodynamic treatment of surface phenomena, the thickness of the boundary regions can often be ignored or their effect eliminated by selection of a convenient location for the interface I_{GL}. The liquid–liquid interface, I_{LL}, of Figure 1b is similarly associated with interfacial regions, R_A and R_B, which can be treated like the gas–liquid interface in most analyses. Since few liquids are completely immiscible, mutual saturation is taken as the equilibrium condition.

Surface Energy of Gas–Liquid Interfaces. Each unit of a liquid surface is associated with a quantity of free energy which is called the *free surface energy*. Work equivalent to the increase in free surface energy must be added to a liquid to increase its surface area. The free energy content of a surface is expressed in ergs/cm². A pure liquid tends toward the condition of minimum energy, which is the shape of minimum area. Thus the shape of a free-falling droplet would be spherical under idealized conditions. The tendency of a pure liquid to minimize its surface can be explained on the basis of intermolecular attractive forces. Even though a liquid is a freely flowing fluid mass, the individual molecules are so close together that van der Waals-type forces are the dominant attraction between molecules. These are very short range forces that may be considered to decrease as the sixth power of the intermolecular distance. Thus a molecule in the interior of a liquid would not be subject to a net attractive force in any direction because the number of molecules in the sphere surrounding it would, on the average, be the same in all directions. However, a molecule at the surface of the liquid would be subject to a strong inward attraction because the number of molecules in the hemisphere of the vapor close enough to exert an attractive force pulling it out of the liquid would be small as compared to the number in the hemisphere of liquid pulling inward from the surface. A reasonable ratio of vapor to liquid molecules would be 1:1000. This unbalanced attraction would cause as many molecules as possible to move out of the surface, reducing its area to a minimum.

Surface Energy of Liquid–Liquid Interfaces. Each unit area of the interface between two mutually insoluble liquids is associated with a quantity of energy called the *interfacial free energy,* expressed in ergs/cm². Expansion of the interfacial area requires the addition of energy. Conversely, the interface tends to decrease to the surface of minimum area. Breaking of an emulsion is an example of a decrease in the area of a liquid–liquid interface. Molecules at a liquid–liquid interface are subject to a more balanced sphere of attraction than molecules at a gas–liquid interface because the number of molecules on both sides of a liquid–liquid interface is of the same order of magnitude. Thus there is a strong force of attraction between two liquids in contact and the interfacial free energy is always less than the surface free energy of the more energetic liquid.

Surface and Interfacial Tension. Some of the gross properties of liquid surfaces are suggestive of a "skin" that exercises a contracting force or tension parallel to the surface. Mathematical models based on this effect have been used in explanation of surface phenomena such as capillary rise. The terms surface tension and interfacial tension relate to these models which do not reflect the actual behavior of molecules and ions at interfaces. The widespread usage of the terms is perhaps unfortunate. *Surface tension* is the force per unit length required to create a new unit area of gas–liquid surface. It is expressed as dyn/cm and is numerically equal to the free surface energy in ergs/cm². Similarly, *interfacial tension* is the force per unit length required to create a new unit area of liquid–liquid interface and is numerically equal to the interfacial free energy.

Energy of Adhesion. About sixty years ago, Antonoff proposed that the interfacial energy between two mutually insoluble liquids, A and B, is equal to the difference in the separately measured surface energies of each phase:

$$\gamma_{AB} = \gamma_A - \gamma_B \tag{7}$$

where γ is free surface or interfacial energy. Liquids A and B were assumed to be mutually saturated with each other. The term γ_{AB} represents the energy that would have to be added to the system to separate the liquids. The rule holds true for most systems. Another early investigator, Dupré, propounded an equation that defines the *work of adhesion,* W_{AB}, between two liquids, ie the energy necessary to increase the interfacial area by one square unit:

$$W_{AB} = \gamma_A + \gamma_B - \gamma_{AB} \tag{8}$$

It is apparent from the equation that the quantity of energy required to separate the two liquids, A and B, increases as the interfacial tension between them decreases. The lower the interfacial energy, the stronger the adhesion.

An attraction also exists at the interface between a liquid and an insoluble solid and the interfacial tension is accordingly lower than the sum of the surface tensions of the two phases. Dupré's equation is also applicable to the solid–liquid interface and has the form

$$W_{SL} = \gamma_{SA} + \gamma_{LA} - \gamma_{SL} \tag{9}$$

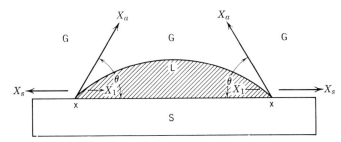

Fig. 2. Contact angle at the oil–solid–air boundary line in the roll-back process of oily solid detergency.

However, the surface tension of the solid, γ_{SA}, and the solid–liquid interfacial tension, γ_{SL}, cannot be measured directly by simple means. The work of adhesion of the solid to the liquid, W_{SL}, is usually determined by other techniques.

Contact Angle. The line of contact between the three phases of a G–L–S system is the locus of all points from which the angle of contact between the liquid and the solid can be measured. Figure 2 depicts such a system. The drop of liquid, L, is resting on the solid, S, and both of these phases are exposed to the gas, G, which consists of the equilibrium vapor pressure of the liquid in air. The drop is assumed to be small enough for the flattening pressure of gravity to be negligible. The line x–X_a is tangent to the liquid at its contact with the solid. The angle θ that the tangent makes with the surface of the solid is called the *contact angle*. The equilibrium value of the contact angle is an indicator of the energy relationships between liquid–liquid and liquid–solid interfaces. The contact angle is related to the free surface energies through the Young-Dupré equation:

$$\gamma_{SA} = \gamma_{SL} + \gamma_{LA} \cos \theta \tag{10}$$

Combining with the Dupré equation for the energy of adhesion of a solid–liquid interface, equation 9, gives

$$W_{SL} = \gamma_{LA} (1 + \cos \theta) \tag{11}$$

It is apparent from eq. 11 that $W_{SL} = 2\gamma_{LA}$ when the contact angle is zero, ie $\cos \theta = 1$. Under this condition the attraction of the liquid for the solid is exactly equal to the attraction of the liquid for itself and complete wetting of the solid by the liquid is possible at equilibrium. If the liquid attracts the solid more strongly than it attracts itself, then $W_{SL} > 2\gamma_{SA}$ which is a possible condition even though the negative contact angle that it implies is impossible. No contact angle or *nil* is used to distinguish $W_{SL} > 2\gamma_{LA}$ from *zero* for $W_{SL} = 2\gamma_{LA}$. The droplet of Figure 2 has a circular line of contact with the solid which is shown in the cross-sectional diagram only at the intercepts, points x. The tangent to the droplet, X_a, is a vector that represents the tendency of the air–liquid interface toward the spherical shape of minimum energy content. There are two interfaces in the plane of the solid, liquid–solid, and gas–solid. The liquid–solid interface tends to minimize itself as represented by the vectors X_l parallel to the solid surface and directed toward the center of the circle of contact. The surface force represented by the vectors X_s is too weak to effect contraction of the solid surface. Nevertheless, such a force does exist and works toward minimizing the area of the air–solid interface. In the system of Figure 2, the area of the air–solid interface may be reduced by substituting a liquid–solid interface which is the tendency represented by the vectors X_s. For a contact angle of zero, $\cos \theta = 1$, and at equilibrium, $X_s = X_a + X_l$. A contact angle of nil would represent the condition $X_s > X_a + X_l$ in which equilibrium could not be attained and the liquid would continue to spread over the solid surface. Contact angles of 90° or greater are associated with very low solid–liquid adhesion. In practical surfactant technology this condition would be apparent because of the lack of wetting of the solid by the liquid. A contact angle of 180° which would indicate the complete absence of solid–liquid adhesion is not known to exist. A hysteresis effect is nearly always observed in the measurement of contact angles, the advancing angle being greater than the receding angle.

Spreading. The decrease in the free surface energy of a system caused by the spreading of a liquid over the surface of a solid or another liquid is called the *spreading coefficient.* The total surface energy must be decreased by the spreading process which implies a greater attraction between unlike molecules than between like molecules. For a liquid–solid system, the decrease in the free energy, ϕ, as a result of the spreading liquid, L, over solid, S, is

$$\phi = \gamma_{SA} - \gamma_{LA} - \gamma_{SL} \tag{12}$$

Combining with Dupré's equation for solids, equation 9, gives

$$\phi = W_{SL} - 2\gamma_{LA} \tag{13}$$

Thus the decrease in free surface energy of the total system when the liquid spreads over the solid equals the energy of adhesion, W_{SL}, minus the energy of cohesion, 2 γ_{LA}. The energy of cohesion is the energy that must be added to a liquid system to separate a column of liquid of unit cross section, thus creating two units of new surface area. If the spreading coefficient, ϕ, is positive, the liquid will spread over the solid and the greater the positive value the more readily spreading will occur. The spreading of a liquid over a plane solid proceeds slowly to equilibrium but in many practical systems capillary action or mechanical agitation speeds the wetting process. The spreading coefficient of a liquid–liquid system is calculated directly by substituting the surface and interfacial tensions in

$$\phi = \gamma_O - \gamma_W - \gamma_{WO} \tag{14}$$

where γ_O represents the surface tension of the oil phase, γ_W, the surface tension of the surfactant solution, and γ_{WO}, the interfacial tension. The greater the positive value of ϕ the greater the ease of spreading.

Effects of Surfactants on the Properties of Solutions. A surfactant changes the properties of a solvent in which it is dissolved to a much greater extent than would be expected from its concentration. This marked effect is due to (1) adsorption at the solution interfaces, (2) orientation of the adsorbed surfactant ions or molecules, (3) micelle formation in the bulk of the solution, and (4) orientation of the surfactant ions or molecules in the micelles. These effects are caused by the amphipathic structure of a surfactant molecule and the magnitude of the effects depend to a large extent on the solubility balance of the molecule. (For hydrophilic-lipophilic balance see Emulsions, Vol. 8, p. 131.) An efficient surfactant is usually relatively insoluble as individual ions or molecules in the bulk of a solution, eg 10^{-2} to 10^{-4} moles/liter.

A schematic representation of adsorption and orientation in a solution of an anionic surfactant is shown in Figure 3. This illustration is intended to show:

1. A relatively greater number of adsorbed ions in the G–L interface than in the bulk of the solution.

2. A relatively greater number of adsorbed ions on the S–L interface (breaker walls) than in the bulk of the solution.

3. The adsorbed molecules are oriented with their solvent-liking moieties in the solvent and their solvent-disliking moieties respectively in the G–L interface and in contact with the S–L surface.

4. The surfactant molecules aggregated in the micelles are oriented with the solvent-liking moieties exposed to the solvent and shielding the solvent-disliking moieties in the center of the micelles.

5. The adsorbed ions are in equilibrium with the micelles through the relatively small concentration of individual solute ions in the bulk of the solution.

If the G–L interface were replaced by an L–L interface, eg an oil layer on an aqueous solution, the orientation of the ions in the illustration would not be changed. In practical surfactant systems, L–L interfaces are often the surfaces of emulsified droplets and L–S interfaces are frequently the surfaces of suspended solids.

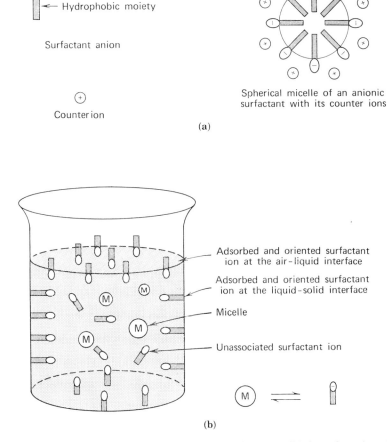

Fig. 3. Schematic diagram of an anionic surfactant solution at equilibrium above its critical micelle concentration. LEGEND: (**a**) components, (**b**) locations of the components at equilibrium.

Adsorption at G–L and S–L Interfaces. Positive adsorption, the concentration of one component of a solution at a phase boundary, results in a lowering of the free surface energy of the solution. Accumulation of a surfactant at a solution interface means that the attractive forces between its molecules or ions are less than the attraction between solvent molecules. As thermal diffusion brings surfactant molecules into the surface, they accumulate there because they cannot reenter the solution against the stronger mutual attraction of the solvent molecules. Negative adsorption occurs when the attraction between solute molecules is greater than the attraction between solvent molecules. This condition exists in concentrated aqueous solutions of inorganic compounds such as NaOH and is associated with a surface tension slightly higher than for pure water.

The quantitative relationship between the degree of adsorption at a solution interface, G–L or L–L, and the lowering of the free surface energy was deduced by Gibbs using thermodynamic methods (57). His equation is rigorous but awkward for calculations. A frequently used approximate form of the Gibbs adsorption isotherm, equation 15, is applicable to dilute binary solutions where the activity coefficient is unity and the radius of curvature of the surface is not too great:

$$\Gamma_s = - \frac{C_s}{RT} \cdot \frac{d\gamma}{dC_s} \tag{15}$$

It states that the surface excess of solute, Γ_s, is proportional to the concentration of solute, C_s, multiplied by the rate of change of surface tension, $d\gamma$, with respect to solute concentration. The concentration of a surfactant in a G–L interface can be calculated from the linear segment of a plot of surface tension versus concentration and similarly for the concentration in an L–L interface from a plot of interfacial tension. In typical applications of the approximate form of the Gibbs equation, Caryl (11) calculated the area occupied by a series of sulfosuccinic ester molecules at the air–water interface and Mankowich (58) calculated the energies of adsorption at the air–water interface for a series of commercial nonionics.

The adsorbed layer at G–L or S–L surfaces in practical surfactant systems may have a complex composition. The adsorbed molecules or ions may be close packed so as to form almost a condensed film with solvent molecules virtually excluded from the surface, or they may be widely spaced and behave somewhat like a two-dimensional gas. The adsorbed film may be multilayer rather than a monolayer. Counterions are sometimes present with the surfactant in the adsorbed layer. Mixed monolayers are known which involve molecular complexes, eg one-to-one complexes of fatty alcohol sulfates with fatty alcohols (59). Competitive or preferential adsorption between multiple solutes occurs at G–L and L–L interfaces. It is an important effect in foaming, foam stabilization, and defoaming.

Adsorption at S–L Interfaces. Practical applications of surfactants more often than not involve in some manner the adsorption of a surfactant on a solid surface. This adsorption is always associated with a decrease in free surface energy, the magnitude of which must be determined indirectly. The force with which the adsorbate is held on the adsorbent may be grossly classified as physical, ionic, or chemical. Physical adsorption is a weak attraction primarily due to van der Waals forces. Ionic adsorption occurs between charged sites on the substrate and oppositely charged surfactant ions. It is usually a strong attractive force. The term chemisorption is applied when the adsorbate is joined to the adsorbent by covalent bonds or forces of comparable strength; it is not an important factor in surfactant technology. The surface condition of a solid adsorbent markedly affects its adsorption characteristics. Important considerations are smoothness, cleanness, particle size and packing of powders, presence of capillary systems, etc. Typical substrates on which adsorption effects are important include metals, glass, plastics, textile fibers, sand, crushed minerals, plant foliage, paper, and the mixed solid "dirt" that collects on clothing, linen, walls, and floors. Analysis of the shape of adsorption isotherms (see Adsorption) has been the technique most widely used in investigations of adsorption mechanisms, but their interpretation has not been elucidated for the numerous combinations of adsorbent–adsorbate and their interactions that are encountered in multicomponent surfactant systems.

Physical (60) and ionic adsorption may be either monolayer or multilayer. Capillary structures in which the diameters of the capillaries are small, ie one to two molecular diameters, exhibit a marked hysteresis effect on desorption. Sorbed surfactant solutes do not necessarily cover all of a solid interface and their presence does not preclude adsorption of solvent molecules. The strength of sorption of surfactants generally follows the order cationics > anionics > nonionics. Surfaces to which this rule applies include metals, glass, plastics, textiles (61), paper, and many minerals. The pH is an important modifying factor in the adsorption of all ionic surfactants but especially for amphoterics which are least soluble at their isoelectric point. The speed and degree of adsorption are increased by the presence of dissolved inorganic salts in surfactant solutions (for textile fibers see ref. 62).

The state of the adsorbed layer has been studied by various methods: electron diffraction patterns, x-ray diffraction, interferometer, and electron microscope. The contact angle of pure liquids on solid surfaces, ie wetting behavior, has been used effectively in investigations of the properties of adsorbed monolayers (63,64). Adsorption can be demonstrated visually by dipping a clean glass plate that is readily water wettable into a solution of a cationic surfactant. On withdrawal the plate will be water repellent due to the orientation of the adsorbed layer. When a complete and closely packed film of surfactant molecules or ions is adsorbed on a solid, the substrate no longer exerts any effect on the contact angle. Preferential adsorption or competition between surfactant solutes for the surface of solid substrates is an important effect and the basis of preferential wetting.

Micelles. Surfactant molecules or ions at concentrations above a minimum value characteristic of each solvent–solute system associate into aggregates called *micelles.* The formation, structure, and behavior of micelles have been extensively investigated. The term *critical micelle concentration* (CMC) is used to denote the concentration at which micelles start to form in a system comprising solvent(s), surfactant(s), possibly other solutes, and a defined physical environment. If the properties of a surfactant solution are plotted as a function of the concentration of the surfactant, the properties will usually vary linearly with increasing concentration up to the CMC at which point there will be a break in the curve. This effect is illustrated schematically for aqueous solutions of sodium lauryl sulfate in Figure 4 (65). Earlier, Hess, Philipoff, and Kiessig (65a) reported experimental data on this compound in a similar composite chart. Other properties than those shown in the figure have also been used for the determination of CMC, eg refractive index, dialysis, and dye solubilization. Most of the studies of micellar size and properties have involved aqueous systems, but nonaqueous systems have received some attention (66,67).   The orientation of surfactant ions in an aqueous solution with the hydrophilic moieties exposed to the water was illustrated in Figure 3.   In a nonaqueous system the orientation is reversed and the lipophilic moieties are exposed to the organic solvent.   The CMC of surfactants in aqueous solutions depends on the structure of the compounds and the environment, but for many anionics at low electrolyte concentrations and room temperature it is close to 10^{-2} moles/liter (68); for nonionics under comparable conditions it is less, about 10^{-4} moles/liter.

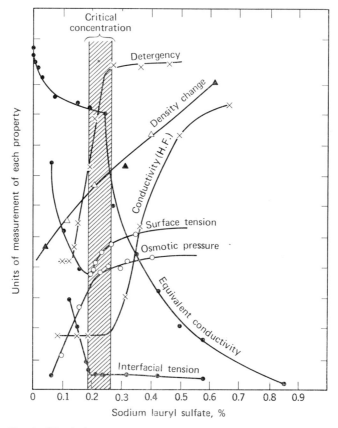

Fig. 4.   Physical-property curves for aqueous sodium dodecyl sulfate.

The size and shape of micelles have been subjects of much investigation.   The size is expressed as the micellar mol wt or as the *aggregation number*, the number of units making up the micelle.   Mankowich (69) has reported micellar mol wt for a representative cross section of surfactants: eg sodium dodecylbenzenesulfonate, 1000–1700; sodium   dioctyl   sulfosuccinate,   7200;   isooctylphenoxyheptaethyleneoxyethanol 66, 700.   Tartar and co-workers (70) studied sulfate, sulfonate, and cationic surfactants.   Herrmann has reported micellar properties of the dimethyldodecylamine oxides (53).   In a series of surfactants where the hydrophilic group is unchanged but the size of the hydrophobic group is increased, CMC values decrease with increasing size of the hydrophobe for both ionic and nonionic types.   If the hydrophobic group is held constant, CMC values decrease with decreasing ethylene oxide content of nonionics.

Increasing the electrolyte concentration decreases CMC values for both anionics and nonionics. The CMC of anionic micelles increases as the temperature increases, whereas the CMC of nonionics decreases with the increase in temperature as would be expected from the cloud point phenomenon. Since the mid-1950s, micellar properties of homogeneous nonionics have been studied and in some cases compared with polydisperse nonionics (71). The CMC and other micellar behavior of homogeneous and polydisperse nonionics of comparable composition are quite similar. Micellar structure has been investigated with respect to shape and composition. A spherical and spheroidal–cylindrical shape has been postulated for small micelles in relatively dilute solutions. Other proposed micellar structures are: a lamellar structure for ionic micelles; a double layer micelle; and a rod-shaped micelle. Probably all of these types exist under certain conditions, and transitions from one type to another occur as the environment changes. In solutions containing two or more surfactant types, micelles of each species may coexist, but usually mixed micelles are formed. Mixtures of nonionic and anionic surfactants are of considerable technical importance and reports of their properties have begun to appear in the literature since 1960, eg Corkill and others (72) and Schick and Manning (73). Changes in the environment (eg temperature, solvents, electrolytes, solubilizates) all exert marked effects on micellar properties. Some of these include complicated phase changes, viscosity effects, gel formation, and liquid crystals. Of the simpler changes, high concentrations of the water-soluble alcohols in aqueous solution often dissolve micelles, and in nonaqueous solvents addition of water frequently causes a sharp increase in micellar size.

Properties and Uses

Practical applications of surfactants usually involve a composite of functional properties, and optimum performance normally requires the use of a mixture of surfactants plus nonsurfactant additives. Before surfactant uses are reviewed, functional properties, nonsurfactant additives, and mixtures of surfactants will be described briefly.

Functional Properties. The key surfactant functions were noted in Table 1 to highlight them in comparison to less basic properties. All but two of these noted properties have been the subject of earlier articles: Detergency, Vol. 6, pp. 853–893; Emulsions, Vol. 8, pp. 117–153; and Foams, Vol. 9, pp. 884–901. Wetting (and rewetting) and micellar solubilization will be reviewed briefly here to round out this category of phenomena. Stabilization, a composite property, will also be described.

Wetting (74). Wetting of a solid by a surfactant solution may represent either the displacement of air or some other gas from the solid surface by the solution or the displacement of a liquid, eg an oil, from the solid surface. The latter case, which is sometimes called preferential wetting, is discussed in Volume 6, pp. 885–887, in connection with oily soil detergency. *Wettability* represents the tendency of a solid to be wetted and *wetting power* the tendency of a liquid to wet a solid (75). The wetting of one liquid by another immiscible liquid is visually apparent by the spreading of a film to create a large liquid–liquid interface, and lack of wetting is evidenced by the tendency of one liquid to form droplets in the form of a lens on the surface of the other.

The attraction between a solid or liquid to be wetted and the wetting solution determines the degree or completeness of wetting that can be attained. The energy of adhesion, $\gamma_{AB} = \gamma_A - \gamma_B$, relates directly to the contact angle of the wetting solution with the substrate to be wetted, as described earlier. If the contact angle is zero or nil, the substrate will be wetted completely at equilibrium. Wetting will be incomplete if the contact angle is positive. Contact angles greater than 90° are associated with such incomplete wetting that the substrate is sometimes loosely described as "unwettable" by the solution. This is a technically inaccurate description since it implies a contact angle of 180°, a condition which is not known to exist. In practical applications, the speed of wetting may be as important as the completeness of wetting at equilibrium. Many investigators have pointed out that the rate of migration of surfactant molecules from the bulk of the solution to maintain the concentration at the interface is one limiting factor on the speed of wetting. Dynamic methods for measurement of the lowering of surface free energy have been used to estimate the significance of this factor. The effectiveness of mechanical agitation, thermal agitation, or capillarity in bringing the solid or liquid to be wetted quickly into intimate contact with the wetting solution often influences the speed of wetting more than the migration rate of the surfactant.

Uses of wetting agents vary widely and include such diverse applications as wetting of textile fibers by processing liquors; wetting of pesticide powders to form aqueous suspensions suitable for spraying; conversion of oil-wet sand to water-wet sand to release the crude oil adsorbed on it so that it is free to migrate to the producing well; and penetration of corroded or oily metal surfaces by cleaning solutions. Evaluations of surfactants as wetting agents are usually made by means of laboratory tests that simulate actual use. The best known practical wetting test was developed by Draves and Clarkson to determine the speed of wetting of unboiled cotton skeins. Unfortunately it has been used to compare the effectiveness of surfactants as wetting agents without recognition of the limited significance of the results.

The physical chemical requirements for rewetting are the same as for wetting and many products are effective in both applications. The most significant difference is that a good rewetter is usually a viscous liquid or waxy solid at 100% concentration rather than a crystalline material. Rewetting agents are applied in aqueous solutions to textiles or paper and the substrate is dried. On subsequent exposure to moisture the substrate rewets quickly. Typical applications are on paper or textile towels and on materials at process holding points in textile or paper mills.

Micellar Solubilization. The spontaneous dissolving of a normally insoluble substance by a relatively dilute solution of a surfactant is called *solubilization*. The substance dissolved is referred to as the *solubilizate* and the surfactant as the *solubilizer*. There are no simple quantitative relationships between solubilizing power of a surfactant and the micellar or surface properties of its solutions. Solubilization is primarily a phenomenon of importance in dilute solutions. In more concentrated solutions it is sometimes difficult to distinguish between solubilization and *cosolvency*, which is a term applied to a mixture of solvents that take into solution a higher concentration of solute than would be expected from the sum of their individual solubilizing powers. Solubilization does not introduce another phase and solutions containing solubilized material are thermodynamically stable. It is a reproducible phenomenon but the rates of attainment of equilibrium differ greatly when approached from different directions.

Solubilization is a micellar phenomenon that occurs only at concentrations above the CMC. Four modes of solubilization have been postulated:

1. Inclusion of the solubilizate in the interior of the solubilizer micelle of Figure 3. Probably most applicable to nonamphipathic solubilizates, eg hydrocarbons and water.

2. Orientation of the solubilizate molecules in the solubilizer micelle parallel to the solubilizer molecules or ions. Probably most applicable to weakly amphipathic compounds, eg fatty alcohols.

3. Adsorption of the solubilizate on the surface of the micelle. Probably most applicable to solubilizates with low solubility in the solvent and in the interior of the micelle, eg dimethylphthalate on potassium laurate micelles.

4. Inclusion of the solubilizate in the polyoxyethylene exterior of nonionic micelles. Particularly applicable to substances with an affinity for the polyoxyethylene chains, eg substituted phenols.

The molecular constitution of micelles tends to change as the quantity of solubilizate in a solution is increased: the number of micelles tends to decrease and the number of surfactant molecules per micelle tends to increase. The solubilization end point for ionic surfactants, ie saturation, is evidenced by the appearance of an emulsion or a suspension. Determination of the true saturation end point of nonionics is complicated because solubilization of hydrocarbons tends to depress the cloud point. A micellar mechanism is probably not involved in the solubilization of polymers, eg keratin, by ionic surfactants. Complex formation with the polymer or adsorption on the polymer is a more likely explanation. Nonionic surfactants are not generally useful for solubilizing polymers.

Solubilization is of considerable importance in nonaqueous applications of surfactants, particularly where water is the solubilizate. Typical applications are in drycleaning solutions and engine lubricants. Essential oils, vitamins, cosmetic emollients, and textile-mill processing oils are typical solubilizates in aqueous systems. Mixtures of surfactants are generally better solubilizers than the same surfactants used individually. Ionic–nonionic combinations are especially effective.

Stabilization. Disperse systems, ie emulsions and suspensions, are often sensitive to coalescence or agglomeration caused by temperature changes, agitation, addition of electrolytes, or aging. Surfactant additives that protect emulsions and suspensions from coalescence or agglomeration are called stabilizers. Protection against agitation is called "mechanical stabilization" and protection against temperature changes is referred to as "freeze–thaw stabilization." Stabilization is not a separate functional property such as emulsification or dispersion. Rather, the addition of stabilizers to a system increases the total concentration of surfactants and provides a balance of emulsifying and dispersing properties that will maintain the dispersed condition over a range of environmental changes. Typical uses of stabilizers are in natural and synthetic rubber latices, pigment dispersions, and emulsion polymerizations (76).

Formulations. Formulated surfactant products may be roughly divided into two major groups. One group is designed to perform "surfactant types" of useful functions, eg cleaning, wetting, foaming, emulsifying, and dispersing. The other group is designed to convey a nonsurfactant functional ingredient to the point of use, eg a herbicide or insecticide toxicant, a textile-mill processing oil. In order to estimate the size of surfactant markets accurately, it is necessary to exclude consumption of surfactant compounds in nonsurfactant uses. For example, metallic soaps constitute about 10 wt % of napalm, a solidified fuel, but surface-active effects of the soap are not important in this type of product. In addition to the primary surfactants the components of formulated surfactant products may be classified as (1) nonsurfactant functional additives, (2) inert fillers, and (3) functional surfactant additives.

Nonsurfactant Functional Additives. The art of surfactant formulation is directed

Table 42. List of Surfactant Uses by Industry

Use	Effect of surfactant
Agriculture	
phosphate fertilizers	shorten manufacturing cycle and prevent caking during storage
spray applications of herbicides, insecticides, and fungicides	wetting, dispersing, and suspending of powdered pesticides and emulsification of pesticide solutions; promote wetting, spreading, and penetration of the toxicant
Building and Construction	
paving	improve the bond of asphalt to gravel and sand, ie prevent "stripping"
concrete	promote air entrainment for control of density, plasticity, insulating properties, etc
Elastomers and Plastics	
emulsion polymerization	solubilization: monomers and catalyst dissolve and react in surfactant micelles; emulsification of monomers; stabilization of latexes
foamed polymers	introduction of air and control of cell size
latex adhesive	promote wetting and thus improve bond strength
plastic articles	antistatic agents
plastic coating and laminating	wetting agents
Food and Beverages	
food processing plants	clean and/or sanitize walls, floors, and processing equipment
fruits and vegetables	improve removal of pesticide residues and aid in wax coating
bakery products and ice cream	solubilize flavor oils, control consistency, and retard staling
beverages	solubilize flavor oils
crystallization of sugar	improve washing and reduce processing time
cooking fats and oils	in frying, prevent spattering due to superheating and sudden volatilization of water
Industrial Cleaning	
janitorial supplies	detergents and/or sanitizers for walls, floors, and windows
miscellaneous cleaning	detergents for railroad cars, trucks, airplanes, tunnel walls, engines, etc
descaling	wetting agents and corrosion inhibitors in acid cleaning of boiler tubes and heat exchangers
soft goods	detergents for laundry and drycleaning
wax strippers	improve wetting and penetration of the old finish
Leather	
skins	detergent and emulsifier in degreasing
tanning	promote wetting and penetration
hides	emulsifiers in fat-liquoring
dyeing	promote wetting, penetration, and level dyeing
Metals	
concentration of ores	wetting and foaming, ie collectors and frothers in ore flotation (qv)

Table 42 (*continued*)

Use	Effect of surfactant
cutting and forming	wetting, emulsification, lubrication, and corrosion inhibition in rolling oils, cutting oils, drawing lubricants, buffing and grinding compounds
casting	mold release additives
rust and scale removal	wetting, foaming, and corrosion inhibition in pickling (ie acid cleaning) and electrolytic cleaning
grease removal	emulsification and wetting in emulsion cleaning preparations
plating	wetting and foaming in electrolytic plating baths
	Paper
pulp treatment	deresinification, pitch dispersion, and washing
paper machine	defoaming, felt washing, color leveling and dispersing
calender	wetting and leveling in coating and coloring operations
towels and pads	rewetting, ie improve absorption of moisture
	Paints and Protective Coatings
pigment preparation	flushing, ie promote preferential wetting by the paint vehicle; dispersing and wetting of the pigment during grinding
latex paints	emulsify the oil or polymer, disperse the pigment, stabilize the latex, retard sedimentation and pigment separation, modify wetting and rheological properties
waxes and polishes	emulsifying waxes, stabilize emulsions and wet substrates in finishes for floor and automobiles; antistat
	Petroleum Production and Products
drilling fluids (qv)	emulsify oils, disperse solids, and modify rheological properties of drilling and completion fluids for oil and gas wells
mist drilling (see Vol. 7, p. 291)	convert intrusion water to foam in air drilling
workover of producing wells	emulsify and disperse sludge and sediment in clean-out of wells; modify wetting of formation at producing zone
producing wells	demulsify crude petroleum and inhibit corrosion of well tubing, storage tanks, and pipe lines
secondary recovery	in flooding operations, release crude oil from the formation surface, ie preferential wetting
refined petroleum products	detergent, sludge dispersant, and corrosion inhibitor in fuel oils, crank-case oils, and turbine oils
	Textiles
preparation of fibers and filaments	detergent and emulsifier in raw-wool scouring; dispersant in viscose rayon spin baths; lubricant and antistat in spinning of hydrophobic filaments
gray goods preparation	wetting and detergency in slashing and sizing formulations; wetting and detergency in kier boiling and bleaching of cotton, and carbonizing of wool; detergency in scouring piece goods; emulsification of processing oils
dyeing and printing	wetting, penetration, solubilization, emulsification, dye leveling, detergency, and dispersion
finishing of textiles	wetting and emulsification in finishing formulations; softening, lubricating, and antistatic additives to finishes

to finding a combination of components that will be compatible and perform satisfactorily at the least cost to the user. Frequently a surfactant is the most expensive component of a formulation and the mixture is designed so that less-expensive inorganic additives contribute as much as possible to the functional performance of the product. Volume 6, pp. 856–858, and Vaughn et al. (77), describe the properties of the important nonsurfactant additives except for the hydrotropes and solvents which serve useful but nonsurfactant functions. Hydrotropic agents are used to solubilize the ingredients in concentrated liquid surfactant formulations. The most common *hydrotropes* are the sodium or potassium salts of benzene-, cumene-, toluene-, or xylenesulfonates. These highly soluble solutes when present at relatively high concentrations, ie 5–15 wt %, increase the solubility of sulfonate and sulfate surfactants in concentrated aqueous compositions. Solvents are also incorporated in surfactant products to obtain homogenous concentrates, and also as functional additives. For example, ethanol is used as a solvent to clarify liquid shampoos. Pine oil and/or deodorized kerosene are often function components of industrial and consumer detergent products.

Inert Fillers. Many surfactants are viscous liquids or low-melting solids that are difficult to handle as 100% active materials. Sodium sulfate, clays, or other inexpensive fillers are added as diluents and carriers to the concentrated surfactants to obtain free-flowing dry powders. Sometimes a portion of the sulfonating or sulfating reagent from the manufacturing process is neutralized and left in finished products as a filler.

Functional Surfactant Additives. Foam boosters, viscosity builders, and coemulsifiers are the most important functional additives to surfactant formulations. The fatty acid alkanolamides and the alkylamine oxides are the outstanding examples of products in this category. They are effective surfactants on the basis of their own properties but one of their principal uses is to enhance the foaming and detergency of less-expensive materials, eg LAS. In these applications, the performance of the mixture exceeds a projection based on the sum of the contributions of the components tested individually. The alkanolamides also increase the viscosity and emolliency of aqueous solutions. The lipophilic emulsifiers are another group of functional surfactant additives. Many of these materials are so hydrophobic that they have almost no utility when used alone, but in mixtures with hydrophilic emulsifiers they are exceedingly useful as cosolvents, solubilizers, dispersants, and emulsifiers.

Uses of Surfactants. Household and personal products tend to dominate the literature on surfactant technology because the sales volume per product is large enough to support research and justify investments in manufacturing facilities. Industrial applications of surfactants usually represent a much smaller sales volume per item and the product research is often conducted either by the user or by a service company that supplies a variety of items to the consuming industry. Methodology or criteria for selection of surfactants for screening in possible applications apparently has not been extensively studied (78).

Household and Personal Products. Detergency is the predominant function of household and personal products and the trend since the decline of soap and the advent of synthetic detergents has been toward functional specialization. A list of the surfactant products now offered for home use confirms the effectiveness of this approach to improved performance viz: heavy-duty laundry detergents, softening rinses, hand-dishwashing detergents, scouring powders, scouring pads, wall and floor cleaners, window cleaners, car-wash detergents, rug shampoos, wool detergents, fine-fabric detergents, metal cleaners, wallpaper removers, soap or detergent bars, hair shampoos, hair rinses, facial-cleansing creams, dentifrices, waterless hand cleaners, herbicide and insecticide sprays, and furniture polishes. At one time most of these applications were all dependent on soap as the surface-active agent.

Industrial Uses. Surfactants are widely used outside of the household for cleaning and for many other purposes. Often the volume or cost of the surfactant consumed in an industrial process is small in comparison to the benefits derived from its use. The illustrative list of surfactant applications by industry given in Table 42 is indicative of the growing importance of this series of products.

Biodegradable Surfactants and Water Pollution

The U.S. surfactant industry made a commitment in April, 1963, to replace ABS, the largest-volume synthetic surfactant, by LAS, a more biodegradable surfactant, in a move to facilitate the degradation of detergent products in sewage plants. The changeover was consummated in June of 1965 but its secondary effects on the surfactant industry are still being worked out. In the shakeup, some suppliers of surfactant raw materials withdrew and new manufacturers entered the market. The new intermediates that became available at a reasonable cost as a result of the changeover are affecting the relative volumes of industrial surfactants that were not a primary consideration in the replacement decision. It is too soon to know whether the actions already taken by the industry are a sufficient contribution to the easing of the water-pollution problems of the U.S.A.

Historical Background. Progressive deterioration in the quality of the water in the rivers and lakes of the United States became increasingly apparent during the 1930s and the obvious reason was the discharge into them of increasing quantities of raw or partially treated wastes from industries and municipalities. By 1950, incidents of foam on rivers and at sewage-treatment plants began to attract sensational press coverage with the insinuation that synthetic detergents, which had begun to replace soap on a large scale, were the cause of the country's water problems. Knowledgeable individuals in industry and government recognized that the foam was a symptom rather than the cause of the water-pollution problem. Nevertheless, the scanty evidence then available indicated that some types of synthetic detergents were more resistant than soap to degradation in sewage-treatment plants.

The major companies in the surfactant industry working through the Association of American Soap and Glycerine Producers (now the Soap and Detergent Association) set up a Technical Advisory Council in 1951 to investigate the problems of detergents and water pollution (79). This group was charged with coordinating industry programs, cooperating with qualified nonindustry groups, and supporting the necessary research at universities, within the industry, and with other authorities. The scope of activities of this committee extended well beyond surfactant biodegradability, the concern of this article.

Heavy-duty household laundry detergents are the largest volume products of the surfactant industry. On the "as-sold basis" nonsoap detergents grew from about 30 million lb in 1940 to over 5 billion pounds in 1966. The key ingredient that made this growth possible was ABS, an inexpensive alkylbenzenesulfonate in which the alkyl group was a highly branched propylene tetramer. The ABS represented about 10–20 wt % of the formulated detergent. Research soon established that degradation of surfactants by the bacteria in sewage-disposal plants is slower and less complete if the hydrophobic chain is branched rather than linear. In the early 1950s no economically feasible technology was known for replacing ABS by a biodegradable substitute. The logical approach to the problem was replacement of the propylene tetramer by an equally inexpensive linear 12-carbon alkylation feedstock from a petrochemical source. However, technological breakthroughs in the early 1960s opened up several possible routes to biodegradable alkylbenzenesulfonates:

1. Separation of *n*-paraffins from kerosene feedstocks in molecular sieves (or alternatively by complexing with urea). Alkylation with the *n*-paraffins involves only conventional processing, ie monochlorination followed by a Friedel–Crafts reaction or dehydrohalogenation and alkylation.

2. Syntheses of linear 1-olefin or alcoholic detergent hydrophobes from ethylene by the Ziegler process using an aluminum catalyst. The trialkylaluminum intermediate in this process can be oxidized to yield linear secondary alcohols suitable for detergent bases or catalytically decomposed to yield 1-olefins that can be used as alkylate feedstocks or hydrated to alcoholic hydrophobes. See Alcohols, higher, synthetic.

3. The 1-olefins obtained by cracking of petroleum waxes can also be used, either as alkylation feedstocks or hydrated to alcoholic detergent bases.

The advent of these new processes made it possible for spokesmen of the detergent industry in April, 1963, to commit the industry publicly to a changeover to more biodegradable detergents by the end of December, 1965. The replacement of ABS by its linear successor, LAS, was actually completed six months ahead of schedule. The direct cost of new plant construction to produce the biodegradable product types was estimated at $150 million. The total cost, including research, product reformulations, and market testing, is unknown.

Biodegradation. Microorganisms have an inherent ability to convert organic matter, including surfactants, into new cell material, food, and energy. The predominant mechanisms by which surfactant hydrophobes are attacked have been described as β-oxidation, methyl oxidation, and aromatic oxidation (80). In β-oxidation, the most important process, a linear hydrocarbon chain is oxidized two carbons at a time; a branch in the chain interrupts the degradation. Methyl oxidation, which is less well understood, attacks terminal methyl groups. Aromatic oxidation proceeds through catechol(1,2-benzenediol) as an intermediate which is cleaved to form an aliphatic dicarboxylic acid. The polyoxyethylene chains of nonionics are probably degraded stepwise through a carboxylation and hydrolysis mechanism that splits glycol units from the chain (81). From a practical viewpoint, secondary and tertiary carbons in aliphatic chains and some phenolic nuclei slow the biodegradation process to rates that are unacceptable in present-day sewage-treatment systems. Very long polyoxyethylene chains are also degraded slowly (82,83). In terms of products (84,85), carboxylic acids and salts, linear alcohol sulfates, sulfated fatty acids, sulfated fatty amides, sulfated esters, glycol esters, glycerol esters, and fatty alkanolamides are most readily biodegradable. The ethoxylated and sulfated linear alcohols, linear alkylbenzenesulfonates, and ethoxylated linear alcohols (up to about 70 wt % of polyoxyethylene) are readily biodegradable. The residual polyoxyethylene chains from high-polyethylene-content nonionics are not surface active and are not a problem in sewage systems at this time. Ethoxylated linear alkylphenols are more slowly biodegradable than aliphatic-based nonionics. There is still some question about the acceptability of these products for all uses (86,87). Unacceptable products on the basis of biodegradability are the branched-chain substituted alkylphenol derivatives, branched-chain substituted alkylbenzenesulfonates, and the derivatives of branched-chain aliphatic alcohols, ie sulfates or sulfated ethoxylates.

Development of methods to measure biodegradability of surfactants paralleled the development of biodegradable materials. Three methods out of the many screened have received widespread acceptance. Two of these, the river die-away (88) and shake-flask methods (89) are suitable for quick screening and/or routine use. The third, a semicontinuous activated-sludge method, is more time consuming but is accurate and reproducible enough to serve as a reference method (90). The determination of *biological oxygen demand* (91), usually abbreviated to BOD (see also Water), also provides useful data on biodegradation processes.

Current Status of the Water Pollution Problem. The task of converting the organic constituents of household and industrial detergents to a satisfactory level of biodegradability was accomplished on schedule by a cooperative effort of the surfactant industry without the pressure of restrictive legislation. However, the total job is unfinished. Algae and plant growths are fouling the lakes and rivers of the U.S.A. due to *eutrophication* (qv in a Supplement Volume), ie excessive fertilization. The phosphate builders in household detergents are a contributor to this problem and substantial research is in progress either to minimize future dependence on this detersive ingredient or to develop improved methods of treating it in sewage plants (92).

Consequences of the ABS-to-LAS Changeover. The changes in the surfactant industry following the replacement of ABS by LAS affected products that were not directly involved in the conversion. Usage of nonbiodegradable surfactants other than ABS began to fall off sharply and the usage of new products started to grow to fill the gap. These secondary realignments were also influenced by the availability of new hydrophobic raw materials.

Ethoxylated nonylphenols, the largest volume nonionic surfactant product group and the most diversified of all surfactant types in usage pattern, were hardest hit. The nonyl substituent on the phenol was not only highly branched and resistant to biodegradation, it was a coproduct of the propylene tetramer used to alkylate benzene in the production of ABS. Replacement of nonylphenoxypoly(ethyleneoxy)ethanols has not proceeded as fast as the ABS-to-LAS conversion because many of the industrial applications of these surfactants do not release waste products directly into sewage systems. Nevertheless two replacement trends are in progress. One direct approach is replacement of branched-chain alkylphenol hydrophobes by their linear substituted counterparts. This changeover is proceeding smoothly with a minimum of technical difficulties. The other approach is the replacement of an ethoxylated alkylphenol by an ethoxylated aliphatic alcohol. The availability of low-cost alcohols from the processes that yield LAS feedstocks have made this type of replacement possible and the greater ease in biodegradation of the alcohol derivatives provides motivation for the change. Another product realignment involves the high-foaming sulfates of ethoxylated nonylphenols. These products had a strong position as components of hand-dishwashing compositions, which are discarded directly into sewage systems. Since ethoxylated alcohol sulfates are now competitive in performance and cost this replacement is proceeding at a fast pace.

The long-term effect of the ABS-to-LAS changeover on other surfactant product types in industrial applications is most apparent in formulations of products for new uses or complete reformulations of old products. The trend is to use only surfactant components that are easily biodegradable even though the particular usage condition does not impose this restriction.

Economic Aspects

The surfactant chemical industry in the United States produced approximately 3 billion lb of 100% active surfactants of all types in 1966. Assuming no increase in inventories, 589 million lb or 54% of this production was either converted by the manufacturers into formulated products and sold or consumed in their processes. The balance of 1,315 million lb was marketed for $304,083,000. Most of the concentrated material that was sold was formulated by the buyer and resold at a lower concentration of active ingredient but at a higher mark-up. No statistics are available on the total sales of formulated surfactant products of all types but the Soap and Detergent

Table 43. U.S. Production and Sales of Surfactants, 1966 (93)

Products	Production, 1000 lb	Sales Quantity, 1000 lb	Value, $1000	Av value/lb, $
anionic surfactants				
carboxylic acids and salts	962,222			
sulfonic acids and salts	963,812			
alkylbenzenesulfonates	596,416	137,936	22,560	0.16
petroleum sulfonates	246,912	50,084	10,006	0.21
sulfosuccinates	9,450	8,854	4,760	0.54
naphthalenesulfonates	8,277	6,614	2,615	0.40
N-methyl-N-oleoyltaurates	2,797	2,589	1,335	0.52
all other sulfonates	99,960			
sulfuric acid esters and salts	111,925			
sulfated alcohols	41,371			
natural fats and oils, sulfated	30,421	19,520	3,824	0.20
sulfated acids, amides, esters	21,504	14,466	4,346	0.30
alkylphenols, ethoxylated and sulfated	9,601	8,166	1,911	0.23
alcohols, ethoxylated and sulfated	9,208			
all other sulfated esters	120,673			
phosphate esters and salts				
total anionic surfactants	*2,050,915*	*661,260*	*130,594*	*0.20*
nonionic surfactants				
ethoxylated alkylphenols	234,032	205,858	35,905	0.17
ethoxylated aliphatic alcohols	209,839	131,573	23,855	0.18
carboxylic esters	146,370	120,871	39,916	0.33
carboxylic amides	93,020	63,240	18,575	0.29
miscellaneous nonionics	2,432	1,260	1,095	0.87
total nonionic surfactants	*685,693*	*522,802*	*119,346*	*0.23*
cationic surfactants				
amines, no oxygen	59,636			
amines, containing oxygen	38,518			
amines with amide linkages	17,451	15,364	6,992	0.46
quaternaries	46,238			
all other cationics				
total cationic surfactants	*161,843*	*126,882*	*50,918*	*0.40*
amphoteric surfactants	5,052	4,852	3,225	0.66
total surfactants	*2,903,503*	*1,315,796*	*304,083*	*0.23*

Association reported sales of over 5 billion lb of heavy-duty household detergent powders in 1966. Table 43 lists the U.S. production and sales of 100% active surfactants by chemical compositions for 1966. The data are based on Tables 19A and 21A of the Tariff Commission report on U.S. production and sales of synthetic organic chemicals (93) in 1966 but it was recast as follows:

1. The hydrotropes, ie benzene-, cumene-, toluene-, and xylenesulfonates, were eliminated from the data of Table 19A as nonsurfactants.

2. The ligninsulfonates were eliminated from the data of Table 19A as nonsurfactants.

3. The data on oil-soluble petroleum sulfonates from Table 21A, Miscellaneous Chemicals (in the Tariff Commission Report), were included in Table 43 on the basis that these products are really surfactants.

4. All of the data in Table 43 were reorganized and abbreviated.

The statistical data throughout this article have been referred to a single year, 1966, and trend effects have been described qualitatively. There were three reasons for this treatment of the data:

1. The Tariff Commission revised and updated the classifications under which production and sales data were reported for 1966. The new groupings are an improvement but they complicated comparisons with previous years.

2. The realignments in product volumes as a consequence of the ABS-to-LAS changeover in 1965 are not yet reflected in the latest statistical data which lag about two years behind the calendar. Thus historical trend data would have been misleading for several of the product groups.

3. Concentrating on a single year made it possible to orient each product volume with respect to total production with a minimum distraction from the technological content.

According to a current estimate (94), ie February 1969, "all alkylate (alkylbenzene for sulfonation) supplies to the U.S. detergent industry are of the linear type,... and as of late 1968... assuming a production rate of 540 million lbs/yr and a capacity of 580 million lbs/yr, the industry operating rate is right at 93%." It was also stated that emphasis appears to have moved to mol wt and isomer distribution. High 2-phenyl-products, approx 30%, result from the $AlCl_3$ alkylation route as compared to approx 20% from the normal HF catalysis procedures. Lower-mol-wt sulfonates find applications in light-duty liquids and higher-mol-wt sulfonates are preferred in heavy-duty laundry detergents. It was also stated that if "alkylate" is 10¢/lb, a 1-olefin of Ziegler quality would have to be available at 9.2¢/lb for 1-olefin sulfonates to compete with LAS on an equal performance basis.

Table 44 lists the 110 U.S. companies that produced or marketed the surfactants listed in this article. The interests of surfactant chemical producers, marketers, and users as well as of technical personnel in the related disciplines are well served by trade associations, publications, and scientific societies. The Soap and Detergent Association and the Chemical Specialties Manufacturers Association (CSMA) represent the companies that make and use surfactants. Trade news and practical technology are reported in *Soap and Chemical Specialties*, *Detergents and Specialties*, *Drug and Cosmetic Industry*, and the *Proceedings of the Chemical Specialties Manufacturers Association*. The *Journal of the American Oil Chemists' Society*, the *Journal of Colloid and Interface Science*, and the appropriate American Chemical Society journals provide media for scientific publications.

Table 44. Manufacturers or Sources of Surfactant Chemicals

Code	Manufacturer or Source
AAC	Alcolac Chemical Corp.
AAP	American Aniline Products, Inc.
ACI	Aceto Industrial Chemical Corp.
ACY	American Cyanamid Co.
AKS	Arkansas Co., Inc.
AML	Amalgamated Chemical Corp.
AMO	Amoco Chemicals Corp.
APD	Atlas Chemical Industries, Inc.
ARC	Armour Industrial Chemical Co.
ARD	Ardmore Chemical Co.
ASC	Ashland Chemical Co.
BAC	Baker Castor Oil Co.
BCN	Lehn & Fink Products Corp., Beacon Div.
BKS	Tenneco Chemicals, Inc., Berkshire Color Div.
BRD	Baird Chemical Industries, Inc.
BRI	Britex Corp.
CCA	Carlisle Chemical Works, Inc., Advance Div.
CCW	Carlisle Chemical Works, Inc.
CIB	Ciba Chemical & Dye Co.
CLI	Clintwood Chemical Co.
CMG	Nyanza, Inc.
CO	Continental Oil Co.
CRC	Crown Chemical Corp.
CRO	Croda, Inc.
CRT	Crest Chemical Corp.
CST	Charles S. Tanner Co.
CTL	Continental Chemical Co.
CUL	Culver Chemical Co.
DEP	DePaul Chemical Co., Inc.
DEX	Dexter Chemical Corp.
DRW	Drew Chemical Corp.
DUP	E. I. du Pont de Nemours & Co., Inc.
EFH	E. F. Houghton & Co.
EK	Eastman Kodak Co.
EMK	Emkay Chemical Co.
EMR	Emery Industries, Inc.
ENJ	Enjay Chemical Co.
FET	Finetex, Inc.
FIN	Fine Organics, Inc.
FIR	Firestone Tire & Rubber Co.
FOR	Foremost Chemical Products Co.
GAF	GAF Corporation
GGY	Geigy Chemical Corp.
GLY	Glyco Chemicals, Inc.
GNM	General Mills, Inc.
HAL	C. P. Hall Co. of Illinois
HAR	A. Harrison & Co., Inc.
HDG	Hodag Chemical Corp.
HK	Hooker Chemical Corp.
HMP	W. R. Grace & Co., Hampshire Chemical Div.
HOR	Humble Oil and Refining Co.
HPC	Hercules, Inc.
HPP	High Point Chemical Corp.
HRT	Hart Products Corp.
JCC	Jefferson Chemical Co., Inc.
LUB	Lubrizol Corp.
LUR	Laurel Products Corp.
MIR	Miranol Chemical Co., Inc.
MOA	Mona Industries, Inc.
MON	Monsanto Co.

Table 44 (*continued*)

Code	Manufacturer or Source
MOR	Mineral Oil Refining Co.
MRS	Mars Chemical Corp.
MTX	Moretex Chemical Products, Inc.
MYW	Stepan Chemical Co., Maywood Div.
NLC	Nalco Chemical Co.
NOP	Diamond Shamrock Chemical Co., Nopco Chemical Div.
NTL	National Lead Co.
OMC	Olin Mathieson Chemical Corp.
ORO	Chevron Chemical Co., Additives Div.
ONX	Millmaster Onyx Corp., Onyx Chemical Div.
OXR	Onyx Oils & Resins, Inc.
PAR	Pennsylvania Refining Co.
PCS	Emery Industries, Inc., Western Div.
PET	Petrochemicals Co., Inc.
PG	Proctor & Gamble Co.
PIL	Pilot Chemical Co.
PRO	Protean Chemical Corp.
QCP	Quaker Chemical Corp.
RCD	Richardson Co.
RH	Rohm and Haas Co.
ROZ	Rozilda, Inc.
RTF	Retzloff Chemical Co.
RW	Robinson Wagner Co., Inc
S	Sandoz, Inc.
SBC	Scher Bros., Inc.
SCO	Scholler Bros., Inc.
SCP	Standard Chemical Products, Inc.
SDW	Sterling Drug, Inc., Winthrop Laboratories Div.
SEY	Seydel-Woolley & Co., Inc.
SFA	Stauffer Chemical Co., Specialty Chemical Div.
SHC	Shell Oil Co., Shell Chemical Co. Div.
SHO	Shell Oil Co.
SIN	Sinclair Refining Co.
SLC	Soluol Chemical Co., Inc.
SNW	Sun Chemical Corp., Chemical Products Div.
SON	Witco Chemical Co., Inc., Sonneborn Div.
SPP	Southern Chemical Products Co.
STP	Stepan Chemical Co., Industrial Chemicals Div.
SUR	Surfact-Co., Inc.
SWT	Swift & Co.
SYC	Synthetic Chemicals, Inc.
SYN	Synthron, Inc.
TCC	Tanatex Chemical Corp.
TCH	Trylon Chemical Corp.
TCI	Texise Chemicals, Inc.
TMH	Thompson-Hayward Chemical Co.
TNN	Tennessee Corp.
TX	Texaco, Inc.
TXC	Tex Chem Co.
TXT	Textilana Corp.
UCC	Union Carbide Corp., Chemicals Div.
UVC	Universal Chemicals Corp.
VAC	Varney Chemical Corp.
VAL	Valchem
VNC	Vanderbilt Chemical Corp.
VND	Van Dyk & Co., Inc.
WAY	Philip A. Hunt Chemical Corp., Wayland Chemical Div.
WON	Woonsocket Color & Chemical Co.
WSN	Washine Chemical Corp.
WTC	Witco Chemical Co., Inc.
WYN	Wyandotte Chemicals Corp.

Health and Safety

Three considerations are involved in evaluating the safety of a surfactant intended for commercial sale. First is the question of direct hazard to the user. Second is the consequence of long-term exposure of the environment to this new component. The third, which is in a different category, deals with the effects of prolonged ingestion of "edible surfactants" by humans or animals.

In general, "anionic and nonionic surfactants are relatively nontoxic to mammals, falling in the same range as sodium chloride or sodium carbonate" (95). Cationics are only slightly more toxic. The foregoing generalizations are not a carteblanche certification of the safety of all surfactants on mammals and each product must be tested, not only as a pure material but also in the formulation in which it will be used. The surfactant industry has generally recognized that many of its products come into intimate contact with the skin or eyes of users and that they are used for cleaning clothes, food, and food utensils. As a result, surfactant products are normally submitted by the manufacturer to an independent laboratory for evaluation of acute oral toxicity in rats, skin sensitization and skin irritation on humans (96,97), and eye irritation in rabbits (98). These findings are made available to prospective customers. Surfactants intended for incorporation in dentifrices or for ingestion in foods are subject to strict regulation by the Federal Government. Prolonged chronic-toxicity testing with animals followed by clinical studies with humans is usually a prerequisite to approval of the prototype compounds suggested for these uses (99).

The usage of surfactants has increased to the point where scientists in government and industry have begun to study their possible effects as a new factor in the human environment. The preponderance of evidence at this time indicates that no serious health hazards have been created.

Test Methods

Methods of chemical analysis, measurement of surface-active properties, and evaluation of performance under simulated use conditions are all important elements of surfactant technology. The voluminous literature on these topics is not amenable to summarization and this section is essentially an introductory bibliography.

The analytical approach to the general case of an unknown commercial surfactant must assume that it is a complex mixture comprised of some combination of anionic, nonionic, cationic, and amphoteric surfactants plus inorganic builders and/or solvents. Unless the sample history suggests a short-cut procedure to the assay, the recommended steps (100) in the analysis are: "(a) separation of nonsurfactant and inorganic material from the total surfactant mixture; (b) classification of the surfactant; (c) separation of the individual surfactant; and (d) quantitative determination."

Methods for classification of mixtures are described by Karabinos and others (101,102). The British Society of Public Analysts (103) has published another scheme. Separation of the sample after the components have been classified may depend on extraction, distillation, centrifugation, ion exchange, or precipitation processes. Burger (104) and Weeks and others (105) have suggested techniques for separation of surfactant mixtures. The final consideration, quantitative determination of the surfactant, will depend on the chemical composition of the unknown and sometimes on the instrumentation that is available. Methods for the quantitative determination of extremely low concentrations of ABS and LAS have been developed in recent years (106) and improved methods have been described for measurement of low concentrations of polyoxyethylene surfactants (107).

The complete analysis of a surfactant sometimes involves determination of the hydrophilic/hydrophobic balance and/or the molecular structure. Comparisons to reference samples of known composition are often helpful in this as well as in other surfactant analytical procedures. Instrumental methods are effective for the identification of surfactant structures, particularly infrared spectra (108) and nuclear magnetic resonance (109). x-Ray investigations have contributed to elucidation of the structure of surfactant molecules.

Measurement of Surface Activity. Each surface-active property can be measured in a variety of ways and the method of choice often depends on the characteristics of the substance to be tested. The most frequently determined properties probably are surface tension, interfacial tension, contact angle, and critical micelle concentration.

Surface and Interfacial Tension. Reviews of methods for measuring these properties started appearing before 1900. Harkins (110) carefully reviewed theories and experimental methods in 1945. The du Nouy Tensiometer, ie ring method, is probably the most widely used determination of static surface and interfacial tension (111). Other frequently used methods are drop weight (112), pendant drop (113), maximum bubble pressure (114), capillary rise, and sessile drops. Dynamic surface tension can be measured by a speedup of the bubbling rate in the maximum bubble-pressure method (115) or the change in wavelength and form when a jet of liquid issues from an elliptical orifice (116). Dynamic methods are useful because they provide information on the time required for surfactant molecules to migrate to the interface.

Contact Angle. A number of methods for direct determination of the contact angle have been proposed, but the measurement is difficult and the results are not always reproducible. The roughness of the solid surface and the difference between the advancing and receding angle lowers the precision of the measurements. The tilted plate is the simplest and most direct method for this determination (117).

Critical Micelle Concentration. The rate at which the properties of surfactant solutions vary with concentration changes at the concentration where micelle formation starts. Surface and interfacial tension, equivalent conductance (118), dye solubilization (119), iodine solubilization (120), and refractive index (121) are properties commonly used as the basis for methods of determination of CMC.

Performance Tests. Laboratory tests that simulate full-scale applications are used extensively in the development of new surfactant formulations and in the control of industrial processes in which surfactants are functional components. Performance tests tend to be individualized because they are designed to fill the specific requirements of each laboratory of company that uses them. However, the need for commercially constructed test equipment and the need to communicate the results of practical tests exerts a pressure for standardization of equipment and procedures. The committees of trade or industry associations and Committee D-12 of the American Society for Testing and Materials are prime sources of standardized surfactant performance tests. Trade sources include the American Association of Textile Chemists and Colorists, American Standards Association, Chemical Specialties Manufacturers Association, and the Toilet Goods Association. A comprehensive list of surfactant test equipment, and of performance tests has not been published, but Harris (122) has compiled some of the frequently used tests in a convenient booklet.

Bibliography

"Surface Active Agents" in *ECT* 1st ed., Vol. 13, pp. 513–536, by D. M. Price, Oakite Products, Inc. "Nonionic Surfactants" in *ECT* 1st ed., Suppl. 2, pp. 490–522, by R. L. Mayhew and F. E. Woodward, General Aniline & Film Corporation.

1. *Business Week*, 42–43 (Mar. 11, 1950).
2. J. Mitchell and F. D. Snell, *Ind. Eng. Chem.* **31**, 48–51 (1939).
3. G. S. Hartley, *Aqueous Solutions of Paraffin-Chain Salts*, Hermann & Cie, Paris, 1936, p. 45.
4. R. A. Gibbons, *Nature* **200**, 665–666 (Nov., 1963).
5. H. P. Dupuy, American Oil Chemists' Society Nomenclature Subcommittee, *J. Am. Oil Chemists' Soc.* **45**, 390A–397A (1968).
6. B. A. Mulley, in M. J. Schick, ed., *Nonionic Surfactants*, Vol. I of *Surfactant Science*, Marcel Dekker, Inc., New York, 1967, Chap. 13, pp. 422, 431.
7. J. Rubinfeld, E. M. Emery, and H. D. Cross, *J. Am. Oil Chemists' Soc.* **41**, 822–826 (1964).
8. G. S. Hartley, *Trans. Faraday Soc.* **37**, 130 (1941).
9. E. E. Dreger, G. I. Keim, G. D. Miles, L. Shedlovsky, and J. Ross, *Ind. Eng. Chem.* **36**, 610–617 (1944).
10. B. G. Wilkes and J. N. Wickert, *Ind. Eng. Chem.* **29**, 1234–1239 (1937).
11. C. R. Caryl, *Ind. Eng. Chem.* **33**, 731–737 (1941).
12. E. Götte, *Die Chemie* **57**, 67 (1944).
13. H. C. Borghetty and C. A. Bergman, *J. Am. Oil Chemists' Soc.* **27**, 88–92 (1950).
14. U.S. Pat. 2,689,170 (Sept. 14, 1954), W. J. King (to Colgate-Palmolive Peet Co.).
15. U.S. Pats. 2,174,110 (Sept. 26, 1959), and 2,263,312, C. F. Reed (to E. I. du Pont de Nemours & Co., Inc.).
15a. W. H. Lockwood, *Chem. Ind.* **62**, 760–763 (1948).
16. W. C. Browning, in F. Asinger, ed., *Proc. IVth Intern. Congr. Surface Active Substances, Brussels, 7–14 Sept., 1964, Vol. 1, Sect. A (of the Congress)*, Gordon and Breach Science Publishers, New York, pp. 141–154.
17. J. M. Davis and E. F. Degering, *Proc. Indiana Acad. Sci.* **56**, 116–118 (1946).
18. W. E. Truce and J. F. Lyons, *J. Am. Chem. Soc.* **73**, 126–128 (1951).
19. A. I. Vogel, *J. Chem. Soc.* **1948**, 607–610, 610–615.
20. W. A. Sweeny and A. C. Olson, *J. Am. Oil Chemists' Soc.* **41**, 815–822 (1964).
21. R. Leslie, *Mfg. Chemist* **21**, 417–420, 422 (1950).
21a. A. B. Brown and J. O. Knoblock, *ASTM Spec. Tech. Publ. 224*, 213–247 (1958).
22. Brit. Pat. 661,701 (Nov. 28, 1951), J. M. Cross (to GAF Corporation).
23. D. M. Marquis, S. H. Sharman, R. House, and W. A. Sweeny, *J. Am. Oil Chemists' Soc.* **43**, 607–614 (1966).
23a. S. Tomiyama, M. Takao, A. Mori, and H. Sekiguchi, *J. Am. Oil Chemists' Soc.* **46**, 208–212 (1969).
24. J. K. Weil, R. G. Bristline, and A. J. Stirton, *J. Phys. Chem.* **62**, 1083 (1958).
25. J. K. Weil, A. J. Stirton, R. G. Bristline, and E. W. Maurer, *J. Am. Oil Chemists' Soc.* **36**, 241 (1959).
26. R. G. Bristline, A. J. Stirton, J. K. Weil, and E. W. Maurer, *J. Am. Oil Chemists' Soc.* **34**, 516 (1957).
27. J. Nusslein, *Parfum. Cosmet. Savons* **2**, 554 (1959); *Chem. Abstr.* **54**, 7074f (1960).
28. *Synthetic Organic Chemicals, United States Production and Sales, 1966*, United States Tariff Commission, *TC Publ. 248*, U.S. Government Printing Office, Washington, D.C., 1968, Table 19B, pp. 148, 149.
29. L. N. Ferguson, *J. Am. Chem. Soc.* **77**, 5288 (1955).
30. H. Arai, *J. Colloid Interface Sci.* **23**, 348–351 (1957).
31. P. H. Elworthy and C. B. Macfarlane, *J. Chem. Soc.* **1964**, 311.
32. J. M. Cross, *Proc. Chem. Specialties Mfrs' Assoc.* (June, 1950), 135, 143.
33. U.S. Pat. 2,931,777 (April 5, 1960), H. A. Shelanski (to GAF Corporation).
34. M. N. Fineman, G. L. Brown, and R. J. Meyers, *J. Phys. Chem.* **56**, 963 (1952).
35. L. Schechter and J. Winstra, *Ind. Eng. Chem.* **48**, 86 (1956).
36. C. Draves, *Am. Dyestuff Reptr.* **28**, 421 (1939).
37. J. Ross and G. D. Miles, *Oil Soap* **18**, 99 (1941).
38. H. G. Nadeau, D. M. Oaks, W. A. Nichols, and L. P. Carr, *Anal. Chem.* **36**, 1914 (1964).

39. L. Gold, *J. Chem. Phys.* **20,** 1651 (1952); **28,** 91 (1958).
40. J. H. McFarland and P. R. Kinkel, *J. Am. Oil Chemists' Soc.* **41,** 742–745 (1964).
41. G. J. Stockburger and J. D. Brandner, *J. Am. Oil Chemists' Soc.* **40,** 590 (1963).
42. T. Malkin and T. H. Bevan, *Progr. Chem. Fats Lipids* **4,** 64 (1957).
43. A. N. Wrigley, F. D. Smith, and A. J. Stirton, *J. Am. Oil Chemists' Soc.* **34,** 39 (1957).
44. W. B. Satkowski and W. B. Bennet, *Soap Chem. Specialties* **33** (7), 37 (1957).
45. U.S. Pat. 2,089,212 (Aug. 10, 1937), W. Kritchevsky (to Ninol Laboratories).
46. W. S. Lennon and I. M. Rosenbaum, *Am. Perfumer* **72** (4), 76 (1958).
47. L. J. Garrison and J. H. Pasleau, *Detergent Age* (Jan., 1968), 27–29, 98.
48. I. R. Schmolka, in M. J. Schick, ed., *Nonionic Surfactants,* Vol. I of *Surfactant Science,* Marcel Dekker, Inc., New York, 1967, Chap. 10.
49. R. J. Thimineur, *Detergent Age* (June, 1967), 23–25.
50. R. R. Egan, *J. Am. Oil Chemists' Soc.* **45,** 481–486 (1968).
51. U.S. Pat. 3,001,945 (Sept. 26, 1961), H. F. Drew and R. E. Zimmer (to Proctor and Gamble Co.).
52. U.S. Pat. 2,999,068 (Sept. 5, 1961), W. Pilcher and S. L. Eton (to Proctor and Gamble Co.).
53. K. W. Herrmann, *J. Phys. Chem.* **66,** 295 (1962).
54. D. B. Lake and G. L. K. Hoh, *J. Am. Oil Chemists' Soc.* **40,** 628 (1963).
54a. H. L. Sanders, J. B. Braunwarth, R. B. McConnell, and R. A. Swenson, *J. Am. Oil Chemists' Soc.* **46,** 167–170 (1969).
55. H. S. Mannheimer, *Soap Chem. Specialties* **30,** 37, 99, 100 (June, 1954).
55a. Reference 28, p. 147.
56. J. W. McCutcheon, *Detergents and Emulsifiers, 1968 Annual,* John W. McCutcheon, Morristown, N.J., 1968.
57. N. K. Adam, *The Physics and Chemistry of Surfaces,* 3rd ed., Oxford University Press, London, 1941, pp. 107–117.
58. A. M. Mankowich, *J. Am. Oil Chemists' Soc.* **43,** 615–619 (1966).
59. R. Matalon, *J. Colloid Sci.* **8,** 53–63 (1953).
60. J. W. McBain and J. C. Henniker, *Colloid Chem.* **7,** 47–66 (1950).
61. A. S. Weatherburn and C. H. Bayley, *Textile Res. J.* **22,** 797–804 (1952).
62. L. H. Flett, L. F. Hoyt, and J. Walter, *Am. Dyestuff Reptr.* **41,** 139–143 (1952).
63. H. W. Fox and W. A. Zisman, *J. Colloid Sci.* **7,** 428–442 (1952).
64. G. J. Kahan, *J. Colloid Sci.* **6,** 571–575 (1951).
65. W. C. Preston, *J. Phys. Colloid Chem.* **52,** 84–97 (1948).
65a. K. Hess, W. Philipoff, and H. Kiessig, *Kolloid-Z.* **88,** 49 (1939).
66. C. R. Singleterry, *J. Am. Oil Chemists' Soc.* **32,** 446–452 (1955).
67. S. Kaufman and C. R. Singleterry, *J. Colloid Sci.* **10,** 139–150 (1955).
68. R. Goto et al., *J. Chem. Soc. Japan* **75,** 73 (1950).
69. A. M. Mankowich, *J. Phys. Chem.* **58,** 1027–1030 (1954).
70. H. V. Tartar and A. L. M. Lelong, *J. Phys. Chem.* **59,** 1185–1190 (1955); J. F. Voeks and H. V. Tartar, *J. Phys. Chem.* **59,** 1190–1192; A. D. Abbott and H. V. Tartar, *J. Phys. Chem.* **59,** 1193–1194; H. V. Tartar, *J. Phys. Chem.* **59,** 1195–1199.
71. E. H. Crook, D. B. Fordyce, and G. F. Trebbi, *J. Phys. Chem.* **67,** 1987 (1963).
72. J. M. Corkill, J. F. Goodman, and J. R. Tate, *Trans. Faraday Soc.* **60,** 986 (1964).
73. M. J. Schick and D. J. Manning, *J. Am. Oil Chemists' Soc.* **43,** 133 (1966).
74. K. Durham, "Wetting" in *Surface Activity and Detergency,* Macmillan and Co., Ltd., London, 1961, Chap. 3, pp. 52–71.
75. H. J. Osterhof and F. E. Bartell, *J. Phys. Chem.* **34,** 1399–1411 (1930).
76. A. F. Helin, J. M. Gyenge, D. A. Beadell, J. H. Boyd, R. L. Mayhew, and R. C. Hyatt, *Ind. Eng. Chem.* **45,** 1330–1336 (1953).
77. T. H. Vaughn, H. R. Suter, and M. G. Kramer, *Ind. Eng. Chem.* **46,** 1934–1937 (1954).
78. H. L. Sanders, *Soap Chem. Specialties* **27,** 39–42, 55, 57 (Dec., 1951).
79. T. E. Brenner, in J. N. Pitts and R. L. Metcalf, eds., *Advances in Environmental Sciences,* Vol. I, Interscience Publishers, a division of John Wiley & Sons, Inc., New York, in press.
80. R. D. Swisher, *J. Am. Oil Chemists' Soc.* **40,** 648 (1963).
81. Q. W. Osburn and J. H. Benedict, *J. Am. Oil Chemists' Soc.* **43,** 141 (1966).
82. E. Ruschenburg, *Vom Wasser* **30,** 232 (1963); *Chem. Abstr.* **61,** 16315b (1964).
83. F. A. Blankenship and V. M. Piccolini, *Soap Chem. Specialties* **39** (12), 75 (1963).
84. E. C. Steinle, R. C. Myerly, and C. A. Vath, *J. Am. Oil Chemists' Soc.* **41,** 804–807 (1964).

85. L. J. Garrison and R. D. Matson, *J. Am. Oil Chemists' Soc.* **41**, 799–804 (1964).

86. R. L. Huddleston and R. C. Allred, *J. Am. Oil Chemists' Soc.* **42**, 983–986 (1965).

87. S. J. Patterson, C. C. Scott, and K. B. E. Tucker, *J. Am. Oil Chemists' Soc.* **45**, 528–532 (1968).

88. P. J. Weaver, *Soap Chem. Specialties* **41**, 45 (1965).

89. Subcommittee on Biodegradation Test Methods, *J. Am. Oil Chemists' Soc.* **42**, 989 (1965).

90. Subcommittee on Biodegradation Test Methods, *J. Am. Oil Chemists' Soc.* **42**, 990 (1965).

91. C. A. Vath, *Soap Chem. Specialties* **40** (2), 56–58, 182 (1964); *Soap Chem. Specialties* **40** (3), 55–58, 108 (1964).

92. Joint Task Force to Investigate Eutrophication, *U.S. Dept. of the Interior, News Release, Aug. 4, 1967, Haskell 343-9134; Ibid., Dec. 28, 1967, Haskell 343-5461.*

93. Reference 28, Table 19A, pp. 47–50, and Table 21A, p. 56.

94. H. A. W. Hill, T. H. Butler, and J. G. Moffett, Jr., *Detergents Specialties* **6** (2), 22–28 (1969).

95. R. D. Swisher, *Surfactant Effects on Humans and Other Mammals*, The Soap and Detergent Association, Scientific and Technical Report No. 4, Nov. 1966.

96. H. A. Shelanski and M. V. Shelanski, *Proc. Sci. Sect. Toilet Goods Assoc.* **20**, 46 (1963).

97. J. H. Draize, *Food Drug Cosmet. Law J.* **10**, 722 (1955).

98. J. H. Draize and E. A. Kelley, *Proc. Sci. Sect. Toilet Goods Assoc.* **17**, 1 (1952).

99. Food and Drug Administration, Div. of Pharmacology, *Appraisal of the Safety of Chemicals in Foods, Drugs and Cosmetics* (1959).

100. H. G. Nadeau and S. Siggia, in M. J. Schick, ed., *Nonionic Surfactants*, Vol. I of *Surfactant Science*, Marcel Dekker, Inc., New York, 1967, Chap. 24.

101. J. V. Karabinos, G. E. Kapella, and G. E. Bartels, *Soap Chem. Specialties* **6**, 30, 41 (1954).

102. E. J. Quinn and J. V. Karabinos, *Soap Chem. Specialties* **32**, 11, 39 (1956).

103. Society of Public Analysts and Other Analytical Chemists, Analytical Methods Committee, *Analyst* **76**, 279 (1951).

104. K. Burger, *Z. Anal. Chim.* **196**, 22 (1963).

105. L. E. Weeks, M. E. Ginn, and G. E. Baker, *Proc. Chem. Specialties Mfrs. Assoc.* (May, 1957), 150–155.

106. *Standard Methods for the Examination of Water and Wastewater*, 12th ed., Am. Public Health Assoc., New York, 1965, pp. 296, 299.

107. N. T. Crabb and H. E. Persinger, *J. Am. Oil Chemists' Soc.* **41**, 752–755 (1964).

108. D. Hummel, *Identification and Analysis of Surface Active Agents by Infrared and Chemical Methods*, Text Volume and Spectra Volume, Interscience Publishers, a division of John Wiley & Sons, Inc., New York, 1962.

109. M. M. Crutchfield, R. R. Irani, and J. T. Yoder, *J. Am. Oil Chemists' Soc.* **41**, 129 (1964).

110. W. D. Harkins, in A. Weissberger, ed., *Physical Methods of Organic Chemistry*, Vol. I, Interscience Publishers, New York, 1945, Chap. 6.

111. H. W. Fox and C. H. Chrisman, Jr., *J. Phys. Chem.* **56**, 284–287 (1952).

112. R. C. Brown and H. McCormack, *Phil. Mag.* **39**, 420–428 (1948).

113. S. Fordham, *Proc. Roy. Soc. London* **A194**, 1–16 (1948).

114. A. S. Brown, R. U. Robinson, E. H. Sirois, H. G. Thiboult, W. McNeil, and A. Tofias, *J. Phys. Chem.* **56**, 701–705 (1952).

115. M. Picon, *Ann. Pharm. Franc.* **6**, 84–93 (1948).

116. K. L. Sutherland, *Australian J. Chem.* **7**, 319–328 (1948).

117. Ref. 57, pp. 180–185, 413.

118. A. B. Scott and H. V. Tartar, *J. Am. Chem. Soc.* **65**, 692 (1943).

119. M. L. Corrin and W. D. Harkins, *J. Am. Chem. Soc.* **69**, 679–688 (1947).

120. S. Ross and J. P. Olivier, *J. Phys. Chem.* **63**, 1671 (1959).

121. H. B. Klevens, *J. Phys. Colloid Chem.* **52**, 130–148 (1948).

122. J. C. Harris, *Detergency Evaluation and Testing*, Interscience Publishers, Inc., New York, 1954.

General References

A. W. Adamson, *Physical Chemistry of Surfaces*, 2nd ed., Interscience Publishers, a division of John Wiley & Sons, Inc., New York, 1967.

P. Becher, *Emulsions, Theory and Practice*, 2nd ed., Reinhold Publishing Corp., New York, 1965.

B. Levitt, *Materials and Processes*, Vol. 1, *Formulary*, Vol. 2 of *Oils, Detergents and Maintenance Specialties*, Chemical Publishing Co., New York, 1967.

J. L. Moilliet, B. Collie, and W. Black, *Surface Activity*, 2nd ed., D. Van Nostrand Company, Inc., Princeton, N.J., 1961.

L. I. Osipow, *Surface Chemistry—Theory and Industrial Applications*, Reinhold Publishing Corp., New York, 1962; *ACS Monograph Series No. 153.*

N. G. Gaylord, ed., *Polyalkylene Oxides and Other Polyethers*, Part 1 of *Polyethers*, Vol. 13 of *High Polymers*, Interscience Publishers, Inc., New York, 1963.

E. Rideal, Conference President, *Wetting*, Society of the Chemical Industry, Monograph No. 25, Gordon & Breach Publishers, Inc., New York, 1957.

J. T. Davies and E. K. Rideal, *Interfacial Phenomena*, Academic Press, Inc., New York, 1961.

M. J. Schick, ed., *Nonionic Surfactants*, Vol. I of *Surfactant Science*, Marcel Dekker, Inc., New York, 1967. (Also includes *Polyoxyethylene Alkylamines, Nonionics as Ionic Surfactant Intermediates, Amine Oxides, Physical Chemistry, Analytical Chemistry, Biology and Physiology.*)

A. M. Schwartz and J. W. Perry, *Surface Active Agents*, Interscience Publishers, Inc., New York, 1949.

A. M. Schwartz, J. W. Perry, and J. Berch, *Surface Active Agents and Detergents*, Interscience Publishers, Inc., New York, 1958.

K. Shinoda, T. Nakagawa, B. Tamamuski, and T. Isemura, *Some Physico-Chemical Properties of Colloidal Surfactants*, Academic Press, Inc., New York, 1963.

J. P. Sisley, *Encyclopedia of Surface-Active Agents*, translated from the French by P. J. Wood, Chemical Publishing Co., Inc., New York, Vol. 1, reprinted 1961, Vol. 2, 1964.

P. A. Winsor, *Solvent Properties of Amphiphilic Compounds*, Butterworth Scientific Publications, London, 1954.

CHAPIN E. STEVENS
Management Research Consultants

SWEETENERS, NONNUTRITIVE

The number of distinct tastes is very large, but generally it is assumed that these are combinations of four basic tastes—sweet, sour, bitter, saline (see also Vol. 9, p. 348). Sourness is a characteristic of protonic acids, and saltiness is a taste found with many salts of the group I metals. The sweet and the bitter tastes, however, are not confined to such well-defined classes of chemicals. In fact, sweetness and bitterness are found in nearly every chemical class.

Attempts have been made to correlate sweetness and structure with theories involving *glucophor* and *auxogluc* groups (1,28), but these leave a great number of sweet-tasting chemicals unexplained. (This terminology is related to the theory of color proposed by Witt in 1876 (see also Vol. 5, p. 766), in which he termed a color-bearing group a *chromophore*, and a color-increasing group an *auxochrome*. Oertly and Meyers (28) coined the analogous terms *glucophor* and *auxogluc* to designate chemical groups that would cause sweetness, or intensify sweetness, respectively.)

The association of sweetness with sugars is understandable historically, although chemically incorrect. Sugar in form of honey, as indicated by rock paintings in the caves near Valencia, Spain, was harvested and used in Neolithic times, and cane sugar was reported by Theophrastus in 300 BC.

Sucrose, glucose, fructose, lactose, and maltose are common, commercial sugar sweeteners today (see Sugar). However, not all sugars are sweet. Many saccharides, like cellobiose, are tasteless. D-Mannose exists in two anomeric forms; one is sweet and the other is bitter.

Sorbitol and mannitol are sweet-tasting polyols (see Alcohols, polyhydric) structurally related to glucose and fructose. Both of these polyols occur in nature. Mannitol was given its name because someone thought it to be a constituent of the manna reported in the Old Testament.

Table 1. Relative Sweetness of Various Organic Chemicals

Chemical	Formula	Sweetness[a] (sucrose = 1)
sucrose	$C_{12}H_{22}O_{11}$	1
lactose	$C_{12}H_{22}O_{11}$	0.4
maltose	$C_{12}H_{22}O_{11}$	0.5
galactose	$C_6H_{12}O_6$	0.6
D-glucose	$C_6H_{12}O_6$	0.7
D-fructose	$C_6H_{12}O_6$	1.1
invert sugar		0.7–0.9
D-xylose	$C_5H_{10}O_5$	0.7
sorbitol	$C_6H_{14}O_6$	0.5
mannitol	$C_6H_{14}O_6$	0.7
dulcitol	$C_6H_{14}O_6$	0.4
glycerol (qv)	$C_3H_8O_3$	0.8
glycine	H_2NCH_2COOH	0.7
sodium 3-methylcyclohexyl-sulfamate	$CH_3C_5H_8NHSO_3Na$	15
p-anisylurea	$CH_3OC_6H_4NHCONH_2$	18
sodium cyclohexylsulfamate (cyclamate)	$C_6H_{11}NHSO_3Na$	30–80
chloroform	$CHCl_3$	40
glycyrrhizin	$C_{29}H_{44}O–(COOH)O–C_6H_8O_5–O–C_6H_9O_6$	50
aspartyl-phenylalanine methyl ester	$HOOCCH_2CH(NH_2)CONHCH(CH_2C_6H_5)COOCH_3$	100–200
5-nitro-2-methoxyaniline	$H_2NC_6H_3(OCH_3)NO_2$	167
5-methylsaccharin	$CH_3C_6H_3CONHSO_2$	200
p-ethoxyphenylurea (dulcin)	$C_2H_5OC_6H_4NHCONH_2$	70–350
6-chlorosaccharin	$ClC_6H_3CONHSO_2$	100–350
n-hexylchloromalonamide	$C_6H_{13}CCl(CONH_2)_2$	300
sodium saccharin	$C_6H_4CONNaSO_2$	200–700
stevioside	$C_{38}H_{60}O_{18}$	300
2-amino-4-nitrotoluene	$CH_3C_6H_3(NH_2)NO_2$	300
naringin dihydrochalcone	$C_{12}H_{21}O_{10}(OH)_2C_6H_2COCH_2CH_2C_6H_4OH$	300
p-nitrosuccinanilide	$O_2NC_6H_4NCOCH_2CH_2CO$	350
1-bromo-5-nitroaniline	$H_2NC_6H_3(Br)NO_2$	700
5-nitro-2-ethoxyaniline	$H_2NC_6H_3(OC_2H_5)NO_2$	950
perillaldehyde anti-aldoxime	$CH_2=C(CH_3)C_6H_8CH=NOH$	2000
neohesperidine dihydro-chalcone	$C_{12}H_{21}O_{10}(OH)_2C_6H_2COCH_2CH_2C_6H_3(OCH_3)OH$	2000
5-nitro-2-propoxyaniline (P-4000)	$H_2NC_6H_3(OC_3H_7)NO_2$	4000

[a] Many factors affect sweetness, and different methods have been used to determine sweetness ratios. The sweetness of sucrose, the usual standard, will change with age due to inversion. Sweet taste depends upon concentration of the sweetener, temperature, pH, type of medium used, and sensitivity of the taster. The usual test methods are dilution to threshold sweetness in water and duplication of the sweetness of a 5 or 10% sucrose solution, although other techniques have also been employed. Where different sweetness values have been reported, the most commonly accepted ones have been cited in this table (1,18,22).

Besides these sweet-tasting sugars and closely related polyols there is a very great number of synthetic chemicals that taste sweet. Two startling observations about these chemicals are that they are chemically unrelated to the carbohydrates and that, generally, they are structurally unrelated to each other.

A number of inorganic salts are known to be sweet, especially the formate, acetate, propionate, and isovalerate salts of lead and beryllium. Most famous of these is lead acetate, commonly known as "sugar of lead," and reportedly used for nefarious purposes by the Borgias about 500 years ago.

Among the organic chemicals, chloroform has a sweet taste, and it has been known since 1831. *Dulcin* (*p*-ethoxyphenylurea) was discovered in 1883 by Berlinerblau (9), and it formerly was used in this country as a commercial sweetener. *Saccharin* (see below) was discovered in 1879 by Remsen and Fahlberg (15,35) and has been in use commercially since 1900.

The variety of chemicals reported to taste sweet is indicated in Table 1. This list is meant to be illustrative and does not include all of the host of chemicals which have been reported to have a sweet taste.

Although the chemicals in Table 1 are fascinating in their variety, most of them have no practical use as sweetening agents. In order for a chemical to be employed in foods and drugs, it must be readily available, economical, stable, compatible with other ingredients present, and must be safe under normal conditions of use (25b). Of the nonnutritive chemical sweeteners, only cyclamate and saccharin meet all of these criteria.

Definitions. The terms "synthetic" and "artificial" sweeteners have fallen into disfavor for describing the noncarbohydrate sweeteners. The practical difference between sweeteners is a nutritional one. The sugars and related polyols are converted to carbon dioxide, water, and energy by the body; hence, these sweeteners have nutritional value. Chemicals like cyclamate and saccharin have no food value, and properly are described as nonnutritive sweetening agents. This term is becoming accepted by food technologists.

Nonnutritive sweeteners are used for special purposes to avoid inherent properties of the sugars. For diabetics they do not have the insulin requirement many sugars have. The nonnutritive sweeteners have no food calorie value for people on reducing diets. In connection with tooth-decay problems, the nonnutritive sweeteners do not have the cariogenic potential of the sugar carbohydrates, because they do not serve as food for microorganisms. Additionally, they are nonhygroscopic, do not caramelize as sugars do, and are highly concentrated sources of sweetness. These properties account for the special dietary and technological uses of the nonnutritive sweetening agents (7).

Saccharin

Saccharin (insoluble saccharin, 2,3-dihydro-3-oxobenzisosulfonazole, 1,2-benziso-thiazol-3(2*H*)-one, *o*-sulfobenzimide, *o*-benzosulfimide, benzoic sulfimide, Gluside, Garantose, Saccharinol, Saccharinose, Saccharol, Saxin, Sykose) (**1**) was synthesized originally by Ira Remsen and C. Fahlberg in the course of an academic investigation of the oxidation of *o*-toluenesulfonamide at John Hopkins University in 1879 (15). The sweetness was discovered accidentally when Fahlberg ate a piece of bread and noticed it had a distinctly sweet taste. He traced the taste to a chemical he had handled in the laboratory. Insoluble saccharin often is used in pharmaceutical tablets. In liquid products and in foods the soluble sodium or calcium salt is customarily preferred. Ammonium saccharin is used occasionally in sweetening solutions.

Saccharin, USP XVII (26), $C_6H_4CONHSO_2$, occurs as intensely sweet, white crystals or as a white crystalline powder, mp 226–230°C. One gram dissolves in 290 ml water or in 31 ml alcohol, in 12 ml acetone, in about 50 ml glycerol, and in 25 ml boiling water; saccharin is freely soluble in solutions of alkali carbonates, and slightly soluble in chloroform and ether. In dilute solutions, it is about 500 times sweeter than sucrose. In distilled water, 60 mg is equivalent in sweetening power to about 30 g of sucrose. Solutions of saccharin are acid to litmus.

Sodium saccharin, NF XII (23), $C_6H_4CONSO_2Na.2H_2O$, is a white crystalline powder with an intensely sweet taste. It contains no less than 98% of anhydrous sodium saccharin after drying at 120°C for 4 hr. One gram is soluble in about 1.2 ml water or about 50 ml alcohol. When in powdered form, it usually contains less than half the theoretical amount of water of hydration.

Calcium saccharin, NF XII, $(C_6H_4CONSO_2)_2Ca.3\frac{1}{2}H_2O$, occurs as white crystals or as a white crystalline powder with an intensely sweet taste. It contains no less than 95% anhydrous calcium saccharin on dry basis. Loss on drying at 125°C for 4 hr does not exceed 15%. One gram dissolves in about 1.5 ml water or in about 33 ml 92% ethyl alcohol.

SOLUBILITY, TASTE

Complete solubility data for saccharin, sodium saccharin, and calcium saccharin in water, alcohol, and glycols have been compiled by Salant (24). Saccharin is chemically stable under all conditions ordinarily encountered in food preparation and processing and, in aqueous buffered solutions of pH 3.3, 7.0, and 9.0, remains stable at temperatures of up to 150°C for 1 hr (13). Sweetness ratios for saccharin relative to sucrose of from 200:1 to 700:1 have been reported. Based on dilution of a solution in distilled water to threshold sweetness, saccharin is about 300 times as sweet as sucrose. Sodium and calcium saccharins are comparable in sweetness.

REACTIONS

The structure of saccharin (**1**) makes many types of reactions possible. The imido hydrogen is acidic and, therefore, saccharin forms salts with bases. Many metallic

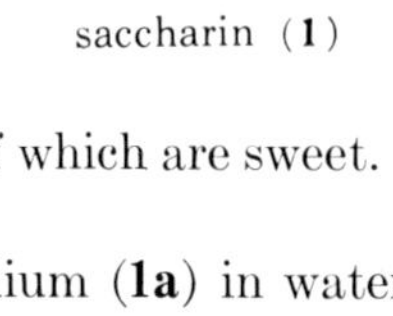

saccharin (**1**)

salts have been prepared, not all of which are sweet. The copper salt is astringent, and the nickel salt only slightly sweet.

Chlorination of saccharin sodium (**1a**) in water solution yields 2-chlorosaccharin (8). Saccharin sodium will react with a great variety of halogen compounds to give N-alkyl- or N-aryl-substituted saccharin (8). Saccharin condenses with phenols (36)

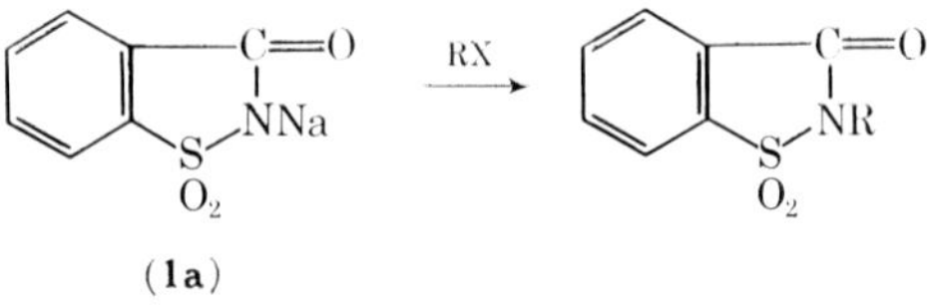

(**1a**)

to give sacchareins of type (**2**).   Heating saccharin with 40% formaldehyde in sulfuric acid yields, 2,2′-methylenedisaccharin (2,2′-methylenebis(1,2-benzisothiazol-3-(2*H*)-one)) (**3**).

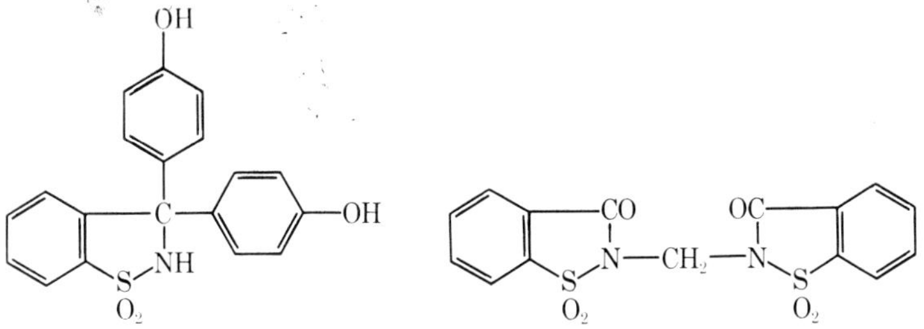

OH

C—OH

S—NH
O₂

(**2**)

CO
S—N—CH₂—N—S
O₂   O₂

(**3**)

The chemistry of saccharin and its derivatives has been investigated by Mameli and Mannessier-Mameli (21).

MANUFACTURE

The best-known process for manufacturing saccharin today consists essentially of the same method used by Remsen and Fahlberg in 1879 (15,35).   Toluene and chlorosulfonic acid react at 0–5°C to form a mixture of o- and p-toluenesulfonamides.   The mixture is separated, and the o-toluenesulfonamide is oxidized to o-carboxybenzenesulfonamide (o-sulfamoylbenzoic acid).   This compound loses a mole of water to become saccharin (**1**) (see Scheme 1).   The p-toluenesulfonamide is also an important by-

Scheme 1

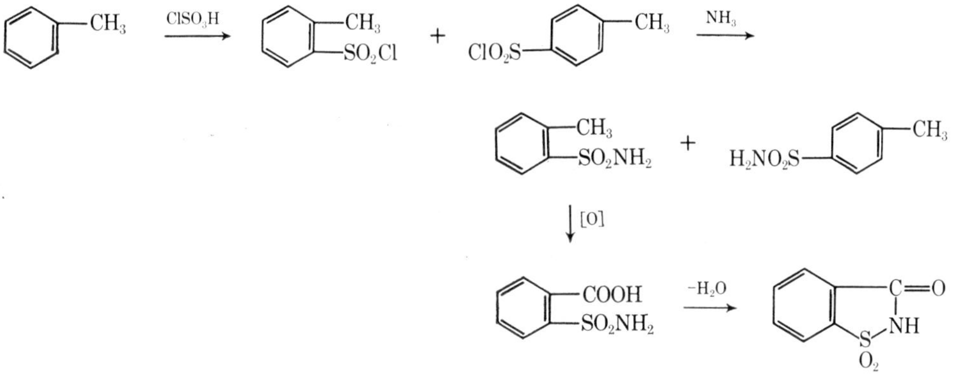

—CH₃ $\xrightarrow{ClSO_3H}$ —CH₃ —SO₂Cl   +   ClO₂S— —CH₃ $\xrightarrow{NH_3}$

—CH₃ —SO₂NH₂   +   H₂NO₂S— —CH₃

↓ [O]

—COOH —SO₂NH₂ $\xrightarrow{-H_2O}$ C=O S—NH O₂

(**1**)

product of saccharin manufacture and is used as a raw material in the production of chloramine T (see Antiseptics, Vol. 2, p. 616; Bleaching agents, Vol. 3, p. 557; Chloramines and chloroamines) and sulfonamide plasticizers (see also Sulfonamides).

Many modifications of this basic process, particularly of the oxidation step, have been proposed so as to achieve the best possible yields and conversions.   Orelup (37) mixed chromic acid with sulfuric acid at over 50% concentration, and today this is the method most widely used for oxidation.   Altwegg and Collardeau (36) found the addition of sulfates of iron, chromium, or manganese to be helpful.   In Löwe's (29) electrolytic method o-toluenesulfonamide is suspended in a weak solution of alkali carbonate,

This reaction is favored by the presence of lead, cerium, or manganese. Klages (34) used an electrolytic process with addition of permanganate as an oxygen carrier. Alkaline potassium permanganate and alkaline potassium ferricyanide have also been employed. A synthesis of saccharin based on anthranilic acid, which is commercial in the United States, is shown in Scheme 2 (11). Numerous other syntheses of sac-

Scheme 2

charin have been devised, and some of these have been used commercially in various parts of the world for one reason or another (12,16).

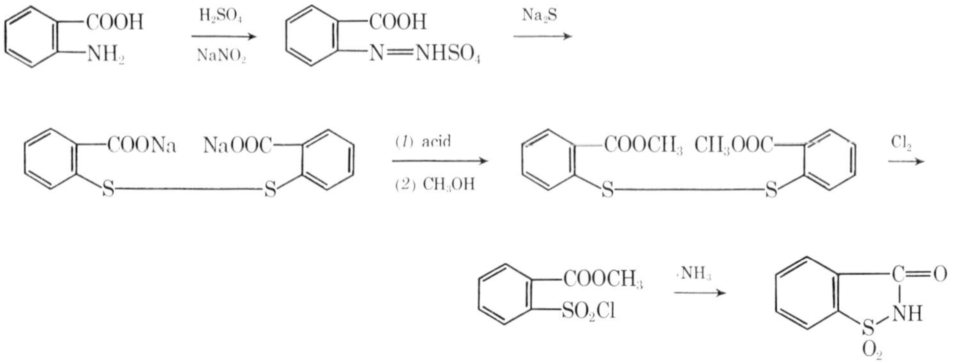

National Formulary, 12th ed. (23), and the *Food Chemicals Codex* (16a) (see also Vol. 4, p. 337) set forth specifications for saccharin, sodium saccharin, and calcium saccharin on melting point, loss on drying, heavy metals, residue on ignition, readily carbonizable substances, benzoic acid and salicylic acid, and assay. Analytical methods are also given.

Cyclamate

Sodium cyclamate (sodium cyclohexylsulfamate) (**4**) was first synthesized by Michael Sveda during the preparation of a series of sulfamates as potential antipyretics at the University of Illinois in 1937. The sweetness was discovered accidentally when Sveda noticed that his cigarette tasted sweet. He traced the taste to the chemical he had been handling, and proceeded then to investigate the taste of this chemical and of a number of analogs. Sodium cyclamate, calcium cyclamate, and cyclamic acid are used in foods, beverages, and pharmaceuticals.

Sodium cyclamate, NF XII, $C_6H_{11}NHSO_3Na$, is an odorless, white crystalline powder with an intensely sweet taste. Minimum purity is 98% after drying at 105°C for 1 hr. Loss on drying at 140°C for 2 hr is no more than 1%. One gram dissolves in about 5 ml water or in about 24 ml propylene glycol. Sodium cyclamate is insoluble in alcohol, benzene, chloroform, and ether. Aqueous solutions are neutral.

Calcium cyclamate, NF XII, $(C_6H_{11}NHSO_3)_2Ca \cdot 2H_2O$, is an odorless, white crystalline powder with an intensely sweet taste. Minimum purity is 98% on anhydrous basis. Loss on drying at 140°C for 2 hr is no more than 9%. One gram dissolves in about 4 ml water, in 60 ml ethyl alcohol, or in about 1.5 ml propylene glycol. Calcium cyclamate is insoluble in benzene, chloroform, and ether. Aqueous solutions are neutral.

Cyclamic acid, $C_6H_{11}NHSO_3H$, is an odorless, white crystalline solid with a sweet-tart taste, mp between 170 and 180°C. Minimum purity is 98% on anhydrous basis. Loss on drying at 105°C for 1 hr is no more than 1%. One gram dissolves in about 13 ml water, 25 ml ethyl alcohol, 9 ml glycerol, or 25 ml propylene glycol. Cyclamic acid is slightly soluble in chloroform and insoluble in hexane. The pH of a 10% aqueous solution is between 0.8 and 1.6.

SOLUBILITY, TASTE, USES

The cyclamates are very soluble under all conditions encountered in food processing. They have prolonged shelf life and broad compatibility with colors, flavors, food ingredients, drugs, and pharmaceutical excipients. The sweetness of the cyclamate salts relative to sucrose may vary from 25 to 140, depending upon the product in which they are used. Cyclamates are about thirty times as sweet as sucrose by dilution of solutions in distilled water to threshold sweetness. Sodium and calcium cyclamates are comparable in sweetness. The potassium and magnesium salts are also sweet, but they have limited commercial use (46a). The most widely employed cyclamate is the calcium salt, because it is suitable for sodium-restricted diets as well as for low-calorie and low-carbohydrate diets. Physical properties of the cyclamates have been described by Beck (4).

Cyclamic acid has both the tart taste of an acid and the sweetness of a cyclamate. It may be used where both tastes are desired. It is particularly useful in effervescent tablets. Cyclamic acid has flavor enhancement properties also at subthreshold levels, below 0.02% concentrations.

REACTIONS

The cyclamates generally are chemically unreactive. One of the few known reactions, the cleavage of the nitrogen–sulfur bond by nitrous acid, is the basis of the most widely used analytical methods:

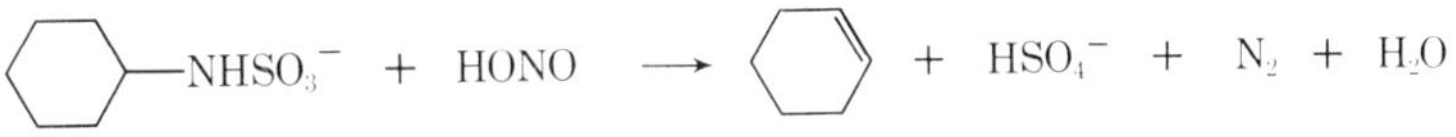

Analytically, the cyclamate can be determined either gravimetrically as the sulfate by precipitation as barium sulfate, $BaSO_4$, or titrimetically by detecting the appearance of excess nitrous acid with a starch–iodide indicator. This test is based on the stoichiometric reaction of sodium nitrite with the cyclamate present.

MANUFACTURE

The most useful methods of making cyclamates involve sulfonation of cyclohexylamine in the presence of a base. Ordinarily the sulfonation is conducted in the presence of excess cyclohexylamine, so that the cyclohexylammonium cyclamate is isolated. This so-called "double salt" can be converted to the sodium or calcium salt by treating it with sodium hydroxide, or calcium hydroxide, respectively.

The original method of Audrieth and Sveda (2,38) was sulfonation with chlorosulfonic acid (see Scheme 3), and this is a useful way of making sulfamates in the labora-

Scheme 3

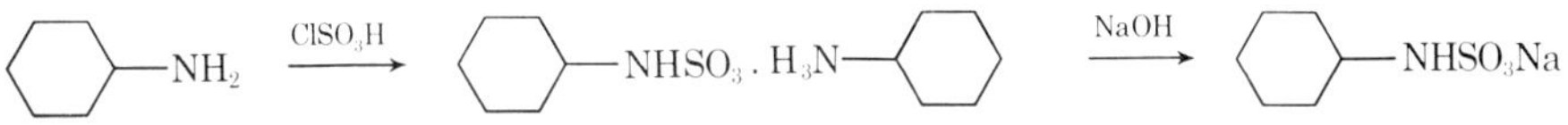

(4)

tory. Cyclohexylamine is sulfonated by dissolving it in carbon tetrachloride, cooling the solution to 5°C, and slowly adding chlorosulfonic acid. The cyclohexylammonium salt of cyclohexylsulfamic acid precipitates from the reaction mixture. This precipitate is collected by filtration and dissolved in dilute sodium hydroxide, and the mass is evaporated to dryness. The dry residue is recrystallized from water to give pure sodium cyclohexylsulfamate.

Commercial processes involve sulfonation with sulfamic acid, a sulfamate salt, or sulfur trioxide. Tertiary bases, such as triethylamine or trimethylamine, can be used as the condensing agent. It is also possible to prepare cyclamate by the catalytic reduction of phenylsulfamates. Some of these reaction schemes are outlined below. In all cases the amine salts of cyclamate can be converted to sodium, calcium, potassium, or magnesium salts by treatment with the appropriate metal hydroxide.

Syntheses have been reported that start with cyclohexylisocyanate and with cyclohexylhydroxylamine; when cyclohexylamine is used, among the sulfonating agents that have been reported are diammonium imidosulfonate and ethyl chlorosulfonate, dioxane–sulfur trioxide complex, sulfur trioxide–amine addition compounds, or ammonium nitrite sulfonate. None of them have commercial value (40,42–49,51–53).

A number of analogs of cyclamate have been made and evaluated as sweetening agents. The 3-methylcyclopentylsulfamate (**5**) is almost as sweet as cyclamate (39).

The *n*-hexyl analog (**6**), however, is not sweet; methylation of the nitrogen atom of cyclamate destroys sweetness (**7**) (2); and ring substituents generally give tasteless or bitter chemicals. Sweetness is assumed to reside with the cyclamate anion, since insoluble salts or salts which are not highly ionized in solution are not very sweet. For example, ammonium cyclamate is considerably less sweet than the sodium salt and is also considerably less highly ionized.

Dihydrochalcones

A series of intensely sweet-tasting dihydrochalcones has been developed by R. M. Horowitz and co-workers at the USDA laboratories in Pasadena, California (50). These compounds can be derived from flavone glycosides that occur naturally in citrus peels (Scheme 4).

Scheme 4

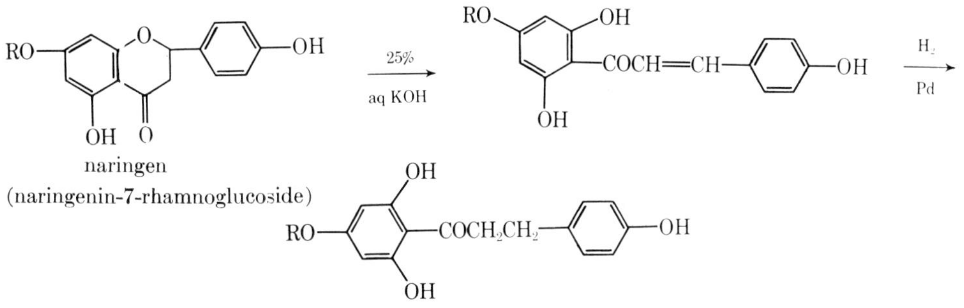

R = neohesperidosyl =

2-*O*-α-L-rhamnosyl-β-D-glusoyl (**8**)

Three dihydrochalcones of interest are naringin dihydrochalcone (**8**), neohesperidin dihydrochalcone (**9**), and hesperetin glucoside dihydrochalcone (**10**).

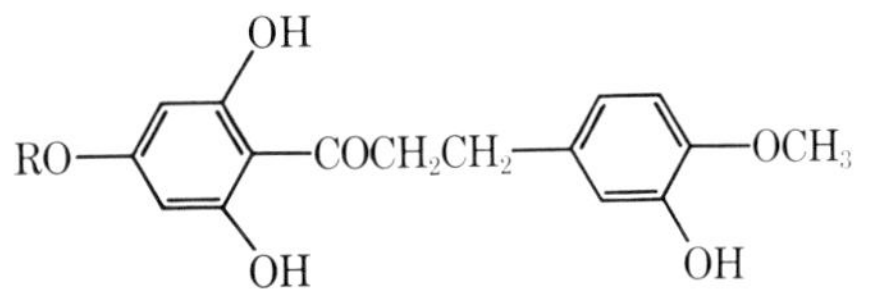

R = neohesperidosyl (**9**)

R = β-D-glucosyl (**10**)

Although naringin itself is bitter (see Vol. 8, p. 203; Vol. 10, p. 173), naringin dihydrochalcone is claimed to be as sweet as saccharin, and neohesperidin dihydrochalcone to be as much as ten times as sweet as saccharin (2000–4000 times as sweet as sucrose). Hesperetin glucoside dihydrochalcone is about seventy to 100 times as sweet as sugar. A number of other dihydrochalcone analogs have also been synthesized and evaluated as sweeteners (19). These dihydrochalcones appear to be nontoxic. However, their low solubility at acidic pH and a residual anise-type aftertaste may limit their practical uses.

Glycyrrhizin

Glycyrrhiza, or licorice, the dried rhizomes and roots of *Glycyrrhiza glabra* L., has been known for more than 4000 years. It was called "sweet root" by the Greeks. Glycyrrhiza is about fifty times as sweet as sucrose.

Glycyrrhizic acid, or **glycyrrhizin,** is extracted from glycyrrhiza. It forms intensely sweet platelets, mp 220°C, from glacial acetic acid. It is freely soluble in hot water, soluble in hot dilute alcohol, and insoluble in absolute alcohol or ether. On acid hydrolysis glycyrrhizin yields two molecules of glucuronic acid and one molecule of glycyrrhetinic acid.

The **ammonium salt of glycyrrhizic acid,** $C_{42}H_{61}O_{10}(NH_4)_3$ (**11**), is about 100 times

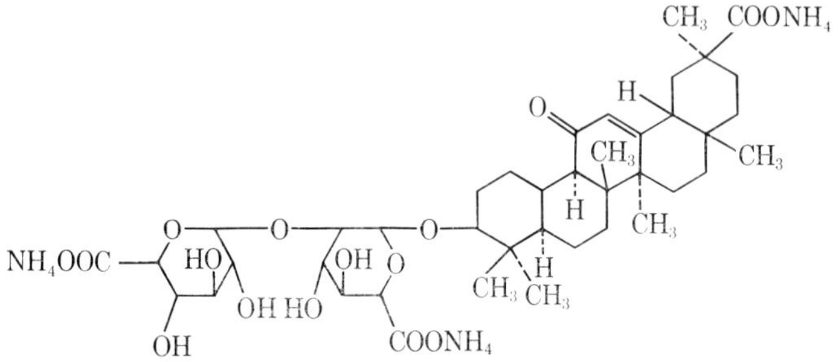

(11)

as sweet as sucrose. It also has a licorice taste, but can be used in confectionery products, frozen desserts, or liquid pharmaceuticals where both sweetness and a licorice taste may be desirable (see also Confectionery).

Aspartyl-Phenylalanine Methyl Ester

The methyl ester of the dipeptide L-asparty'-L-phenylalanine (**12**) is reported to be 100–200 times as sweet as sucrose (25a).

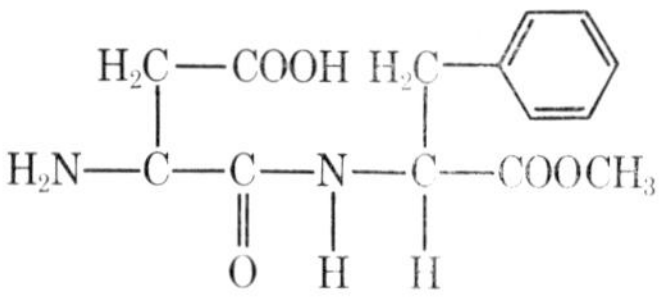

(12)

This compound was the most promising of a series of dipeptide esters prepared by R. H. Mazur and co-workers. Poor stability in acidic solutions may preclude its use in soft drinks and fruit products, but it may find application in other types of products if the FDA approves it as a food additive.

Polyols

The polyols are not nonnutritive sweeteners, although they, too, are used in special dietary foods. Sorbitol, mannitol, glycerol, and propylene glycol are the most commonly used polyols. (See also Alcohols, polyhydric; Glycerol; Glycols, Vol. 10, p. 649.)

The structural similarity of fructose, sorbitol, mannitol, and glycerol would lead one to expect these polyols to taste sweet and to become metabolized, as does fructose.

```
   CH₂OH              CH₂OH              CH₂OH              CH₂OH
    |                  |                  |                  |
    C=O           H—C—OH           HO—C—H            H—C—OH
    |                  |                  |                  |
 HO—C—H          HO—C—H           HO—C—H              CH₂OH
    |                  |                  |
  H—C—OH           H—C—OH            H—C—OH
    |                  |                  |
  H—C—OH           H—C—OH            H—C—OH
    |                  |                  |
   CH₂OH              CH₂OH              CH₂OH

   fructose           sorbitol          mannitol           glycerol
```

Sorbitol actually is metabolized and has the same caloric value as the sugars. However, it is utilized slowly and generally is assumed to have no insulin demand. Sorbitol, then, is useful as a replacement for sucrose or for glucose in foods for diabetics. It is employed in candies and confections and in ice cream–type products (see also Milk and milk products). Also, sorbitol is claimed to be less cariogenic than sucrose and is used in "sugarless" chewing gum. Since sorbitol is about half as sweet as sucrose, cyclamate or saccharin often is added with it to bring the food to the expected point of sweetness.

Mannitol is not well absorbed by the body. About half of the ingested mannitol usually is excreted unchanged, so that mannitol is assumed to furnish 2 kcal per gram instead of the 4 kcal per gram of sugars. The use of mannitol in chewable tablets is important but, in foods, is limited by cost and by the rather low laxative threshold.

Glycerol serves to depress the freezing point of low-calorie frozen foods. All of the polyols are useful as conditioning agents, especially as humectants in confections and baked goods.

Uses

Essentially the market for nonnutritive sweeteners is the market for cyclamate, saccharin, and mixtures of the two. The greatest use is for mixtures, as combinations permit higher sweetness levels with fewer aftertaste problems (27,41). These sweeteners are incorporated into a wide variety of foods, beverages, pharmaceuticals, and toiletries for a number of different reasons.

Foods and Beverages. The primary commercial use of nonnutritive sweeteners is for the production of low-calorie foods and beverages (see also Carbonated beverages, Vol. 4, p. 339). Sugars furnish four food calories (1 food calorie = 1 kcal) per gram, while cyclamate and saccharin have no food value. For weight reduction in the treatment of obesity or for weight maintenance diets, the nonnutritive sweeteners contribute palatability without calories. For example, a 12-oz bottle of carbonated beverage sweetened with sugar has about 160 food cal per bottle; with nonnutritive sweeteners the beverage has only 2 or 3 food cal from the acidulant and flavors.

Obesity has been cited as a leading health problem in the United States. Statistics show that overweight causes a decrease in life expectancy and also is associated with an increase in the incidence of heart diseases, digestive diseases, diabetes, and cancer (17). In addition to concern about health, fashion emphasis on slimness encourages weight watching by the majority of Americans.

The nonnutritive sweeteners can be used in almost any food or beverage where sweetness is desirable. They are used in bottled and canned soft drinks, soft drink powders, canned fruits and juices, puddings and gelatin desserts, salad dressings, frozen desserts, jellies and jams, metered calorie foods, and condiments. They have also been incorporated into some baked goods and candies, but not all of the technological problems in these applications have been solved. Table 2 indicates the 1965 use patterns based on tonnages of cyclamate and saccharin sold to the food industry (3).

Table 2. U.S. Use Pattern for Cyclamate and Saccharin in Foods, 1965

Use	Percent of total food use	Quantity, 1000 lb		
		Cyclamate	Saccharin	Both
carbonated beverages	53	6,060	606	6,666
dry beverage bases	17	1,944	194	2,138
diet foods	13	1,486	149	1,635
sweetener formulations	12	1,372	137	1,509
miscellaneous	5	572	57	629
total	100	11,434	1,143	12,577

Soft drinks and soft drink bases represent the largest segments of the low-calorie food industry. The consumption of tablets and sweetening solutions in the home is close to being the next-biggest use of these sweeteners. Development of markets for low-calorie baked goods and confections has been hampered by technological problems of overcoming loss of solids when sugar is removed.

Foods for Diabetics. Another major use of nonnutritive sweeteners is in the preparation of foods for diabetics. Saccharin performed this role from 1900 until 1950, when cyclamate was introduced. Now it is common to use cyclamate–saccharin mixtures in products for diabetics. Neither cyclamate nor saccharin has an insulin requirement.

Pharmaceutical Products. The nonnutritive sweeteners are widely employed in pharmaceutical products to mask the unpleasant taste of drugs. Frequently they are superior to sugars for this purpose. In addition to their ability to cover bitterness and other unpleasant tastes, nonnutritive sweeteners make it possible to formulate oral liquids with lower viscosity and fewer "cap lock" problems, as well as smaller tablets, which have better stability for longer shelf life, are nonhygroscopic, and do not caramelize in the drying or compression stage (14,20).

Toiletries. The nonnutritive sweeteners are frequently incorporated as flavoring agents in toothpaste, mouth washes, and gargles.

Table 3. How Sucrose, Cyclamate, and Saccharin Differ

Properties	Sucrose	Sodium cyclamate	Sodium saccharin
formula	$C_{12}H_{22}O_{11}$	$C_6H_{11}NHSO_3Na$	$C_6H_4CONNaSO_2 \cdot 2H_2O$
chemical class	carbohydrate	salt	salt
sweetness	1 (standard)	30–140	200–700
melting pt, °C	170–186 (dec)	480–500 (dec)	> 300 (dec)
solubility, g/100 ml	68	21	100
specific gravity	1.176 (40% soln)	1.002 (1% soln)	1.00 (0.1% soln)
relative viscosity	5.187 (40% soln)	1.004 (1% soln)	1.00 (0.1% soln)
food calories, kcal/g	4	0	0

Technological Uses. Whereas the dietary uses of nonnutritive sweeteners are based on metabolic differences between them and the nutritive sweeteners, technological differences are based on other effects of their physical and chemical properties. Some typical differences between nutritive and nonnutritive sweeteners are shown in Table 3 (7).

From this table one can envision various technological uses of nonnutritive sweeteners. For example, cyclamate can replace sucrose in the curing of bacon. When fried crisp, the bacon does not scorch, because cyclamate does not caramelize as does sugar during the frying process (5).

Economic Aspects

The production of saccharin began in 1900 and in the United States reached a peak above 500,000 lb per year during World War I, when sugar was very difficult to get. After that it remained fairly stable between 300,000 and 400,000 lb per year, until the advent of cyclamate in 1950. Initially cyclamate was quite expensive, near $4.00/lb,

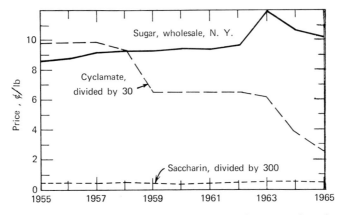

Fig. 1. Prices, in terms of equivalent sweetness, of sugar, cyclamate, and saccharin.

but improved processes, greater volume of use, and competition combined to bring the price down steadily. Both cyclamate and saccharin are considerably cheaper on a cost/use basis than are sugars, as indicated in Figure 1 (3).

The production of cyclamate and saccharin in the United States from 1957 to 1965 is shown by Table 4 (3). Combined production exceeded 15 million lb per year by 1967 (7). The price history of cyclamate and saccharin from 1955 to 1967 is illustrated by Table 5 (3).

It is not possible to convert tons of nonnutritive sweeteners used exactly into tons of sugar replaced because the perception of sweetness of cyclamate and saccharin

Table 4. U.S. Production of Cyclamate and Saccharin, million lb

Year	Cyclamate	Saccharin
1957	0.5	1.5
1960	1.25	1.75
1963	4.25	1.5
1964	9.7	2.4
1965	10.3	2.6
1967	15.0	3.4

Table 5. Average U.S. Selling Price, $/lb

Year	Cyclamate	Soluble saccharin
1955	2.95	1.60
1959	1.95	1.57
1963	1.86	1.60
1965	0.80	1.40
1967	0.55	1.17

relative to sugar is so variable (see footnote to Table 1). Also, it is impossible to measure the impact of nonnutritive sweeteners on the nutritive sweetener markets with complete accuracy because some uses of nonnutritive sweeteners are supplemental (direct sugar replacement cannot be said to be involved in the case of new products not formerly made with or without sugar).

Outlook

The markets for low-calorie foods should increase as more variety and better-quality products become available. Technological uses based on differences in physical properties between nonnutritive sweeteners and sugars may continue to be developed. Although new sweetening agents will no doubt be found, any nonnutritive sweetener must meet costly FDA requirements for proof of safety. Additionally, a new sweetener must face the competition of cyclamate and saccharin, which are well established and inexpensive.

Bibliography

1. Amerine, M. A., R. M. Pangborn, and E. B. Roessler, *Principles of Sensory Evaluation of Food*, Academic Press, Inc., New York, 1965.
2. Audrieth, L. F., and M. Sveda, *J. Org. Chem.* **9**, 89 (1944).
3. Ballinger, R. A., *Agri. Econ. Rept. No. 113*, Economic Research Service, USDA, 1967.
4. Beck, K. M., *Food Technol.* **11** (3), 156 (1957).
5. Beck, K. M., R. L. Jones, and L. W. Murphy, *Food Eng.* **30**, 114 (May 1958).
6. Beck, K. M., *Food Prod. Develop.* **1** (1), 19 (Feb.–March 1967).
7. Beck, K. M., *Amer. Chem. Soc. Div. Marketing & Economics Papers* **9** (1), 294 (April 1968).
8. A. Chattaway, *J. Chem. Soc.* **87**, 1884 (1905).
9. Berlinerblau, J., *J. Prakt. Chem.* **30**, 103 (1883).
10. Beyer, O., *Handbuch der Saccharin-Fabrikation*, Rascher & Co., Zürich, 1923.
11. *Chem. Eng.* **61** (7), 128 (1954).
12. Dalal, N. B., and R. C. Shah, *Current Sci. (India)* **18**, 440 (1949); (through) *Chem. Abstr.* **44**, 4881c (1950).
13. DeGarmo, O., G. Ashworth, C. Eaker, and R. J. Munch, *J. Amer. Pharm. Assoc. Sci. Ed.* **41**, (1), 17 (1952).
14. Endicott, C. J., and H. M. Gross, *Drug Cosmetic Ind.* **85**, 176 (1959).
15. Fahlberg, C., and I. Remsen, *Chem. Ber.* **12**, 469 (1879).
16. Field Information Agency, *Office Tech. Services Rept.*, PB-901 (Oct. 10, 1945).
16a. Food Protection Committee, NAS–NRC, *Food Chemicals Codex*, Publ. No. 1406, National Academy of Sciences–National Research Council, Washington, D.C., 1966.
17. *J. Obesity* **1**, 16 (1964).
18. Karrar, P., *Organic Chemistry*, 4th Engl. ed., transl. by A. J. Mee, Elsevier Publishing Co., New York, 1950.
19. Krbechek, L., G. Inglett, M. Holik, B. Dowling, R. Wagner, and R. Riter, *J. Agr. Food Chem.* **16** (1), 108 (1968).

20. Lynch, M. J., and H. M. Gross, *Drug Cosmetic Ind.* **87**, 324 (Sept. 1960).
21. Mameli, E., and A. Mannessier-Mameli, *Gazz. Chim. Ital.* **70**, 855 (1940).
22. Moncrieff, R. W., *The Chemical Senses*, 3rd ed., CRC Press, Cleveland, Ohio, 1967.
23. *National Formulary*, 12th ed., Mack Printing Co., Easton, Pa., 1965.
24. Salant, A., *Handbook of Food Additives*, Chemical Rubber Co., Cleveland, Ohio, 1968, Chap. 14.
25. Sanders, H. J., *Chem. Eng. News* **44**, 100 (Oct. 10, 1966) and 108 (Oct. 17, 1966).
25a. *Science* **162**, 1511 (Dec. 27, 1968).
25b. The Ad hoc Committee on Nonnutritive Sweeteners, Food Protection Committee, NAS–NRC, *Nonnutritive Sweeteners* (An Interim Report to the U.S. Food and Drug Administration, Dept. of Health, Education, and Welfare), National Academy of Sciences–National Research Council, Washington, D.C., Nov. 1968.
26. *United States Pharmacopeia*, 17th revision, Mack Printing Co., Easton, Pa., 1965.
27. Vincent, H. C., M. J. Lynch, F. M. Pohley, F. J. Helgren, and F. J. Kirchmeyer, *J. Amer. Pharm. Assoc. Sci. Ed.* **44**, 442 (July 1955).
28. Wicker, R. J., *Chem. Ind.*, 1708 (Oct. 8, 1966).
29. Brit. Pat. 174,913 (Jan. 5, 1922), H. Löwe.
30. Brit. Pat. 662,800 (Dec. 12, 1951), (Abbott Laboratories).
31. Brit. Pat. 669,200 (March 26, 1962), (Abbott Laboratories).
32. Brit. Pat. 930,289 (July 3, 1963), (Abbott Laboratories).
33. Can. Pat. 770,637 (Oct. 31, 1967), V. D. Shah (Abbott Laboratories).
34. Swiss Pat. 78,277 (Nov. 1, 1918), W. Klages.
35. U.S. Pat. 319,082 (June 2, 1885), C. Fahlberg.
36. U.S. Pat. 1,507,565 (Sept. 9, 1924), J. Altwegg and J. Collardeau (Société Chimique des Usines du Rhône).
37. U.S. Pat. 1,601,505 (Sept. 28, 1926), J. Orelup.
38. U.S. Pat. 2,275,125 (March 3, 1942), L. F. Audrieth and M. Sveda (E. I. du Pont de Nemours & Co., Inc.).
39. U.S. Pat. 2,785,195 (March 12, 1957), K. M. Beck and A. W. Weston (Abbott Laboratories).
40. U.S. Pat. 2,800,501 (July 23, 1957), W. W. Thompson (Du Pont).
41. U.S. Pat. 2,803,551 (Aug. 20, 1957), F. J. Helgren (Abbott Laboratories).
42. U.S. Pat. 2,804,472 (Aug. 27, 1957), D. J. Loder (Du Pont).
43. U.S. Pat. 2,804,477 (Aug. 27, 1957), H. S. McQuaid (Du Pont).
44. U.S. Pat. 2,805,124 (Sept. 3, 1957), W. W. Thompson (Du Pont).
45. U.S. Pat. 2,814,640 (Nov. 26, 1957), D. R. V. Golding (Du Pont).
46. U.S. Pat. 2,826,605 (March 11, 1958), W. W. Thompson (Du Pont).
46a. U.S. Pat. 2,845,353 (July 29, 1958), Charles Riffkin and Gilman N. Cyr (Olin Mathieson Chemical Corp.).
47. U.S. Pat. 3,043,864 (July 10, 1952), N. Okuda and K. Suzuki (Daiichi Seiyaku Co.).
48. U.S. Pat. 3,060,231 (Oct. 23, 1962), P. Mueller and R. Trefzer (Ciba Corp.).
49. U.S. Pat. 3,082,247 (March 19, 1963), M. Freifelder (Abbott Laboratories).
50. U.S. Pat. 3,087,821 (April 30, 1963), R. M. Horowitz and B. Gentili (U.S.A. Secretary of Agriculture).
51. U.S. Pat. 3,194,833 (July 13, 1965), M. Freifelder and B. Meltsner (Abbott Laboratories).
52. U.S. Pat. 3,361,799 (Jan, 2, 1968), O. G. Birsten and J. Rosin (Baldwin-Montrose).
53. U.S. Pat. 3,366,670 (Jan. 30, 1968), O. G. Birsten and J. Rosin (Baldwin-Montrose).

KARL M. BECK
Abbott Laboratories

SYNDETS. See Surfactants.

SYNTANS. See Leather, Vol. 12, p. 325.

SYNTHESIS GAS. See Ammonia; Gas, manufactured; Methanol.

T

TACK. See Rubber compounding, Vol. 17, p. 626.

TACONITE. See Iron, Vol. 12, p. 7.

TALC

The term "talc" covers a wide range of natural minerals, most of which are high magnesium silicates. It is a hydrous magnesium silicate, $Mg_3SiO_{10}(OH)_2$, theoretically 31.7% MgO, 63.5% SiO_2, and 4.8% H_2O. The mineral talc is usually, although not always, a major constituent of mineral mixtures offered commercially as "talc."

Minerals commonly associated with talc are tremolite ($CaMg_3(SiO_3)_4$), serpentine ($3MgO.2SiO_2.2H_2O$), anthophyllite (($OH)_2.Mg_7.(Si_4O_{11})_2$), and chlorite. The latter is a talclike mineral in which varying proportions of aluminum are substituted for magnesium in the brucite layer. (Prochlorite, for example, is $9MgO.3Al_2O_3.5SiO_2.-8H_2O$.) Impurities such as dolomite ($Ca, MgCO_3$), calcite ($CaCO_3$), iron oxide, carbon, quartz, and manganese oxide may also be present, although these limit the commercial value of the talc.

Talc deposits probably were formed by hydrothermal alteration or contact metamorphism of preexisting rocks. The degree of alteration and the nature of the rocks from which the talc was formed largely determine purity and particle form. The whiter, purer talcs derive chiefly from dolomite and dolomitic limestone; those from ultrabasic igneous rocks usually contain intermediate minerals, such as serpentine.

Generally speaking, the purest talcs have the greatest commercial value. Those used for cosmetics, pharmaceuticals, selective adsorption, and electrical ceramics approach theoretical purity and are also characterized by a white color.

Talc, soapstone, and pyrophyllite are grouped together by the U.S. Bureau of Mines for reporting purposes, although they differ in physical and chemical properties, as well as in end use. *Soapstone* is a talclike material of varying composition, but it contains impurities which prevent its use in applications requiring white color or chemical purity. *Pyrophyllite* is the aluminum analog of talc, having a theoretical composition $Al_2SiO_4O_{10}(OH)_2$. It has many of the characteristics of talc, and may be substituted for it in some applications.

Properties

Pure talc mineral is characterized by softness (Mohs scale 1), hydrophobic surface properties, and slippery feel. The crystal form may be foliated, lamellar, fibrous, or massive. Although pure talc is the standard for softness on the Mohs scale, some commercial talcs may exhibit harder properties because of the presence of impurities and associated minerals, such as dolomite, calcite, tremolite, and quartz. The electron micrograph in Figure 1 illustrates the lamellar structure of a relatively pure Montana talc.

Crude talcs range in color from white to green and brown. After being ground to powder form, all pure talcs are varying degrees of white. A typical sample of high-quality talc will give a reading of 90–95% General Electric brightness. High-quality talcs in oil or plasticizer suspensions range from 40 to 60% reflectance, and are blue-white to yellowish in cast.

The index of refraction of talc is 1.54–1.59 and specific gravity is 2.7–2.8. Pure talc is heat-stable up to 900°C. Differential thermal analysis (see Thermal analysis) shows a major peak at 900–1000°C, representing an endotherm caused by loss of the chemically combined water of the talc mineral. A minor peak at 710°C may be present, corresponding to the loss of CO_2 from a small amount of dolomite.

Figure 2 illustrates the structure of pure talc mineral. It consists of a brucite sheet sandwiched between two silica sheets, forming talc layers which are superimposed indefinitely. Each layer is electrically neutral; adjacent layers are held together only by weak van der Waals forces. The characteristic slippery property of talc results from these layers sliding over one another.

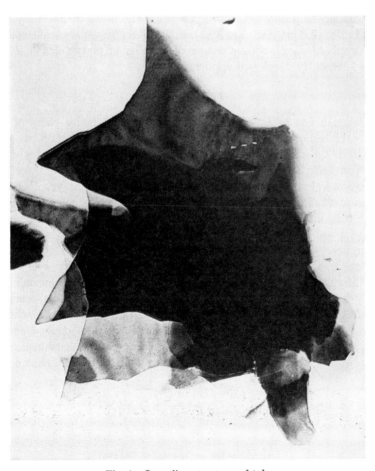

Fig. 1. Lamellar structure of talc.

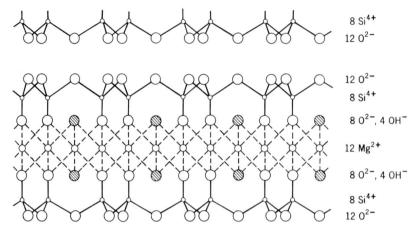

Fig. 2. Crystal structure of pure talc mineral, $(OH)_8Mg_{12}Si_{16}O_{40}$ or $(OH)_2Mg_3(Si_2O_5)_2$.

Talc is inert in most chemical reagents, although it exhibits a marked alkaline pH (typically 9.0–9.5). It is, however, soluble in hot concentrated phosphoric acid. Its cation exchange capacity is also very low, on the order of 2.4 meq/100 g for a finely ground talc (17.6 m²/g surface area).

The hydrophobic/organophilic nature of lamellar or platy talcs is of importance in a number of recently developed applications.

Occurrence

Talc, although not as common as clay, is found in many parts of the world. Deposits of real international importance, however, can be counted on two hands.

The United States is the world's largest producer of talc. The states of New York, California, Vermont, Texas, and Montana, in that order, account for more than three fourths of a volume now (1969) approaching 1 million tons/yr. New York talc, which occurs in St. Lawrence County, while of good, white color, is intimately associated with tremolite. This enhances its value in the production of ceramic wall tile, but restricts its use to applications where softness, slip, and hydrophobicity are of minor importance. California talcs occur in and around Death Valley and vary widely from very pure talc to tremolite, depending on location. All commercial deposits are characterized by excellent whiteness. Vermont talcs found near Johnson and Windsor are relatively impure and require special processing for applications demanding high quality. Montana talcs from mines near Cameron and Dillon approach theoretical purity, have good color, and are strongly hydrophobic. Texas talcs from Hudspeth County in western Texas are contaminated with carbon and dolomite, which restricts their use to ceramics; the carbon goes off in the form of oxides below the maturing temperature of ceramic wall tile.

Although the U.S. Bureau of Mines lists Japan as the largest producer of talc, that country produces no high-quality mineral, only soapstone and pyrophyllite. Actually, Japan imports a substantial amount of talc from the Peoples' Republic of China (Manchuria), Korea, India, and the U.S.S.R., the principal Asian sources of talc. Western Europe is a major source of talc. Although France produces a greater tonnage of the mineral, the first-quality cosmetic-grade talc comes from Italy. Western Australia has recently become an important source of high-quality talc. Most of its product is sold in Europe to the electrical ceramics (steatite) industry.

Mining and Processing

Mining methods vary from straightforward drill-blast-shovel open pits to complicated, carefully timbered underground operations. Where color and chemical purity are important, screening, washing, and selection by hand or electron beam may be used.

Traditional processing involves crushing with jaw and/or gyratory crushers; rotary or flash drying, if necessary; and milling with roller-type or ball/pebble mills. Maximum particle size is controlled by air classification. The product is collected in cyclones. For dust control "baghouse" dust collectors are used. These materials are normally ground to a specification of $99+\%$ through a 200 mesh (74 μ) or $99+\%$ through a 325 mesh (44 μ). An increasing proportion of talc produced is to subsieve specification, which in the talc industry means 30 μ or smaller. Some materials are reduced to a maximum particle size of 6 μ, in fluid-energy equipment using superheated steam. Such products have a mean surface diameter of under 1 μ, and specific surfaces approaching 20 m^2/g. The term Mistron, and related expressions such as Mistron Vapor and Mistron Frost, are trademarks of United Sierra Division, Cyprus Mines Corporation, describing such ultrafine talcs.

There are a number of methods of reducing talc to subsieve maximum particle size. In most cases, these depend on high energy input (fluid energy using superheated steam or ultrahigh-speed vertical hammer mills); but in some cases air classification with or without mechanical rotors is used to remove oversized particles from conventionally milled talc. Classification products are not the same as ultrafine grinds, since different particle-size distribution and specific surface result from the two approaches. See Size reduction; Size measurement of particles.

Wet-processing of talcs became significant during the 1960s. Talcs which are unsuitable in their natural state for high-quality end uses are upgraded by flotation and acid leaching to the degree of chemical purity and color needed.

Specifications and Standards

Most talcs have brand names which define the properties of interest to the user. Differences in source and type of raw material, particle shape, impurity limits, fired and unfired color, particle-size distribution, surface area, and oil and water adsorption distinguish various brands. There are a number of more general talc specifications. *The U.S. Pharmacopoeia XVII* specifies impurity limits for talc. The Toilet Goods Association Specification No. 10 (Talc) has its own version. The U.S. Government publishes a series of property and performance specifications in its Federal Specification No. TT-P-403A for paints, while ASTM Standards No. D-605-66T apply as industry standards for the same use.

Analytical and Test Methods

Chemical analysis for talc involves solubilizing by fusion with alkalis and subsequent detection of magnesia and silica by chemical means. Routine chemical analysis would normally also detect oxides of calcium, iron, and alkalis. x-Ray fluorescence is commonly used for talc chemical analysis, without fusion of the talc.

Differential thermal analysis and x-ray crystallography show characteristic patterns for talc and its associated minerals and principal impurities. Particle-size distribution is normally determined by sedimentation methods; for many applications, Hegman gage readings provide an excellent and quick measurement of maximum particle size. Specific surface is determined by techniques based on B-E-T nitrogen gas adsorption. (See Vol. 1, p. 431.)

There is a wide range of special tests to identify properties of importance to consumers. Some of the properties often tested are oil absorption, color, bulk density (fluffed and packed), and abrasiveness.

Economic Aspects

The world total of talc business may surprise those who think of talc only as face powder.

The U.S. Bureau of Mines reports world production of the talc group as being about 4 million tons in 1967. A good estimate of value of this tonnage would be $75,000,000.

Table 1 gives a rough breakdown of the world production pattern.

Prices vary widely, depending on chemical purity, fineness of grind, color, and slip. Roofing-grade talc (ground and packed in bags) from Vermont or Texas sells for as little as $15.00/ton. Ultrafine talcs from Montana and cosmetic talcs from Italy command more than $100.00/short ton.

Table 1. World Production of Talc and Soapstone

Source	Approx tonnage, 1000 short tons	Approx value, $1000	Major markets	Major end uses
North America	800	20,000	world	ceramics, paint, paper, cosmetics
Western Europe	500	20,000	world	paper, ceramics, paint, cosmetics
Far East, India, and Australia	400	10,000	Eastern Asia, Europe	paint, cosmetics, ceramics
South America	100	5,000	local	roofing, insecticides, rubber
subtotal	1,800	55,000		
others (including U.S.S.R.)	500			
		20,000		
pyrophyllite (all countries)	1,700			
total	4,000	75,000		

Uses

Ceramics has been the largest consumer in the United States of talc-group minerals for more than two decades. This is attributable to the fact that virtually all of the ceramic wall tile produced in the U.S.A. contains a large percentage (up to 65%) of talc (usually tremolitic) or pyrophyllite. The value of talc in preventing delayed glaze crazing, lowering firing temperatures, and reducing fired shrinkage account for its widespread use in this country.

In Europe an important use of talc is in ceramics; electrical ceramics and steatite applications, however, outweigh wall tile. Talcs of high chemical purity and granular particle structure are the bases for low-loss insulators used in a wide variety of electronic and electrical uses.

The next most important application in the U.S.A., and probably for world talc consumption as well, is in protective coatings. Talc improves exterior durability, controls viscosity, brushing and gloss properties, as well as reducing paint formulation costs.

The world paper industry is a major talc consumer. Talc use in the U.S.A. has shifted from ordinary filler to control of pitch and other oleoresinous impurities during the last fifteen years. Ultrafine, high-purity, platy, particle-shaped talcs of high specific surface selectively adsorb these impurities and prevent their deposit on pulp- and paper-making machinery. In Europe and Japan, use as an inexpensive filler continues to overshadow more technical applications.

The cosmetics and pharmaceuticals industries are important talc consumers. Face and body powder, as well as tablets and pills, require talc of excellent purity, color, and slip. Within the last five years, because of improved processing methods, the U.S.A. has succeeded in becoming nearly self-sufficient in producing this type of talc, and thus no longer relies on Italy for its major supply.

Other major end uses of talc are as insecticide carriers, as rubber dusting and textile filling materials, and as an additive in asphalt roofing compounds. These account for large tonnage, but a relatively small proportion of total value, since they usually need only low-quality talcs.

New uses which depend on selective adsorption or organic preference are rubber and plastics reinforcing and oil-spill cleanup.

Bibliography

"Talc" in *ECT* 1st ed., Vol. 13, pp. 566–572, by Hans Thurnauer, American Lava Corporation.

General References

G. W. Brindley and Irene S. Stemple, "A Structural Study of Talc and Talc-Tremolite Relations," *J. Am. Cer. Soc.* **43** (1), 34–42 (1960).

Emerson W. Emrich, "Tremolitic Talc—Its Modern Role in Ceramics," *J. Can. Cer. Soc.* **31** (1962), 52–60.

A. E. J. Engel and Lauren A. Wright, "Talc and Soapstone," in *Industrial Minerals and Rocks*, 3rd ed., American Institute of Mining, Metallurgical, and Petroleum Engineers, 1960, pp. 835–850.

W. W. Gaskins, "Historical Background Development on Use of Talc in Ceramic Bodies," *Am. Cer. Soc. Bull.* **31** (10), 392–395 (1952).

H. T. Mulryan, "Talc," *Paper AIME Southwest Metals and Minerals Conference, May 17, 1968.*

Thornton L. Neathery, Herbert P. LeVan, H. William Ahrenholz, and James F. O'Neill, *Talc and Asbestos at Dadeville, Ala.,* Report of Investigations 7045, U.S. Dept. of Interior, Bureau of Mines, U.S. Govt. Printing Office, Washington, D.C., November 1967.

J. A. Pask and M. F. Warner, "Fundamental Studies of Talc: Construction of Talcs," *J. Am. Cer. Soc.* **37** (3), 118–128 (1954). (A superb reference on the theoretical composition of talc and related minerals.)

Malcolm Ross, William L. Smith, and William H. Ashton, "Triclinic Talc and Associated Amphiboles from Gouverneur Mining District, New York," *Am. Mineralogist* **53,** 751–769 (May–June, 1968).

Hans Thurnauer and A. R. Rodriguez, "Notes on the Constitution of Steatite," *J. Am. Cer. Soc.* **25** (15), 443–450 (1942).

Minerals Yearbook, U.S. Dept. of Interior, Bureau of Mines, U.S. Govt. Printing Office, Washington, D.C., 1967.

Mistrons for Paper Applications, Brochure 1-Pr, United Sierra Division, Cyprus Mines Corp., Trenton, N.J.

Talcs for Protective Coatings, Brochure 1-Pt, United Sierra Division, Cyprus Mines Corp., Trenton, N.J.

Mistron Vapor in Rubber Compounds, Brochure 3-R, United Sierra Division, Cyprus Mines Corp., Trenton, N.J.

Mistron Vapor and Mistron ZSC for Oil Slick Cleanup, Technical Bulletin, United Sierra Division, Cyprus Mines Corp., Trenton, N.J., May 15, 1968.

Lauren A. Wright, *Talc and Soapstone*, Bulletin 176, Mineral Commodities of California, California Division of Mines, Dec. 1957, pp. 623–634.

Cosmetic and Pharmaceutical Data Book, Whittaker, Clark, and Daniels, Inc., New York, 1964.

Paint Data Book, Whittaker, Clark, and Daniels, Inc., New York, 1964.

H. T. MULRYAN
United Sierra Division
Cyprus Mines Corporation

TALCUM POWDER.   See Cosmetics, Vol. 6, p. 360.

D-**TALITOL,** $CH_2OH(CHOH)_4CH_2OH$.   See Alcohols, polyhydric, Vol. 1, p. 575.

TALL OIL

Tall oil is the major by-product of the kraft or sulfate pulping process. It is a mixture of rosin and fatty acids together with unsaponifiables. It is obtained by the acidification of the rosin and fatty acid sodium soaps recovered from the concentrated black liquor in the kraft or sulfate pulping process. See also Fatty acids; Pulp; Terpenes.

The Swedish pulp industry made the first contribution to the name "tall oil." From their sulfate pulp process, they obtained an oil by-product which they called "tallolja" from the Swedish word "tall," which means pine, and the suffix "olja," which means oil. Thus, the literal translation is "pine oil." Since pine oil was already an established article of commerce both in the United States and Europe, this caused confusion. The new "pine oil" was an entirely different type of product. The Germans cleared the confusion by giving to the material the name "tallöl." This combined the Swedish word for pine and the German word "öl," meaning oil. In the United States, the decision was made to use the "tall" portion of the word, but to translate literally the "öl" portion; thus the name or term "tall oil" was developed (1).

The domestic production of crude tall oil has grown at a very rapid rate since World War II: 150,000 tons in 1952; 320,000 tons in 1957; 450,000 tons in 1962; and an estimated 625,000 tons in 1968. Further increases in production depend upon the growth of the sulfate kraft pulp industry and improved methods for the recovery of the sodium soaps.

Recovery of the Sodium Soaps from Sulfate Liquors

In the sulfate or kraft process, the chipped pine wood is digested with a solution of sodium sulfide, Na_2S, sodium hydroxide, NaOH, and sodium carbonate, Na_2CO_3. The digestion proceeds, under high temperature and pressure, in a vessel called a digester.

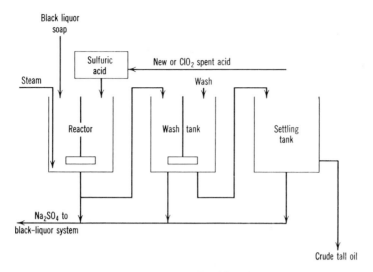

Fig. 1. Crude-tall-oil batch acidulation process.

During the digestion or pulping process, the cellulose fibers are released from other wood constituents. The highly alkaline solution, or "white liquor," used in the digestion process forms soluble sodium salts of the lignin, the rosin, and the fatty acids, the fatty acids originally having been present as esters. The soaps and spent cooking liquor are washed from the wood pulp by water, and this wash solution is added to the black liquor which separates from the pulp as the entire mass is blown from the digester into the blow pit or receiving tank. The black liquor and the soap solution washed from the pulp are concentrated in multiple-effect evaporators to about 15 to 50% solids. As the total solids content of the black liquor is increased by the process of evaporation, the soap rises to the surface of the liquor. The soap is skimmed mechanically from the surface of the black liquor at a concentration of 21–28% solids. The skimming operation is carried out in a tank which receives the liquor from, usually, the fourth effect of the evaporators and returns it to the third effect. If the concentrated black liquor is allowed to cool, the soap will rise to the surface, but because of the economics involved in the operation of the evaporators, this is not always possible. The soap must be recovered or skimmed continuously at the established temperature existing between the two effects. By removing the soap from the black liquor during the evaporation process, the fouling of the evaporator tubes is minimized, and the evaporators may be operated more efficiently.

There are several different designs of skim tanks or soap separating tanks, but usually a simple tank for retention time is adequate. The soap skim tank usually contains one or more baffle plates in order to prevent channeling of the liquor as it flows from the inlet to the outlet. The soap is removed by means of a mechanically operated sweep or a drag chain to which small steel plates have been attached. The soap is pumped continuously away from the removal point, and the skimmed liquor is returned continuously to the evaporators.

The soap skimmings contain approximately 55% resin and fatty acids, as sodium salts, 35% water, and 10% black-liquor solids. The fuel value is in the range of 8000–9000 Btu/lb if the resinate is burned in the recovery units.

Maximum yields of soap have been reported from loblolly pine and longleaf pine, ranging from 180 to 300 lb of soap per air-dry ton of pulp. The equivalent yield of tall oil would be in the range of 95–159 lb per ton of pulp.

The sodium soap or resinate skimmed from the surface of the black liquor is pumped into storage tanks. During the storage period, any entrained black liquor settles out and is returned to the pulp-mill black-liquor system.

If the soap is to be acidified, and not sold as "raw soap," it is boiled with sulfuric acid either by batch or continuous operation, as shown in Figures 1 and 2.

The reactor for the batch system of converting the soap must be a steel tank lined with acid-resistant tile. The equipment for the continuous acidification process is usually made of type 316 S.S. (stainless steel).

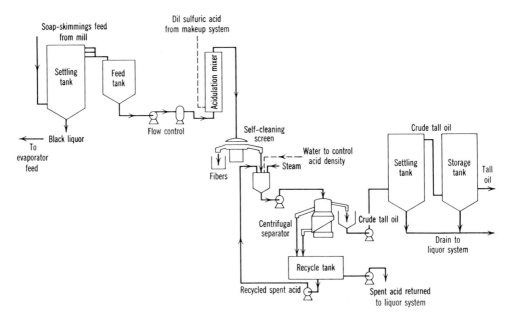

Fig. 2. Continuous tall-oil acidulation process.

The acidification converts the sodium soaps to free rosin and fatty acids. The strength of the acid should be in the range of 5–9N, whether it is fresh 66°Bé sulfuric acid or chlorine dioxide spent acid from the chlorine dioxide generators used for producing the bleaching agent for the pulp bleaching process. The reaction mixture, containing the liberated tall oil, is either allowed to settle or fed into a centrifuge. Three phases are formed: the clear, brown tall oil; the lignin-fiber phase; and the spent-acid phase. After the crude tall oil has been removed from the reaction mixture, the other two phases are returned to the pulp-mill black-liquor system; these phases may or may not be neutralized before entering the black-liquor system. The crude tall oil is washed with hot water to remove residual sulfuric acid, and then allowed to settle in storage tanks to reduce the water content. The settled oil must meet specifications on moisture, ash, acid number, etc, and, if within these specifications, it is ready for shipment or further processing into raw materials for the chemical industry.

Composition and Refining

The main components of crude tall oil are fatty acids, rosin acids, and unsaponifiables. These are the same components as are found in the ether extractives of the pine wood. A number of articles have been written describing the composition of various tall oils from different parts of the United States, Canada, and Scandinavia. Compositions of some crude tall oils are shown in Table 1 (1). The composition is dependent primarily upon the geographic location where the pine trees are grown.

Table 1. Composition of Some Crude Tall Oils

Pine-tree source	Fatty acids, %	Rosin acids, %	Neutral fraction, %
Swedish	40–58	30–50	6–15
Finnish	37–59	32–49	6.8–11.3
Finnish (whole trees)	29–36	52–57	9–11
Finnish (sawmill waste)	49–62	30–39	5–12
Danish	50	43	6.7
American	18–53	35–65	8–24
Canadian mixed sample	46	28	25
S. E. Virginian	55–56	39–40	4.8–5.8
N. E. North Carolinan	53–54	40–41	5.3–6.1
S. W. North Carolinan	51–53	41–42	6.1–6.9
E. Central S. Carolinan	46–48	45–47	6.2–7.4
E. Central Georgian	45–48	45–48	6.2–7.4
S. E. Georgian	43–46	47–51	6.3–7.4
S. E. Texan	45–48	46–48	5.3–7.1

Crude whole tall oil is composed of fatty acids, rosin acids, and unsaponifiables or sterols. Even though the demand for the crude continues to rise and new uses for it are constantly being found, its use is still limited due to its disagreeable, mercaptan-like odor and dark-brown color. The rosin acid content decreases the value of the fatty acids in the soap industry, while the rosin acids cannot be used for sizing paper unless they contain a very low fatty acid content; however, if the components are separated, each one becomes very valuable and much better opportunities for sale are realized.

A great number of refining methods have been developed, physical, chemical, and combinations of both. Some of the methods are for improving the color and odor of the whole crude oil, while others are for separating the various components almost completely.

Table 2. Distilled Tall Oil, Composition and Properties

Average composition, %		Typical properties	
fatty acids	60–85	color, Gardner	4–12
rosin	14–37	sp gr, 25°C (77°F)	0.940–0.950
neutral materials	1–3	acid number	180–190
		saponification number	185–195
		viscosity (Gardner-Holdt)	B–E
		flash point (open cup), °C (°F)	182–210 (360–410)

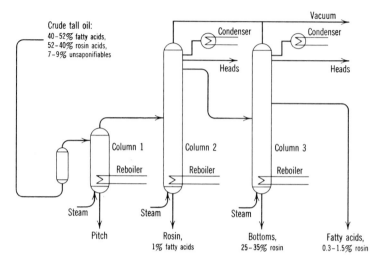

Fig. 3. Tall-oil fractionation.

Most of the components in crude tall oil are decomposed or transformed when subjected to high temperatures. Therefore, to prevent decomposition, the distillation is usually carried out under high vacuum and in the presence of superheated steam. The separation obtained by simple distillation is generally very small and is limited to the removal of the most evil-smelling first cut and the dark pitchlike residue from the rosin and fatty acids. A typical analysis of distilled tall oil is shown in Table 2 (2).

Due to the quality of the distilled tall oil, its use as a raw material for more valuable products is limited and, therefore, the use of fractionating columns has become almost standard practice in the refining processes for tall oil.

A typical fractional distillation process is shown in Figure 3 (3). The crude oil is first dehydrated, then passed through a heat exchanger in order to increase the temperature of the oil entering the flash feeder and the stripping tower. Pitch is removed from the bottom of the stripping tower, and the rosin, fatty acids, and neutrals are taken overhead to a fractionating tower. From this first fractionating tower, a pure rosin is obtained from the bottom of the tower, an odor or heads cut from the top of the tower, and an intermediate fatty acid cut from near the top of the tower. The intermediate fatty acid cut is fed into either another fractionating tower or the same tower. High-purity fatty acids are taken off from the mid-section of the tower, odor and heads cut from the top of the tower, and distilled tall oil from the bottom of the tower.

Processing crude tall oil by fractionation yields the following percentages (2): fatty acids, 25%; rosin acids, 40%; secondary products composed of distilled tall oil,

Table 3. Properties of Major Tall-Oil Fatty Acids

Common name	Systematic name	Mp, °C	Bp, °C(mm)
palmitic	hexadecanoic	62.9	352(760)
palmitoleic	9-hexadecenoic	−1.5	
steric	octadecanoic	69.9	376(760)
oleic	*cis*-9-octadecenoic	13.4	250(30)
linoleic	*cis*-9-, *cis*-12-octa-decadienoic	−6.5	202(1.4)

Table 4. Tall-Oil Rosin, Composition and Properties

Average composition, %		Typical properties	
rosin acids	90–95	color, USDA rosin scale	X–N
fatty acids	2–3	acid number	162–172
neutral materials	3–7	saponification number	170–180
		softening point, °C (°F)	73–83 (163–181)

Table 5. Tall-Oil Heads, Composition and Properties

Average composition, %		Typical properties	
rosin	0.1–1.5	color, Gardner	10–18
fatty acids	40–75	acid number	75–150
neutral materials	25–60	saponification number	105–180
		sp gr, 25°C (77°F)	0.911–0.920
		flash point (open cup), °C (°F)	188–199 (370–390)

heads, and tall-oil pitch, 35%. The properties of these products are given in Tables 3, 4, and 5 (2).

Composition of Tall-Oil Pitch. Tall-oil pitch is the residue remaining after the distillation and fractionation of tall oil. Enkvist has studied tall-oil pitch in great detail. The pitch contains decomposition products of rosin and fatty acids, such as rosin anhydrides, estolides, and hydrocarbons resulting from the dehydration and decarboxylation of rosin and fatty acids. There are also hydroxy acids of both the rosin and the fatty type as well as higher alcohols, sterols, hydrocarbons, and sulfur lignin. The composition and properties of tall-oil pitch are given in Table 6 (2).

Table 6. Tall-Oil Pitch, Composition and Properties

Average composition, %		Typical properties	
rosin acids and esters	12–30	color, Gardner, 5% in benzene	11–18
fatty acids and esters	35–50	acid number	20–60
		saponification number	80–135
neutral materials	20–35	sp gr, 25°C (77°F)	0.990–1.010
		softening point, °C (°F)	25–55 (77–131)
		flash point (open cup), °C (°F)	260–271 (500–520)

Refining of Crude Tall Oil with Adsorbents. The improvement in color and odor which may be obtained through the use of bleaching clays, activated carbon, and silica gel is rather small compared to that obtained by distilling the crude oil. This method, therefore, is used only in combination with other physical methods.

Combined Chemical and Physical Treatments. Due to the high viscosity of the crude oil, treatment directly with a chemical agent is difficult and costly unless the oil is diluted with a water-insoluble solvent. The solvent selected should be one in which oxy rosin and oxy fatty acids are insoluble; for example, petroleum ether or naphtha.

The chemical refining of the solution is usually made with strong sulfuric acid. Most of the color bodies, odor bodies, and the unsaponifiables are condensed to tarlike products. The temperature, during the addition of the acid and during the period of

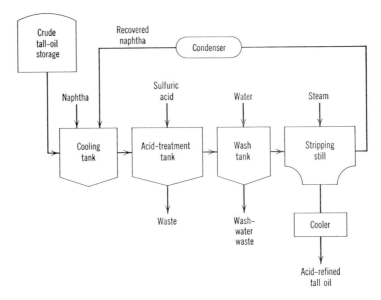

Fig. 4. Acid refining process for tall oil.

treatment, must be held in the range of 0–20°C. This is necessary in order to reduce the risk of side reactions which will reduce the yield of refined product. Sulfuric acid above 90% concn is generally used. After the treatment, the oil–solvent solution is removed from the tarlike impurities and given several water washes in order to remove the residual sulfuric acid and the sulfonation products formed. The solvent must be removed by steam stripping in order to prevent deterioration of the color of the oil.

The composition and properties of acid-refined tall oil are given in Table 7 (2). A flow diagram of the process is shown in Figure 4 (2).

Table 7. Acid-Refined Tall Oil, Composition and Properties

Average composition, %		Typical properties	
fatty acids	50–70	color, Gardner	8–12
rosin	25–42	sp gr, 25°C (77°F)	0.900–1.000
neutral materials	5–7	acid number	155–170
		saponification number	160–175
		viscosity (Gardner-Holdt)	Z–Z$_2$
		flash point (open cup)	204–216 (400–420)

Continuous Methods. Continuous extraction has been used extensively in the refining and separation of fats and fatty acids other than tall-oil fatty acids. The Solexol process, developed by the M. W. Kellogg Company, uses propane and has been applied to the process of separating the fatty and rosin acids in tall oil. The Pittsburgh Plate Glass Company method uses furfural, sometimes mixed with naphtha. The separation of the fatty acids from the rosin acids by these processes is far from complete and the degree of purity of the products is not high.

The yields of fatty and rosin acids obtained from the continuous extraction method of refining crude tall oil are higher than those obtained by distillation, but the operating costs are higher and the separated products cannot be used as extensively as the pure components from the fractionation process.

Various other refining methods have been developed, such as neutralization, separation, thermal methods, partial cracking, and partial condensation, but none of these have found widespread application in the industrial fields.

Composition of the Fatty Acids. The fatty acids in tall oil are mixtures of mostly 18-carbon, unsaturated acids. The acids are oleic, linoleic, and saturated fatty acids.

The saturated fatty acids consist mainly of palmitic acid, but include minor quantities of stearic, lignoceric (C_{24}), and cerotic (C_{26}) acids. Also, there is a small percentage of palmitoleic acid, which is generally listed as oleic.

Typical composition of tall-oil fatty acids in low-rosin tall-oil fatty acids is shown in Table 8 (2). The properties of commercial-type tall-oil fatty acids are given in Table 9 (2).

Table 8. Typical Composition of Tall-Oil Fatty Acids in Low-Rosin Tall-Oil Fatty Acids

Fatty acids	% in low-rosin tall-oil fatty acids
palmitic	1
palmitoleic	
stearic	2
oleic	51
linoleic (nonconjugated)	40
linoleic (conjugated)	5
unknown	4

Table 9. Properties of Commercial-Type Tall-Oil Fatty Acids

	Type I[a]		Type II[a]		Type III[a]	
	Min	Max	Min	Max	Min	Max
acid number	197		192		190	
rosin acids, %		1.0		2.0		10.0
neutral materials, %		1.0		2.0		10.0
fatty acids, %	98		96		90	
color, Gardner		4		5		10.0
iodine number	125	135				

[a] Grouped by rosin content.

General Reactions of Tall-Oil Fatty Acids

Fatty acids are capable of undergoing many types of reactions, including condensation and polymerization, oxidation, halogenation, dehydration, and isomerization, as well as conversion into numerous derivatives such as amides, amines, nitriles, alcohols, mono- and polyesters, sulfates, and sulfonates.

For the fatty acid molecule, the two general points of reaction are (1) the carboxyl group and the methylene group activated by it, and (2) the double bond in unsaturated acids and the adjacent allylic methylene group. The reactive points for oleic acid are shown on the following page (3):

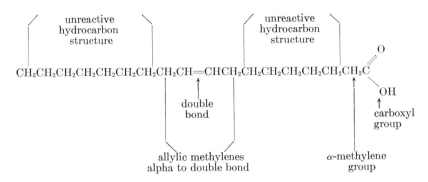

Salt and Soap Formation. Salts are formed by the reaction or treatment of a fatty acid with a base or base-exchange salt. The sodium, potassium, and ammonium salts are water soluble, and, therefore, are used widely in the preparation of detergents and wetting and emulsifying agents. Water-insoluble salts such as lead, aluminum, and calcium are used in the production of greases. Heavy-metal salts of the unsaturated acids such as lead, manganese, and cobalt are used primarily as driers in the protective-coating industry. Metallic salts such as sodium, calcium, tin, lead, and zinc are used as catalysts for various chemical reactions. See Driers and metallic soaps.

The metallic salts of the fatty acids are produced by replacing the hydrogen of the carboxyl group with a metal. This can be carried out by the action of a base, hydroxide, or oxide on a fatty acid, or by double decomposition of a soluble salt of a fatty acid and a salt of a mineral acid, or by saponification of glycerides or other esters of fatty acids with a base on metallic oxide. The reactions are:

$$C_{17}H_{33}COOH + NaOH \rightarrow C_{17}H_{33}COONa + H_2O$$

$$2\ C_{17}H_{33}COONa + MgCl_2 \rightarrow (C_{17}H_{33}COO)_2Mg + 2\ NaCl$$

Esters. Esters of tall oil are formed by the action of an alcohol on a tall-oil fatty acid. If the alcohol is monohydric, one molecule of water is liberated. The reverse reaction is hydrolysis:

$$RCOOH + R'OH \leftrightharpoons RCOOR' + H_2O$$

If the alcohol is polyhydric, such as glycerol, one molecule of water is liberated for each of the three hydroxyl groups:

$$
\begin{array}{ccc}
CH_2OH & & CH_2OOCR \\
3\ RCOOH + CHOH & \rightarrow & CHOOCR + 3H_2O \\
CH_2OH & & CH_2OOCR
\end{array}
$$

The fatty acids esterify more rapidly than the rosin acids. The esterification of tall-oil fatty acids is carried out at an elevated temperature or with the aid of an acid catalyst such as H_2SO_4, HCl, or H_3PO_4. In order to carry the reaction to completion (reduce the acid number to the lowest possible value), either an excess of alcohol must be used, or else the water formed during the reaction must be removed as the reaction proceeds (2).

Amides. Replacement by an NH_2 group of the hydroxyl group in the carboxyl of the fatty acids results in the formation of the corresponding amides. This replacement may be accomplished directly from the acids or indirectly from acid anhydrides, acid halides ammonium salts, or amines. One method for accomplishing this is to react the fatty acid with ammonia to form the ammonia soap which undergoes dehydration to the amides:

$$RCOOH + NH_3 \rightarrow RCOONH_4$$

$$RCOONH_4 \rightarrow RCONH_2 + H_2O$$

At high temperatures the amide is converted to the nitrile:

$$RCONH_2 \rightarrow RC \equiv N$$

The nitrile reacted with hydrogen forms the amine:

$$RC \equiv N + 2\ H_2 \rightarrow RCH_2NH_2$$

The acid amides made by the use of the tall-oil fatty acids are useful as waterproofing agents, protective coatings, paper sizes, lubricant modifiers, and plasticizers.

Reactions at the Double Bonds. When heated to high temperatures under pressure, concentrated aqueous soaps of linoleic and linolenic acids undergo isomerization.

Oxidation. Linoleic acid, if quantitatively split by oxidation at both double bonds without subsequent oxidation of the primary oxidation products, will produce one mole each of the following acids: caproic, malonic, and azelaic. Linolenic acid under similar oxidative conditions will produce one mole propionic, two moles malonic, and one mole azelaic acid. The primary product formed by the fission may be partly or completely oxidized to lower-molecular-weight acids, and, therefore, may not produce one mole of each.

Oxidative cleavage is the process of rupture of the ethylenic linkage in the carbon chain followed by oxidation of the cleaved carbons to carboxyl groups. If the starting raw material is an unsaturated acid, such as oleic acid, which contains a carboxyl group at the terminal position, then the fragments of oxidative cleavage will be a mono- and a dibasic acid (3).

Agents such as ozone, chromic acid, permanganate, or nitric acid are used to cause oxidative cleavage of the double bond.

There are two types of permanganate oxidation: (1) oxidation in aqueous alkaline media at low temperatures, 0–30°C, and (2) oxidation in nonaqueous (acetone) or acidic media at elevated temperatures. This second type produces fission products through rupture of the molecule at the double bonds. Fission generally results when highly unsaturated acids are oxidized at 0°C, in fairly concentrated aqueous sodium carbonate–potassium permanganate solutions.

The cleavage products have many potential uses, due to the fact that the dibasic acid recovered is a basic raw material for the production of polymers, plasticizers, and lubricants.

Hydrogenation. The product formed from hydrogenation is either completely or partially saturated. With the addition of one mole of hydrogen to a molar quantity of oleic acid a mole of stearic acid is produced:

$$CH_3(CH_2)_7C \!\!=\!\! C(CH_2)_7\ COOH \xrightarrow{\ H_2\ } CH_3(CH_2)_7C \!\!-\!\! C(CH_2)_7COOH$$

For the production of hydrogenated products on either an industrial scale or in the laboratory, only four catalysts have been found to be satisfactory. These are platinum, palladium, nickel, and copper chromite. Only the nickel and chromite are used on an industrial scale. The reaction takes place under pressure, from atmospheric to 400 atm, and at temperatures from room temperature to 400°C. Higher pressures are more desirable than higher temperatures. If the nickel catalyst is used for the saturation of the double bonds of the fatty acids, molecular hydrogen and low temperatures and pressures are used. For the reduction of carboxyl groups, copper chromite catalyst and fairly high pressures and temperatures are employed.

Halogenation. Halogenation serves as a basis for analytical methods used in determining the degree of unsaturation of fatty acids and glycerides. These methods require the addition of iodine, chlorine, or bromine to the double bonds which are present in the reacting acid or ester. When iodine monochloride is used in this method, the iodine value or amount of iodine absorbed gives a measure of the amount of unsaturated acids present (4).

Fatty Acid Sulfates and Sulfonates. If sulfuric acid is added to a double bond with the formation of a carbon–oxygen–sulfur linkage, the reaction is known as sulfation and the product known as a sulfate:

$$—C{=}C— + H_2SO_4 \rightarrow \underset{\overset{|}{H}\quad\overset{|}{OSO_3H}}{—C{-}C—}$$

If the acid is added with the formation of a carbon–sulfur linkage, the reaction is known as sulfonation, and the product is a sulfonate:

$$—C{=}C— + H_2SO_4 \rightarrow \underset{\overset{|}{H}\quad\overset{|}{SO_3H}}{—C{-}C}$$

True sulfonic acids may be prepared by several methods, but particularly by carrying out the sulfonation in a fairly anhydrous medium.

The "sulfonated" oils and acids available on the market consist of various mixtures of sulfated oil, sulfated acids, lower esters of sulfuric acid esters, hydroxy acids, etc, depending on the nature of the raw material and the conditions of "sulfonation" (sulfation). When fatty acids are treated with sulfuric acid under special conditions, only small proportions of sulfonated derivatives are produced, with some exceptions. It is for this reason that the process is often called sulfation rather than sulfonation.

Sulfonated oils are valuable not only because of the many raw materials from which they can be made, but also because of the variety of end products that can be prepared from one and the same raw material.

Polymerization. In order to achieve polymer formation, a minimum number of functional groups are required to be present. In the case of fatty acids the functional groups may be unsaturated linkages, hydroxyl groups, and carboxyl groups, two or more of which must be present in heat-polymerization reactions; the saturated acids cannot undergo heat polymerization per se. However, if only double bonds are present then only addition polymerizations are possible. The heat polymerization of the nonconjugated fatty acids such as linoleic and linolenic cannot take place through a diene mechanism unless a previous shift of isolated to conjugated double bonds has taken place (4).

Applications of Tall Oil

The production of tall oil is not related to that of industrial vegetable oils, including edible oils, which fluctuate frequently with the supply and demand for agricultural

Table 10. Applications of Tall-Oil Fatty Acids

Applications	Total production, %
protective coatings, inks, and metallic driers	30
soaps and detergents	15
flotation acids and collectors	9
esters, plasticizers, and chemical intermediates	30
miscellaneous	16

products. Due to the low cost and availability of crude tall oil, many applications have been found for it as well as for the separated fractions, fatty acids, rosin acids, and pitch. Some of the principal industrial applications of tall-oil fatty acids are given in Table 10.

The use of tall-oil fatty acids has grown at a rapid rate in the surface-coatings industry, due to the abundant supply and low cost. The coating vehicles produced have exceptional color stability and nonyellowing characteristics due to the absence of triene acids in the tall-oil fatty acids.

Tall-oil fatty acids used for modifying alkyd resins give specific improved properties, due to the lack of trienes, over saturated coconut or unsaturated soya and linseed oils. Color retention is much better due to the absence of linolenic acid. Speed of drying is greatest with linolenic acid. Intermediate with linoleic, an alkyd made with oleic, is nondrying. However, the degree of yellowing follows the same tendency, the alkyd made with linolenic acid being the first to yellow.

Phthalic anhydride is the major polybasic acid used in the production of alkyds, and glycerol and pentaerythritol are the principal polyhydric alcohols. Tall-oil fatty acids are used in producing short-oil baking alkyds (solvent or fusion process), medium-oil alkyds (fusion process), and long-oil alkyds (fusion process). Solubility of the oil-modified resins varies with the oil length. As the percentage of fatty acids used in making the alkyd is increased, greater compatibility with petroleum thinners will be obtained, and therefore reduced cost. The long-oil resins generally are used for exterior applications and the medium- and short-oil resins for interior applications.

Metallic Driers. During World War II, when naphthenic acids were in short supply, the use of tall-oil soaps as metallic driers increased rapidly. Lead, manganese, cobalt, and other metals are used as driers or catalysts for promoting oxidation.

The tallate driers have higher specific gravities than the naphthenate driers, a higher nonvolatile content, and a drying action comparable to that of naphthenate driers. See Driers and metallic soaps.

Tall-Oil Esters. Tall-oil fatty acids react with alcohols to produce esters. The reaction is reversible and, therefore, the esters may be hydrolyzed to give acids and alcohols. The type and relative quantity of the alcohol and acid used and the reaction temperature determine the point of equilibrium.

Esters of tall oil are used in the making of vehicles for paints and varnishes, printing inks, core oils, putty, and calking compounds.

Surfactants. The interaction of tall oil with ethylene oxide yields an ether ester. Esters of this type form the basis for nonionic detergents. They have low foam level and are compatible with both anionic and cationic detergents. See Surfactants.

Saponification Products. Tall-oil fatty acids may be saponified by treatment with bases. The alkali metal hydroxides form the basis for the preparation of hard soaps, soap powders, liquid soaps, jellied soaps, water-soluble soaps of various types, and soaps which serve as emulsifying agents for insecticides and disinfectants. They are also of value in making drycleaning soaps, soaps used as emulsifiers for lubricating oils in the preparation of cutting oils, soaps which emulsify petroleum oils in the formulation of stamping and drawing compounds, soaps used for metal cleaning and degreasing, and soaps used for rubber polymerization.

Tall-Oil Rosin and Pitch

Composition of Rosin and Unsaponifiables. The rosin acids in tall oil are identical with those found in wood and gum rosin: they are diterpene carboxylic acids. The main constituent is abietic acid which is in equilibrium with its isomer, neoabietic acid. See Terpenes and terpenoids.

Tall oil also contains other rosin acids which differ from abietic, either in the number or location of the double bonds or in the structure of the side chain. The distribution of these acids in tall-oil rosin estimated by Harris (5) are as shown in Table 11.

Table 11. Distribution of Rosin Acids in Tall Oil

Rosin acid	%	Rosin acid	%
abietic acid	30–40	dehydroabietic acid	5
neoabietic acid	10–20	dextropimaric acid	8
dihydroabietic acid	14	isodextropimaric acid	8
tetrahydroabietic acid	14		

The unsaponifiable matter in tall oil is a mixture of hydrocarbons, long-chain alcohols, and sterols. The hydrocarbons are formed from the decarboxylation of rosin acids. The high-molecular-weight monohydric alcohols are mainly phytosterols, but there are also small percentages of lignoceryl (C_{24}) alcohol and β-sitosterol. The approximate percentages of these components are: lignoceryl alcohol, 10%; β-sitosterol, 30%; hydrocarbons, 60%.

Reactions of Tall-Oil Rosin. Most of the chemical reactions of tall-oil rosin are due mainly to the presence of the carboxyl group. The rosin acids react with alkali to form soaps:

$$RCOOH + NaOH \rightarrow RCOONa + H_2O$$

The rosin acids also react with metallic oxides and metallic hydroxides to form soaps.

The acids can also be esterified with monohydric or polyhydric alcohols. The esterification of rosin acids requires high temperature and pressure equipment when using the lower-boiling alcohols. They may also be etherified with ethylene oxide to form nonionic surfactants.

The rosin acids react with ammonia to form ammonia soaps which undergo dehydration to amides:

$$RCOOH + NH_3 \rightarrow RCOONH_4$$
$$RCOONH_4 \rightarrow RCONH_2 + H_2O$$

At high temperatures the amide is converted to the nitrile:

$$RCONH_2 \rightarrow R\equiv CN$$

The nitrile may be hydrogenated to form the amine:

$$RC{\equiv}N + 2\,H_2 \rightarrow RCH_2NH_2$$

Due to the tertiary carboxyl gorup, the rosin acids are susceptible to decarboxylation by heat treatment in the presence of mineral acids or at temperatures above $275°C$:

$$RCOOH \rightarrow RH + CO_2$$

The unsaturated rosin acids undergo many reactions involving the double-bond linkage: reactions such as hydrogenation, disproportionation, polymerization, and condensation with maleic anhydride. In the latter reaction, the conjugated double bonds appearing in a single-ring nucleus of the levopimaric structure are responsible for the maleic anhydride reaction, which is essentially the same as the Diels-Alder reaction.

Uses of Rosin Acids. The most common process of separating the rosin acids from the fatty acids in tall oil is that of fractional distillation. Almost complete separations are obtained and the rosin is equivalent to gum and wood rosin. See Rosin.

Hydroabietyl alcohol is used as a resin and as a plasticizer in the protective coatings industry and also as an intermediate in the preparation of ether and ester derivatives. The viscous, water-white alcohol is made by the hydrogenation of the methyl ester of rosin.

Phenolic resins made with tall-oil products have many applications in surface coatings, printing inks, adhesives, binders for flooring, and other surface compositions. The tall oil imparts flexibility and toughness to the phenol–formaldehyde resins.

Rosin soaps are used to emulsify the monomers with water as the first step in the polymerization (emulsion polymerization) for making synthetic rubber (SBR and neoprene). Disproportionated rosin accounts for over 50% of the consumption of polymerization emulsifiers. Disproportionated rosin is rosin that has been modified to make it more resistant to air oxidation. Modification is rapid if the rosin is heated with a catalyst such as sulfur, selenium, iodine, or noble metal; however, heating to a high temperature without a catalyst will also cause the shift in hydrogen between the rosin acids, converting abietic acid to dehydroabietic acid with the formation of smaller amounts of the other pyroabietic-type rosin acids.

Tall-Oil Pitch. This is the residue from the bottom of the stripping tower during the flash-distillation step prior to separating the fatty acids from the resin acids by fractionation.

Tall-oil pitch is used as an emulsifying agent for asphalt emulsions in the manufacture of weather-resistant fiberboard; it has also found extensive use in the manufacture of adhesives and printing inks. The polyol esters of tall-oil pitch modified with maleic anhydride are used in enamels for drums and coatings for underground pipe lines.

Specifications and Test Methods

Methods of analyzing whole or refined tall oils have been standardized by the American Society for Testing and Materials and by the American Oil Chemists' Society.

The principal specifications for testing tall oil are listed in Table 12 (2). Individual suppliers of crude tall oil or tall-oil products have developed modified and simplified methods which meet individual needs. Gas-chromatographic methods are used extensively for determining the individual components in the rosin and fatty acids.

Table 12. Testing Specifications for Tall Oil

Specification	Distilled oils, fatty acids, heads		Pitch	Rosin
	AOCS Spec	ASTM Spec	ASTM Spec	ASTM Spec
acid number	Tela–64T	D 803–61		D 465–59
ash	Tm 1a–64	D 803–61	D 803–61	D 1063–51
color, Gardner		D 803–61		
color, Rosin				D 509–55
fatty acids		D 803–61	D 803–61	D 1585–63
flash and fire point	Tn 1a–64	D 803–61	D 803–61	D 803–61
color after heating	Td 3a–64	D 1981–61		
iodine value[a]	Tg 1a–64T	D 1959–61	D 1959–61	
moisture	Ca 2a–45	D 803–61	D 803–61	
refractive index	Tp 1a–64	D 555–61	D 555–61	
rosin acid, less than 15%	Ts 1a–64	D 1240–54		
rosin acid, more than 15%		D 803–61	D 803–61	D 1585–63
sampling	Ta 1a–64T	D 1466–61	D 1466–61	D 509–55
saponification value	Tl 1a–64	D 803–61	D 803–61	D 464–59
softening point			E 28–58T	E 28–58T
specific gravity	To 1a–64	D 1963–61	D 1963–61	D 1963–61
titer	Tr 1a–64	D 1982–61		
unsaponifiables	Ca 6b–53	D 803–61	D 803–61	D 1065–56
viscosity (Gardner-Holdt)	Tq 1a–64T	D 803–61		
viscosity (SFS)			E 102–62	

[a] Not reliable in presence of high rosin and neutral materials content.

Storage and Shipping

Storage tanks for crude tall oil are usually made of steel, and should be equipped for heating and have a bottom drain and a manhole for clean-out. If the heat is internal, the coils should be of type 316 S.S., and placed at least six inches above the bottom of the tank. A more economical method of heating is to place the coils on the outside bottom of the tank. This allows removal of the coils in case of leaks and facilitates maintenance. External heat exchangers are sometimes used in place of the steam coils. Centrifugal pumps with steam-jacketed casings are generally recommended, although other types of pumps may be used. Pipe lines are usually of steel, at least 3 in. diam, steam traced and insulated. The oil in storage should be held between 120 and 140°F to facilitate pumping and handling.

Crude tall oil is shipped in 8000-, 10,000-, 12,000-, and 20,000-gal tank cars and also shipped in 55-gal steel drums. The tank cars must be equipped with steam coils in order to facilitate unloading. Loaded drums are best heated in a "hot-room" or a box equipped with a steam coil. A temperature of 175°F is usually sufficient to dissolve the rosin acid crystals.

Tall-oil fatty acids are shipped in 4000-, 8000-, and 10,000-gal aluminum or resin-lined tank cars and in resin-lined 55-gal drums. These fatty acids require the same precautions in storage and handling as other fatty acids of the semidrying type, such as soya fatty acids. Storage tanks of aluminum are recommended as the best type, although phenolic-resin-coated steel tanks are also recommended. A blanket of inert gas should be kept over the acids in order to prevent oxidation. Type 316 S.S. is recommended for pumps, heating coils, processing kettles, and pipe lines. Metals such as bronze, brass, copper, and iron must be avoided, as these metals are oxidation catalysts and cause darkening of the acids. Distilled tall oil requires the same precautions in storage and handling as the tall-oil fatty acids. Tall-oil rosin is usually shipped in galvanized iron drums.

There are two precautions that must be observed in the handling process; one is to prevent crystallization, the other to prevent oxidation.

Oxidation does not occur during normal handling operations; however, if the rosin is in a molten condition under prolonged storage or at a temperature above 300°F, a blanket of inert gas must be provided in order to prevent darkening. Crystallization can be avoided or prevented if certain precautions are followed: these are (*1*) to pass through the critical temperature range 190–280°F as quickly as possible, (*2*) to store melted rosin above 280°F, and (*3*) to avoid decarboxylation by holding the processing temperature below 570°F.

Rosin, when heated, will melt into a clear liquid at a temperature of about 212°F, whereupon crystallization and solidification may take place. If this happens, then the rosin will remelt only if heated above 280°F.

Bibliography

"Tall Oil" in *ECT* 1st ed., Vol. 13, pp. 572–577, by R. H. Stevens, Herty Foundation.

1. William Brushwell, *Am. Paint J.*, **38** (Aug. 6, 1954).
2. Pulp Chemicals Association, Tall Oil Products Division, *Tall Oil and Its Uses*, F. W. Dodge Corp., New York, 1965.
3. E. Scott Pattison, *Industrial Fatty Acids and Their Applications*, Reinhold Publishing Corp., New York, 1959.
4. K. S. Markley, *Fatty Acids*, Interscience Publishers, Inc., New York, 1947.
5. G. C. Harris, *Tappi Monograph Ser.* No. 6, 167 (1948).

DAN C. TATE
U. S. Plywood-
Champion Papers Inc.

TALLOW. See Fats and fatty oils; Meats and meat products, Vol. 13, p. 183.

TANKAGE. See Feeds, animal, Vol. 8, p. 866.

TANK CARS. See Packaging, Vol. 14, p. 434.

TANNIC ACID, TANNING MATERIALS. See Leather and leather processing.

TANTALUM AND TANTALUM COMPOUNDS

Tantalum, Ta, at. no. 73, at. wt 180.948, sp gr 16.6, mp 2996°C, appears in group VA of the periodic table directly below niobium (qv) with which it is closely associated in nature and to which it is very similar in its properties. Tantalum has only one natural isotope, ^{181}Ta, but several radioactive isotopes have been made. The most common valence of the element is 5.

Tantalum is best known as a refractory metal with a combination of unique properties which make it useful in a number of unrelated commercial applications. It is very ductile and can be worked cold into fine wire or thin foil. It is completely inert to strong acids at ordinary temperatures and yet is very reactive to almost all substances at high temperatures.

The history of tantalum begins with its discovery by Ekeberg in 1802. His difficulty in finding a solvent for the oxide prompted him to name the element tantalum in honor of the mythological Tantalus. The work of Ekeberg and that of Hatchett (1), discoverer of columbium in 1803, do not report the presence of two elements (tantalum and niobium) in their earth oxides, so it might be assumed that they both were working with mixtures of the two elements. In 1844, H. Rose (2) reported that there were two similar elements in the earth oxides obtained from columbite; he referred to one as tantalum and named the other niobium (for Niobe, daughter of Tantalus). Any remaining confusion was removed in 1866 when Marignac (3) made his classical separation of tantalum and niobium by means of the difference in the solubilities of their complex potassium fluorides.

The first ductile tantalum was made by W. von Bolton in Germany in 1903, and tantalum was first used commercially as a filament in electric lamps. About 11 million tantalum lamps were made before tungsten wire replaced tantalum for this application in 1909. From then until 1922 the uses of tantalum were limited to certain dental and surgical instruments. Tantalum was first produced in the U.S.A. in the laboratory of Fansteel Inc., North Chicago, Ill., by C. W. Balke in 1922 and has been in continuous commercial production since that time. The production and use of tantalum have increased greatly since 1950 and there is no reason to believe that this trend should not continue.

The appearance of three books (4–6) devoted entirely to tantalum and niobium (columbium) and a comprehensive treatment of tantalum in another (7) testify to the growing interest in these metals.

Occurrence

Tantalum is found in a number of oxide minerals (8) (see Table 1), which almost invariably contain niobium also. It does not occur naturally in the free state. The most important tantalum-bearing minerals are tantalite and columbite which are variations of the same natural compound $(Fe,Mn)(Ta,Nb)_2O_6$. The mineral is called tantalite when the tantalum pentoxide (Ta_2O_5) content exceeds the niobium pentoxide (Nb_2O_5) content. Columbite is considered an ore of tantalum when it contains 20% or more of Ta_2O_5. Other tantalum minerals except microlite have little or no significance as sources of tantalum.

Tantalite–columbite occurs in some pegmatites in quantities which seldom exceed a few pounds per ton and in alluvium derived from such pegmatites. Although the mineral is found in many places in North America, there is no important mining for it

Table 1. Tantalum Minerals

Name	Composition	Ta_2O_5 content, %	Color and luster	Sp gr	Mohs hardness	Crystal structure	Streak
tantalite–columbite	$(Fe,Mn)(Ta,Nb)_2O_6$	0–86	black, metallic	5.2–7.8	$6-6\frac{1}{2}$	orthorhombic	brown to black
manganotantalite	$Mn(Ta,Nb)_2O_6$	40–82	black, metallic	6.0–7.8	$6-6\frac{1}{2}$	orthorhombic	brown to black
tapiolite	$Fe(Ta,Nb)_2O_6$	40–85	black, metallic	6.0–7.8	$6-6\frac{1}{2}$	tetragonal	brown to black
skogbolite	$FeTa_2O_6$	86	black, metallic	7.8	$6\frac{1}{2}$	tetragonal	brown to black
microlite	$Ca_2(Ta,Nb)_2O_6(OH,F)$	60–70	pale yellow to light brown, nonmetallic	5.2–6.2	$5\frac{1}{2}$	isometric	light gray
simpsonite or calogerasite	$Al_2Ta_2O_8$ + CaO as an impurity	70–72	cream to gray, non-metallic	5.9–6.5	$6\frac{1}{2}-7$	hexagonal	white to pale yellow
thoreaulite	$SnTa_2O_7$ + CaO and Nb_2O_5 as impurities	60–75	white to light brown or gray, nonmetallic	7.6–7.9	6	monoclinic	white to pale yellow
stibiotantalite	$(Sb,Bi)(Ta,Nb)O_4$	35–60	dark to light brown, resinous	5.5–7.5	5–7	orthorhombic	light yellow
yttrotantalite	$(Fe,Ca)_2(Y,Er,Ce,U)_2(Ta,Nb)_4O_{15}$ + 4 H_2O	30–45	black, vitreous	5.5–6.8	$5-5\frac{1}{2}$	orthorhombic	gray to light brown
tanteuxenite	$(Y,Er,Ce,U)(Ta,Nb)(Ti)O_6$	20–55	black or brown, resinous	5.5–5.9	$5\frac{1}{2}-6\frac{1}{2}$	orthorhombic	gray to light brown

in this country.   Much of tantalum ore used in the United States prior to about 1939 was mined from a rich alluvial deposit in the Pilbarra District of northwestern Australia.   The mineral concentrate, which was mined by the most primitive methods, contained from 60 to 70% Ta_2O_5.   Much of the tantalite concentrates used in the United States since 1945 has been obtained as a by-product of tin mining in the Republic of Congo (Kinshasa).   The cassiterite and tantalite–columbite are concentrated together and then separated magnetically.   Although the Congo is still a major source of tantalum ores, several other areas throughout the world are now important contributors.   Brazil has recently become a very important source of tantalum ore.   The mineral is mined in many places by numerous small operators using rather primitive methods.   It is often co-mined with other values, particularly beryl.   A total of 1.5 million lb of tantalum concentrates was imported during 1968; the main suppliers were the Democratic Republic of the Congo (Kinshasa) and Brazil, 25% each; Mozambique, 24%; and Australia, 5%.

The relatively small amount of tantalum in the earth's crust and low concentrations in known deposits keep the cost of Ta_2O_5 in ore concentrates quite high.   Also, increasing demand, irregular production of ore, and warehousing of the concentrates by users cause the price to vary considerably from year to year and, for spot ore, from month to month.   The average estimated price per lb of Ta_2O_5 in 30% ore for the years 1962–1968 are shown below.

Year	1962	1963	1964	1965	1966	1967	1968
Price, $	9.50	3.60	3.00	4.75	8.00	12.25	8.00–14.00

Tin Slags.   Cassiterite deposits, such as those found in the Republic of Congo and in Nigeria, Portugal, Malaya, and Thailand, contain important amounts of tantalite–columbite and probably thoreaulite.   During the concentration of the tin mineral, much of the tantalum and niobium are removed by magnetic separators, but that which remains with the cassiterite is finally collected in the smelting slag.   Tin slags from the Congo and from Portugal often contain from 12 to 15% $(Ta,Nb)_2O_5$ of which about one half is Ta_2O_5, and the slags from Thailand run as high as 12–14% Ta_2O_5.   In spite of their relatively low metal contents these slags have become important sources of tantalum, particularly during periods when the price of ore is high.   A U.S. Bureau of Mines report shows that during 1965, 1966, and 1967 a total of 47,955,000 lb of tin slags containing 2,516,000 lb of Ta_2O_5 was reported received by consumers (see Table 2).

Chemical Analysis of Ores.   The high cost of Ta_2O_5 in tantalum ores makes the accurate analyses of these ores very important to both the supplier and user.   Unfortunately, there is yet to be developed a rapid, simple, and accurate method for the determination of tantalum and niobium in ores.   The chemical similarity of these elements hindered their early identification and has made their separation, both industrial and analytical, difficult to this day.

The oldest procedure to be used for the separation of tantalum and niobium is the

Table 2.   Receipts of Tin Slags by Consumers, lb

Tin slag	1965	1966	1967
gross weight	8,822,000	10,220,000	28,919,000
Ta_2O_5 weight	429,000	560,000	1,527,000

classical Marignac method which takes advantage of the great difference in the solubilities of potassium fluorotantalate (K_2TaF_7) and potassium niobium oxyfluoride (K_2NbOF_5) in water containing a little free HF. This method gives reasonably accurate results with clean minerals of high tantalum content but leaves much to be desired when used on high-niobium ores or ores containing much titanium.

A procedure developed by W. R. Schoeller is based on the difference in the solubilities of oxalotantalic and oxaloniobic acid complexes with tannin in acid solutions. This procedure requires quite a bit of individual skill and patience by the analyst because of its many repetitive fractionating steps. Several modifications of this classical system have been developed and used.

Analytical methods using x-ray fluorescence spectrography are comparatively rapid, but often lack accuracy because of interferences from elements commonly found in varying amounts in tantalum ores.

Probably the most acceptable method yet developed for the analysis of tantalum ores is based on the separation of tantalum and niobium from their impurities and from each other by ion exchange using Dowex I (The Dow Chemical Company) resin. An analytical procedure based on work by Kraus, Moore, and Nelson (9,10) and Hague, Brown, and Bright (11), and developed and published by Kallmann, Oberthin, and Liu (12) has been described in some detail.

In this procedure a sample of finely divided mineral is dissolved in a mixture of HCl ($12M$) and HF ($24M$) in a heated polyethylene beaker covered by a sheet of polyethylene which is held tightly to the sides of the beaker with a rubber band. Certain refractory mineral combinations may require a sodium bisulfate fusion for complete decomposition but, in any event, the sample is finally dissolved in the HCl–HF mixture. The resulting solution (from either procedure) containing the dissolved ore is passed through the column containing Dowex I resin on which the tantalum and niobium are retained, and the impurities such as titanium and tungsten pass through. The niobium is removed from the resin first by elution with a water solution containing 14 w/v % of NH_4Cl and 4 v/v % of HF. Then the tantalum is eluted with another portion of the same mixture which has been neutralized with NH_4OH to a pH of 6. Next, the two solutions containing the tantalum and the niobium are treated to precipitate their values by first complexing the HF with boric acid and then adding cupferron. The precipitates are collected, ignited, and weighed as Ta_2O_5 and Nb_2O_5. Modifications of this method are used extensively for the evaluation of tantalum–niobium ores.

A rapid method for the approximate evaluation of tantalite–columbite mineral, based on the relationship of Ta_2O_5 content to specific gravity, has been used for many years for a preliminary examination of samples submitted by prospectors. The results are surprisingly close to the ultimate analysis when clean, sound pieces of the mineral are used for specific gravity determinations. A graph was prepared by plotting many analyses of clean minerals against their specific gravities; some figures from this curve are shown below.

Ta_2O_5, %	0	10	20	30	40	50	60	70	80
Sp gr	5.27	5.51	5.75	6.00	6.26	6.54	6.85	7.20	7.78

Extraction

The manufacture of tantalum metal is accomplished by (*1*) the extraction and purification of a pure tantalum compound, (*2*) the reduction of such a compound to

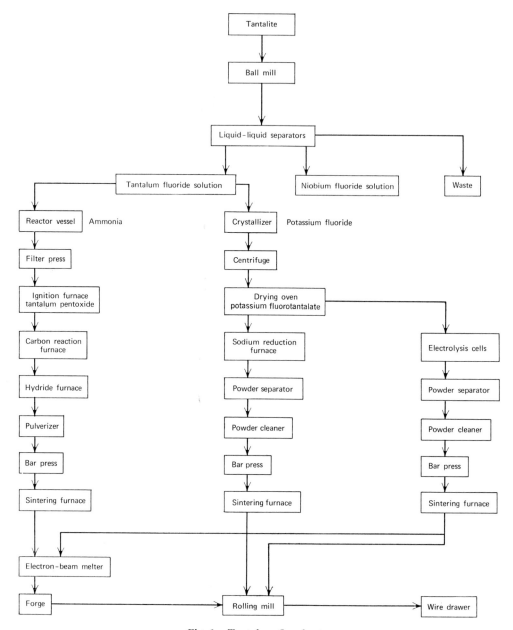

Fig. 1. Tantalum flowsheet.

pure metal, and (3) the consolidation of the metal (powder, pellets, or sponge) into workable forms such as ingots, bars, or rods. The extraction of tantalum is complicated by the unusually refractory nature of its minerals and by the need to separate it from the ever-present and chemically similar niobium. Tantalum containing niobium is inferior to pure tantalum in most of its applications.

The first successful industrial process used to extract tantalum from tantalite–columbite employed an alkali fusion to decompose the ore, acid treatment to remove most of the impurities, and the historic Marignac (3) fractional-crystallization method to separate the tantalum from the niobium and to purify the resulting K_2TaF_7. This method alone was used to produce all of the tantalum manufactured prior to about 1957 and is still used on a limited scale. Since that time, more and more metal has been produced by hydrofluoric acid extraction and liquid-liquid separation (13). This method was developed by Werning and Highbie at the U.S. Bureau of Mines, Albany, Oregon (14) and by H. A. Wilhelm and co-workers at the Ames Laboratory of the U.S. Atomic Energy Commission (15,16). Modifications of the basic methods (17,18) have been developed and are used by most producers of tantalum and niobium at this time.

Fractional Crystallization. The steps involved in the industrial application of the Marignac separation of the complex fluorides of tantalum and niobium are as follows:

1. The finely pulverized ore (200 mesh) is fused with NaOH to form sodium tantalate and niobate, and iron and manganese hydroxides.

2. The fusion cake is leached in water and treated with HCl to dissolve the iron and manganese, and to convert the sodium salts of tantalum and niobium to insoluble hydrated oxides.

3. After washing with water, the white slurry is dissolved in HF and then sufficient KF is added to the hot solution to form K_2TaF_7 and K_2NbOF_5.

4. The hot solution is filtered and allowed to cool slowly to crystallize the K_2TaF_7.

5. The tantalum salt may be recrystallized if a higher purity is required.

Liquid–Liquid Extraction. The principles involved in the liquid extraction system are based on the effect of acidity on the solubilities of the fluorides of tantalum, niobium, titanium, zirconium, iron, manganese, etc in methyl isobutyl ketone (MIBK). When an acid solution of these fluorides is allowed to contact MIBK, the tantalum can be taken into the organic phase at a relatively low acidity but the niobium only at a high acidity. Under both of these conditions the other elements remain in the aqueous phase. The difference in the solubilities is sufficient to give clean extractions of pure tantalum and niobium in only a few contacts.

The separations are accomplished by either of the following procedures: *(1)* Extraction of the tantalum first, by mixing a low-acidity feed solution with barren MIBK, and then extraction of the niobium by increasing the acidity of the feed and mixing it with more fresh MIBK, or *(2)* extraction of both tantalum and niobium from a strongly acidic aqueous feed by mixing with fresh ketone and then stripping of the niobium from the organic phase by mixing it with a less concentrated acid solution.

In either case, the values remaining in the MIBK are recovered by stripping with dilute acid. In industrial practice the following steps are used:

1. Finely pulverized ore (200 mesh) is fed slowly into a strong hydrofluoric acid solution contained in a temperature-controlled tank lined with Inconel nickel–chromium–iron. Digestion is continued for several hours to decompose the minerals completely.

2. The solution is filtered and adjusted to the required acidity and fed into the mixer-settler system.

3. The resulting aqueous solutions containing pure tantalum or niobium fluoride are converted to hydrated oxides by precipitation with ammonia or to double fluorides by the addition of potassium fluoride.

Tin Slags. Because of their low $(Ta,Nb)_2O_5$ contents and their high hydrofluoric acid-consuming impurities, it is not economical to extract the values from lower-grade tin slags by direct solution in hydrofluoric acid. Several rather complex methods for the upgrading of these slags are used to prepare them for liquid extraction. Although these processes are of a proprietary nature and are not generally available, it is known that they usually include smelting with carbon in an electric furnace to form the metal carbides and a metalfree slag. The smelted product is crushed and magnetically separated to collect the iron, tantalum, and niobium carbides. Further concentration and purification of the tantalum and niobium values may include dissolving the carbides in iron and then treating the melt with lime and air to separate the earth oxides from the iron melt as a synthetic calcium–tantalum–niobium ore. The tungsten, tin, and some of the silica remain in the pig iron. The concentrates produced by upgrading tin slags, particularly if they contain carbides, often require an alkali fusion to make them completely soluble in HF.

Reduction

There are three well-established methods of reduction used in the manufacture of tantalum, and several others have been developed. The choice of method is determined by economic considerations and by the particular requirements for the proposed use of the metal.

Reduction by Sodium. The first pure ductile tantalum was made in Germany by W. von Bolton at Siemens und Halskie AG. He employed a modification of the sodium-reduction methods described much earlier by J. J. Berzelius in 1825 and H. Rose in 1856. In this method, sodium-metal pellets and dry K_2TaF_7 were placed in alternate layers in an upright iron cylinder which was sealed and then fired to a red heat to start the reaction. The resulting product was a mixture of fine tantalum powder, alkali fluorides, and an excess of sodium. The cooled reaction cylinder was opened and the mass saturated with methanol to dissolve the free sodium. The mass was mechanically removed from the cylinder and treated with water to deactivate the sodium and dissolve the fluorides. However, infrequent but potentially dangerous explosions were reported to have occurred during the reactions and during the recovery of the powder. The collected tantalum powder was given several acid digestions and water washes, and the colloidal material which was formed was removed by a hydrofluoric acid wash.

Sophisticated modifications of this sodium reduction procedure are used to produce commercial quantities of tantalum at this time. Sodium-reduced tantalum powder is comparatively fine in particle size and notably low in carbon. It is used primarily in the manufacture of tantalum capacitors.

Reduction by Electrolysis. The reduction of tantalum by the electrolysis of fused K_2TaF_7 was started in 1922 and is still in regular industrial use. The original cell consists of a graphite anode and a cast-iron pot which serves as the cathode. Tantalum powder is deposited as small dendrites on the wall and bottom of the pot when high-density current is passed through a bath of K_2TaF_7 and Ta_2O_5 (or other oxides). The cell is batch operated until the powder deposit almost fills the pot. After cooling to room temperature, the metal–salt mass is removed from the pot, crushed, pulverized, and air- and table-separated to collect the metal powder, which is cleaned by washing it in strong acids followed by water washing. The powder produced by electrolysis is well suited for production of tantalum bars by powder metallurgy. A typical analysis is tantalum, 99.8%; iron, 0.01%; titanium, 0.001%; and carbon, 0.13%.

Several variations of the foregoing method are used to produce tantalum powder. Often, the cell container is made of graphite and the cathode of metal. This arrangement permits a more-or-less continuous electrolytic procedure because the loaded cathode can be removed at intervals and replaced by a new one. Other variations include the addition of other alkali halides to the K_2TaF_7 to increase its fluidity at lower bath temperatures.

Reduction by Carbothermic Reaction. The earliest recorded attempts to make tantalum were by carbon reduction of Ta_2O_5. However, the resulting products were hard and brittle, probably due to the presence of carbon and/or oxygen in the metal.

Tantalum and niobium were produced on a limited industrial scale from 1935 to 1939 by the high-temperature reaction of tantalum carbide and tantalum oxide (19). In this method, the carbide was made by heating a mixture of Ta_2O_5 with lampblack, and then the TaC produced was mixed with Ta_2O_5, pressed into bars, and heated at about 2000°C under vacuum to produce metal bars.

$$5\,TaC + Ta_2O_5 \rightarrow 7\,Ta + 5\,CO$$

Production of tantalum by this method was abandoned because of the lack of control of the residual carbon and oxygen in the metal bars. However, during the late 1950s a fresh interest in carbon reduction was kindled by the need for greater production rates and for larger bars. Also, it was found that the requirements for the feedstock for the newly developed electron-beam furnaces were not as critical as those for powder-metallurgy rolling bars. Now, large quantities of tantalum (and niobium) are made via carbothermic reduction. In modern practice, a blend of Ta_2O_5 and carbon is pressed into firm pieces which are heated by induction to make tantalum metal.

$$Ta_2O_5 + 5\,C \rightarrow 2\,Ta + 5\,CO$$

The reaction product is heated in hydrogen to form the very brittle hydride which is pulverized to a fine powder. The hydride powder is pressed into bars, which are sintered under vacuum, making them suitable as feedstock for electron-beam melters.

Reduction by Other Methods. Other methods of reduction include the following:

1. The deposition (vapor-plating) of tantalum on a metal or nonmetal base to form a coherent coating (20) from a mixture of hydrogen and $TaCl_5$ at temperatures from 800 to 1400°C.

2. The Kroll process, in which anhydrous $TaCl_5$ is reduced by magnesium under helium or argon is described by Johansen and May (21).

3. The quantitative reduction of K_2TaF_7 by aluminum and copper. When K_2TaF_7 and aluminum are heated to 1100°C, a refractory acid-insoluble compound, Al_3Ta, is formed; if this compound is heated with copper at 1100°C, the result is free tantalum powder in an alloy of copper and aluminum. The tantalum is recovered by dissolving the copper and aluminum from the alloy in acid (22).

Consolidation

The high melting point and reactivity of tantalum prohibit its consolidation by ordinary melting and casting methods. W. von Bolton produced the first ductile tantalum by arc-melting a powder compact to a button on a steel plate in a vacuum. Later, he developed and used a vacuum-sintering technique to produce workable bars. Modifications of these methods and the more recently developed consumable electrode, arc-melting method and the electron-beam melting method are now used to consolidate the metal.

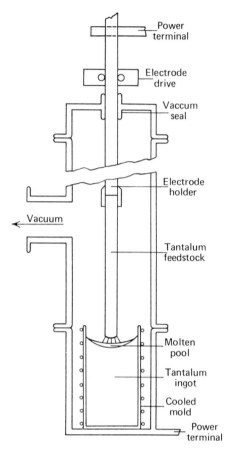

Fig. 2. Vacuum arc melter.

Pressing. The consolidation of tantalum begins with the pressing of the metal powder. Two types of pressing equipment, mechanical and isostatic, are used to make the compacts, and pressures from 20 to 50 tons per in.² are applied. Mechanical pressing is usually employed when the bars are to be sintered by resistance. The powder is spread evenly in a sturdy rectangular compound die set and the pressure is applied through top and bottom punches, and often, also, to the side. By this means a bar with precise dimensions is produced. Mechanically pressed tantalum bars are usually limited to about 10 kg in weight and 30 in. in length. Hydrostatic (isostatic) compacting allows more freedom in bar size and shape. The metal powder is poured into a rubber or neoprene mold which is supported by an inexpensive steel shell. Bars pressed in this manner are usually sintered by induction-heating or become the feedstock for electron-beam melting furnaces.

Sintering. The sintering process consolidates and purifies a metal at temperatures well below its melting point. It is particularly useful with metals such as tantalum which are very reactive and have high melting points. Pressed bars are sintered for several hours at temperatures ranging from 2000 to 2400°C in a good vacuum. Heating is accomplished by passing a high current through the bar, by induction, or by radiation from a susceptor, or from resistance elements. Sintering in vacuum removes

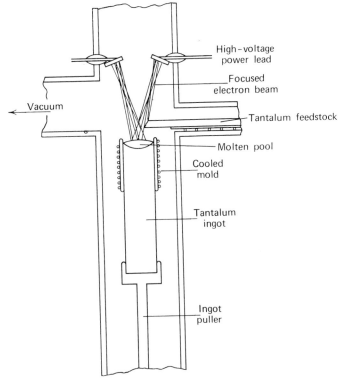

Fig. 3.   Electron-beam melter.

high-vapor-pressure impurities such as salts, some oxides, and lower-melting metals; carbon and oxygen contents are reduced through loss as carbon monoxide.   Depending on which of the latter impurities is dominant, Ta_2O_5 or carbon is added to permit maximum purification through the carbon monoxide reaction.   Tantalum bars are usually resintered at least once after being forged or rolled to lower the porosity.

Tantalum metal made via the sintering method has certain metallurgical characteristics which are useful in the forming and drawing of thin sheet and in the drawing of fine wire.   On the other hand, residual interstitial impurities normally found in this metal contribute to porosity in weldments.

Vacuum Arc Melting.   Large tantalum ingots which are required for the manufacture of large tantalum sheets are made by arc or electron-beam melting of pressed and sintered bars.   In the arc furnace a heavy direct current arc is drawn between a tantalum bar, which is a consumable electrode, and a pad of tantalum metal on the bottom of a water-cooled mold (see Fig. 2).   The current is usually supplied by silicon rectifiers.   The heat of the arc melts the lower end of the electrode (the tantalum feedstock), and the molten metal drops into the cooled mold below.   A shell of tantalum immediately solidifies on the inside wall of the mold, thereby forming a tantalum crucible which now holds a shallow pool of molten metal.   The tantalum electrode is continuously lowered as it melts and fills the mold.   When the mold is full, the operation is stopped and the ingot is allowed to cool before removal from the furnace.   A pressure, usually below 10^{-2} mm Hg, is maintained throughout the entire process. A limited amount of purification occurs during this melting process.   Ingots 10 or more in. in diameter can be made, and ingots 6–9 in. in diameter and 70 in. long are common. Melting rates of several hundred lb of tantalum per hr are normal.

Electron-Beam Melting.   The latest and most sophisticated method to be used to consolidate tantalum is melting by electron bombardment.   In this process a beam of high-velocity electrons accelerated by a high potential between the cathode and anode in an electron gun is focused by an electromagnetic field to the end of a pre-sintered (or pressed only) tantalum bar (the feedstock) and the surface of a pool of molten metal in the water-cooled mold below (see Fig. 3).   The tantalum feedstock is pushed continuously into the furnace as it melts and drops into the pool below and the ingot, as it is formed, is lowered down through the mold into the cooling chamber. This vacuum melting process effectively removes the gaseous and the more volatile metallic impurities contained in the feedstock.   It should be noted that the heating capacity and the feed rate of the electron-beam melter are independent of each other; therefore, the molten metal may be exposed to the high vacuum (at least 10^{-4} mm Hg) for any reasonable length of time.   If further purification is required, the ingot is re-melted in the same furnace but in this case the feedstock is lowered vertically into the furnace, rather than from the side.

Tantalum metal made from electron-beam-melted ingots is noted for its high purity, excellent ductility, and good weldability.   It is characterized, also, by its large grain size and lower tensile strength as compared with that from sintered bars.   Tantalum metal is beam-melted at a rate of about 200 lb per hr and ingots 8 in. in diameter and 120 in. long, weighing more than $1\frac{1}{2}$ tons, are in regular production.   They are prepared for rolling, first by machining to remove the rough surface, and then by forging or extruding into suitable slabs.

Metal Working.   Sintered bars or melted ingots are very ductile and can be rolled cold into sheet and foil.   Seamless tubing drawn from sheet is readily available in sizes from $\frac{1}{4}$ in. to 2 in. in diameter.   Capillary-size tubes have been made.   Tantalum wire is made by cold-rolling and swaging the square-bar stock into small rods, oxidizing the surface of the rod to aid in retention of the drawing lubricant, and then drawing the coated (oxidized) rod through diamond dies to size.   Drawing bare tantalum is not practical because the metal galls.

Tantalum can be reduced in cross section by 75–90% before it requires annealing. It is not worked hot because it reacts with all common gases above 250°C.   Recrystallization is accomplished in an hour at about 1200°C in a good vacuum.   Table 3 shows the effects of recrystallization on worked tantalum sheet and wire.

Fabrication.   Tantalum is usually fabricated in the annealed condition.   It is very ductile and can be formed or drawn into shapes when properly lubricated.   It is not suitable as a bearing metal because it seizes or galls when rubbed against itself and most

Table 3. Effects of Recrystallization on Worked Tantalum Sheet and Wire

	Sintered				Beam melted			
	0.020-in. wire		0.020-in. sheet		0.020-in. wire		0.020-in. sheet	
Property	Worked	Recrystallized	Worked	Recrystallized	Worked	Recrystallized	Worked	Recrystallized
tensile strength, psi	90,000	45,000 to 55,000	90,000	45,000 to 50,000	75,000	35,000 to 45,000	75,000	33,000 to 45,000
elongation, %	<2	25 to 30	1	35	<2	25 to 35	2	35 to 40

other metals. It can be lap- or seam-welded under water, arc-welded under carbon tetrachloride, and inert-gas-welded when protected by pure helium or argon. Fabricated articles include structural assemblies used in electronic vacuum tubes and simple and multitube heat exchangers used in corrosive environments in the chemical industry. The metal is used to clad steel and copper pipe and to line large chemical-reaction vessels. Tantalum can be successfully machined with sharp tools when carbon tetrachloride or perchloroethylene is applied.

Properties

Physical Properties. The physical properties of tantalum are shown in Table 4. It should be kept in mind that many of the properties of the metal vary with its state of work and with its purity. For this reason some of the values shown may not be precise.

Reactions. The presence of a naturally occurring oxide film on the surface of tantalum makes it inert to most acid chemicals below about 150°C. Only those substances

Table 4. Typical Properties of Tantalum

Property	Value
lattice type	body-centered cubic
lattice constant at 20°C, Å	3.3026
density at 20°C, g/cm³	16.6
melting point, °C	2996
boiling point, °C	5425 ± 100
vapor pressure at 1727°C, mm	9.5×10^{-11}
specific heat at 20°C, cal/(g)(°C)	0.036
linear coefficient of expansion, per °C	6.5×10^{-6}
thermal conductivity at 20°C,	
cal/(sec)(cm²)(°C/cm)	0.130
electrical resistivity, $\mu\Omega$-cm	
at 20°C	13.5
at 1000°C	54
at 1500°C	71
temp coef of elec resistivity	
at 0–100°C, per °C	0.00382
thermionic work function, eV	4.12
total emissivity	
at 1500°C	0.21
at 2000°C	0.26
magnetic susceptibility (cgs)	0.93×10^{-6}
tensile strength, psi	
at room temp	35,000–70,000
at 500°C	25,000–45,000
at 1000°C	13,000–17,000
Young's modulus, psi	
at room temp	27×10^6
at 500°C	25×10^6
at 1000°C	22×10^6
Poisson's ratio	0.35
working temp	room
recrystallization temp, °C	1050–1400
stress relieving temp, °C	900
nuclear cross section for thermal	
neutrons, b/atom	21.3

which are capable of dissolving this film and preventing it from reforming react with the element. It is very slowly attacked by strong alkalis, more readily by fuming sulfuric acid (oleum), rapidly by hydrofluoric acid, and vigorously by a mixture of hydrofluoric and nitric acids.

Tantalum is very reactive at elevated temperatures. It reacts with oxygen or air to form Ta_2O_5; the reaction begins at 260°C and becomes vigorous at about 800°C. It reacts with molecular hydrogen above 250°C and with atomic hydrogen at room temperature to form the very brittle hydride. It has been reported (23) that tantalum containing dissolved oxygen can absorb molecular hydrogen at room temperature when it is undergoing deformation. However, all of the hydrogen is released when the hydride is heated above 800°C in a vacuum. All of the halogens react with tantalum to form the metal halides, fluorine at room temperature, chlorine at about 200°C, bromine at about 300°C, and iodine (24) beginning at about 300°C, but more rapidly above 340°C. Carbon and boron react directly with tantalum to form tantalum carbide, TaC, and tantalum boride, TaB_2.

Corrosion Resistance. The complete inertness of tantalum to so many chemicals has made it the standard for corrosion resistance in severe acid environments. Its remarkable resistance to corrosion is responsible for an important part of its industrial application. Tantalum has been tested against literally hundreds of corrosive substances and long lists of results have been published. However, the most important corrodants based on industrial usage are sulfuric, hydrochloric, and nitric acids, organic chemicals, and liquid metals.

Tantalum is inert to sulfuric acid below about 150°C, and the attack below 175°C is not significant (see Table 5). Corrosion at all temperatures is uniform (without

Table 5. Corrosion Rates of Tantalum in Sulfuric Acid

Concentrated sulfuric acid		Fuming sulfuric acid	
Temperature, °C	Corrosion rate, mils/yr	Temperature, °C	Corrosion rate, mils/yr
175	0.1	23	0.3
200	1.5	70	92.0
250	29.0	130	3900.0
300	342.0		

pitting) and hydrogen embrittlement does not occur. This statement is supported without exception by a large number of corrosion tests at several concentrations and by many years of service by heat exchangers installed in sulfuric acid concentrators. However, it has been reported (25) that embrittlement occurred when strips of tantalum were sealed in glass tubes with 80–95% sulfuric acid and heated to the boiling points of the acid in an autoclave.

Tantalum is inert to hydrochloric acid in all concentrations and at all temperatures up to about 95°C. Twenty percent acid (constant boiling mixture) does not corrode the metal below 190°C. Corrosion rates for 37% (concentrated reagent) and for 20% hydrochloric acid are given in Table 6.

It has been reported (26) that tantalum samples tested against concentrated hydrochloric acid at 190°C for 90 hr (confined under pressure) had corrosion rates from 6 to 24 mils/year and became enbrittled.

Table 6. Corrosion Rates of Tantalum in Hydrochloric Acid

Hydrochloric acid, 37%		Hydrochloric acid, 20%	
Temperature, °C	Corrosion rate, mils/yr	Temperature, °C	Corrosion rate, mils/yr
100	0.02	190	0.00
110	0.11	200	0.13
120	0.60	220	0.90

Tantalum is not attacked by nitric acid in all concentrations up to 70% and at all temperatures up to at least 190°C (27,28). Numerous industrial installations using tantalum equipment have been in operation for many years without reported failures caused by corrosion.

In general, tantalum is completely resistant to organic compounds and is used in heat exchangers, spargers, and reaction vessels in several important organic reactions, particularly when corrosive inorganics are involved. However, an important exception has been reported by Eric Rabald (29) who noted that mixtures of anhydrous methanol with chlorine, bromine, or iodine cause pit-type corrosion on tantalum at 65°C. This is of particular interest because tantalum is not attacked individually by methanol, the halogens involved, or the product, methyl halide, even at somewhat higher temperatures. Also, pit-type corrosion on tantalum is rare. Rabald concluded that the corrosive action was caused by the occurrence of the intermediate, haloformic acid.

Tantalum is resistant to several liquid metals, and is used in the handling of these materials and in the construction of heat-transfer systems for them. It shows good resistance in the following media up to the temperatures shown:

Metal	Temp, °C	Metal	Temp, °C	Metal	Temp, °C
Bi	900	Li	1000	Na–K	1000
Ga	450	Mg	1160	Na	1000
Pb	1000	Hg	600	Zn	500

The occurrence of a galvanic couple or a stray voltage can adversely affect the usefulness of tantalum in a corrosive medium to which it is completely resistant. If tantalum is permitted to become the cathode in an electrolyte, either because it is connected to a metal which is being chemically attacked by the electrolyte or because of a stray voltage, it may become embrittled by the atomic hydrogen which is being liberated on its surface. In solutions of hydrofluoric acid which prevent the formation of the protective oxide film, tantalum is less noble than silver, copper, lead, nickel, iron, and niobium but is more noble than zinc, manganese, aluminum, and zirconium (30).

Metallography

The preparation of a good metallographic surface on recrystallized tantalum requires a little more than the usual care and patience because of the metal's characteristic low hardness and excellent resistance to chemical attack. The following procedure is in regular use: (1) Mount the flat specimen in a plastic or tantalum holder; (2)

wet grind on 240- and then 400-grit silicon carbide paper; (3) polish on nylon cloth with 30-μ diamond paste and kerosene; (4) repeat (3) using 9-μ diamond paste; (5) polish on micro cloth with 1-μ diamond paste; (6) etch in a solution of 15 ml HF, 15 ml H_2SO_4, and 15 ml H_2O activated with 5–20 drops of 30% H_2O_2; (7) repeat steps (5) and (6) until a satisfactory surface is obtained.

Alloys

Tantalum forms continuous solid-solution alloys with niobium, tungsten, molybdenum, and body-centered cubic titanium. These alloys and a number of other tantalum alloys have been studied and reported (31). However, only a very few have found important uses.

High-tantalum alloys are designed to improve the physical characteristics of the metal without lessening its important corrosion resistance; the most effective alloying metal in this respect is tungsten. Small additions of tungsten to tantalum create stronger yet ductile alloys whose corrosion properties are about the same as, and in some cases superior to, those of pure tantalum (see Table 7).

Table 7. Properties of Tantalum–Tungsten Alloys

Alloy	Elongation, %	Tensile strength, psi	Corrosion resistance in sulfuric acid, mils/yr	
			175°C	200°C
tantalum	42	38,000	0.20	1.9
tantalum–2.5% tungsten	36	53,000	0.23	1.0
tantalum–5% tungsten	32	66,000	0.21	1.1
tantalum–10% tungsten	28	98,000	0.22	1.7

Two high-tantalum alloys which have good creep- and corrosion-resistance properties are said to be useful for handling hot liquid metals in nuclear-power systems. Their compositions are shown below.

Composition	T-111	T-222
tungsten, %	7–9	9.6–11.2
hafnium, %	1.8–2.4	2.2–2.8
carbon, ppm	less than 40	80–170

Applications

The uses of tantalum are determined largely by its inertness to chemical attack at moderate temperatures, reactivity at high temperatures, good strength and ductility, and by the dielectric properties of its electrolytic oxide film. Its applications are inhibited somewhat by its relatively high cost.

Capacitors. Tantalum is a superior metal for use in electrolytic capacitor anodes because of the inertness and stability of its electrolytic oxide film. The tantalum capacitor is the standard for reliable performance. For many years, about one half of the tantalum produced has been used to make capacitors. There are three types of con-

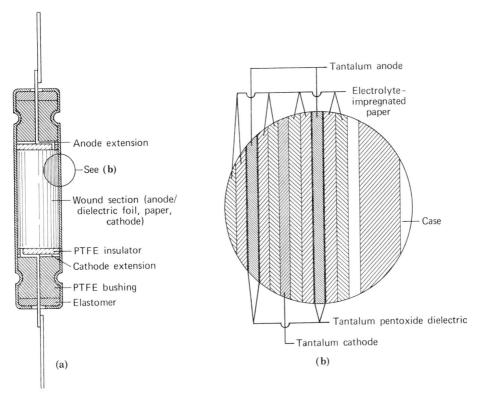

Fig. 4. (**a**) Tantalum foil capacitor; (**b**) sectional enlargement of (**a**). Courtesy Transistor Electronics, Inc.

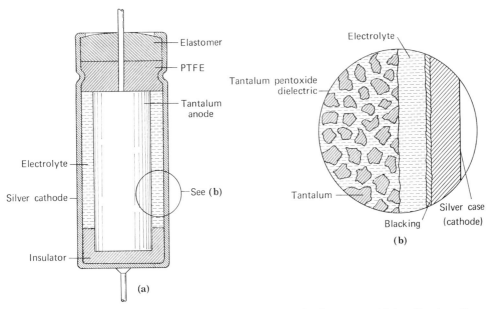

Fig. 5. (**a**) Tantalum wet-electrolyte capacitor; (**b**) sectional enlargement of (**a**). Courtesy Transistor Electronics, Inc.

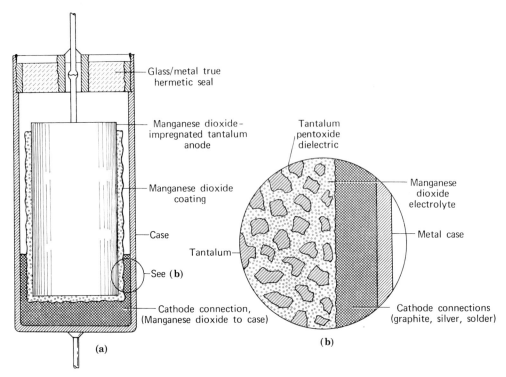

Fig. 6. (**a**) Tantalum solid-electrolyte capacitor; (**b**) solid sectional enlargement of (**a**). Courtesy Transistor Electronics, Inc.

struction: foil (Fig. 4), porous wet anode in aqueous electrolyte (Fig. 5), and porous-anode dry-electrolyte (Fig. 6).

Foil capacitors are made by rolling up two strips of thin foil separated by a paper saturated with a glycol-base electrolyte. The anode strip is etched to increase its surface and then electroformed to develop the dielectric film. These capacitors can be electroformed to more than 400 V for use at about 250 V, but have the lowest capacitance per unit volume of the three types. Their production volume, also, is the lowest.

Porous-anode, wet-electrolyte capacitors are composed of the anode, an electrolyte, which is a solution of either sulfuric acid or lithium chloride, and a silver container. The anode is made by pressing a compact of tantalum powder around a tantalum wire and sintering to just weld the particles together without closing the voids. This procedure produces a very high surface area per unit volume, which results in high capacitance-per-volume rating. The working voltages of capacitors of this type are usually limited to about 150. Porous anodes are made from either sodium-reduced powder or from a powder made by hydrogenating and pulverizing high-purity arc-melted or electron-beam melted tantalum ingots. Most low-voltage (20 V or less) units contain sodium-reduced powder, while the higher-voltage (35 V or above) units are made with hydrogenated and milled powders produced from ingots.

Solid-electrolyte capacitors have the highest capacitance per unit volume of the three types. They operate well in a wide temperature range, have excellent leakage properties, and, like the others, give good idle or shelf life and long reliable service life. They permit the ultimate in miniaturization.

The solid electrolyte is manganese dioxide, which is incorporated into the electroformed porous anode by dipping it in a solution of manganous nitrate, and then decomposing the salt by heating. These operations are repeated until the voids are filled and the anode is coated with manganese dioxide. The anode is coated, next, with carbon and then with a silver-rich, conducting paint. After attaching a cathode terminal by soldering, the capacitor is encased in a metal container or a molded (or dipped) epoxy covering. About nine-tenths of the tantalum capacitors manufactured are of the solid-electrolyte, porous-anode type.

Chemical Equipment. Mill products account for about one-fourth of the tantalum produced, and the most important single product made from tantalum sheet is corrosion-resistant chemical equipment. Fabricated tantalum equipment used in the chemical industry includes bayonet heaters, vapor condensers, multitube heat exchangers, U-tubes, spargers, thermowells, rupture diaphragms, orifices, and many others. Tantalum plugs are used to repair perforations in glass-lined steel equipment. Tantalum equipment is widely used in sulfuric acid concentrators, in temperature controllers for chromium-plating systems, and in the distillation and condensation of acids and acidic chemicals. It is used in the manufacture of pharmaceuticals and fine chemicals where contamination cannot be tolerated. It is also used in several organic chemical reactions.

Most tantalum equipment can be constructed from sheet less than 0.015 in. thick because of its inertness and adequate strength. This permits a very high heat transfer which reduces the metal area required, and, thereby, the cost of the equipment. When greater strength is required, or when lower heat transfer can be tolerated, tantalum-clad steel or copper is used.

The availability of larger tantalum sheets from electron-beam-melted ingots has made it practical to line large 500–2000 gal reaction tanks because fewer welded seams are needed. Many such installations are in use.

Vacuum Tubes. Good high-temperature strength, low vapor pressure, and the "gettering effect" (see Vol. 8, p. 20) have made tantalum an important component metal in special-purpose vacuum tubes. It is easily formed and welded into anodes and grids, which can be cleaned easily in strong acids. Tantalum components can be outgassed at 2000°C and operated at 1200°C.

Surgical Applications. The complete inertness of tantalum to body fluids and tissues has made it attractive as an implant metal for the human body; however, the superior strength and rigidity of stainless steel and the castability of the high-cobalt alloys have led to their much greater use as prosthetic materials (32). Tantalum has been used for suture wire, for cranial repair plates, and for wire gauze for abdominal muscle support in hernia-repair surgery. The powder has been used in x-ray studies of the respiratory system in research on dogs.

A recent paper by Jay A. Nadel, M.D., et al. (33) discusses in detail the use of tantalum powder in the preparation of bronchograms of the lungs of living dogs. Excellent roentgenograms were obtained when only 1 ml of pure tantalum powder (2.5 μ mean particle size) was insufflated into the airways of the lungs. The powder adhered firmly to the mucus lining and thereby resisted early dislodging by coughing, but was mostly eliminated by ciliary activity and by coughing within four days thereafter. The studies showed that tantalum caused no unfavorable tissue reactions, either acute or chronic. Excellent bronchograms were made on tantalum-treated human lungs postmortem, also. The writers stated that because of the advantages of tantalum powder enumerated in their report, "it should be a useful diagnostic procedure in man."

Economic Aspects

Using the reports of annual imports of tantalum concentrates as a base, it is estimated that the production of tantalum and tantalum products in the U.S.A. is a little less than 1 million lb per yr.

The base selling prices of tantalum metal products are shown in Table 8.

Table 8. Selling Prices of Tantalum Metal Products, $/lb

Form of tantalum	1963	1964	1965	1966	1967	1968
sheet, 0.060 in.	45	30	35	40	50	40
foil, 0.0005 in.	70	55	60	60	76	60
powder	28–40	22–35	28–40	28–40	31–43	30–31

The current price of tantalum carbide is about $16.00/lb.

Tantalum Compounds

The refractory nature of tantalum prevents the formation of many ordinary simple compounds of this element. Of those that have been prepared, only a very few may be considered important.

ALUMINUM TANTALIDE. Aluminum tantalide, Al_3Ta, with sp gr 7.02, is a gray refractory powder which forms when aluminum metal is added to potassium fluotantalate at about 1000°C. It is quite insoluble in acids and alkalis. It oxidizes very slowly when heated in air above 500°C. It melts in a vacuum at about 1400°C when it begins to lose some aluminum.

TANTALIC ACID, TANTALATES. See Tantalum oxides and tantalic acid.

TANTALUM BORIDE. Tantalum boride, TaB_2, with sp gr 11.15, mp about 3000°C, Mohs hardness 8+, is a gray metallic powder. It is quite insoluble in acids and alkalis. It may be prepared by heating tantalum and boron in a vacuum at about 1800°C, by induction-heating a mixture of Ta_2O_5, B_2O_3, and C, or by the electrolysis of fused Ta_2O_5, B_2O_3, CaO, and CaF_2 (34).

TANTALUM BROMIDE. See Tantalum halides.

TANTALUM CARBIDE. Tantalum carbide, TaC, with sp gr 13.9, mp 3880°C, is a crystalline, very fine, gold-to-brown-colored powder. It is insoluble in all acids except a mixture of hydrofluoric and nitric acids. Its Mohs hardness is between 9 and 10. It is an interstitial compound with a face-centered cubic lattice. Tantalum carbide with a hexagonal structure has also been reported (35). Stoichiometric tantalum carbide may be prepared by the direct carburization of tantalum powder with the appropriate amount of lampblack, or by the reaction of tantalum oxide and lampblack at about 1900°C in an inert atmosphere. The valency of tantalum does not determine the stoichiometric composition of the carbide. Tantalum carbide is converted to the pentoxide when heated to redness in air. It is easily decomposed for analytical purposes by fusion with potassium pyrosulfate or by solution in a mixture of hydrofluoric and nitric acids.

Tantalum carbide is added to tungsten carbide and cobalt to produce hard-carbide cutting tools which have a low coefficient of friction and a high resistance to mechanical shock. Tantalum carbide accounts for about one-tenth of all tantalum production. See also Carbides (Industrial, heavy metal; Cemented); Tool materials.

TANTALUM HALIDES. **Tantalum pentachloride,** $TaCl_5$, with sp gr 3.68, mp 216.0°C, bp 242°C, is a white (when pure) crystalline salt which hydrolyzes in water but is soluble in absolute alcohol. It also hydrolyzes on exposure to moist air. It is formed when tantalum metal is heated in pure dry chlorine above 200°C. It may also be prepared by heating a mixture of tantalum pentoxide and carbon in pure dry chlorine. It decomposes to tantalum and hydrogen chloride when heated above 600°C in hydrogen.

Tantalum oxytrichloride, $TaOCl_3$, is a crystalline salt that forms, with some pentachloride, when tantalum pentachloride is distilled in dry air. It hydrolyzes in water.

Tantalum tribromide, $TaBr_3$, is formed when the pentabromide is reduced with hydrogen at 700°C (36). It reacts with water and alkali, liberating hydrogen and forming $Ta_2O_5 \cdot 2H_2O$.

Tantalum pentabromide, $TaBr_5$, sp gr 4.67, mp 265°C, bp 348.8°C, is a yellow crystalline salt which hydrolyzes in water. It can be prepared by heating tantalum metal in pure bromine gas above 300°C. Vapor pressures of the liquid are reported in reference 36.

Tantalum pentaiodide, TaI_5, mp 496°C, bp 543°C, forms as shiny black crystals when tantalum metal is heated to a bright-red heat in iodine. It hydrolyzes when exposed to air but does not decompose below its boiling point when protected. It loses iodine when heated somewhat above 1000°C (36). Vapor pressures of the liquid are reported in reference 36.

Tantalum pentafluoride, TaF_5, sp gr 4.74, mp 96.8, bp 229.5, is a colorless crystalline salt which is soluble in water without hydrolysis. It may be prepared conveniently by reacting anhydrous hydrogen fluoride with tantalum pentachloride at room temperature. It is formed also when tantalum metal is heated in a stream of fluorine.

Tantalum forms a number of double fluorides, of which potassium fluorotantalate is best known.

Potassium fluorotantalate (potassium tantalum fluoride), K_2TaF_7, sp gr 5.24, mp 7.20 ± 10°C, crystallizes as colorless rhombic needles when potassium fluoride is added to a solution of tantalum fluoride with an excess of hydrofluoric acid. It hydrolyzes when boiled in water containing no free hydrofluoric acid. Its solubility in acidulated water varies from 60 g/100 ml solution at the boiling point to less than 0.5 g/100 ml cold. The difference in solubility characteristics of K_2TaF_7 and K_2NbOF_5 is used in the industrial separation of tantalum from niobium. Potassium fluorotantalate was produced first by Berzelius in 1825 and is the most important salt of tantalum today.

Tantalum fluoride forms complexes with the fluorides of the alkali metals, the alkaline earth metals, certain heavy metals, ammonia, and pyridine. C. W. Balke (37) investigated and described the following: $2NH_4F \cdot TaF_5$, $3NaF \cdot TaF_5$, $2NaF-$

$TaF_5.H_2O$, $2RbF.TaF_5$, $ZnF_2.TaF_5.7H_2O$, $CuF_2.TaF_5.4H_2O$, $LiF.TaF_5.2H_2O$, $NaF.-TaF_5$, $CsF.TaF_5$, $2CsF.TaF_5$, $C_5H_5N.HF.TaF_5$, and $3(C_5H_5N.HF).TaF_5.2H_2O$. An oxyfluoride complex, $2KF.TaO_2F_3.H_2O$, was also found.

TANTALUM HYDRIDE. Tantalum hydride, TaH, sp gr 15.1, is a gray, brittle material having a metallic luster. Tantalum metal absorbs hydrogen by cathodic electrolysis or when heated in hydrogen at a red temperature. Hydrogen is absorbed to the extent of $TaH_{0.76}$ or about 740 volumes (38). The absorption is accompanied by an expansion of the body-centered crystal lattice and by an increase in molecular volume of the tantalum. The absorbed hydrogen is liberated when the hydride is heated above 800°C and cooled in a vacuum. Tantalum hydride exhibits superconductivity at low temperatures (39). It resists attack by acids.

TANTALUM NITRIDE. Tantalum nitride, TaN, with sp gr 13.80, mp 2800 ± 50°C, forms in hexagonal dull-gray crystals when tantalum is heated in pure nitrogen at about 1100°C. Nitrogen is liberated if the nitride is heated to 2000°C and cooled in a vacuum. Tantalum nitride is insoluble in acids but is easily decomposed by potassium hydroxide with the evolution of ammonia. It is an interstitial compound, like the carbide. It does not exhibit superconductivity above $1.20°K$ (40).

TANTALUM OXIDES AND TANTALIC ACID (41). **Tantalum(II) oxide** is not easily prepared, but its existence has been reported. Tantalum tribromide decomposes in water to a brown powder, $TaO_2.2H_2O$, which changes to the pentoxide in air at room temperature (42). An impure Ta_2O_4 is probably formed when the pentoxide is partially reduced with carbon at 1900°C.

   Tantalum pentoxide (tantalum oxide), Ta_2O_5, sp gr 8.2, mp 1800°C, is a rhombic, white powder, which is insoluble in water and in most acids and alkalis. It reacts slowly with hot hydrofluoric acid. It can be taken up by fusion with potassium pyrosulfate or alkali-metal hydroxides or carbonates. It is prepared by the ignition in air of tantalum metal, tantalum hydride, or tantalum carbide, or by heating tantalic acid. Tantalum oxide reacts with carbon at 1900°C to form the carbide and with sulfur monochloride, S_2Cl_2 at a dull-red heat to form the pentachloride.

   Tantalic acid, $HTaO_3$, or probably more correctly $Ta_2O_5.nH_2O$, is the name given to hydrated forms of tantalum oxide. It is a white insoluble precipitate which forms when (1) a potassium pyrosulfate fusion containing tantalum is leached with water, (2) a solution of tantalum fluoride is made ammoniacal, (3) a solution of alkali tantalates is acidulated with hydrochloric acid, or when (4) a halide of tantalum is hydrolyzed by boiling in water.

   Tantalic acid forms organic complexes with tannic, oxalic, tartaric, salicylic, citric, and pyrogallic acids. These complexes are very useful to the analytical chemist. The following are the most important:

   1. A voluminous, characteristic, yellow precipitate is produced when tantalic acid is formed in the presence of a tannin; it is completely insoluble in water or dilute hydrochloric acid.

   2. The oxalic and tartaric complexes of tantalic acid, on the other hand, are soluble in water.

   3. The pyrogallol–tantalic acid complex which is colored is used in the spectrophotometric determination of tantalum (43).

Tantalic acid is very weakly acidic; it readily reacts and dissolves with either hydrofluoric acid or potassium hydroxide. When tantalic acid is ignited, tantalum pentoxide is formed.

Tantalic acid forms several series of tantalates. Some of these occur in nature (see Table 1) and many others have been prepared in the laboratory.

Potassium tantalate or *orthohexatantalate* (4:3 ratio), $4K_2O.3Ta_2O_5.16H_2O$, is a colorless monoclinic salt which is soluble in water. It is the most common potassium salt of tantalum and is prepared by dissolving a fusion of potassium hydroxide and tantalum pentoxide in water and crystallizing the salt by evaporation. Cesium and rubidium form tantalates in this series which carry only fourteen molecules of water.

Potassium metatantalate (1:1 ratio), $K_2O.Ta_2O_5$, is a white insoluble salt prepared by leaching calcined potassium hexatantalate with water.

Potassium pertantalate, K_3TaO_8, is a white anhydrous salt which forms when tantalic acid is dissolved in a solution of potassium hydroxide and hydrogen peroxide. It decomposes with the evolution of oxygen when placed in boiling water. When treated with dilute sulfuric acid, a white precipitate, *metapertantalic acid*, $HTaO_4.nH_2O$, is formed.

Sodium orthohexatantalate (4:3 ratio), $4Na_2O.3Ta_2O_5.25H_2O$, is the white insoluble compound which is formed when a fusion of tantalum pentoxide and sodium hydroxide is leached with water. It is slightly soluble in water but insoluble in solutions of sodium hydroxide or sodium chloride. It is converted to tantalic acid when treated with hydrochloric acid.

Sodium pentatantalate (7:5 ratio), $7Na_2O.5Ta_2O_5.24H_2O$, is similar to the orthohexatantalate. It is formed when sodium hydroxide is added to an aqueous solution of potassium tantalate or potassium fluorotantalate.

Sodium metatantalate (1:1 ratio), $Na_2O.Ta_2O_5.2H_2O$, is obtained when the orthohexatantalate is calcined and then extracted with water to remove the free alkali. It is a white insoluble material which, like the other sodium tantalates, is converted to tantalic acid when treated with hydrochloric acid.

Sodium metapertantalate, $NaTaO_4.NaTaO_5.13H_2O$, and sodium orthopertantalate, $Na_3TaO_8.H_2O$, were prepared by Melikoff and Pissarjewsky (44) and are described as white amorphous powders, sparingly soluble in water, whose solutions liberate oxygen when heated. The per-salts are produced by the addition of hydrogen peroxide to solutions of the tantalates.

TANTALUM SULFIDE. Tantalum sulfide, Ta_2S_4, is a black crystalline powder which is stable below 1300°C. It is insoluble in water and very slowly attacked by hydrofluoric, sulfuric, and nitric acids. It is decomposed by fusion in potassium hydroxide or pyrosulfate. It is formed by heating tantalum metal to a red heat in sulfur vapor.

Bibliography

"Tantalum and Tantalum Compounds" in *ECT* 1st ed., Vol. 13, pp. 600–613, by D. F. Taylor, Fansteel Metallurgical Corporation.

1. C. Hatchett, *Phil. Trans. Roy. Soc. London* **92,** 49–66 (1802).
2. H. Rose, *Pogg. Ann. Phys. Chem.* **63,** 317–341 (1844).
3. J. C. Marignac, *Ann. Chim. Phys.* **8,** 5 (1866).

4. G. L. Miller, *Tantalum and Niobium*, Academic Press, Inc., New York, 1959.
5. F. T. Sisco and E. Epremian, eds., *Columbium and Tantalum*, John Wiley & Sons, Inc., New York, 1963.
6. F. Fairbrother, *Chemistry of Niobium and Tantalum*, American Elsevier Publishing Co., Inc., New York, 1967.
7. C. A. Hampel, ed., *Rare Metals Handbook*, 2nd ed., Reinhold Publishing Corp., New York, 1967.
8. E. S. Dana, ed., *System of Mineralogy*, 6th ed., John Wiley & Sons, Inc., New York, 1937.
9. K. A. Kraus and G. E. Moore, *J. Am. Chem. Soc.* **71**, 38–55 (1949); **73**, 2900 (1951).
10. K. A. Kraus and F. Nelson, *ASTM Spec. Tech. Publ. 195* (1954).
11. J. L. Hague, E. D. Brown, and H. A. Bright, *J. Res. Natl. Bur. Std.* **53**, 261 (1954).
12. S. Kallmann, H. Oberthin, and R. Liu, *Anal. Chem.* **34**, 609–613 (1962).
13. D. F. Taylor, *Chem. Eng. Progr.* **54**, 47–50 (1958).
14. J. R. Werning and K. B. Highbie, *Ind. Eng. Chem.* **46**, 2491 (1954); **46**, 644 (1954).
15. H. A. Wilhelm and R. A. Foos, *U.S. At. Energy Comm. Rept. ISC-694* (Aug. 1954).
16. E. L. Koerner, Jr., M. Smutz, and H. A. Wilhelm, *U.S. At. Energy Comm. Rept. ISC-802* (Dec. 1956).
17. C. H. Chilton, *Chem. Eng.* **65**, 104–107 (1958).
18. U.S. Pat. 3,117,833 (1964), J. A. Pierret (to Fansteel Inc.).
19. C. W. Balke, *Trans. Electrochem. Soc.* **85**, 89–95 (1944).
20. C. F. Powell, I. E. Campbell, and B. W. Gonser, *J. Electrochem. Soc.* **93**, 258 (1948).
21. H. A. Johansen and S. L. May, *Ind. Eng. Chem.* **46**, 2499 (1954).
22. U.S. Pat. 2,905,549 (1957), D. F. Taylor, R. L. Baughman, and L. F. Yntema (to Fansteel Inc.).
23. A. Clauss and H. Forestier, *Compt. Rend.* **246**, 3241–3243 (1958).
24. R. F. Rolsten, "Preparation and X-Ray Study of Some Tantalum Halides," *J. Am. Chem. Soc.* **80**, 2952 (1958).
25. F. S. Badger, *Ind. Eng. Chem.* **50**, 1608–1611 (1958).
26. C. R. Bishop and M. Stern, *Corrosion* **17**, 379–385 (1961).
27. M. Stern and C. R. Bishop, "Corrosion and Electrochemical Behavior," in reference 5.
28. C. A. Hampel, *Corrosion* **14**, 557–560 (1958).
29. E. Rabald, *Werkstoffe Korrosion* **12**, 695–698 (1961).
30. *Corrosionomics* **5** (5), Fansteel Inc., North Chicago, Ill., 1960, p. 5.
31. G. L. Miller, "Binary Alloy Systems," in *Tantalum and Niobium*, Academic Press, Inc., New York, 1959, Chap. 11.
32. D. C. Ludwigson, *J. Metals* **16**, 226–229 (1964).
33. J. A. Nadel, M.D., et al., "Tantalum Powder as a Medium for Bronchography in Canine and Human Lungs," *Invest. Radiology* **3**, 229 (1968).
34. J. H. Norton, H. Blumenthal, and S. J. Sindeband, *J. Metals* **1**, 749 (1949).
35. F. H. Elinger, *Trans. Am. Soc. Metals* **31**, 89 (1943).
36. K. M. Alexander and F. Fairbrother, *J. Chem. Soc.* **1949**, S 223.
37. C. W. Balke, *J. Am. Chem. Soc.* **27**, 1140 (1905).
38. M. von Parani, "Tantalum and Hydrogen," *Z. Elektrochem.* **11**, 555 (1905).
39. F. Horn and W. Zweigler, *J. Am. Chem. Soc.* **69**, 2762 (1947).
40. G. F. Hardy and J. H. Hulm, *Phys. Rev.* **93**, 1004 (1954).
41. R. Young and T. Hastings, *J. Am. Chem. Soc.* **64**, 1740 (1942).
42. Reference 6, Chap. 3.
43. J. I. Dinnin, *Anal. Chem.* **25**, 1803 (1953).
44. P. G. Melikoff and L. Pissarjewski, *Z. Anorg. Chem.* **20**, 345 (1899).

Donald F. Taylor
Fansteel Inc.

TAPIOCA.   See Starch, Vol. 18, p. 672.

TAR ACIDS.   See Cresols, Vol. 6, p. 437; Tar and pitch.

TAR AND PITCH

Most organic substances, when subjected to a high temperature in the absence of air, undergo, to a greater or lesser extent, simultaneous decomposition to small molecules and polymerization to high-molecular-weight char or coke with the production of a dark-colored by-product to which the generic terms "tar" or "pitch" are given. The differentiation between these two terms is not precise; when the by-product is a liquid of fairly low viscosity at ordinary temperature, it is regarded as a tar; when the by-product is of very viscous, semisolid or solid consistency, it is designated as a pitch. Thus on distillation of vegetable or animal oils or fats, small amounts of residual products known as "vegetable-oil pitch," "wool-grease pitch," "stearin pitch," and so on are produced. Such products, of ill-defined composition and properties, are, however, made in the minimum quantities and have little industrial importance; mainly, they are burned as a means of disposal.

The distillation of crude petroleum yields a pitchlike residual product termed "bitumen" or "asphalt." In America it is referred to as asphalt, but in Europe the term "asphalt" is generally restricted to naturally occurring lake asphalt, the residues from crude-oil distillation being termed "bitumen." These are important industrial materials, produced in millions of tons annually, but they are not included in the subject matter of this article. Their production, properties, and uses are dealt with in the article on Asphalt (Vol. 2, p. 762).

Currently over 350 million long tons (2240 lb) of coal are destructively distilled (carbonized) for the production of coke or town gas (world estimate) and it is this source which provides the raw material for the tar-distilling industry (see Carbonization). The subject of this article is therefore coal tar and its solid or semisolid distillation residue, coal-tar pitch.

Before embarking on this main theme, mention should be made of wood tar and pine tar. Fairly large tonnages of wood (1.5 million tons annually in the U.S. alone) are carbonized for the manufacture of charcoal with the production of by-product tar in about 10 wt % yield. However, only a minor proportion of the wood is treated in by-product recovery ovens and much of the tar recovered is burned as fuel to heat the carbonizing retorts. Wood tar (from hard woods) and pine tar (from resinous woods) are thus of comparatively minor industrial importance. They are chemically complex and reactive materials whose composition varies with the nature of the wood carbonized. When distilled, they yield light and heavy oil and residual wood-tar pitch or pine-tar pitch (sometimes referred to as Stockholm pitch or Archangel pitch). A large number of organic chemicals, such as ketones, lactones, aliphatic acids, methoxy-substituted phenols, and furan derivatives, have been identified in, or isolated from, wood-tar distillate oil (1), but industrial utilization has been confined to the use of the crude fractions as preservatives for ropes and as froth-flotation agents. Turpentine and dipentene are obtained from the front ends of pine-tar oils, the heavier fractions of which are used for the antirot treatment of cordage and as a perfuming agent in soaps, shampoos, and other toilet preparations. Pine-tar pitch is used as a sealant, as a fixative in the grinding of optical lenses, for rotproofing jute fabrics, and as a basis for marine antifouling paints.

Historical. Although coal was first carbonized in Britain toward the end of the eighteenth century to produce tar as a substitute for the wood tar used in shipbuilding the tar industry owes its inception to the development of gas-lighting in England during the first twenty years of the nineteenth century. By 1820, gasworks, in which coal was carbonized in small iron retorts, had become established in most cities and towns in Britain, and the disposal of the by-product tar was becoming an increasing problem. At first it was burned under the retorts, but, in 1818, Accum demonstrated that crude coal tar could be distilled to yield a volatile oil, which could be used as a substitute for turpentine, and a residue which had valuable properties as a protective paint. This established the early pattern of tar processing until about 1830, when the use of tar in the manufacture of ropes was discontinued and, at the same time, copper sheathing of ship hulls became general and tarring was abandoned. Fortunately a new outlet for the heavier tar oil (creosote) arose with the development in 1838 by Bethell of his process for the preservation of railway ties by pressure impregnation. This coincided with the growing use of coal-tar pitch in the making of coal briquets and a more profitable and stable pattern of processing developed. Small tar distilleries, employing primitive batch stills, were established at, or near, the gasworks to make coal-tar naphtha or light oil, which had a growing outlet as a rubber solvent, creosote for timber preservation, and pitch for briquetting.

The development of the coal-tar color industry in Britain during the latter half of the nineteenth century increased the value of crude tar and even when this industry had become the monopoly of the large German cartels, most of the crude intermediates were imported from Britain. The adoption of by-product coke ovens with benzole recovery in Germany, following their development in France by Knob and Carvès, rendered Germany independent of the importation of tar chemicals; the price of crude tar in Britain fell by 90% from 1880 to 1895.

A somewhat similar pattern of development took place in both Germany and the United States, particularly after the changeover to by-product coking ovens; by the commencement of the twentieth century, tar distillation had become established as a separate and important industry in all these countries. Subsequent developments which, with different time lags, have affected all countries, have been the replacement of pot stills by continuous units; the centralization of tar distilling in fewer, large firms; and the development of new major outlets for the products of tar refining. Notable in this context have been the development of fluxed coal-tar pitch as a road binder and as a liquid fuel, the invention of phenol–formaldehyde resins, and the rise of phthalic anhydride—made, until recently, entirely by the oxidation of coal-tar naphthalene—as a major industrial chemical.

Coal-Tar Production

The carbonization of coal is now carried out for three distinct purposes. One major product desired is a hard coke suitable for use in blast furnaces for the reduction of iron ore. For this purpose the coal is heated in coke ovens in which the flue temperature is on the order of 1250–1350°C and the time of carbonization varies from 17 to 30 hr. The gas made in this process may be considered the major by-product; it is purified and used as town gas.

In those countries where the by-product gas from metallurgical coke ovens is insufficient to satisfy the demand for town gas, and natural gas is unavailable, coal is carbonized at gasworks. Coke ovens, operated under slightly less drastic conditions and on a wider selection of coals, are the main gas-making plant operated in Germany, France, Russia, and Japan; the major by-product is a more reactive coke which, although less suitable for metallurgical use, is satisfactory for domestic heating. In

Great Britain, however, the earlier horizontal retorts used for town-gas production have been almost completely replaced by continuous vertical retorts. These operate at a flue temperature of 1000–1100°C but the volatile products of carbonization are rapidly swept from the retort by the introduction of steam in an amount between 10 and 20 wt % of the coal carbonized.

The third objective of coal carbonization is a minor, though growing, one. This is low-temperature carbonization, in which coal is heated in retorts at temperatures in the 600–800°C range to produce a very reactive coke suitable for use as a smokeless fuel in open fires. See also Carbonization.

In addition to the by-product tars produced in coke ovens, continuous vertical retorts, and low-temperature retorts, oil-gas tars and carburetted water-gas tars may

Table 1. Production of Coal Tar in Various Countries

Country	Production, 1000 tons			
	1962	1964	1966	1967
U.S.A.	2,778	3,257	4,100	4,160
Great Britain				
coke oven	982	1,075	997	954
continuous vertical retorts	1,166	1,079	929	798
low temperature	80	110	138	168
others	378	327	243	199
total	2,606	2,591	2,307	2,119
West Germany				
coke oven	1,720	1,730	1,570	1,420
others	278	231	173	141
total	1,998	1,961	1,743	1,561
U.S.S.R. (estimated)	2,600	2,870	3,350	3,500
Japan	947	1,075	1,246	1,421
estimated world production (excluding China)	14,000	14,860	15,300	15,350

be mentioned. These are not, strictly speaking, derived from coal but from the cracking of the petroleum gas-oils used to increase the calorific value of water gas or producer gas. Their production has now become almost obsolete. Some small amounts of tar are produced in Europe by the complete gasification of coal in Lurgi Spühlgas plants. In composition this is similar to continuous vertical-retort tar if bituminous coal is used, but more similar to low-temperature tar if brown coal is the material gasified. See also Gas, manufactured.

Thus, except in Great Britain, almost all the tar made in the world is of coke-oven origin. In Britain continuous vertical-retort tar rose to a peak production of 1,240,000 tons in 1957; since then it has decreased due to the replacement of coal by petroleum distillates as the feedstock for the production of town gas. This decrease is expected to accelerate in the near future as North Sea natural gas replaces manufactured gas and it is expected that by 1972, the tar industry in Britain, like that in the other major industrial countries, will be almost solely dependent on coke-oven tar. Table 1 gives some statistical information on tar production in the major producing countries.

Properties of Coal Tar

The tars recovered from commercial carbonizing plants are not the primary products of the thermal decomposition of coal. These initial products undergo, to a greater or lesser degree, depending on the carbonizing temperature and their residence time in the retort, a complex series of secondary reactions. Although the carbonization conditions have the greatest effect on the chemical nature of the organic by-products, the nature of the coal also has some influence, but appears to affect quantity rather than quality except that the sulfur content of coal tar is roughly proportional to that of the coal from which it is derived. The type of by-product recovery plant and how it is operated are also of some importance. Thus crude tar from direct-recovery carbonizing plants will have experienced more secondary cracking in the main than the tar from plants employing the indirect-recovery or semidirect-recovery systems.

Many attempts have been made to isolate and identify the primary products of coal carbonization by carefully heating coal under high-vacuum, short-distillation-path conditions. However, in view of the widely different products obtained in these researches, it is doubtful whether this objective was achieved. The vacuum tars isolated by Juettner and Howard (2) were semisolid, yellow or brown materials containing only small amounts of volatile components. They contained 30% of neutral ether-insoluble compounds of average molecular weight 400. Similar results have been reported by Sun, Ruof, and Howard (3); in their work a number of American coals were subjected to molecular distillation and the distillate separated into pentane-insoluble and pentane-soluble fractions. The yields of condensate varied considerably with the coal. Pittsburgh coal gave the highest yield (12%) and Pocohontas coal the lowest (2.5–3.5%). The pentane-soluble fraction from the Pittsburgh coal vacuum tar had a molecular weight of 350 and the pentane-insoluble fraction, one of 400. Griefner (4) has reported that the pyrolysis of a Pittsburgh seam coal at 10^{-4} mm Hg pressure yielded an enamel-like deposit whose infrared spectrum was almost identical with that of anthraxylon (vitrain) of which the coal was largely composed.

However, at higher pressures the decomposition appears to be quite different. Pictet (5–7) claimed to have recovered 4 wt % of a tar by heating a Loire "fat" coal ("gras," see Vol. 5, p. 658) to 450°C at 15–17 mm Hg pressure in iron retorts and to have found this material free of phenols or carboxylic acids, but rich in fully or partly reduced ring compounds. By heating British coals under moderate vacuum and maintaining the temperature at each level until gas generation had virtually ceased, Burgess and Wheeler (8) found the first change to occur at 200°C when water and carbon oxides were evolved. At 270–300°C decomposition of sulfur compounds was noted and at 310°C a thin, reddish-brown oil began to distill, gas being generated in only small quantities at this stage. At 350°C rapid evolution of a gas whose main components were methane, ethylene, hydrogen, and carbon dioxide was noted, and a viscous oil condensed. From this stage onward, there was increasing rapidity of decomposition to 450°C, at which temperature liquid condensation had virtually ceased, and the gas consisted mainly of methane and hydrogen. The total yield of liquid condensate amounted to 6.5% and, on distillation to 300°C, equal amounts of distillate and pitch were produced. The distillate contained 40–45% unsaturated hydrocarbons, 40% naphthenes and paraffins, 12–15% cresols and xylenols, and only 7% aromatic compounds which, apparently, were naphthalene derivatives.

It would thus appear that the initial decomposition of coal is in effect a depolymerization and that, if the ambient pressure is sufficiently low, the coal fragments, of molecular weight in the 300–400 range, distill and may be condensed. At higher pressures, however, the depolymerized coal undergoes more deep-seated decomposition into gaseous products and simpler paraffins and naphthenes (taken as including both fully and partially saturated ring compounds). Or, alternatively, the decomposition may be into simple molecules and free radicals, some of which almost immediately recombine to yield the "primary" tar. This point is still the subject of controversy. As the primary tar travels through the hot char in the retort it undergoes the reactions which, on thermodynamic grounds, might be expected. Paraffins and naphthenes are aromatized, the naphthenes disappearing before the paraffins; phenols and phenolic compounds are dehydroxylated to aromatic hydrocarbons and substituted aromatics; phenol and heterocyclic compounds lose their alkyl side chains, particularly those which are longer than methyl. The proportion of condensed-ring compounds containing more than three fused rings and the molecular weight of the more complex molecules increase.

Coke-oven tars are the least "primary" tars; that is, in their formation the secondary reactions have been allowed to proceed to their greatest extent. Such tars are complex mixtures of aromatic and heterocyclic ring compounds contaminated with only small amounts (less than 5%) of nonaromatic hydrocarbons. Substituent groups (hydroxyl or alkyl) have been largely removed, so that the "tar acid" content of coke-oven tar is normally less than 5% and unsubstituted aromatic hydrocarbons are more prominent than their alkyl derivatives; such substitution as does occur is restricted to one or more methyl groups. The degree of condensation of the molecules increases as the boiling range is ascended. Single-ring compounds (benzene, toluene, xylene, phenol, cresols, xylenols, pyridine, and methylpyridines) account for about 3% of the tar. These are followed by fused six- and five-membered ring systems (hydrindene, indene, coumarone, and indole) which make up a further 2–3%. Then follow systems containing two six-membered rings, two six-membered and one five-membered ring, and three six-membered rings. This range accounts for 30–35% of the tar; naphthalene and phenanthrene are the major components with the other unsubstituted aromatics (acenaphthene, fluorene, and anthracene) also prominent. Oxygen compounds, with the oxygen atom in a five-membered ring, are the most common heterocyclic compounds, followed by bases with the nitrogen as $=$N— in a six-membered ring or as —NH— in a five-membered ring; ring compounds with a sulfur atom in five-membered rings are also present, particularly in the lower molecular weight range. This same pattern is preserved in the higher molecular weight fractions which—as far as present analytical techniques have been able to elucidate their structures—appear to consist predominantly of unsubstituted or methyl-substituted aromatic hydrocarbons containing from four to eight fused rings, either in single units or joined to each other by single C–C bonds, to give incompletely condensed molecules of irregular shape. Compounds containing more than one heterocyclic atom are rare, as are compounds containing partly saturated ring systems; in most of the structures which contain ring —CH_2— groups, these groups are part of a five-membered ring. Tars produced in continuous vertical retorts can be considered to be more primary than coke-oven tars. They contain larger amounts of paraffins, naphthenes, and partly saturated ring systems and considerably greater amounts of phenolic compounds; the majority of the aromatic hydrocarbon and heterocyclic structures are substituted with one or more methyl or, more rarely, ethyl groups.

Table 2. Properties of Coal Tars

Property	Type of tar							
	Coke oven					Continuous vertical retort British		Low-temperature British average
	British		German		American average			
	Average	Range	Average	Range		Average	Range	
yield, liter/tonne gal/ton	34.4 7.4[a]	17.2–44.6 3.7–9.6[a]	27.4		27.8 6.4[b]	72.5 15.6[a]	64.0–76.6 13.8–16.5[a]	93.0[a]
density, at 20°C	1.169	1.138–1.180	1.175	1.14–1.20	1.180	1.074	1.066–1.083	1.029
viscosity, Redwood mole-sec at 60°C	179	96–400			680	91	78–99	62
water, %	4.9	3.2–6.5	2.5	0.2–5.0	2.2	2.0	2.1–6.3	2.2
carbon, % (on dry tar)	90.3	86.8–93.5	91.4	90–93	91.3	86.0	85.3–87.2	84.0
hydrogen, % (on dry tar)	5.5	5.1–6.0	5.25	5–6	5.1	7.5	7.2–7.8	8.3
sulfur, % (on dry tar)	0.84	0.68–0.98	0.75	0.6–1.0	1.2	0.90	0.67–1.16	0.74
nitrogen, % (on dry tar)	0.95	0.73–1.07	0.86	0.6–1.2	0.67	1.21	0.84–1.65	1.08
ash, % (on dry tar)	0.24	0.03–0.47	0.15	0.05–0.25	0.03	0.09	0.03–0.24	0.10
toluene insolubles, % (on dry tar)	6.7	2.7–7.5	5.5	2–12	9.1	3.1	0.9–5.1	1.2
components wt % (on dry tar)								
benzene	0.25	0.12–0.42	0.4		0.12	0.22	0.14–0.26	0.01
toluene	0.22	0.09–0.35	0.3		0.25	0.22	0.17–0.29	0.12
o-xylene	0.04	0.02–0.07			0.04	0.06	0.05–0.08	0.05
m-xylene	0.11	0.06–0.18	0.2		0.07	0.3	0.11–0.16	0.10
p-xylene	0.04	0.02–0.07			0.03	0.05	0.05–0.07	0.04

ethylbenzene	0.02	0.02–0.04	0.03	0.02			0.01–0.05	0.02
styrene	0.01	0.02–0.06	0.04	0.02			0.02–0.03	0.04
phenol	1.44	0.49–1.36	0.99	0.61	0.08–0.7		0.14–1.15	0.57
o-cresol	1.48	0.77–1.53	1.33	0.25		0.5	0.10–0.34	0.32
m-cresol	0.98	0.58–1.33	1.05	0.45		0.2	0.16–1.0	0.45
p-cresol	0.87	0.50–1.03	0.86	0.27		0.4	0.07–0.70	0.27
xylenols	6.36	2.70–3.58	3.08	0.36		0.2	0.13–1.30	0.48
higher-boiling tar acids	12.89	6.57–11.10	8.09	0.83			0.31–2.09	0.91
naphtha fraction (bp 150–200°C)	3.63	2.86–3.84	3.21	0.97			0.52–2.66	1.18
naphthalene	0.65	2.15–3.84	3.18	8.80	5–13	10.0	7.29–11.31	8.94
1-methylnaphthalene	0.23	0.46–0.64	0.54	0.65		0.5	0.60–0.86	0.72
2-methylnaphthalene	0.19	0.62–0.74	0.68	1.23		1.5	1.15–1.63	1.32
acenaphthene	0.19	0.50–0.80	0.66	1.06		0.3	0.42–1.28	0.96
fluorene	0.13	0.33–1.23	0.51	0.84		2.0	0.46–1.80	0.88
diphenylene oxide	0.19	0.56–0.84	0.68			1.4	1.40–2.00	1.50
anthracene	0.06	0.18–0.30	0.26	0.75		1.8	0.52–1.38	1.00
phenanthrene	1.6	0.40–2.90	1.75	2.66		5.7	2.30–8.80	6.30
carbazole	1.29	0.14–1.43	0.89	0.60		1.5	0.58–1.73	1.33
tar bases	2.09	1.81–2.47	2.09	2.08	0.2–2.0	0.73	1.25–2.60	1.77
medium-soft pitch (70°C, R and B softening pt)	26.0	41.0–49.3	43.7	63.5	45–65	54.4	49.5–63.9	59.8

a Imp. gal/long ton.
b U.S. gal/short ton.
1 long ton = 2240 lb.
1 short ton = 2000 lb.
1 tonne = 1000 kg = 2204 lb.
1 Imp. gal = 1.2 U.S. gal = 4.54 liters.

Low-temperature tars are the most nearly primary of the commercial coal tars. In these, nonaromatic hydrocarbons (paraffins and olefins) amount to 30–35%; phenols make up 20–25%; and almost all the 40–50% aromatic hydrocarbons present contain one or more alkyl groups.

A feature of the phenols extracted from both continuous vertical-retort tars and low-temperature tars is their high content of indanols (hydroxyhydrindenes); the tar bases recovered from low-temperature tars contain a considerable proportion of primary bases such as aniline and toluidine.

It must, however, be emphasized that, even among the same types of tar, considerable variations in chemical composition occur. Only a small number of the components of coal tars are present in amounts sufficient to justify their recovery, and only a few of these have industrial uses. Table 2 lists the tar components which have either current or potential industrial possibilities and gives the amounts which have been found in the different types of tar. This table also illustrates the variations which can be found in tars of the same type.

The Primary Distillation of Coal Tar

As produced, crude coal tar is of value only as a fuel; formerly, relatively large amounts of crude or dehydrated tar were burned, particularly at steel works. This practice has largely been abandoned and now 98% of the tar made in Britain and West Germany and 85% of the tar produced in the U.S. is distilled.

Although 10–30-ton mild-steel pot stills are still in use at some small tar works, continuous stills with capacities varying from 100 to 700 tons/day are now generally used. There are a considerable number of different designs of continuous tar stills in operation, but all are basically similar in principle. Their essential features are a tube-still furnace, through which the tar flows continuously, flash chambers in which water and volatiles are separated from the crude and dehydrated tars, and one or more bubble-cap fractionating columns in which the tar vapors are separated into a series of distillates of progressively increasing boiling range.

The tube furnace is essentially a rectangular chamber lined with refractory brick and divided into two sections by a curtain wall which has apertures to enable the hot flue gases to pass from one compartment to the other. One section serves as a combustion chamber in which coke-oven gas, fuel oil, or creosote/pitch is burned at specially designed nozzles projecting into the chamber. The hot flue gases are drawn by a fan from the combustion chamber into the second, or convection, chamber, before being exhausted to the chimney stack. In some designs there is provision for recirculating the flue gas through the furnace before it is withdrawn to the chimney. The heating tubes, through which the crude and dehydrated tars are pumped, are generally arranged horizontally and parallel on the furnace walls; the connecting bends generally protrude through the furnace shell for ease of cleaning. There are usually two separate coils; the smaller one—the waste heat coil—is located in the convection chamber and the main coil may either be positioned entirely within this chamber— in which case it is screened from direct radiation from the furnace—or may be located partly in the convection section and partly in the combustion chamber; in this latter design some of the heat is transmitted to the tubes by direct radiation.

The flash chambers consist essentially of large vertical cylindrical vessels either empty or fitted with staggered baffles; in some plants there is an upper section filled with mild-steel ferrules.

Other items of a primary tar still are shell tube heat exchangers in which the crude tar is heat-exchanged with the residue and/or distillate oils.

Two major problems are associated with continuous tar distillation. Coal tar contains two types of components which are highly corrosive to ferrous metals. The ammonium salts (principally ammonium chloride) in the entrained liquor remain in the tar on dehydration and tend to dissociate in the hotter parts of the plant with the production of hydrochloric and other acids which cause rapid wastage of any part of the plant in which the tar vapors and steam are present above 240°C and also of the condensers on the dehydration flash tower and the fractionation-column overhead stream. This form of corrosion is controlled by the addition of alkali (caustic soda or sodium carbonate solution) to the crude tar.

The higher-boiling phenols—the so-called *resinols*—are corrosive to mild steel, the attack increasing rapidly above 300°C. Fortunately they are not so aggressive toward cast iron, chrome steels, or stainless steels and the furnace tubes in continuous tar plants are generally constructed of one of these metals. Nevertheless, to ensure satisfactory life from the furnace coils, particularly in plants processing continuous vertical-retort tar or low-temperature tar, the temperature of the tar in the tubes should be kept at a minimum.

There is, however, a much more important reason for operating tar tube-still furnaces to avoid overheating the tar. Coal tar is thermally unstable and, if heated above a certain temperature, will decompose with the formation of coke which can rapidly block the tubes. This danger is again more acute in plants handling continuous vertical-retort tars and low-temperature tars which have a decomposition temperature considerably lower than coke-oven tars. To guard against overheating the tar, various means are adopted in different designs. Most plants operate the furnace tubes under a back pressure, which may be as high as 150 psi in order to minimize vaporization in the tubes. In some designs the tubes are screened from radiant heat; in others, twin coils are employed to reduce the heat flux. Flue-gas recirculation, which reduces the overall flue-gas temperature, is a feature of some modern plants. In one popular design, the hot residue is recirculated with the dehydrated tar; this cuts down the percentage of vapors in the circulating fluid and, by increasing the velocity through the tubes, improves the heat-transfer rate. Other designs utilize a double-flash system in which the second stage is carried out under reduced pressure; this reduces the temperature to which the tar must be raised to yield a residual pitch of the desired softening point.

Continuous tar stills can therefore be divided into those which employ a single-pass, single-flash system; those which employ a single-pass, multiple-flash system; and those in which the residue is recirculated. Examples of each of these main variants differ, however, in the design of tube furnace, in the number of fractionation columns used, and in the extent to which heat exchange is employed.

Single-Pass, Single-Flash Continuous Stills. The Pro-Abd (Société pour l'Exploitation des Procédés Ab-Der-Halden) design, illustrated in Figure 1, is typical of a once-through plant employing a single atmospheric pressure side-stream column (9). This design is employed at a number of distilleries in Great Britain, France, and Holland.

Crude tar from storage, after passing through screening filters and being doped with aqueous alkali, is pumped through a series of heat exchangers and then through the waste-heat coil in the furnace. It is then, at a temperature of 150–160°C, injected into the dehydrator where the water and lighter oils flash off. These, after cooling by

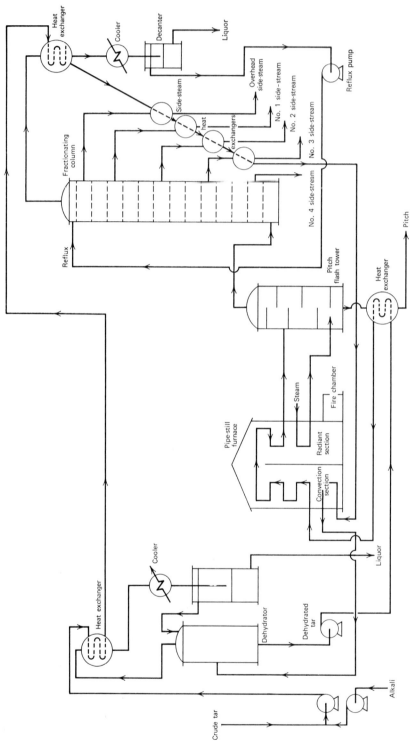

Fig. 1. Pro-Abd design of continuous tar still.

heat exchange, are condensed and the water separated from the oils in a decanter; the light oils are returned to the dehydrator. (This is not universal practice; in some plants the condensed light oils are added as reflux to the top of the fractionating column.) The dehydrated tar is heat-exchanged with the hot pitch and vapors, and then pumped through the main furnace coil, emerging at 350–400°C and at a pressure of 30–50 psi into the pitch flash chamber in which volatile oils are disengaged from the residual pitch or base tar. Superheated steam is injected into the base of the flash chamber to assist the removal of the volatile products. The mixture of oil vapors and steam enters the base of the fractionating column, from which the various fractions are taken off as a light overhead fraction and heavier side-streams.

This newer design of Pro-Abd plant is generally operated to give a base tar or soft pitch as the residue. In the older design, which is still in operation at a number of refineries in Great Britain and other European countries, steam is not added to the flash chamber; the residue is treated separately with superheated steam in a vessel termed a "cornu" (retort) located in a setting on the top of the furnace.

The Newton Chambers plants operated by Lancashire Tar Distillers, Cadishead near Manchester; the Foster Wheeler plants of the Midland-Yorkshire Tar Distillers, Oldbury near Birmingham; and the continuous plants used by the Barrett Division of Allied Chemicals and Dye Corporation are of the same basic design. The older type of Koppers plant (10), which is still in operation in both England and Germany, differs from the Pro-Abd design in employing a number of distillation columns in series instead of a single side-stream column. The "Giprokoks"-designed plants encountered in Russian tar distilleries also operate on the single-pass, single-flash principle but employ two side-stream columns, one of which replaces the pitch flash chamber (11). The heated tar issuing from the main furnace coil is fed to the first column about one-third up from the base. Pitch is withdrawn from the base of this column and a heavy-oil side-stream from near the top. Uncondensed vapors pass to the second column near the base and the remaining fractions are taken as side-streams from this column. By this means, better stripping of oil from the pitch is achieved.

Another variant of the once-through, single-flash design is employed at the Duis-burg-Meiderich works of Rütgerswerke AG and in the Badger's plant, operated by Dominion Tar and Chemical Co. Ltd. at their Hamilton, Ontario works (12). In these plants the pitch flash chamber and fractionating column are operated under vacuum.

Single-Pass, Multiple-Flash Continuous Stills. The modern Koppers design of continuous tar plants (13), operated in both Germany and Great Britain, is illustrated in Figure 2. The crude tar, after being strained through wire gauze screens and the customary addition of alkali, is raised to a temperature of 150°C by heat exchange and enters the dehydrator where water and light oils are removed. The topped tar is then pumped through the furnace coils from which it emerges at 300–320°C into the main atmospheric distillation column. From this column an overhead fraction, two side-streams, and a bottoms fraction are taken. The overhead product is condensed and separated into light oil and liquor; the lower side-stream passes to a stripping column. The top product from the stripping column passes back to the main atmospheric column as reflux, while the bottoms product passes to a third atmospheric pressure column to be separated into naphthalene oil and a light wash oil. The base stream from the main atmospheric fractionating column is pumped through another coil in the furnace to bring its temperature back to 300–320°C and is then injected into a

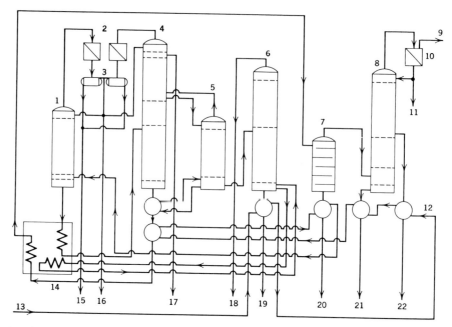

Fig. 2. Modern Koppers continuous tar-distillation plant. Reproduced from H. G. Franck and G. Collin, *op. cit.* Courtesy Springer-Verlag.

LEGEND:

1. dehydration column	8. anthracene oil column	15. water
2. condensers		16. light oil
3. decanters	9. to vacuum pump	17. carbolic oil
4. main atmospheric column	10. condenser	18. naphthalene oil
5. stripping column	11. wash oil II	19. wash oil I
6. wash-oil column	12. crude tar	20. pitch
7. flash chamber	13. crude tar	21. anthracene oil II
	14. tube furnace	22. anthracene oil I

vacuum flash chamber. The heavier oils released here are split into heavy wash oil and heavy and light anthracene oils in a vacuum side-stream column; the residual pitch flows from the base of the vacuum flash chamber.

A much more elaborate multiflash system is operated by Rütgerswerke AG at their Castrop-Rauxel plant. In this plant the crude tar is continuously dehydrated in a baffled column and the dehydrated tar brought to 250°C by heat exchange with hot pitch and injected into a large fractionating column which comprises forty bubble-cap trays above a 10-m packed section. This column operates at atmospheric pressure and has its own gas-fired reboiler. From it are taken an overhead carbolic oil stream, a naphthalene oil side-stream, and a residue fraction. The naphthalene oil fraction is upgraded in a twenty-plate stripping column and the combined residues from the atmospheric column and the stripping column pass to the second fractionating column which is similar in dimensions and design to the first but which operates at 200 mm Hg pressure. From this column is taken a methylnaphthalene fraction as overheads, wash oil, and a fluorene/acenaphthene oil as side-streams, and a residue. The wash-oil side-stream is treated in a twenty-plate stripping column to remove lighter and heavier

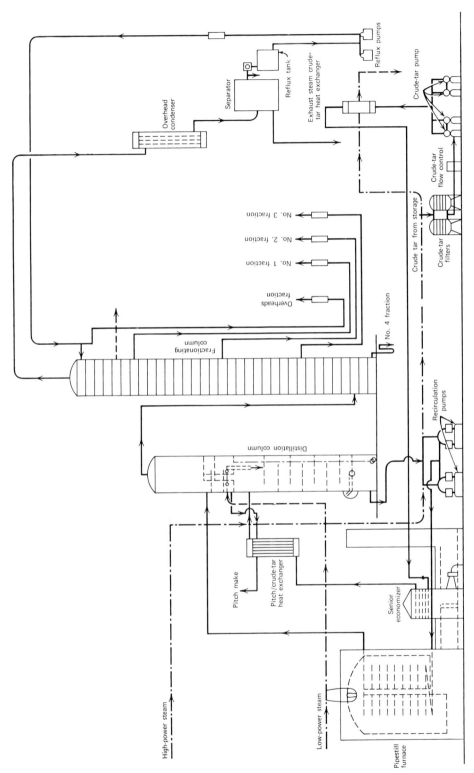

Fig. 3. Modern Wilton still process.

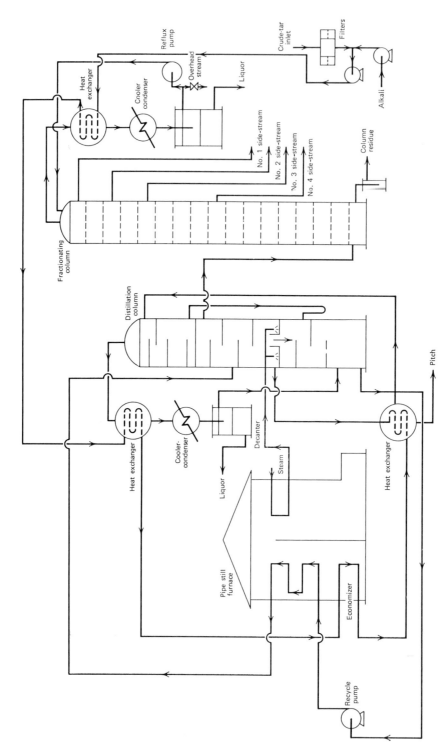

Fig. 4. Wilton continuous tar-distillation plant with three-section distillation colu.mn.

material, the former returning to the second fractionating column as reflux and the latter joining the residue from the second column. These combined residues pass to the third fractionating column which operates at 70 mm Hg pressure; in this, residual oils are separated from pitch. The residual oils pass to a fourth fractionating column operated at 20 mm Hg pressure where they are separated into a close-cut anthracene/phenanthrene fraction and a crude carbazole fraction; the latter is finally fractionated in a fifth column to give carbazole of 90–95% purity and a heavy-oil residue.

All the fractionating columns at the Castrop-Rauxel plant except the stripping columns and the carbazole columns have separate gas-fired reboilers.

Recycle Continuous Stills. Wilton stills, designed and erected by Chemical Engineering Wiltons Ltd. (now part of the Simon Carves Group of Stockport, England) are in operation in Great Britain, the U.S., South Africa, Australia, and in various European countries. The latest type, which usually distills 200–400 tons/day of crude tar, is illustrated in Figure 3 (14). Crude tar, after screening and doping with alkali, is pumped through a series of heat exchangers and a waste-heat coil and then injected into the lower section of a dual flash chamber (termed the "distillation column"), where it meets hot pitch overflowing from the upper section. The water and light-oil vapors released in the lower section pass up through a liquid seal into the upper part. The mixture of dehydrated tar and pitch is pumped from the base of the distillation column, through the furnace coil and, at a temperature of 360°C (if a medium-soft pitch is desired as the residue) enters the upper chamber of the distillation column, where the oil vapors flash off assisted by the injection of superheated steam. These vapors and the vapors from the lower section issue from the top of the distillation column into the base of the side-stream fractionating column, while the pitch, which accumulates at the base of the upper section of the distillation column, is partly withdrawn as product and partly allowed to overflow into the lower section where it mixes with the crude tar before recycle through the furnace coils.

For the continuous distillation of relatively small amounts of tar (50–200 tons/day), the early design of Wilton plant (15) is particularly popular. The distillation column in this design is in three sections (Fig. 4). The top section acts as a dehydrator, the topped tar produced there overflowing into the bottom section where it meets recycle pitch from the midsection. The mixture of dehydrated tar and pitch, after passing through the furnace coils, enters the midsection of the distillation column into which superheated steam is also injected. The light oil and liquor vaporized in the top section are condensed and separated, the oil fraction being added to the top of the fractionating column as reflux. The heavier-oil vapors disengaged in the midsection pass in the usual manner to the base of the fractionating column from which an overhead fraction, various side-streams, and a heavy-oil residue are taken; the pitch make is taken off from the base of the midsection of the distillation column.

Other Designs of Continuous Tar-Distillation Plants. A few types of continuous tar plant which do not employ a tube furnace are still in operation. The Raschig continuous plant—a German design—consists, in essence, of a series of pans heated by superheated steam and operating at progressively lower pressure (16). The tar flows in cascade through these pans, the vapors produced in each being fractionated in separate vacuum fractionating columns.

At one large U.S. refinery, the crude tar is first dehydrated by heat exchange and the dehydrated tar pumped via a crude tar/topped tar heat exchanger, into a bubble-cap fractionating column equipped with gas-fired reboiler. In this column about 20%

of the tar (a fraction containing the bulk of the naphthalene and phenols) is recovered as distillate; the topped-tar residue, after cooling in the heat exchanger, is further distilled in pot-stills to yield refined tar or pitch of the specification desired.

Coal-Tar Products

Nature of Primary Fractions from Crude Tar. The two main objectives in the primary distillation of crude tar are to obtain a pitch or refined-tar residue of the desired softening point and to concentrate, as far as possible in certain fractions, those components which are subsequently to be recovered.   In the case of continuous vertical-retort tar, the main aim is to concentrate the phenol, cresols, and xylenols in the carbolic-oil fraction, whereas, in the processing of coke-oven tar, the main objective is to concentrate naphthalene and anthracene in the naphthalene oil and anthracene oil, respectively.

The degree of fractionation employed is, except in the case of the Rütgerswerke Castrop-Rauxel plant, generally no better than is required to achieve these purposes.

Table 3. Typical Fractions Taken in Continuous Tar Distillation to Medium-Soft Pitch

| | Type of tar | | | | | |
| | Continuous vertical retort | | | Coke oven | | |
Fraction no.	Names	Boiling range,[a] °C	Wt % of crude tar	Names	Boiling range,[a] °C	Wt % of crude tar
1	crude benzole, light oil	106–167	2.4	crude benzole, light oil	99–160	0.6
2	naphtha, carbolic oil, phenolic oil	167–194	3.1	naphtha, light oil,	168–196	2.9
3	heavy naphtha, carbolic oil, naphthalene oil	203–240	9.3	naphthalene oil	198–230	14.6
4	naphthalene oil	215–254	3.5	wash oil, benzole absorbing oil, light creosote	224–286	2.8
5	wash oil, benzole absorbing oil, light creosote	238–291	10.2	anthracene oil, heavy creosote	247–355	8.0
6	creosote	271–362	11.5	heavy oil	323–372 (90%)	9.5
7	heavy creosote, heavy oil	285–395 (50%)	12.1			
residue	medium-soft pitch		40.5	medium-soft pitch		56.6
liquor and losses			7.4			5.0

[a] 5–95% sidearm flask.

The Rütgerswerke plant produces not only a highly concentrated naphthalene fraction, but also fractions which contain high concentrations of fluorene and acenaphthene, anthracene and phenanthrene, and carbazole. These concentrates are further treated to produce these aromatic hydrocarbons in a technically pure form; almost all the pure polynuclear aromatic hydrocarbons (except naphthalene) used throughout the world are products of this plant.

At other plants the number of distillate fractions does not exceed seven, and at many refineries the number is smaller. Table 3 lists typical fractions which might be taken but it must be emphasized that the boiling ranges and the yields on the crude tar will vary somewhat at each plant, depending on the plant design, the nature of the crude tar, and the secondary refining operations carried out at each plant. It should also be pointed out that there are no universally recognized names for primary tar fractions; the same term may be used at two different works to designate fractions of very different boiling range.

REFINED PRODUCTS

From Primary Fractions Distilling up to 150°C. Chemically the crude-benzole fraction of tar is similar to the crude benzole recovered as a separate fraction at gasworks and coke ovens (see Vol. 3, p. 382) and is usually blended with this for further processing. This processing comprises a "defronting" operation by steam stripping which removes the components distilling below benzene (17). The defronted benzole may then be fractionated in batch or continuous stills to give crude benzene, crude toluene, crude xylenes, and a residue of naphtha; each of these fractions may be further purified to meet the specification requirements for the various grades of *benzene, toluene,* and *mixed xylenes.* Alternatively, the crude benzole may be refined and the refined product fractionated. The refining consists essentially of removing non-aromatic hydrocarbons and thiophene derivatives; the most widely used process is to mix the crude benzole or crude-benzole fraction with a small amount of concentrated sulfuric acid, which, in addition to polymerizing olefins, effects selective sulfonation of sulfur-containing impurities. It has been shown that this sulfonation reaction is reversible (18) and, for most economic results, very intimate mixing of the crude benzole with 2–4% concentrated sulfuric acid and almost immediate separation of the layers is recommended. Pulsed column contactors are being increasingly used for this purpose (19).

The alternative to sulfuric acid treatment is catalytic hydrorefining, which is employed at a number of U.S., British, Russian, and German refineries, mainly on the crude-benzene fraction (20–22). In this process the vaporized hydrocarbon feedstock and hydrogen are passed over a cobalt molybdate-on-alumina catalyst at about 400°C and 500 psi pressure. This converts any olefins to paraffins or naphthenes and effects reduction of thionaphthene compounds to hydrogen sulfide. The refined product, after washing with alkali to remove hydrogen sulfide, must in general be further treated by some suitable solvent-extraction process to remove the small amount of nonaromatic hydrocarbons which it contains. The Universal Oil Product Co. "Udex" process (23), the Shell Development Co. sulfolane extraction process, and the process recently developed by Metallgesellschaft AG, which employs N-methylpyrrolidone as the selective solvent (24), are all in use for this purpose. See also Hydroprocesses.

Gasworks benzole or its fractions are generally too rich in nonaromatic hydrocarbons—even after sulfuric acid refining—to yield synthesis-grade benzene and toluene at an economic cost; the main outlet for gasworks benzole is as an aromatic additive to gasoline, for which purpose it is only necessary to reduce the sulfur content to 0.4%.

Up to the start of World War II almost all the benzene and toluene used by the chemical industry was derived from coal carbonization, but since then the rise of the petrochemical industry has completely changed the picture; today, over 85% of the benzene, over 95% of the toluene, and all the pure xylene isomers used by the U.S. chemical industry are petroleum based. Coal-tar xylenes are not separated but are sold as mixed isomers for solvents.

Benzole forerunnings (fronts) contain *carbon disulfide* as a major component and, formerly, this was recovered either by conversion to sodium xanthate or by absorption in ammonium sulfide. The forerunnings also contain *cyclopentadiene* which, until recently, was recovered by storing the forerunnings under pressure at 100°C until the cyclopentadiene had polymerized to dicyclopentadiene (25) (bp 170°C) from which the other components of the forerunnings could be readily separated by distillation. Depolymerization of the diene was subsequently accomplished by heating to its boiling point or by passing the vapors, under vacuum, through a heated tube. Cyclopentadiene (qv) is the starting material for the production of the insecticides aldrin and dieldrin which, until recent legislation restricted the use of persistent organochlorine insecticides, were widely employed in agriculture. Benzole forerunnings are now mainly disposed of by burning.

From Primary Fractions Distilling in the 150–200°C Range. This fraction of coal tar provides the greater part of the pyridine bases as well as solvent and heavy naphthas and coumarone resins.

Pyridine Bases (26–28). The fractions of crude tar which distill in the 150–200°C range are first washed with 10% aqueous caustic soda to remove any phenols and then contacted with a slight excess of 25–35% aqueous sulfuric acid. The "pyridine sulfate" layer is separated from the phenol- and base-free oils. The crude aqueous solution of pyridine base sulfates is sometimes diluted with water and allowed to stand; any resinous material which forms on the surface is skimmed off. It is then steamed or boiled to free it from coextracted neutral oils before being neutralized by the addition of alkali. At some plants 16% caustic soda is used for "cracking" (or "springing") pyridine sulfate; at others, ammonia or sodium carbonate is employed. Whichever alkali is used, the acid concentration is adjusted before neutralization so that an almost saturated solution of sodium or ammonium sulfate, in which pyridine bases are substantially insoluble, is formed. The crude bases are separated from the alkali sulfate solution and dried, either by addition of solid caustic soda or by azeotropic distillation with benzene. The dry bases are then fractionated to yield (1) a small amount of pyridine–water azeotrope (approximately $C_5H_5N \cdot 3H_2O$) which is recycled to the dehydration stage of the process, (2) once-run *pyridine*, (3) once-run α-picoline, (4) a fraction known as 90/140 bases which consists mainly of β-picoline, γ-picoline, and 2,6-lutidine, and (5) higher-boiling fractions termed 90/160 and 90/180 bases. Each of these fractions may be refractionated to yield material suitable for specific purposes. The separation of *β-picoline*, *γ-picoline*, and *2,6-lutidine* by fractional distillation is impossible since they boil less than one degree apart. They do, however, form azeotropes with water which, though still boiling close together, can be separated by high-efficiency fractionation. See also Pyridine.

In the United States the more usual practice is to extract tar acids and tar bases from the total distillate oils boiling up to 230°C. This operation yields crude tar bases which contain, in addition to the pyridine bases, primary bases such as aniline and toluidines and higher bases such as quinoline, isoquinoline, and methylquinoline.

Until recently the main uses for pyridine bases were as solvents, for the synthesis of rubber chemicals, and for the synthesis of drugs. Pyridine and its 2-benzyl and 2-amino derivatives are the starting products for a number of analgesics, stimulants, and antihistamine preparations. The main outlet for β-picoline is for oxidation to nicotinic acid, and for γ-picoline the major use is for the synthesis of isoniazid (isonicotinic acid hydrazide), used in the treatment of tuberculosis.

Recently the development of the nonpersistent herbicides diquat and paraquat has provided a new market for pyridine which is now by far the largest. See Weed killers.

α-Picoline has minor uses in the pharmaceutical field; its three main outlets are for the production of 2-vinylpyridine, for the synthesis of 2-β-methoxyethylpyridine, and for the synthesis of Amprolium (a registered trademark of Merck & Company, Inc.), formerly called Mepyrium. 2-Vinylpyridine, made by condensing α-picoline with formalin to give 2-hydroxyethylpyridine and dehydrating this product, is used as a copolymer with butadiene and styrene in the manufacture of tires. 2-β-Methoxyethylpyridine, Promintic (a registered trademark of Imperial Chemical Industries Ltd.), is a widely used anthelmintic for cattle and Amprolium is employed in combating coccidiosis in poultry.

The higher-boiling tar base mixtures, ie 90/160 and 90/180 bases, are employed as denaturants, special solvents, and corrosion inhibitors.

Naphthas. The tar-acid-free and tar-base-free 150–200°C fraction of coal tar is generally refractionated (sometimes after treatment with concentrated sulfuric acid) to yield rectified or unrectified *solvent naphtha* and *heavy naphtha*. Sometimes the grades of naphtha made are termed *90/160, 90/180,* and *90/200 naphthas*, indicating that 90% distills at 160, 180, or 200°C. The naphthas are fairly widely used as solvents in paints and polishes.

Coumarone Resins (29). These should really be called indene resins. They are made by taking a special fraction of coke-oven naphtha which distills substantially in the range 170–185°C and which contains at least 30% indene. This fraction, free from tar acids and bases, is heated with or without a catalyst to polymerize the indene and part of the coumarone; the unpolymerized oil is removed by distillation. Thermal polymerization or the use of sulfuric acid as catalyst has been replaced by the use of boron trifluoride as its complex with either acetic acid or phenol as the catalytic agent in making coumarone resins. These resins vary from pale amber to dark brown in color and are made in various grades having softening points of up to 120°C. They find uses in the production of flooring tiles and in paints and polishes. See also Hydrocarbon resins.

From Primary Fractions Distilling in the Range 200–250°C. This range includes the carbolic and naphthalene oils and yields the most valuable tar chemicals.

Tar Acids (30–32). Tar acids or phenols are recovered from oils in this range by extracting them with a slight excess of 10% caustic soda. Extraction is carried out at a temperature just above the crystallization point of the oil; batch-stirred vessels or continuous-extraction columns may be employed. The aqueous extract (known as crude sodium phenate, crude sodium carbolate, or sodium cresylate) is separated from the dephenolated oils, which pass forward for the recovery of naphthalene. The sodium cresylate is boiled or treated with live steam, and/or solvent-extracted to remove coextracted neutral oils and bases, and then "sprung" or decomposed by passing down a tower countercurrent to a stream of gas containing carbon dioxide. The product from this springing tower separates into two layers—an aqueous solution of sodium carbonate and an upper layer of crude tar acids. These are separated and the crude tar acids, which contain about 20% of dissolved carbonate, are either neutralized with sulfuric acid or treated again with carbon dioxide until about half the sodium carbonate is converted to bicarbonate. On settling, the aqueous solution of sodium sulfate or sodium carbonate/bicarbonate separates and is run off. If the crude tar acids are treated by "aftercarbonation," the carbonate/bicarbonate solution is added to the aqueous carbonate from the springing tower and recausticized by treating with quicklime and removing the calcium carbonate precipitate ("lime mud") by filtration or centrifuging. The regenerated caustic soda is adjusted to the correct concentration and recycled to the extraction stage.

The crude tar acids are refined by batch or continuous fractional distillation. They are first fractionated to give "phenol water" (which is recycled), once-run tar acids, and a residue of phenolic pitch. The once-run tar acids are then fractionated to give pure *phenol*, pure *o-cresol*, mixtures of *m-* and *p-cresols* containing specific amounts of the meta isomer and a residue of *xylenols* which may be further separated by batch fractionation. Depending on the demand for the various cresols and xylenols, crude tar acids may be less efficiently distilled and simply separated into phenol and mixtures of cresols and xylenols which conform to certain specifications. Such mixtures are known in commerce under the generic term of *cresylic acids*. See also Cresols.

The amount of phenol separated from coal tar is entirely inadequate to meet the demands of industry for this chemical and most of the phenol used by the chemical and allied industries is synthesized from benzene; currently, for example, in the U.S. about 90% of the phenol used is synthetic (see Phenol). On the other hand, most of the cresols and all of the xylenols used industrially are derived from coal tar.

Phenol is one of the most widely used industrial chemicals. It is the starting point for one of the routes to nylon and for the manufacture of aspirin and other important drugs. Other major outlets are in the production of phenol–formaldehyde resins; in the manufacture of pentachlorophenol, a product widely used as a fungicide and wood preservative; in the production of 2,4-dichlorophenoxyacetic acid, which is widely used as a selective weed killer; and in the manufacture of *p-tert*-butyl- and *p*-octylphenols which are employed in the production of oil-soluble resins.

o-Cresol is mainly used as the starting material for the manufacture of dinitro-*o*-cresol, an old established insecticide and herbicide, and in the production of 2-methyl-4-chlorophenoxyacetic acid (MCPA), another widely used selective weed killer. The major uses for cresylic acids are for the manufacture of tritolyl phosphate plasticizers ("tricresyl phosphates") and for the production of thermosetting resins; minor outlets include froth-flotation agents, metal degreasing agents, resin solvents for wire coating, antioxidants, synthetic tanning agents, and nonionic detergents. 2,4-Xylenol is employed in the production of 2,4-dimethyl-6-*tert*-butylphenol which is used as an antioxidant; 3,5-xylenol has an outlet in the production of 4-chloro-3,5-xylenol (or PCMX, *p*-chloro-*m*-xylenol), used as a bactericide and fungicide. 2,6-Xylenol is the raw material for the so-called PPO (polyphenylene oxide) resins recently developed by

General Electric Co. They are claimed to have outstanding mechanical, thermal, and electrical properties.

Naphthalene. Naphthalene is the most abundant single compound in coke-oven tar of which it makes up, on the average, about 9%. The older method of recovering it from dephenolated carbolic or naphthalene oil is to allow the oils to cool slowly in open pans, and allow the residual oil to drain from the crude crystalline naphthalene. The crude naphthalene is then macerated and centrifuged, which gives "whizzed" naphthalene, and finally, the centrifuged material is subjected to a pressure of 350 atm at 60–70°C for several minutes in a mechanical press (33). By this means the less pure, lower-melting-point layers of the crystal are expressed as liquid, leaving a product with a crystallizing point of 78–78.5°C. This grade was found satisfactory for oxidation to phthalic anhydride. Material of 78–79°C crystallizing point, no matter how it is produced, is still referred to as "hot-pressed-grade naphthalene."

The old hot-pressing plants have been almost completely replaced by other installations for recovering hot-pressed-grade naphthalene. In the U.S. (34) and at some British refineries (35) fractional distillation of dephenolated naphthalene oil is the process employed, but this process cannot be used on the oil of lower concentration derived from continuous vertical-retort tars.

The plant employed for the fractionation of coke-oven naphthalene oils consists of a small dehydrating column in which the feedstock is mixed with some of the overhead product from the second, or "fronts," column. The dehydrated naphthalene oil from the base of the dehydrating column is fed to the "fronts" column near the top. In this column, material boiling lower than naphthalene is removed as overheads and employed to dehydrate the crude naphthalene oil. The residue from the fronts column is fed to the middle of the naphthalene column from which hot-pressed-grade naphthalene is taken off as the overhead product and as a heavy fraction from the bottom. Fronts and bottoms fractions are allowed to cool to atmospheric temperature in pans and the crude crystal naphthalene which forms is drained from oil and recycled with fresh feedstock. The distillation columns used in naphthalene distillation plants have generally forty to fifty bubble-cap plates and are operated either at atmospheric pressure with oil-heated reboilers or under moderate vacuum, in which case superheated steam may be used for heating.

This process has one major disadvantage. Components of naphthalene oil such as thionaphthene (C_8H_6S) and dodecanes (which are present in continuous vertical-retort carbolic and naphthalene oils in amounts up to 10%) are concentrated with the naphthalene. Thus, the process is only applicable to substantially paraffin-free coke-oven oils and, even with these feedstocks, it yields a hot-pressed-grade naphthalene containing about 1% sulfur. Since modern phthalic anhydride plants employ catalysts which are sulfur-sensitive, some desulfurization of distilled naphthalene, either by treatment with sulfuric acid or metallic sodium (36) or by catalytic refining (37), is generally desirable.

In Great Britain, Germany, and Russia the generally preferred process for the production of hot-pressed-grade naphthalene consists of first of all adjusting the concentration of naphthalene in the feedstock to give a crystallizing point of 55°C. This feedstock is then cooled to 30–35°C in closed, stirred tanks; the resultant slurry of naphthalene crystals and mother-liquor oils is continuously centrifuged and the crystals washed on the centrifuge with a warm dilute caustic soda solution. The washed crystals are then melted and the aqueous layer which separates is added to the centrifuge wash liquor for recycle (38). The naphthalene from the melter is of hot-pressed quality and is generally transported as liquid to the phthalic anhydride plants.

The mother-liquor oils from the centrifuge still contain about 30% naphthalene and, in the case of coke-oven oils, it is general practice to refractionate these to give a naphtha fraction, a naphthalene concentrate, and a heavy fraction. The concentration of the naphthalene fraction is such that, when mixed with the appropriate amount of fresh naphthalene oil, the crystallizing point of the mixture will be close to 55°C. In practice, it is impossible to treat the total mother liquor in the refractionating plant since, if this is done, coboiling impurities build up and the quality of the naphthalene falls. A part—generally 15–20%—of the mother-liquor oil must be removed from the system although additional naphthalene may be recovered by cooling this purge oil and recycling the crude drained naphthalene recovered from it.

At the Rütgerswerke AG refinery at Castrop-Rauxel and at the Caerphilly plant of the British National Coal Board, a variation of this process is employed (39). The naphthalene oil, without pretreatment to recover tar acids, is cooled by direct contact with twice its volume of cold water, and the mixture of naphthalene crystals, mother-liquor oils, and water is centrifuged. The crystal cake on the centrifuge is washed with hot water. The oils and water are separated and the naphthalene melted to separate the occluded water in the crystals; the combined aqueous layers are recycled after passage through a cooler and the mother-liquor oils refractionated.

In general, continuous vertical-retort carbolic oil, after removal of phenols, contains only 40–45% naphthalene and is processed for naphthalene recovery only when the demand for naphthalene warrants this. The usual practice follows the indirect cooling-centrifuging-washing process described above, with two important differences. Firstly, it is necessary to refractionate the oil to increase its crystallizing point to the 55°C level, and secondly, the mother-liquor oils are not fractionated to recover a naphthalene concentrate for recycle. Their content of coboiling impurities, particularly dodecane, is too great to permit recycle. They are either rejected or refrigerated to obtain a second crop of crystal naphthalene which can be recycled.

To complete the description of naphthalene recovery, mention should be made of the Pro-Abd "zone-refining" process (40) and the methanol purification process employed at the Avenue site of the British National Coal Board near Chesterfield (41). The Pro-Abd process has been found useful for upgrading crude naphthalene of 72–76°C crystallizing point. The unit consists of a rectangular tank in which is set a nest of coils through which either steam or water may be circulated. The tank is filled with molten crude naphthalene, which is crystallized by circulating cooling water through the coils. When the contents have solidified. a tap at the base is opened and hot water is circulated through the coils until the temperature is just below the desired crystallizing point of the product. This condition is maintained until no more oil drains from the base of the tank, at which point steam is circulated in order to melt out the purified naphthalene.

The recovery of naphthalene from washed, coke-oven naphthalene oil at the Avenue plant is carried out in tall cylindrical tanks equipped with internal heating or cooling coils. Feedstock is charged into these tanks and cooled to around 35°C. Mother liquor is allowed to drain from the base of the tank for a few hours, after which the tank is filled with once-run methanol until the solvent level is above the surface of the crystallized naphthalene. After standing for 1 hr, the methanol is run off and replaced by redistilled methanol, which is again left in contact with the solid naphthalene for 1 or 2 hr before draining. Finally the purified naphthalene is melted by circulating steam in the coils and discharged to storage. The first charge of methanol passes to a still where it is separated from water and naphthalene drain oil. This redistilled methanol is used as the second wash for the next batch; the methanol used as the second wash for the first batch is used as the first wash for the next charge.

The 1966 production of naphthalene in the major industrial countries was:

Country	Production, long tons
U.S.A.	363,000 (including 155,000 from petroleum)
West Germany	153,000
Great Britain	84,700
France	57,000
Japan	86,000
Belgium	17,000
U.S.S.R. (estimated)	120,000

By far the major use of naphthalene is for the production of phthalic anhydride; in 1966, 91% of British production was used in this way. The other outlets are mainly for the manufacture of dyestuffs intermediates (through 1-naphthol, 2-naphthol, naphthylamines, naphthalenesulfonic acids, etc), and (through 1-naphthol) of carbaryl insecticide (see Vol. 11, pp. 689, 711, 734).

For these other purposes, hot-pressed-grade naphthalene must be further purified to a crystallizing point of 79.5–80°C (99% pure or better). This is generally carried out by agitating liquid naphthalene with 10% of 94–95% sulfuric acid, followed by water washing, alkali washing, and, finally, by efficient fractional distillation or sublimation.

From Primary Fractions Distilling in the Range 250–300°C. No tar chemicals are extracted commercially from this range of oil. A fraction distilling mainly in the range 240–270°C is employed at coking installations as wash oil for scrubbing benzole from coal gas, but most of the oils in this range are used in creosote blends.

From Primary Fractions Distilling in the Range 300–350°C. Coke-oven anthracene oils, on cooling, deposit crystals of crude anthracene which contain 12–25% anthracene, 20–35% phenanthrene, and 7–15% carbazole. Crude anthracene crystals are separated from the drained anthracene oil by centrifuging and, after digesting with light creosote, are recentrifuged to yield a product containing 40–45% anthracene, 10–20% phenanthrene, and 20–30% carbazole. This product, known as *40's anthracene*, is sold to the dyestuff manufacturers who upgrade it to 95% anthracene by recrystallization from kerosene and then from high-boiling pyridine bases. The purified anthracene is then oxidized to anthraquinone.

BULK PRODUCTS

Pitch. Pitch, the residue from the primary distillation of tar, can be made in different viscosity grades depending on how far the distillation is taken. If the distillation is continued to the desired softening point, the residue is termed a "straight-run" pitch to distinguish it from a "cut-back" or "fluxed-back" pitch, ie a straight-run pitch of harder consistency fluxed back to the desired softening point with tar-distillate oil. The softer grades of pitch, having softening points by the Ring and Ball

(R and B) method (see Vol. 2, p. 791) below 50°C, are generally referred to as base tars or refined tars; other grades are soft pitch (50–75°C, R and B softening point), medium-hard pitch (85–95°C, R and B softening point), and hard pitch (softening point above 95°C, R and B).

Pitches of all grades behave essentially as Newtonian liquids. Their major industrial uses are in the fields of binders, adhesives, protective coatings, and impregnants. Their physical properties vary somewhat with the softening point and type of tar from which they are derived; however, in designing plants for handling pitches and refined tars, the data in Table 4 can be used.

Table 4. Some Physical Properties of Coal-Tar Pitches in SI Units

Property	
viscosity at the R and B softening pt, °C (42)	800 N-sec/m² (8,000 P)
viscosity at the Krämer and Sarnow softening pt, °C (43)	5,500 N-sec/m² (55,000 P)
viscosity at penetration of 200 (44) (see Vol. 2, p. 791)	2×10^4 N-sec/m² (2×10^5 P)
viscosity at ductility pt	10^7 N-sec/m² (10^8 P)
viscosity at Fraass brittle pt (45)	4×10^8 N-sec/m² (4×10^9 P)
viscosity at t°C (46)	$\log \eta_t = -4.175 + \dfrac{711.8}{86.1 - t_s + t}$ where η_t = viscosity at t°C, P t_s = R and B softening pt, °C
coefficient of thermal expansion (47)	0.00047–0.00056/°C
specific heat capacity (48)	$4.187 \left(\dfrac{0.873}{d_{20}} - 0.413 + 0.00093t \right)$ kJ/(kg)(deg K) (or $\dfrac{0.873}{d_{20}} - 0.413 + 0.0093t$ cal/(g)(deg C)) where d_{20} = density at 20°C; t = temperature, °C
thermal conductivity (49)	0.0037 W/(m)(deg K) or 0.00214 Btu/(hr) (ft²) (deg F/ft)

Base tars and soft pitches are generally stored and transported as liquids. Other grades may be stored or handled as solids or liquids; the modern trend is toward the production and transport of medium-soft pitch and even hard pitches as liquids or as particulate solids in order to avoid the carcinogenic hazard associated with the inhalation of, or prolonged skin contact with, pitch dust. It should perhaps be mentioned here that the danger of contracting cancer by contact with coal tar or coal-tar products is greatly exaggerated. This hazard undoubtedly exists but is confined to prolonged and continuous (many years' duration) exposure to finely divided solid pitch. Even in occupations in which such conditions prevail, the dangers can be greatly minimized by the use of protective clothing, goggles, and face masks, by the use of barrier creams on exposed parts of the body, and particularly, by a high standard of personal hygiene.

Nevertheless, it is the aim of the tar refiners in all countries to avoid the use of pitch bays, in which large quantities of pitch are stored and broken up for loading when required, by storing pitch liquid in steam-heated tanks and transporting it in heated road or rail tankers (50) or by installing equipment for producing pitch in the form of flakes, "pencils," or "pastilles." "Flake" pitch is made by cooling the pitch on a moving steel band (51), "pencil" or "rod" pitch by directly cooling thin streams of pitch in water (52), and "pastillated" pitch by allowing the molten pitch, precooled to about 100°C above its softening point, to fall in blobs onto a continuous, direct-cooled metal belt from a container which has at its base a large number of orifices which can be rapidly opened and closed (53).

Briquetting Pitches (54,55). In some European countries one of the largest uses of coal-tar pitch is the briquetting of coal fines. Ground bituminous coal is mixed with 8–10% of powdered medium-soft pitch, this mixture is heated to about 90°C in a pug mill, and the plastic mass is pressed into bricks or ovoids. A recent development is the production of smokeless briquets in Great Britain and Belgium. In the British "Phurnacite" and Multiheat processes, either Welsh steam coal or anthracite fines are briquetted with pitch and the briquets are partly carbonized (56); in the Belgian process, the briquets, made from lean coal fines and pitch, are subjected to a short heating with air so that a thin skin of coke is formed on the outside (57).

Electrode Pitch. Coal-tar pitch is the preferred binder for the electrodes used in aluminum-reduction furnaces, in electric-arc steel-melting furnaces, and for the manufacture of carbon brushes and other carbon ceramic articles. The first provides the largest market; about three-quarters of the electrode pitch market in the U.S. is represented by that used for both self-baking and prebaked electrodes in aluminum smelters. A pitch of high density (1.30 kg/liter at 20°C) and with a softening point in the range 90–100°C (R and B) is preferred, although some specifications allow a somewhat lower density minimum and a higher softening point. See also Carbon.

Roofing Pitch (59). Until some ten years ago the use of coal-tar pitch in the construction of membrane roofing for flat-topped buildings was a major outlet for coal-tar pitch in the U.S. and Canada. The method of construction involved building up a surfacing consisting of alternate layers of tar-impregnated paper and soft coke-oven pitch. The hot pitch was mopped onto the paper, a second layer of paper laid on the hot pitch, and so on until the necessary number of layers (usually three to five) had been applied. The top pitch layer was covered with slag or gravel to protect it from light and air. The use of coal-tar pitch for this purpose declined due to the introduction of competitive materials such as butyl rubber and special bitumens, but it is now regaining its popularity particularly for flat or shallow-pitched roofs; for steep-pitched roofing or for shingles, asphalt is preferred (60). The so-called tar-paper and tarred-felt roofing components which are supplied in rolls consist of heavy paper, felt, or hessian, impregnated and/or coated with bitumen and not with pitch. See also Roofing materials.

Fiber-Pipe Pitch (61). Fairly large amounts of pitch are used in the manufacture of pitch fiber pipes. These are made by pressure-impregnating dried fiber tubes with a soft pitch (65–70°C, R and B) at 165°C under vacuum. A highly aromatic pitch of low-quinoline-insoluble content is used for this purpose; suitable material can be made by distilling centrifuged coke-oven tar in a pipe still.

Pitch fiber pipes are now fairly extensively used in the U.K. and the U.S. for drainage, sewage, carrying of industrial effluent and, to a minor extent in the U.S. only, for potable water. They are generally buried, but some have been used as flues and ducts for cooled industrial gaseous effluents. The main use, however, is for sewage, drainage, irrigation, and transport of industrial effluents.

Pitch Coke (62). A major outlet for coal-tar pitch in Russia and Germany, accounting for 400,000–500,000 tons of pitch/yr, is the manufacture of pitch coke which is used as the solid grist in the manufacture of certain types of electrodes and carbon ceramics; see Carbon. Coking is carried out in modified coke ovens which are charged with molten hard pitch (140–145°C, R and B softening point) for 20 hr at a flue temperature of 1300°C. Pitch coke production was formerly carried out by Koppers Co., Inc. at Warren, Ohio, but this plant has now been closed. The Lummus Co. has recently extended its delayed petroleum coking process to the production of pitch coke and a plant to make pitch coke in this way has been erected in Japan.

Protective Coatings. Strictly speaking, protective coatings should come under the heading of fluxed-pitch products, but it is more convenient to deal with them at this point. They are of three types which collectively consume an annual world total of between 200,000 and 300,000 tons of pitch.

The simplest types are the so-called "black varnishes" which consist of soft pitch fluxed back to brushing or spraying consistency with coal-tar naphtha (63). These are still quite widely used for the protection of industrial steelwork and as antifouling marine paints. They are, however, being increasingly displaced by the pitch–epoxy and pitch–polyurethan coatings (64). The components of these pitch–resin coatings consist of soft coke-oven pitch, an epoxy or polyurethan resin, a suitable hardener, a mineral filler, and a volatile aromatic solvent. These components are mixed to give two components, one containing the resin and the other, the hardener. Thus, the pitch, resin, and filler with some of the solvent may make up one part and the hardener, dissolved in the remainder of the solvent, the other. In other formulations, the resin dissolved in part of the solvent makes up one component and the other ingredients form the second part. The two parts are mixed in the correct proportions just prior to application. These coatings provide long-term protection for structural steelwork in industrial corrosive atmospheres and are extensively used for the protection of the inside and outside surfaces of water pipes and for durable wearing courses on steel bridge decks.

The third type of protective coating based on coal-tar pitch covers the plasticized-pitch, pipe-coating enamels which are extensively used for the protection of the outside of buried gas, oil, and water pipe lines (65). These are made by digesting 25–30% of powdered coal at 310–320°C in a mixture of coke-oven medium-soft pitch and coke-oven heavy oil. To this mixture, while fluid, is added 30–35% of a mineral filler, such as slate flour or talc, to give a final product with a softening point (R and B) of 105–125°C and a penetration of 1–2 mm when tested with a needle loaded with 100 g for 5 sec at 25°C and which also meets the other requirements of the relevant specifications (eg American Water Works Association Specification C203-67 or British Standard Specification 4164/67).

To ensure good adhesion, the pipe is first primed with a primer consisting of chlorinated rubber and chlorinated paraffin wax (or chlorinated diphenyl) dissolved in a mixture of toluene and trichloroethylene. The molten enamel is flooded onto the primed pipe and coated with a wrapping of fiber glass impregnated with coal tar. This wrap is applied under tension while the enamel is still plastic so that it partly penetrates the thick enamel layer and, when the enamel has cooled and hardened, the protective coating is completed by a second wrapping of impregnated fiber glass.

Miscellaneous Uses for Pitch. Other uses for coal-tar pitch are as a sealant in dry-battery manufacture, as a component in molded battery boxes, and for the production of clay pigeons, which are simply discs molded from hard pitch loaded with a mineral filler such as clay or limestone dust. A growing outlet for soft pitch or refined tar is in the so-called tar-bonded refractories, used as liners in the converters of the modern oxygen steelmaking processes. They consist of a mixture of pitch or tar binder and crushed, calcined dolomite or magnesite. This mixture may be rammed into shape in the hearth of the converter and calcined in situ, or shaped into blocks which are later calcined.

Creosote. In earlier sections of this article, it was noted that the tar distiller produces, as part of his operations, a number of residual oils such as naphthalene drain oil, wash oil, drained anthracene oil, and heavy oil. These oils when blended to meet some specified requirements are referred to as "creosotes" or "creosote oils."

The major outlets for creosotes are as timber preservatives, as fluxing oils for coal-tar pitch and bitumen, for the production of carbon black, and as winter wash oils for spraying dormant fruit trees.

Timber preservation creosote, conforming to such specifications as British Standard Specification 144 or the American Wood-Preservers Specification P 1-65, is mainly a blend of wash oil, drained anthracene oil, and heavy oil. There are three main processes for creosoting timber. The full-cell, or Bethell, process is used for treating marine piling and other heavy-duty installations including railway ties in Britain and some European countries. In this process the timber is first subjected to a vacuum in a pressure-tight cylinder which is then filled with hot creosote and subjected to an air pressure of 120–150 psi. The empty-cell, or Lowry, process, also used for treatment of railway ties, employs a cycle in which the timber is covered with hot creosote and subjected to a pressure of up to 150 psi for several hours, after which the pressure is released and the air trapped in the cells is allowed to expand, forcing the creosote from the cells. Surplus creosote is drained from the impregnation vessel which is finally evacuated for a short time before the timber is discharged. For the preservation of transmission poles, fence posts, farm buildings, etc, where a dry outside finish is desired, the Rueping process is generally employed. This differs from the empty-cell process in that the timber is initially subjected to air pressure before the cylinder is charged with creosote at a somewhat higher pressure. After charging, the pressure is increased to about 150 psi and the cycle is then similar to that in the empty-cell process (66).

For partial combustion to carbon black, the creosote employed is chiefly a mixture of anthracene oil and heavy oil; for winter wash oil for dormant fruit trees a mixture of drained naphthalene oil, wash oil, and anthracene oil containing residual-tar acids is preferred.

Blends of Pitch and Creosote. *Road Tar.* The use of tar as a binder in the construction and maintenance of roads is a major outlet for the bulk products of tar distillation. World consumption of road tar is about 1.5 million tons per annum (500,000 tons per annum in Great Britain, 250,000 tons per annum each in the U.S. and West Germany, and 200,000 tons per annum in France). Road tar is generally made by fluxing back a soft or medium-soft pitch with a mixture of wash oil, drained anthracene oil, and heavy oil to meet the viscosity and other requirements of the appropriate specifications, such as British Standard Specification 76, ASTM Designation D 490-47, and the German DIN 1995. Alternatively, the distillation of crude tar may be adjusted to give road tar as a residue but such "straight-run" road tars are now seldom made.

Different grades of road tar are used for different purposes and the various grades are designated according to their viscosity levels. The most convenient scale is the equiviscous temperature (evt) scale which is employed in Great Britain and is coming into increasing use in Europe. The evt of a tar is defined as the temperature at which the viscosity is 50 sec measured by the standard tar viscometer using a 10-mm cup (42). It corresponds approximately to a kinematic viscosity of 200 St and is approx 20°C higher than the R and B softening point.

In Britain about 40% of the road tar is used in surface dressing; this is recognized as the most satisfactory, inexpensive method of maintaining good riding and nonskid properties of a road surface. A fairly fluid tar (32–46°C evt, equivalent to ASTM grades RT 8, 9, and 10) is used, depending on the prevailing road temperature. The profile of the road should be first corrected by filling in potholes, etc; then the tar, at a temperature of 100–140°C, is sprayed on the dry road surface at a rate of between 4 and 5 yd²/imp. gal (0.74–0.93 m²/liter). The application of tar is immediately followed by covering the road surface with single-size stone chippings or gravel of between 6.35 and 19 mm size, so that the surface of the road is covered by a dense, uniform layer of stone firmly adhering to the surface. Finally this structure is consolidated by rolling (67).

The rest of the road tar in Britain is utilized in production of premixed materials for new road construction (68). For roadbases, a dense mixture of stone, slag, or gravel aggregate containing a fairly high proportion of fine material is mixed in a paddle mixer with 4–6% of a viscous tar (50–60°C evt corresponding to ASTM grades RT 11 and 12) at a temperature of 100–120°C, depending on the binder viscosity. The hot mix is transported from the mixing plant to the laying site in sheeted trucks, laid by machines, and consolidated by road rollers while still plastic.

Wearing course macadams may be either open-textured, medium-textured, or dense, depending on the size grading of the stone aggregate and the amounts of filler added. In general, the more open the texture desired, the smaller the filler content and the lower the tar viscosity used. For open-textured materials a tar of 32–40°C evt (ASTM grades RT 9 and 10) would be used, whereas for dense tar surfacing the binder viscosity would normally be in the 55–60°C evt range (eg ASTM grades RT 11 or 12).

Coal-Tar Fuels (69). The industrial markets for coal-tar pitch, creosote, and their blends are not sufficient to utilize the total production, and fairly large quantities of mixtures of pitch and creosote are used as liquid fuels. In Great Britain, this balancing outlet accounts for 800,000 tons of tar products; in the U.S. about 400,000 tons, and in West Germany, 250,000 tons of coal-tar fuels are consumed. Coal-tar fuels are made in various grades from a light grade, which is essentially creosote, to a heavy grade, which is essentially medium-soft pitch. The most widely used grade contains approximately equal amounts of medium-soft pitch and tar oils and is used extensively in steel works where its low sulfur content and high flame luminosity offer advantages over alternative fuels.

Bibliography

"Tar and Pitch" in *ECT* 1st ed., Vol. 13, pp. 615–632, by E. O. Rhodes, Koppers Company, Inc.

1. A. W. Goos and A. A. Reiter, *Ind. Eng. Chem.* **38,** 132 (1946).
2. B. Juettner and H. C. Howard, *Ind. Eng. Chem.* **26,** 1115 (1934).
3. B. Sun, C. H. Ruof, and H. C. Howard, *Fuel* **37,** 299 (1958).
4. B. Griefner, *Fuel* **37,** 345 (1958).

5. A. Pictet and M. Bouvier, *Ber.* **46,** 3362 (1913).

6. A. Pictet, O. Kaizer, and A. Labouchère, *Compt. Rend.* **165,** 113 (1917).

7. A. Pictet, *Gas J.* **142,** 333 (1918).

8. M. J. Burgess and R. V. Wheeler, *J. Chem. Soc.* **105,** 358 (1916).

9. *Chem. Ind. (London),* June 28, **1958,** 804.

10. *Gas World* **149,** 734 (1959).

11. I. P. Isanenko et al., *Coke Chem. (U.S.S.R.) (Eng. Trans.)* **11,** 47 (1958).

12. *Chem. Eng. Prog.* **55,** 84 (1959).

13. W. Ger. Pat. 1,241,837 (1967), (to Heinrich Koppers GmbH).

14. *Gas J.* **288,** 355, 384 et seq. (1956).

15. *Chem. Ind. (London),* June 25, **1960,** 776.

16. *BIOS (British Intelligence Objectives Subcommittee) Survey No. 25,* "The German Coal Tar and Benzole Industries during the Period 1939–1945," H. M. Stationery Office, London, 1950, p. 34.

17. O. Clyne and T. Scott, *Coking* (Monthly Suppl. to *Gas World*) **147,** 53 (1958).

18. W. M. Hyslop, W. A. P. Carter, and E. Marsden, *Coke Gas* **37,** 331 (1961).

19. Brit. Pat. 932,938 (1963), (to A.P.V. Co. Ltd.).

20. *Chem. Eng.* **66,** 110 (1959).

21. F. Sonntag, *Erdöl Kohle* **13,** 752 (1960).

22. *Gas World* **152,** 726 (1960).

23. H. W. Groté, *Chem. Eng. Prog.* **54** (8), 43 (1958).

24. Brit. Pat. 1,049,455 (1966), (to Metallgesellschaft AG).

25. J. Orlowski et al., *Przemysl Chem.* **40** (9), 517 (1961); (through) *Chem. Abstr.* **61,** 2876 (1964).

26. J. L. Boyle, *Ind. Chemist* **29,** 251 (1953).

27. D. McNeil, *Chem. Proc. (London)***13** (10) Processing Suppl., 53 (1967).

28. P. Arnall, *Chem. Prod.* **24** (11), 451 (1961).

29. R. C. Peter, *Ind. Chemist* **31,** 141 (1955).

30. A. Marx, *Brennstoff-Chem.* **30,** 37 (1949).

31. P. V. Clifton and W. H. A. Webb, *Ind. Chemist* **32,** 526 (1956).

32. K. A. Adey, *Gas J.* **303,** 475 (1960).

33. J. A. Davy, *Gas World* **71,** Coking and By-Products Sect., 10 (1919); *Gas J.* **148,** 489 (1919).

34. U.S. Pat. 2,440,707 (1948), (to Koppers Co., Inc.); Brit. Pat. 620,753 (1949), (to Koppers Co., Inc.).

35. A. P. V. Co. Ltd., *Coking* (Monthly Suppl. to *Gas World*) **133,** 2 (1951).

36. E. Treszczanowicz and S. Ciborowski, *Przemysl Chem.* **6,** 132 (1950); (through) *Chem. Abstr.* **46,** 3989 (1952).

37. G. Gilbert, R. C. Weil, and R. H. Hunter, *Ind. Eng. Chem.* **53,** 993 (1961).

38. T. G. Woolhouse, *J. Appl. Chem.* **7,** 573 (1957).

39. Brit. Pat. 732,652 (1955), (to Rütgerswerke AG).

40. J. C. D. Molinari, *Ind. Chemist* **37,** 323 (1961).

41. Brit. Pat. 686,166 (1949), (to W. Butler and Co. Ltd.).

42. P. W. Walker, "Paper No. 142," *Bur. Std. J. Res.,* (1930); "Serial No. P3-67," *Standard Methods for Testing Tar and Its Products,* 6th ed., Standardization of Tar Products Test Committee, Gomersal, England, 1967.

43. G. Krämer and S. Sarnow, *Chem. Ind.* **26,** 55 (1903); "Serial No. P2-62," *Standard Methods for Testing Tar and Its Products,* 5th ed., Standardization of Tar Products Test Committee, Gomersal, England, 1962.

44. "Test for Penetration of Bituminous Materials," ASTM D-5-65, American Society for Testing and Materials, *Book of ASTM Standards,* Philadelphia, Pa., 1965.

45. A. Fraass, *Asphalt und Teerstrassenbautechnik* **13,** 367 (1930).

46. A. J. Hoiberg, ed., *Bituminous Materials: Asphalts, Tars and Pitches,* Interscience Publishers, a division of John Wiley & Sons, Inc., Vol. III, 1966, p. 147.

47. *Ibid.,* p. 150.

48. D. K. H. Briggs and W. D. Drake, *Chem. Ind. (London)* **1957,** 666.

49. D. K. H. Briggs and F. Popper, *Fuel* **33** (2), 222 (1954).

50. *Chem. Eng. News* **40,** 81 (1962).

51. *Chem. Proc.* **6,** 8 (1960).

52. Brit Pat. 1,061,620 (1967), (to Koppers Co., Inc.).

53. Rosin Engg Co. Ltd., *Process Engineering*, 1967, p. 40.

54. "Brikettierung der Steinkohle," in W. Hagen and G. A. H. Meyer, eds., *Der Deutsche Steinkohlenbergbau*, Vol. 3, Verlag Glückauf GmbH, 1958.

55. F. Wulf, *Chem-Ing-Technik* **32**, 198 (1960).

56. W. I. Jones, *Inst. Gas Engr. J.* **4**, 115 (1964).

57. J. Dupont, *Ann. Mines Belg.* **1960**, 851.

58. B. E. A. Thomas, *Coking* (Monthly Suppl. to *Gas World*) **56**, 51 (1960).

59. *Koppers Built-up Roofing: Specification Manual*, Tar Products Division, Koppers Co., Inc., Pittsburgh, 1964.

60. *Roofing/Siding/Insulation* No. 60, Jan. 1969.

61. *Pipes and Pipelines* **4**, 28, 39 (1959); **5**, 85(1960); **7**, 57 (1962).

62. I. N. Peresadenko, *Coke Chem. (U.S.S.R.)* (7), 24 (1957).

63. N. T. Shideler, *Bitumen, Teere, Asphalte, Peche* **9**, 47 (1958).

64. A. K. Long and R. H. Goodnight, *Mater. Protection* **2**, 92 (1963).

65. J. J. McManus, W. L. Pennie, and A. Davies, *Ind. Eng. Chem.* **58**, 43 (1966).

66. G. M. Hunt and G. A. Garratt, *Wood Preservation*, McGraw-Hill Book Co., Inc., New York, 1953, p. 206.

67. *The Technique of Surface Dressing with Tar, Pamphlet D.2*, British Road Tar Association, London, 1959.

68. *Road Construction with Tar: A Guide to the Choice of Specifications*, British Road Tar Association, London, 1966.

69. W. H. Huxtable, ed., *Coal Tar Fuels*, Association of Tar Distillers, London, 1961.

General References

D. McNeil, *Coal Carbonization Products*, The Commonwealth and International Library, Pergamon Press, London, 1966.

H. G. Franck and G. Collin, *Steinkohlenteer: Chemie, Technologie, und Verwendung*, Springer-Verlag, Berlin-Heidelberg-New York, 1968.

H. J. V. Winkler, *Der Steinkohlenteer und seine Aufarbeitung*, Verlag Glückauf GmbH, Essen, 1951.

D. McNeil
The Coal Tar Research Association

TAR SANDS

Tar sands (also known as oil sands and bituminous sands) are sand deposits which are impregnated with dense, viscous petroleum. Tar sands are found throughout the world, often in the same geographical area as conventional petroleum. The largest deposit is in the Athabasca area in the northeastern part of the Province of Alberta, Canada. This reserve contains over 700 billion bbl. For comparison, this is about one sixth of the U.S. shale oil reserves and about one sixteenth of the U.S. coal reserves. Tar sands, oil shale, and coal are currently candidate sources of synthetic fuels. Despite the relatively smaller size of the Athabasca reserve, it is the only one which has yet been exploited commercially.

Reserves of tar sands, each containing over 15 million bbl of bitumen, have been located in the United States, Venezuela, Albania, Rumania, Malagasy, and the U.S.S.R. The only really sizable deposit besides the Athabasca is in eastern Venezuela.

This reserve is estimated to contain 200 billion bbl of bitumen, which exceeds all the other reported reserves combined, except the Athabasca tar sands.

Tar sands have the interesting property that the bitumen is often rather easy to separate from the sand by a wide variety of methods. Tar sands have provided, at least in the U.S. and Canada, grist for the mills of innumerable kitchen-sink inventors. An extensive patent literature (1) testifies to this fact. Despite the fact that tar sand deposits have been known for many years and the fact that bitumen separates rather easily from the sand, it is only recently that tar sands have assumed technical importance. (For the best compendia of general information on tar sands, see references 2–4.) The first venture for manufacturing synthetic crude from the sands, Great Canadian Oil Sands, Ltd. (GCOS), is now in commercial operation. GCOS rated production is 45,000 bbl/day; actual production as of August, 1968, was approaching this figure.

Although several of the U.S. tar sand deposits have been briefly investigated, the bulk of the data available on tar sands refers to the Athabasca deposit. This deposit was first recorded in 1788. Serious mapping and exploration awaited the work of S. C. Ells of the Federal Canadian Department of Mines and Technical Surveys, starting in 1913. From that time until about 1945, except for the continuing research program of the Research Council of Alberta, little interest was expressed in the Athabasca deposit. During World War II, with the real possibility of an oil shortage in Canada and the United States, an extensive program of exploration was undertaken by the Canadian Government. Between 1940 and 1950 pilot plants were sponsored by both the Federal Canadian Government and the Government of the Province of Alberta. During 1948–1949 the hot water separation process was demonstrated on pilot scale under the technical supervision of Dr. K. A. Clark. In 1950 the Blair Report (5) was published. This engineering study concluded that production of synthetic crude oil from the Athabasca tar sands was technically and economically feasible. Since 1955 industrially sponsored research has been steadily increasing, leading to three formal proposals for commercial ventures.

Among the in situ methods for recovering bitumen from tar sands are fire floods, a steam drive process, and atomic explosion. Processes operating on tar sand which has been mined include direct coking of the tar sand; and hot water, cold water, and solvent processes for extracting bitumen from the sand. Bitumen itself is too dense (6–10° API) and viscous (5000–50,000 P at 50°F) to be either salable or transportable. Many upgrading processes have been proposed, including partial coking, conventional delayed coking with catalytic hydrodesulfurization of the coker distillate, and direct catalytic hydrovisbreaking. Commercial ventures for bitumen recovery from the Athabasca tar sands have been proposed by Shell Canada, Ltd. (steam drive in situ recovery process followed by thermal cracking and hydrotreating); Cities Service Athabasca, Ltd. and Great Canadian Oil Sands, Ltd. (mining, hot water extraction of bitumen, coking, and hydrotreating); and Syncrude Canada, Ltd. (mining, hot water extraction, H-oil hydrovisbreaking).

Occurrence and Reserves

Various definitions have been applied to energy reserves (6). What are usually called proved reserves have a rather limited and specific meaning. These are reserves recoverable under current conditions of technical and economic feasibility. *Proved reserves* give an accurate, short-term estimate of the working inventory of a particular resource. The proved U.S. reserves of crude oil, for instance, have remained relatively constant during the 1960s despite the fact that 8–9% of this figure has been consumed each year. What this really means is that economic conditions within the U.S. petroleum industry are such that about an eleven-year proved reserve/production ratio is regarded as an acceptable economic balance between the present risk of commiting capital to exploring for more crude and the future risk of a deficiency in crude supply.

Ultimate reserves, or in-place reserves, are defined much more broadly as the largest reasonable estimate of the total amount of a particular resource. Not only discovered, but also "discoverable" (based on reasonable geological extrapolations) resources are included. The estimate is not limited to today's economic conditions or recovery technology. Because of the differences in definition, it is not meaningful to compare reserves using different calculation bases.

Table 1 compares proved and ultimate reserves for a number of energy sources.

Table 1. Energy Reserves (7–9)

| Resource | Reserves[a] | | | | Predicted U.S. consumption, 1960–2000[a] |
| | Proved | | Ultimate | | |
	U.S.A.	World[b]	U.S.A.	World[b]	
crude oil	0.2	2.3	6.0	37.0	1.3
natural gas[c]	0.3	0.9	3.2	19.6	1.1
shale oil	0.3	0.9	23.2	79.0	
coal	4.6	18.0	55.0	320.0	0.5
uranium[d]	0.2	0.7	1.2×10^5		
deuterium[e]				7.5×10^9	
tar sands			0.01	6.1	

[a] Expressed in arbitrary units; each unit = 10^{18} Btu = 0.167×10^{12} Bbl crude oil.

[b] Including U.S. reserves.

[c] Including natural gas liquids.

[d] Proved reserves assume 1% recovery of maximum theoretical fission energy content and mining cost of $5–10/lb of U_3O_8; ultimate reserves assume 100% theoretical energy content and no mining cost limit.

[e] Energy obtained by nuclear fusion.

Although tar sands are not a major energy reserve, they certainly are significant in comparison to projected energy consumption over the next several generations. Recently, in the popular press, *ultimate* tar sand reserves have been compared to *proved* crude oil reserves. Such a comparison creates the misleading impression that tar sands are a fantastically large resource. Table 2 compares various deposits of tar sand.

As noted previously, proved U.S. crude oil reserves have remained approximately constant during the 1960s. Nevertheless, the reserve/production ratio has decreased constantly and perceptibly during the decade. This has, particularly recently, caused increasing concern among oil companies as to their long-term positions on crude oil. Right now several major petroleum companies have committed, or are considering committing, major amounts of funds to development of "synthetic fuels." Synthetic fuels are fuels made from any source other than conventional crude oil, specifically tar sands, shale oil, and coal. Among these contenders, tar sands is clearly the front

Table 2. Major Tar Sands of the World Listed in Order of Reserve Size (9)

Location and name of deposit	Age of reservoir rock	Areal extent, sq. miles	Pay thickness, ft Range	Pay thickness, ft Average	Bitumen saturation, wt %	Character of oil °API at 60°F	Character of oil Sulfur, %	Overburden thickness, ft	In-place reserves, million bbl
Canada									
Athabasca, Alberta	Lower Cretaceous	9,000	0–300	175				0–1,900	625,900
Bluesky-Gething, Alberta		1,875	0–400					700–2,600	51,500
Grand Rapids, Alberta		1,625	400	280				300–1,400	33,400
total "Athabasca" tar sands		12,500		150	2–18	10.5	4.5	0–2,600	710,800
Melville Island, N.W.T.	Trias	?	60–80		?–16	10	0.9–2.2	0–2,000a	?
Eastern Venezuela									
Oficina–Temblador tar belt	Oligocene	9,000	3–100	100		10		0–3,000a	200,000
Malagasy, Bemolanga	Trias	150	80–300	100	10		0.7	0–100	1,750
U.S.A.									
Asphalt Ridge, Utah	Oligocene and Upper Cretaceous	17a	11–254	98	11	8.6–12	0.5	0–2,000	900
Sunnyside, Utah	Upper Eocene	54a	24–200	100	9	10–12	0.5	0–150	500
Albania, Selenizza	Miocene–Pliocene	8	33–330	50a	8–14	4.6–13.2	6.1	shallow	371a
U.S.A.									
Whiterocks, Utah	Jurassic	3	900–1,000		10	12	0.5	nil	250
Edna, Cal.	Miocene–Pliocene	10	0–1,200a	250	9–16	<13	4.2	0–600a	165
Peor Springs, Utah	Upper Eocene	<3	1–250	34a	9a			shallow	87
Eastern Venezuela									
Guanoco	recent alluvium	<2	2–9	4	64	8	5.9	nil	62
Trinidad, La Brea	Upper Miocene		0–270	135	54	1–2	6.0–8.0	nil	60
U.S.A.									
Santa Rosa, N.M.	Trias	7a	0–100	20	4–8	4–8		0–40	57
Sisquoc, Cal.	Upper Pliocene	0.3	0–185	85	14–18			15–70	50
Asphalt, Ky.	Pennsylvanian	11	5–36	15	8–10			6–30	48
Rumania, Derna	Pliocene	0.7	6–25	15	15–22		0.7	shallow	25
U.S.S.R.									
Cheildag, Kobystan	Middle Miocene	0.1a		200	5–13			shallow	24
U.S.A.									
Davis-Dismal Creek, Ky.	Pennsylvanian	3	10–50	15	5			15–30	22
Santa Cruz, Cal.	Miocene	2	5–50	11	10–12			0–100	20
Kyrock, Ky.	Pennsylvanian	1.4a	15–40	20	6–8			15	18

a Estimated.

runner. That is to say, production from the tar sands is today a commercial reality. The next most likely prospect may be shale oil. However, a commercial shale oil venture seems no closer today than it was five years ago. The case of coal liquefaction is similar—although the technology is available now, the economics point five to ten years into the future.

Fig. 1. Province of Alberta, Canada.

Athabasca Tar Sands. *Location and Geology.* The Athabasca tar sands, actually three deposits, are located in the northeast part of the Province of Alberta, Canada. Figures 1 and 2 give the geographical location; Figure 3 gives a geological cross section of the three deposits. The Athabasca tar sand deposits are the only deposits currently

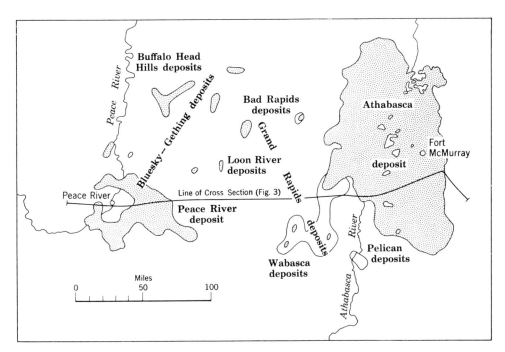

Fig. 2. Location of evaluated tar sands deposits of northern Alberta (10).

considered as candidates for large-scale commercial exploitation. They are also the only deposits which are known to have been investigated scientifically in any amount of detail.

The main geological features of the Athabasca deposit can be seen in Figure 3. The floor of the deposit is limestone of Devonian age. Above the Devonian base occur in order the McMurray, Clearwater, and Grand Rapids formations. The McMurray formation is a layer of sand, cross-bedded in some locations with lenses of clay and shale. Where the McMurray formation has been impregnated with bitumen, it is the tar sands. Along the Athabasca River, north of the town of Fort McMurray, for several miles east and more particularly to the west, the Clearwater and Grand Rapids formations may be absent. These formations are sandstone and shale layers without bitumen saturation. Where they have weathered away, outcrops of tar sand can be observed along the Athabasca River bank for about a hundred miles to the north of Fort McMurray.

There are two schools of thought regarding the origin of the oil. One (11) is that the oil was formed locally and has neither migrated a great distance, nor been subjected to large overburden pressures. Since under these conditions the oil cannot have been subjected to thermal cracking, it is geologically young and therefore dense and viscous. The opposing theory (12) assumes a remote origin for the oil, both geographically and in geological time. The oil, originally like a conventional crude, is assumed to have migrated into the sand deposit, which may originally have been filled with water. After the oil migrated, the overburden pressures were relieved, and the light portions of the crude evaporated, leaving behind a dense viscous residue. This theory would explain the water layer surrounding sand grains in the Athabasca deposit (discussed below). However, because the metals and porphyrin contents

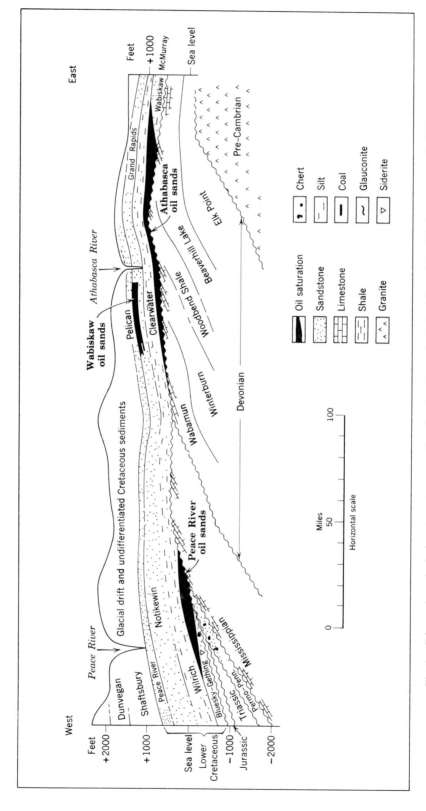

Fig. 3. Schematic geological east-west cross section showing the geological setting of the Athabasca tar sands (10).

of bitumen are similar to those of some conventional Alberta crude oils of Lower Cretaceous age and because Athabasca bitumen has a relatively low coking temperature, the bitumen may be of Lower Cretaceous age. This is the age of the McMurray formation, which is geologically young. This evidence supports the theory that the oil was formed in situ and is a precursor, rather than a residue of some other oil. The issue is not settled.

Recoverable Reserves. Two conditions of vital concern for the economic development (7) of a tar sand deposit are the concentration of the resource, or the percent bitumen saturation, and its accessibility, usually measured by the overburden thickness. Information of this type is available only for the Athabasca deposit and is summarized in Figures 4 and 5. Recovery methods may be generally divided into

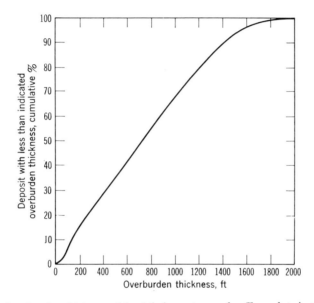

Fig. 4. Overburden thickness of the Athabasca tar sands. From data in reference 10.

those which depend on mining combined with some further processing and those which attempt to operate on the oil sands in situ. The mining methods are applicable to shallow deposits, characterized by an overburden ratio (overburden depth/thickness of tar sand deposit) on the order of 1.0. Since the Athabasca tar sands have a maximum thickness of about 300 ft, and average about 150 ft in thickness, the data in Figure 4 indicate that no more than 10% of the in-place deposit is minable within current concepts of the economics and technology of open-pit mining. This 10% portion may be considered as the *proved* tar sand reserves.

At the other end of the overburden scale, in situ processes are used. Each of these depends on injecting a driver substance into the ground through injection wells and recovering bitumen through production wells. All such processes need a relatively thick layer of overburden to contain the driver substance within the formation between injection and production wells. If, in this context, a thick overburden layer can be taken to mean upward of 250 ft, then much of the Athabasca deposit may be suitable for in situ recovery. If on the other hand a much larger depth, say 1000 ft, is required, then Figure 4 shows that only about another 30% of the deposit would be suitable for in situ recovery.

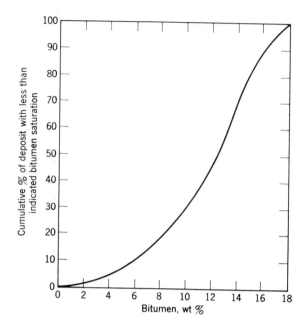

Fig. 5. Bitumen saturation of the Athabasca tar sands. From data in reference 10.

For tar sands of 10 wt % bitumen saturation, 2 tons of tar sand must be processed to recover 1 bbl of bitumen. By simple arithmetic, if the ore contains only 5 wt % bitumen, twice the amount of ore must be processed to recover the same 1 bbl of bitumen. The point is that there is a lower limit to the bitumen saturation of the tar sands which can be processed economically. For a mining process, this lower limit may be on the order of 10 wt % so that, as Figure 5 shows, about 30% of the Athabasca tar sand deposit would be excluded from consideration. For an in situ process, the lower limit may be somewhat less. Nevertheless, considering the limitations both of overburden thickness and of bitumen content, it is clear that when proved reserves are calculated for the Athabasca deposit (or for any of the tar sands deposits) this figure will be much smaller than the total in-place reserves.

History of the Athabasca Tar Sands

Evidently the Cree Indians, native to the Athabasca region of northeastern Alberta, Canada, have known about the tar sands for well over 200 years. By the late eighteenth century, the Hudson's Bay Company had moved into the Athabasca region and was attempting to set up trading posts. Yet it remained for an itinerant New England fur trader, one Peter Pond, to be the first to record an outsider's observation of the tar sands. In 1788 Pond told how the Indians used "a sticky substance oozing from the river banks to waterproof their canoes." Peter Pond established a successful trading post near the site of the present town of Fort McMurray (see Fig. 1) where the Clearwater and Athabasca Rivers join. In 1870, the post received its present name, Fort McMurray.

The first scientific interest in the tar sands was taken by the Canadian Government in 1890. R. G. McConnell, a geologist, reported on the tar sands during a reconnaissance of the Athabasca district. In 1897–1898 the first drilling was accomplished, at

Pelican Rapids on the Athabasca River 80 miles southwest of Fort McMurray; tar sands were reached at a depth of 740 ft. Thus, by the beginning of the twentieth century, the existence of the Athabasca tar sands was confirmed and it was thought that the reserves were large. The development to the point of a large-scale commercial venture to process these reserves occupied the next sixty-seven years. Between 1930 and 1960, the development was mainly a story of small commercial enterprises which were formed, failed, and were reformed with some regularity. Behind the story of unsuccessful entrepreneurs runs the unbroken thread of the life-long efforts of two men, S. C. Ells and K. A. Clark. Sidney C. Ells was, from 1913 until his retirement in 1945, a geologist with the Federal Canadian Department of Mines and Technical Surveys. He was involved in a number of the early attempts to commercialize the tar sands. Dr. Karl A. Clark was, from 1920 until his retirement in 1954, associated with the Research Council of Alberta. In this position he pioneered the development of a hot water separation process, one of several possible methods for recovering bitumen from tar sands.

S. C. Ells' first exploration of the Athabasca was made in 1913. He sampled the outcrops of tar sand along the Athabasca River and commenced the first surveys. He returned to the area for a number of years and produced the first comprehensive maps. In 1922 Ells succeeded in interesting a group of New York City policemen in forming the Alcan Oil Company. This company failed forthwith and in 1923 the assets were taken over by R. C. Fitzsimmons, who formed International Bitumen Company. International Bitumen was the first to exploit the tar sands commercially. In 1930 a works was operated at Bitumount about sixty miles north of Fort McMurray on the east bank of the Athabasca; several thousand barrels of tar were recovered and sold in Edmonton as a roofing material. Also in 1930 Dr. Clark set up a small pilot plant on the Clearwater River under the auspices of the Research Council of Alberta. This unit had been operated for several years previously in Edmonton. It was the first on-site experimental unit devoted to developing an efficient separation process.

In 1930 still another chain of development efforts was started. In consultation with S. C. Ells, Max W. Ball formed the Canadian Northern Oil Sands Products, Ltd., later reformed as Abasand Oils, Ltd. In 1936 Abasand started construction of a 250-ton-per-day separation plant on the Horse River, just south of Fort McMurray. During 1937 to 1941 construction was undertaken on a second plant, rated at 400 tons/day. In the summer of 1941 some 17,000 bbl of bitumen were produced and refined to distillate petroleum products. In November of the same year the plant burned down. In 1942 the separation plant was rebuilt, but in 1943 Ball's financing failed. The Dominion Government then took over the Horse River separation plant and during 1944 the plant was redesigned and revised, with rated capacity of 100 tons/day. This was to be the pilot unit for a larger 500-ton-per-day plant which was completed in 1945. These plants never operated; they burned to the ground on June 15, 1945.

The International Bitumen Company operations were not continued after 1930. In 1942 L. R. Champion received the assets of International Bitumen and formed Oil Sands, Ltd. By 1944 Champion had arranged with the Alberta Research Council to help in financing a test plant. In 1948 Champion's financing failed, however, and the Government of the Province of Alberta took over the newly built test plant at Bitumount. This plant was operated during 1948 and 1949 under the supervision of W. E. Atkins. Technical support was provided by the Research Council under Dr. Clark's direction. These operations were reported in detail (13,14). An independent engineering analysis based on this work, the Blair Report (5), was a detailed study of the technical and economic feasibility of a tar sands separation venture. The Blair Report was optimistic and spurred the interest of several investigators during the next decade. In 1953 the Oil Sands, Ltd. interests were reformed as Great Canadian Oil Sands, Ltd. (GCOS). At the same time, the Government moved to divest itself of the Bitumount holdings. In 1955 these were sold to Can-Amera Oil Sands Development Company. During 1955–1959 the facility was again operated by Can-Amera and Royalite Oil Company.

Between 1957 and 1967 three extensive pilot plant operations were conducted in the Athabasca region, each leading to a proposal for a commercial venture. During 1957–1962 Shell Canada, Ltd. tested in situ recovery of bitumen from the tar sands. Between 1959 and 1962 a group headed by Cities Service Athabasca, Ltd., and including Imperial Oil, Ltd., Richfield Oil Corp., and Royalite Oil Company, Ltd., operated a pilot plant at Mildred Lake, based on a hot water extraction process. During 1963–1965 Great Canadian Oil Sands, Ltd. operated a pilot plant at the present commercial plant site (see Fig. 1) near Mildred Lake. Since 1965 Mobil Oil Company has conducted tests on in situ recovery. In 1967 Petrofina established a pilot facility across the Athabasca River from the site of the GCOS plant. The operations of the latter two pilot plants remain proprietary; they have not been described in the open literature.

The ruins of several of the early tar sand ventures may yet be seen. The burned-out remains of the Abasand plant are easily located on the Horse River south of Fort McMurray, near what is now a community fishing ground. Likewise, just across the Clearwater River from Fort McMurray, the remains of the first Clark test plant are visible. At Bitumount, both the International Bitumen Company plant and the Oil Sands, Ltd. test plant are still standing. Only the Oil Sands, Ltd. plant was not destroyed by fire.

Properties and Characteristics of the Athabasca Tar Sands

This section on properties is based entirely on the Athabasca tar sands, rather than tar sands generally; data of the type discussed are available only for the Athabasca deposit.

Bulk Properties. Tar sand has been defined (10) as sand saturated with a "highly viscous crude hydrocarbon material not recoverable in its natural state through a well by ordinary production methods." Technically, the material should perhaps be called bituminous sand rather than tar sand since the hydrocarbon is a bitumen (ie, a carbon disulfide-soluble oil). In petroleum refining, "tar" is a term reserved to mean the residue of a thermal process. The term "oil sand" is used also, possibly in allusion to the synthetic crude oil which can be manufactured from the bitumen.

Tar sand is a mixture of sand, water, and bitumen, arranged as shown in Figure 6. The sand component is predominantly quartz in the form of rounded or subangular particles, each of which is wet with a film of water. Surrounding the wetted sand grains and somewhat filling the void volume among them is a film of bitumen. The balance of the void volume is filled with connate water plus, sometimes, a small volume of gas. Usually the gas is air; however, methane has been reported from some test

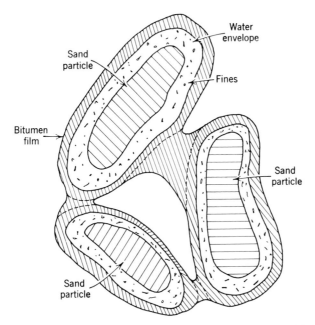

Fig. 6. Typical arrangement of tar sand particles (15). Courtesy Research Council of Alberta.

borings in the Athabasca deposit. The sand grains are packed to a void volume of about 35%. This corresponds to a tar sand mixture of roughly 83 wt % sand; the balance is bitumen and water. In fact, it is found with considerable regularity that the bitumen and water total about 17 wt % of the tar sands.

Two figures of merit are applied to tar sands with respect to hot water processing: percent bitumen and percent fines. Percent bitumen may be determined analytically by solvent extraction. Toluene is a suitable solvent, and the extraction may be so arranged that both the water and bitumen contents are measured directly. The toluene makes a better extractant if it is stored over sodium hydroxide; the reason for this is not known. Percent fines as used in this article refers to the weight per-

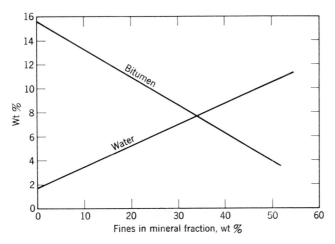

Fig. 7. Relationship of tar sand fines, water, and bitumen contents. From data in reference 16.

Table 3. Bulk Properties of Athabasca Tar Sand

Property	Range of values	Average	Reference
bulk density, g/cm³			
bitumen content, % dry wt			
>10	1.75–2.09	1.90	17
unknown	1.86–2.36	1.972	17
unknown	1.98–2.08[a]		17
unknown	2.10–2.19[b]		17
porosity, vol %			
bitumen content, % dry wt			
>10	34–46	40.7	17
unknown	17.6–43.3	31.4	17
unknown		40[a]	17
unknown		34[b]	17
specific heat, cal/(g)(°C)			
bitumen content, % dry wt			
100		0.35	18
air permeability, millidarcy[c]			
bitumen content, % dry wt			
>10	0–215	50	17
4–10	0–600	100	17
<4	0–35	10	17
thermal conductivity, at 45°C, cal/(sec)(cm²)(°C/cm)			
bitumen content, % dry wt			
17.1[d]	0.0035		18
17.1[e]	0.0027–0.0032		18
11.7[e]	0.0021		18
8.6	0.0024		18
3.0	0.0017		18

[a] 200 ft below surface. [c] See reference 18a for [d] Undisturbed sample.
[b] 1000 ft below surface. definition of darcy. [e] Remolded sample.

centage of the dried, extracted tar sand mineral which passes a fixed mesh size such as 325 mesh (44 μ). The percent fines may be conveniently determined by screening. Figure 7 summarizes the analytical findings on a number of core samples obtained from test borings in the GCOS Lease 86 located in the Mildred–Ruth Lakes area. The direct correlation of water content with fines and the inverse correlation of bitumen content with fines are evident.

Compositions of tar sand and tar sand–water mixtures may conveniently be represented by using a triangle diagram, as shown in Figure 8. The three vertices represent 100 wt % bitumen, 100 wt % mineral, and 100 wt % water. Typical compositions for tar sand and for various streams encountered in the hot water processing of tar sand are summarized by the circled areas in Figure 8. Table 3 summarizes a number of values of bulk properties of tar sands.

Properties of Tar Sand Minerals. Usually, more than 99% of the tar sand mineral is composed of quartz sand and clays. In the remaining 1%, over twenty-five minerals have been identified, mostly calciferous or iron based. Sand ranges from the largest grains (99.9% is finer than 1000 μ) down to 44 μ. This size is 325 mesh, the smallest size which it is practical to determine by dry screening. Mineral between 44 and 2 μ is referred to as silt. Mineral sized below 2 μ (equivalent spherical diameter) is clay.

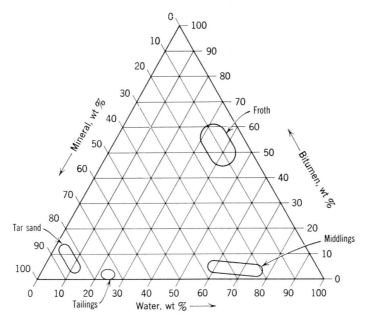

Fig. 8. Use of triangle diagram to represent composition of tar sand–water mixture.

Clays are aluminosilicate minerals, for some of which definite chemical compositions have been established. However, as used here and below, clay is only a size classification and is usually determined by a sedimentation method. According to the previous definition of fines, the fines fraction equals the sum of the silt and clay fractions. Over a wide range of fines contents the clay fraction is a relatively constant 30% of the fines. Using data from the sieve analyses of the tar sand mineral from a number of core samples, Carrigy (19) has classified tar sands into three groups according to their particle size distribution (see Table 4).

Table 4. Classification of Tar Sand by Particle Size (19)

	Group number		
Characteristic of sand	*1*	*2*	*3*
relative size of sand	largest	medium	smallest
location in formation	bottom	middle	top
average particle diameter, μ	130–600	90–180	44–120
fines $< 44\ \mu$, %	10	2–10	10–60
average bitumen content, wt %	12	14	variable

Bitumen Properties. Although there are wide variations both in the bitumen saturation of tar sands (0–18 wt % bitumen) and in the particle size distribution of the tar sand mineral, the chemical composition of Athabasca bitumen is relatively constant over a wide geographical area. Table 5 summarizes bitumen properties of samples from a number of geographical locations. Its density at 60°F is slightly greater than that of water. About 50% of the bitumen is distillable without cracking. Elemental analyses are relatively constant. Sulfur averages 4.5–5.0 wt % and nitrogen 0.4–0.5 wt %. Figure 9 summarizes viscosity values reported for samples from Bitumount, Abasand,

Table 5. Properties of Athabasca Bitumen from Various Sources

Property	Mildred–Ruth Lakes sample no.				Shell Canada, Ltd.	Abasand sample no.				Clearwater River	Ells River	Bitumount sample no.		From Ft. McMurray	
	1	2	3	4	7	1	2	3	4			1	2	75 miles south	120 miles west
gravity, °API (Vol. 14, p. 835)		6.5	8.3	8.6	7										
specific gravity, 60/60°F	1.006					1.027	1.031		1.022		1.007	1.007		1.006	1.022
distillation temp, °F, ibp		505													
5%		544		430	575										
10%		610		560	660										
30%		795		820	840										
50%		981		1010	965										
end pt		1030													
recovery, %		50													
molecular weight			539			800	600–700								
elemental analysis, wt %															
carbon	83.4	83.2	83.12			83.1	81.9	83.3	83.0	83.6	83.3	83.3		83.4	82.9
hydrogen	10.4	10.4	10.59			10.28	9.5	10.4	10.2	10.3	10.4	10.4		10.4	10.3
oxygen	1.2	0.94	1.14			1.36	2.9	0.8	2.5	0.2	1.3	1.2		0.9	0.9
nitrogen	0.5	0.36	0.40	0.29		0.30	0.4	0.4	0.5	0.4	0.4	0.4		0.6	0.5
sulfur	4.5	4.2	4.75	4.4		4.96	5.3	5.1	3.8	5.5	4.6	4.7		4.7	5.4
metals, ppm															
vanadium		250	290			210									
nickel		100	82												
iron			75												
copper		5	2												
hydrocarbon type, wt %															
asphaltenes		19						23.4					17.9		
resins		32						29.0					34.7		
oils		49						47.6					45.0		
carbon residue, wt %		10[a]		13.6[b]											
heating value, Btu/lb	17,810								17,860		17,690	17,910		17,870	17,700
reference	20	16	21	22	23	21	21	20	20	20	20	20	24	20	20

[a] Ramsbottom.   [b] Conradson.

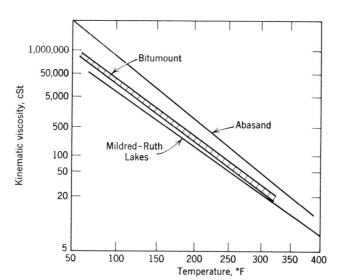

Fig. 9. Bitumen viscosity.

and the Mildred–Ruth Lakes area (GCOS). Figure 10 shows the variation of bitumen density with temperature. A curve for water is superimposed. Note that the water and bitumen curves cross twice, at about 100°F and about 240°F. The maximum density difference occurs at 160–180°F, near the operating temperature of the hot water bitumen extraction process.

Properties of Refined Products. Inspections on synthetic crude oils made from Athabasca bitumen by various processes are summarized in Table 6. When the synthetic crude is not desulfurized, sulfur content is about 4%; sulfur and nitrogen removal can be accomplished down to parts-per-million levels. Properties of coke made from Athabasca bitumen are summarized in Table 7.

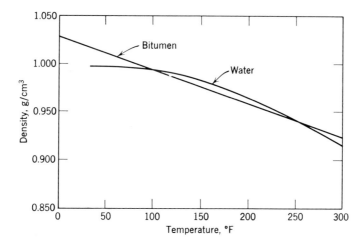

Fig. 10. Density of bitumen and water.

Table 6. Properties of Synthetic Crude Oil Refined from Athabasca Bitumen

| | Source of samples | | | | | | | |
| | GCOS | | Cities Service Atha-basca | Shell Canada, Ltd. | Direct fluid coking | | UOP[a] pilot plant | Feed for hydro-treating tests |
Property	Pilot plant	Commer-cial			Aba-sand	Bitu-mount		
gravity, °API	37.6	38.3	30.2	32.8	15.6	15.8	25.5	15.4
distillation temperature, °F								
ibp	210	162			176	182	118	
5%	277	221			338	412	182	
10%	300	254	265		460	482	245	
30%	379	408	455	400	630	600	438	
50%	486	507	585	540	682	650	550	
90%	680	615		885			750	
end pt	833	715					760	
recovery, %	99						97	
elemental analysis, wt %								
carbon	86.3							84.4
hydrogen	13.4							11.2
nitrogen	0.02		0.096	0.09				0.24
oxygen								0.10
sulfur	0.03	0.022	0.182	0.29	4.0	3.9	3.6	4.1
heavy metals,[b] ppm	0.04							
hydrocarbon type, wt %								
asphaltenes	0							
resins	0							
oils (aromatic)	21							
oils (saturated)	79							
UOP[a] "K"							11.0	
process	delayed coking; hydrotreating		fluid coking; hydro-treating	thermal cracking; hydro-treating	direct coking of tar sand 977°F		delayed coking	destruc-tive batch distil-lation
reference	16	25	22	23	24	24	26	27

[a] Universal Oil Products Co.   [b] Vanadium, nickel, and copper.

Table 7. Properties of Coke from Athabasca Bitumen

| | Sample number | | | |
Property	1[a]	2[a]	3[a]	4[b]
proximate analysis, wt %				
volatile	10.4	14.3	13.0	10.85
fixed carbon	84.3	77.0	82.9	
ash	5.3	8.7	4.1	2.95
heating value, Btu/lb	14,300	14,000	14,710	
sulfur, wt %	6.0	6.0	6.0	6.42

[a] Source: Sun Oil Company.   [b] Reference 26.

Technology of the Recovery of Values from Tar Sands

There are two basic approaches to recovering bitumen. The tar sand may be mined and transported to a processing plant where the bitumen is extracted and the sand is discharged. Alternatively the separation of bitumen from sand may be accomplished without ever moving the sand, that is, in situ. In situ processes have a great deal in common with secondary recovery of conventional crude oil.

Each of the recovery processes which has been described in the open technical literature is discussed below. A number of additional processes, presently of minor importance, are described in patents (1). Since the scale of operations described varies from laboratory batch experiments to a 10-ton-per-hr pilot plant, comparisons of the relative merits of the various processes must be made with the greatest care. The term yield, or bitumen recovery, is subject to so many definitions and possible methods of calculation that comparisons are possibly meaningless. Also, practically no economic data are available. Despite these shortcomings, process flow sheets may readily be compared. Fundamental process requirements, such as heat, can also be calculated and reliably compared.

IN SITU PROCESSES

Conventional crude oil is collected (produced) from the oil-bearing formations by drilling wells down into the formation. The oil is driven from the formation up through the wells (production wells) by energy stored in the formation, such as the pressure of natural gas. When this natural energy of the formation is expended or, as in the case of the Athabasca tar sands, if it never was present, then energy must be injected into the formation via other wells (injection wells) in order to stimulate production. A final essential for a successful in situ process is a means of communication between the injection wells and the production wells.

Thermal Methods of Recovery. In thermal recovery, or fire flooding, energy is generated in the formation in the form of heat. The heat is supplied by actually igniting oil in the formation and sustaining it in a state of combustion or partial combustion. The high temperatures generated decrease the viscosity of the oil and make it more mobile. More importantly, however, the high formation temperatures actually cause coking of the oil, so that an upgraded product rather than bitumen itself is the fluid recovered from the production wells. Thermal recovery processes are referred to as forward combustion or reverse combustion, depending on whether the combustion front moves with or counter to the direction of air flow. In either case burning occurs at the interface where air contacts hot, unburned oil. Thus, if the flame front is ignited near the injection well, it will propagate toward the production well (forward combustion). However, if the front is ignited near the production well, it will move in the opposite direction (reverse combustion). In forward combustion the hydrocarbon products released from the zone of combustion move into a relatively cold portion of the formation. Thus, there is a definite upper limit to the viscosity of the liquids which can be recovered by a forward combustion process. On the other hand, since the air passes through the hot formation before reaching the combustion zone, burning is complete; the formation is left completely cleaned of hydrocarbons. In reverse combustion some hydrocarbons are left in the formation. The relative advantage of reverse combustion is that the combustion products move into a heated portion of the formation and so are not subject to a strict viscosity limitation.

Although thermal recovery, or fire flooding, has been practiced for secondary recovery of conventional crude oil, no information has been published on results of field tests in tar sands. Laboratory tests have been made on reverse combustion in samples of Athabasca tar sands (28). The tests produced an upgraded oil, amber in color, of 25°API gravity and 15 cP viscosity. Temperatures and combustion zone velocities observed were a function of the rate at which air was fed to the combustion zone. At air fluxes above 20–40 scf/(ft²)(hr), formation temperatures are in the coking range for Athabasca bitumen (ie, above 650°F).

Emulsion-Steam Drive Process. If the viscous bitumen in a tar sand formation can be made mobile by admixture of either a hydrocarbon diluent or an emulsifying fluid, then a relatively low-temperature secondary recovery process may be possible. If the formation is impermeable, communication problems will exist between injection and production wells. However, it is possible to propagate a solution or dilution process along a narrow fracture plane between injection and production wells.

Shell Canada, Ltd. tested an emulsion process in field trials between 1957 and 1962 (29). Emulsification was preferred to the use of a hydrocarbon diluent because diluent is more expensive than the emulsifying fluid (water) and relatively large amounts of diluent would be required to reduce the viscosity of the very viscous Athabasca bitumen. The viscosity of a bitumen-in-water emulsion (20–30% bitumen) is essentially the viscosity of water.

Field trials were conducted between 1957 and 1959 on the use of a proprietary nonionic surfactant in water. During a somewhat larger and more comprehensive program between 1960 and 1962, a combination caustic solution (sodium hydroxide in water) and steam drive technique was tested. For this test, a five-spot pattern of wells was drilled (four injection wells at the four corners of a square with a producing well located in the center).

Shell discovered that, contrary to previous theoretical predictions (30), horizontal fractures could be formed in the McMurray formation, so that communication could be established between the injection and the production wells. As a result of the 1960–1962 experimental program, Shell concluded that in commercial operation, 70% displacement of the in-place oil would be possible from that fraction of the ore body which was wet, or "swept," by the caustic solution (29). That fraction itself, called the "sweep efficiency," would range from 70 to 100%. Therefore, the overall recovery would be between 50 and 70% of the in-place oil. In the experimental program, the ratio of steam injected to bitumen recovered was about 0.685 tons steam/ bbl bitumen. At this operating ratio, formation temperatures reached a maximum of 275°F. Interpreting the experimental data, Shell concluded the following: an injection rate of about 0.5 ton steam/bbl bitumen would be required in commercial operations; operating formation temperature would be 350°F; the fluid recovered from the producing wells would be an emulsion of 25–30% bitumen in water; a practical well spacing would be 4 acres per producing well; and wells would be spotted in a uniform geometric pattern, such that each producing well would be surrounded by four injection wells.

The ratio of steam injected per bbl of bitumen produced is important as far as the economics of an emulsion process are concerned. This can be shown from a brief consideration of the theoretical heat requirements. Net heating value of 1 bbl of bitumen is 6.24 million Btu. One ton of steam represents approx 2 million Btu as latent heat of vaporization. Thus, 0.5 ton steam/bbl bitumen represents (at 100%

efficiency) a fuel requirement of 16% of the bitumen recovered. If, now, the thermal efficiency of the steam drive process is impaired, for instance by heat losses upward in the formation to the overburden or downward from the formation, the numerator of the steam-to-bitumen ratio will be increased. Conversely, as the tar sand grade (percent bitumen) decreases, a larger amount of sand must be heated for each barrel of bitumen recovered. Thus, the denominator of the steam-to-bitumen ratio will decrease. If this expected thermal efficiency is much reduced, then a relatively large and economically significant amount of the recovered bitumen will be required for fuel.

Atomic Explosion. In 1958 a group headed by Richfield Oil Company (31), and including Imperial Oil, Ltd. and the Cities Service Athabasca, Ltd., proposed the test firing of an atomic bomb in the Athabasca oil sands. Project Oil Sand was the title of their proposal to the U.S. Atomic Energy Commission (which would supply the nuclear device) and the Oil and Gas Conservation Board of the Province of Alberta. The proposal was given technical study at the time it was made; action has been deferred by the Canadian Government.

The location proposed was Pony Creek, sixty-four miles south of Fort McMurray. It was planned that a nine-kiloton device be exploded at a depth of 1250 ft. A cavity some 230 ft in diameter would be created, which would contain up to one half the energy of the blast as useful thermal energy. This energy presumably would reduce the viscosity of the bitumen contained in the cavity. This bitumen, if sufficiently heated and reduced in viscosity, could then be produced in a conventional manner from a production well which would be drilled at the test site after the blast.

Project Oil Sand was designed using the data in hand as of 1958. It has not been discussed in the open literature since 1963. The recent success of Project Gasbuggy (recovery of natural gas in Nevada by means of nuclear explosion) may rekindle interest in Project Oil Sand. Certainly, at the present time the experiment could be much more critically designed.

MINING

The alternative to an in situ processing scheme is to mine the tar sands, transport them from their place in the formation to a processing plant, extract the bitumen value, and dispose of the waste sand. In order to support synthetic crude production in a plant of economically viable size, an immense mining operation is called for. For instance, the GCOS project, which produces 45,000 bbl/calendar day of synthetic crude requires a tar sand mining rate of about 100,000 tons/day. This figure refers to the tar sand (ore) only and does not include the overburden which must be stripped away in order to expose the tar sands for mining. This mining rate is on the order of those of the largest mines in North America, such as the open-pit iron ore mines of Labrador and of Minnesota. Because of the large scale of mining involved, only open-pit methods have been proposed for the Athabasca tar sands. As noted above, one important parameter in an open-pit mining scheme is the overburden ratio (the thickness of overburden which must be scraped away to expose unit thickness of the ore body). For the GCOS project, the overburden ratio is approximately 0.4 (16). The mining of deposits with overburden ratios as high as 2.5–3.5 has been discussed (32), but has not been seriously proposed.

Because of the relatively low unit value of tar sand as an ore, mining and transportation costs must be rigorously minimized. This means, among other things,

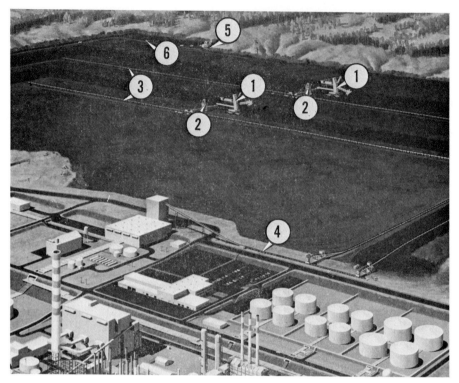

Fig. 11. Schematic plan of GCOS mining operations. Courtesy Sun Oil Company.

the feed must receive only a minimum amount of handling between mine and processing plant. On the other hand, for economy of operation in the processing plant, continuous units must be designed to operate with a relatively steady feed rate, round-the-clock. Such processing is usual in petroleum refineries; it is very definitely the exception in mining. Thus, quite apart from the large size scale, tar sand mining presents the unique problem of assuring a relatively steady feed rate to the processing plant, round-the-clock and year-round. In addition to this requirement, which exists for any tar sand formation, the mining of the Athabasca tar sands presents two other significant problems: (*1*) tar sand in-place requires very large cutting forces and is extremely abrasive to the cutting edges exposed to it, and (*2*) both the equipment and pit layouts must be designed to operate during the long Canadian winters at temperatures as low as 60°F below zero.

Basically there are two approaches to the open-pit mining of tar sands. The first is to use a few mining units of custom design, which will necessarily be very expensive. For instance, large units which have been considered are bucket wheel excavators, dredges (both hydraulic and bucket ladder), and supersized drag lines. The second approach is to use a multiplicity of smaller mining units of conventional design and relatively much lower unit costs. For example, scrapers and truck-and-shovel operations have been considered. Each method has advantages and its own peculiar risks (32). The first approach has been adopted by GCOS (16,33); the second approach has been proposed by Syncrude Canada, Ltd. (34).

Main features of the GCOS pit design are shown in Figure 11. The ore body is divided into two layers, or benches, each nominally seventy-five ft in height. The

Fig. 12. Bucket wheel excavator. Courtesy Sun Oil Company.

pit floor and the dividing plane between the upper and lower bench are roughly horizontal. Mining is done by two bucket wheel excavators, located at *1* in Figure 11. Figure 12 is a photograph of two bucket wheel excavators feeding tar sands to the GCOS extraction plant. (Note that both excavators are, temporarily, on the same bench because the pit is being developed.) Tar sands loosened from the face of each bench by the bucket wheel are discharged onto a crawler mounted conveyor or belt wagon, indicated at *2*. The belt wagons in turn discharge onto movable conveyors, shown at *3*. These conveyors are advanced from time to time in the direction of mining. The movable conveyors discharge onto trunk conveyors which in turn feed the main conveyor, shown at *4*. This conveyor is shown also in Figure 12. Maximum design capacity of each bucket wheel is 9000 tons/hr, more than enough to feed the entire plant. However, because of uncertainties as to the amount of time required for maintenance and unscheduled shutdowns, it was considered necessary to install two bucket wheel excavators at the outset. The overburden stripping operation is accomplished by an electric shovel, shown at *5* in Fig. 11. The shovel discharges to off-road trucks of eighty-five ton capacity which transport the overburden material out of the mine area to a suitable discharge spot.

Main features of the proposed Syncrude pit design are shown in Figure 13. The Syncrude mining operation (32) would be based on scrapers of conventional design and of approx 40-yd^3 capacity per unit. The pit is laid out in two benches and has very roughly a "race track" shape. Central to the pit is a drive-over dump station. The scrapers drive over this station without stopping and discharge their load to a conveyor which moves the tar sand to the plant area. Scrapers are also to be used for overburden stripping. The Syncrude application (34) is for production of 80,000 bbl/day of synthetic crude and specialty oils, which requires a rate of 104,000 yd^3/day, or 72 yd^3/min. This implies that one 40-yd^3 scraper must discharge its load of tar sands every 30 sec.

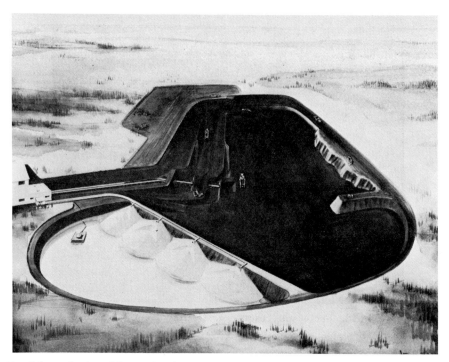

Fig. 13. Schematic plan of Syncrude mining operations (32). Courtesy *Journal of Petroleum Technology.*

Each mining method involves its own peculiar scale-up and operating risks and costs. Both GCOS and Syncrude tested small bucket wheel excavators on tar sands. It has been demonstrated that these units of less than one tenth the commercial size do provide the cutting action and the necessary power to mine tar sands. The major unknown for bucket wheels is the service factor. Scrapers have also been tested and demonstrated successfully for mining tar sands. The major unknown in a large scraper mining operation is the very real traffic problem. With the necessity to dump one scraper every 30 sec and with haul distances which may approximate one mile, large traffic problems may be foreseen. The two operations may also be compared as to their spare capacity requirements and equipment utilization. When very large units of mining equipment, such as the bucket wheel excavator, are used, extra capacity necessarily also comes in large increments and is expensive. Thus, the need to provide spare mining capacity practically forces poor utilization of this capacity. On the other hand, with big equipment, unit mining costs will be low. Unit mining costs may be expected to be high if smaller mining units, such as scrapers, are used. On the other hand, a few extra scrapers, purchased at relatively low cost, may provide the necessary overcapacity and insurance against unscheduled breakdown. Thus, if the scraper mining scheme operates according to design, nearly all the equipment will be in use all the time. A final major point of comparison between the two methods has to do with the time value of capital. It was necessary for GCOS to commit the funds for the purchase of the bucket wheels considerably in advance of plant startup. The cost of scrapers may be spread over the entire life of the project. It is reasonable to assume that both types of mining operation, and other alternatives, have been studied in considerable detail. The fact that two different conclusions have been reached as to the best mining method indicates that the managements involved believe the pros and cons for each mining method are comparable.

PROCESSING OF MINED TAR SANDS FOR BITUMEN RECOVERY

Direct Coking of Tar Sands. Direct coking of tar sands using a fluidized-bed technique has been tested by the Canadian Department of Mines and Technical Surveys, Mines Branch (24). Figure 14 is a simplified flow sheet of the pilot plant. Tar sand is fed to a first vessel which is a coker or still, operating at about 900°F. In the coker, the tar sand is heated by contact with a fluidized bed of clean sand from which the coke has been removed by burning. Volatile portions of the bitumen are distilled from the sand grains. Residual portions are thermally cracked, resulting in the deposition of a layer of coke around each sand grain. Coked solids are withdrawn from the coker down a standpipe, fluidized with air, and transferred to a second vessel. This vessel is a burner or regenerator; it operates at about 1400°F. In the regenerator most of the coke is burned off the sand grains. The clean hot sand is withdrawn through a standpipe. Part (20–40%) is rejected; the balance of the clean hot sand is recirculated to the coker to provide the heat for the coking reaction. Products leave the coker as a vapor, which is condensed in a product receiver. Reaction off-gases from the receiver are recirculated to fluidize the clean, hot sand which is returned to the coker. Condensate from the product receiver forms a heavy synthetic crude oil, the main reaction product. Typical properties of the synthetic crude are summarized in Table 6. Operating data from a number of coking runs on tar sands at different temperatures are summarized in Table 8. The main point to note is that to raise the coker temperature, it is necessary to raise the temperature in the burner and/or increase the recirculation rate (recycle ratio) of hot sand to the coker. At the highest recycle ratio, 5.0, the

Table 8. Operating Data for Athabasca Tar Sand Direct Coking Pilot Plant (24)

| | Source of tar sand | | | | | |
| | Abasand run no. | | | Bitumount run no. | | |
Operating data	*1*	*2*	*3*	*1*	*2*	*3*
feed						
composition, wt %						
bitumen	17.0	16.4	16.4	13.5	14.5	15.8
water	0.3	0.3	0.3	0.35	nil	0.9
rate						
lb/hr	83	86.4	83	107	85.4	79
lb/(hr)(ft²)	434	450	434	560	445	412
lb/(hr)(ft³) (bed volume)	169	176	169	219	173	161
operating conditions						
coker temperature, °F	925	977	1067	932	977	1022
burner temperature, °F	1303	1286	1436	1220	1265	1400
recycle ratio, lb clean sand						
to coker/lb tar sand to						
coker	2.9	4.4	5.0	4.4		3.9
oil product						
yield, vol %	84.0	83.5	73.5	85.7	86.0	82.5

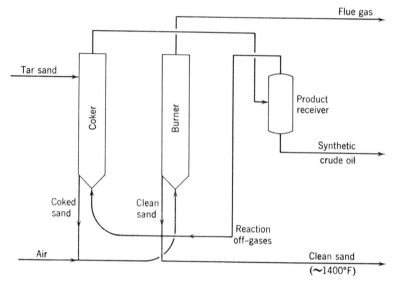

Fig. 14. Direct fluid coking of tar sands.

weight ratio of sand to oil in the coker is about 35. For comparison, typical catalyst-to-oil weight ratios in fluidized-bed catalytic cracking are 8 : 10.

Direct coking of tar sands using a fluidized-solids technique has much to recommend it. The process is a simple, direct treatment of the tar sand. The technology involved is similar to that in fluid catalytic cracking, so that it is reasonable to expect that large units could be engineered and scaled up reliably. This process has the particular advantage, relative to the hot water process (discussed below), that feeds of high fines content offer no particular difficulty. However, there are two possibly serious disadvantages to direct coking. Firstly, large amounts of sand must be circulated relative to the oil throughput. Under reaction conditions the sand may prove to be abrasive, causing material handling problems. Secondly, the sand discharged from the process is hot (1400°F) and thus represents a significant heat loss. No practical way has yet been suggested for recovering the large amount of sensible heat in the reject sand from a direct coking process. To heat the sand to 1400°F requires about 240 Btu per lb of tar sand. The heating value of 1 lb of tar sand (12 wt % bitumen) is about 2100 Btu. Thus, the process heat loss from this one source alone represents over 10 wt % of bitumen contained in the tar sands.

Anhydrous Solvent Extraction Process. An anhydrous solvent extraction process for bitumen recovery was developed by Cities Service Athabasca Limited (15). The work was carried out on laboratory scale during 1959–1961. The anhydrous process has four major steps, shown schematically in Figure 15. The solvent used in the experimental work was not specified. Presumably it was a light hydrocarbon.

In the first, or mixer, step fresh tar sand is mixed with recycle solvent which contains some bitumen and minor amounts of water and mineral. Solvent-to-bitumen ratio (by weight) is adjusted to about 0.5. The drain step, which is summarized by a single block in Figure 15, is actually the heart of the solvent extraction process. This step consists of a three-stage countercurrent wash. Settling and draining time is about 30 min for each stage. After each extraction step, a bed of sand is formed and

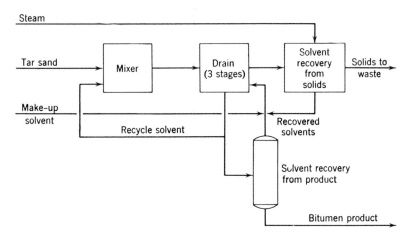

Fig. 15. Anhydrous bitumen recovery process.

the extract is drained through the bed until the interstitial pore volume of the bed is emptied. In typical runs, drain rates were on the order of 10 gal/(min)(ft²); they depended on the extract viscosity, sand bed depth, and applied pressure differential. Maximum pressure differential was 15 in. Hg. It was observed from time to time that the bed plugged with fine mineral or emulsion. In these cases drainage rate was essentially zero and the particular extraction stage in which the condition occurred was totally ineffective.

The last two steps of the process are devoted to solvent recovery. Stripping of the solvent from the bitumen is straightforward. The step of solvent recovery from the solids holds the key to the economic success of an anhydrous process (Table 9). In theory (15) 93% of the feed bitumen is recovered. Note, however, that solvent loss must eventually be made up from the bitumen product, probably by some process such as coking which will have less than 100 vol % yield. Thus, a more meaningful recovery figure is that equivalent to 100% solvent recovery. This figure is 89.3% if solvent stripping from the solids is accomplished. It is doubtful that the amount of steam indicated in the material balance is adequate to accomplish much stripping of solvent from the reject solids. If no such stripping is accomplished bitumen recovery falls from 93 to 90%. Solvent losses increase from 1 to 18% of circulation. This is an intolerably large loss; the corresponding bitumen recovery, corrected to 100% solvent recovery, is only 19%.

Cold Water Separation Processes. Two cold water bitumen separation processes have been developed to the point of small-scale continuous pilot plants. One process (35), developed by the Mines Branch of the Canadian Department of Mines and Technical Surveys in 1949–1950, uses a combination of cold water and solvent. This process was demonstrated in a 200-lb-per-hr continuous pilot plant. The first process step is called disintegration and is carried out in a pebble mill. This step accomplishes the disintegration of the charge and its mixing with water, diluent, and reagents. The diluent is kerosene; it is added in about 1:1 weight ratio to the bitumen in the feed. Total water addition for the process is two to three times the weight of tar sands. The pH is maintained in the range 9–9.5 by the addition of approximately 1.5 lb of soda ash/ton of tar sand. In addition to the soda ash, wetting agents are added. The pebble mill effluent is mixed with additional water, and in a raked classifier the sand is settled from

Table 9. Calculated Material Balance in Anhydrous Bitumen Recovery Process (15)[a]

| | Component, lb | | | | |
Stream	Bitumen	Solvent	Mineral	Water	Total
mixer step					
tar sand	380.0		2639.4	234.3	3254.5
recycle solvent	761.5	860.5	29.3	18.3	1669.6
drain step					
makeup solvent		10.4			10.4
solvent recovered					
from product		266.7			266.7
from sand	11.4	192.3			203.7
feed from mixer	1142.3	860.5	2668.7	252.6	4924.1
product	1115.6	1127.2	41.8	25.6	2310.2
solids-to-solvent					
recovery	38.1	202.8	2626.9	277.0	3094.7
solvent recovery step					
from product					
feed to stripper	354.1	266.7	12.5	7.3	640.6
bitumen product	354.1		12.5	7.3	373.9
from solids					
steam				149.1	149.1
solids to waste	26.7	10.4	2626.9	376.1	3040.1

Recoveries and losses	With solvent recovery from solids	Without solvent recovery from solids
solvent loss, % of circulation	1.0	18.0
bitumen recovery, % of feed bitumen	93.0	90.0
bitumen recovery, equivalent to		
100% solvent recovery, %	89.3	19.0

[a] Calculated on the basis of 1 bbl bitumen recovered.

the bulk of the remaining mixture. The water and oil overflow the classifier and go to the final process step, thickeners, which concentrate the oil. It was noted during experimental work that clay in the tar sand feed has a distinct effect on the process; it forms hard-to-break emulsions which are wasted with the underflow from thickeners step and detract from process recovery. The experimental work on the Mines Branch process was carried out with Abasand tar sands. Recall that this is a feed of low fines content. Oil product from the cold water separation process has a nominal composition by weight as follows: oil (bitumen diluted 1 to 1 with kerosene) 73%, mineral 2%, water 25%.

The sand reduction process (35a) is similar to the Mines Branch cold water process except no solvent is used. In the first step the tar sand feed is mixed with water at about 70°F in a screw conveyor. Water is added in the ratio of 0.75–3 tons/ton tar sand, with the lower range being preferred. The mixed pulp from the screw conveyor is discharged into a rotary drum screen, which is submerged in a water-filled settling vessel. The bitumen forms agglomerates, which are retained by the 20-mesh screen. These agglomerates sink through the settling vessel and are withdrawn as oil product. The sand readily passes through the 20-mesh screen and is withdrawn from the bottom of the settling vessel as a waste stream. The process is called sand reduction because its objective is the removal of sand from the tar sand to provide a feed suitable for a fluid coking process. Approximately 80% removal of sand is claimed. Nominal composition of the oil product is 58 wt % oil (bitumen), 27 wt % mineral, and 15 wt % water. The sand reduction process is said to be tolerant of fines (defined as less than 200-mesh mineral matter) up to about 25 wt % of the total tar sand mineral.

A process called spherical agglomeration has been described (36) by Puddington et al. at the National Research Council, Ottawa. The process, which has been briefly applied to tar sands (37), is remarkably like the sand reduction process. Water was added to tar sands and the mixture was ball-milled. The bitumen formed dense agglomerates of 75–87 wt % bitumen, 12–25 wt % sand, and 1–5 wt % water.

Hot Water Process. The hot water bitumen extraction process is, and probably will remain closely linked with the name of Dr. K. A. Clark. Dr. Clark first described the process in 1923 (38). From that start he devoted himself to research on the hot water extraction process more or less continuously through the pilot plant program at Bitumount in 1948–1949. Since that time, two major industrially sponsored pilot plant efforts have been made using the hot water process. The first of these was led by Cities Service Athabasca, Inc. in association with Imperial Oil, Ltd.; Richfield Oil Corp.; and Royalite Oil Company, Ltd. This program was carried out during 1959–1962 at Mildred Lake near the present GCOS plant site. The second effort was by GCOS during 1963–1965 at the plant site.

Despite some differences in detail, the hot water processes described, respectively, by Clark (39), Cities Service (22), and GCOS (16) have a great deal in common. The essentials of the hot water process are shown as a simplified flow sheet in Figure 16. In the first step, conditioning, also referred to as mixing or pulping, tar sand feed is heated and mixed with water to form a pulp of 60–85% solids at a temperature of 180–200°F. Broadly speaking, this process takes place in two stages. First the lumps of tar sand as mined are reduced in size by ablation. Successive layers of each tar sand lump become warmed and slough off revealing the inner, cooler layers. Secondly, the pulp so formed is mechanically mixed, reacted with any chemicals added, and further heated to the process temperature. Conditioning can be accomplished by open steam heating in a horizontal rotating drum. A great deal of research has been done on the effect of high shear mixing (40), water content of the pulp, and reaction of the caustic soda or other conditioning reagents with the tar sands (21,41). It has been shown, however, that all of these reactions are relatively rapid compared to the step of feed lump size reduction by ablation (16). Thus, from the point of view of equipment scale-up, conditioning can be regarded essentially as a heat transfer process. The effluent from the conditioning drum is screened to remove tramp material or tar sand lumps which were not sufficiently reduced in size. The screened pulp is mixed with any added water, adjusted to the proper consistency for pumping, as described below, and sent to the second step, the separation cell.

The separation cell acts like two settlers, one on top of the other. The lower settles sand down and the upper settles bitumen up (ie floats the bitumen). The bulk of the sand in the feed is removed from the bottom of the separation cell as tailings. A major portion of the feed bitumen floats to the surface of the separation cell and is removed as froth. A middlings stream, the third stream removed from the separation cell, consists mostly of water, but with some suspended fine mineral and bitumen particles. A portion of the middlings may be returned for mixing with the conditioning drum effluent in order to dilute the separation cell feed properly for pumping. The

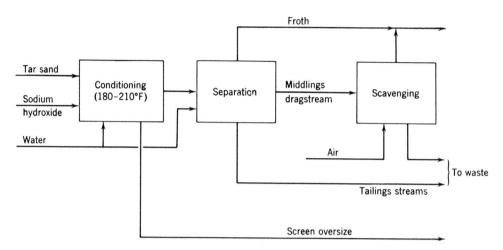

Fig. 16. Hot water bitumen recovery process.

balance of the middlings is called the drag stream. The drag stream is withdrawn from the separation cell to be rejected after processing in the scavenger cells. Tar sand feed contains a certain portion of fine mineral which, if allowed to build up in concentration in the middlings, increases the viscosity and eventually will cause all settling to cease in the separation cell. It is in order to control the fines concentration in the middlings that the drag stream is required as a purge. The amounts of water that come in with the feed and leave with the separation cell tailings and froth are relatively fixed. Thus, the size of the drag stream directly determines the makeup water requirement for the separation cell. The separation cell is simply an open straight-sided vessel with a cone bottom. Mechanical rakes on the bottom move the sand toward the center for discharge. Wiper arms rotating on the surface push the froth to the outside of the separation cell where it overflows into launders for collection.

The third step in the hot water process is scavenging. Enough bitumen may leave the process in the drag stream to make another recovery step economic; this depends on the drag stream size and composition. Scavenging may be accomplished by froth flotation using air. The scavenger froth is combined with the separation-cell froth to be further treated and upgraded to synthetic crude oil. Tailings from the scavenger cell join the separation-cell tailings stream and go to waste. Conventional froth flotation cells are suitable for the scavenging step.

The three major process steps may also be explained in terms of the separation mechanism, viewed on the microscale. Recall Figure 6, which described sand grains surrounded by a water film, surrounded by a bitumen film. The conditioning process provides enough shearing-agitation to rupture these bitumen films and cause the bitumen to disassociate from the sand grains as suspended flecks of oil. In a sense, then, after the pulp leaves the conditioning drum, the separation of bitumen from sand has actually been accomplished; the remainder of the process is simply for the purpose of collecting the separated materials. In the separation cell, the bitumen particles rise to the surface of the middlings and agglomerate to form a coherent mass, which is collected as a froth floating on the surface of the middlings. On an air-free basis, bitumen froth has a density about equal to, or slightly greater than, that of the middlings on which it floats. It is the inclusion of upward of 30 vol % of gas bubbles that causes the

Table 10. Calculated Material Balance for Hot Water Bitumen Extraction Process (16)[a]

| Component | Process inputs, lb | | Process outputs, lb | | | |
	Tar sand	Water	Screen oversize	Froth	Tailings	Middlings dragstream
bitumen	260		2.6	211.2	23.1	23.1
mineral	1660		16.6	38.8	1360.0	244.6
water	80	1000	0.8	181.0	456.9	441.3
total	2000	1000	20.0	431.0	1840.0	709.0

[a] Calculated on the basis of 1 ton tar sand processed.

bitumen flecks to readily float and form froth. Since the process is carried out at about 180°F, much of the gas is water vapor. The balance is air which has been entrained during conditioning and pumping to the separation cell. No air is added to the separation cell. Based on laboratory studies and the Bitumount pilot plant work, Clark described a step called flooding between the conditioning and separation steps. The purpose of the flooding step was to achieve high-shear mixing without air entrainment. Considerable importance was attached to this step, particularly to the exclusion of air. Air entrainment was said to lead to increased mineral content in the froth. From the GCOS pilot plant work it was concluded that no special provisions for flooding need be made; the diluted pulp can be transferred to the separation cell by centrifugal pumps. In the scavenging step, an attempt is made to recover bitumen particles which do not float in the separation cell. These particles evidently are finer or less air-avid than were the bitumen particles which were collected in the separation cell. Therefore, air must be added in the scavenging cell to accomplish recovery of these more refractory bitumen particles. Table 10 shows the material balance assembled from the data of Fear and Innes (16).

The thermodynamics of the hot water separation process have been formulated elegantly (21). The system has extremely complicated surface chemistry involving interfaces among various combinations of solids (including both silica sand and aluminosilicate clays), water, bitumen (which contains polar sulfur- and nitrogen-containing molecules), and air. Although the mathematical framework for expressing the various relationships has been provided, data are lacking. The control of pH in the process does seem to be critical. Preferred range of pH is 8.0–8.5. This range can be achieved with any of the monovalent bases. Polyvalent cations must be excluded from the process because they tend to flocculate the clays and thus raise the middlings viscosity in the separation cell. The relationships among clay concentration, flocculating ion concentration, and middlings viscosity are described in reference 41a.

A process termed hot water extraction has been applied on laboratory scale by the U.S. Bureau of Mines (USBM) to U.S. tar sand (42). This process is distinctly different from hot water separation as described above because a solvent is used. In the USBM hot water process a 33°API fuel oil containing 20–25 vol % aromatics is added as solvent in 1-to-3 weight ratio based on the feed bitumen content. Solvent is added in the conditioning stage. The product of this process resembles closely that of the Canadian Mines Branch cold water process. The composition of froth recovered from Edna, California tar sands was 73 wt % diluted bitumen, 6 wt % mineral, and 21 wt % water.

Despite the complication of the use of a high-boiling solvent, the same fundamental mechanisms seem to apply to the USBM process. Tar sand from the Vernal deposit in Utah (8.7–13.9% bitumen, 2% fines) was processed with bitumen recovery of 96%. Tar sand from the Sunnyside deposit in Utah actually occurs as an extremely hard asphalt rock that must be crushed to small size to facilitate complete disintegration and displacement of the bitumen from the sand grains. In the crushing operation, large quantities of silt are produced (fines content is 9–17%). This increases the water requirement relative to the Vernal tar sand and decreases the recovery to 90%. The tar sand deposit at Edna, California (11% bitumen, 6% fines) is unusual in that it contains, in the connate water, large concentrations of iron and calcium salts. With these present, bitumen cannot be extracted by the hot water process. However, if the tar sand is washed with hot water before conditioning to remove the polyvalent cations, then the hot water process can be successfully applied. The effect of the polyvalent cations is to form, under the basic processing conditions, gelatinous slimes. These prevent proper froth floatation and reduce recovery to 50% or less.

UPGRADING THE VALUE OF BITUMEN

There are two objectives in product upgrading. The first is the conversion of froth from those processes which yield froth as a product to the hydrocarbon bitumen. The second objective is upgrading the bitumen itself to a more salable product which can be generally described as a synthetic crude oil. Refining of synthetic crude to useful consumer goods such as gasoline and home heating oil can then be accomplished by conventional means.

Froth Cleanup Processes. Three types of froth cleanup processes have been described in the literature; no detailed data have been published on any of these. Froth from the hot water process may be mixed with a hydrocarbon diluent, such as coker naphtha, for viscosity reduction and centrifuged. The GCOS process (25) is a two-stage centrifuging operation, each stage consisting of multiple centrifuges of conventional design installed in parallel. Bitumen product contains 1–2 wt % mineral (dry bitumen basis) and 5–15 wt % water (wet diluted basis). Cities Service Athabasca, Ltd. proposed a two-stage froth cleanup process. The first stage accomplishes the bulk of the mineral removal by water-washing; the second stage is thermal dehydration. A third process, proposed by Shell, is electrical dehydration. This process was also proposed by GCOS in their original application to the Oil and Gas Conservation Board (1960–1962). It is analogous to electrostatic methods for the desalting of conventional crude oil.

Partial Coking. A partial coking or thermal deasphalting process has been proposed (43) to provide minimal upgrading of bitumen. The objective of the process is to remove mineral and water from a hot-water process froth, yielding a dehydrated and mineral-free bitumen product which still contains most of the asphaltenes and Ramsbottom carbon content. Partial coking consists simply of distilling hot-water process froth at atmospheric pressure. The process has been carried out batchwise in laboratory tests over a period of from 30 min to 4 hr. Thermal cracking begins as the liquid temperature passes 650°F. The distillation is continued to 700–850°F. When the heating is done slowly (50°F liquid temperature rise per hr) coke production rate is approximately 1 wt % of feed per hr. The coke forms about the entrained mineral particles as nuclei. In the process of forming 1–4 wt % coke, up to 50 vol % of the feed is recovered as distillate. After this treatment the residue may be filtered to yield an

Table 11. Inspections of Coker Distillate[a] Fractions (24)

Inspection	Composite	Distillation range, °F						Residue
		ibp to 356	356 to 464	464 to 536	536 to 608	608 to 644	644 to 750	
specific gravity, 60°/60°F	0.960	0.7720	0.8497	0.8801	0.9009	0.9165	0.9439	1.019
refractive index		1.4348	1.4719	1.4860	1.4980	1.5061	1.5234	
sulfur, wt %	4.01	1.70	2.59	2.69	3.21	2.76	3.51	4.92
viscosity, cSt								
at 100°F	43.2	1.24	1.65	2.73	3.98	8.51	27.7	10,721.0
at 210°F	5.7	0.77	0.8	1.12	1.58	2.12	3.9	77.8
percent of coker distillate								
by vol		6.6	5.9	3.6	5.8	3.4	17.8	54.7
by wt		5.1	5.0	3.2	5.7	3.1	16.8	55.7
asphaltenes, wt %	1.2	nil	nil	nil	nil	trace	trace	3.75
resins, wt %	18.7	0.94	1.8	2.4	3.0	4.1	4.4	39.4
oily material, wt %	77.8	99	98.2	97.6	97.0	95.2	93.9	57.9
aromatics, wt %		7.4	16.1	17.3	12.8	19.7	17.4	
acid soluble, wt %		63.3	51.2	45.5	48.8	45.7	54.6	
acid insoluble, wt %		29.3	32.7	37.2	38.4	34.6	27.8	

[a] Produced by direct fluidized solids coking of Abasand tar sands (977°F).

Table 12. Inspections of Coker Distillate[a] Fractions (24)

Inspection	Composite	Distillation range, °F						Residue
		ibp to 356	356 to 464	464 to 536	536 to 608	608 to 644	644 to 750	
specific gravity, 60°/60°F	0.954	0.7875	0.8477	0.8747	0.9000	0.9218	0.9465	1.003
refractive index		1.4384	1.4680	1.4815	1.4952	1.5098	1.5252	
sulfur, wt %	4.0	1.71	1.87	2.12	2.70	3.03	3.61	4.74
viscosity, cSt								
at 100°F	52.0	2.1	1.88	2.91	5.14	9.81	28.7	4550.0
at 210°F	5.2	1.06	0.87	1.15	1.59	2.27	4.0	54.0
percent of coker distillate								
by vol		3.5	6.1	5.7	7.7	4.0	17.2	50.0
by wt		2.8	5.2	5.0	6.9	3.7	16.2	50.2
asphaltenes, wt %	0.5	nil	nil	nil	nil	trace	trace	1.03
resins, wt %	22.6	1.40	1.66	1.74	2.2	3.9	6.7	26.6
oily material, wt %	72.5	98.0	98.0	97.6	97.0	94.5	92.7	71.7
aromatics, wt %		4.9	11.4	12.4	18.4	33.3	38.4	
acid soluble, wt %		44.8	41.3	39.0	39.6	29.5	38.6	
acid insoluble, wt %		50.3	47.3	48.6	42.1	37.1	25.0	

[a] Produced by direct fluidized solids coking of Bitumount tar sands (944°F).

Table 13. Product Yields from the Delayed Coking of Bitumen

Product	Scale of operation		
	Pilot plant	Pilot plant	Commercial (GCOS)
product yields, wt %			
H₂S	1.2		
hydrocarbon gases[a]	7.0		
total gases[a]		8.3	7.9
gasoline[b]	15.4	12.1	12.7
kerosene		10.1	15.0
gas oil	55.0	41.4	36.2
fuel oil		4.2	6.0
coke	21.0	22.7	22.2
unaccounted	0.4	1.3	
gas composition, mole %			
H₂	11.0	24.2	
CH₄	47.1	32.9	
C₂H₄	1.8	2.3	
C₂H₆	14.2	11.6	
C₃H₆	6.1	3.4	
C₃H₈	11.7	7.6	
C₄H₈	3.6		
C₄H₁₀	4.5	0.6	
H₂S and others		17.4	
reference	26	44	25

[a] C_4 and lighter.   [b] C_5 and heavier.

essentially ashfree product.   This ashfree residue now is suitable for several applications, such as metallurgical coke and production of bituminous paints, for which the original mineral content would have disqualified it.

Direct Coking and Delayed Coking. The commercially proposed tars and ventures have in common the objective to market an upgraded (and hence, relatively more valuable) product, and to satisfy the sizable need for fuel at the bitumen recovery site. Coking meets this particular combination of needs efficiently and economically.   The operation can be carried out in a number of ways, including direct coking of tar sands (see above) and fluid coking, delayed coking, and destructive batch distillation of bitumen.   In each case the charge is converted to distillate oil and coke.   The coke fraction of the product satisfies the need for fuel.   The coker distillate is a partially upgraded material in itself and is a suitable feed for hydrodesulfurization to produce a sweet synthetic crude.   Coking followed by hydrodesulfurization is the process route recommended in the Blair report (5).   It is the process used commercially by GCOS.

Operating conditions and product yields for the direct coking of tar sands have been described above.   Inspections of the whole coker distillate are given in Table 6. Properties of distillate fractions are detailed in Tables 11 and 12.   As noted above, chemical composition of the bitumen in the Athabasca deposit does not vary over rather wide geographical areas.   Thus, it is not surprising that the distillates made from Abasand tar sands (Table 11) and Bitumount tar sands (Table 12) are quite similar. In both distillates, sulfur is well distributed throughout the boiling range.   Aromatics content of both distillate samples is low compared to that of delayed coker distillates. In fact, none of the Abasand fractions boiling below 750°F had over 20% aromatics.

Table 14. Product Inspections of Delayed Coking of Bitumen

| | Scale of operation | | | | |
| | Pilot plant | | Commercial design basis | | |
Inspection	Gasoline	Gas oil	Naphtha	Kerosene	Gas oil
coker distillate,[a] wt %	19.5	69.6	16.5	13.7	51.8
gravity, °API	51.9	16.6	46.8	32.9	18.3
sulfur, wt %	1.86	4.04	2.2	2.7	3.8
bromine no.	80	47	61	36	20
nitrogen, total, ppm			150	400	2000
FIA,[b] vol %					
aromatics			19	39.2	62.1
olefins			32	14.4	2.0
paraffins and naphthenes			49	46.4	35.9
distillation					
temperature, °F					
ibp	126	443	180	380	515
5%	165	466	202	396	530
10%	186	486	220	409	550
30%	232	550	268	428	600
50%	275	621	295	441	645
70%	315	690	314	458	697
90%	358	715	347	477	780
95%			360	490	807
end pt	400	760+	400	535	850
recovery, %	98.5	97.5			
viscosity, 100°F, SUs		70.8			
reference	26	26	44	44	44

[a] The total distillable (ie, gas and liquid) coker product. It includes the streams labeled H$_2$S, hydrocarbon gases, gasoline, kerosene, gas oil, and fuel oil, in Table 13.

[b] Fluorescent Indicator Absorption, ASTM Method D-1319.

This result is a bit surprising considering that the parent bitumen contained over 50% asphaltenes and resins.

As the temperature of coking (in the range 800–1000°F) is decreased and the residence time correspondingly increased, operating conditions shift from fluid coking and approach once-through or delayed coking. In delayed coking the charge oil is heated to a temperature usually between 875 and 950°F to initiate the coking reactions. The heated oil then is fed to large drums, where all the material which will vaporize is allowed to do so. The residue is left behind to polymerize to coke. The various coking operations produce different coke yields; lower coking temperatures and longer residence times (as in delayed vs fluidized coking) favor higher coke yields. Figure 17 summarizes the range of values which have been obtained in coke and distillate yields.

Both pilot plant and commercial yield data are available on delayed coking of Athabasca bitumen and are summarized in Table 13. Table 14 summarizes inspections on fractions of delayed coker distillate. Corresponding inspections on the whole synthetic crudes from which these fractions are taken have been summarized in Table 6. Sulfur is distributed throughout the boiling range of the delayed coker distillate, as it was with the direct coker distillate. Nitrogen, which averaged 5000 ppm in the bitumen feed, is more heavily concentrated in the higher-boiling fractions; neverthe-

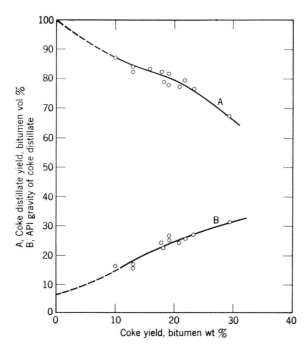

Fig. 17. Yields and gravities of various coker distillates produced from bitumen (26).   Courtesy Research Council of Alberta.

less, it is present in all distillate fractions.   Note that the gas oil has the high aromatics
content typical of coker gas oils.

Figure 18 gives a generalized correlation for the coke sulfur content from a number of possible feeds.   These data are compatible with the data on distillate fractions,
and again show that coking does not produce significant concentration of the sulfur in
any one fraction.   Incidentally, these data also emphasize that with a high sulfur feed
such as bitumen, a high sulfur coke will be produced.   Table 15 summarizes a sulfur
balance over a pilot plant delayed coking run.

Hydrotreating.   *Hydrogenation of Coker Distillate.*   All proposals to recover oil
from the Athabasca tar sands include the step of desulfurizing the synthetic crude oil
product.   Because the sulfur is so well distributed throughout the boiling range, catalytic hydrodesulfurization is the only process which has been seriously considered.
The Mines Branch of the Federal Canadian Government has maintained an ongoing

Table 15. Sulfur Balance for Pilot Plant Delayed Coking of Bitumen (26)

	Product yield, wt %	Sulfur in product, wt %	Sulfur in bitumen, %
bitumen charge	100.0	5.32	100.0
products			
C$_4$ and lighter gas	8.2	13.8	21.2
debutanized gasoline	15.4	1.86	5.5
gas oil distillate	55.0	4.04	41.7
coke	21.0	6.42	25.4
unaccounted for	0.4		6.2

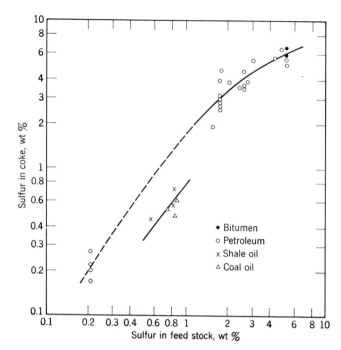

Fig. 18. Sulfur contents of coke produced by thermal cracking (26). Courtesy Research Council of Alberta.

program of research on hydrotreating of coker distillates (27,45) from bitumen and more recently of bitumen itself (46).

Results of hydrotreating a coker distillate (27,45) using cobalt–molybdena on alumina catalyst are summarized in Figures 19–21. Feed for these tests is described in Table 6. Catalyst deactivation rate, in continuous operation at fixed conditions, can be expressed by the term $\Delta(SG)/\Delta\theta$

$$\Delta(SG)/\Delta\theta = 1.24(10^6)/P^{3.1}$$

operating conditions: temperature = 896°F

liquid hourly space velocity (LHSV) = 2.0 vol/(vol)(hr)

pressure = 1000–3000 psig

where (SG) = specific gravity; P = pressure, psig; and θ = time, hr.

In order to take advantage of optimum operating conditions for various distillate fractions, the GCOS coker distillate is treated as three separate fractions: naphtha, kerosene, and gas oil. GCOS uses the Unifining process (Universal Oil Products Company); operating conditions have not been published. In the operation proposed by Shell Canada, Ltd., feed is to be treated in two fractions, naphtha–kerosene and heavy gas oil. Inspections on feeds and products of these desulfurizing operations are summarized in Table 16.

Hydrogenation of Bitumen. Direct hydrogenation of bitumen has been tested by the Mines Branch of the Federal Canadian Government (46) in a fixed-bed continuous-flow pilot plant similar to that used for hydrogenating coker distillate. The feed consisted of Abasand cold water process bitumen and blends of this bitumen with a distillate produced at the Bitumount pilot plant. The blend used in most of the tests

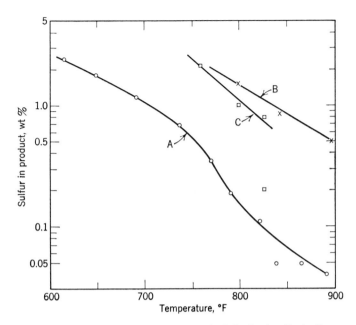

Fig. 19. Effect of temperature on catalytic hydrodesulfurization.

Curve	Feed	Hydrogen pressure, psig	LHSV, vol/(vol)(hr)	Reference
A	coker distillate	1000	1.82	45
B	coker distillate	1000	2.0	27
C	diluted bitumen	2000	0.5	46

is described in Table 17.   The catalyst in the fixed-bed reactor was the same cobalt–molybdena on alumina catalyst (Union Oil Company Type N-5) used in the high-pressure hydrogenation tests on coker distillate.   The catalyst was used in two forms, as received (oxide form) and sulfided (850°F, 1 atm hydrogen sulfide, 1 hr).

The effect of temperature on sulfur removal is shown by curve C of Figure 19. Note that although the desulfurization achieved is comparable to that possible with coker distillate, much more severe operating conditions are required.   This requirement of increased severity of treatment can be illustrated in a different way by comparing Figures 21 and 22.   These two figures show the amount of sulfur reduction achieved for a given amount of specific gravity reduction.   Hydrogen consumption data were not provided for the bitumen hydrogenation tests.   If, however, hydrogen consumption follows specific gravity reduction for the bitumen hydrogenation as it did for coker distillate (Fig. 21), then, because a given sulfur reduction requires more specific gravity reduction for diluted bitumen than for coker distillate, it is reasonable to assume that the same sulfur reduction also requires more hydrogen consumption. The economics of hydrotreating are directly and largely influenced by the amount of hydrogen chemically consumed.   To compare direct hydrotreating with the coking-hydrotreating sequence described above, the cost of this extra hydrogen must be balanced against possible savings resulting from eliminating the need for delayed cokers.

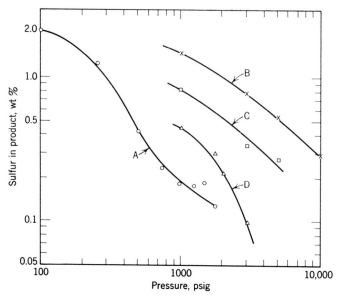

Fig. 20. Effect of pressure on catalytic hydrodesulfurization of coker distillate.

Curve	Temperature, °F	LHSV, vol/(vol)(hr)	Co–Mo/Al₂O₃ catalyst (Union Oil Co.)	Reference
A	790	1.85	N	45
B	797	2.0	N-5	27
C	842	2.0	N-5	27
D	896	2.0	N-5	27

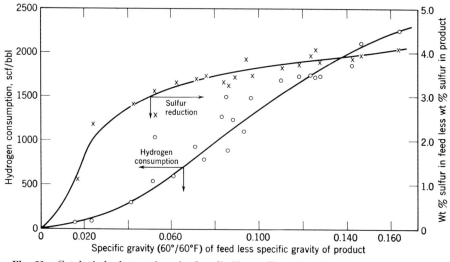

Fig. 21. Catalytic hydrotreating of coker distillate. From data in references 27 and 45.

Catalyst life for hydrotreating diluted bitumen was tested in several 100-hr continuous runs. Catalyst in the sulfided form showed a deactivation rate (LHSV = 0.5, 840°F, 2000 psig) of 5.5×10^{-4} units of specific gravity per hr. A similar test at 1.0

Table 16. Hydrodesulfurization of Coker Distillate Fractions

Inspection	GCOS									Shell Canada, Ltd.			
	Naphtha			Kerosene			Gas oil			Naphtha and kerosene		Heavy gas oil	
		Product			Product			Product					
	Feed	Pilot plt.	Com.	Feed	Pilot plt.	Com.	Feed	Pilot plt.	Com.	Feed	Product	Feed	Product
coker distillate, wt %	16.5			13.7			51.8						
synthetic crude, vol %		30.6	30.8		19.0	27.2		50.4	42.0				
gravity, °API	46.8	50.9	55.3	32.9	39.7	38.6	18.3	28.7	27.5	28.4	41.5	10.6	20.2
sulfur, ppm	22,000	50	15	27,000	50	50	38,000	800	410	29,800	500	41,500	5,100
nitrogen, total, ppm	150	18	2[a]	400	1	50[a]	2,000	trace	500[a]	600	100	22,900	1,700
FIA, vol % aromatics	19	18		29.3	13.8	12.7	62.1	29.8	25.3				
olefins	32			14.4	<1.0		2.0						
paraffins and naphthenes	49			46.4	85.7		35.9						
distillation temp, °F													
ibp	180	174	162	380	388	358	515	499	498				
5%	202	260	194	396	398	385	530	512	526				
10%	220	274	206	409	402	398	550	522	540				
30%	268	282	238	428	411	418	600	561	568				
50%	295	296	278	441	415	438	645	611	588				
70%	314	310	316	458	423	460	697	655	615				
90%	347	334	369	477	433	496	780	740	675				
95%	360	344	396	490	448	513	807	785	706				
end pt	400	366	462	535	468	533	850	869	715				
recovery, %								90					
viscosity, 100°F, cSt					1.8								
operating conditions													
inlet pressure, psig	800			1,500			1,500			1,200	1,500		
outlet temperature, °F										725	725		
LHSV, vol/(vol)(hr)										1.0	1.0		
hydrogen consumption, scf/bbl										700	1,000		
reference	44	25	25	44	25,47	25	44	25,47	25	23	23	23	23

NOTE: plt. = plant; Com. = commercial.

[a] Typical properties.

Table 17. Hydrodesulfurization of Diluted Bitumen

Inspection	Feed	Oxide catalyst[a]				Sulfided catalyst[b]					
		Whole product	Product fractions			Whole product	Product fractions				
whole product, vol %			60	17	23		47.2	12.8	13.3	10.9	15.8
gravity, °API	10.1	28.4				32.5					
sulfur, wt %	4.02	0.93	trace	0.18	2.85	1.97	trace	0.04	0.12	0.27	4.08
distillation temperature, °F											
ibp				660	800+			480	540	660	800+
5%	385	230									
10%	480	310				255					
30%	674	485				390					
50%		600				480					
70%		720				625					
90%											
95%											
end pt			660	800			480	540	660	800	
recovery, at 800°F, %	46.5	76.8				84.2					

[a] Pressure, 2000 psig; temperature, 810°F; LHSV, 0.5 vol./(vol)(hr).   [b] Pressure, 2000 psig; temperature, 806°F; LHSV, 0.5 vol/(vol)(hr).

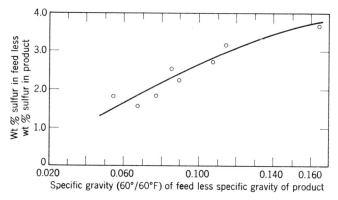

Fig. 22. Catalytic hydrotreating of bitumen. From data in reference 46.

LHSV showed double this deactivation rate. Extrapolating these data, the rate at 2.0 LHSV would have been 22×10^{-4} units of specific gravity per hr, or 15 times the corresponding rate (LHSV = 2, 896°F, 2000 psig) observed for hydrotreating coker distillate. The deactivation rate for coker distillate was observed using the catalyst in the oxide form. When the catalyst is used in the oxide form for treating diluted bitumen, no regular increase in specific gravity with time is observed in 70 hr at 850°F or in 100 hr at 800°F. O'Grady and Parsons (46) speculate that the greater cracking activity of the sulfide form of the catalyst leads to more rapid coke buildup on the catalyst. At temperatures of 800°F and below, the oxide catalyst form has low enough cracking activity for coke precursors to be washed away from the catalyst surface by the liquid phase portion of the reaction medium. Inspections on products and product fractions are summarized in Table 17. Table 17 illustrates the greater cracking activity of the sulfide catalyst form (480°F vs 600°F mid-boiling point in the product). The oxide catalyst form is somewhat more active for sulfur removal at equivalent operating conditions; however, both catalysts yield an 800+°F residuum which is only slightly improved if at all in sulfur content. On the other hand, brief tests showed that this residuum is no more refractory than the (undiluted) feed bitumen and thus might be recycled if desired.

Commercial Ventures

Following the issue of the Blair report in 1950, there was a spate of activity in applications for leases in the Athabasca tar sands. Between 1950 and 1955 exploration leases covering a large proportion of the tar sands were issued. These leases generally provided exploration rights only and could be maintained annually by payment of a nominal sum. Exploration leases now cover practically the entire deposit. Starting about 1955 serious pilot plant efforts were undertaken which have led at the present time to three applications for commercial production from the Athabasca tar sands (33,34,48,49). The application of Great Canadian Oil Sands, Limited has been granted and GCOS is now in commercial production. Major points of the three formal applications are compared in Table 18.

Great Canadian Oil Sands, Limited. Great Canadian Oil Sands, Ltd. was formed in 1953 from the holdings of Oil Sands, Ltd. GCOS is in a direct line of descent from the Bitumount pilot plant. In 1953 GCOS's stock-in-trade was a hot water bitumen ex-

Table 18. Proposed Commercial Tar Sand Ventures

Project	Shell Canada, Ltd.	Cities Service Athabasca, Ltd.[a]	Great Canadian Oil Sands, Ltd.[b]	Syncrude Canada, Ltd.[c]
project size				
bitumen, bbl/day	130,000	134,000	57,700	
synthetic crude, bbl/day	100,000	100,000	45,000	80,000[d]
investment, million $		274.0[e]	230.0[f]	192.5[g]
processing sequence				
mining	in situ	bucket wheels (two)	bucket wheels (two)	scrapers
bitumen recovery	API separator	dense phase process[h]	hot water	
bitumen upgrading	electrical dehydrator	thermal dehydrator	centrifuge	
refining (a)	thermal crack	fluid coking	delayed coking	H-oil hydro-visbreaking
(b)	hydrodesulfurize	hydrodesulfurize	hydrodesulfurize	
status	application 1962 withdrawn 1968	application 1962 action deferred	started commercial operations Sept. 1967	application 1968
references	23,49	22,48	16,25,33,47	34

[a] In association with Imperial Oil Ltd., Richfield Oil Corp., and Royalite Oil Co., Ltd.

[b] A subsidiary of Sun Oil Company, Ltd.

[c] Consortium of Cities Service (30%); Atlantic Richfield (30%); Imperial Oil Ltd. (30%); Royalite Oil Co., Ltd. (10%).

[d] Synthetic crude, 50,000 bbl/day; low sulfur fuel, 25,000 bbl/day; naphtha, 5000 bbl/day.

[e] Estimated.　　　　　[g] Estimated; excludes　　　　[h] A hot water

[f] Actual costs.　　　　　pipeline and powerhouse.　　　extraction process.

traction process based on this earlier work. However, repeating the often-told story, GCOS lacked financial backing. At about the same time Sun Oil Company became interested in the tar sands through Sun's Canadian exploration work. Sun became a three-quarter holder of Lease No. 4 in the Mildred–Ruth Lakes area, along with Abasand Oils, Ltd., the original lease holder. Since the original exploration work of S. C. Ells the Mildred–Ruth Lakes area was reputed to be a prime candidate for a tar sands mining venture. The World War II drilling program (50) of 1942–1947 confirmed this. Abasand had acquired Lease 4 after World War II. In 1957 GCOS obtained an option to sublease from Sun and Abasand. In 1960, GCOS applied (33) to the Oil and Gas Conservation Board of the Province of Alberta for permission to produce 31,500 bbl/day of synthetic crude oil. Sun, as three-quarter holder of Lease 4, now seriously began to consider backing GCOS financially. In 1963 a pilot plant and lease evaluation program (51) were started and GCOS, with Sun backing, filed their revised application for production of 45,000 bbl/day of synthetic crude; this application was approved. The pilot plant program went into high gear through 1965 (16). Dedication ceremonies for the plant were held Sept. 30, 1967. Figure 23 describes the hot water extraction process used by GCOS for recovery of bitumen from the tar sands. Figure 24 is an overall flow sheet and material balance for the project. At this writing, 1 yr after plant startup, the project is approaching production at the design rate. The startup period has been protracted; however, this is not altogether unexpected for a

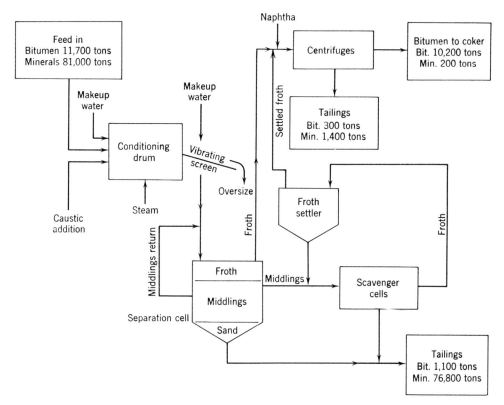

Fig. 23. GCOS bitumen recovery process (44). All figures are per calendar day. LEGEND: Bit., bitumen; Min., minerals. Courtesy *Oil and Gas Journal.*

refinery which is not only a grass-roots operation located in a wilderness, but also the first of its kind. Initial commercial operation has proved out the design bases of the GCOS project (25) and smooth continuous operation is now being achieved.

Products from the GCOS operation are synthetic crude oil (40.8° API; 45,000 bbl/day), sulfur (314 long tons/day), and fuel gas, fuel oil, and coke (Fig. 24). The latter three are all consumed internally as plant fuel. The crude oil product is piped to Edmonton through a 266-mile pipeline laid by GCOS for the purpose. Edmonton is the western terminus of the Interprovincial Pipeline. In this line the GCOS crude moves east for sale. The by-product sulfur is moved by truck and rail from the plant site via Fort McMurray to Edmonton and thence to its markets.

Cities Service Athabasca, Ltd., and Syncrude Canada, Ltd. Cities Service has been central to a second chain of effort, which also began in the mid-1950s with a somewhat less direct connection to the Bitumount pilot plant. This pilot plant ended up being owned by the Alberta Government which had no use for the property. It was sold to Can-Amera and Royalite Oil Company, Ltd. (Royalite is held by British American Oil Company, which in turn is related to the U.S.-based Gulf Oil Corporation.) In 1958 Royalite entered into a joint program with Cities Service Research and Development Co. They were joined soon afterward by Richfield Oil Corporation and Imperial Oil, Ltd. Cities Service established a new subsidiary, Cities Service Athabasca, Inc., to act as operator for the group. Further pilot plant work was carried out briefly in 1958

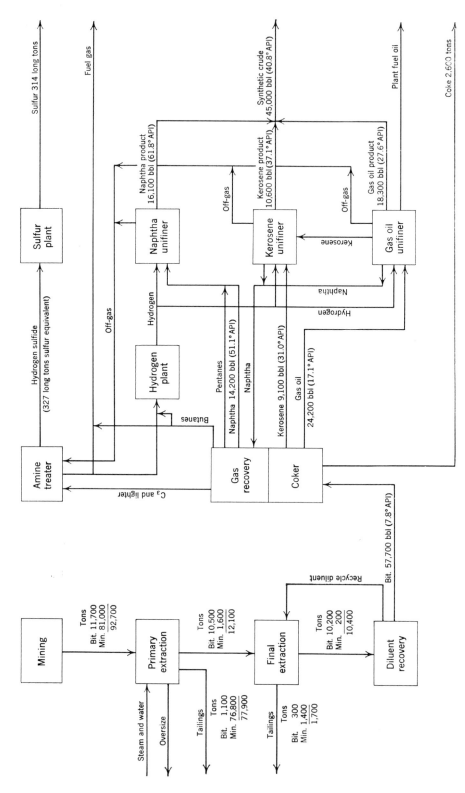

Fig. 24. Overall flowsheet for GCOS process (16). All figures are per calendar day. LEGEND: Bit., bitumen; Min., minerals. Courtesy World Petroleum Congresses.

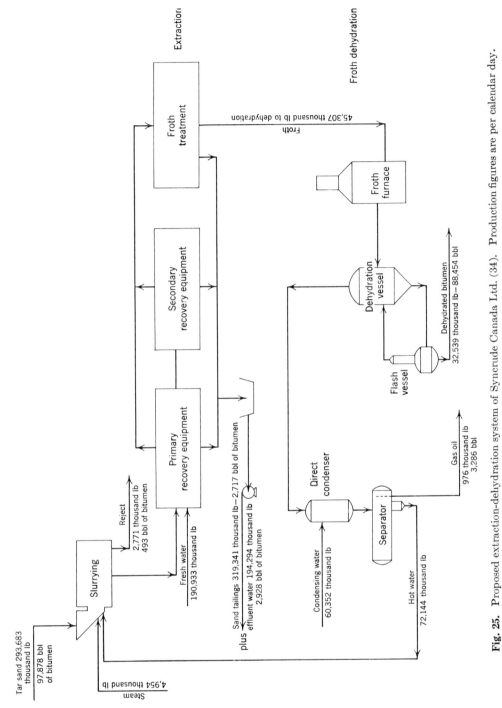

Fig. 25. Proposed extraction-dehydration system of Syncrude Canada Ltd. (34). Production figures are per calendar day.

at the Cities Service lab at Lake Charles, Louisiana.   In 1959 an extensive pilot facility was opened near Mildred Lake on the west bank of the Athabasca River, twenty-five miles north of Fort McMurray.   This pilot plant was operated from 1959 to 1962 (22). The pilot plant work resulted in the Cities Service Athabasca application in 1962 (48).

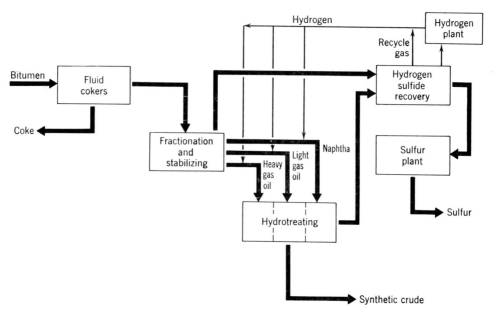

Fig. 26. Proposed bitumen upgrading process of Cities Service Athabasca Ltd. (22).

The Cities Service bitumen recovery scheme was also a hot water extraction process; the flowsheet, showing rates as revised by Syncrude Canada, Ltd., is summarized in Figure 25. Bitumen upgrading is shown in Figure 26. The process is essentially the same as that proposed by GCOS, except that fluid coking is used instead of delayed coking. Fluid coking is a coking process offered for license by Esso Research and Engineering Company, which is a part of the New Jersey Standard Oil Company family, as is Imperial Oil, Ltd. This process should not be confused with direct coking of tar sands as studied by the Mines Branch of the Federal Canadian Government. This latter process also uses a fluidized solids technique.

At the time of the Cities Service Athabasca application, the Oil and Gas Conservation Board had in effect a policy whereby production from the tar sands was limited to 5% of the commercial crude oil production of the Province of Alberta. Under this restriction, the GCOS application could be allowed, but action on the applications of Cities Service and of Shell (each for 100,000 bbl/day) was deferred. In early 1968, the Province revised this limitation and raised the allowable production from the tar sands to 150,000 bbl/day.

When the application was not approved, Cities Service shut down the Mildred Lake pilot facility. Laboratory work continued in Edmonton under the leadership of a reformed operating company, Syncrude Canada, Ltd. Cities Service and Imperial Oil, Ltd. remained as 30% owners. Royalite Oil Company, Limited remained as a 10% owner. The original Richfield interest was picked up by Atlantic Richfield. (Atlantic Refining Company and Richfield Oil Corporation had merged in the meantime.) Under the new policy of the Oil and Gas Conservation Board, Syncrude submitted a revised application early in 1968 (34). This application involved major changes in concept from the original Cities Service Athabasca application. One of the principal changes was dropping the coking-hydrotreating process step in favor of H-oil, a residuum hydrotreating process (Fig. 27). If the Syncrude project proceeds, it will be the

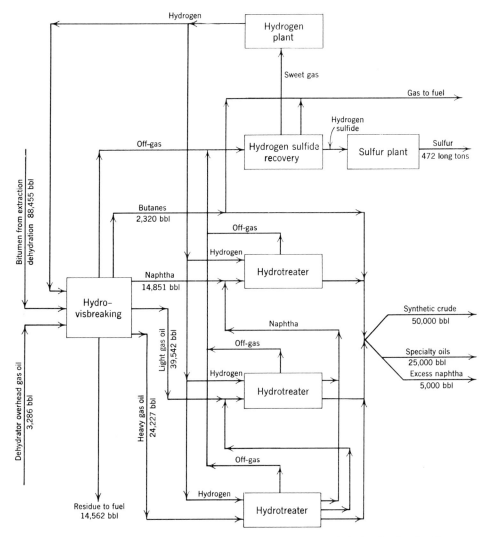

Fig. 27. Proposed bitumen upgrading system of Syncrude Canada Ltd. (34). Production figures are per calendar day.

first commercial application of the H-oil process to a high metals (above 200 ppm) residual stream. The H-oil process was developed jointly by Cities Service and Hydrocarbon Research, Inc. in the early 1960s.

Shell Canada, Ltd. Shell Canada, Ltd. has put forward the only proposal (49) for an in situ bitumen recovery process. Shell's process is based on their pilot plant work, carried out between 1957 and 1962 (23,29). This work included extensive field trials of two in situ processes; the first process uses surfactants and the second, dilute caustic solution along with steam to emulsify the in-place bitumen. The second process, called steam drive, is the one they proposed to commercialize. Shell's proposed bitumen refining scheme is summarized in Figure 28. This scheme is analogous to that of GCOS and Cities Service Athabasca, Ltd. except that the thermal cracker produces a liquid pitch for use as refinery fuel, rather than coke. The Oil and Gas Conservation Board

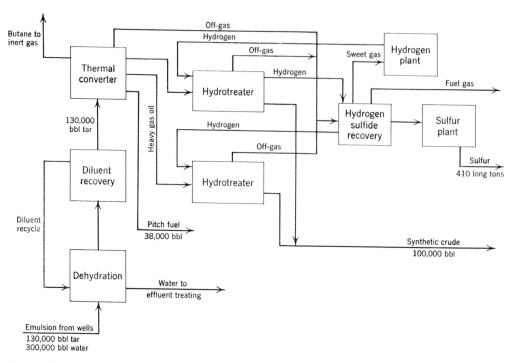

Fig. 28. Processing scheme proposed by Shell Canada Ltd. (23).   Production figures are per calendar day.

deferred action on Shell's application (also 100,000 bbl/day); in 1968, Shell withdrew their application.

Bibliography

"Tar Sands" in *ECT* 1st ed., Vol. 13, pp. 633–645, by K. A. Clark, Research Council of Alberta, and G. B. Shea (U.S. Deposits), U.S. Department of the Interior.

1. M. A. Carrigy, comp., *Preliminary Report 65-3, Athabasca Oil Sands Bibliography (1789–1964)*, Research Council of Alberta, Edmonton, Alberta, Canada, 1965.
   This is the definitive bibliography on tar sands through 1964.   No attempt is made in the following references to match Carrigy's completeness.   Rather, the objective is to provide enough (particularly recent) references to give the serious researcher an entry into the tar sands literature.   References 2, 3, and 4 should form the backbone of any working library on tar sands.
2. *Proceedings of the First Athabasca Oil Sands Conference*, King's Printer, Edmonton, Alberta, Canada, Sept. 1951.
3. M. A. Carrigy, ed., *Athabasca Oil Sands: A Collection of Papers Presented to K. A. Clark on the Seventy-Fifth Anniversary of his Birthday*, Research Council of Alberta, Edmonton, Alberta, Canada, Oct. 1963.
4. "Occurrence and Prospects of Tar Sands," Panel Discussion No. 13 in *Proceedings of the 7th World Petroleum Congress*, Vol. 3, Elsevier Publishing Co., Amsterdam, 1967, pp. 549–655.
5. S. M. Blair, *Report on the Alberta Bituminous Sands*, Government of the Province of Alberta, Edmonton, Alberta, Canada, 1950.
6. D. C. Ion, "The Significance of World Petroleum Reserves" in *Proceedings of the 7th World Petroleum Congress*, Vol. 1B, Elsevier Publishing Co., Amsterdam, 1967, pp. 25–36.
7. R. A. Baillie and T. S. Mertes, "Development and Production of Oil from the Athabasca Tar Sands" in *Proceedings of the Southwestern Legal Foundation: Sixth Annual Institute on Explora-*

tion and Economics of the Petroleum Industry, Matthew Bender & Co., New York, 1968, pp. 241–271.

8. A. B. Cambel, *Energy, R&D and National Progress*, U.S. Government Printing Office, Washington, D.C., 1964.

9. P. H. Phizackerley and L. O. Scott, "Major Tar Sand Deposits of the World" in reference 4, pp. 551–571.

10. *A Description and Reserve Estimate of the Oil Sands of Alberta*, Oil and Gas Conservation Board of the Province of Alberta, Calgary, Alberta, Canada, 1963.

11. G. W. Hodgson, E. Peake, and B. L. Baker, "The Origin of Petroleum Porphyrins: The Position of the Athabasca Oil Sands" in reference 3, pp. 75–100.

12. T. A. Link, "Source of Oil in Oil Sands of Athabasca River, Alberta, Canada," in reference 2, pp. 55–65.

13. W. E. Atkins, *Report to the Board of Trustees of the Oil Sands Project*, Government of the Province of Alberta, Canada, 1950.

14. D. S. Pasternack, *Report on Operations at Bitumount during 1949*, Research Council of Alberta, Edmonton, Alberta, Canada, 1949.

15. J. H. Cottrell, "Development of an Anhydrous Process for Oil Sand Extraction" in reference 3, pp. 193–206.

16. J. V. D. Fear and E. D. Innes, "Canada's First Commercial Tar Sand Development" in reference 4, pp. 633–650.

17. M. A. Carrigy, "The Physical and Chemical Nature of a Typical Tar Sand: Bulk Properties and Behavior" in reference 4, pp. 573–581.

18. K. A. Clark, *Can. J. Res.* **22F,** 174–180 (1944).

18a. A. E. Scheidigger, *The Physics of Flow Through Porous Media*, University of Toronto Press, Toronto, 1957, p. 59.

19. M. A. Carrigy, "The Significance of a Grain Size Classification of the Sands of the McMurray Formation, Alberta" in *Proc. 5th World Petrol. Congr., Sect. 1*, Fifth World Petroleum Congress, Inc., New York, 1959, pp. 575–590.

20. K. A. Clark, "Guide to the Alberta Oil-Sand Area along the Athabasca River between McMurray and Bitumount and to the Oil-Sand Separation Plant of the Government of Alberta at Bitumount" in reference 2, pp. 343–366.

21. C. W. Bowman, "Molecular and Interfacial Properties of Athabasca Tar Sands" in reference 4, pp. 583–604.

22. R. A. Given, *Paper No. 63-15, National Petroleum Refiners Association Meeting*, April, 1963.

23. A. D. Hoskins, "How Hydrogen is Used to Upgrade 7-DEG-API Athabasca Tar to Sweet Crude Oil," *Proc. Am. Petrol. Inst., Sect. III* **44,** 426–429 (1964).

24. W. S. Peterson and P. E. Gishler, "The Fluidized Solids Technique Applied to Alberta Oil Sands Problem" in reference 2, pp. 207–236.

25. G. F. Andrews, E. W. Dobson, and H. M. Lewis, "Great Canadian Oil Sands Experience in the Commercial Processing of Athabasca Tar Sands," *Am. Chem. Soc., Div. Petrol. Chem., Preprints* **13** (2), F5–F18 (1968).

26. M. J. Sterba, "Thermal Coking of Oil from Alberta Bituminous Sand" in reference 2, pp. 257–270.

27. A. R. Aitken, W. H. Merrill, and M. P. Pleet, *Can. J. Chem. Eng.* **42,** 234–238 (Oct. 1964).

28. R. H. Perry, D. W. Green, and J. M. Campbell, *J. Petrol. Tech.* **12** (5), 11–12 (1960); R. L. Reed, D. W. Reed, and J. H. Tracht, *J. Petrol. Tech.* **12** (5), 13–14 (1960); J. E. Warren, R. L. Reed, and H. S. Price, *J. Petrol. Tech.* **12** (5), 14–15 (1960); V. J. Berry, Jr. and B. R. Parrish, *J. Petrol. Tech.* **12** (5), 15–16 (1960).

29. T. M. Doscher, R. W. LaBelle, L. H. Swatsky, and R. W. Zwicky, "Steam-Drive—A Process for In Situ Recovery of Oil from the Athabasca Oil Sands" in reference 3, pp. 123–141.

30. T. M. Doscher, "Technical Problems in the Processing of Mined Sand for Oil Recovery" in reference 4, pp. 625–632.

31. M. L. Natland, "Project Oilsand" in reference 3, pp. 143–155.

32. F. K. Spragins, *J. Petrol. Tech.* **19** (10), 1337–1343 (1967).

33. "Report to the Lieutenant Governor in Council with Respect to the Application of Great Canadian Oil Sands, Ltd.," Nov. 17, 1960; "Supplemental Report to the Lieutenant Governor in Council with Respect to the Application of Great Canadian Oil Sands, Ltd.," Sept. 19, 1962;

"Report on an Application of Great Canadian Oil Sands, Ltd. under Part VI of the Oil and Gas Conservation Act," Feb. 14, 1964, Oil and Gas Conservation Board, Government of the Province of Alberta.

34. Application to the Alberta Oil and Gas Conservation Board; under Part VI-a of the Oil and Gas Conservation Act by Atlantic Richfield Co., Cities Service Athabasca, Inc., Imperial Oil, Ltd., Royalite Oil Co., Ltd., May 9, 1962; amended to May 3, 1968.

35. L. E. Djingheuzian, "Cold Water Method of Separation of Bitumen from Alberta Bituminous Sand" in reference 2, pp. 185–199.

35a. J. A. Bichard, C. W. Bowman, R. M. Butler, and J. L. Tiedje, "Separation of Oil from the Athabasca Oil Sands by Sand Reduction," in reference 3, pp. 171–191.

36. J. R. Farnand, H. M. Smith, and I. E. Puddington, *Can. J. Chem. Eng.* **39**, 94–97 (April, 1961).

37. "Oil Sands Separated by Concentration," *Can. Chem. Process.* **47** (10), 82–83 (Oct., 1963).

38. K. A. Clark, *Report 8, Annual Report 1922*, Research Council of Alberta, Edmonton, Alberta, Canada, 1923, pp. 42–58.

39. K. A. Clark, *Trans. Can. Inst. Mining Met.* **47**, 257–274 (1944).

40. W. H. Seitzer, "Hot Water Processing of Athabasca Oil Sands: I. Oil Flotation in a Stirred Reactor" in reference 25, pp. F19–F24.

41. R. M. Bean and E. W. Malmberg, "Hot Water Processing of Athabasca Oil Sands: II. Microscope Studies of the Conditioning Process," pp. F25–F37 of reference 23.

41a. E. W. Malmberg and W. M. Robinson, "Hot Water Processing of Athabasca Oil Sands: III. Laboratory Studies on Settling, Middlings Viscosity, and Influence of Electrolytes" in reference 25, pp. F38–F49.

42. G. B. Shea and R. V. Higgins, *Report of Investigation 4246*, 1948; *4871*, 1952, U.S. Bureau of Mines.

43. D. S. Pasternack, "Low-Ash Asphalt and Coke from Athabasca Oil-Sands Oil" in reference 3, pp. 207–229.

44. *Oil Gas J.* **65**, 69–88 (Oct. 23, 1967).

45. T. E. Warren, F. L. Booth, R. E. Carson, and K. W. Bowles, "Hydrodesulfurization of Coker Distillate from Athabasca Bitumen" in reference 2, pp. 289–305.

46. M. A. O'Grady and B. I. Parsons, *Report R-194, The Hydrogenation of Alberta Bitumen Over Cobalt–Molybdate Catalyst*," Canadian Dept. of Energy, Mines and Resources, Mines Branch, Ottawa, Canada, Sept. 1967.

47. P. F. Lovell, H. E. Reif, R. O. Burk, P. H. Hertel, and B. T. Abbott, *Oil Gas J.* **64**, 66–72 (Aug. 15, 1966).

48. Application by Cities Service Athabasca, Inc. to the Alberta Oil and Gas Conservation Board for Approval of a Scheme of Operation for the Recovery of Oil or a Crude Hydrocarbon Product from Oil Sands Located in the Mildred Lake Area of the Athabasca Tar Sands, May 9, 1962; amended to Nov. 15, 1962.

49. Application by Shell Canada, Ltd. to the Alberta Oil and Gas Conservation Board for Approval of a Scheme of Operation for Recovery of Oil or a Crude Hydrocarbon Product from Athabasca Oil Sands, Sept. 6, 1962.

50. *Results of Investigation, 1942–1947*, Vol. 1 of *Drilling and Sampling of the Bituminous Sands of Northern Alberta*, Canadian Department of Mines and Resources, Mines, Forest, and Scientific Services Branch, Bureau of Mines, Ottawa, Canada, 1949.

51. D. E. Ward, *Geological Development for Mining of Oil Sands*, Paper No. 875-21-D, American Petroleum Institute, Division of Production, Rocky Mountain District, Dallas, Texas, April 19, 1967.

FREDERICK W. CAMP
Sun Oil Company

TARTARIC ACID

Tartaric acid, $C_4H_6O_4$, is a dibasic dihydroxy acid. The article of commerce is the natural form, (+)-tartaric acid. This isomer, which has been known since antiquity, occurs in grapes as the acid potassium salt. In the fermentation of grape juice to wine the salt deposits in the vats. Free crystallized tartaric acid was first obtained from such fermentation residues by Scheele in 1769.

Properties

Physical Properties. Commercial (+)-tartaric acid, NF, when crystallized from aqueous solutions above 5°C, is obtained in the anhydrous form. The crystals are colorless or translucent. Below 5°C, tartaric acid forms a monohydrate, unstable even at room temperature. The anhydrous crystals belong to the monoclinic system and melt at 160–170°C. Sp gr at 20°C is 1.76. The optical rotation of an aqueous solution varies with the concentration. For a concentration c between 20 and 50% $[\alpha]_D^{20} = 15.050° - 0.1535c$. The solid crystals are levorotatory, α_D of a 1-cm layer being $-114°$. Tartaric acid is a strong organic acid with dissociation constants $pK_1 = 1.04 \times 10^{-3}$ and $pK_2 = 4.55 \times 10^{-5}$ (25°C). The acid dissociation constants of the alcoholic hydroxyls are $pK_3 = 15.5 \pm 0.5$ and 15.0 ± 0.5; $pK_4 = 17.5 \pm 0.5$ and 16.5 ± 0.5, where the first value is in KOH and the second in NaOH (1).

The solubility of (+)-tartaric acid is given in Table 1. One hundred grams absolute ethyl alcohol dissolves 20.4 g tartaric acid at 18°C; 100 g ether dissolves 0.3 g at 18°C.

Table 1. Solubility of (+)-Tartaric Acid

Temp, °C	Soly, g/100 g H_2O	Temp, °C	Soly, g/100 g H_2O	Temp, °C	Soly, g/100 g H_2O
0	115	30	156	70	244
5	120	40	176	80	273
10	125	50	195	90	307
20	139	60	218	100	343

Isomerism. Tartaric acid can be obtained in four forms. Formulas (**a**) and (**b**) represent *dextro-* and *levo-*tartaric acid, the prefix referring to the direction of rotation of polarized light; (**c**) is *meso-*tartaric acid, which is inactive due to "internal compensation." In addition, there is the racemic mixture of (**a**) and (**b**), commonly called racemic acid.

```
    COOH         COOH         COOH
     |            |            |
   HCOH         HOCH         HCOH
     |            |            |
   HOCH         HCOH         HCOH
     |            |            |
    COOH         COOH         COOH

    (a)          (b)          (c)
```

Attempts to name the optically active tartaric acid by D and L prefixes have resulted in hopeless ambiguity and controversy. That (**a**) represents the absolute configuration of dextrorotatory tartaric acid has been established relatively recently (2).

Table 2. Physical Constants of Tartaric Acids

Properties	(+)	(−)	Racemic	Meso
mp, °C (anhydrous)	169–170	169–170	205–206	159–160
soly in water, at 20°C, g/100 g H₂O	139	139	20.6	125
soly of acid potassium salt, at 25°C, g/100 g H₂O	0.84	0.84	0.72	16.7
moles of water in hydrate of calcium salt	4	4	8	3

The ambiguity arises because tartaric acid can be defined by the configuration at carbon-2, as is done with amino acids, or by the configuration at carbon-3, the carbohydrate convention (3–5). The amino acid convention names the natural isomer of tartaric acid (**a**) D-tartaric acid; in the carbohydrate convention it is L-tartaric acid. The literature contains arguments in support of both conventions.

Compound (**a**) can be designated unequivocally by calling it (+)-tartaric acid or L-threaric acid (from the sugar L-threose), by the sequence rule (6), or by subscript notation (7). By the sequence rule (**a**) is (RR)-tartaric acid and (**b**) is (SS)-tartaric acid. Using subscript notation, (**a**) can be Ds-tartaric acid (referred to the amino acid serine) or Lg-tartaric acid (referred to the sugar glyceraldehyde) (8).

To avoid adding to the confusion, in this article the natural isomer will be designated (+)-tartaric acid, the nonnatural isomer (−)-tartaric acid, and the mixture DL-tartaric acid, or racemic acid.

(+)-Tartaric acid occurs in numerous plants and fruits, although it is not as widely distributed as citric or L-malic acid. The only commercial source is the residues from the wine industry.

(−)-Tartaric acid has been found in the fruit and leaves of *Bauhinia reticulata*, a tree native to Mali (western Africa). Like the (+)-acid, it forms anhydrous monoclinic crystals.

Racemic acid is not a primary product of plant processes, but is readily formed from the (+)-acid by heating with strong alkali or strong acid or by heat alone. As the classical example of an optically inactive compound originating from the combinations of molar proportions of the dextro and levo isomers, it is of considerable historical interest. The methods by which such racemic compounds can be separated into the optically active modifications were devised by Pasteur and first applied to racemic acid. Racemic acid crystallizes as the hydrate $(C_4H_6O_6)_2 \cdot 2H_2O$ in triclinic prisms. It becomes anhydrous on drying at 110°C and melts incongruently at 205°C. Calcium racemate, $(C_4H_4O_6Ca)_2 \cdot 8H_2O$, is even less soluble in water than calcium tartrate; thus, a dilute racemic acid solution is precipitated by a saturated calcium sulfate solution while active tartaric acid is not.

meso-Tartaric acid is not found in nature. It is obtainable from the other isomers by prolonged boiling with caustic alkali. The free acid crystallizes as a monohydrate, $C_4H_6O_6 \cdot H_2O$, in monoclinic prisms. On drying at 110°C, it becomes anhydrous and melts at 159–160°C.

Table 2 compares the physical properties of the isomers.

Synthesis. No synthetic process has yet been devised which would free commercial tartaric acid production from dependence upon wine industry by-products. One reason is that, under present conditions, the price of finished tartaric acid and tartrates depends closely upon the price of the source materials, the argols. The cost of argols fluctuates considerably in relation to abundance of supply. In a scarce year, the price of natural-based tartrates might rise to where the synthetically produced forms could be competitive. However, in a succeeding year of abundant, low-priced argols, synthetic tartrates would be excluded and there would be nothing to sustain directly the investment in equipment.

Another consideration is that, while some of the known synthetic methods yield the (+)-isomer (natural form), others yield the mixed isomers including racemic and/or the meso isomer. Products consisting of other than the natural isomer would have to receive clearance for food and drug use from regulatory bodies in various countries. At present it appears that a synthetic DL-tartaric acid and its salts are in commercial channels only in Japan.

The following appear to be the major types of syntheses which have been explored:

Fermentation. The production of (+)-tartaric acid by bacterial fermentation of glucose has been described by Kamlet (9). This isomer also can be formed by fermentation of 5-keto-D-gluconic acid, according to the process of Lockwood and Nelson (10). These fermentation methods are well removed from the range of commercial feasibility.

Oxidation of 5-Keto-D-Gluconic Acid. The conversion of 5-keto-D-gluconic acid by chemical oxidation also has been accomplished. The starting compound, which is obtained by fermentation from gluconic acid or glucono-δ-lactone (and ultimately from glucose), has a structure which favors a break between carbons 4 and 5, yielding the 4-carbon skeleton of the tartaric molecule. According to the method of Pasternack and Brown (11) the conversion is effected by gaseous oxygen with vanadium pentoxide or manganese dioxide serving as catalyst. Other suitable catalysts are salts of cobalt or titanium. Barch's method (12) utilizes nitric acid as the oxidizing agent and vanadium or salts of vanadium as the catalysts. Both methods, which are relatively costly, claim formation of (+)-tartaric acid with only minor quantities of other isomers.

Oxidation of Carbohydrates. This method, in which nitric acid is the oxidizer, has been applied to various carbohydrates, but mainly glucose. There are several publications on this synthesis (13–17).

The main problem which elevates the cost of this oxidative method is separating the tartaric acid. It is not clear from these reports how much of the natural (+)-tartaric is formed, although in theory the molecule of dextrose splits between carbons 4 and 5, which should yield a 4-carbon residue with a (+)-structure and hence (+)-tartaric acid. The break at this point also yields a 2-carbon residue which leads to oxalic acid. In practice some (−)- and meso-tartaric and other acids are formed.

Oxidation of Fumaric or Maleic Acid. A process for the oxidation of fumaric or maleic acid to yield DL- or meso-tartaric acid was described by Terry and Milas (18). Braun (19) applied this to fumaric acid alone to obtain DL-tartaric. Both laboratories used a chlorate as the oxidizing agent and catalyzed with osmium tetroxide, a toxic and expensive substance. Church and Blumberg (20), in later research, used maleic acid as the starting substance, hydrogen peroxide as the oxidizer, and tungstic acid as the catalyst. They state that the yield of DL-tartaric is high and requires minimal purification. The maleic or fumaric oxidation process is marginal as to competitive costs. It would seem most feasible with maleic if a captive source of the anhydride or maleic scrub liquor were available.

Reactions. When free (+)-tartaric acid is heated above its melting point (170°C), amorphous anhydrides are formed which on boiling with water regenerate the acid.

Table 3. Diesters of (+)-Tartaric Acid

Ester	Mp, °C	Bp, °C	Sp gr	$[\alpha]_D^t$
methyl	48 and 61.5	$165–166_{11.5}$	1.2903_4^{62}	$+6.15^{90}$
ethyl	17	$155–156_{15}$	1.2112_4^{18}	$+7.48^{20}$
n-propyl	liquid	174_{12}	1.1361_4^{18}	$+11.7^{14}$
isopropyl	liquid	$157–158_{16}$	1.1274_4^{18}	$+15.7^{14}$
n-butyl	22	186_{14}	1.0886_4^{18}	$+10.3^{19}$
isobutyl	70	195_{13}	1.0213_4^{80}	$+19.9^{100}$

Further heating causes simultaneous formation of pyruvic acid, $CH_3COCOOH$, and pyrotartaric acid, $HOOCCH_2CH(CH_3)COOH$, and finally a black, charred residue. Hydrogen peroxide in the presence of ferrous salt forms dihydroxymaleic acid, $HOOCCOH{=}COHCOOH$. Nitrating the acid yields a dinitro ester which on hydrolysis is converted to dihydroxytartaric acid, $HOOCC(OH)_2C(OH)_2COOH$. The latter goes to tartronic acid, $HOCH(COOH)_2$, on oxidation with nitric acid. Acetyl chloride or acetic anhydride forms diacetyltartaric anhydride, $OC.CH(OOCCH_3).CH\text{-}$
$\text{---------------}O\text{---}$
$(OOCCH_3).CO$, readily hydrolyzable to diacetyltartaric acid.

Tartaric acid is reduced stepwise with concentrated hydriodic acid, first to D-malic acid, $HOOCCHOHCH_2COOH$, and then to succinic acid, $COOH(CH_2)_2COOH$. Ammoniacal silver solution is reduced with the formation of a silver mirror.

In common with certain other hydroxy organic acids, tartaric has the ability to complex many metal ions. Because of this property, tartaric acid and its salts are useful as sequestering agents. They hold metal ions in solution but prevent them from reacting in the usual manner. See below under Uses.

Salts and Esters. Tartaric acid forms stable acid (monobasic) and neutral (dibasic) salts; also acid and neutral esters. The salts of commercial importance are: *Acid potassium tartrate*, NF (potassium hydrogen tartrate, cream of tartar, potassium bitartrate), $KHC_4H_4O_6$, soly, g/100 ml water, 0.6 at 20°C, and 6.1 at 100°C. *Potassium sodium tartrate*, NF (Rochelle salt), $KNaC_4H_4O_6.4H_2O$, soly, g/100 ml water, 26 at 26°C, and 66 at 100°C. *Potassium antimony tartrate* (antimony potassium tartrate, USP, tartar emetic), $K(SbOH)_2C_4H_4O_6.\frac{1}{2}H_2O$, soly, g/100 ml water, 8.7 at 25°C, and 35.7 at 100°C. *Calcium tartrate*, $CaC_4H_4O_6.4H_2O$, is the usual intermediate in the commercial production of tartaric acid. The neutral strontium and barium salts are similar compounds of low solubility in water. The neutral heavy-metal salts are water-insoluble, but soluble in excess of neutral or alkaline solutions of alkali tartrates.

The neutral esters of the lower aliphatic alcohols, formed by the usual esterification methods, are liquids or low-melting solids shown in Table 3.

Analysis. When a few milligrams of tartaric acid are heated in a steam bath with 2 ml concentrated sulfuric acid containing 0.5% pyrogallol, an intense violet color is produced. A similar color is developed with resorcinol and sulfuric acid when heated to 130°C. These color reactions are not given by citric or malic acid. Paper chromatography is the best method for identification and approximate quantitative estimation in the presence of other organic acids (21,22). The usual quantitative determination is by precipitation of the acid potassium salt with an excess of potassium acetate or citrate and acetic acid in dilute alcohol and subsequent titration of the precipitate. The commercial analysis for tartars, which is based on this procedure, is known as the *Goldenberg analysis* (23). Polarimetric methods, whereby advantage is taken of the greatly enhanced rotatory power obtained in the presence of uranyl acetate or sodium molybdate, are also in use (24). A spectrophotometric method with copper benzidine, capable of determining microgram quantities of tartaric and other organic acids, has been reported by Draganic (25).

Physiological Properties. Tartaric acid and tartrates are poorly absorbed from the intestine. Their metabolism is different from that of citric acid in that tartaric acid is only slightly oxidized. The acid that is absorbed is excreted unchanged in the urine. Acid tartrates tend to increase the acidity of the system and in large doses are injurious to the kidneys (26). Large quantities injected parenterally immobilize the blood calcium and endanger heart action.

A review of the metabolism of tartaric acid containing 209 references has been published by Dupuy (27). So far as is known, all nutritional and physiological investigations have been made with the (+)-isomer.

Manufacture of Tartaric Acid and Its Salts

The raw materials available for the manufacture of tartaric acid and tartrates are by-products of wine making. Crude *tartars* are recoverable from the following sources:

1. The press cakes from grape juice, unfermented or partly fermented (marcs or pomace). The residues are boiled up with water, and alcohol, if present, is distilled off. The hot mash is settled, decanted, and the clear liquor cooled to crystallize. The recovered high-test crude cream of tartar, *vinaccia*, has an 85–90% cream of tartar content.

2. *Lees*, the dried slimy sediments in the wine fermentation vats, consisting of yeast cells, pectinous substances, and tartars. At present these are a minor source of tartrate for manufacturing purposes. Their content of total tartaric acid equivalent ranges from 16 to 40%.

3. The crystalline crusts formed in the vats in the secondary fermentation period are known as *argols*. These products contain more than 40% total tartaric acid; they are high in potassium hydrogen tartrate and low in calcium. Sablons are argols, high in calcium, originating from Italy.

It is usually advantageous to combine the manufacture of tartaric acid, cream of tartar, and Rochelle salt in one plant. This permits the most favorable disposition of the mother liquors from the three processes. Some plants include a system for potassium salt recovery.

The chemical reactions involved are as follows: formation of calcium tartrate from crude potassium acid tartrate,

$$2\ KHC_4H_4O_6 + Ca(OH)_2 + CaSO_4 \rightarrow 2\ CaC_4H_4O_6 + K_2SO_4 + 2\ H_2O$$

formation of tartaric acid from calcium tartrate,

$$CaC_4H_4O_6 + H_2SO_4 \rightarrow H_2C_4H_4O_6 + CaSO_4$$

formation of Rochelle salt from argols,

$$2\ KHC_4H_4O_6 + Na_2CO_3 \rightarrow 2\ KNaC_4H_4O_6 + CO_2 + H_2O$$

and formation of cream of tartar from tartaric acid and Rochelle salt liquors,

$$2\ H_2C_4O_6 + 2\ KNaC_4H_4O_6 + K_2SO_4 \rightarrow 4\ KHC_4H_4O_6 + Na_2SO_4$$

Preparation of Calcium Tartrate. The oldest procedure is the *decantation process*, in which fresh wet lees or finely ground dry lees are treated with sufficient hydrochloric acid to dissolve all tartrates. The acidified magma is diluted with sufficient water to obtain at least 50% supernatant solution after settling. The acid liquor is drawn off and the insolubles are washed by repeated suspension in water and decantation. The combined extracts are neutralized with ground limestone or hydrated lime, leaving the end reaction slightly acid to litmus to reduce coprecipitation of the phosphates of iron and aluminum. The process requires only wooden vats and simple gravity filters, but the simplicity of the equipment does not compensate for the large volumes of solution required and consequent solubility losses.

Tartar recovery from winery still slops (still residues) may be accomplished by *exchange adsorption* on an ion exchanger in the chloride form. Common salt solution serves as the regenerant. Concentration of the tartrate in solution is increased fifteen to eighteen times over that in the original slop. High-purity calcium tartrate is the final product (28).

In the *neutral pressure process* the ground tartars are suspended in water, heated to boiling with direct steam, and then nearly neutralized with a slurry of hydrated lime. The magma is autoclaved at 50 lb pressure for two or three hours. After cooling to 30°C in an open tank, the batch is heated with calcium chloride in slight excess, further cooled, filtered, and washed. Then it is promptly acidified with sulfuric acid to prevent bacterial activity. It is good practice to keep all plant equipment scrupulously clean at all times and to use a suitable chemical sterilizer whenever the plant is idle, even for a short time.

Roasting Process. The crude material is ground to pass a 20–30 mesh screen. Roasting time is from 2 to 6 hr at 115–165°C, depending on the crude. The roasted material is brought to neutrality with hydrated lime slurry in a wood precipitation tank provided with a cooling coil. A slurry of precipitated calcium sulfate is added until 20% excess is present. The reaction mixture is cooled to 30°C, filtered, and washed with cold water. The filtrate is saved for recovery of potassium sulfate. This is effected by treatment with sodium carbonate to precipitate calcium. The slurry is filtered and concentrated in a triple-effect evaporator. Crystallized potassium sulfate is collected on drain boxes.

Decomposition of Calcium Tartrate. The washed press cake is slurried up with weak wash water from a previous acid charge and acidified with cold 70% sulfuric acid to a pH of 0.8 at 15°Bé (see Vol. 6, p. 758). The batch is filtered on wooden vacuum filter boxes and the calcium sulfate–pomace cake washed with cold water. The wash liquors, down to 3°Bé, are combined with the strong liquors, the weaker washings being used for make-up of the next charge. The liquor is evaporated in vacuum pans heated by exhaust steam. The clear filtrate is evaporated under vacuum until a heavy magma of crystals is obtained. The charge is passed through lead-lined stirred granulators and centrifuged to remove mother liquor. Mother liquor is boiled down again in vacuum to yield a second crop of crystals. The filtrate from this crop is treated to yield a third crop, although this is of poorer quality and is often used to make calcium tartrate (29) or cream of tartar (30). Troublesome impurities are salts of aluminum, iron, copper, and lead. Copper and lead can be eliminated as sulfides, and iron as ferrocyanide. Aluminum can be considerably reduced by treating the warm old liquor with potassium sulfate; on cooling with agitation, potassium alum will crystallize and is separated by centrifugation.

Finished Tartaric Acid. A concentrated solution of the crystals is made in wooden tanks. Sulfate is removed by adding barium carbonate and iron with calcium ferro-cyanide. The solution is filtered and transferred to storage tanks. It is drawn from these and evaporated to crystallization in vacuum tanks. There are subsequent steps, depending upon whether a crystalline or granulated finished product is desired. Prices quoted in late 1968 were 43–47¢/lb for powder and fine granular tartaric acid.

Manufacture of Rochelle Salt (31). Blended argols are roasted for 5 hr at 160–165°C, transferred to a tank containing wash liquor from a previous charge, and treated with a slight excess of soda ash. The addition is made rapidly, with stirring as the temperature is brought to 80°C. When evolution of carbon dioxide has ceased, calcium is reduced to a minimum by addition of potassium oxalate. Filtration is conducted in a plate-and-frame press. Strong liquors from this filtration are used in the manufacture of Rochelle salt and the weaker wash water for cream of tartar. The Rochelle liquor is evaporated to about 41°Bé at 100°C. A check titration is made using phenolphthalein as indicator and adjustment is made with either soda ash or cream of tartar. Sufficient sodium sulfide is added to remove iron, and decolorizing charcoal to remove coloring matter. The charge is filtered through a stainless-steel filter press and run into stainless-steel granulators equipped with cooling jacket and cooling coils. When cold, the Rochelle salt is centrifuged, washed with water in the centrifuge, and dried.

Prices quoted during the third quarter of 1968 were 42½–43¢/lb for granular or powder Rochelle salt.

Manufacture of Cream of Tartar (31). Cream of tartar is usually produced by combining tartaric acid solutions available from the manufacture of tartaric acid with Rochelle salt solution derived from suitable crude potassium bitartrate such as high-grade argols or recovered cream of tartar. Potassium sulfate is added on the basis of 1 mole K_2SO_4 for 2 moles of free tartaric acid introduced. The acid liquor is heated to 60°C and treated with decolorizing carbon. Heavy metals are removed by convenient means. Filtration is done through a wooden plate-and-frame press, the filtrate being received in storage tanks. After other purification steps, the neutral Rochelle liquor is filtered again and the filtrate collected. Hot neutral and acid liquors are run simultaneously into granulators fitted with cooling coils. During the precipitation the pH is held between 3.2 and 3.5. The precipitated cream of tartar is centrifuged, washed, and dried.

Sulfur Dioxide Process. The principle of the process is to saturate a water suspension of argols with sulfur dioxide, whereby cream of tartar as well as calcium tartrate is dissolved to an approx 7% solution. The pomace can then be removed on a pressure filter. On boiling the filtrate or applying vacuum, sulfur dioxide is driven off, thus reprecipitating the tartars in purified form. Most of the sulfur dioxide can be recovered by absorption in a new batch. The calcium tartrate present in the raw material is preferably converted to cream of tartar by the addition of an equivalent quantity of potassium acid oxalate or potassium sulfate previous to the treatment with sulfur dioxide.

Other Processes. Obviously, cream of tartar can be produced directly from the argol soda ash cook without diverting any part of it to the manufacture of Rochelle salt. In this case, the whole batch is neutralized with sufficient acid liquor, as previously described.

The price quoted for cream of tartar in late 1968 was 37–38¢/lb for granular or powder.

Tartar Emetic. Plant equipment should be of stainless steel. Potassium bitartrate

Table 4. Imports into the U.S. of Potassium Bitartrate and Cream of Tartar,[a] lb

Country	1963	1964	1965	1966	1967
France	272,036	159,872	6,200	5,500	22,025
West Germany					100,000
United Kingdom	502,590	2,400			
Spain	530,761	778,646	634,844	764,525	730,788
Italy	1,725,920	1,328,141	1,211,423	1,633,675	1,382,525
Greece					22,046
Australia		637,136	600,000	150,000	200,000
Japan	55,200				
total	3,086,507	2,906,195	2,452,467	2,553,700	2,457,384
value, $	662,612	620,164	553,265	593,769	591,110

[a] U.S. Dept. of Commerce, Bureau of the Census, U.S. Imports, FT 135.

Table 5. Imports into the U.S. of Tartaric Acid,[a] lb

Country	1963	1964	1965	1966	1967
France	228,527	198,208	188,931	278,615	356,220
Spain	3,858,540	3,192,351	2,749,346	3,552,179	2,994,492
Italy	856,245	1,174,911	1,328,980	2,046,746	2,058,060
West Germany					79,366
Sweden				33,069	
United Kingdom		1,565			
Gibraltar		33		30,000	
Switzerland					11
total	4,943,312	4,567,068	4,267,257	5,940,609	5,488,649
value, $	1,236,372	1,169,638	1,143,014	1,623,017	1,880,716

[a] U.S. Dept. of Commerce, Bureau of the Census, U.S. Imports FT 135.

and antimony oxide, Sb_2O_3, are added simultaneously to water in a reaction vessel fitted with heating coils and an agitator. The reaction mixture is diluted and put through a filter press, then collected in jacketed granulators where crystallization takes place after cooling. The crystals are centrifuged, washed, and dried.

Tartar emetic USP was quoted in 1968 at 89¢/lb.

Economic Aspects

In 1955 the United States imported 15 million lb of crude tartars, equivalent to about half that weight of pure tartaric acid. These crude tartars came from such wine-producing places as France, North Africa, Italy, Portugal, and Argentina. These imports were the source materials for tartaric acid and its salts manufactured by the American chemical industry.

Imports declined drastically after 1955. Instead, the American chemical industry purchased increasing quantities, for resale, of the refined tartaric acid and tartrates produced by chemical manufacturers abroad according to American specifications.

Imports of the finished products for 1963–1967 are shown in Tables 4 and 5.

Uses

Tartaric acid is used like citric acid as an acidulant in carbonated and still beverages, including beverage powders (see Carbonated beverages). Customarily it has been used with grape-flavored beverages, but recently lower-cost citric acid has been found to blend satisfactorily with this flavor. Tartaric acid has been used also as an acidulant in the manufacture of gelatin desserts and in fruit jellies, especially in pectin jellies for candies when relatively low pH is necessary for proper setting. In the manufacture of starch jelly candies, tartaric acid and cream of tartar are used to modify the starch so that the product will flow freely while being cast. Tartaric acid is well suited to the manufacture of hard candies because its melting point permits it to fuse into the "glass" and it does not contribute moisture. Its degree of acidity is such that it is favored for extra-sour candies.

Tartaric acid has uses in the textile industry. In calico printing it controls the liberation of chlorine from bleach powder. In dyeing it serves as a mordant and as a resist for alumina and other basic mordants. The acid is employed in certain types of photographic work for printing and developing. Some of the iron salts are light-sensitive and hence are used in blueprinting.

The complexing ability of tartaric acid and its salts has been employed to advantage in metal cleaning and finishing. These chemicals are used as paste and powder cleansers and as bath components in electrolytic polishing of copper and its alloys, aluminum, and ferrous metals. They are employed also in baths for removal of rust, scale, and oxide. Rochelle salt is well known as an important bath component in electroplating of many metals and alloys—gold, silver, copper, zinc, tin, lead, tungsten, iron, molybdenum. There are reports of the use of tartrates in baths for nonelectrolytic deposition of metals (32) and in phosphatizing of ferrous metals (33). Tartrates also are important sequesterants in aluminum etching (34).

Caustic solutions containing an iron–tartrate complex are used as solvents for determination of the degree of polymerization of cellulosic materials (35).

Tartaric acid has been found to function as a polymerizing agent for methylmethacrylate (36,37).

Rochelle salt has additional uses, as in the silvering of mirrors. Rochelle salt crystals exhibit piezoelectricity and this property makes them valuable, when suitably cut, as components of crystal-controlled electronic oscillators. Medicinally, this salt is the major ingredient of mild saline cathartic preparations like compound effervescing powder or Seidlitz powders. In food, it can be used as an emulsifying agent in the manufacture of processed cheese. In the laboratory it is an ingredient of Fehling's solution for the determination of reducing substances, especially sugars.

Cream of tartar is used in baking powder and in prepared baking mixes. Its limited solubility in the cold inhibits the reaction with bicarbonate until baking temperature is reached, thus releasing the major portion of the carbon dioxide at the optimum time. Cream of tartar also is useful in the aeration of angel food cake. A slurry of cream of tartar is an excellent cleaner of brass. It is used in the electrolytic tinning of iron and steel, in gold and silver coating of various metals, and in some metal-coloring processes.

Solutions of cream of tartar have been used for rinsing and storing metal components between acid plating and pickling. This application is of special importance in plating titanium and other metals which tend to form an oxide coating after abrasive or chemical etching and a water rinse. A rinse with a 5% tartrate solution avoids oxide formation and permits excellent adhesion of plate (38).

Tartar emetic is used medicinally in small doses as an expectorant in cough syrups, in larger doses as an emetic. As an intravenous injection in the treatment of various tropical infections it has been superseded by less toxic forms of antimony. Formerly, tartar emetic was used to a certain extent for the control of various kinds of insects. The compound is used as a mordant in fixing basic colors on cotton, leather, and fur. The fastness to washing and light of antimony–tannin–basic dyestuff lakes is used to good advantage in textile printing. Incorporation of tartar emetic in vinyl chloride formulation has been found to inhibit or retard discoloration.

Bibliography

"Tartaric Acid" in *ECT* 1st ed., Vol. 13, pp. 645–656, by Richard Pasternack, Chas. Pfizer & Co., Inc.

1. M. Beck, B. Csiszar, and P. Szarvas, *Magy. Kem. Folyoirat* **70**, 217 (1964); *Chem. Abstr.* **61**, 5012e (1964).
2. J. M. Bijvoet, A. F. Peerdeman, and A. J. Van Bommel, *Nature* **168**, 271 (1951).
3. *Chem. Eng. News* **30**, 4522 (1952).
4. *Ibid.*, **31**, 1777 (1953).
5. M. A. Rosanoff, *J. Am. Chem. Soc.* **28**, 114 (1906).
6. R. S. Cahn, C. K. Ingold, and V. Prelog, *Experientia* **12**, 81 (1956).
7. H. B. Vickery, *J. Biol. Chem.* **169**, 237 (1947).
8. J. N. Baxter, *J. Chem. Educ.* **41**, 619 (1964).
9. U.S. Pat. 2,314,831 (March 24, 1943), J. Kamlet (to Miles Laboratories).
10. U.S. Pat. 2,559,650 (July 10, 1951), L. B. Lockwood and G. E. N. Nelson (to the United States of America, as represented by the Secretary of Agriculture).
11. U.S. Pat. 2,197,021 (April 16, 1940), R. Pasternack and E. V. Brown (to Chas. Pfizer & Co., Inc.).
12. U.S. Pat. 2,417,230 (March 11, 1947), W. E. Barch (to Standard Brands).
13. U.S. Pats. 2,419,019 and 2,419,020 (April 15, 1947), R. A. Hales (to Atlas Powder Co.).
14. U.S. Pat. 2,419,038 (April 15, 1947), M. T. Sanders (to Atlas Powder Co.).
15. U.S. Pat. 2,390,196 (July 10, 1945), S. Soltzberg (to Atlas Powder Co.).
16. U.S. Pat. 2,247,230 (Sept. 30,1941), W. E. Stokes and W. E. Barch (to Standard Brands).
17. Polish Pat. 43,618 (Dec. 30, 1960), R. Bogczek.
18. E. Terry and N. A. Milas, *J. Am. Chem. Soc.* **47**, 1412 (1925).
19. U.S. Pat. 2,000,213 (May 7, 1935), G. Braun (to Standard Brands).
20. J. M. Church and R. I. Blumberg, *Ind. Eng. Chem.* **43**, 1780 (1951).
21. B. T. Overell, *Australian J. Sci.* **15**, 28 (1952).
22. E. F. Phares, F. H. Mosbach, F. W. Denison, Jr., and S. F. Carson, *Anal. Chem.* **24**, 660 (1952).
23. A. H. Allen, *Commercial Organic Analysis*, 5th ed., Vol. I, The Blakiston Co., Inc., New York, 1923, p. 724.
24. G. Buogo, *Giorn. Chim. Ind. Appl.* **16**, 120 (1934).
25. Z. D. Draganic, *Anal. Chim. Acta* **28**, 394 (1963); *Chem. Abstr.* **59**, 1098g (1963).
26. A. Osol, R. Pratt, and M. D. Altschule, *The United States Dispensatory and Physicians' Pharmacology*, 26th ed., J. B. Lippincott Co., Philadelphia, Pa., 1967.
27. P. Dupuy, *Ann. Inst. Natl. Rech. Agron. Ser.* **E 9**, 139 (1960); *Chem. Abstr.* **55**, 21192 (1961).
28. R. R. Legault, L. L. Nimmo, C. E. Hendel, and G. K. Notter, *Ind. Eng. Chem.* **41**, 466 (1949).
29. H. D. Davis, *Tartaric Acid Process in Germany*, FIAT Final Rept. 1049 (1947).
30. A. Del Bono, *Giorn. Chem. Ind. Appl.* **15**, 451 (1933).
31. J. W. Black, *Ind. Chemist* **15**, 270 (1939).
32. U.S. Pats. 2,827,398 and 2,827,399 (March 18, 1958), P. H. Eisenberg (to Sylvania Electric Products, Inc.).
33. U.S. Pat. 3,307,979 (March 7, 1967), W. B. Upham (to Lubrizol Corp.).
34. F. J. Prescott, J. K. Shaw, and J. Lilker, *Metal Finishing* **51**, 65 (1953).
35. W. B. Achwal, T. W. Narayan, and W. M. Purao, *Tappi* **50**, 90A (June 1967).
36. U.S. Pat. 3,306,883 (Feb. 28, 1967), A. Ravve and J. T. Khamis (to Continental Can Co.).
37. B. C. Mitra, P. Ghosh, and S. R. Polit, *Indian J. Appl. Chem.* **29**, 1 (1966).
38. D. C. Horner, *Electroplating Metal Finishing* **21**, 113 (April 1968).

D. F. Chichester
Chas. Pfizer & Co., Inc.

TAUROCHOLATE, SODIUM.   See Bile constituents, Vol. 3, p. 484.

TEA

Two distinct taxa of tea have been separated by Wight (1) at species level: the China species, *Camellia sinensis* (L.) and the Assam species, *Camellia assamica* (Masters). Wight describes the China species as a shrub, characterized by more or less virgate stems, 1.0–3.0 m tall; it has relatively small, hard, dark-green leaves with a dull (matt) surface. The Assam species is described as a small, much-branched tree, 10–15 m tall (sometimes with a trunk one-third its height). The supple light-green leaves are 15–20 cm long, and have a glossy surface.

Teas made from the two species differ fundamentally, especially in their cup characters: China and Assam teas cannot be substituted for each other.

Subsidiary forms of the China species were described by Fortune (3) and those of the Assam species by Watt and Mann (4). A "southern form" of tea, occurring to the southeast of Assam, is named by Wight (1) as *Camellia assamica*, subsp *lasiocalyx* (Planch., MS). The species and their subsidiary forms intercross with ease.

Intergrades between the Assam and the China species arose during the nineteenth century, after tea seed collected from widely scattered areas of China was introduced into Assam. Tea seed produced in Assam for commercial plantings gave rise to tea populations spoken of as "jats," named after the permanent tea seed garden from which they originated. Within each jat or cultivar the populations are internally mixed, depending on the genetical history of the tea trees comprising the seed garden. Thus they may form an array of leaf form intergrades between the subsidiary forms of each species or between *C. assamica* and *C. sinensis*. Surveys conducted by Wight (1), however, demonstrated that within hybrid populations there is generally a preponderance of features which bias a population toward *assamica* or *sinensis*, so that truly intermediate plants are rare (Fig. 1).

Roberts et al. (5), who investigated the taxonomy of several *Camellia* species by paper chromatographic methods, showed that while the tea species are closely similar to each other in chemical composition, containing flavan-3-ols, depsides, flavanols, and leucoanthocyanins, they bear no obvious relationship to the chemical composition of the nontea *Camellias*. The southern form is similar in content to the tea species, but contains in addition large amounts of another unidentified phenolic compound, which is designated as IC.

China tea, *C. sinensis*, contains relatively large amounts of triglycosides of quercetin and kaempferol. These substances are found at the most in trace amounts in Assam tea, where they are possibly nontypical.

Later work on tea chemistry has not always discriminated between teas in relation to their genetical constitution. Because of the mixed nature of much of the world's planted tea, however, the characteristics of teas reaching the market tend to differ appreciably from one batch to the other, depending on the kinds of plants in the plantations from which the leaf was harvested. Teas also vary markedly in this way from one part of an estate to another, according to the source of the seed with which each section was planted. In addition, it is well known that climatic factors, especially ambient temperature, rainfall, and hours of sunshine, affect the cup characters of tea made from a specific unit, and produce marked seasonal variations throughout the year.

Added to these variations are differences which arise as a result of differences in processing and sorting methods, and the resultant teas reaching the market present a widely differing array of leaf grades, quality, flavor, color, briskness, and strength. Because of these differences the tea trade employs tea-tasters and blenders skilled in

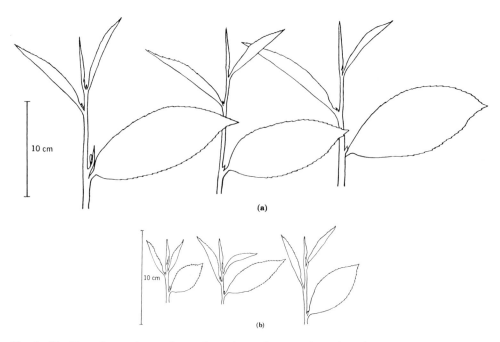

Fig. 1. Plucking shoots drawn from plantations of preponderantly (**a**) *Camellia assamica;* (**b**) *Camellia sinensis.*

combining teas of differing characteristics, in order to provide the consumer with an all-round pleasant blend of features characteristic of the various standard brands, and to maintain these as nearly uniform as is possible throughout the year.

Soil and Climate. Tea can be grown over a considerable range of conditions from mediterranean climates to hot, humid tropics. Production is centered in equably warm places with a mean ambient temperature of 22.5°C or higher, and a well-distributed rainfall of 70 in. or more, but commercially viable plantations have been established in much cooler and drier places.

Production, which depends on the availability of an adequate supply of water and nutrients for uptake by the roots, is curtailed in most traditional tea-producing areas during dry or cold weather.

Irrigation is used by some producers to improve the continuity of the flow of leaf for processing.

Nutrition. High levels of production depend on replacement of nutrients lost from the soil by leaching or by removal with the crop. Nutrient uptake by tea roots is optimum for the nutritional requirements of the plant at pH 5.6. The approach to nutrition changed recently, following the demonstrations at the Tea Research Institute of East Africa (6) that when weeds are eliminated and soil disturbance ceases, as for example with chemical weed control, surface-feeding tea roots absorb phosphates. Phosphate nutrition was always inadequate so long as hand cultivation of tea fields was practiced, and resulted in root destruction. Based on their findings, the Institute (7) developed a new approach to nutrition, using a system of modified forest management; emergent roots explore a layer of mulch which is allowed to build up at the soil surface. A standard fertilizer using NPK 5:1:1 is applied in proportion to the amount of crop removed. Foliar-analysis methods developed by Willson (8) indicate the

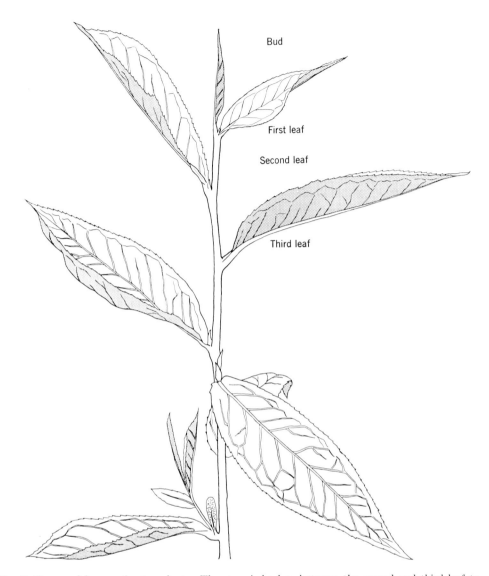

Fig. 2. Stem and leaves of a tea plant. The stem is broken between the second and third leaf to harvest the young shoot for processing. (Tea Research Institute of East Africa Clone 6/8.)

nutrient status of mature fields and permit additional corrective doses of specific nutrients to be applied where they are needed.

Field Methods. Traditionally, seedlings have been used as planting material, but increasingly varieties selected for superior yield and teamaking characters are propagated vegetatively and planted as clones. Some clones, for example TRIEA Clone 6/8, possess cup characters that are a combination of Assam and China teas. Teamaking potential is generally estimated by tea-tasters, but it has been shown by Forrest (9) that the catechin composition of regularly plucked shoots of a clone is characteristic of that clone. He suggests that plant improvement programs based on selection for high levels of epicatechin and epigallocatechin in the shoots could indicate clones which would produce brighter teas. A few all-clonal estates are being developed, mainly in Assam and Uganda.

On flat land, tea normally is planted in parallel rows, the systems being modified for contour planting on sloping land. Current plantation systems require between 8000 and 13,000 plants per hectare. The branches of the young plants are either pegged down or given a series of prunes so as to form a flat-topped bush one meter high when in production. Mature tea bushes form a continuous sheet of foliage conforming to the topography of the land. Young shoots are harvested as they appear above the level of the table of mature leaves.

Tea was traditionally grown in China on small farms; bulk production on large estates originated in Assam in 1833. Tea is again coming to be regarded as a suitable crop for small-scale production, provided freshly harvested leaf can be easily transported to central processing plants. Small-holding schemes are currently being developed in many countries: perhaps the best example is in Kenya, where some 40,000 small farmers are growing tea on holdings of average size of about ¼ hectare.

Plucking (Harvesting). The young foliage is harvested. The terminal bud is removed together with two, three, or four leaves. Roberts (10) showed that the best tea is made from the terminal bud plus the two youngest leaves, and most of the black tea of commerce is made from the traditional "two leaves and a bud" (Fig. 2).

Frequency of harvesting is related to growth rate: Intervals between plucking rounds normally vary between five and fourteen days. In Georgia, U.S.S.R., plucking has been fully mechanized (11). There the tea is planted in rows, and a self-propelled combine harvester straddles the rows and selectively grasps and plucks the shoots that are ready.

In Japan, shears are used in some places, either hand-operated or worked from shoulder-mounted motorized units.

Most of the world's tea is plucked by hand, and it is probable that this method will continue because of the major unemployment situation which could arise from large-scale mechanization.

Manufacture of Black Tea

Young fresh leaves and shoots of *Camellia assamica* have the approximate composition given in Table 1 (12). They are characterized by a high concentration of compounds of the flavonoid group, predominantly catechins. These flavonoids are changed during processing, largely by the action of the enzyme polyphenol oxidase (catechol oxidase), into oxidation and condensation products which give the characteristic color and taste to infusions of black tea.

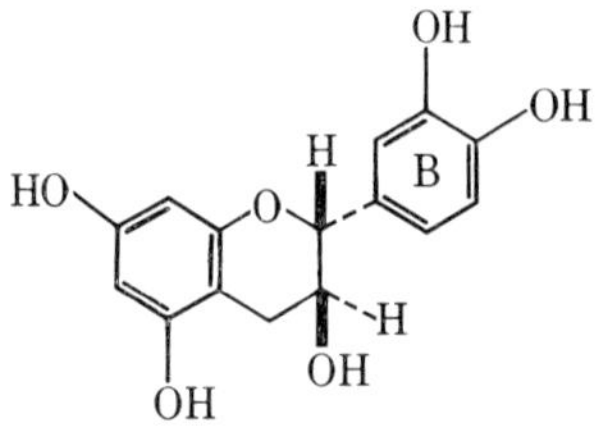

(+)-catechin

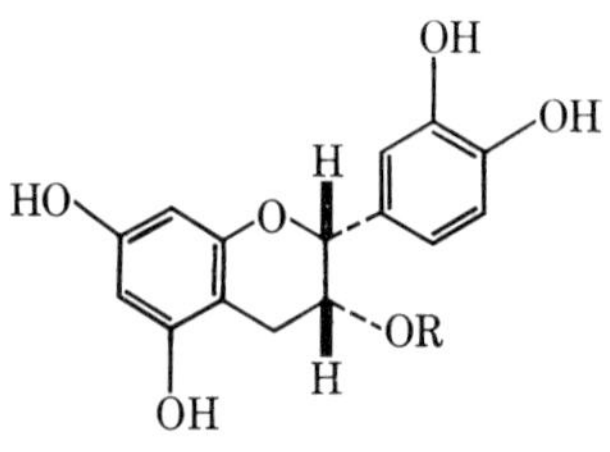

(−)-epicatechin, R = H;
(−)-epicatechin gallate,
R = 3,4,5-trihydroxybenzoyl

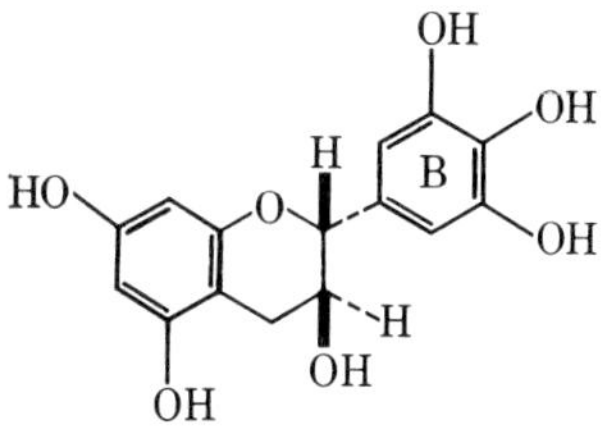

(+) gallocatechin

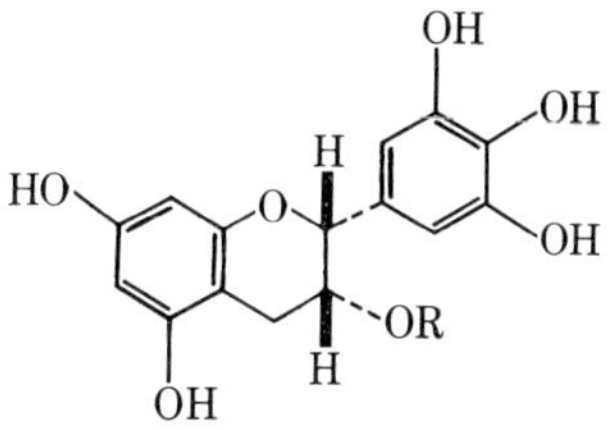

(−)-epigallocatechin, R = H;
(−)-epigallocatechin gallate,
R = 3,4,5-trihydroxybenzoyl

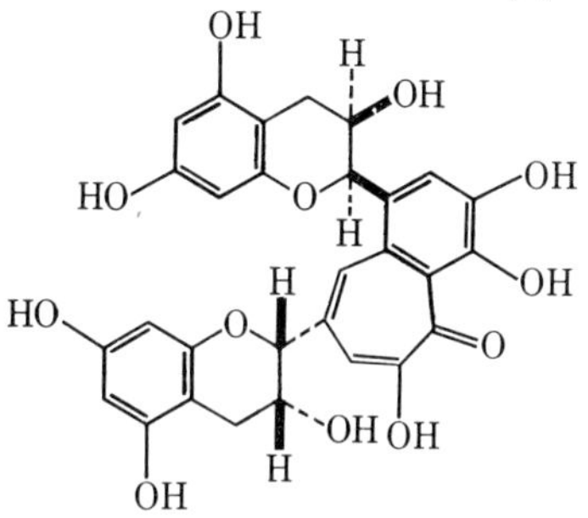

theaflavin

Table 1. Approximate Composition of Green Tea Shoots (Assam Variety) (12)

Substances	Dry weight, %
Soluble in hot water	
flavanols	
(−)-epigallocatechin gallate	9–13
(−)-epicatechin gallate	3–6
(−)-epigallocatechin	3–6
(−)-epicatechin	1–3
other flavanols	1–2
flavanols and flavanol glycosides	3–4
leucoanthocyanins	2–3
acids and depsides	~5
caffeine	3–4
amino acids	4
simple carbohydrates	4
organic acids	0.5
Partially soluble in hot water	
polysaccharides	
starch	1–2
pectic substances, pentosans, etc	~12
proteins	~15
ash	~5
Insoluble in water	
cellulose	~7
lignin	~6
lipids	3
pigments	~0.5
Volatile	0.01–0.02

Withering. The process begins by dehydration, or withering, of the freshly plucked shoots after they are brought in from the field. In *chung withering* the leaf is spread thinly on hessian or nylon and air-dried through the wilting point until it is reduced to about 50–85% of its fresh weight; the final weight depends on the method of processing. In the more efficient *trough withering*, dehydration is accomplished by passing air supplied by reversible fans through loosely packed fresh leaf in troughs. The withering process takes 16–20 hr. Much work has been done on the chemical changes which take place during withering, but it is basically a means of reducing the water content of fresh shoots and rendering them malleable.

Rolling. It has been shown by Wickremasinghe et al. (13) that the polyphenol oxidase enzyme is localized within the epidermal cells and vascular bundles of the leaf. In the living plant the enzyme is not in contact with the polyphenols located in the vacuoles of the palisade cells. The basis of the next stage of manufacture is to bring the enzyme and substrate together by disruption of the leaf tissues, in a process known as *rolling*.

Rolling is achieved in orthodox manufacture by subjecting the withered leaf to a wringing action in a rolling machine. Popular alternative methods are (*1*) the CTC (crushing, tearing, and curling) process, in which the withered leaf is abraded and fragmented between revolving cutters; (*2*) the McTear rotorvane process which operates on the principle of the mincing machine by squeezing and then cutting the leaf; or (*3*) a combination of these two processes.

In one method of processing the Legg tobacco cutter is used to shred unwithered leaf, sometimes in combination with the rotorvane.

Fermentation. The tea industry still retains the word fermentation, used in an old connotation, to describe the series of oxidations and condensations initiated by the rolling process. During the fermentation process the fragmented leaf is stacked in aerated troughs or on open trays.

Flavanol Conversion. Of the many flavanols in fresh leaf, epigallocatechin gallate is present in the largest amount, followed by epicatechin gallate, epigallocatechin, and epicatechin. Enzymatic oxidation of these substances produces new substances not present in the fresh leaf, the theaflavins and thearubigins.

It has been shown by Brown et al. (14) that the formulation of theaflavin is compatible with its formation by oxidative coupling involving (−)-epicatechin and (−)-epigallocatechin and their gallates as precursors, by a process known as dimerization. They have also shown the thearubigins to be polymeric proanthocyanidins. Roberts (15) emphasized the importance of the theaflavins and thearubigins in the cup characters of black tea, and showed how the characters of briskness, color, brightness, and strength in the liquors relate to the changes occurring with time as fermentation proceeds. Thus, when theaflavins rise to a maximum and then decrease during enzymatic oxidation, the liquors first increase in briskness and brightness, and then become less brisk and bright. As the thearubigins begin to accumulate in the later stages of fermentation, the strength of the liquors increases.

Roberts (16) proposed a simple diagram (Fig. 3) to show the progressive waxing and waning of cup characters with time, and also (16) showed the relationship between fermentation temperatures and the rapidity with which the processes go forward (Table 2).

The enzyme chiefly involved in flavanol oxidation is polyphenol oxidase, or more specifically, catechol oxidase. This enzyme is specific for dihydric phenols and related

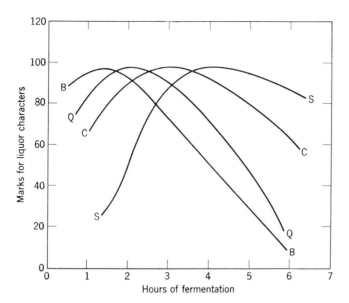

Fig. 3. Liquor characters relative to fermentation time. LEGEND: B, briskness; C, color; Q, quality; S, strength.

Table 2. Temperature and Optimum Fermentation Times for Liquor Characters, hr

Character	Temperature			
	60°F	70°F	80°F	20°F
strength	4¾	4½	4	3½
color (milk)	4¼	3¾	3	<2
quality	3½	2½	2	<2
briskness	<2	<2	<2	<2

compounds. All the flavanols and many of the minor phenolic components of green leaf are substrates. The flavanols, together with the monomeric leucoanthocyanins, are consumed during fermentation (16).

Quality. Roberts' expositions of the broad principles of fermentation, appearing in a series of papers in the *Biochemical Journal*, were valuable in demonstrating the part which theaflavins and thearubigins play as factors in determining the liquoring of black tea. However, other factors are concerned, and Sanderson (17) has drawn attention to the imperfect state of knowledge on the subject of tea "quality."

Difficulties arise in defining quality, which may mean a quantitatively measurable character associated with the taste of one or several specific compounds, or may be a description applied to a tea possessing all-round good cup characters, of which color, brightness, briskness, strength, aroma, and quality itself are all components. It is used in the former sense when describing Assam second-flush teas or Uva teas in which positive quality detectable by tea-tasters arises in specific teas at certain times of the year.

Roberts and Sanderson (18) showed that there was a negative relationship between the total free amino acid content of fresh young leaf and the quality of the clone from which it came. These and other related findings led Sanderson (17) to suggest that

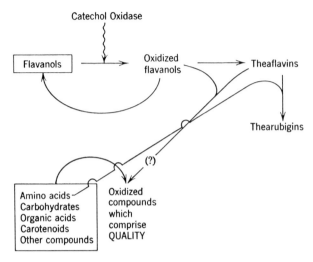

Fig. 4. Sanderson's proposed scheme for tea fermentation.

free amino acids and possibly other leaf components are involved in the formation during fermentation of chemical quantities which determine quality in black tea.

Sanderson's fermentation scheme takes account of amino acid involvement and also of the possible cyclic role played by the flavanols in the formation of quality. Quality formation thus presents itself as another feature of flavanol oxidation going on independently of the enzymatic dimerization process of theaflavin formation (Fig. 4).

Brown et al. (14) have shown that the theaflavins and the thearubigins are formed concurrently and independently during the fermentation process. The theaflavins arise from flavanols as a result of polyphenol oxidase activity. The thearubigins have a polymeric proanthocyanidin structure, and the authors conclude that they are presumably formed by the oxidative coupling of flavanol precursors.

The theaflavins are progressively reduced during the latter part of the fermentation process, but the manner in which they are resolved is not yet known.

Flavor (30). Flavor, known to be a characteristic feature of teas made from populations of *Camellia sinensis*, or populations containing a proportion of plants apparently *Camellia sinensis*, or forms intermediate between *sinensis and assamica*, is more pronounced in such teas when they are grown slowly in cool conditions. When growth is artificially slowed down in these conditions, for example, when the flush is stunted by attacks of green fly, flavor can become very pronounced.

Wickremasinghe and Swain (19) showed that high levels of the amino acids leucine and isoleucine are detrimental to the development of flavor during the fermentation process. At the Ceylon Tea Research Institute, Tirimanna and his colleagues (20) have shown that leucine and isoleucine are produced in larger quantities in leaf grown in warm conditions than in teas grown in cool climates, and are working on the prospect of removing flavor inhibitors such as the leucines during fermentation, especially in low-country teas, so as to produce more flavory teas.

Briskness. The cup character of briskness is defined in a tea-taster's glossary as a "live characteristic, indicating some degree of pungency and maltiness." Pungency is described as "having astringency without bitterness." Briskness was shown by Roberts (15) to be associated with the presence of caffeine (qv) and theaflavin.

Caffeine, which was identified in tea leaves as long ago as 1827 by Oudry (21), is present in fresh leaf to between 3 and 4% of dry weight, and remains relatively unchanged during the fermentation process.

Caffeine is a water-soluble alkaloid, 1,3,7-trimethylxanthine, which acts mainly on the higher centers of the central nervous system to produce a condition of wakefulness and increased mental activity. It thus contributes to the refreshing and stimulating character of tea as a beverage.

In making brisk teas it is advantageous to stop the fermentation after appreciable quantities of theaflavins have formed, but before there is time for the process to proceed to the point where theaflavin is depleted and the teas are dull.

Color. As fermentation proceeds, the color of the fermenting material changes from green through olive-green to light-brown or orange. Fermentation is normally stopped when the brown or orange color is brightest; if it is allowed to continue the color changes continue through dark brown to chocolate. Teas made at this late stage are strong, but have no briskness.

Some of the chlorophyll in the fermenting leaf was found by Wickremasinghe and Perera (22) to be transformed into a black compound, phaeophytin, by the removal of magnesium in the acid conditions of fermentation, and some was changed into chlorophyllide by the enzyme chlorophyllase. Chlorophyllide was changed to a brown compound, phaeophorbide, by the removal of magnesium. The authors presented evidence that the intensity of blackness was a function of the amount of chlorophyll in the fresh leaf, and that brownness could be intensified by rolling processes which bruised the leaf more severely and thus brought more chlorophyllase into contact with the substrate. For more detailed accounts of the fermentation process, reference should be made to the papers by Millin and Rustidge (12), Sanderson (17), and Brown et al. (14).

Firing (Drying). At the conclusion of fermentation, the changes are abruptly arrested by heat. The fermented leaf is exposed to hot air in a dryer. The leaf is carried through the machine on a series of slowly moving metal trays, falling from one level to another into warmer and drier air, until the completely dried tea falls off the last tray at the exit aperture or mouth. Hot air is drawn into the base of the dryer at an inlet temperature of 190–210°F, and meets the driest tea first, gradually cooling and absorbing moisture from the successive wetter layers of drying tea until it meets the fermented leaf as it first enters the dryer. On leaving the dryer, the exit temperature of the warm air has fallen to 130°F.

Dryer inlet and exhaust temperatures, and the drying time for the tea, are all carefully controlled because of the rapidity with which adverse characters and taints otherwise develop. Drying time takes from 15 to 30 min, depending on the type of dryer. If a rapid throughput is necessary at times of heavy leaf production, the inlet temperature is sometimes raised to 220°F and the time is reduced.

Sorting. The dried leaf is sorted mechanically or by air flotation into leaf grades, and packed at a moisture-content level of 3 ± 1% in plywood, foil-lined chests for transportation. Tea is hygroscopic and readily absorbs moisture from the air; at moisture contents in excess of 6% it deteriorates quickly. As a consequence, care has to be taken during transportation and storage to prevent exposure to water vapor. It was shown by Roberts and Smith (23) that deterioration of tea during storage under adverse conditions of moisture content and temperature is associated with a breakdown of the theaflavins, resulting in a production of carbon dioxide. This change can be minimized by maintaining a low moisture content in the tea.

Creaming Down. Tea "cream" is a finely divided suspension of small particles which forms when a strong infusion of black tea cools. Smith (29) has shown that the principal constituents of cream are theaflavins, thearubigins, and caffeine, with smaller amounts of other flavanoids and other nitrogen compounds, chlorophyll, and inorganic material, all of which are present in the original black tea.

Variations on the Black Tea Process

Current trade in black teas is preponderantly in quick-liquoring broken and small-leaf grades, prepared for blending and sale as standard brands, either loose in small packets, or in tea bags. There is also an appreciable market for orthodox tea grades which have been prepared for fermentation in a traditional roller during manufacture. Part of this market is concerned with supplying more expensive fine grades, often containing large proportions of the dried buds or tips, for discerning consumers.

Teas grown in cooler climates, especially teas made from tea populations in which *Camellia sinensis* plants predominate, require a fuller wither, followed by a comparatively higher pressure during the rolling process, and a longer fermentation, in order that the more flavory character of the tea will emerge in the cup.

Some processors, particularly in Ceylon and Darjeeling, may in some seasons dry their teas at the conclusion of fermentation at temperatures between 220 and 250°F. This results in a distinctive high-fired character being produced in the made tea.

Several different forms of tea are produced for small specialized outlets; examples are brick tea, made by compressing green or black tea for consumption with yak butter, mainly in Tibet, and oolong tea, made in China and Taiwan by hot firing after hand processing.

Made tea very readily absorbs flavors, taints, and perfumes, and this propensity is made use of in some other specialized kinds of tea. In preparing Lapsang Soochong China tea, the fresh leaf is withered on tarred fishnetting, which imparts a distinctive taste to the tea. Another example is jasmine tea, in the preparation of which dried flowers, in this case *Jasminum sambae*, are mixed with warm newly dried China tea to impart fragrance and aroma. Equally, care has to be taken in storing tea near such produce as onions, phenolic soap, or roasted coffee.

Green Tea. Green tea is prepared and consumed mainly in Japan. In 1966, 160 million lb of green tea were made and consumed in that country, compared with 10 million lb of black tea. Only small amounts of black tea were produced in Japan, and the rest imported, mainly from Ceylon.

The product is prepared from fresh leaf, as soon as possible after plucking, but where fresh leaf has to be stored for periods up to 24 hr, it is kept cool and unwithered by being spread on perforated metal sheets, and having cold air blown through the leaf at intervals.

In manufacture, the polyphenol oxidase and possibly other enzymes are inactivated completely by steaming the leaf for 20 sec as it passes along a conveyor, so that no flavanol conversion can take place. The steamed green leaf is then partially dried and rolled for 30 min, in boxes through which hot air is passed, until it loses about 40% of its moisture, after which it is rolled for 10–15 min in a conventional roller.

The rolled leaf is then dried for 10 min in a drum dryer at 100°C, twisted, and re-dried at 80°C for 15–20 min until the moisture content is below 5%, after which the dried green tea is fragmented and polished. The processed leaf develops an olive-green color during drying. The infusion is green or greenish-yellow and has a delicate flavor.

Instant Tea. Instant teas fall into two categories: those prepared from fresh leaf and those prepared from already-manufactured black tea. Several processes are in use. The chemical engineering problems have been overcome independently and in different ways by the interests concerned, and the processing systems are either secret or carefully protected by patent cover.

In preparing instant tea from *fresh leaf*, the methods are devised so as to allow the changes which take place to proceed as nearly as possible as in traditional fermentation. The fresh leaf is macerated, sometimes by normal rolling routines, and the substrate is allowed to ferment. At the conclusion of fermentation the soluble solids are separated from the inactive plant debris by aqueous extraction. The extract is then concentrated and vacuum freeze-dried or spray-dried. At each stage the temperature is carefully controlled to prevent the development of undesirable flavors and to preserve the color and brightness in the liquors made from the resultant product.

The extraction of water-soluble solids from *black tea* for preparation of instants is essentially similar to normal infusion, and is followed by concentration and drying of the liquor.

Originally instant teas were developed for traditional markets as possible alternatives to black tea. A range of cold-water-soluble flavored and sweetened instants has also been developed specifically for the soft-drink trade, and an iced-tea market has been created.

Furuya (28) reports that a method of making cold-water-soluble instant green tea was developed in the tea technology division of the Japan Tea Research Station, Shizuoka.

Commercial production of instant green tea started on a small scale in Japan in 1962 and is now being developed. In preparing it, the soluble solids are extracted from dried ground green tea with hot water. The extracted liquid is concentrated to contain about 20% solids and is then vacuum-dried or freeze-dried into a soluble powder with 2–3% moisture.

Supply and Distribution

Production and consumption of tea is given in Tables 3 and 4.

Tea Production in the United States

According to Ukers (26), tea seeds and plants were first brought into the country in 1795 by American captains in the China trade, and introduced by a French botanist, A. Michaux, into his botanical gardens in the Middleton Estate, fifteen miles from Charleston, S.C. In 1848 Dr. Julius Smith attempted to start a tea industry near Greenville, S.C., and in 1850 a further plantation was made at McIntosh, Ga., by a Dr. Jones, but these early projects were not successful.

In 1858 the United States Government sent Robert Fortune to China for seeds which were distributed to planters in several southern states, but it was not until 1880 that large-scale experiments were carried out near Summerville, S.C., by J. Jackson for the U.S. Commissioner for Agriculture, using surviving plants from previous plantings and seed from China, Japan, and India. Jackson's plantings had been brought into production before the experiments stopped, and this experiment was followed by further plantings at Summerville in 1890 by Dr. Charles U. Shephard. With yearly appro-

Table 3. Production and Exports, 1966, 1000 metric tons (24)

Country	Production	Exports
India	376.0	179.2
Ceylon	222.3	200.0
China	160.0	35.9
Africa	84.3	75.0
Japan	82.0	1.8
U.S.S.R.	58.4	
Pakistan	28.5	2.3
Latin America	22.0	15.9
others	157.5	110.9
world total	1191.0	621.0

Table 4. Net Imports for Consumption, 1966, 1000 metric tons (25)

Country	Imports
U.S.A.	60.1
Canada	19.0
West Indies and Latin America	6.6
U.K. and Ireland	229.7
rest of Western Europe	30.4
U.S.S.R. and Eastern Europe	27.2
Asia	75.3
Africa	87.2
Australia and New Zealand	35.5
major producing countries	7.0
total	578.0

priations of Government aid between 1900 and 1915, the development became the Pinehurst Tea Garden, and 125 acres of tea were brought into production, with the highest annual yield reaching 15,000 lb. In 1915 this enterprise was abandoned.

Meanwhile in 1901 the American Tea Growing Company was established between Charleston and Savannah, S.C., and had plans to plant up to 2000 acres of tea, but the venture only lasted until 1903. Other smaller plantings were made near Pierce, Texas, with inconclusive results, and a few trees have been grown in the open in California, but the early experiments ended before 1920.

Sanderson (27) reports that in 1956 a small portion of Dr. Shephard's tea at Summerville was revitalized through a project headed by Dr. W. Carroll Barnes of Clemson College Agricultural Station near Charleston, with the support of Thomas J. Lipton, Inc. The project was initiated to provide Lipton's laboratories at Englewood Cliffs, N.J., with a variety of teas for research into tea aroma and flavor, tea biochemistry, tea analytical chemistry, instant tea chemistry, and related subjects. In 1963 Lipton purchased another farm near Charleston, where about 20 acres of tea are now under cultivation for use in their research program.

Other projects in tea cultivation are in progress at the University of Florida, the Tuskegee Institute in Alabama, and the University of California. Fruitland Nurseries at Augusta, Ga., and possibly other nurseries, propagate tea as an ornamental plant.

Bibliography

"Tea" in *ECT* 1st ed., Vol. 13, pp. 656–666, by George F. Mitchell, General Foods Corporation.

1. W. Wight, *Current Sci. (India)* **31**, 298–299 (1962).
2. W. Wight, *Nature* **183**, 1726–1728 (1959).
3. R. Fortune, *Report upon the Tea Plantations in the North-Western Provinces,* Indian Goverment, 1851, p. 13.
4. G. Watt and H. H. Mann, *The Pests and Blights of the Tea Plant,* 2nd ed., Office of the Superintendent, Goverment Printing, Calcutta, India, 1903, pp. 14–19.
5. E. A. H. Roberts, W. Wight, and D. J. Wood, *New Phytologist* **57**, 211 (1957).
6. K. C. Willson, *Tea (Nairobi, Kenya)* **8** (3), 2 (1967).
7. *Tea Growers' Handbook 1969,* Tea Research Institute of East Africa, Kericho, Kenya, 1969.
8. K. C. Willson, *J. Exptl. Agr.* (1969) (in press).
9. G. I. Forrest, *Studies in Tea Biochemistry and Fermentation, Final Report,* Swazi Tea Research Station, Swazi, Malawi, 1967.
10. E. A. H. Roberts, *Tocklai Exptl. Sta. Tea Encyclopaedia Serial 26/1* (1951).
11. *Tchai* (in Russian), several authors, Tbilisi, 1963.
12. D. J. Millin and D. W. Rustidge, "Tea Manufacture," *Process. Biochem.* **11** (1967).
13. R. L. Wickremasinghe, G. R. Roberts, and B. P. M. Perera, *Tea Quart.* **38**, 310 (1967); *paper presented at 7th Intern. Congr. Biochem., Tokyo, 1967.*
14. A. G. Brown, W. B. Eyton, A. Holmes, and W. D. Ollis, *Nature* **221**, 742–744 (1969).
15. E. A. H. Roberts, *"Two and a Bud,"* **9**, 3–8 (1962).
16. E. A. H. Roberts, *Tocklai Exptl. Sta. Tea Encyclopedia Serial 56* (1949).
17. G. W. Sanderson, *Tea Quart.* **36**, 172–182 (1965); also reprinted in *World Coffee and Tea* **7**, 55–58, 65–68 (1967).
18. G. R. Roberts and G. W. Sanderson, *J. Sci. Food Agr.* **15**, 14 (1966).
19. R. L. Wickremasinghe and T. Swain, *Chem. Ind. (London)* (**1964**), 1574–1575.
20. A. S. L. Tirimanna, *Tea Quart.* **38**, 293–295 (1967).
21. A. Biétrix, *Le Thé,* J.-B. Baillière et Fils, Paris, 1892, p. 81.
22. R. L. Wickremasinghe and V. H. Perera, *Tea Quart.* **37**, 75 (1966).
23. E. A. H. Roberts and R. F. Smith, *J. Sci. Food Agr.* **14**, 698 (1963).
24. FAO Committee on Commodity Problems, Third ad hoc Consultation on Tea, *Memoradum Tah 68/2 (Corr.)* (Jan. 6, 1969).
25. International Tea Committee, London, *Annual Bulletin of Statistics* (1968) and Suppl. (Dec. 1968), Table D-1.
26. W. H. Ukers, *All About Tea,* Tea and Coffee Trade Journal Co., New York, 1935, pp. 213–215.
27. G. W. Sanderson, Thomas J. Lipton, Inc., Englewood Cliffs, N.J., private communication to author.
28. K. Furuya, *Japan. Agr. Res. Quart. (J.A.R.Q.)* **2**, 19–23 (1967).
29. R. F. Smith, *J. Sci. Food Agr.* **19**, 530–534 (1968).
30. T. Yaminishi, *J.A.R.Q.* **4**, 25–32 (1967).

ERNEST HAINSWORTH
Tea Research Institute
of East Africa

TELLURIUM AND TELLURIUM COMPOUNDS

Tellurium, Te, at. no. 52, at. wt 127.61, is between selenium and polonium in group VIb, and between antimony and iodine in period 5, of the periodic table. The configuration of its six outer electrons is $5s^25p^4$, and its five inner shells are completely filled (2,8,18,18,6). Tellurium is more metallic than oxygen, sulfur, and selenium, yet it resembles them closely in most of its chemical properties. Whereas oxygen and sulfur are nonmetals and electrical insulators, selenium and tellurium are metalloids and semiconductors, while polonium is a metal. Tellurium forms inorganic and organic compounds very similar to the corresponding sulfur and selenium compounds. Its important oxidation states are -2, 0, $+4$, and $+6$.

Tellurium was discovered by Müller in 1782 in Transylvanian gold ore. It was named by Klaproth in 1798 from the Latin *tellus*, meaning earth (1).

Properties (2–11)

Physical Properties. At least twenty-one tellurium isotopes are known, with mass numbers from 114 to 134. Eight isotopes are stable (120,122–126,128,130). The rest are radioactive with lifetimes from 2 min to 154 days; the heaviest six are fission products. Tellurium illustrates the rule that elements with even atomic numbers have more isotopes than elements with odd atomic numbers. The neighboring antimony has two isotopes, and iodine one only. Because of the preponderance of heavy isotopes, tellurium has a higher atomic weight than iodine.

At ordinary temperature and pressure, solid tellurium, unlike sulfur and selenium, exists in one modification only. It crystallizes in a hexagonal lattice with parameters $a = 4.4570$ Å and $b = 5.9290$ Å, and trigonal symmetry. The so-called amorphous variety consists of very thin hexagonal crystals. Tellurium crystals are markedly anisotropic in many physical properties, such as compressibility, strength, thermal expansion, optical absorption, refraction of polarized light, electrical conductivity, and galvanomagnetic properties. The structural diagram of tellurium shows five solid phases at 300–475°C and 0–40,000 kg/cm².

Tellurium forms a continuous range of isomorphous solid solutions with gray selenium. These solutions contain chains with more or less randomly alternating Se and Te atoms. Tellurium solidified from the liquid is crystalline, grayish white with a metallic luster resembling antimony and tarnishing somewhat on exposure to air, rather brittle, and easily pulverized. The specific gravity at 20°C is 6.24 (crystalline) and 6.0–6.02 (precipitated); it increases markedly under compression. The relative hardness on the Mohs scale is 2.0–2.5, the modulus of elasticity is 6×10^6 psi, and the Poisson ratio at 30°C is 0.33. Thin films of tellurium are reddish brown to purple. They are opaque to visible light and transparent to infrared. Finely divided tellurium is dark gray when powdered mechanically, grayish brown when precipitated with oxygen from alkaline telluride solutions or with sulfur dioxide from acidified solutions, and black when precipitated by reduction with zinc, tin, or iron. Colloidal tellurium prepared by reducing aqueous telluric acid with hydrazine is red.

The heat capacity of solid tellurium at 25°C is 6.14 cal/g-atom, the entropy at 25°C is 11.88, and the heat of fusion is 4.27 kcal/g-atom. Tellurium shrinks 5–7% in volume on solidification. It melts at 450°C to a dark liquid resembling molten lead. The viscosity at the melting point is 1.8–1.95 cP. The vapor pressure between 786 and 1110°K is given by the following equation (12):

$$\log p_{mm} = 7.5999 - (5960.2/T)$$

where $T = $ °K. The extrapolated boiling point is 990°C, and the heat of vaporization is 11.0 kcal/g-atom. The golden-yellow vapor absorbs light in the visible and ultra-violet regions and contains species from monatomic Te to Te_5. The Te_2 species is predominant. The heat of formation of a Te_2 molecule from the standard state of a Te(g) atom is 48 kcal/mole, and the dissociation energy of $Te_2(g)$ to form atoms is 53 kcal/mole. The heat conductivity of polycrystalline tellurium at 20°C is 0.01433 cal/(cm-sec)(°C) and varies irregularly with temperature. In single crystals it is markedly anisotropic and is affected by impurities and lattice imperfections.

The electrical resistance of polycrystalline tellurium, as with any semiconductor, varies greatly with the amount and kind of impurities and decreases markedly with increasing temperature, and especially with compression. The photoelectric effect is only approx 0.01% as strong as in gray selenium. The thermal emf is 50–600 μV per deg Celsius, depending on the kind and concentration of impurities. Tellurium has diamagnetic susceptibility, which, like the Hall effect, is anisotropic and affected by impurities. The Hall effect varies irregularly with temperature and shows two sign reversals in the solid state and one in the liquid state. Tellurium and many of its alloys and intermetallic compounds have semiconductor and thermoelectric properties (12a–12d).

The Te–Te bond energy is 33 kcal/mole. The covalent radius is 1.37 Å, and the electronegativity on the Pauling scale is approx 2.1. The first ionization potential is 9.01 eV. The first electron affinity may be as high as 2.3 eV, and the second (to form Te^{2-}) is about -3 eV.

Chemical Properties. Although chemically tellurium resembles sulfur and selenium, it is more basic, more metallic, and more strongly amphoteric. Its behavior as an anion or a cation, depending on the medium, eg,

$$TeO_2 + 2\,KOH \rightarrow K_2TeO_3 + H_2O$$

$$TeO_2 + 4\,HCl \rightleftharpoons TeCl_4 + 2\,H_2O$$

explains the three types of redox reactions in the acid and in the alkaline mediums. In an acid medium, the following reactions take place:

$$Te - 4\,e \rightarrow Te^{4+} \qquad Te^{4+} + 4\,e \rightarrow Te \qquad Te^{4+} - 2\,e \rightarrow Te^{6+}$$

In an alkaline medium,

$$Te - 4\,e + 3\,H_2O \rightarrow TeO_3^{2-} + 6\,H^+ \qquad TeO_3^{2-} + 4\,e + 6\,H^+ \rightarrow Te + 3\,H_2O$$

$$TeO_3 - 2\,e + H_2O \rightarrow TeO_4^{2-} + 2\,H^+$$

Tellurium forms ionic tellurides with active metals, and covalent compounds with other elements. The valence states are -2 (H_2Te, Na_2Te, $CuTe$), $+4$ (TeO_2, $TeBr_4$, $TeOCl_2$), and $+6$ (TeO_3, H_6TeO_6, TeF_6). Solid crystalline tellurium tarnishes slightly in the air, and more rapidly and to a greater degree in the powdered state. Moist precipitated tellurium oxidizes on drying, especially at >100°C. Molten tellurium is readily oxidized to tellurium dioxide, which can be volatilized by blowing air through the melt. Tellurium reacts with halogens and halogenating agents, and mixes in all proportions with sulfur and selenium. Oxidation with concentrated nitric acid, and ignition of the resulting $2TeO_2 \cdot HNO_3$, yields very pure TeO_2. Tellurium reacts with concentrated, but not with dilute, sulfuric acid to form $TeSO_3$,

$$Te + H_2SO_4 \rightleftharpoons TeSO_3 + H_2O$$

Dilution with water reverses the reaction, and heating the solution liberates sulfur dioxide. When added to solutions of tellurides, tellurium forms colored polytellurides. Unlike selenium, tellurium is not soluble in aqueous sodium sulfite. Consequently, this offers a method for separating the two elements. Like selenium, tellurium is soluble in hot caustic alkalis, with the exception of ammonium hydroxide. Cooling reverses the reaction. Since tellurium forms solutions of anions (Te^{2-}) and cations (Te^{4+}), tellurium films can be deposited on inert electrodes of either sign.

Elemental tellurium reduces chlorides such as $AsCl_3$, $AuCl_3$, and $PbCl_4$ to the element; it reduces $FeCl_3$ to $FeCl_2$, and SO_2Cl_2 to SO_2. Oxidation of metals by tellurium gives metallic tellurides. Tellurium itself is oxidized by such strong reagents as $Na_2Cr_2O_7$, $KMnO_4$, $Ca(OCl)_2$, and $HClO_3$. Tellurium dioxide and tellurous acid and its salts are readily reduced to the element with $SnCl_2$, Na_2AsO_3, H_2S, and $Na_2S_2O_4$ and are oxidized to the Te(VI) state with PbO_2, CrO_3, Cl_2, and $KMnO_4$. TeO_4^{2-} ions are reduced to TeO_3^{2-} with Se, H_2S, and HCl. Solid tellurium oxides can be reduced by heating with hydrogen, carbon, and carbon monoxide.

The stability of organic compounds of elements in group VIb decreases in the order sulfur > selenium > tellurium. The organic compounds of tellurium are listed in Table 2, page 768.

Occurrence (13–15)

At 0.047 atom per 10,000 atoms Si, tellurium is about the fortieth element in the order of cosmic abundance. Along with platinum, palladium, and ruthenium, it ranks about seventy-first in the order of crustal abundance. The average amount in crustal rocks is 0.01 ppm. The chalcophile elements, sulfur, selenium, and tellurium, are primary components of intrusive and extrusive magmas, of volcanic gases, and hence of volcanic sulfur deposits. Nevertheless, selenium and tellurium are not essential components of the common igneous rock-forming minerals. Tellurium is widely distributed in the earth's crust in deposits of many different types, from magmatic and pegmatitic to hydrothermal, especially where these deposits are associated with epithermal gold and silver deposits.

There are small concentrations but large quantities of tellurium in copper porphyries, in massive pyritic copper sulfide and nickel sulfide deposits, and frequently in lead sulfide deposits. In pyritic deposits, tellurium is concentrated chiefly in pentlandite, $(FeNi)_9S_8$; chalcopyrite, $CuFeS_2$; and pyrite, FeS_2 (in decreasing order), and least in sphalerite, ZnS; and pyrrhotite, FeS. Other tellurium-bearing deposits are copper–molybdenum, lead–zinc, gold, tungsten–bismuth, uranium, and mercury–antimony. The S:Se:Te ratio varies widely among the deposits and within the same deposit. At times, tellurium concentration exceeds that of selenium, and often it increases with depth. Little is known about tellurium in sedimentary rocks, though some shales contain 0.1–2 ppm and manganese nodules from the Pacific and Indian Ocean floors contain 0.5–125 ppm.

Like selenium, tellurium forms most often binary minerals; but where selenium isomorphously replaces a part of the sulfur in sulfides, tellurium occurs only as discrete tellurium minerals of microscopic size. Tellurium is a major component of about forty mineral species, including twenty-four tellurides, seven tellurites, two tellurates, native tellurium, and a selenium–tellurium alloy. It is a minor constituent of an undetermined number of minerals. It occurs in combination with oxygen, sulfur, and ten other elements with high atomic numbers. At least ten tellurium minerals occur with gold and silver, ten with bismuth, and six with iron. Some of the better known minerals are hessite, Ag_2Te; petzite, Ag_3AuTe_2; calaverite, $AuTe_2$; sylvanite, $AuAgTe_4$; altaite, $PbTe$; tetradymite, Bi_2Te_2S; rickardit, $Cu_{4-x}Te_2$; nagyagite, $Au(Pb, Sb, Fe)_8(Te, S)_{11}$; and tellurite, TeO_2.

Like selenium, tellurium minerals are widely disseminated but do not form an ore. Hence, there are no deposits that can be mined for tellurium alone, and there are no "reserves." Resources estimated at tens of millions of pounds, however, are found in the base-metal sulfide deposits mined for copper, nickel, gold, silver, and lead, where the recovery of tellurium, like that of selenium, is incidental.

Manufacture

Recovery. The percentage of tellurium recovered from copper ore is indeed small. About 90% is lost in flotation concentration, and from 20 to 60% is lost in each metallurgical operation—roasting, smelting, converting, fire refining, and slimes treatment (see also Copper). Losses are also high in the metallurgical treatment of lead and zinc ores, by-products of which are sometimes sent to a copper smelter.

Almost all of the tellurium of commerce is recovered from electrolytic copper-refinery slimes, in which it is present from a trace to 8% (see also Selenium).

When the slimes are decopperized by aerating in dilute sulfuric acid, or by digesting with strong acid and then water-leaching, much of the tellurium is dissolved. This tellurium is recovered by cementing (precipitation on metallic copper), leaching the cement mud with dilute caustic soda, and neutralizing the solution with sulfuric acid. The precipitate from the neutralization contains tellurium as tellurous acid suitable for recovery.

The decopperized slimes are treated by one of the following methods: (1) refining with soda ash in a doré or cupeling furnace (17–19), (2) combined oxidation and alkalization by roasting or baking a slimes–soda mix, (3) deselenizing roasting and caustic soda leaching, or (4) boiling the slimes with caustic soda (20,21). The soda slag from (1) or the roasted product of (2) is water-leached to extract sodium tellurite. The insoluble sodium tellurate remaining in the leached slag is returned to the copper-anode furnace. The liquor from (3) and (4) contains lead. In all cases, the solution contains selenium and impurities. Whatever the method, the liquor is neutralized to pH 6–6.2 with sulfuric acid in order to precipitate impure tellurous acid as tellurium mud (22). In addition to tellurous acid, the mud contains lead sulfate, silica, and other impurities. The mud is purified by redissolving in caustic soda and reprecipitating. Impurities such as lead may be removed by careful precipitation from the caustic solution with sodium sulfide. Fractional neutralization of the initial impure caustic solution yields tellurous acid of a purity acceptable for reduction to the metal.

Three methods are used to recover tellurium from the precipitated tellurous acid: (1) direct reduction by heating with flour under cover of borax (heavy fuming of tellurium dioxide and the formation of organic decomposition products are drawbacks; reduction by heating with sulfur is rapid and leaves a clean melt, but the heavy fumes are obnoxious), (2) dissolving in hydrochloric acid or in sulfuric acid to which crude common salt is added, followed by precipitation of tellurium with sulfur dioxide, and subsequent filtration, washing, drying, and melting (a drawback is that some oxidation of the precipitate takes place during drying) (23), (3) dissolving in caustic soda to give a solution containing 200–275 g/l of tellurium as sodium tellurite, electrolyzing the solution in a cell with stainless-steel electrodes at 1.5 V per cell and 6–18 A/ft^2, followed by removing, washing, drying, and melting of the cathode deposit (24) (this is the most satisfactory method).

Purification. The high boiling temperature of tellurium precludes purification by atmospheric distillation, but low-pressure distillation is feasible. Heavy-metal impurities (iron, copper, tin, silver, lead, antimony, bismuth) are left in the still residue, and volatile selenium is a persistent contaminant, reaching 500 ppm in distilled tellurium.

A rather laborious purification method consists of dissolving tellurium in strong nitric acid, hydrolyzing to a white $2TeO_2.NO_3$ precipitate by diluting and boiling, separating and washing (redissolving and rehydrolyzing, if desired), dissolving in hydrochloric acid, and reducing with sulfur dioxide.

Ultrahigh-purity tellurium is prepared by zone refining in a hydrogen or inert-gas atmosphere. Single crystals of tellurium, tellurium alloys, and metal tellurides are grown by the Bridgman and Czochralski methods (see Semiconductors) (10).

Commercial Tellurium Products. *Tellurium dioxide*, TeO_2, theoret 79.9% Te, is made by drying precipitated tellurous acid at 100°C. The acid is purified, if necessary, by redissolving in caustic soda solution and neutralizing with sulfuric acid.

Sodium tellurate, Na_2TeO_4, theoret 53.7% Te, is made by oxidizing sodium tellurite solution with hydrogen peroxide.

Ferrotellurium, which usually has a Te content near the theoretical 69.5%, is made by melting iron and tellurium powders in about stoichiometric proportion.

Tellurium diethyldithiocarbamate, $((C_2H_5)_2NCSS)_4Te$, theoret 25.8% Te, is made by reacting diethylamine, carbon disulfide, and tellurium dioxide, in alcoholic solution.

Metal tellurides for use in semiconductors are made in the following ways: (*1*) direct melting, (*2*) melting with excess tellurium and volatilizing the excess under reduced pressure, (*3*) passing tellurium vapor in an inert gas carrier over a heated metal, (*4*) high-temperature reduction of oxy compounds with hydrogen or ammonia (10).

Economic Aspects (15,25–27)

Tellurium has been produced commercially in the United States since 1918 and in Canada since about 1934. Table 1 lists U.S. and Canadian producers, as well as producers in Japan and Europe. In addition to those mentioned in the table are some producers in Yugoslavia, the U.S.S.R., East Germany, and probably China.

Production and trade figures are published by the U.S. Bureau of Mines, Washington, the American Bureau of Metal Statistics, New York, and the Dominion Bureau of Statistics, Ottawa, Canada.

Annual tellurium production in the free world is about 300,000 lb. Approximately 85% of this is produced in the United States and Canada. In 1966, 199,000 lb of tellurium were produced in the U.S. (mainly from copper porphyry ores) and 72,000 lb in Canada (mainly from pyritic copper ores and to a lesser extent from copper–nickel ores). In Japan, the average annual production from 1963–1964 was 16,000 lb, and in Peru it was 37,000 lb. Production figures for other countries are few and incomplete; they are not available in communist-block countries.

For several years, the demand for tellurium was below production capacity. As a result, producers have some stocks of refined metal and a substantial supply of unprocessed tellurium-bearing by-products and residues, much of which could be economically treated. In the last few years, use has risen substantially and is in close balance with the quantities refined.

The main application of tellurium is in metallurgy as an additive to steel and copper to provide machinability. Appreciable quantities are also employed as accelerators in the rubber industry. Other important uses are in semiconductors, thermoelectric alloys, cast iron, and glass formulations for special applications, although only small quantities of the metal are used for these purposes.

The United States and Canada are self-sufficient in tellurium. Unlike selenium, the metal and its compounds are not as yet included in the U.S. Government National Stockpile list of Critical and Strategic Materials. The Government, however, offers

Table 1. Producers of Tellurium

Producer	Location	Remarks
United States		
American Smelting & Refining Co.	Baltimore, Md.	copper refinery
International Smelting & Refining Co. (controlled by The Anaconda Co.)	Perth Amboy, N.J.	copper refinery
U.S. Metals Refining Co. (a division of American Metal Climax, Inc.)	Carteret, N.J.	copper refinery
U.S. Smelting, Refining & Mining Co.	East Chicago, Ind.	lead producer
Canada		
Canadian Copper Refiners Ltd. (a subsidiary of Noranda Mines, Ltd.)	Montreal East, Quebec	copper refinery
International Nickel Co. of Canada, Ltd.	Copper Cliff, Ontario	copper–nickel refinery
Japan		
Mitsubishi Metal Mining Corp.	Osaka	copper refinery
Nihon Kogyo Kabushiki Kaisha	Hitachi	copper refinery
Europe		
Norddeutsche Affinerie	Hamburg, Germany	copper refinery

financial assistance in exploration costs. Tellurium exports are not limited by any regulations. Imports are dutiable at 6% on the metal and 8% on the compounds. These rates are scheduled to be reduced to 4% and 5%, respectively, by 1972.

Until 1954, the price of commercial-grade tellurium was $1.50–1.75/lb. It increased gradually, and since 1962 it has been $6.00/lb. The price of the high-purity grade is $12/lb, while the extra-high-purity grade costs $30/lb (early 1969).

Specifications and Standards

There are no official specifications, but some producers publish their own standards, and some users specify the weight and shape of the pieces, a screen analysis of the powder, and a maximum content of certain impurities.

The following three grades of tellurium are available: (1) commercial or refined, containing >99.0% (usually >99.4%) tellurium, with impurities usually <0.5% selenium, <0.3% lead, <0.1% iron, and <0.02% copper—sold as lump 3-in. down, 1-, 2-, and 6-lb blocks, 1- and 2-lb sticks, −200 mesh powder, and 1-, 2-, and 3-g tablets; (2) high-purity, containing >99.95% tellurium (though 99.99% is claimed by some makers), with impurities usually <500 ppm selenium, <25 ppm lead, <15 ppm arsenic, <10 ppm zinc, and <15 ppm total of iron, copper, nickel, chromium, antimony, bismuth, mercury—usually sold in shotted form; and (3) ultrahigh-purity, claimed to contain min 99.999% tellurium.

Analytical Methods (7,11,14,28–30)

Tellurium is usually detected by the formation of a black precipitate with sulfur dioxide in dilute hydrochloric acid, or a reddish-brown tellurium sulfide with hydrogen sulfide. Elemental tellurium and tellurides, but not tellurites and tellurates, give a purplish-red color when warmed with concentrated sulfuric acid.

Depending on the tellurium content and the nature of the material being analyzed, tellurium can be determined by a number of gravimetric (31), volumetric, polarographic, potentiometric (32), photometric, emission-spectrographic, and x-ray-fluorescence methods. In addition, atomic-absorption-spectrophotometric procedures have been developed.

Gravimetric-determination methods are not entirely satisfactory for tellurium. Precipitation as the element with sulfur dioxide (preferably with the addition of hydrazine) is affected by coprecipitation of other elements and by oxidation of the precipitate on drying. Tellurium dioxide can be precipitated from Te(IV) solutions with ammonia, pyridine, and hexamethylenetetramine, but heavy metals and other elements are coprecipitated, unless complexed with a reagent such as EDTA (30a), citric acid, and tartaric acid.

A common volumetric-determination method involves treatment of the sample with a 1:1 nitric–sulfuric acid mixture to dissolve the tellurium as tellurite; addition of potassium bisulfate and repeated fuming with sulfuric acid to volatilize the selenium; boiling with 10% (v/v) sulfuric acid to dissolve the tellurite, followed by threefold dilution with water and titration with potassium permanganate,

$$5\ TeO_3^{2-} + 2\ KMnO_4 + 3\ H_2SO_4 \rightarrow 5\ TeO_4^{2-} + 2\ K_2SO_4 + MnSO_4 + 3\ H_2O$$

This reaction is not entirely stoichiometric, and the titrant must be standardized against pure telluric acid.

When the tellurium concentration is $<0.01\%$, a preconcentration technique is used together with a spectrophotometric or atomic-absorption method. A direct spectrographic method is used when the concentration is several parts per million.

Health and Safety Aspects (33–36)

Less is known about the toxicity of tellurium than of selenium, tellurium being less toxic. Elementary tellurium and the stable metallic tellurides, such as those of copper, zinc, cadmium, bismuth, and lead, are relatively inert and are not thought to be a health hazard. All other tellurium compounds, however, should be handled with care. This includes the reactive tellurides, the volatile and the soluble compounds, and especially hydrogen telluride and the organics. Some of these compounds can enter the body through the skin and by the inhalation and ingestion of dust, fumes, or vapors. Hydrogen telluride is very toxic, although contrary to published statements it is less toxic than hydrogen sulfide. The soluble tellurites are more toxic than selenites and arsenites. The toxic effects of the compounds arise on reduction to the relatively harmless elemental tellurium and to dialkyl (chiefly methyl) tellurides. Tellurium, as well as tellurium compounds and metabolism products, is present in exhaled breath, sweat, urine, and feces. No definite pathological effects have been observed, but moderate exposure to tellurium dioxide fumes and dust, and short exposure to hydrogen telluride, may cause a dryness and metallic taste in the mouth, as well as extremely unpleasant breath. Not all individuals are susceptible to the same degree.

As with selenium, industrial precautions include the common sense measures of good housekeeping, adequate ventilation, personal cleanliness, and frequent changes of clothing. Gloves should be worn at all times, and dust masks and chemical goggles should be used where needed. Prolonged or repeated contact of the skin with tellurium-containing solutions and compounds should be avoided. Oral administration of ascorbic acid, recommended at one time to alleviate the unpleasant breath, is no longer in favor; for, by reducing tellurium compounds, ascorbic acid may enhance their toxic effects. Chlorophyll preparations are now used for deodorizing the breath.

Tellurium and its commercial products do not present a fire hazard. They should be stored in a dry, ventilated area. There are no shipping restrictions.

Inorganic Compounds

Tellurium forms inorganic and organic compounds very similar to those of sulfur and selenium. Its oxidation states are -2, 0, $+4$, and $+6$. The most important tellurium compounds are the tellurides, the halides, the oxides, and the oxyacids. For detailed descriptions of tellurium compounds, including references to original work, see Friend (2), Mellor (3), Yost and Russell (5), Sidgwick (6), Pascal (7), and Bagnall (11). Techniques and methods of preparation are given in *Inorganic Syntheses* (37) and in Brauer (38). The chemical relations of tellurium compounds are illustrated in Figure 1 (39).

Although the chemical behavior of tellurium compounds has been reasonably well studied, some of the physical constants that have been published are uncertain and should be accepted with reservation.

Tellurides. Most elements form compounds with tellurium. Chizhikov and Shchastlivyi (10) describe binary compounds of tellurium with sixty-nine elements, and alloys with two others. Fifty-eight of the elements are metals, three are metalloids, and ten are nonmetals. Most of the tellurides can be prepared by direct reaction. The reaction varies from very vigorous with alkali metals to sluggish—and requiring a high temperature—with hydrogen. The alkali and alkaline-earth tellurides are colorless ionic solids rapidly decomposed by air. In solution, they are hydrolyzed less than sulfides and selenides but very easily oxidized. The solutions dissolve excess tellurium, forming dark-red polytellurides. The alkali-metal tellurides are strong reductants and reduce tellurites to metallic tellurium. Hydrotellurides, such as NaHTe, are also known. Some metals form more than one telluride, and some metal tellurides show nonstoichiometry. Many tellurides possess semiconductor properties.

Hydrogen Telluride. This colorless, toxic gas has an odor resembling arsine. The liquid and solid states are also colorless. Hydrogen telluride is thermodynamically unstable but can be prepared from the elements in poor yield at approx 650°. A more convenient method is by the action of water on aluminum telluride in the absence of air, or by electrolysis of cold 15–50% sulfuric acid with a tellurium cathode. Hydrogen telluride and its aqueous solution decompose slowly in the air. Unless perfectly dry, the compound also decomposes when exposed to light. Hydrogen telluride is a strong reducing agent and is rapidly oxidized. It reacts with alkalis and the solutions of many metal salts to form the corresponding tellurides. Hydrogen telluride solutions are weakly acidic and ionize to HTe^- and Te^{2-}.

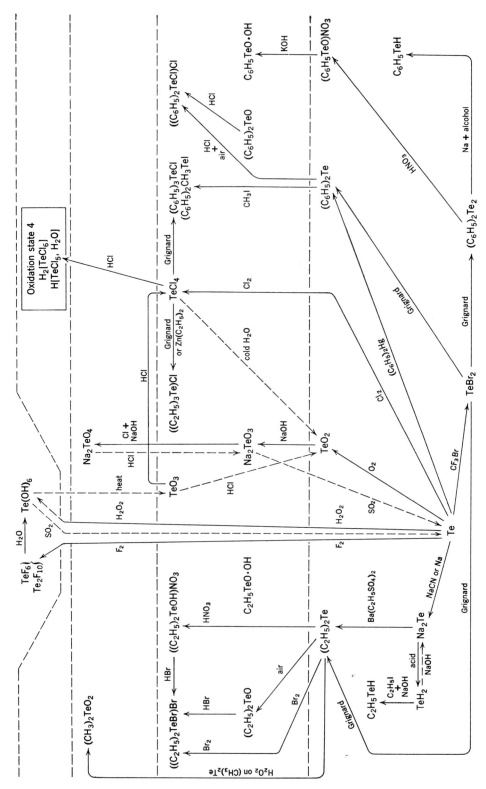

Fig. 1. Chemical relations of the compounds of tellurium. Courtesy Longmans Green & Co. Ltd, London (39).

Tellurium Sulfide. In the liquid state, tellurium is completely miscible with sulfur. The Te–S phase diagram shows a eutectic at 105–110°C when the sulfur content is 98–99 atom % (94–98 wt %). Tellurium–sulfur alloys have semiconductor properties. Bands attributed to the TeS molecule have been observed.

Tellurium Selenides (or selenium tellurides). Tellurium selenides are unknown. The molten elements are miscible in all proportions. The mixtures are not simple solid solutions but have a complex character. Like the "sulfides," the "selenides" possess semiconductor properties.

Carbon Sulfotelluride, CSTe. This compound exists as a yellow-red liquid with a garlic odor. It is decomposed by light, even at −50°C, to carbon disulfide, carbon, and tellurium.

Carbonyl Telluride, COTe. Not very much is known about this compound. It is formed in poor yield by passing carbon monoxide over tellurium at a high temperature. It is less stable than the selenide.

Tellurium Nitride, Te_3N_4. This unstable, citron-yellow solid detonates easily when heated or struck but can apparently be kept under dry chloroform. It is said to explode on contact with water, possibly because of the heat of wetting.

Tellurium Halides. Tellurium forms the dihalides $TeCl_2$ and $TeBr_2$, but not TeI_2. It forms tetrahalides with all four halogens. Te_2F_{10} and TeF_6 can also be prepared. No monohalide, Te_2X_2, is believed to exist. Tellurium does not form well-defined oxyhalides as do sulfur and selenium. The tellurium halides show varying tendencies to form complexes and addition compounds with nitrogen compounds such as ammonia, pyridine, simple and substituted thioureas and anilines, and ethylenediamine, as well as with sulfur trioxide and the chlorides of other elements.

Tellurium Tetrafluoride, TeF_4. This compound forms white, hygroscopic needles melting at 129.6°C. It decomposes at 194°C to TeF_6 and is readily hydrolyzed. TeF_4 attacks glass, silica, and copper at 200°C, but it does not attack platinum at temperatures below 300°C.

Tellurium Decafluoride, Te_2F_{10}. A stable, volatile, colorless liquid, this compound melts at −33.7°C and boils at 59°C.

Tellurium Hexafluoride, TeF_6. This compound melts at −38°C and sublimes at −39°C, forming a colorless gas. TeF_6 hydrolyzes slowly to orthotelluric acid. It is reduced with tellurium to TeF_4.

Tellurium Dichloride, $TeCl_2$. A black, hygroscopic solid, $TeCl_2$ melts at 208°C to a black liquid and boils at 328°C to a bright-red vapor. The solid is stable when pure. It disproportionates in organic solvents and is decomposed by acids and alkalis; $TeCl_2$ is hydrolyzed to H_2TeO_3, Te, and HCl, and decomposed by HCl to Te and H_2TeCl_6. It is oxidized by air to TeO_2 and HCl.

Tellurium Tetrachloride, $TeCl_4$. The white, hygroscopic crystals of $TeCl_4$ melt at 225°C to a dark-red liquid. The vapor (bp approx 390°C) is also red. $TeCl_4$ is prepared by the action of chlorine on tellurium or of SCl_2, CCl_4, or $AsCl_3$ on tellurium or TeO_2. The crystals are soluble in benzene, toluene, and ethyl alcohol, but not in ether. $TeCl_4$ hydrolyzes in cold water to TeO_2 and in hot water gives a clear solution. With dilute HCl, it yields H_2TeO_3, TeO_2, $HTeCl_5$, and H_2TeCl_6, and with concd HCl it forms $TeCl_6^{2-}$. On evaporation to dryness, $TeCl_4$ forms $H_2TeCl_6 \cdot 2H_2O$, which decomposes at 350°C to TeO_2. With phenyl magnesium chloride, it yields $Te(C_6H_5)_3$-Cl. $TeCl_4$ forms many addition compounds and ligands.

Tellurium Dibromide, $TeBr_2$. This compound must be prepared very carefully, as it is unstable and has a strong tendency to disproportionate to $TeBr_4$ and Te.

Tellurium Tetrabromide, $TeBr_4$. Its yellow, hygroscopic crystals decompose at temperatures above 280°C and melt at 363°C under bromine vapor. $TeBr_4$ boils at 414–427°C, dissociating into $TeBr_2$ and bromine. It is soluble in ether and chloroform but not in CCl_4. The compound is readily hydrolyzed.

Tellurium Tetraiodide, TeI_4. The gray-black crystals of this compound are volatile and decompose into the elements at temperatures above 100°C. They melt at 280°C in a sealed tube.

Tellurium Oxychlorides. $Te_6O_{11}Cl_2$ and $TeOCl_2$ have been reported, and $TeOBr_2$ has been prepared.

Tellurium Oxides, Oxyacids, and Salts. Two oxides, TeO_2 and TeO_3, are known; both are more stable than SeO_2 and SeO_3. The existence of the monoxide, TeO, is in doubt.

Tellurium Dioxide, TeO_2. The white crystals of this compound melt at 733°C to a clear, dark-red liquid and vaporize at 790–940°C. TeO_2 is made by dissolving tellurium in $6N$ HNO_3 and decomposing the resulting $2TeO_2.HNO_3$ at 400–430°C, by heating Te in air or oxygen, or by thermal dehydration of H_6TeO_6. It is slightly soluble in water, forming H_2TeO_3, and readily soluble in halogen acids, forming complex anions, such as $TeCl_6{}^{2-}$. It dissolves in alkali-metal carbonates only on boiling. The standard redox potential is intermediate between those of SO_2 and SeO_2. In solution, TeO_2 is a weaker oxidant than SeO_2 for SO_2. Tellurium dioxide is amphoteric, with minimum solubility at pH 3.8–4.2, its isoelectric point. It forms tellurites, M_2TeO_3, with alkali metals, but not with NH_3. With some acids it forms basic salts, such as $TeO_2.2HCl$, $TeO_2.3HCl$, $TeO_2.2HBr$, $2TeO_2.HNO_3$, $2TeO_2.SO_3$, and $2TeO_2.HClO_4$. Heating with metal oxides yields tellurites, but with higher oxides, such as PbO_2, or with oxidants such as KNO_3 or $KClO_3$, tellurates are formed. Heating with metals such as Al, Cs, and Zn, with C (at red heat), or with S, ZnS, HgS, or PbS, reduces TeO_2 to Te. Hydrogen does not reduce it completely even at high temperatures, and H_2O_2 oxidizes aqueous TeO_2 suspension to H_4TeO_6.

Tellurium Trioxide, TeO_3. This compound exists in two modifications, the yellow-orange α-form and the grayish β-form. The α-form, sp gr 5.07, decomposes at >360°C to TeO_2. It is prepared by dehydrating H_6TeO_6 at 300–360°C. α-TeO_3 is a strong oxidant; it reacts violently with such metals as Al or Sn, and with such nonmetals as C, P, and S. Although insoluble in water, dilute mineral acids, and dilute alkalis, it dissolves in hot concentrated alkalis, with the formation of tellurates. α-TeO_3 is reduced to TeO_2 and $TeCl_4$ by boiling concd HCl (with the liberation of Cl_2). The β-form, a grayish solid, sp gr 6.21, is obtained by heating orthotelluric acid or α-TeO_3, alone or with H_2SO_4, for 10–12 hr at 300–350°C. It is less reactive than the α-form. Although insoluble in concentrated alkalis, the β-form is attacked by fused KOH. It is soluble in concd Na_2S solution. Hydrogen will reduce it at 400°C. The β-form does not react with water at 150°C in the presence of acid or alkali. Most likely, it is a polymer, but there are no structural data for either modification of TeO_3.

Tellurous Acid, H_2TeO_3. This unstable white solid dehydrates readily to TeO_2. It is prepared by the acidification of tellurite solution with dilute HNO_3, or by cold hydrolysis of a tetrahalide. H_2TeO_3 is a much weaker acid than H_2SeO_3. Both normal and acid tellurites are known. Alkali-metal tellurites are obtained from alkali hydroxides and TeO_2; other tellurites are prepared by double decomposition with alkali-metal tellurites, or by fusing TeO_2 with metal oxides or carbonates. The alkali-metal tellurites are water soluble, the alkaline-earth tellurites less so. Other tellurites are insoluble. Tellurites are oxidized to tellurates by heating in air or by treating a solution with H_2O_2 and other oxidants. In acid solution the salts are reduced to Te by SO_2, Sn, Zn, Cu, and some organic compounds.

Orthotelluric Acid, H_6TeO_6. Its white crystals are sparingly soluble in cold water and easily soluble in hot water and mineral acids, with the exception of HNO_3. Orthotelluric acid is made by oxidizing Te or TeO_2 (for example, by refluxing with H_2O_2 in concd H_2SO_4). It exists in a cubic α-form and a monoclinic β-form, which is stable at room temperature. The β-form is obtained from the α-form by heating. Orthotelluric acid tends to polymerize. It is weakly dibasic, forming salts not higher than dibasic, such as KH_5TeO_6, $Li_2H_4TeO_6$, and $Na_2H_4TeO_6$. An exception is Ag_6TeO_6. Heating dehydrates H_6TeO_6 to TeO_3, and then to TeO_2 and O. The acid is a fairly strong oxidant, liberating I from KI and oxidizing HCl and HBr. It is reduced by H_2S, SO_2, Zn, Fe^{2+}, and hydrazine. It forms complex acids and salts with other elements.

Polymetatelluric Acid, $(H_2TeO_4)_n$ (where n = approx 10). This white, amorphous, hygroscopic solid is obtained by the partial dehydration of orthotelluric acid at 100–200°C in air. Polymetatelluric acid always contains some of the ortho-acid and reverts to it in solution. It forms esters and salts. Orthotelluric and polymetatelluric acids are the only two telluric acids known.

The so-called allotelluric acid, a colorless syrup, is a mixture of orthotelluric and polymetatelluric acids. It is prepared by heating the ortho-acid in a sealed tube at 305°C.

The water-soluble alkali-metal and alkaline-earth tellurates are prepared by chlorinating alkaline solutions of the tellurites or by heating solid tellurites with KNO_3, $KClO_3$, or PbO_2. The insoluble tellurates are made by double decomposition of alkali-metal salt solutions.

Other Inorganic Compounds

Telluropentathionates, $(Te(S_2O_3)_2)^{2-}$. Alkali-metal and ammonium salts have been prepared. The S_2O_3 group can be replaced by ethyl xanthate diethyldithiocarbamate.

Tellurium pseudohalides, such as the dicyanide, $Te(CN)_2$, the dithiocyanate, $Te(SCN)_2$, and thiourea complexes with $Te(SCN)_2$, have been prepared. They are similar to the halides in properties.

Basic tellurium nitrate, $2TeO_2.NO_3$, is made by dissolving Te in $8N$ HNO_3. Thermal decomposition begins at 190°C and is complete at 300°C.

Basic tellurium sulfate, $2TeO_2.SO_3$; *selenate*, $2TeO_2.SeO_3$; and *tellurate*, $2TeO_2.TeO_3$, are known. The sulfate is made by slow evaporation of TeO_2 solution in H_2SO_4 and is stable up to 440–500°C. It is hydrolyzed slowly by cold, and rapidly by hot water.

Tellurium perchlorate, iodate, and methylthiosulfate, as well as Te(IV) salts of aliphatic and aromatic acids, have been prepared.

Organic Compounds

The chemical properties of organosulfur, organoselenium, and organotellurium compounds are markedly similar. Because bond stability with carbon decreases with the increasing atomic number of the element, thermal stability decreases while oxida-

Table 2. Organic Tellurium Compounds

Compound	Formula	Melting point, $°C_{mm}$	Boiling point, $°C_{mm}$
tellurols or telluromercaptans	RTeH		
ethanetellurol	C_2H_5TeH		90
benzenetellurol	C_6H_5TeH		
alkyl, aryl, and cyclic tellurides			
dimethyl telluride or methyl telluride	$(CH_3)_2Te$		82
diphenyl telluride	$(C_6H_5)_2Te$	53.4	$182_{16.5}$
tetraphenyl telluride	$(C_6H_5)_4Te$	104–106	
tetrahydrotellurophene	$TeCH_2(CH_2)_2CH_2$		
ditellurides	R_2Te_2		
diphenyl ditelluride	$C_6H_5.Te—Te.C_6H_5$	53–54	
tellurium monohalides have not been reported			
alkyltellurium trihalides	$TReX_3$		
methyltellurium tribromide[a]	CH_3TeBr_3		
dialkyltellurium dihalides	$R_2Te_2X_2$		
dimethyl tellurium dichloride	$(CH_3)_2TeCl_2$	92 (α), 134 (β)	
trialkyltellurium monohalides have not been reported			
telluronium salts	R_3TeX, $R_2R'TeX$, $RR'R''TeX$		
trimethyltelluronium iodide	$(CH_3)_3TeI$		
methylphenyl-p-tolyltelluronium iodide[b]	$(C_6H_5)(p\text{-}CH_3C_6H_4)(CH_3)TeI$		
telluroxides	$RR''TeO$		
diphenyl telluroxide	$(C_6H_5)_2TeO$	185	
tellurones	R_2TeO_2		
dimethyl tellurone or methyl tellurone	$(CH_3)_2TeO_2$		
tellurane 1,1-dioxide monohydrate	$C_5H_{10}TeO_2.H_2O$		
telluroketones	$RCTeR'$		
dimethyl telluroketone	$CH_3.CTe.CH_3$	$63–66_{9–10}$	
tellurinic acid	$RTeO.OH$		
phenyltellurinic acid	$C_6H_5TeO.OH$	211	
tellurocyanates are not known			
heterocyclic compounds			
1,4-oxatellurane	$OCH_2CH_2TeCH_2CH_2$		
3,5-telluranedione	$CH_2COCH_2TeCH_2CO$	182	

[a] Dec 140°C.

[b] Optically active.

tion susceptibility increases so much that alkyl tellurides are oxidized rapidly by air at room temperature. A result is that comparatively little has been written concerning the chemistry of organotellurium compounds. Nevertheless, several reviews are available (11,40,41).

Organotellurium compounds range from the simple CSTe (see also Tellurides) to complex heterocyclic compounds. The various types of tellurium compounds, along with specific examples, are listed in Table 2.

Not included here are the many organic complexes of inorganic tellurium compounds and of their ions.

For detailed descriptions of the laboratory preparation of many common organo-tellurium compounds, see references 40 and 42–44.

Uses

Free-Machining Steels. Tellurium has been shown to be the best additive for improving machinability in several types of ferritic steel. Its effectiveness in this area has caused a considerable increase in tellurium consumption. The Inland Steel Corp., East Chicago, Ind. (45–46), developed what is currently the largest single outlet for tellurium as an additive to plain-carbon, leaded, and leaded resulfurized steels. The presence of 0.023–0.057% tellurium in cold-drawn steels, containing 0.06–0.09% carbon, 0.28–0.37% sulfur, and 0.15–0.22% lead, increases their machinability by 30–52% while increasing the feed rates. This saves much time and investment, especially with high-speed automatic-screw machines, in manufacturing large numbers of rela-tively small parts requiring much machining content. The machined surface finish is superior, the life of the cutting tool is longer, the metal chips are more uniform, and there is less buildup on the tool edges. Tellurium addition affects the mechanical properties very little, raises the recrystallization temperature only slightly (without affecting the heat-treatment properties), and has a minor effect on grain refining. In addition, it is less detrimental than sulfur in lowering the corrosion resistance. Tel-lurium can also be added to low- and high-alloy steels that are normally difficult to machine (47).

Chilled Castings (48–54). Since about 1940, tellurium has been used to control the chill depth of iron castings. Hard, wear-resistant, chilled surfaces were originally produced on gray iron castings by pouring molten iron against a metal surface, a thin layer of white iron forming on rapid cooling. The high cost and the limited life of metal molds led to the development of chilled surfaces by adjusting the carbon–silicon–sulfur content of the molten iron and by adding such carbide stabilizers as chromium and vanadium. The melt composition was difficult to control even under the best operating conditions, and the castings were often unacceptable. This problem was eliminated, however, by adding less than 0.1% tellurium to the melt.

Tellurium is 100–150 times as effective as chromium in producing a given depth of chill. It is a powerful carbide stabilizer, minute quantities converting gray iron to white. Since tellurium is very volatile, it is added to the ladle just before pouring. It may be added as pellets, tablets, powder (in aluminum or copper containers), ferro-tellurium or copper telluride granules, or any other convenient form. Alternatively, the mold is treated by coating the desired areas of the mold surface with a tellurium-bearing wash (55), by surfacing the sand mold with a layer of tellurium-rich sand, or by use of tellurium-containing tape (56).

The result is a hard, abrasion-resistant surface, important in many applications of cast iron. The depth of the chill may be controlled by regulating the amount of tellurium added. The casting invariably shows a sharp demarcation line between the chilled and unchilled regions; there is no intermediate or mottled zone. Yet, the chilled portion shows excellent resistance to spalling from thermal or mechanical shock. Tellurium-treated iron is more resistant to sulfuric and hydrochloric acids than is un-treated, unchilled gray iron. The amount of tellurium added is 0.005–0.1%, about 60% of this being lost by volatilization. Excessive addition of tellurium causes poros-ity in the castings.

Tellurium-chilled iron is used in mining, automotive, railroad, and other equipment. Tellurium corewashes eliminate troublesome localized shrinkage in castings (55). These corewashes contain about 25% tellurium, the balance consisting mainly of silica flour and some bentonite.

Other Ferrous-Metal Uses. Addition of tellurium sharply decreases the rate of nitrogen absorption in liquid iron and steel. This allows the use of cheaper, lower-purity oxygen in the basic oxygen steelmaking process and might be useful in decreasing the nitrogen pickup during supplementary scrap melting.

Tellurium can be used in making malleable iron. It is not as widely used as other graphitizing additives, but active research is under way.

Copper and Copper Alloys. A 99.5% Cu–0.5% Te alloy has been marketed for many years (57,58). Both the electrical and thermal conductivity of this alloy are about 90% that of pure copper. The machinability rating is 80–90, compared with 100 for free-cutting brass and about 80 for unalloyed copper.

Tellurium is sometimes added as a master alloy, often with some phosphorus as a deoxidizer. Most major users add tellurium in elemental lump form.

Unlike lead and other additives, tellurium has no adverse effect on the hot-working properties of copper and does not cause segregation and firecracking. Although the alloy is somewhat less ductile at room temperature than is pure copper, it may nevertheless be extensively hot- and cold-worked, although intermediate annealing is required when the cross-section reduction is >40%. Machining methods are the same as for free-cutting brass. Because the copper telluride particles are harder than the lead particles in free-machining brass, carbide-tipped tools must be used. The alloy is recommended for situations demanding a high production rate with no significant sacrifice in conductivity. Tellurium–copper has found an outlet in the electrical, radio, and communications industries, and in similar fields. The combination is also employed in welding and cutting tips. It was widely used in military applications during World War II. In copper–zinc alloys, the benefits of tellurium decrease with increasing zinc content and almost disappear when the zinc content exceeds 35%.

Telnic bronze, an alloy which hardens with age, contains 98.3% Cu, 1.0% Ni, 0.2% P, and 0.5% Te. Its machinability rating is 80. The hot-working properties of Telnic bronze are comparable to those of commercial bronze with a high copper content and are superior to any lead-containing free-machining copper alloy. Its tensile strength is high, and the electrical conductivity is about one half that of copper (see also Copper alloys).

Lead Alloys. A tellurium–lead alloy containing 0.02–0.1% tellurium, with or without antimony, was introduced in 1934 (59). Tellurium has a deoxidizing action on lead. The alloy shows very uniform elongation and retains fine structure to its breaking point. This is attributed to the film of lead telluride, which is insoluble in the lead matrix and prevents the growth of lead grains over a wide temperature range.

The addition of tellurium confers on lead useful work- and precipitation-hardening properties, improves resistance to wear, vibration, and mechanical breakdown, and imparts resistance to corrosion. These properties are utilized in marine-cable sheathing, where tellurium refines the grain size and improves mechanical properties without impairing corrosion resistance. It successfully replaces tin (1–3% Sn) in the sheathing. Thinner sheaths can be extruded, and the extrusion pressure for 0.05% Te lead is about the same as for a 3% Sn alloy. Tellurium is added as a master lead–tellurium alloy, containing a convenient percentage of tellurium in such quantity as to give a final concentration of about 0.06% Te.

The enhanced corrosion resistance of tellurium–lead brought about its widespread use in the chemical industry, especially in equipment that is exposed to sulfuric acid (see also Lead alloys).

Other Metals. Adding 0.1–1% Te to tin improves the work-hardening properties, the tensile strength, and the creep resistance. Tellurium also controls structure and improves uniformity and fatigue resistance in babbitt-type alloys by restricting the tendency to segregate.

Tellurium has been recommended as an additive to magnesium to increase corrosion resistance. The addition is highly exothermic but can be controlled by adding one tellurium tablet at a time to a sufficiently large bath of liquid magnesium.

Thermoelectric Materials. Tellurium is a component of most thermoelectric materials designed for operation at normal temperatures. The most desirable alloys are bismuth–antimony–selenium–tellurium, although bismuth–tellurium and lead–tellurium compositions are also important. Thermoelectric materials offer the possibility of manufacturing various cooling or heating devices which have no moving parts and can be simply plugged into any convenient direct-current power source. Alternatively, thermoelectric devices can convert heat to electricity. There exist numerous specialized applications, such as small cooling boxes, water coolers, limited remote-power generators, solar-energy converters, and small-scale control apparatus. For large-scale applications, further improvements in materials and engineering design are necessary (see also Thermoelectric energy conversion).

Rubber. At one time the rubber industry provided the largest single outlet for tellurium, but now the new steel uses have taken a long lead. Powdered tellurium is used as a secondary vulcanizing agent in natural rubber and in styrene–butadiene. In many cases, adding 0.5% Te increases the rate of vulcanization and improves the aging and mechanical properties of sulfurless and low-sulfur stocks. Tellurium is particularly effective when used with tetramethylthiuram disulfide (bis(dimethylthio-carbamoyl)disulfide), $((CH_3)_2NCSS)_2$, and with selenium diethyldithiocarbamate (see also Selenium) in sulfurless cures. It is used frequently to eliminate porosity in thick-molded sections. Tellurium rubber is extremely resistant to heat and abrasion. It is used in all-rubber-jacketed portable cables in mining, dredging, welding, etc, and in conveyor belts for special applications.

Tellurium diethyldithiocarbamate, $((C_2H_5)_2NCSS)_4Te$, in combination with mercaptobenzothiazole, with or without tetramethylthiuram disulfide, is the fastest known accelerator for butyl rubber. It is used extensively in butyl tubes for buses and similar vehicles and in other butyl applications.

Miscellaneous. Tellurium chloride, as well as tellurium dioxide in hydrochloric acid solution, is used to impart a permanent and attractive black antique finish to silverware, aluminum, and brass. In addition, small quantities of tellurium have been employed in glass and ceramics to produce blue to brown colors. Tellurium has also served as a base for ultramarine-type and cadmium sulfotelluride pigments (60). Patents have been granted for the use of tellurium in petroleum refining and in lubricants, and as a catalyst in the manufacture of organic chemicals (61,62). A tellurium preparation, similar to selenium sulfide, has also been developed for the control of seborrheic dermatitis of the scalp (63).

Low-melting glasses have been developed from tellurium dioxide and from the sulfides, selenides, and arsenides of the arsenic-group elements (64,65). Tellurium dioxide glasses have higher dielectric constants and better infrared transmission than ordinary silicate glasses; they are free of silicon but are more fragile. The chalcogenide glasses are dense, free of silicon and oxygen, and have high expansivity and high refractive indices. The uses of these glasses range from transparent insulators to silver-black semiconductors. Small quantities of tellurium have been used in lasers and as a dopant in semiconductors. Tellurium rectifiers have been patented (66).

Since 1955, tellurium has been used in delay electric blasting caps, where the controlled and predictable behavior of all reactive components is critically important. The caps offer a range of delay firings from 0.012 to 15.6 sec. Selenium and tellurium, in a mixture with lead, act as oxidants in gasless ignition charge; and, in combination with barium peroxide, act as reductants for the fuse powder (67,68) (see also Selenium).

Cuprous telluride, Cu_2Te, and cobalt telluride, $CoTe$, have been reported as useful outdoor fungicides for textiles (69).

A very small, yet very important application of tellurium is in making radioactive iodine isotopes for the treatment of thyroid gland diseases.

Bibliography

"Tellurium and Tellurium Compounds" in *ECT* 1st ed., Vol. 13, pp. 666–676, by E. M. Elkin, Canadian Copper Refiners Ltd., and J. L. Margrave, University of Wisconsin.

1. M. A. Weeks and H. M. Leicester, *Discovery of the Elements*, 7th ed., *J. Chem. Educ.*, Easton, Pa., 1968.
2. J. Newton Friend, *A Text-book of Inorganic Chemistry*, Vol. 7, Part 2, "Sulphur, Selenium, and Tellurium," Charles Griffin & Co., London, 1931.
3. J. W. Mellor, *A Comprehensive Treatise on Inorganic and Theoretical Chemistry*, Vol. 11, Longmans, Green & Co., Inc., London, 1931.
4. *Gmelins Handbuch der Anorganischen Chemie*, 8th ed., Deutsche Chemische Gesellschaft, Verlag Chemie, Berlin, System-Nummer 11, 1940.
5. D. M. Yost and H. Russell, Jr., *Systematic Inorganic Chemistry of the Fifth- and Sixth-Group Nonmetallic Elements*, Prentice-Hall, Inc., New York, 1944.
6. N. V. Sidgwick, *The Chemical Elements and Their Compounds*, Vol. 2, Oxford University Press, London, 1950.
7. P. Pascal, *Nouveau Traité de Chimie Minérale*, Tome 13, Deuxième Fascicule, Masson & Cie., Editeurs, Paris, 1960.
8. R. C. Brasted, *Comprehensive Inorganic Chemistry*, Vol. 8, D. Van Nostrand Co., Inc., Princeton, N. J., 1961.
9. A. F. Wells, *Structural Inorganic Chemistry*, 3rd ed., Oxford University Press, London, 1962.
10. D. M. Chizhikov and V. P. Shchastlivyi, *Telluri Telluridy* (Tellurium and the Tellurides), Nauka Publishing House, Moscow, 1966 (in Russian) (English translation in preparation).
11. K. W. Bagnall, *The Chemistry of Selenium, Tellurium, and Polonium*, Elsevier Publishing Co., Amsterdam, 1966.
12. L. S. Brooks, *J. Am. Chem. Soc.* **74**, 227–229 (1952).
    (a) N. B. Hannay, *Semiconductors*, Reinhold Publishing Corp., New York, 1959.
    (b) A. F. Ioffe, *Physics of Semiconductors*, Infosearch Ltd., London, 1960, and Academic Press, Inc., New York.
    (c) A. F. Ioffe, *Semiconductor Thermoelements and Thermoelectric Cooling*, Infosearch Ltd., London, 1957.
    (d) I. B. Cadoff and E. Miller, *Thermoelectric Materials and Devices*, Reinhold Publishing Corp., New York, 1960.
13. B. Mason, *Principles of Geochemistry*, 3rd ed., John Wiley & Sons, Inc., New York, 1966.
14. N. D. Sindeeva, *Mineralogy and Types of Deposits of Selenium and Tellurium*, Interscience Publishers, a division of John Wiley & Sons, Inc., New York, 1964.
15. A. M. Lansche, "Selenium and Tellurium—a Materials Survey," *U. S. Bur. Mines Inform. Circ. 8340*, Government Printing Office, Washington, D. C., 1967.
16. J. H. Schloen and E. M. Elkin, *Trans. AIME* **188**, 764–777 (1950); "Treatment of Electrolytic Copper Refinery Slimes," in A. Butts, ed., *Copper*, Reinhold Publishing Corp., New York, 1954, Chap. 11.

17. F. Benard, *Trans. AIME* **106**, 369–397 (1933); **159**, 521–529 (1944).
18. A. I. Gaev, T. S. Dolzhenko, and B. V. Trutnev, *Tsvet. Metal.* **11** (10), 64–70 (1938).
19. R. H. Waddington, *Can. Metals Met. Ind.* **3**, 153–8 and 190–2, 199 (1940).
20. M. Heberlein, *Metall u. Erz* **30**, 363–6 (1933).
21. J. H. Schloen and E. M. Elkin, *Trans. Can. Inst. Mining Met.* **49**, 143–90 (1946).
22. U. S. Pat. 2,349,697 (May 23, 1944), N. R. Brierly (to The American Metal Co. Ltd.).
23. U. S. Pat. 2,076,738 (April 13, 1936), O. C. Martin and C. W. Clark.
24. U. S. Pat. 2,258,963 (Oct. 14, 1941), W. G. Woll and R. T. Gore (to International Smelting & Refining Co.).
25. American Bureau of Metal Statistics, 4th Annual Issue for 1968, New York, 1969.
26. U. S. Dept. of the Interior, Bureau of Mines, *Minerals Yearbook* (published annually), Government Printing Office, Washington, D. C.
27. Canada Dept. of Energy, Mines and Resources, Mineral Resources Division, *Canadian Minerals Yearbook* (published annually), The Queen's Printer, Ottawa.
28. V. Lenher, in N. H. Furman, ed., *Standard Methods of Chemical Analysis*, Vol. 1, 5th ed., D. Van Nostrand Co., Inc., New York, 1939, pp. 775–93.
29. T. E. Green and M. Turley, in I. M. Kolthoff and P. J. Elving, eds., *Treatise on Analytical Chemistry*, Vol. 7, Part 2, Interscience Publishers, a division of John Wiley & Sons, Inc., New York, 1961, pp. 137–205.
30. D. I. Ryabchikov and I. I. Nazarenko, in I. P. Alimarin, *Analysis of High Purity Materials*, Israel Program for Scientific Information, Jerusalem, 1968.
    (a) K. L. Cheng, *Anal. Chem.* **33** (6), 761–764 (1961).
31. C. Duval and U. M. Doan, *Anal. Chim. Acta* **5**, 569–572 (1951).
32. P. W. Bennett and S. Barabas, *Anal. Chem.* **35** (2), 139–141 (1963).
33. F. A. Patty, ed., *Industrial Hygiene and Toxicology*, Vol. 2, Interscience Publishers, a division of John Wiley & Sons, Inc., New York, 1963.
34. N. J. Sax, *Dangerous Properties of Industrial Materials*, 3rd ed., Reinhold Publishing Corp., New York, 1968.
35. W. M. Gafafer, ed., *Occupational Diseases*, Publication No. 1097, U. S. Dept. of Health, Education, and Welfare, Public Health Section, Government Printing Office, Washington, 1964.
36. E. A. Cerwenka, Jr. and W. C. Cooper, *Arch. Environ. Health* **3**, 189–200 (1961).
37. *Inorganic Syntheses* (McGraw-Hill Book Co.) **1**, 121 (1939); **2**, 189 (1946); **3**, 140, 143, 145 (1950); **4**, 88, 93 (1953).
38. G. Brauer, *Handbook of Preparative Inorganic Chemistry*, Vol. 1, Academic Press, Inc., New York, 1963.
39. P. J. Durrant and B. Durrant, *Introduction to Advanced Inorganic Chemistry*, Longmans, Green & Co., London, 1962, p. 881.
40. J. Newton Friend, *A Text-Book of Inorganic Chemistry*, Vol. 11, Part 4, "Organometallic Compounds," Charles Griffin & Co., London, 1937, pp. 166–260.
41. E. Krause and A. von Grosse, *Die Chemie der Metallorganischen Verbindungen*, Bornträger, Berlin, 1937 (through reference 11).
42. *Organic Syntheses*, published annually since 1921, John Wiley & Sons, Inc., New York.
43. J. Houben, ed., *Die Methoden der Organischen Chemie (Weyls Methoden)*, Georg Thieme Verlag, Stuttgart, 1925–1941. (Reproduced by Edwards Brothers, Inc., Ann Arbor, Mich.)
44. V. Migrdichian, *Organic Syntheses*, Vols. 1 and 2, Reinhold Publishing Corp., New York, 1957.
45. U.S. Pats. 3,152,889 and 3,152,890 (Oct. 13, 1964), M. O. Holowaty (to Inland Steel Co.).
46. U.S. Pat. 3,169,857 (Feb. 16, 1965), A. E. Rathke and A. T. Morgan (to Inland Steel Co.).
47. U.S. Pats. 2,009,713–2,009,716 (July 30, 1935), F. R. Palmer (to Carpenter Steel Co.).
48. Brit. Pat. 510,757 (Aug. 8, 1939) Meehanite Metal Corp. and O. Smalley.
49. Brit. Pat. 552,390 (April 3, 1943), British Cast Iron Research Association, E. Morgan and E. Hinchcliffe.
50. U.S. Pats. 2,250,488 and 2,250,489 (July 29, 1941), C. H. Lorig and D. E. Krause (to Battelle Memorial Institute).
51. U.S. Pats. 2,253,502 (Aug. 26, 1941) and 2,331,886 (Oct. 19, 1943), A. L. Boegehold (to General Motors Corp.).
52. U.S. Pat. 2,281,460 (April 28, 1942), O. Smalley (to Meehanite Metal Corp.).
53. C. R. Austin, *Foundry* **77** (7), 74–7 (1949).

54. E. A. Loria, *Foundry* **79** (6), 126–9, 212, 214, 216, 218 (1951).
55. J. O. Vadeboncoeur, *Trans. Am. Soc. Metals*, Preprint No. 51 (1945).
56. U. S. Pat. 2,979,793 (April 18, 1961), R. L. Wilson, F. B. Herlihy, and T. J. Wood (to American Brake Shoe Co.).
57. U. S. Pat. 2,027,807 (Jan. 14, 1936) H. L. Burghoff and D. E. Lawson (to Chase Co., Inc.).
58. Kenneth Rose, *Materials and Methods* **23** (4), 1027–1042 (1946).
59. Brit. Pat. 441,524 (June 8, 1934), W. Singleton, W. Hulme, B. Jones, and Goodlass Wall and Lead Industries Ltd.
60. U.S. Pat. 3,012,899 (Dec. 12, 1961), A. Giordano (to Harshaw Chemical Co.).
61. V. Kollonitsch and C. H. Kline, *Hydrocarbon Process. Petrol. Refiners* **43** (6), 139–42 (1964).
62. U.S. Pat. 3,409,561 (Nov. 5, 1968), N. Ferlazzo, G. Caporali, and N. Giordano (to Montecatini Edison S.p.A.).
63. U.S. Pat. 2,933,432 (April 19, 1960), A. Lichtin.
64. G. W. Brady, *J. Chem. Phys.* **27** (7), 300–3 (1957).
65. A. D. Pearson, *Glass Ind.* **45** (12), 666–669, 712–713 (1964); **46** (1), 18–21 (1965).
66. U.S. Pat. 2,740,925 (April 3, 1956), C. A. Escoffery (to International Rectifier Corp.).
67. Can. Pat. 570,919 (Feb. 17, 1959), T. J. Mulqueeny (to Olin Mathieson Chemical Corp.).
68. U.S. Pat. 3,094,933 (June 25, 1963), D. T. Zebree (to Hercules Powder Co.).
69. R. J. Brysson, B. J. Trask, and A. S. Cooper, Jr., *Am. Dyestuff Reptr.* **57** (12), 23–4 (1968).

General References

A. A. Kudryavtsev, *Khimiya i Tekhnologiya Selena i Tellura* (Chemistry and Technology of Selenium and Tellurium), 2nd ed., Metallurgiya Publishing House, Moscow, 1968.

E. M. ELKIN
Canadian Copper Refiners Limited

TEMPERATURE MEASUREMENT

Temperature is a most important factor in our lives. It influences our physical well-being and our enjoyment of the outdoors, and also affects the direction and rate of many laboratory reactions and industrial processes.

Temperature is a basic concept in the theory and use of heat. If two bodies at different temperatures are placed in contact, heat will flow from the body at higher temperature to the body at lower temperature. For example, if you put your hand in a pail of hot water heat will flow from the water into your hand, warming it, and consequently you will know that the temperature of the water is higher than that of your hand. Conversely, if you put your hand in a pail of cold water heat will flow from your hand into the water, cooling your hand, and you will know that the water temperature is lower than that of your hand.

Temperature determines whether a substance such as water exists as a solid, liquid, or gas; it affects the volume of solids, liquids, and gases, and the electrical resistance of metals and insulators. Temperature is a controlling factor in most chemical reactions, and in the development of desired properties in metals and many other manufactured materials and products. The accurate measurement of temperature is therefore very important in modern science and industry. Special temperature scales and temperature measuring instruments have been devised to facilitate temperature measurements and to make sure that the numbers which we use to represent temperature are the same from time to time and from place to place.

Temperature Scales

Celsius and Fahrenheit Temperature Scales. The temperature scales most commonly used are the Celsius and the Fahrenheit. They were originally based on the melting point of ice and the boiling point of water, both under the standard pressure of 760 mm of mercury. On the Celsius scale, formerly called centigrade, these points were assigned the values of 0 and 100, respectively, while on the Fahrenheit scale they were designated as 32 and 212, respectively. Celsius and Fahrenheit temperatures can be interconverted by the formulas:

$$(°C) = [(°F) - 32]/1.8$$

$$(°F) = 1.8(°C) + 32$$

The following forms of the equations will be found convenient:

$$(°C) + 40 = [(°F) + 40]/1.8$$

$$(°F) + 40 = 1.8[(°C) + 40]$$

Two other scales, used extensively in technical and scientific practice, are based on experimental evidence that the volume of a perfect gas would be reduced to zero if its temperature were decreased to $-273.15°C$ ($-459.67°F$). This is the lowest possible temperature and is called *absolute zero*. The absolute or Kelvin temperature of a body is its temperature in Celsius degrees above absolute zero; that is, the *Kelvin temperature* is the Celsius temperature plus 273.15°. The absolute temperature of a body may also be expressed in Fahrenheit degrees. This is called the *Rankine temperature* and it is the Fahrenheit temperature plus 459.67°.

The Celsius and Fahrenheit scales have been named after the two scientists who originally developed them. Gabriel Daniel Fahrenheit, a German physicist, is credited with inventing the mercury-in-glass thermometer in 1714. Previously he had demonstrated with the use of an alcohol thermometer, that the freezing point of water was constant, that is, the level of the alcohol was always at the same point in a mixture of ice and water. He chose as the zero of his scale the lowest temperature which he could reproduce in the laboratory, that of a mixture of ice and common salt, and then he divided the range from zero to the temperature of the human body into twelve divisions. Later, Fahrenheit found that the divisions were of more convenient size if he made them one-eighth as large as the original divisions. This made body temperature 96 divisions. With his new mercury thermometer Fahrenheit could extend his scale to the boiling point of water which he demonstrated was constant at 212 divisions. During the next century the standard of temperature measurement was the mercury-in-glass thermometer with its scale divided linearly over the 180° interval from the freezing point of water (32°) to its boiling point (212°). The Fahrenheit scale is still used in most English-speaking countries for everyday household and industrial measurements. In 1742 Anders Celsius, a Swedish astronomer, divided his thermometer scale into 100 divisions (or degrees) between the freezing point of water which he called 0° and the boiling point which he called 100°. This scale was adopted by scientists and was known as the centigrade scale in southern Europe and in English-speaking countries. It was called the Celsius scale in Scandinavia, Russia, Japan, the Netherlands, and German-speaking countries. In 1948 the Ninth General Conference on Weights and Measures, representing thirty-three nations that subscribed to the Treaty of the Meter, adopted the name Celsius for this scale. This action was taken in the interest of uniformity of practice. The change to Celsius made the whole system of temperature scales more consistent by naming this scale after the inventor rather than designating it by a descriptive term such as centigrade or centesimal. But this change has been recognized and accepted only very slowly by American scientists and engineers, and even today the designation centigrade is still frequently used.

The use of the pressure of a gas confined in a fixed volume as a measure of its temperature was being explored even before the invention of the mercury-in-glass thermometer. The precision of the gas thermometer was slowly improved and in 1887 the International Committee of Weights and Measures adopted the centigrade scale of the hydrogen thermometer as the international standard. The most accurate mercury-in-glass thermometers available at that time were used to define a mercury-in-glass scale which did not agree exactly with the hydrogen scale. Corrections were devised and mercury thermometers were used as standards, their readings being corrected to the hydrogen scale, so that the standard hydrogen scale could be reproduced in many laboratories without the need for a multiplicity of hydrogen thermometers. The standard range was limited to that between 0 and 100°C, the best reproducibility was about ±0.002°C, and there were differences of as much as 0.01°C between different "standard" thermometers. Even at this early date, the need for an international standard was recognized, and it was realized that the standard scale must be transferred to portable thermometers.

Thermodynamic Temperature Scale. The fundamental importance of the concept of temperature was demonstrated with the development of the theory of thermodynamics. Lord Kelvin showed in 1848 that it was possible to define temperature in terms of energy, and he proposed the thermodynamic scale which is independent of the properties of any particular substance. His development of this scale was based on the theory of the perfect heat engine employing the Carnot cycle. If this engine operates with its source at 100°C and its sink at 0°C, a certain amount of work is done during each cycle. If the same engine, operating through a certain temperature interval, does one-hundredth as much work as between 100 and 0°, that temperature interval is 1 deg. This is true no matter where the interval is taken on the temperature scale, above or below 0°C.

Lord Kelvin also showed that the ideal gas scale, based on the performance of a perfect gas which obeys Boyle's law and Charles' law, is identical with the thermodynamic scale. This gas scale can be realized in a laboratory with a gas thermometer using a real gas at constant pressure or constant volume. If readings are taken over a range of different pressures and the results are extrapolated to very low pressure, they will agree with the ideal gas scale. The thermodynamic temperatures have been determined, by means of gas thermometers, for a large number of fixed points such as the triple points, melting points, and boiling points of pure substances. A triple point, where the solid, liquid, and gas phases of a pure substance are in equilibrium, is achieved by isolating this pure substance in a hermetically sealed container and giving it a temperature treatment such that the three phases exist simultaneously in the container. Triple points are ideal for use as fixed points because they can be reproduced at will, and the temperature is independent of the surroundings. Freezing points are preferred to boiling points because they are disturbed less by changes in atmospheric pressure.

The Kelvin thermodynamic temperature scale as originally established was based on the fundamental interval of 100°C between the freezing point and the boiling point of water. The temperatures of other fixed points were determined by gas thermometers calibrated on this same fundamental interval. The zero of this scale is that temperature at which all of the heat has been extracted from the working substances used in the Carnot cycle; this temperature is also the zero of the perfect gas thermometer. It was determined that this zero point was −273.15°C. But, as Lord Kelvin had pointed out in 1854, a fundamental absolute scale should have only one fixed point in addition to zero. In 1954, a hundred years later, the Kelvin thermodynamic scale was redefined by giving the value 273.16 to the triple point of water. The unit of the scale was changed to the kelvin, represented by the symbol K, and defined as the fraction 1/293.16 of the thermodynamic temperature of the triple point of water. This triple point was chosen as the single fixed point because it had been found to be the most accurately and easily reproducible point of all the fixed points which had been determined. As a result of this action, the fundamental interval 0–100°C lost its basic significance, and the freezing point of water, 0.01°C below the triple point, lost its position as a primary fixed point.

The thermodynamic scale, although satisfactorily rooted in theory, is experimentally the most cumbersome. A gas thermometer suitable for use as a primary standard is a complicated piece of equipment. It must be operated with painstaking care and corrections must be applied to all of the readings. Consequently this thermometer can be used only in a special laboratory, and its principal use has been in the determination of fixed-point temperatures on the thermodynamic scale. For practical temperature measurements it has been necessary to employ other types of thermometers and to develop means of relating temperature measurements with these other thermometers to the thermodynamic temperature scale.

The International Practical Temperature Scale of 1968. The International Temperature Scale adopted in 1927 was intended to be as nearly identical with the thermodynamic scale as was possible. It was based upon six fixed points which were assigned their thermodynamic temperatures. The scale was divided into three major ranges, and in each range the method of measuring temperature was specified for the most precise modern thermometer suitable for use in this range. The temperatures of the fixed points and the methods of interpolating were revised in 1948, and in a text revision of 1960, procedural changes were made and the name of the scale was changed to the International Practical Temperature Scale of 1948 (IPTS-48) (1).

As the accuracy of determining thermodynamic temperatures improved during the years following 1948 and the thermodynamic temperatures of many fixed points were revised, it became apparent that the temperature values assigned to several fixed points on IPTS-48 differed from their true thermodynamic temperatures by amounts much greater than the obtainable limits of accuracy. This led to another revision of the practical temperature scale by the General Conference of Weights and Measures, in 1968. The resulting International Practical Temperature Scale of 1968 (IPTS-68) has the defining fixed points given in Table 1. The estimated uncertainties of these

Table 1. Defining Fixed Points, International Practical Temperature Scale of 1968

Assigned values		Defining fixed points	Estimated uncertainty, K
K	°C		
1337.58	1064.43	freezing point, gold	0.2
1235.08	961.93	freezing point, silver	0.2
692.73	419.58	freezing point, zinc	0.03
505.1181	231.9681	freezing point, tin	0.015
373.15	100	boiling point, water	0.005
273.16	0.01	triple point, water	exact by definition
90.188	−182.962	boiling point, oxygen	0.01
54.361	−218.789	triple point, oxygen	0.01
27.102	−246.048	boiling point, neon	0.01
20.28	−252.87	boiling point, equilibrium hydrogen	0.01
17.042	−256.108	17.042°K point[a]	0.01
13.81	−259.34	triple point, equilibrium hydrogen	0.01

[a] Equilibrium between the liquid and vapor phases of equilibrium hydrogen at a pressure of 33,330.6 nm^{-2} (25/76 standard atmosphere).

fixed points are also given in Table 1. Except for the triple point of water and the boiling point of water, all of the fixed points have been changed by amounts much larger than the present uncertainties. With these changes in the fixed points and with the modifications which have been made in the defining equations used to measure intermediate temperatures, all temperatures measured on IPTS-68 agree with the true thermodynamic temperatures within the limits of the present accuracy of measurement of the absolute thermodynamic temperatures. The platinum resistance thermometer is used as the primary standard from −259.34°C, the lowest temperature defined on IPTS-68, to 630.74°C. The Pt-90% Pt,10% Rh thermocouple is the primary standard from 630.74 to 1064.43°C, the freezing point of gold. The optical pyrometer is the primary standard for temperatures above 1064.43°C.

In the United States the National Bureau of Standards (NBS) has the responsibilities of establishing the primary temperature scale and of disseminating calibration information. This is done by the distribution of standard reference materials which undergo observable transitions at specific temperatures, and by using the primary scale and associated primary instruments to make secondary calibrations on portable temperature measuring instruments which are then used throughout the country as secondary standards (2). This service is of great value to scientists and industrial personnel who wish to measure and maintain accurate values of temperature. It is especially important to manufacturers of temperature measuring instruments who can use the standard reference materials and secondary standard instruments in their own plants to calibrate the instruments which they make. The result is that almost all temperature measuring instruments in use in this country today have calibrations traceable to NBS and therefore based on the same primary scale.

The complete text of IPTS-68 has been published in the April 1969 issue of *Metrologia* (3). A short article has appeared in *Nature* (4), and a brief note in the *NBS Technical News Bulletin* (5). Each of these publications gives a table of approximate differences between IPTS-68 and IPTS-48. It is expected that almost all calibrations made during and after late 1969 will be in accord with IPTS-68.

Measurements Based on Expansion

Liquid-in-Glass Thermometers. The most widely used instrument for the measurement of temperatures, in the range of temperatures from about -170 to $+500°C$, is the liquid-in-glass thermometer which consists of a small-bore glass tube with a thin-walled bulb at its lower end and contains sufficient mercury, alcohol, or other fluid to fill the bulb and partially fill the tube. The fluid level in the tube rises and falls with increase or decrease of the temperature of the fluid in the bulb. The upper end of the tube is sealed although it often terminates in a small bulb or reservoir to hold fluid which rises to the top of the tube when the thermometer is overheated, thus safeguarding against bursting. Graduations, engraved on the wall of the tube or on an associated scale, are calibrated in terms of temperature corresponding to the level of the top of the liquid column.

Mercury is the liquid commonly used for temperatures above its freezing point $(-39°C)$. An organic liquid, eg, an alcohol, with a low freezing point must be used to measure lower temperatures. When the mercury thermometer is to be used to measure high temperatures, the space above the mercury column is filled with nitrogen at a pressure of 30–300 psi to prevent evaporation or boiling of the mercury that would cause errors in calibration. The liquid-in-glass thermometer is suitable only for visual readings which are recorded only to the extent that maximum and minimum temperatures experienced since the last resetting can be indicated by iron floats moved by the mercury column and left by it at the highest or lowest position attained.

The glass of the thermometer must be selected for stability, and must be very thoroughly annealed. The bulb, at high temperature and pressure, is subject to a permanent increase of volume, causing the thermometer indication to be too low.

The most accurate mercurial thermometers are graduated and calibrated for the total immersion of all the mercury, including that in the stem, at the temperature being measured. If part of the mercury column extends outside the region in which the temperature is being measured, a correction based on the length in degrees of the emergent column, on the difference in temperature between the emergent column and the bulb, and on the relative expansion of mercury and glass, must be applied to the reading.

Table 2 states the graduation intervals appropriate for the temperature ranges listed, the tolerances allowed by the NBS in issuing reports of calibration, the accuracies which may be expected from the ranges and types represented, and the decimal figure to which the corrections are stated in the report. This table has been compiled using data given in NBS Monograph 90, *Calibration of Liquid-in-Glass Thermometers* (6). In this table "accuracy" refers to the best temperature measurement which can be made when all corrections are applied. "Tolerance" is the maximum scale error allowed, and these tolerances have been accepted by the makers of precise mercury thermometers. They represent good manufacturing practice without imposing undue hardship on the manufacturers.

The values given in Table 2 apply only to the highest-grade mercury thermometers which are the only ones admitted for certification by NBS. A typical chemical thermometer with a range from -5 to $+150°C$ graduated in 1-deg intervals has a tolerance of ±1 deg.

Beckman Thermometer. The Beckman differential thermometer has a scale about 1 ft long, with a total range of 5 or 6 deg C in 0.01-deg divisions. It is so con-

Table 2. Tolerances for Celsius Total Immersion Mercury Thermometers

Temp range, °C	Graduation interval, °C	Tolerance, °C	Accuracy, °C	Corrections stated to, °C
Thermometers for low temperature				
−35 to 0	1 or 0.5	0.5	0.1–0.2	0.1
−35 to 0	0.2	0.4	0.02–0.05	0.02
Thermometers graduated under 150°C				
0 up to 150	1 or 0.5	0.5	0.1–0.2	0.1
0 up to 150	0.2	0.4	0.02–0.05	0.02
0 up to 100	0.1	0.3	0.01–0.03	0.01
Thermometers graduated under 300°C				
0 up to 100	1 or 0.5	0.5	0.1–0.2	0.1
above 100 up to 300	1 or 0.5	1.0	0.2–0.3	0.1
0 up to 100	0.2	0.4	0.02–0.05	0.02
above 100 up to 200	0.2	0.5	0.05–0.1	0.02
Thermometers graduated above 300°C				
0 up to 300	2	2	0.2–0.5	0.2
above 300 up to 500	2	4	0.5–1.0	0.2
0 up to 300	1 or 0.5	2	0.1–0.5	0.1
above 300 up to 500	1 or 0.5	4	0.2–0.5	0.1

structed that a portion of the mercury in the bulb can be transferred to a reservoir so as to bring the top of the mercury column into the graduated section, for the various temperature ranges in which differences may be measured. It is used only for measuring differences in temperature. The accuracy attainable is estimated to be between 0.002 and 0.005 deg in the measurement of any interval within the limits of the scale.

Bimetallic strip thermometers consist of a strip made up of two metals with widely differing coefficients of thermal expansion welded or brazed together face to face throughout their length. The strip may be nearly straight, or it may be formed into a spiral to obtain greater sensitivity. A rise in temperature changes the curvature of the strip since the two metals expand at different rates. The low-expansion metal is usually a nickel–iron alloy called Invar. Invar is a registered trademark of the Soc. Anon. de Commentry-Fourchambault et Decazeville (Aciéries d'Imphy). The high-expansion metal, for temperatures up to about 125°C, may be brass. For higher temperatures, up to about 425°C, the high-expansion metal is generally a nickel steel or a nickel-chromium steel. The response to temperature changes is nearly linear, and errors inherent in the strip are slight. If one end is fixed, a pointer linked to the free end can be caused to move over a scale calibrated in temperature, or a pen can be made to move across a moving chart to record the temperature. Care must be exercised in the design of this instrument or the mechanical linkage may introduce appreciable errors. Bimetallic strips are also commonly used to actuate electrical contacts to control the temperature of rooms, air baths, or ovens. In one form the bimetallic strip is a spiral inside a slender metal tube, and the indicating pointer moves over a circular calibrated scale, coaxial with the tube. It can replace the mercury thermometer for many uses.

Filled-System Thermometers

Gas-Filled Thermometers. The constant-volume gas thermometer, mentioned in connection with the establishment of the thermodynamic temperature scale, belongs to the category of gas-filled thermometers and is the most precise of this type. It is not used outside of standardizing laboratories because of its complexity and size. For industrial use a gas-pressure thermometer consists of a pressure-measuring element of the Bourdon tube type (see Pressure measurement) connected by capillary tubing to a bulb which is exposed to the temperature to be measured. The system is filled under pressure with an inert gas, usually nitrogen. Since the pressure of a gas in a closed container is proportional to its absolute temperature, the measuring element can be calibrated in temperature degrees, with a uniformly divided scale. Since the gas in the measuring element and in the connecting tube is not at the temperature of the bulb, the bulb volume must be large so that the errors introduced by differences of temperature of the pressure-measuring element and the capillary may be insignificant. It should have at least forty times the volume of the rest of the system. Because of this fact, and because of the lag in transmitting pressure changes through the capillary, the length of the latter is limited to a maximum of 200 ft, and is preferably much shorter.

The initial pressure in the gas thermometer is usually between 150 and 500 psi. The torque produced is then ample to operate a recording pen when the scale span is 400 deg F or more. Scale spans of less than 120 deg F are not recommended. With a scale span of 400 deg C, or more, the reproducibility of readings is on the order of $\pm \frac{1}{4}\%$ of the span. The response time tends to be long, partly because of the necessity of transmitting pressure changes through a tube of fine bore and partly because of the large volume and poor thermal conductivity of the nitrogen. To give sufficient volume, the bulb usually has a diameter of $\frac{7}{8}$ in., resulting in slow response. Response time may be reduced by securing the desired volume by the use of a long, $\frac{1}{4}$ in. tube, usually in the form of a 2 in. coil.

Temperature may be indicated by a pointer moving over a graduated scale, or recorded on a circular chart by a pen actuated by the pressure-measuring element. Scale spans for the recorders are rarely less than 200 deg F, but for indicators the range may be narrower.

Variations in barometric pressure normally are not large enough to appreciably affect the indications, but major changes in altitude must be corrected for in calibration.

Gas-pressure thermometers are used at temperatures between $-450°$F and $+1000°$F, which fall partially or entirely outside the limits for vapor-pressure systems, and for applications where their lesser accuracy and larger bulb size do not, for the particular application, outweigh the higher cost of the liquid-expansion type.

Vapor-Pressure Thermometers. Vapor-pressure thermometers make use of the fact that, in a closed vessel which contains nothing but a liquid and its vapor, the liquid partially fills the enclosure, and the pressure is dependent only on the nature of the liquid and on its temperature. Very extensive use is made of this relationship between vapor pressure and temperature in the measurement and recording of industrial temperatures. The vapor-pressure thermometer resembles the gas-pressure thermometer in consisting of a bulb, a connecting tube of fixed length, usually from 5 to 250 ft long, and a pressure-sensitive element. The bulb is partly filled with a fluid with a boiling point low enough to produce a working pressure of 75–500 psi in the temperature range to be covered. The upper end of the range must be lower than the critical point of the liquid. Various liquids such as methyl chloride, sulfur dioxide, ether, ethyl alcohol, and toluene are used. They are selected for suitable vapor pressure vs temperature relationships and inertness to metals in the system and availability in a pure form. Such liquids are available covering a range from 180 to 300°C.

Vapor pressure increases with temperature more rapidly as the temperature rises so that the vapor pressure-temperature curve is nonlinear, and charts graduated in temperature have their degree marks much farther apart at the upper end of the range than at the lower. A recorder with a chart range from 10 to 100°C may have graduations 2 deg C apart from 10 to 40°C, and only half a degree apart from 40 to 100°C. Readability is poor at the low end of the range. The reproducibility of vapor-pressure thermometers is on the order of $\pm 1\%$ and in some cases considerably better.

The level of the bulb with respect to the pressure-measuring device is important because, if the temperature of the connecting tube is below the temperature of the bulb, filling-liquid will condense in the connecting tubing. The pressure-measuring device is subjected to the vapor pressure in the bulb plus the hydrostatic head of the column of liquid if the bulb is above the measuring device, or to the vapor pressure in the bulb minus the hydrostatic head if the bulb is below the measuring device. If the operating temperature of the bulb is higher than the temperature of the pressure-measuring device, then the instrument is calibrated for a definite difference of level. Corrections must be applied if the elevation of the bulb is changed.

A major weakness in this type of measuring system is the upset due to shifting of the liquid from the bulb to pressure element or the reverse as the measured temperature crosses the temperature of the instrument.

Liquid-Expansion Thermometers. In a liquid-expansion thermometer the system is completely filled with a suitable liquid. The thermometer consists of a bulb connected by capillary tubing to an element in the shape of a Bourdon helix or spiral which is located in the case of the instrument. An increase in temperature causes expansion of the liquid, the element uncoils to provide the increased volume, and the instrument reading rises. The filling-pressure selected must be such that the boiling point of the liquid is appreciably higher than the top temperature that the system is to measure. Temperatures can be measured from −175 to +300°C (and 550°C for mercury). Although the volume changes are relatively small, the forces exerted can be great for actuating the element, and therefore this type of measurement is considered good for controllers requiring a high degree of stability. Reproducibility on the order of $\frac{1}{4}$ of 1% can be expected.

The major source of error in this type of measurement is the thermal expansion of the liquid not in the bulb. When the tubing length is short, the error is mostly in the Bourdon element, and a bimetal correction element is normally placed in the case to compensate for this error. When the capillary tubing is long either one of two methods is used for correction: (1) A central wire is placed in the capillary tubing and runs along its full length; this wire has a relative expansion coefficient that corrects for the change in volume of the liquid. Normally that is used only in mercury-filled systems. (2) A second capillary tube, closed off at the end rather than having a bulb attached, is run parallel to the capillary from the bulb and operates an identical helical Bourdon in the instrument case. The tube is linked with the original element so that any expansion in this correction capillary end element subtracts from the other system and thereby corrects for the expansion everywhere in the measuring bulb.

Any thermal expansion of the bulb is automatically included in the calibration of the system. The thermal expansion of the capillary tube and sensitive element is completely negligible.

Electrical Methods

Resistance Thermometer. The laboratory-type resistance thermometer, used for the most precise practical temperature measurements, has a carefully mounted and protected sensing element of pure platinum wire with double leads at each end. The International Practical Temperature Scale (IPTS-68) is defined, from 0 to 630.74°C, in terms of the ratio of the resistance of such a sensing element to its resistance at 0°C. There is a quadratic equation which may be used to determine an approximate temperature t':

$$W(t') = R_{t'}/R_0 = 1 + At' + Bt'^2$$

where $R_{t'}$ is the observed resistance, R_0 is the resistance at 0°C, and A and B are constants. The constants A and B can be determined for a particular thermometer by measurement of the resistance ratio $W(t')$ at the boiling point of water or the freezing point of tin, and at the freezing point of zinc. To find the IPTS-68 temperature t, it is necessary to use a correction-equation,

$$t = t' + 0.045 \left(\frac{t'}{100°\text{C}}\right)\left(\frac{t'}{100°\text{C}} - 1\right)\left(\frac{t'}{419.58°\text{C}} - 1\right)\left(\frac{t'}{630.74°\text{C}} - 1\right)°\text{C}$$

The correction introduced by this latter equation is less than 0.05 deg C within this temperature range, so measurements based on the quadratic equation without the correction may be expected to be accurate to within about ±0.1 deg C. Because of the complications introduced by the use of these equations it is much easier to use a computer-generated table giving the resistance ratio at 1 deg C intervals. Linear interpolation within the 1 deg C intervals will yield temperature values well within the limits of precision of the measurements. Tables of this nature are generally furnished as part of the calibration service supplied by NBS and other standardizing laboratories. A laboratory-type thermometer with a suitable calibration can be used to measure temperatures with an accuracy of better than ±0.01 deg C, and changes in temperature of 0.001 deg C are measurable.

The IPTS-68 is defined, from 13.81 to 273.15K, in terms of a standard reference function and equations giving the deviation of the resistance ratio of a particular thermometer from the reference function. Within this temperature range the calculations involved in realizing the IPTS-68 are very complicated, especially since the reference function is a twenty-degree polynomial. It is advisable to use a table with the resistance ratio at 1 deg C intervals. The most convenient table for this purpose is one supplied by a standardizing laboratory, representing the calibration of the particular thermometer being used for the temperature measurement. It is also possible to use a table for the reference function and make corrections to obtain the true temperature, using for these corrections the deviation equation appropriate at this temperature.

Figure 1 is a photograph of a laboratory-type platinum resistance thermometer. When it is used to calibrate temperatures from −183 to +500°C the element is enclosed in a Pyrex glass tube about 46 cm long, and when it is used to calibrate from −183 to +650°C a fused silica tube is used. A special thermometer used in low-tem-

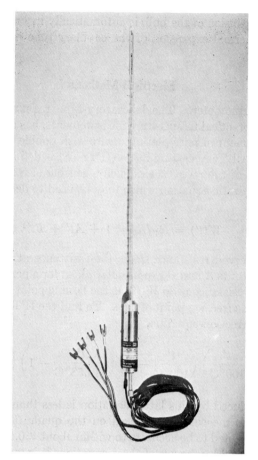

Fig. 1. Laboratory-type platinum resistance thermometer.

perature calorimetry from -261 to $+250°C$ has the sensitive element enclosed in a small platinum tube about 6 cm long. The value chosen for R_0 is usually approximately 25.5 ohms. Platinum increases in resistivity by about 0.39% of its resistivity at 0°C per deg C rise in temperature. At 100°C the value of the resistance R will therefore be about 35.5 ohms, an increase of 10 ohms, or of 0.1 ohm per degree. To measure to 0.01 deg C with an error of less than 1% it should be possible to measure R to the nearest 0.00001 ohm. Such resistance measurements require measuring equipment of the highest attainable precision, maintained at a uniform temperature and carefully calibrated. The measuring instrument may be either a specially designed Wheatstone bridge or a precise potentiometer. The Mueller bridge is commonly used for precise measurements, although equally good precision can be attained with a suitable potentiometer.

It is important to measure the resistance by a method which gives the resistance of a platinum coil, independent of lead resistance. Two leads are attached to each end of the platinum coil for the potentiometric method of measurement. The potentiometer measures the potential drop of a known current through the platinum coil. The bridge method of measuring thermometer resistance is illustrated in Fig. 2. The bridge current is supplied by one or more dry cells, E. Balance is detected by a

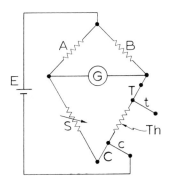

Fig. 2. Bridge measurement of thermometer resistance.

galvanometer G.   There are two equal arms, A and B.   The sensing element of the thermometer, Th, is in one leg, and the fourth leg of the bridge has a standard resistor, S, adjustable in very fine steps.   The four leads of the thermometer are labeled c, C, T, and t.   The connection shown may be called the normal connection.   Lead C is in the standard leg, lead T is in the thermometer leg, and lead c is the battery connection.   A balance is made with this thermometer connection and the resistance of S is recorded. Then the thermometer connections are reversed end for end so that T is in the stan-

Fig. 3. Industrial platinum resistance thermometer.

dard leg, C is in the thermometer leg, and t is the battery connection. A balance is made with this reversed thermometer connection and S′, the new value of S, is recorded. The mean of the two recorded resistance values is the true resistance of the sensing element.

Industrial Resistance Thermometers. For industrial temperature measurements, resistance thermometers are available with the platinum sensing elements inbedded in ceramic inside a protective metal casing (Fig. 3). They are used either bare or in protecting metal wells, mounted in flat or curved walls, in the bottoms or lids of furnaces, in ovens, kilns, lehrs (in glass manufacturing), tanks, or pipes. A heavy metal head is generally provided to protect the lead connections. Three carefully matched leads allow bridge measurements of resistance without the complication of reversing the connections. The calibrations of these industrial resistance thermometers are matched to standard tables of resistance vs temperature supplied by instrument manufacturers. Over the range of -190 to $+550°C$ the thermometers can be used for temperature measurements accurate to $±0.3\%$ of the total range, and for shorter spans to $±0.2\%$. They can be used with special indicators and recorders, generally making bridge-type measurements, which are calibrated to read directly in temperature. Matched copper leads can be run for long distances so that from one central location temperatures can be measured at many widely distributed remote points in a building or in a production process. Nickel and copper resistance thermometers are also used in many industrial temperature measurements.

Thermistors. Sensing elements made of semiconducting materials having high temperature coefficients of resistance are called thermistors. Their high coefficients give them a much greater sensitivity to small temperature changes than can be obtained with pure metal sensing elements. In addition to high sensitivity, thermistors have the advantage of very high room-temperature resistance which eliminates the need for lead-wire compensation. Their size and shape can be varied to give fast speeds of response. Also if they are mass-produced they cost much less than metal sensing elements. Thermistors are used to make approximate temperature measurements, and to measure small temperature differences, but they cannot approach the accuracy and reproducibility of metal resistance thermometers.

Thermoelectric Thermometers (Thermocouples)

If two wires of different materials are in good electrical contact at a pair of ends and the junction is heated, an electromotive force (emf) is developed. The two wires form a thermocouple. If the other two ends are joined through a current-detecting instrument, it is found that a current flows in this closed circuit as long as the heated junction is hotter than the other (reference) junction. If the reference junction is kept at a constant known temperature, the emf generated depends upon the temperature of the hot junction and can be used as a measure of this temperature. This constitutes a thermoelectric thermometer. If the circuit has a constant resistance, the current can be used as a measure of the emf. The current-measuring instrument can be graduated in millivolts, or, for a given thermocouple and reference junction temperature, in the temperature of the measuring junction. This is the millivoltmeter or deflection method which presupposes that the resistance of the circuit remains unchanged. The emf may preferably be measured by balancing it against a known emf by means of a potentiometer (see Electroanalytical methods). In this case no current flows in the thermocouple circuit and the emf measurement is independent of the circuit resistance.

The most commonly used thermocouples have been given letter designations by the Instrument Society of America, in order to avoid the use of trade names in specifications. These letter designations have been adopted universally in the United States and have been used in standards published by the American Society for Testing and Materials (ASTM) and the United States of America Standards Institute (USASI). The standard types and their ranges are listed below. The nominal compositions of the noble metal thermocouples (Types B, R, and S) and the original names of the base metal thermocouples (Types E, J, K, and T) are given in parentheses. Standard tables of emf vs temperature have been published for these thermocouples. These tables are the actual specifications. For example any thermocouple which matches the Type K table is a Type K thermocouple regardless of the emf-vs-temperature characteristics of the individual alloys forming the two legs.

Type S (Pt–$Pt_{90}Rh_{10}$), the most important thermocouple because of its accuracy and reproducibility from 0 to 1500°C, is chemically inert and is stable in oxidizing atmospheres. It is used to define the IPTS from the freezing point of antimony (630.74°C) to the gold point (1064.43°C). It has a thermoelectric power of about 10 μV per deg C which is less than that of base-metal thermocouples but is adequate with modern instrumentation. It is not used below 0°C because its thermoelectric power becomes very small at low temperatures. It must never be exposed to reducing atmospheres at temperatures above 500°C because it deteriorates as a result of gas absorption and of deposition on it of metals reduced from the oxides of the protecting tube and ceramic insulators.

Type R (Pt–$Pt_{87}Rh_{13}$) is inert and stable, like the Type S, but it is not used as a standard and has only limited industrial use. It was introduced to match instrument scales which had been established for thermocouples of nominal composition Pt–Pt_{90}-Rh_{10} which were later found to be impure. The use of pure thermocouple wires reduced the emf, but the substitution of $Pt_{87}Rh_{13}$ for the $Pt_{90}Rh_{10}$ alloy compensated this error and allowed the continued use of existing instruments.

Type T (copper vs Adams constantan) (constantan, so-called because of its low coefficient of resistance, is an alloy of about 57% copper and 43% nickel with fractional percentages of manganese and iron; Adams constantan is a variation which when paired with soft copper gives a thermocouple matching a table originally published by L. H. Adams) is usable at temperatures from −250 to +300°C, and for short periods up to 400°C. The thermoelectric power from −200 to −100°C is about 20 μV per deg C. It increases rather uniformly so that from 200 to 300°C it is about 55 μV per deg C. The Type T thermocouple is widely used in laboratory measurement at low temperatures. It fails at temperatures above 300°C because of the oxidation of copper.

Type J (iron–constantan) is the most widely used industrial thermocouple. The iron is not pure, but its composition is very carefully controlled by having small but definite amounts of manganese, copper, nickel, and carbon, and minimum amounts of chromium, sulfur, phosphorus, and silicon. The constantan differs slightly from Adams constantan. The Type J thermocouple is usable from −200 to about 760°C in oxidizing atmospheres and to about 980°C in reducing atmospheres. Its thermoelectric power increases rather uniformly from about 40 μV per deg C below 0°C to about 60 μV per deg C above 300°C.

Type K (formerly only the Chromel-Alumel (Hoskins Manufacturing Co.) thermocouple) is used to designate any thermocouple which matches the Chromel-Alumel tables within specified limits. Alloys which match these tables are available and are suitable for continuous use from about −190 to 1200°C and for short periods to 1300°C. The Type K thermocouple has a thermoelectric power of about 40 μV per deg C. Its long life in oxidizing atmospheres makes it the most useful of the base-metal thermocouples for measuring temperatures above 800°C. Reducing atmospheres and atmospheres containing sulfur dioxide or hydrogen sulfide are injurious, and this thermocouple deteriorates rapidly in atmospheres containing hydrogen or carbon monoxide.

Type E (formerly Chromel P vs Adams constantan) has recently been approved as a standard thermocouple by the United States of America Standards Institute (USASI). It has a thermoelectric power of about 80 μV per deg C from about 300 to 900°C, greater than that of any other thermocouple in general use. It is especially useful for differential temperature measurements because of this high thermoelectric power. Its stability is very good from 0 to 870°C.

Type B ($Pt_{70}Rh_{30}$–$Pt_{94}Rh_6$), a thermocouple recently recommended by USASI, can be used continuously for several hundred hours in the range from 1427 to 1705°C in oxidizing atmospheres, and intermittently for several hours up to 1800°C. The use of two alloy wires provides greater stability at these high temperatures than the Type R or Type S with one pure platinum wire, along with increased mechanical strength. The thermoelectric power in this high temperature range is about 11.5 μV per deg C. At lower temperatures the thermoelectric power decreases, approaching zero at 0°C, so the Type R and Type S thermocouples are preferred for measuring the lower temperatures. The Type B thermocouple has proved most reliable when used in a clean oxidizing atmosphere of air, but it has also been used in neutral atmospheres and in a vacuum.

In addition to the seven standard thermocouple types mentioned above, many other thermocouple combinations are available. The most important of these are the CoAu–silver normal thermocouple for cryogenic use and the $W_{95}Re_5$–$W_{74}Re_{26}$, W_{97}-Re_3–$W_{74}Re_{26}$, W-$W_{74}Re_{26}$, and Ir–$Ir_{40}Rh_{60}$ for high temperatures.

With the aid of the published tables, the temperature of the measuring junction can be determined by a measurement of the emf generated when the reference junction is held at the melting point of ice. Many commercially available measuring instruments designed for use with thermocouples are provided with special circuits so that the thermocouple wires can be connected directly to the instrument binding-posts. Then the reference junction is at the instrument and it is at the temperature of the instrument. By means of the special circuits compensation is made for the difference in the emf of the thermocouple caused by the divergence of the reference junction from 0°C.

The precision attainable in the measurement of temperature with thermocouples depends upon the precision of measurement of the emf and the accuracy upon the agreement of the particular thermocouple used with its standard table. Commercial base-metal thermocouples from stock are usually guaranteed to match the corresponding table to within ±0.75% of the measured emf at temperatures above 260°C and ±2.2°C below 260°C. Selected and calibrated thermocouples may match the table to ±0.375% and correspondingly accurate temperature measurements can be made if the potentiometric method of measuring emf is employed.

Individual Type S thermocouples (Pt–Pt$_{90}$Rh$_{10}$) are often calibrated individually by NBS. In these calibrations the emf of the thermocouple is determined at 1064.43°C (gold point), 961.93°C (silver point), 630.74°C, and 419.58°C (zinc point) with the reference junction at 0°C. The uncertainties in these emf values are estimated not to exceed 2 μV (about 0.2°C). From these values and using standard tables as a guide, tables are provided giving emf values of this individual thermocouple for every degree from 0 to 1450°C. The uncertainties in these values are estimated not to exceed 3 μV (about 0.3°C) in the range 0 to 1100°C and then increase to not more than 20 μV (about 2°C) at 1450°C. The calibration of such a thermocouple is subject to change during use. The magnitude of the change depends on such factors as the temperature, the length of time, and the conditions under which it is used. Therefore it is advisable to keep a calibrated thermocouple of this type as a secondary laboratory standard and use it only to calibrate other working thermocouples.

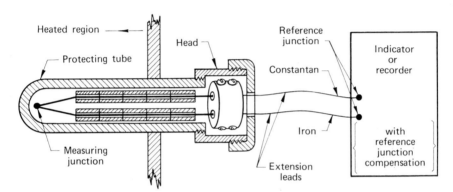

Fig. 4. Thermoelectric thermometer.

Structure of Thermocouples. The measuring junctions of thermocouples are usually welded. During the fabrication of base-metal thermocouples, types E, J, K, or T, the wires are often twisted together for two or three turns before welding to reduce strains on the weld, but it should be remembered that electrical contact of the wires, except at the weld, will introduce an error if there is a temperature difference between the weld and the point of contact. Base-metal thermocouples may be brazed or hard-soldered. The junctions of base-metal thermocouples, for many applications, may be made very quickly and conveniently with a special connector and hand-operated pressure tool. This pressure connection generally outlasts the wire, and its use has the advantage that the wires are not exposed to contamination or to thermal stresses. In the laboratory, when precise temperature measurements are being made, the thermocouple wires terminate in ice baths where they are joined to copper leads. These copper leads are then connected to a potentiometer, carefully designed to be free from spurious parasitic emf's. In this case the reference junctions are in the ice baths. In most industrial applications the maintenance of ice baths is impractical. The thermocouple wires or extension leads are connected to a measuring instrument which has a compensating circuit designed to provide the difference in emf caused by having the reference junction at ambient temperature rather than at the ice point (see Fig. 4). When automatic reference junction compensation is provided by a temperature-sensitive circuit the thermocouple connection is often made on a terminal board inside the instrument to assure that the compensating circuit and the reference junction are at the same temperature.

Extension Leads. The indicating or recording instrument must frequently be placed at a considerable distance from its thermocouple. The thermocouple wires are not suitably insulated and often are too large to be put in suitable conduits. Extension leads are provided for this purpose, properly insulated, and of suitable size. Preferably, the extension leads are of the same materials as the thermocouple wires to which they are joined. In the case of platinum vs platinum–rhodium this is too expensive, and leads of copper and of an alloy of nickel and copper are used. These have approximately the same thermoelectric characteristics as the thermocouple wires to which they are joined in the limited temperature range to which the reference junctions will be exposed.

Protecting Tubes. Although in some cases the thermocouple may be inserted in the region where the temperature is to be measured, such as an oil bath, without a protecting covering, in general the wires are insulated from each other and they are placed in a protecting tube. The insulating and tube materials used depend upon the temperature and the nature of the medium. For temperatures below 100°C enameled wires may be used. For temperatures up to 500°C a glass fiber insulation may be used. For use from the lowest to the highest temperatures the insulation may be ceramic tubes or beads. The protecting tube may be of metal, ceramic, graphite, etc, depending upon the temperature to be measured and the nature of the atmosphere or liquid in which it is placed. The function of the protecting tube is to keep the thermocouple in an atmosphere of dry air and to shield it from mechanical and chemical damage. Many varieties of protecting tubes are available and the manufacturer of thermocouples should be consulted as to which should be used in a particular application.

Pipe-Type (Coaxial) Thermocouples. Thermocouples are often constructed with one element, eg, iron in the form of a pipe, the other (constantan) being an insulated wire inside the pipe and welded to a plug that closes the lower end of the pipe. The iron pipe thus performs the functions of the protecting tube and, if coated with a thin film of chromium or a nickel–chromium alloy, is resistant to oxidation.

Surface Temperatures. One special application for thermocouples is the measurement of surface temperatures of stationary objects. A thermocouple junction held against the surface will approach the temperature of the surface and an approximate surface temperature can be obtained by reading the thermocouple temperature. A more accurate measurement of the surface temperature of a metal can be made if two small shallow holes are drilled close together and the thermocouple wires are inserted and peened into these holes. In this case the metal itself becomes a part of the junction, but this does not cause any error in the measurement. Both of the above methods are subject to error, however, because the thermocouple wires conduct heat away from the junction and this may reduce the junction temperature. This conductionerror can be reduced if the thermocouple wires can be kept close to the surface and thus they conduct less heat away from the junction. There is a special thermocouple probe available, having an automatically controlled heater which supplies the heat necessary to balance the conduction loss, so that the true surface temperature can be measured without any error due to heat conduction. This probe is especially useful in measuring the temperature of small objects such as the components of an electrical circuit which would be disturbed by contact with a conventional thermocouple.

Molten Metals. Temperatures of molten metals may be measured by thermocouples inserted into protecting tubes which have their closed ends immersed in the molten metal. It is often more convenient to use a small portable thermocouple with its measuring junction enclosed in a protective sheath. This thermocouple is dipped into the molten metal momentarily, only until a reading is obtained, and is then withdrawn. An expendable immersion thermocouple is available for use in open-hearth and other melting furnaces. A small cartridge containing the thermocouple junction and short lengths of the thermocouple wires is mounted on the end of a holder made from standard pipe. A cardboard tube is slipped over the pipe to protect it from the molten metal and slag. The operator plunges the end of the pipe with the cartridge through the slag and into the molten metal. The thermocouple junction reaches the temperature of the molten metal in about 5 sec and its temperature is recorded. The pipe is then withdrawn and the cartridge and cardboard tube are discarded and replaced for the next reading. The simplicity of this method and the complete lack of maintenance work at the furnace have made the expendable thermocouple a very economical and popular temperature measuring device. In another application, a small expendable crucible contains a thermocouple which measures the temperature of a molten metal which has been poured into the crucible. A recorder connected to the thermocouple produces a cooling curve from which the temperature of the liquidus arrest can be determined. In the case of steel, the temperature of this arrest, when corrected for the effect of alloying elements, gives the carbon content. The temperature of the arrest gives the carbon equivalent for ductile iron, gray iron, or malleable iron. Also, the cooling curves obtained with nonferrous alloys can often be used to determine the compositions of the alloys.

Uses. Thermocouples were first developed for use in pyrometry, that is, the measurement of temperature higher than 500°C, but they are now competitive with resistance thermometers and the various expansion and pressure types of thermometers in the lower ranges of temperature. They are competitive with radiation methods of measuring temperature up to about 1700°C. They are well adapted to the recording and control of temperature throughout this wide range, and are depended upon with a minimum of personal attention in a number of widely diversified fields of industry.

Precautions. Thermocouples should be made of wires obtained from reputable sources and carefully tested to match the appropriate emf vs temperature table. The installed thermocouple should be checked at suitable intervals. If a permanent thermocouple installation is to be made in a plant, lead wires should be run in grounded metal conduits. The lead wires themselves should have weatherproof, heat-resistant insulating coverings. All joints except at the thermocouple head should be soldered and taped. The leads should not be run through hot regions, for example, over the roof of a poorly insulated furnace. Where more than one thermocouple is to be monitored by a single measuring instrument, the selector switch should be of the double-pole variety, so that both thermocouple leads are disconnected from the circuit when it is transferred to another thermocouple.

Radiation Thermometry

Every solid body emits radiant energy. The intensity of the radiant energy increases if the temperature of the solid body is increased. This is the result of the increased molecular and atomic agitation at the higher temperature. The radiant energy may be sensed if one holds his hand near the heating element of an electric stove or if he walks from the shade into the bright sunlight. This radiant energy, generally called thermal radiation, can be measured and thus the temperature of the radiating body can be determined from a distance. The science of such measurements is called radiation thermometry.

The use of radiation thermometry is advantageous when access to the hot body is difficult, when touching it with a temperature detector would disturb it, or when its environment would disturb the reading of the temperature detector. Applications of the method include measurement of the temperature of moving objects such as billets of steel during the rolling process, and of small objects in a furnace atmosphere which would poison a thermocouple or in an induction furnace where electrical interference from the high-frequency field would make it impossible to obtain a reading from a thermocouple. Radiation thermometers can be used to measure very high temperatures because they are not in direct contact with the object being measured and therefore they do not have to be built to withstand this high temperature.

The Laws of Radiation. The radiation from a solid body may be influenced by its surface conditions or the surroundings. In order to prevent disturbing influences it is customary to consider a completely enclosed cavity with all of its walls at the same temperature. At every point on the internal surface of such a cavity, equilibrium will exist between the radiation which is emitted and that which is absorbed. The radiation which impinges on a surface element is exactly equal to that which emanates from the surface element, and is a function of the temperature alone. The radiation within the cavity is known as thermal radiation or blackbody radiation corresponding to the temperature of the walls. The cavity is called a blackbody.

A small hole may be provided in the wall of a cavity. If the hole is small enough and the cavity is properly designed, the disturbance of thermal equilibrium inside the cavity by the presence of the hole will be negligible, and the radiation emanating from the hole will have the same intensity as that existing within the cavity. The radiation from the hole will be thermal radiation or "blackbody" radiation corresponding to the temperature of the cavity.

The total energy radiating from a blackbody of unit area is given by the Stefan-Boltzmann law:

$$E = \sigma T^4$$

where T is the absolute temperature in kelvins and σ, the Stefan-Boltzmann constant, has the value 5.6697×10^{-12} W/cm^{-2} K^{-4}.

The radiation from a blackbody is distributed continuously over a wide range of wavelengths. The distribution changes with temperature, as is apparent when an object being heated first appears as a dull red, then changes color through orange and straw to a dazzling white. By the use of a spectroscope the radiation may be separated according to wavelength and displayed as a spectrum. If this is done, and if a heat detector such as a small thermometer or thermocouple is used to investigate the distribution of energy, it will be found that most of the radiant energy is beyond the red end of the visible spectrum, in the region called infrared.

If the spectral radiance $N_{b\lambda}$ is defined as the energy of blackbody radiation at a particular wavelength λ, then its value is given by the Planck radiation equation:

$$N_{b\lambda} = C_1 / \pi \lambda^5 \left[\exp \left(C_2 / \lambda T \right) - 1 \right]$$

where C_1 and C_2 are the first and second radiation constants, respectively.

Most real objects radiate, absorb, and reflect energy. If radiation strikes an object, a portion is absorbed and the remainder is reflected:

$$a + r = 1$$

where a represents the absorption coefficient, or the fraction of the incident radiation which is absorbed, and r represents the reflection coefficient, or the fraction of the incident radiation which is reflected. If the object is surrounded by a uniform field of radiation at temperature T, such as exists in a blackbody at this temperature, then it will reach temperature T. Thereafter it will be in equilibrium with this radiation field and it will radiate exactly as much energy as it absorbs. Since the surface of the object absorbs only a fraction a of the incident blackbody radiation, it must radiate this same fraction, which is called the emissivity and is generally represented by the symbol ϵ. It is seen that

$$\epsilon = a$$

and if we make a substitution in the first equation we obtain

$$\epsilon + r = 1$$

These relations were first expressed by Kirchhoff, and the latter equation relating emissivity and reflection coefficient is often called Kirchhoff's law.

It is clear, from the relations between absorption, reflection, and emissivity, that no real object can radiate more energy than a blackbody at the same temperature. In fact any object which exhibits measurable reflection must have an emissivity less than unity. Thus when it is in the open with cooler surroundings its emission will be less than blackbody radiation. This causes one of the most serious problems in the use of radiation thermometers, which are usually calibrated in terms of blackbody radiation.

The Optical Pyrometer. The optical pyrometer in most general use is the "disappearing-filament" pyrometer. Observations are made visually through a special telescope (Fig. 5). The objective lens forms a real image of the object under observation, or target, in the plane of a lamp filament. This filament and the superimposed image are viewed through a magnifying eyepiece. A red glass filter between the filament and the eye serves to cut off radiation of wavelength shorter than about 620 nm. The human eye is not sensitive to light of wavelength longer than about 720 nm so the

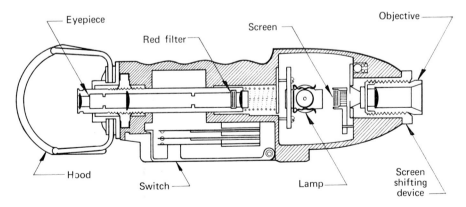

Fig. 5. Optical pyrometer telescope.

band of radiation used lies between these values. The effective wavelength is about 655 nm.

An auxiliary box is generally supplied as part of the pyrometer (Fig. 6). This box contains an adjustable current supply for the pyrometer lamp filament, and means for reading the current. An observation consists of adjusting the filament current until the filament has the same brightness as the superimposed image of the target, and then reading the current. The current-measuring means may be either a potentiometer or an indicating milliammeter. In a commercial optical pyrometer of the industrial type the scale is calibrated directly in degrees. The measuring circuit of such a pyrometer has been adjusted at the factory so that the scale reading matches the temperature of the target. Replacement lamps then may be supplied with auxiliary resistors and instructions for installing a new lamp so that correspondence between scale reading and target temperature is preserved.

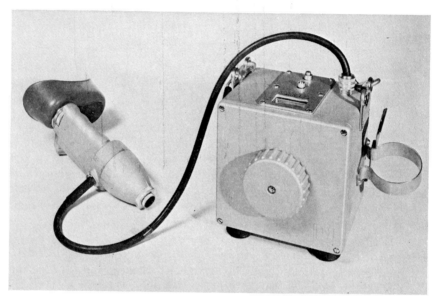

Fig. 6. Optical pyrometer.

In order to maintain the required stability of calibration, the filament temperature of the pyrometer lamp is limited to a maximum of about 1250°C. An absorbing glass inside the pyrometer may be interposed as a screen between the pyrometer lamp and the objective lens. This screen reduces the brightness of the target-image so that the filament brightness may be matched to it without overheating the filament. The apparent temperature S, obtained by using this screen, may be related to the true temperature T by using Wien's radiation equation which is sufficiently accurate for industrial temperature measurements, and which is obtained from Planck's equation by dropping the constant term (-1) in the denominator of the exponential. The apparent spectral brightness is then

$$N^1{}_{b\lambda} = \tau C_1 \lambda^{-5} \exp\left(-C_2/\lambda T\right) = C_1 \lambda^{-5} \exp\left(-C_2/\lambda S\right)$$

where τ is the transmission of the screen. From this equation the following relation may be obtained:

$$\frac{1}{S} - \frac{1}{T} = -\frac{\lambda}{C_2} \ln \tau = A$$

The absorbing glass which is generally used as a screen has a spectral transmission such that A is a constant over the band of wavelengths employed by the pyrometer. By using this constant A value, true temperature T may be computed from apparent temperature S, and a high-range calibration may be provided on the scale of the measuring instrument. With a series of such screens, the range of the optical pyrometer may be extended to extremely high temperature with confidence that it will agree with the IPTS, provided corrections are made for the divergence of Wien's radiation equation from Planck's law.

With an optical pyrometer of this type industrial temperature measurements are commonly made to an accuracy of ± 4 deg C from 800 to 1225°C and of ± 8 deg C up to 1750°C. Even inexperienced observers are consistent in their readings within 5 deg C at temperatures up to 1750°C and experienced observers in a darkened room are consistent to better than 1 deg C.

Other variable current optical pyrometers are available. Some employ the voltage drop through the filament or the resistance of the filament as a measure of the temperature of disappearance. Still another type, lighter and of more compact construction, is operated with the filament-current always at a fixed value. Disappearance of the filament is obtained by adjusting an absorbing wedge which is located between the objective lens and the filament, and thus reducing the apparent brightness of the source to that of the filament. The source temperature is read from a scale which moves with the wedge. The precision of this pyrometer is not as good as that of the adjustable-current types.

Automatic Optical Pyrometers. Recently developed automatic optical pyrometers employ a photoelectric detector and an electronic balancing system to achieve a balance between the brightness of an unknown target and that of the standard lamp. Figure 7 shows a comparison of the methods of balancing used in the manual optical pyrometer and a typical automatic optical pyrometer. In the sketch of the manual instrument the eye observes the image of the target superimposed on the lamp-filament. The brain tells the hand whether to increase or decrease the current in the filament to obtain a brightness match. When a match has been obtained the tempera-

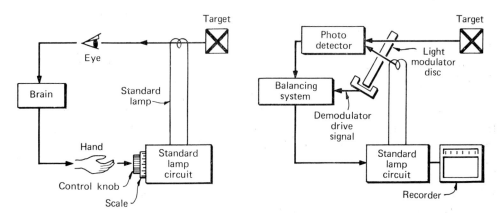

Fig. 7. Methods of balancing visual and automatic optical pyrometers.

ture can be read from the scale, or the filament current can be read by means of an auxiliary instrument not shown in the figure. In the automatic optical pyrometer a photoelectric detector is illuminated alternately by an image of the target and an image of the lamp filament. The signal from the detector is amplified, demodulated synchronously, and used to adjust the lamp current until a brightness match is achieved. A recorder is usually used to monitor the lamp current and may be calibrated in temperature or current. In the latter case a table or graph must be used to convert the current reading into a temperature value. The automatic optical pyrometer makes a rapid precise brightness match. Temperatures can be read in 1 sec to a precision of $\pm 0.1°$C.

Calibration. Above the melting point of gold ($t_{\text{Au}} = 1064.43°$C) the IPTS-68 is defined in terms of Planck's law, using the value 0.014388 mk for the second radiation constant, C_2. The temperature t of a radiating body is determined by measuring the ratio of its spectral radiance, $N_{b\lambda}(t)$, to that of a blackbody at the gold point, $N_{b\lambda}(t_{\text{Au}})$:

$$R = \frac{N_{b\lambda}(t)}{N_{b\lambda}(t_{\text{Au}})} = \frac{\exp\left(C_2/\lambda\left(t_{\text{Au}} + T_0\right) - 1\right)}{\exp\left(C_2/\lambda\left(t + T_0\right) - 1\right)}$$

where T_0 is $273.15°$K.

Primary calibrations are made at NBS using a photoelectric optical pyrometer, very carefully designed to obtain extremely high precision (7).

The first step in a primary calibration is made by sighting the pyrometer on a gold-point blackbody. The observer records the current in the pyrometer lamp which causes the brightness of the filament to match the brightness of the inside of the crucible. Successive readings are taken as the gold is allowed to cool through its freezing point. A plot of the current readings as a function of time will show a plateau at the freezing point. Determination of this current constitutes a primary calibration at the gold point.

To realize a calibration point at a temperature higher than the gold point, a blackbody or a vacuum-lamp with a tungsten strip filament may be used as a high-temperature source. A rotating sectored disc placed between the source and the pyrometer acts as a neutral screen of known transmission. The pyrometer filament current is set to the value found for the gold point. The temperature of the source is then adjusted until a brightness match is observed in the pyrometer. This source temperature is then maintained while the sectored disc is removed and the pyrometer lamp current is adjusted to obtain a new brightness match. The pyrometer current for this new match gives the calibration point for the brightness temperature of the source when observed directly. The actual temperature is computed from the defining equation using the reciprocal of the transmission factor of the disc as the ratio of spectral radiances, and using the effective wavelength of the pyrometer for λ.

A number of primary calibration points are obtained by using discs of various transmission factors. A calibration curve or table may then be made, giving the temperature of a blackbody source which is matched by the pyrometer filament as a function of the filament current. Temperatures below the gold point may be included in the primary calibration. These points may be obtained by using a radiating target with a temperature near the gold point, and observing it with and without rotating discs. It is very convenient to have this downward extension of the calibration, although the optical pyrometer is not recognized as the official interpolating instrument below the gold point. The theory and procedure used in making a primary calibration have been discussed in detail by H. J. Kostkowski and R. D. Lee (8).

NBS will calibrate other pyrometers from the primary pyrometer. A stabilized blackbody or tungsten strip lamp is observed successively using the primary pyrometer and the secondary pyrometer under calibration, and the temperature scale is thus transferred, one point at a time, from the primary pyrometer to the secondary pyrometer. The uncertainty in the calibration of a manual secondary pyrometer is estimated by NBS to be not more than 4 deg C at 800°C, 3 deg C at 1100°C, 5 deg C at 1800°C, 8 deg C at 2800°C, and 40 deg C at 4000°C. The uncertainties of calibration are much smaller for automatic optical pyrometers, for which errors are usually less than 1 deg C below 1250°C.

In laboratories engaged in precise temperature measurements, and in industrial standardizing laboratories, it is customary to keep at least one secondary pyrometer with an NBS calibration to be used in calibrating other working pyrometers. Thus the secondary pyrometer is used as a standard. It is not exposed to the dust and dirt and extreme temperature conditions of the factory, and its calibration may be expected to remain stable for years. Additional assurance of the stability of calibration of the secondary standard pyrometer can be obtained by providing an additional calibrated secondary pyrometer. The two secondary pyrometers can be compared from time to time, and one of them can be returned at intervals to NBS for recalibration without interrupting the work of the laboratory.

Calibration checks may also be made by using a blackbody cavity and measuring its temperature with a calibrated thermocouple. By keeping optical pyrometers clean, and frequently checking the operation of switches and current measuring devices, temperature readings can be reproduced with them, well within the limits of the maximum uncertainties as stated by NBS.

Emissivity. The uncertainties considered above apply to temperature measurements of blackbodies. Additional uncertainties arise in the measurement of surface temperatures. As discussed above, real surfaces emit less energy than blackbodies, and the ratio of the actual radiation to the radiation from a blackbody at the same temperature is known as the emissivity (ϵ). The emissivity may vary from less than 1% for a highly-polished metal surface, to very nearly unity for an oxidized metal surface or a rough refractory surface. A pyrometer reading on a surface yields the "brightness-temperature" of that surface, which may be far below the true temperature if the emissivity is low. Tables are available which give the correction to be applied to brightness-temperature to convert it to true temperature, if the emissivity of the surface is known (9). Other tables give observed emissivities for various surfaces (10). At industrial temperatures, up to 1800°C, the radiation at 0.65 μ varies as a high power of the temperature. This power may be as high as 10 or 20. For this reason the error in absolute temperature is much less than error in the intensity of the radiation. For example at the gold point an emissivity of 90% causes a 10% reduction in the intensity of the radiation, but at 0.65 μ the intensity is proportional to about the 17th power of the temperature, so the error in temperature as read by an optical pyrometer will be only 0.6% or about 8 deg C.

There is no universal method for compensating or correcting pyrometers to eliminate the emissivity error. A number of methods have had some degree of success and have been quite useful in special applications. Clean surfaces of molten metals are good reflectors and consequently have low emissivity.

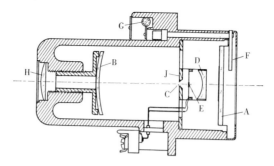

Fig. 8. Section of a radiation pyrometer.

The emissivity of molten cast iron is about 0.4, and special scales called "foundry scales" have been used on optical pyrometers. These scales have been constructed to include a correction for an emissivity of 0.4, and they can be used to read the true temperature of molten cast iron or steel. Particles of slag or iron oxide floating on the metal have higher emissivities and therefore appear as bright spots on the surface; they are "blacker" than the clean metal. The correction for an emissivity of 0.4 is applicable to the clean surface of the metal so the filament should be matched against this darker-appearing surface. An incandescent steel billet usually has a mottled appearance because of scale more or less closely attached to its surface. The scale appears darker than the clean steel surface because it is actually at lower temperature. In this case the brighter spots should be sighted on and a correction corresponding to about 0.8 emissivity applied. A concave portion of an incandescent surface usually appears brighter and therefore hotter than a convex portion of the same surface, that is, it has a higher effective emissivity. It may be possible to provide a small blackbody cavity in an object for the purpose of measuring its temperature. A drilled hole of depth at least five times its diameter is adequate in most cases. A pyrometer reading made by sighting on the bottom of this hole will give the temperature within this drilled cavity. Although this may not be the same as the true surface temperature, it may be just as useful.

Nonblackbodies are reflectors of radiation. The optical pyrometer is calibrated in terms of the radiation emitted by a hot body. If an optical pyrometer is sighted on a sheet of white paper in a well-lighted room, a disappearance of the filament may be secured giving a temperature reading of perhaps 1000°C while the paper is at room temperature. This means that the brightness of the reflected red light is as great as that which would be emitted by a blackbody at 1000°C. Any light from a lamp, window, or other source which is reflected from the surface being measured into the pyrometer telescope introduces an error in the reading, and is to be avoided. In addition to extraneous light, other sources of error to be avoided are: smoke or fumes between the pyrometer and the source, and dust or other deposits on lenses, screens, or lamps.

Other Pyrometers. It is often advantageous to record or control a temperature, in the absence of an operator. The most common form of pyrometer used for this purpose has a thermal receiver. An optical system, sometimes simply a single lens or mirror, is used to focus the radiation onto the receiver, which may be a small disc. This receiver is heated by the radiation and the degree of heating is interpreted in terms of the temperature of the hot body supplying the radiation.

Figure 8 shows schematically the arrangement of the optical system in one form of commercial radiation pyrometer. Radiation from a source enters the quartz window A, is reflected by the spherical mirror B, and is brought to a focus on the diaphragm J, in the center of which there is an aperture C. Radiation passing through C is reflected by the spherical mirror D to the receiver E where an image of C is formed. The surface of J is whitened slightly with magnesium oxide, to make the image of the source visible when viewed through a lens H placed behind B. Since B produces no chromatic aberration and very little spherical aberration, the image of the source is very sharp and a very definite portion of the image can be made to cover C. The corresponding portion of the source therefore supplies the radiation which is focused on E, and the temperature of this portion of the source is measured. A light-trimmer F in front of the window may be rotated by turning the screw G, so that the output signal of the pyrometer may be adjusted. In this way, several radiation pyrometers may be matched in output so that they can be used with one multiple-point recorder.

A pyrometer of this type may be sensitive to radiation of a broad band of wavelengths, including all of the visible radiation and also infrared radiation, of longer wavelength. Such a pyrometer, called a total-radiation pyrometer, has a response approximately proportional to the fourth power of the temperature. Thus it is more sensitive to emissivity errors than is the optical pyrometer, and therefore in practice it is often calibrated in place by means of an optical pyrometer.

It is important, when using radiation pyrometers, to make sure that the sighting path from the pyrometer to the radiation source is free of mechanical obstructions and infrared-absorbing gases such as water vapor and carbon dioxide. The ratio of source distance to the minimum source diameter (distance factor), for the pyrometer described above with a thermopile receiver, is about 24:1 for distances greater than 24 in. At 24 in., the source diameter must be at least 1 in.; at 48 in., 2 in.; etc. For distances greater than 20 in., the pyrometer can be used as a "universal focus" device if properly focused and calibrated for a distance of 24 in. For shorter source distances the distance factor is generally larger, but special pyrometers are available with smaller apertures so that they can sight between the coils of an induction heater onto the work surface. The standard pyrometers are used for all temperatures above 800°F (about 450°C). They have a time constant of 1.8 sec which gives a complete response (to 99% of a sudden change) in 8 sec. For measuring rapid variations in source temperature within this range, pyrometers are available with a time constant of 0.15 sec, giving a complete response in less than 1 sec. Slower pyrometers are also available for use in applications where it is undesirable to follow rapid, erratic changes in temperature. For measuring temperatures as low as 100°F (38°C) there is a pyrometer with a time constant of 1.6 sec and a distance factor which varies from about 7 at the minimum sighting distance of 12 in. to about 10 at sighting distances of 32 in. or more.

Photovoltaic cells are also used in radiation pyrometers constructed as described above. If no filter is used in the radiation path, the detector is sensitive to visible and infrared radiation of wavelength shorter than about 1.2 μ and the effective wavelength is about 0.90 μ. The pyrometers used for lower temperatures, from 800°F (425°C) to 1400°F (760°C), have a distance factor of about 12. Pyrometers made for use at higher temperatures have a distance factor of about 100, which allows reliable temperature measurements to be made from a much greater distance. The insensitivity of these pyrometers to infrared radiation longer than 1.2 μ makes their readings independent of the presence of water vapor and carbon dioxide in the sighting path. They are also less sensitive than total radiation pyrometers to emissivity variations.   When measuring temperatures above 2025°F (1100°C) it is advantageous to filter out all of the radiation of wavelength greater than about 0.9 μ, and thus reduce the effective wavelength to 0.65 μ.   This causes the output signal from the pyrometer to vary as a higher power of the temperature and reduces the emissivity error to the value obtained with an optical pyrometer.   The pyrometers using photovoltaic cells have a very fast response, requiring only 0.001 sec to indicate 99% of an instantaneous change in source temperature.

The radiation pyrometers which have been described are sealed units designed to withstand the conditions prevailing in the vicinity of manufacturing operations, such as glass melting and working, steel melting and rolling, and various other metal working and heat-treating processes.   Many other pyrometers are available, some employing thermistor-bolometer detectors sensitive to long-wavelength infrared radiation, some using photoconductive cells (such as lead sulfide cells) which are sensitive to infrared radiation of wavelengths as great as 2 or 3 μ.   These are especially useful for measuring low temperatures, from ambient up to several hundred degrees.   With all of these pyrometers, particularly the ones which are sensitive to visible radiation, care must be exercised when measuring low temperatures to make sure that the radiation entering the pyrometer is originating at the low-temperature source being measured, and is not radiation emitted by a nearby hot object and reflected from the source being measured.

The temperature of a transparent object generally cannot be measured with a radiation pyrometer.   Kirchhoff's law can be modified to include transparent objects:

$$\epsilon + r + t = 1$$

In this case the sum of the emissivity, ϵ, the reflection coefficient, r, and the transmission, t, is equal to unity.   The emissivity is always small for an object with high transmission, such as a sheet of glass or clear plastic, or a clear nonluminous flame.   A special condition exists, however, in the radiating characteristics of silicate glasses.   At wavelengths between 4 and 8 μ both the reflection coefficient and the transmission of these glasses are quite small and the emissivity is almost unity.   Therefore a radiation pyrometer with filters which exclude all of the radiation outside the wavelength band from 4 to 8 μ can be used to measure the temperature of hot glass while it is being formed or heat-treated.

Uses.   The radiation pyrometer is to be recommended in place of a thermocouple in the following cases: (*1*) where a thermocouple would be poisoned by furnace atmospheres; (*2*) for measurement of surface temperatures; (*3*) for measurement of the temperature of moving objects; (*4*) for measurement of temperatures beyond the range of base-metal thermocouples; (*5*) where mechanical conditions, such as vibration or shock, make a hot thermocouple short-lived; and (*6*) where high speed of response to temperature changes is required.

Color Temperature.   It is a familiar fact that the color of an incandescent body, such as the filament of a tungsten lamp, is dependent on its temperature.   As it is heated, the filament is first black, then dull red, bright red, yellow, and finally "white."   There is a characteristic color for each temperature.   The filament is a gray body and therefore it is less bright than a blackbody at the same temperature, but its color is the same as that of the blackbody, since by definition of a gray body its spectral distribution is the same as that of a blackbody at the same temperature.   Hence when color is used as a basis of measurement, no emissivity corrections are involved.   Since it is very difficult to match two colors exactly, one method of approach is to measure the ratio of intensity of radiation at two different wavelengths, such as red and green. For either a gray or a blackbody, this ratio is the same function of the temperature, and can be used as a measure of temperature, independent of emissivity. Photoelectric sensitive elements are used in this measurement, and a number of two-color pyrometers are available.

The open-hearth melter, wearing goggles of cobalt blue glass which has transmission bands, one in the blue and the other in the red, unconsciously uses a variation of this method. Because of the variation in ratio, the purple sensation changes rapidly with temperature. With experience he is able to estimate temperature around 3000°F within from 30 to 75 deg F.

These color temperatures are not to be confused with the film colors on an iron surface which the blacksmith of former days used to determine when to quench a red-hot tool to secure the desired temper.

Miscellaneous Methods

Melting Points as Measures of Temperature. This method of indicating that a certain temperature has been reached consists in applying a mark, a wash, or a pellet to the body to be heated. Melting of this application takes place at some definite temperature and is detected by observing the change from a rough to a glossy surface. Under the trademark Tempilstick these materials are supplied as a series of compounds ranging in melting point from 113 to 2500°F at intervals from 12.5 to 50°F. They are said to have a mean accuracy of ±1.0% of the stated temperatures. Their use involves no instrumentation and no special training of the operator. A series of marks with crayons of different melting points can serve, on subsequent examination, to indicate the highest temperature attained by the workpiece.

Choice of Method

There is a wide choice open to the person who wishes to measure temperatures. The simplicity of expansion thermometers and their inexpensiveness make their use almost obligatory in many cases. In the range of temperatures from about −183 to +450°C where high precision is not required, liquid-in-glass thermometers are indispensable. If the location where temperatures in this range are to be measured is unfavorable to the installation and reading of a mercury thermometer or if it is required that temperature be recorded or controlled, consideration must be given to pressure-type thermometers, resistance thermometers, and thermocouples. If the recorder can be located within a few feet of the sensitive element, the gas- or vapor-pressure-type instruments are usually adequate and less costly, though inferior in precision to resistance thermometers and thermocouples. Replacement of sensitive elements is a more difficult operation for the pressure-type instruments than for the electrical. In its accepted range, the resistance thermometer has advantages over the thermocouple in sensitivity and precision, and in operation, if desired, from an ac supply, thus eliminating all need for dry cells, standard cells, current standardization, and reference junction compensation. The thermocouple can be inserted in locations inaccessible to resistance thermometers, has a higher speed of response, and is less costly. Resistance thermometers and thermocouples are definitely competitive over the range from −200 to +500°C. For recording and controlling above 500°C the thermocouple and the radiation pyrometers are competitive up to about 1600°C, where the thermocouple drops out.   The optical pyrometer is the most precise means of measuring temperatures above the gold point (1064.43°C).

Bibliography

"Temperature Measurement" in *ECT* 1st ed., Vol. 13, pp. 677–699, by P. H. Dike, Leeds & Northrup Co.

1. H. F. Stimson, *International Practical Temperature Scale of 1948: Text Revision of 1960*, Monograph 37, NBS (1961), U.S. Government Printing Office, Washington, D.C.
2. *Federal Register*, Title 15, Chap. 2, Part 200, "General," and Part 203, "Heat" (copies available from NBS on request).
3. "The International Practical Temperature Scale of 1968," *Metrologia* **5**, 35–44 (1969).
4. C. R. Barber, "International Practical Temperature Scale of 1968," *Nature* **222**, 929–931 (1969).
5. "1968 Actions ... International Committee of Weights and Measures," *NBS Technical News Bulletin* **53** (1), 12–13 (Jan. 1969).
6. J. F. Swindells, *Calibration of Liquid-in-Glass Thermometers*, NBS Monograph 90 (1965), U.S. Government Printing Office, Washington D.C.
7. R. D. Lee, "The NBS Photoelectric Pyrometer and Its Use in Realizing the International Practical Temperature Scale above 1063°C," *Metrologia* **2** (4), 150–162 (Oct. 1966).
8. H. J. Kostkowski and R. D. Lee, *"Theory and Methods of Optical Pyrometry,"* NBS Monograph 41 (1962), U.S. Government Printing Office, Washington, D.C.
9. D. E. Poland, J. W. Green, and J. L. Margrave, *Corrected Optical Pyrometer Readings*, NBS Monograph 37 (1961), U.S. Government Printing Office, Washington, D.C. 20402.
10. G. G. Guboreff, J. E. Janssen, and R. H. Torborg, *Thermal Radiation Properties Survey*, Minneapolis-Honeywell Regulator Company (Honeywell Inc.), Minneapolis, Minn.

General References

1. American Institute of Physics, *Temperature, Its Measurement and Control in Science and Industry*, Vol. 3, Reinhold Publishing Corp., New York, 1962.
   This publication, containing papers presented at the "Fourth Symposium on Temperature, Its Measurement and Control in Science and Industry," is in three parts: Part 1, Basic Concepts, Standards and Methods, F. G. Brickwedde, ed.; Part 2, Applied Methods and Instruments, A. I. Dahl, ed.; Part 3, *Biology and Medicine*, J. D. Hardy, ed.
2. J. F. Swindells, ed., *Precision Measurement and Calibration, Selected NBS Papers on Temperature*, NBS Spec Publ. 300, Vol. 2, U. S. Government Printing Office, Washington, D.C., 1968.
   This is a compilation of previously published papers by the staff of the National Bureau of Standards.   References 2, 4, 5, and 6 are reprinted in this volume.
3. J. A. Hall, *The Measurement of Temperature*, Chapman and Hall, Ltd., London, 1966.
4. R. P. Benedict, *Fundamentals of Temperature, Pressure, and Flow Measurements*, John Wiley & Sons, Inc., New York, 1969.
5. T. R. Harrison, *Radiation Pyrometry and Its Underlying Principles of Radiant Heat Transfer*, John Wiley & Sons, Inc., New York, 1960.
6. D. I. Finch, *General Principles of Thermoelectric Thermometry*, Tech. Publ. D1.1000, Leeds & Northrup Co., North Wales, Pa., 1966.
7. P. H. Dike, W. T. Gray, and F. K. Schroyer, *Optical Pyrometry*, Tech. Publ. D1.4000, Leeds & Northrup Co., North Wales, Pa., 1966.

WILLIAM T. GRAY
Leeds & Northrup Company

TEMPERING AND ANNEALING OILS.   See Petroleum (products), Vol. 15, p. 84.

TERBIUM, Tb.   See Rare earth elements.

TEREPHTHALIC ACID, p-$C_6H_4(COOH)_2$. See Phthalic acids, Vol. 15, p. 462.

TERGITOL. See Surfactants.

TERNE PLATE. See Metallic coatings, Vol. 13, p. 260.

TERPENES AND TERPENOIDS

It is customary to consider the terpenes as derivatives of isoprene. The carbon skeletons of terpenes are thus made up of two isoprene units (monoterpenes), three isoprene units (sesquiterpenes), four isoprene units (diterpenes), and six isoprene units (triterpenes). The units are most often connected head to tail, and less frequently in other arrangements. Simple hydrocarbons of the series have the empirical formula $(C_5H_8)_x$, where x is 2, 3, 4, or 6. Higher terpenes are known, but so far few have importance in technology.

Although the name terpenes might be limited to unsaturated hydrocarbons, in practice it includes not only the isoprene oligomers, but also their oxygenated derivatives (alcohols, ketones, aldehydes, acids, etc), and partial or complete reduction products. These derivatives are often called terpenoids. In the majority of terpenes the polyisoprene chains are closed to form rings. Six-membered rings are most common, but rings of five, four, and three carbons are also well represented. Thus, besides being divided into classes based on the number of isoprene units, the terpenes are further divided on the basis of whether they are acyclic, monocyclic, bicyclic, tricyclic, etc.

Until recently, nearly all technologically important terpenes were of biochemical origin, mostly from phytochemical sources. In the biosyntheses, occasionally a terpene is produced which either lacks part of an isoprene unit, or has an extra part of one. Also, particularly in the triterpenes, migration of methyls has occurred in some cases, so that the final product may no longer have a skeleton strictly comprised of isoprene units. These materials are nevertheless considered to be members of the terpene family.

This article is limited essentially to the technologically important mono- and sesquiterpenes. The technologically important diterpenes are chiefly the rosin acids, which are produced in large tonnages in the form of rosins. These diterpenes are considered in a separate article on Rosin and rosin derivatives. Gibberellic acid is chemically, but not yet technologically, related to pimaric acid, a rosin acid. See Plant growth substances. Vitamin A, an important diterpene, is considered under Vitamins, together with the related tetraterpene, carotene. The technologically important triterpenes are the steroids (qv). See also Flavors and spices; Oils, essential; Perfumes; Turpentine.

Important recent developments in monoterpene technology are the commercialization of processes for making the acyclic odor and flavor terpenoids from β-pinene, and the use of new analytical methods, which made possible the research leading to the development of the new processes. Analytical separations of monoterpenes, sesquiterpenes, and diterpenes are now made chiefly by gas chromatography. Identifications are made mainly by infrared spectrometry, which also supplies much structural information. Additional structural information is obtained by ultraviolet spectrometry, proton magnetic resonance, mass spectrometry, and optical rotatory dispersion. Identification methods, such as physical constants and melting points of derivatives, are still used, but usually only in a supplementary way. Tables 2 and 3 (see below) list physical constants for selected terpenes. The reader is referred to the compendia of infrared spectrograms listed at the end of the bibliography.

Table 1. Structural Formulas, Names, and Numbering Systems of Technologically Important Terpenes

Acyclic monoterpene hydrocarbons

myrcene; 1,6-octadiene, 7-methyl-3-methylene-[a] (**1**)

ocimene[a]; 1,3,6-octatriene, 3,7-dimethyl-[a] (**2**)

alloocimene; 2,4,6-octatriene, 2,6-dimethyl-[a] (**3**)

Monocyclic monoterpene hydrocarbons

p-menthane (cis and trans), p-menthane[a] (**4**)

dipentene (*dl*), limonene (*d* or *l*); p-mentha-1,8-diene[a] (**5**)

ψ-limonene; p-mentha-1(7),8-diene[a] (**6**)

3,8-p-menthadiene; p-mentha-3,8-diene[a] (**7**)

α-phellandrene; p-mentha-1,5-diene[a] (**8**)

β-phellandrene; p-mentha-1(7),2-diene[a] (**9**)

α-terpinene; p-mentha-1,3-diene[a] (**10**)

γ-terpinene; p-mentha-1,4-diene[a] (**11**)

terpinolene; p-mentha-1,4(8)-diene[a] (**12**)

Table 1 (*continued*)

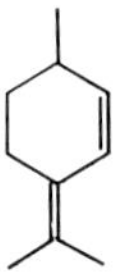

isoterpinolene, 2,4(8)- *p*-menthadiene; *p*-mentha-2,4(8)- diene[a] (**13**)	carvomenthene, 1-*p*-menthene; *p*-menth-1- ene[a] (**14**)	3-*p*-menthene; *p*- menth-3-ene[a] (**15**)	*p*-cymene[a] (**16**)

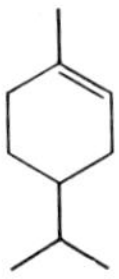

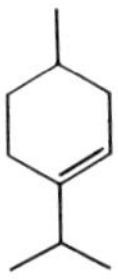

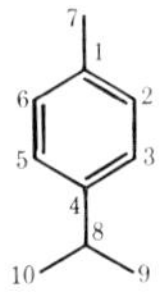

Bicyclic monoterpene hydrocarbons

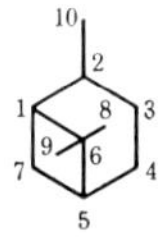

pinane[a] (**17**)	α-pinene; 2- pinene[a] (**18**)	β-pinene; 2(10)- pinene[a] (**19**)	carane[a,b] (**20**)

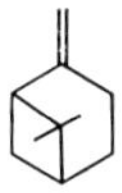

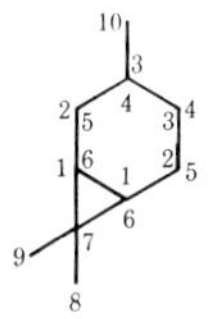

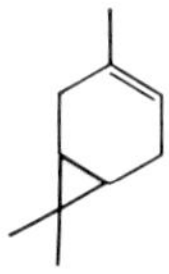

3-carene,[a] Δ-3-carene (**21**)	4-carene, Δ-4-carene; 2-carene[a] (**22**)	camphene[a]; norbornane, 2,2-dimethyl-3-methy- lene- (**23**)

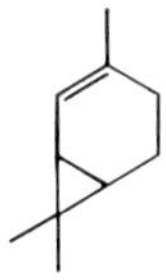

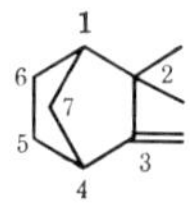

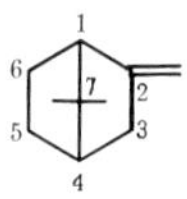

α-fenchene; norbornane, 7,7- dimethyl-2-methylene-[a] (**24**)	tricyclene; tricyclo(2.2.1.0.²,⁶)- heptane, 1,7,7-trimethyl- (**25**)

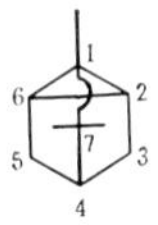

Cineoles

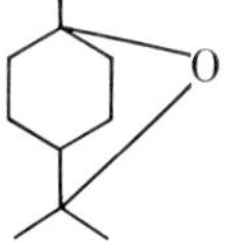

eucalyptol, 1,8-cineole; *p*-men- thane, 1,8-epoxy-[a] (**26**)	1,4-cineole; *p*-men- thane, 1,4-epoxy-[a] (**27**)

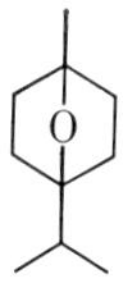

(*continued*)

Table 1 (*continued*)

Acyclic monoterpene alcohols

citronellol; 6-octen-1-ol,
3,7-dimethyl-[a] (**28**)

geraniol (trans), nerol (cis) (shown);
2,6-octadien-1-ol, 3,7-dimethyl-[a] (**29**)

linalool; 1,6-octadien-3-ol,
3,7-dimethyl-[a] (**30**)

myrcenol[a], myrcene hydrate; 7-octen-2-ol,
2-methyl-6-methylene- (**31**)

Monocyclic monoterpene alcohols

dihydro-α-terpineol;
p-menthan-8-ol[a] (**32**)

menthol[a]; *p*-men-
than-3-ol (**33**)

isopulegol; *p*-men-
th-8-en-3-ol[a] (**34**)

terpinen-1-ol; *p*-
menth-3-en-1-ol[a] (**35**)

terpinen-4-ol; *p*-men-
th-1-en-4-ol[a] (**36**)

α-terpineol; *p*-men-
th-1-en-8-ol[a] (**37**)

β-terpineol; *p*-men-
th-8-en-1-ol[a] (**38**)

γ-terpineol; *p*-men-
th-4(8)-en-1-ol[a] (**39**)

δ-terpineol; *p*-menth-1(7)-
en-8-ol[a] (**40**)

3-menthene glycol; *p*-
menthane-3,4-diol[a] (**41**)

terpin; *p*-menthane-
1,8-diol[a] (**42**)

Table 1 (*continued*)

Bicyclic monoterpene alcohols

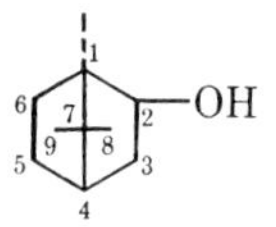

borneol[a] (endo), isoborneol[a] (exo) (shown); 2-born-anol (**43**)

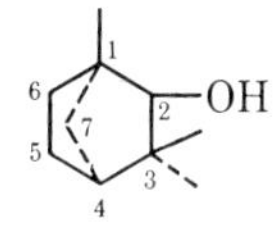

α-fenchol (endo) (shown), β-fenchol (exo), fen-chyl alcohol; 2-norborn-anol, 1,3,3-trimethyl-[a] (**44**)

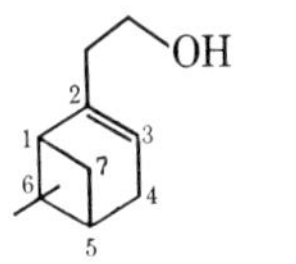

nopol; 2-norpinen-2-eth-anol, 6,6-dimethyl-[a] (**45**)

Monoterpene aldehydes and ketones

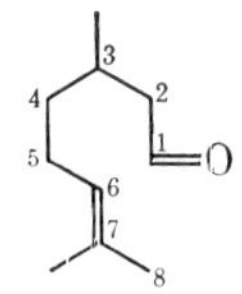

citronellal; 6-octenal, 3,7-dimethyl-[a] (**46**)

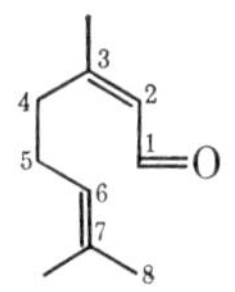

citral, geranial (trans), neral (cis); 2,6-octadienal, 3,7-dimethyl-[a] (**47**)

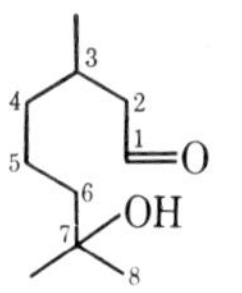

hydroxycitronellal; octanal, 7-hydroxy-3,7-dimethyl-[a] (**48**)

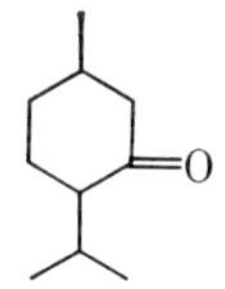

menthone; *p*-men-than-3-one[a] (**49**)

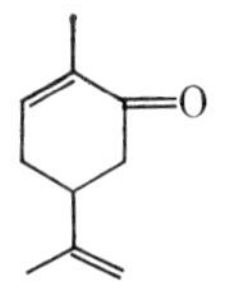

carvone; *p*-mentha-6,8-dien-2-one[a] (**50**)

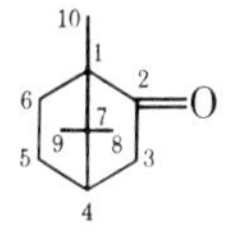

camphor[a]; 2-born-anone (**51**)

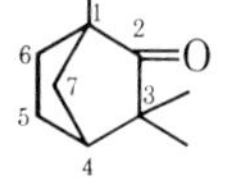

fenchone; 2-norbornanone, 1,3,3-trimethyl-[a] (**52**)

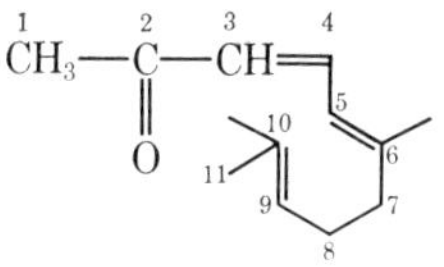

pseudoionone; 3,5,9-un-decatrien-2-one, 6,10-dimethyl-[a] (**53**)

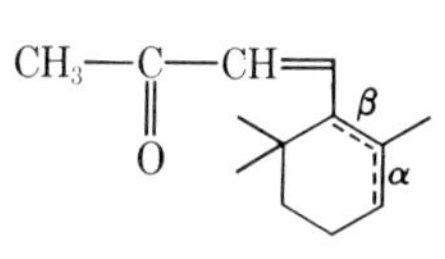

ionones; 3-buten-2-one, 4-(2,6,6-trimethyl-1-cyclohexen-1-yl)-[a] or 3-buten-2-one, 4-(2,6,6-trimethyl-2-cyclohexen-1-yl)-[a] (**54**)

(*continued*)

Table 1 (*continued*)

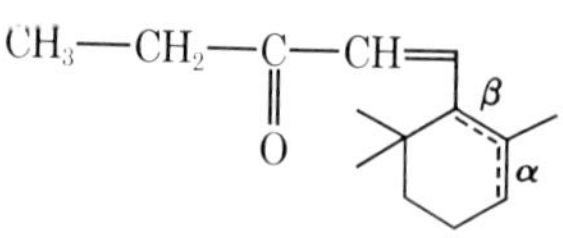

CH₃—CH₂—C—CH=

n-methylionones; 4-penten-3-one, 5-(2,6,6-trimethyl-1-cyclohexen-1-yl)-[a] or 4-penten-3-one, 5-(2,6,6-trimethyl-2-cyclohexen-1-yl)-[a] (**55**)

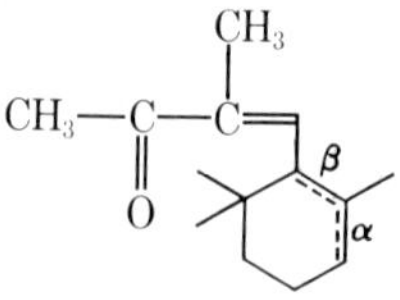

isomethylionones; 3-buten-2-one, 3-methyl-4-(2,6,6-trimethyl-1-cyclohexen-1-yl)-[a] or 3-buten-2-one, 3-methyl-4-(2,6,6-trimethyl-2-cyclohexen-1-yl)-[a] (**56**)

Sesquiterpenes

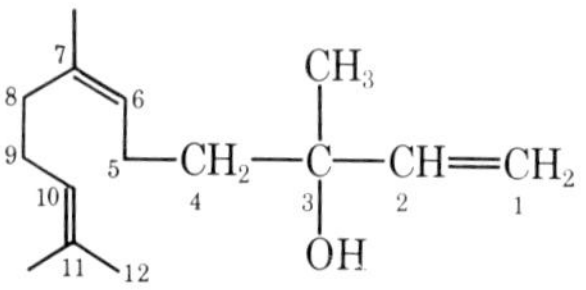

nerolidol; 1,6,10-dodecatrien-3-ol, 3,7,11-trimethyl-[a] (**57**)

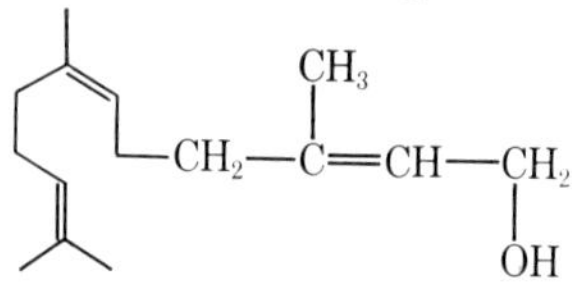

farnesol; 2,6,10-dodecatrien-1-ol, 3,7,11-trimethyl-[a] (**58**)

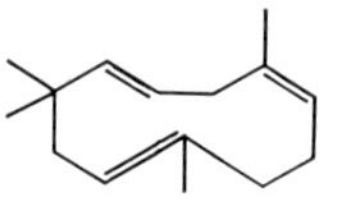

α-caryophyllene; humulene[a] (**59**)

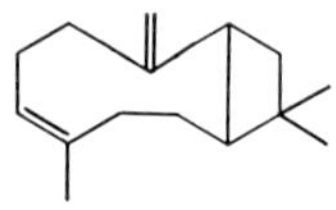

β-caryophyllene[a] (**60**)

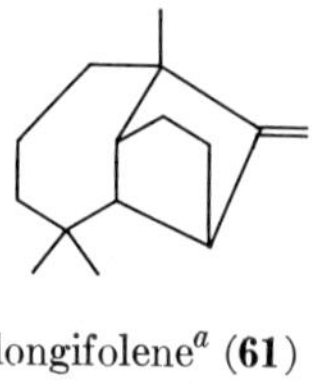

longifolene[a] (**61**)

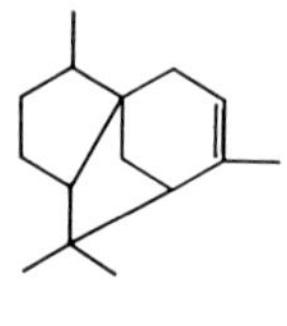

α-cedrene[a] (**62**)

Table 1 (*continued*)

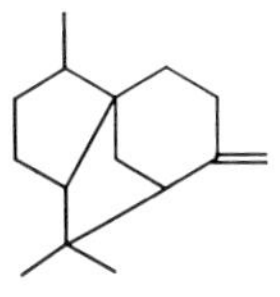

β-cedrene[a] (**63**)

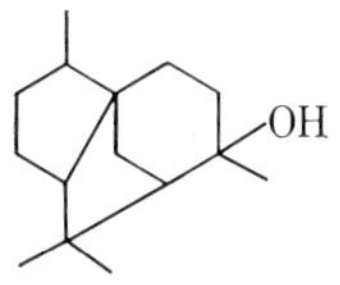

cedrol[a] (**64**)

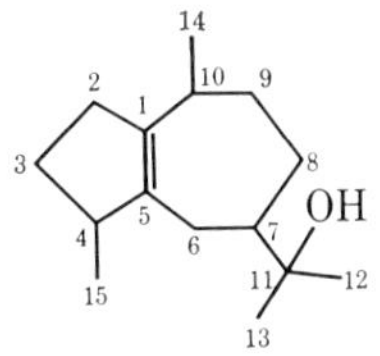

guaiol; guai-1(5)-en-11-ol[a] (**65**)

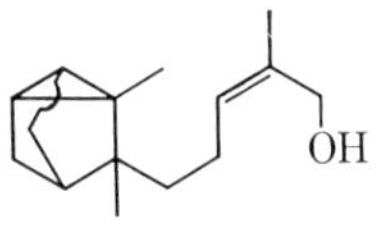

α-santalol; 2-penten-1-ol,
5-(2,3-dimethyltricyclo-
$(2.2.1.0^{2,6})$hept-3-yl)-
2-methyl-[a] (**66**)

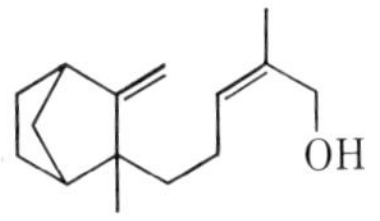

β-santalol[a] (**67**)

NOTE: Where only one name is shown, the common and the CA names are the same.

[a] *Chemical Abstracts* name as of Vol. 66 (June 1967). The CA numbering of pertinent skeletal systems is used, except where indicated. Alternative numbering has been used in the literature for systems other than the *p*-menthane system; *p*-menthane derivatives are universally numbered as shown. No reference to numbering systems is used or needed in the body of this article, but numberings are helpful for literature searches, etc.

[b] Inside numbering given according to old standard; outside numbering according to present CA rules.

The technologically important terpenes are discussed in order of volume, although some departures have been made in order to keep related materials together.

Exact details of current manufacturing processes are sometimes in the nature of trade secrets, and are unavailable even from the patent literature. In the U.S.S.R. a number of classical processes in this category are being reexamined and optimized. The results are published in Russian. Consult *Transactions of the All Union Scientific Research Institute for Synthetic and Natural Perfume Materials* (*Tr. Vses. Nauchn.-Issled. Inst. Sintetich. i Natural'n Dushistykh Veshchestv*). The bibliography lists some of these papers, along with their location in *Chemical Abstracts*.

Terpene nomenclature is following two divergent paths. In technology and much of chemistry, the trivial names are used almost exclusively, and they are used in this article. *Chemical Abstracts*, on the other hand, indexes according to numbered standardized ring and chain systems, particularly in the more recent volumes. Searching under the trivial name, however, gives direct reference to the formal equivalent in most cases. The names and structures of some of the more important terpenes are given in Table 1.

The Monoterpenes

Next to the diterpenes which make up the rosin acids, the monoterpenes constitute the largest tonnage of commercially important terpenes. This group, with three or four exceptions, is derived entirely from essential oils. Materials furnishing large volumes of monoterpenes are turpentine, pine oil, citrus limonene, Japanese mint oil, camphor oil, citronella oil, and lemongrass oil. A few low-volume oils serve as sources for minor isolates. Other essential oils which are used directly for odor and flavor purposes and which do not serve as raw materials for industrial chemical syntheses are considered under Oils, essential. Turpentine sources and characteristics are considered in detail in the article on Turpentine. (Cross references, such as "see under Pinane," are to sections of this article; other references, such as "see Turpentine," are to separate articles.)

Turpentine is by far the largest source of monoterpenes. Except for a relatively small proportion that still goes into solvent uses, such as paint thinner, all of the turpentine produced in the U.S. serves as raw material for chemical processes. The U.S. industry is centered in the Southeast. Gum turpentine is obtained from living trees, wood turpentine from pine stumps, and sulfate turpentine as a by-product from the kraft paper mills. The main pine species from which southeastern turpentines originate are slash pine and longleaf pine. Gum turpentine or sulfate turpentine from these species averages about 30% β-pinene, the balance being chiefly α-pinene. Sulfate turpentine from northern and Pacific slope mills contains chiefly α-pinene. A few kraft mills in western U.S. mountain areas process ponderosa pine and produce a turpentine containing about 30% 3-carene and only a little β-pinene. Steam-distilled wood turpentine from southeastern stumps consists of chiefly α-pinene, less than 5% β-pinene, and 10–15% camphene. Small amounts of monocyclic terpenes, such as dipentene, are found in all turpentines. Crude sulfate turpentines contain small amounts of pine-oil components and sesquiterpene hydrocarbons, which are considered below under appropriate headings. These are removed during processing to refined sulfate turpentine.

The major components of commercial turpentine are α-pinene (**18**) (bp, 156°C); β-pinene (**19**) (bp, 165°C); camphene (**23**) (bp, 158°C); and 3-carene (**21**) (bp, 170°C). Of these components, α-pinene from southeastern gum or sulfate sources is dextrorotatory and has about half the optical activity of pure d-α-pinene. The α-pinene of Mexican turpentine is dextrorotatory to a considerably greater extent and that from Greek turpentine (*Pinus halepensis*) is over 95% optically pure. French turpentine (*Pinus maritima*) gives highly active l-α-pinene, along with l-β-pinene. α-Pinene from southeastern U.S. steam-distilled wood turpentine is nearly racemic. The low rotation of the turpentine from the stumps, when compared to its rotation when taken directly from the live tree, together with the low β-pinene content, suggests that much of the original l-β-pinene has been isomerized to l-α-pinene. β-Pinene from any commercial turpentine is strongly levorotatory, and nearly optically pure. Camphene is racemic, or nearly so, and the carene is dextrorotatory, approaching full optical purity. At present, little or no use is made of the optical activity of these terpenes.

Some properties of selected monoterpene hydrocarbons and the cineoles, which often occur in monoterpene hydrocarbon fractions, are given in Table 2. Some properties of selected oxygenated terpenes are given in Table 3.

The technologically important reactions of the terpenes are of six main types:

1. Acid-catalyzed rearrangements, additions, and eliminations.
2. Thermal rearrangements.
3. Allylic rearrangements.
4. Hydrogenations and other reductions, and dehydrogenations.
5. Stereochemical changes (epimerizations).
6. Oxidations, including halogenations.

The discovery of explanations for the very facile rearrangements of the terpenes has contributed greatly to the general understanding of these processes in organic chemistry. For better understanding of the technology, the rearrangements are shown in detail where they occur in technical processes.

Table 2. Some Properties of Selected Monoterpene Hydrocarbons and Cineoles

Name	Boiling point, °C (760 torr)	Boiling point, °C (100 torr)	Density, d^{20}	n_D^{20}	$[\alpha]_D$	Melting point, °C	GC retention time relative to α-pinene on Carbowax 4000
tricyclene	152	85			0	+65	0.96
α-pinene	156	89	0.8595	1.4658	±51	−50 (−75)	1.00
α-fenchene	157	91.5	0.8697	1.4740	±44		1.22
camphene	158	91			±108	+49	1.28
β-pinene	165	98	0.8722	1.4790	±22	−50 (−61)	1.58
myrcene	167		0.7880^a	1.4680^a	0		1.70
cis-pinane	168	101	0.8575	1.4629	±23	−53	1.25
8-p-menthene	169		0.8142	1.4554	0		trans, 1.35
							cis, 1.60
trans-2-p-menthene	169		0.8100	1.4500	±132		1.17
3-p-menthene	169	102	0.8129	1.4519	±141		1.18
trans-p-menthane	170	103	0.7928	1.4367	0		0.97
3-carene	170	104	0.8617	1.4742	±16		1.82
cis-p-menthane	172	105	0.8002	1.4431	0	−90	1.10
1,4-cineole	172	105.5	0.8986	1.4446	0	−46	2.09
1,8-cineole	174	108	0.9245	1.4574	0	+1	2.57
α-terpinene	175	108	0.8315^a	1.4755^a	0		2.09
carvomenthene	176	110	0.8246^b	1.4563^b	±118		1.72
4(8)-p-menthene	176	110		1.4689	0		1.71
limonene	176.5	110	0.8411	1.4730	±124	−74 (−89, dl)	2.29
p-cymene	177	110	0.857	1.4905	0	−73	3.15
γ-terpinene	182	116	0.8455^a	1.4715^a	0		2.88
3,8-p-menthadiene	183.5	117.5	0.851	1.4876	±140		3.12
2,4(8)-p-menthadiene	185	120	0.8535^a	1.5030^a	±49		3.66
terpinolene	186	120	0.8620	1.4861	0		3.51

$^a T = 25°C.$ $^b T = 18°C.$

α-**Pinene.** *Source and Manufacture.* Various turpentines are rectified to produce α- and β-pinenes of technical purity for particular purposes. Sulfate turpentine is the major source of these individual terpenes, which are sometimes additionally treated

Table 3. Some Properties of Selected Oxygenated Terpenes

Name	Boiling point, °C (760 torr)	Boiling point, °C (100 torr)	Density, d^{20}	n_D^{20}	$[\alpha]_D$	Melting point, °C
fenchone	193	122	0.9452	1.4628	±70	+5
linalool	199		0.8607	1.4616	±22	
α-fenchol	200	133	0.935^a	1.4734	±12.5	48 (39, dl)
citronellal	203		0.851	1.4467	±12	
terpinen-1-ol	208	106 (25)	0.9171^b	1.4701^b	dl	
camphor	209				±45	179
trans-β-terpineol	209	139	0.919	1.4712^c	0	33
trans-dihydro-α-terpineol	209			1.4630	0	35
cis-dihydro-α-terpineol	210		0.8962^d	1.4664	0	47
trans-menthone	210	138	0.8903^b	1.4500	±29	−6
terpinen-4-ol	211	123 (50)	0.9259	1.4762	±29	
neomenthol	212		0.8917^c	1.4604	±20	−22 (+53, dl)
borneol	212				±38	209 (210, dl)
isoborneol	214				±34	212 dl
menthol	216		0.8911^c	1.4615	±50	43 (38, dl)
γ-terpineol	218	132 (50)	0.9412	1.4912	0	70
α-terpineol	219	149	0.9336	1.4831	±112	40 (35, dl)
citronellol	224		0.8550	1.4559	±7	
nerol	225	128 (25)	0.8735^b	1.4736^b	0	
citral	228		0.8972^e	1.4891	0	
geraniol	230	131 (25)	0.8770^b	1.4756^b	0	
carvone	231	157	0.9550^b	1.4990	±62	
hydroxycitronellal		116 (5)	0.9220	1.4494	±10.5	
terpin (ordinary)	258				0	105 (117, hydrate)
α-ionone	258		0.9309	1.4971	±400	
β-ionone	271		0.9461	1.5202	0	−35
nerolidol	276		0.8778^f	1.4795	±15	

^{a} $T = 40°C.$ ^{c} $T = 30°C.$ ^{e} $T = 15°C.$
^{b} $T = 25°C.$ ^{d} $T = 45°C.$ ^{f} $T = 22°C.$

by stirring with sodium or calcium hypochlorite, or by adsorbents, to lower the sulfur content and improve the odor. Typical purities are 90–95% α-pinene by gas chromatographic analysis. α-Pinene which is to be stored under ordinary conditions is usually protected with an antioxidant such as di(t-butyl)-p-cresol. Physical properties of commercial grades of α-pinene are given in manufacturers' literature. Typical are sp gr, 15.6/15.6°C, 0.863; n_D^{20}, 1.466; color, 10–20 APHA; boiling range (5–95%), 156–158°C.

Reactions. The technologically important reactions are detailed under topics given in Uses. α-Pinene undergoes autoxidation readily, yielding oxygenated terpenes with pinane skeletons (1). These oxygenated pinenes undergo a number of interesting transformations but do not seem to have any commercial application (2). α-Pinene undergoes thermal isomerization at increasing rates above 200°C (3). The primary products are dipentene and ocimene. The ocimene is further converted by thermal isomerization to alloocimene unless very short contact times and fast quench conditions are used. The pyrolizate is used to make terpene resins. Acid treatment of α-pinene causes rearrangements to members of the bornyl, fenchyl, and p-menthane series. Technical processes for manufacture of pine oil and camphene are based on these reactions. Hydrogenation of α-pinene yields pinane; the *cis*-isomer is favored (4). Pinane is converted to pinane hydroperoxide by air oxidation on a small commercial scale.

Uses. α-Pinene has two major uses: conversion to synthetic pine oil by hydration with aqueous mineral acids, and isomerization to camphene. See below under Camphene; Pine oils. Considerable amounts of monoterpene monocyclic hydrocarbons (*p*-menthadienes) are formed as by-products in these processes. See below under Monocyclic monoterpene hydrocarbons. Smaller quantities of α-pinene are used for the manufacture of terpin hydrate, terpene resins, and minor products. See below under Terpin hydrate; Terpene resins.

β-Pinene. *Source and Manufacture.* Like α-pinene, β-pinene is obtained by rectification of turpentine, chiefly the sulfate type. Typical commercial purities are 80–95% β-pinene, depending on the use intended. An antioxidant is usually added to β-pinene which is to be stored under ordinary conditions. Physical properties of commercial grades of β-pinene are given in manufacturers' literature. Some typical values are sp gr, 15.6/15.6°C, 0.870–0.873; n_D^{20}, 1.477; color, 10 APHA; boiling range (5–95%), 165–168°C.

Reactions. The technologically important reactions are detailed among topics given under Uses. β-Pinene undergoes hydration to pine oil and isomerization to camphene, thus resembling α-pinene. It is richer in energy (5) and more reactive than α-pinene. Being more expensive than α-pinene, it is used only in reactions where α-pinene cannot serve as well. β-Pinene is readily converted to α-pinene by using certain acids, bases, and hydrogenation catalysts (6). *l*-α-Pinene can be made in good yield this way. The reaction is reversible, with the equilibrium containing 3–6% β-pinene, depending chiefly on temperature. Because of the price differential between the pinenes, some effort has been made to utilize this interconversion to convert the cheaper and more plentiful α-pinene to β-pinene. However, the low amount of β-pinene at equilibrium and the boiling point relationship make for a large heat requirement and high equipment investment, so the process is not economically attractive.

β-Pinene undergoes autoxidation to yield oxygenated terpenes with the pinane skeleton (7), but no commercial application seems to have been made. Natural *l*-β-pinene undergoes thermal isomerization to give myrcene, *l*-limonene, and ψ-limonene (8). This mixture is used for the commercial manufacture of several important chemicals. See below under Myrcene. Hydrogenation of natural β-pinene gives *l*-pinane, chiefly cis, of high optical purity (4). *l*-*cis*-Pinane has been proposed as an intermediate to *d*-linalool and to *d*-citronellol and its derivatives, but these syntheses have not been commercialized. β-Pinene reacts with formaldehyde to give the alcohol nopol.

β-pinene   +   HCHO   →   nopol

Uses. The major uses of β-pinene are for polymerization to terpene resins and pyrolysis to myrcene. See below under Myrcene; Terpene Resins. Nopyl acetate is used as an odorant in perfumes.

Camphene. *Source and Manufacture.* *dl*-Camphene is obtained by the isomerization of α-pinene, using solid acidic minerals such as silica, alumina, titania, and various clays as catalysts (9). The yield and purity of the camphene obtained depends on the selection and treatment of the catalyst. The reaction medium is generally the hydrocarbon itself, and the isomerization is usually carried out at the reflux temperature. The reaction is quite exothermic, inasmuch as it involves the release of the strain energy of α-pinene, and can be dangerous if the heat is not liberated in a controlled manner. A variety of isomeric hydrocarbons is formed but, by suitable selection of catalyst and conditions, a yield of 70–80% camphene and tricyclene is obtained. These two hydrocarbons are in equilibrium with each other in the presence of a protonating catalyst, and together constitute commercial camphene. The symmetrical structure of tricyclene precludes optical activity. For the major technical uses both hydrocarbons give the same products. The other products of the α-pinene isomerization reaction are primarily the monocyclic hydrocarbons (*p*-menthadienes).

α-pinene   camphene   tricyclene   α- and γ-terpinenes   dipentene and terpinolene

This reaction is called the Wagner-Meerwein rearrangement after early workers who made important contributions to the understanding of it. In the commercial process, fenchenes are almost totally avoided, and this suggests that with the best of the solid catalysts, protonation is almost exclusively from one side (see Pine oils). The commercial camphene is separated from the monocyclic hydrocarbons by rectification. Grades are determined by the end use intended. Camphene with a melting point of 46°C and a good odor is required for the manufacture of olfactory products. Physical properties of commercial grades of camphene are given in manufacturers' literature. Glidden-Durkee Division of SCM Corporation gives for its camphene-46: sp gr, 15.6/15.6°C, 0.873; sp gr, 50/15.6°C, 0.847; freezing point, 45.9°C; boiling range (5–95%), 156–159°C; camphene content, 79%, balance principally tricyclene. Specifications of camphene used captively are not published.

Reactions. Most acidic catalysts cause camphene to rearrange, yielding derivatives with an isobornyl structure. The reaction with acetic acid to give isobornyl acetate is typical. Some 6-exo-yl exoisocamphane (pseudobornyl) derivatives (10) are also usually formed. See below under Isobornyl acetate.

Uses. Large quantities of camphene are chlorinated up to about 68% chlorine to give the valuable insecticide toxaphene. The next largest use is the reaction with acetic acid to manufacture isobornyl acetate, a perfume component with a characteristic pine-needle odor, which is also an intermediate for synthetic camphor. Other important uses are the manufacture of the insecticide Thanite (isobornyl thiocyanacetate) (Hercules Incorporated), and of specialty aromatics such as camphene–phenol derivatives.

3-Carene. *Source and Manufacture.* 3-Carene occurs in turpentines derived from *Ginus ponderosa* in the U.S., *Pinus sylvestris* in Europe, and *Pinus longifolia* in India. Concentrations of 3-carene are obtained in the rectification of these turpentines for recovery of the pinenes, chiefly α-pinene.

Reactions. 3-Carene is not used in commercial reactions at the present time. Unlike the pinenes, it does not yield camphene, does not undergo efficient hydration to pine oil, and is not polymerized to a hard terpene resin. It undergoes autoxidation more readily than any of the other major components of commercial turpentines, yielding oxygenated terpenes with a carane skeleton. 3-Carene has high thermal stability (11) and is unaffected by thermal treatment which causes isomerization of the pinenes. In the presence of certain catalysts it forms an equilibrium with its position isomer (12), variously known as 4-carene and 2-carene,

depending on the numbering system used. Hydrogenation of 3-carene yields carane (chiefly cis) and/or 1,1,4-trimethylcycloheptane, depending on catalyst and conditions (13). 3-Carene has been converted to *d*- and *l*-chrysanthemic acids (14). It reacts with acids more sluggishly than do the pinenes, and yields *m*- and *p*-menthadienes. *p*-Menthadienes from acid isomerization of the pinenes are often used in the processes for the manufacture of *p*-cymene; it is important not to get 3-carene or its derivatives into these processes, in order to avoid contamination of the *p*-cymene by *m*-cymene.

Uses. 3-Carene has only solvent uses at the present time.

Monocyclic Monoterpene Hydrocarbons. The important monocyclic monoterpene hydrocarbons are limonene (dipentene) (**5**); terpinolene (**12**); α-terpinene (**10**); γ-terpinene (**11**); isoterpinolene (2,4(8)-*p*-menthadiene) (**13**); 3,8-*p*-menthadiene (**7**); α-phellandrene (**8**); β-phellandrene (**9**); *p*-menthane, *cis*- and *trans*- (**4**); and *p*-cymene (**16**).

Source and Manufacture. Relatively small amounts of the monocyclic monoterpene hydrocarbons are obtained by the rectification of crude sulfate turpentine. Larger amounts arise from extraction of southeastern pine stumps and as by-products in the conversion of α-pinene to synthetic pine oil or camphene. The first-formed monocyclic hydrocarbons from acid isomerization of α-pinene are limonene and terpinolene. These and all other *p*-menthadienes undergo further isomerization in the presence of acid to give a mixture of α- and γ-terpinenes, isoterpinolene, and 3,8-*p*-menthadiene. The last four form an equilibrium composition if contact with the acid is maintained long enough (15). The first three of this group can be fractionated from the equilibration mixture in technical purity. The phellandrenes occur in the monocyclic hydrocarbon fractions of turpentines, and the *p*-menthanes and *p*-cymene occur in the monocyclic hydrocarbon fraction of extract from pine stumps. In addition, small amounts of cineoles occur in the monocyclic hydrocarbon fraction from pine stumps and of sulfate turpentines, and fair amounts are formed in the commercial hydration of α-pinene to synthetic pine oil.

The monocyclic monoterpenes are produced as technical mixtures by fractional distillation from any of the sources mentioned above. Mixtures that meet the physical properties required by government specifications such as TT-D-376C are usually sold as "dipentene." Mixtures with other properties may be called dipentene or be sold under trade names. GC (gas chromatography) analysis (Carbowax column) (Union Carbide Company) of a dipentene of the former type shows the following composition:

Component	Percent	Component	Percent
p-menthanes	6	1,8-cineole	2
carvomenthene (1-menthene)	4	γ-terpinene	2
α-phellandrene	2	p-cymene	19
α-terpinene/1,4-cineole	8	terpinolene	3
dipentene	50	other	2
β-phellandrene	2		

Trade-name solvent-grade monocyclic terpene mixtures are specified by physical properties. Some typical mixtures are given in Table 4.

Table 4. Typical Physical Properties of Trade-Name Monocyclic Terpene Hydrocarbon Solvents[a]

Trade name	Manufacturer	Sp gr, 15.6/15.6°C	n_D^{20}	Color (Hazen)	Distillation range, °C 5%	95%
Solvenol No. 1	Hercules Inc.	0.854	1.475	30	176	184
Solvenol No. 2		0.854	1.473	45	173	182
Unitene LP	Union-Camp Corp.	0.848		35		
Unitene D		0.870	1.476	20	174	187
Glidco Dipentene 300	Glidden-Durkee Div., SCM Corporation	0.855–0.880	1.471–1.485	50, max	170, initial	190
Acintene DP	Arizona Chemical Co.	0.8550	1.4780	40	178	187

[a] Data from manufacturers' literature.

p-Cymene is manufactured by dehydrogenation of the mixed p-menthadienes from any of the above sources. It is necessary to avoid menthadienes from carene-bearing species, which usually contain some sylvestrene (a m-menthadiene). p-Menthane is made by complete hydrogenation of the various monocyclic terpene mixtures. A mixture of about 70% p-cymene and 30% p-menthane results from complete disproportionation of mixed p-menthadienes by refluxing over various hydrogenation catalysts. The two products are separated by column distillation. Commercial p-cymene analyzes over 98% pure by GC. Other properties are sp gr, 15.6/15.6°C, 0.861; n_D^{20}, 1.490; boiling range (5–95%), 176–178°C.

d-Limonene is obtained as a by-product from the citrus juice industry. After extraction of the juice from the fruit in a mechanical extractor, the orange (or other citrus) skins are treated with lime and pressed. (Approx 0.15–0.30% calcium hydroxide is added; this causes a collapse (syneresis) of the spongy structure of the pulp so that the juice is readily expressed.) The press liquor is evaporated to produce citrus molasses (see Vol. 13, p. 617) and the limonene is recovered from the condensate from the evaporators.

The source of the limonene is the oil cells in the skin of the orange. These are also the source of "cold-pressed orange oil" which is used for orange flavoring. Citrus limonene typically analyzes 90–95% pure by gas chromatography. Impurities are fatty aldehydes, myrcene, and terpene alcohols, chiefly acyclic. Citrus limonene which has been allowed to autoxidize contains carvone, carveols, and other oxygenated products. Physical properties of various brands of citrus limonene are given in suppliers' literature.

High-purity dipentene (95%) has been manufactured by thermal isomerization of α-pinene. Yields are 50–60%, with alloocimene and its dimers as coproducts. The dipentene is isolated by rectification.

Reactions. All of the p-menthadienes can be dehydrogenated to p-cymene, hydrogenated to p-menthane, and disproportionated to a mixture of the two. p-Cymene and p-menthane can be autoxidized to their respective hydroperoxides. Partial disproportionation or partial hydrogenation of mixed p-menthadienes can be conducted so as to obtain useful amounts of 3-menthene (16). This reaction has been used for small commercial manufacture of *dl*-menthol. The menthadienes react with maleic anhydride either by Diels-Alder or by substitution.

d-Limonene from citrus is converted to *l*-carvone via the nitrosochloride and oxime (17). It can be partially hydrogenated to give carvomenthene. Autoxidation of limonene readily occurs to give a variety of oxygenated monocyclic terpenes (18).

Uses. The major uses of turpentine-derived monocyclic monoterpene hydrocarbons are dehydrogenation to p-cymene, hydrogenation to p-menthane, and as solvents. Maleic anhydride reaction products are used in the preparation of alkyd resins. See Alkyd resins (Vol. 1, p. 862). Citrus *d*-limonene is used as a raw material for manufacture of *l*-carvone, and as an odor and flavor chemical. p-Cymene is used as the raw material for commercial manufacture of p-cresol, as a heat-exchange medium, and for minor synthetic uses. p-Menthane is used to make p-menthane hydroperoxide, a polymerization catalyst. High-purity dipentene and citrus limonene have found use in sulfurized lubrication oil additives (see Sulfurization), and in terpene resin manufacture. Commercial dipentene is used as an odorant in industrial and household specialty products.

Myrcene. *Source and Manufacture.* Myrcene is manufactured by the pyrolysis of β-pinene (8). β-Pinene is vaporized and passed through a hot tube at about 550°C, whereby the pinene skeleton is cleaved to myrcene, limonene, and ψ-limonene. (See pyrolysis of α-pinene under Terpene resins.) The products are explained by assuming that the reaction proceeds through an allylic diradical:

l-β-pinene

myrcene
75–80%

ψ-limonene
3–4%

l-limonene
10%

Small amounts of cracking products (eg isoprene), and of myrcene dimer (α-camphorene) are also formed.

It should be pointed out that the postulated radicals do not readily induce polymerization or otherwise show the usual behavior of free radicals. The odd electrons are apparently only intramolecular distances apart and so the radicals are not really free in the ordinary sense. The rearrangements then are likely to be intramolecularly concerted.

High-purity myrcene can be isolated from the pyrolysis mixture by careful rectification. However, myrcene readily dimerizes when heated for a long period, and losses due to dimerization may be heavy during a prolonged distillation. Technical-grade myrcene is simply the entire pyrolyzate from 95% β-pinene and has the composition shown above. Some physical properties are sp gr, 15.6/15.6°C, 0.806; n_D^{20}, 1.471. Myrcene is usually protected during storage with an antioxidant. Analysis is generally made by gas chromatography.

Reactions. The important reactions of myrcene are those leading to linalool and geraniol and their derivatives. Hydrogen chloride adds to myrcene to give:

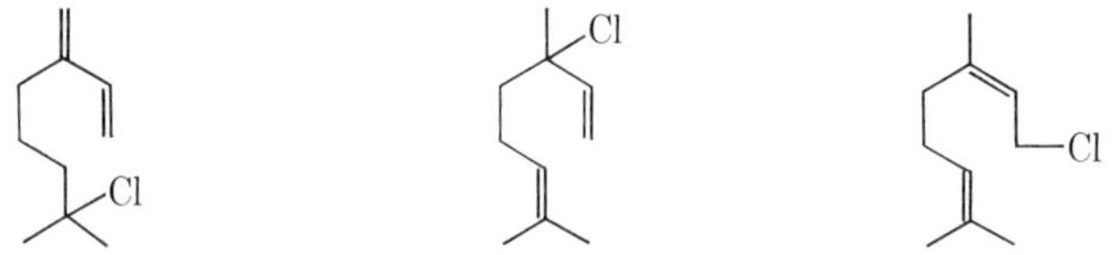

myrcenyl chloride	linalyl chloride	geranyl chloride (trans)
		neryl chloride (cis) (shown)

If copper is present, the addition of HCl takes place preferentially at the conjugated system (19), so that little myrcenyl chloride is formed; or, the addition can be made without copper, and copper then added to effect redistribution of the HCl (20). The primary and tertiary allylic chlorides are in equilibrium with each other in the presence of copper. Linalyl chloride is formed at low temperature and with minimum copper; so is the kinetic product, but it isomerizes to the primary chlorides if allowed to stand with the catalyst at room temperature (allylic rearrangement). The system appears to have reducing properties. Hydrolysis of the mixed chlorides prepared without copper gives a mixture of myrcenol, linalool, α-terpineol, and very little geraniol. Hydrolysis of the geranyl chloride gives chiefly the rearranged products linalool and α-terpineol, the former by allylic rearrangement and the latter by cyclization of the intermediate carbonium ion generated by solvolytic removal of the chloride ion.

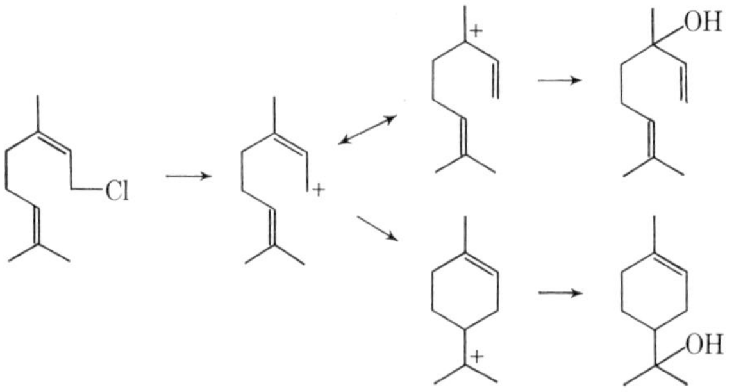

The myrcenol is avoided if copper is used during the addition of HCl. Myrcenol can be made selectively by forming an SO_2 adduct (a sulfolene) at the conjugated part of myrcene, hydrating the isolated double bond, and then removing the SO_2 (21).

$$HC\!\!=\!\!C\text{—}CH_2\text{—}CH_2\text{—}CH\!\!=\!\!C\!\!<^{CH_3}_{CH_3}$$

SO_2 adduct of myrcene

isohexenyl

Usually the hydrochlorination is carried out so as to produce the primary chlorides, and these are converted by reaction with sodium acetate to geranyl, neryl, and linalyl esters. The geraniol/nerol mixture serves as an intermediate for the manufacture of citronellol, citronellal, citral, hydroxycitronellal, the ionones and methylionones, and ultimately vitamin A. By changing conditions, linalool can be made the main product. The geranyl/neryl chloride can be converted directly to citral by treatment with salts of nitronic acid (22). See Nitroparaffins, Vol. 13, p. 864.

$$CH_3\text{—}CH\text{—}CH_3 \qquad CH_3\text{—}C\text{—}CH_3 \qquad CH_3\text{—}C\text{—}CH_3$$
$$| \qquad\qquad\qquad \| \qquad\qquad\qquad \|$$
$$NO_2 \qquad\qquad\qquad NO_2H \qquad\qquad\qquad NO_2Na$$

2-nitropropane   aci-2-nitropropane   sodium salt of 2-propane-
             (2-propanenitronic acid)   nitronic acid

Myrcene can be dihydrochlorinated, one mole of HCl adding at the conjugated system, and the other at the isolated double bond. The dihydrochloride may be used when a product with two oxygen functions, such as hydroxycitronellal, is desired. See under the individual terpenes.

Myrcene can be selectively hydrogenated to form several isomeric dihydromyrcenes (23), sometimes in quite high purity, and to a tetrahydromyrcene, in which only the isopropylidene double bond remains. These hydromyrcenes are useful for preparing specialty perfume alcohols.

Uses. The major use of myrcene is as an intermediate for the manufacture of perfume chemicals, such as geraniol, nerol, linalool, citral, citronellol, citronellal, hydroxycitronellal, and the ionones.

Pine Oils. The major components of pine oils are α-terpineol (**37**); β-terpineol (**38**); γ-terpineol (**39**); α-fenchol (**44**); borneol/isoborneol (**43**); dihydro-α-terpineol (**32**); fenchone (**52**); camphor (**51**); and the phenol ethers estragole and anethole, as shown:

estragole   anethole

In addition, varying amounts of monoterpene hydrocarbons are present. The first six formulas represent the most important components of synthetic pine oil. Natural pine oil from stumps contains the same components except for γ-terpineol, plus all of the remaining components. Sulfate pine oil may contain, in addition, appreciable amounts of sesquiterpene hydrocarbons.

Source and Manufacture. Natural pine oils are produced by distillation of the extract of southeastern pine stumps. Commercial grades are obtained by blending selected distillation cuts. Sulfate pine oil is a distillation cut obtained in the rectification of crude sulfate turpentine, and is considered the poorest grade of pine oil. Synthetic pine oil is produced by the hydration of α-pinene with aqueous mineral acids (24), followed by distillation to separate the excess hydrocarbons. A number of concomitant and sequential reactions take place to give a mixture of products.

In general, the reaction sequence is initiated by protonation of pinene:

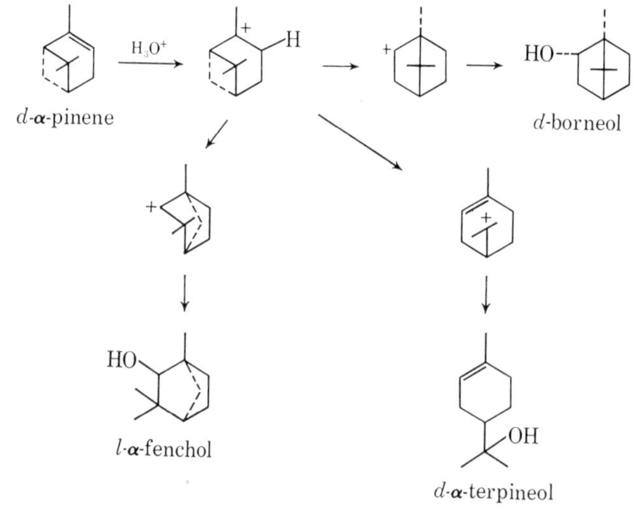

d-α-pinene   *d*-borneol

l-α-fenchol

d-α-terpineol

Apparently two stereochemically distinct carbonium ions are formed initially; one of them rearranges to fenchol and terpineol, and the other to borneol and terpineol (25). Possibly these are the result of protonation of the pinene molecule from front and back sides.

Hydrocarbons are formed when the carbonium ions eliminate a proton:

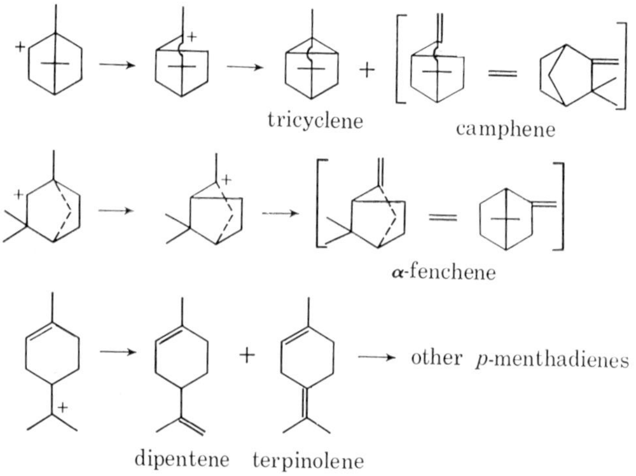

tricyclene   camphene

α-fenchene

dipentene   terpinolene   other *p*-menthadienes

Some α-terpineol undergoes further hydration to terpin when it comes into contact with the process acid. The terpin undergoes partial dehydration to other terpineols and cineoles (see under Terpineols):

terpin α β γ 1,8–cineole   1,4–cineole

The tertiary alcohols also undergo slow dehydration when in contact with the acid, but the secondary alcohols are stable. By controlling the reaction variables (time, temperature, acid strength, mixing) the technical operation is usually carried out so as to produce a maximum of alcohols and a minimum of hydrocarbons and cineoles. The alcohols are separated from the hydrocarbons and cineoles by distillation and constitute the synthetic pine oils of commerce. Different grades of synthetic pine oil are prepared by selection of distillation cuts, and blending.

Commercial pine oils are specified by physical properties, and by alcohol content as determined by dehydration. Some brands are mixtures of natural and synthetic pine oils. Typical properties are given in Table 5. Commercial pine oils with lower alcohol contents than those shown in Table 5 are also available. These grades have a correspondingly higher content of monoterpene hydrocarbons. Other properties sometimes specified are color, flash point, freezing point, and secondary alcohol content. In some uses odor is important. The major difference in odor between natural and synthetic pine oils is due to the presence of phenol ethers (anethole and estragole) in the former.

Detailed analysis is usually carried out by gas chromatography. For example, a commercial pine oil showed the following components, in order of elution on a Carbowax column:

Component	Percent	Component	Percent
hydrocarbons eluting before terpinolene	1.3	β-terpineol	1.5
terpinolene	2.7	estragole	0.6
fenchone	0.6	isoborneol	1.6
camphor	3.6	α-terpineol	59.0
trans-dihydro-α-terpineol	5.8	borneol	7.4
α-fenchol/terpinen-1-ol	10.6	*cis*-anethole	0.4
terpinen-4-ol	3.7	*trans*-anethole	0.5
		miscellaneous	0.7

U.S. production of pine oils for the crop year April 1, 1967, to March 31, 1968, was reported to be 14,256,000 gal.

Reactions. Distillation cuts of the pine oils rich in α-terpineol are acetylated to form terpinyl acetate. Estragole derived from natural or sulfate pine oils is isomerized with caustic alkali to produce anethole. No other commercially important reactions are carried out with pine oil.

Uses. Pine oil is widely used as a frother in the separation of minerals by flotation. See Flotation. The textile industry uses it as a penetrant, dispersing agent, wetting agent, and inhibitor of bacterial growth in practically all wet-processing of cotton, silk, rayon, and woolen goods, including scouring, bleaching, desizing, fulling, degumming, dyeing, and printing. Pine oil is used as a solvent and bactericide in

Table 5. Typical Physical Properties of Commercial Pine Oils[a]

Trade name	Manufacturer	Sp gr, 15.6/15.6°C	Total alcohols,[b] %	Distillation range, °C 5%	Distillation range, °C 95%
Herco	Hercules Inc.	0.934	85	206	220
Yarmor 302		0.941	91	212	210
Unipine 85	Union-Camp Corp.	0.932	87.8	198	222
Unipine 75		0.921	74.5	193	218
Minol	Newport	0.932	82, min	200	220
Pynol		0.934	86, min	204	219
Glidco 150	Glidden	0.924–0.926	83, min	190, min	226, max
Glidco 230		0.934, min	90, min	200, min	226, max
Cropine 29	Crosby	0.920	79	200	219

[a] Data from manufacturers' literature.

[b] Determined by dehydration. The standard procedure is to dehydrate the alcohols to olefins, collect the water formed, and calculate the percent alcohols based on the amount of water obtained, using the formula of pine oil alcohols as $C_{10}H_{17}OH$.

soaps and other disinfecting compounds. It serves as a solvent for chlorinated phenols used in the treatment of lumber and as a preservative for casein and other proteins in adhesives and water paints. Some pine oil fractions are used as odorants in commercial cleaning compounds. Terpineol-rich fractions low in secondary alcohols are used in the manufacture of lower grades of terpinyl acetate.

Terpin Hydrate. *Source and Manufacture.* Terpin (*trans-p*-menthane-1,8-diol) occurs naturally as the hydrate, with one molecule of water of crystallization, in the extract of southeastern pine stumps. After distilling off the terpene hydrocarbons and alcohols, the remaining crude rosin contains anhydrous terpin, which is removed by steam distillation. Crystalline terpin hydrate is recovered from the distillate and purified. By virtue of its high melting point and insolubility in common solvents, terpin hydrate is readily freed of impurities. Terpin hydrate is also manufactured by the hydration of α-pinene. In this process, α-pinene is stirred with dilute sulfuric acid under conditions which favor further hydration of the first-formed α-terpineol. The resulting terpin hydrate crystals are separated and purified. The material is available in NF and in technical grades, the latter being 99% terpin hydrate.

Reactions. Terpin hydrate is partly dehydrated to produce odor-grade terpineols. Terpin hydrate readily loses its water of crystallization when heated above its melting point, producing anhydrous terpin. The loss occurs below the melting point at reduced pressure or in the presence of desiccants. The water of crystallization is regained by contact with moisture.

Uses. Terpin hydrate, NF grade, is used for medicinal purposes, especially for the manufacture of cough syrups in which it functions as an expectorant. The major use of terpin hydrate is as an intermediate for the manufacture of perfume-grade terpineols.

Terpineols. *Source and Manufacture.* Terpineols suitable for manufacture of the lower grades of terpinyl acetate and some other odorant uses are obtained by rectification of natural and synthetic pine oils. These terpineols are largely α-terpineol. Synthetic pine oil yields a product containing some γ-terpineol. Both types usually contain small amounts of borneol. Specifications vary with the manufacturer and are given in manufacturers' literature.

The perfume-grade terpineols are manufactured by the partial dehydration of terpin hydrate. Steam distillation of a weakly acidic aqueous slurry of purified terpin hydrate yields the mixed terpineols (given here according to elution order on a Carbowax column): (*1*) terpinen-1-ol (**35**); (*2*) terpinen-4-ol (**36**); (*3*) *trans*-β-terpineol (**38**); (*4*) δ-terpineol (**40**); (*5*) *cis*-β-terpineol (**38**); (*6*) α-terpineol (**37**); and γ-terpineol (**39**).

Small amounts of *p*-menthadienes and cineoles are produced as by-products. The steam distillate is then rectified to produce the terpineol of commerce. Highest odor grades are produced by the aromatics industry and are known as "terpineol prime" and "terpineol extra." These are selected on the basis of odor, but manufacturers also publish physical properties to go with their grades of these products. A product of this general type but not odor-graded is produced by the naval stores industry (Terpineol 318 (Hercules Incorporated)). The Essential Oil Association of the U.S.A. also publishes physical standards for terpineol. As with all perfume materials, odor quality largely determines the value of the product.

All of the alcohols can be separated by gas chromatography using a Carbowax column, except γ- from α-terpineol, which elute together as a large final peak. The gamma content can be determined by infrared (peak at 11.5 μ). After acetylation all seven acetates can be separated by GC (α-terpinyl acetate last), and this provides a method of complete analysis.

A high-beta-content terpineol can be obtained by acid-catalyzed dehydration of terpin in a nonaqueous system, if a demand should develop for such a material (26).

GC analysis of a terpineol from terpin hydrate showed the following percentage composition (data from Hercules Laboratories):

terpinen-1-ol	2.4	high-boiling β-terpineol	2.5
low-boiling β-terpineol	15.5	γ-terpineol	15.5
terpinen-4-ol	1.3	α-terpineol	62.1
δ-terpineol	0.7		

U.S. production of terpineols was reported to be 3.5 million lb in 1966. Average value was 32¢/lb.

Reactions. The main reaction of commercial significance which is carried out on odor-grade terpineol is esterification, primarily acetylation. Some terpineol is hydrogenated and acetylated to give dihydroterpinyl acetate.

Uses. Odor-grade terpineols and their esters are used as odorants in perfumery.

Menthol. *Source and Manufacture.* By far the largest part of the menthol produced is the *l*-isomer, obtained by crystallization of Japanese mint oil. See Oils, essential. The residual oil after separation of the menthol crystals is known as cornmint oil, and is still rich in menthol. In addition the oil also contains much menthone which is convertible into *l*-menthol. Accordingly, additional *l*-menthol is obtained from cornmint oil by chemical processing and rectification. The *U.S. Pharmacopeia* sets standards for levorotatory and racemic menthols. Non-USP grades together with specifications are sometimes offered in manufacturers' literature.

A small amount of *l*-menthol is produced from natural *d*-citronellal isolated from citronella oil. In this process, catalysts such as copper metal or silica gel (27) are used to cyclize citronellal to isopulegol, which is then hydrogenated to menthol.

The crude menthol from this step contains stereoisomeric menthols besides *l*-menthol, and separation of these is made to obtain *l*-menthol meeting USP standards. High-efficiency rectification, crystallization, and use of crystalline derivatives are employed. The isomer separation may be made at the isopulegol stage (27). The manufacture of *l*-menthol from natural citronellal is a marginal business and depends on low prices for citronellal and high prices for menthol.

It has long been known that *l*-menthol can be made by resolution of *dl*-menthol. Recently it has become possible to make *d*-citronellal from β-pinene (28) (this could then become a source of *l*-menthol):

Neither of these processes seems to have been commercialized.

Racemic menthol is manufactured by the hydrogenation of synthetic thymol. All four isomers of *dl*-menthol are obtained. By use of copper chromite and relatively high temperature and pressure, the mixture is obtained as an equilibrium which contains about 60% *dl*-menthol, the balance being other isomers. The *dl*-menthol is isolated by high-efficiency fractionation and may be further purified through crystalline derivatives to meet USP standards. The other menthol isomers are re-equilibrated by heating with copper chromite and hydrogen. Menthol from thymol (*m*-cresol) is the oldest example of the commercial production of a terpene starting from a nonterpene.

Racemic menthol is also produced commercially from 3-menthene. Mixed *p*-menthadienes, preferably a mixture of α- and γ-terpinenes and isoterpinolene such as is obtained by acid treatment of any *p*-menthadiene (15), are converted to 3-menthene by disproportionation with a Pd catalyst or by partial hydrogenation (16). Alternatively the 3-menthene may be made by hydrogenating α-terpineol or α-terpineol-rich cuts and treating the dihydroterpineol with an acid. The 3-menthene is hydroxylated or epoxidized, and this product is rearranged to menthone by boiling with dilute sulfuric acid (29). The menthone is then hydrogenated to mixed menthols, and the process from this point is the same as the synthesis from thymol. Alternatively the menthone may be reduced with sodium to menthols.

In 1966 the total amount of menthol imported into and produced in the United States was 2.5 million lb. Average value was $4.13/lb.

Reactions. Small amounts of menthols are converted to menthone and to acetate esters. The geometric isomers interconvert when heated with a hydrogenation catalyst and hydrogen, or with metal alkoxides. Menthol has an extensive chemistry, little of which is commercially important.

Uses. Menthol is used in cigarets and cosmetics for its cooling effect, and in medicinals. The cooling effect is associated with the *l*-isomer, so that racemic menthol is not fully equivalent to *l*-menthol in this respect. Menthol, its geometric isomer neomenthol, menthone, and menthyl esters are used to compound artificial peppermint flavors.

Linalool. *Source and Manufacture.* Natural linalool is produced from rosewood oil, in which it occurs as the major component. Natural linalyl acetate is produced from petitgrain oil and from rosewood oil. Other essential oils are sometimes used as a source of linalool. See Oils, essential.

Synthetic linalool is manufactured from myrcene and from an intermediate in the total synthesis of vitamin A. Linalool has been made by the pyrolysis of pinanol, but this does not seem to have developed into a commercial process (see below).

The synthesis from myrcene involves the addition of HCl to technical myrcene, which is the whole pyrolyzate from β-pinene. The addition reaction is run so as to obtain chiefly the primary chlorides, a mixture of geranyl and neryl chlorides. See above under Myrcene. The mixed chlorides are reacted with sodium acetate in the presence of copper to give linalyl acetate (31). An allylic rearrangement takes place in this step.

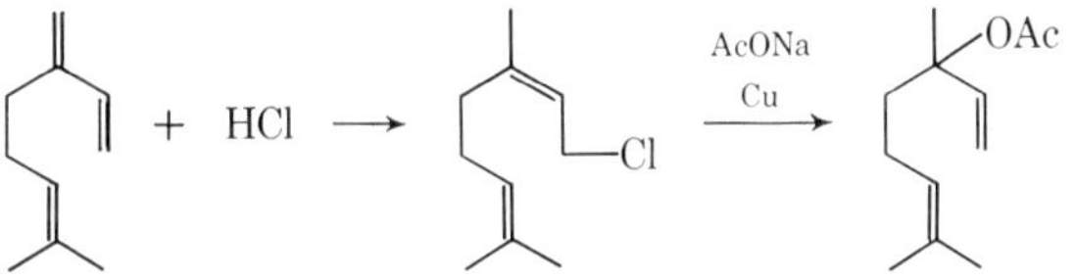

$$\text{(structure)} + \text{HCl} \longrightarrow \text{(structure)}-\text{Cl} \xrightarrow[\text{Cu}]{\text{AcONa}} \text{(structure)}-\text{OAc}$$

Saponification of the acetate then yields the linalool, which is purified by careful rectification (see under Geraniol).

The synthesis through a vitamin A intermediate involves the following sequence, which utilizes the Nef reaction and the Carroll reaction:

$$HC\equiv CNa + CH_3COCH_3 \longrightarrow HC\equiv C-\underset{\underset{OH}{|}}{\overset{\overset{CH_3}{|}}{C}}-CH_3 \xrightarrow{H_2} H_2C=CH-\underset{\underset{OH}{|}}{\overset{\overset{CH_3}{|}}{C}}-CH_3$$

$$2\ CH_3COCH_3 \xrightarrow{\Delta} 2\ \underset{\text{ketene}}{CH_2=C=O} \longrightarrow CH_3-\underset{\underset{O}{\|}}{C}-CH=C=O$$

diketene

$$CH_3-\underset{\underset{OH}{|}}{\overset{\overset{CH_3}{|}}{C}}-CH=CH_2 + CH_3-\underset{\underset{O}{\|}}{C}-CH=C=O \longrightarrow \overset{\overset{CH_3}{|}}{\underset{\underset{\underset{O}{\|}}{O-C-CH_2-CO-CH_3}}{CH_3-C-CH=CH_2}}$$

$$\downarrow -CO_2$$

$$CH_3-\overset{\overset{CH_3}{|}}{C}=CH-CH_2-CH_2-CO-CH_3$$

methyl heptenone

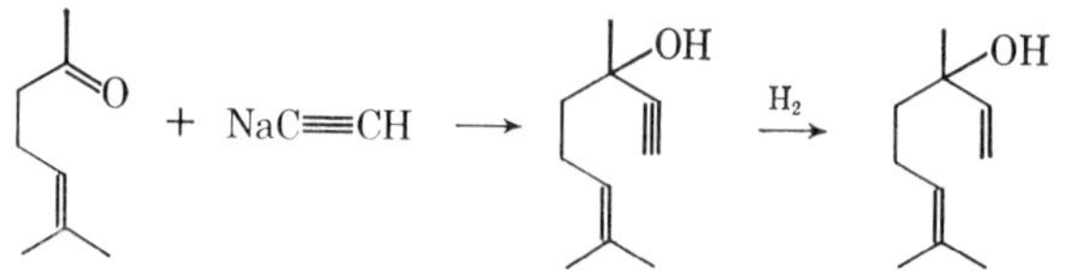

dehydrolinalool   linalool

The selective partial hydrogenation of the acetylenic double bond is usually done with a lead-poisoned palladium catalyst (Lindlar catalyst), but it may be done in other ways. This is an example of the few productions of a terpene from a nonterpene raw material.

Both of the above processes produce *dl*-linalool. Optically active linalool has been made experimentally, but not commercially, by the following method (30):

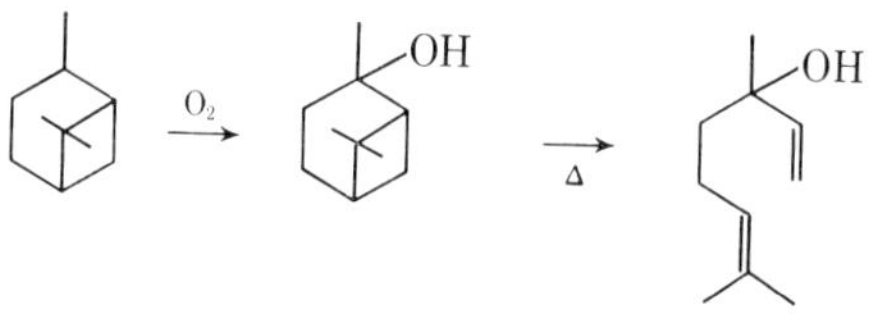

Physical properties of commercial grades of linalool are given in manufacturers' literature. Properties of linalool from rosewood oil are also specified by the Essential Oil Association of the U.S.A. Synthetic linalool shows purities of 98% and higher by GC. Natural linalool is less pure. As with all perfume materials, odor quality, which is not readily described, largely determines the value of the product.

Reactions. The most important reaction of linalool at the present time is conversion to esters, chiefly the acetate. This must be done with great care to avoid extensive rearrangement to geraniol and nerol, and dehydration to hydrocarbons. In the total synthesis route, there is the alternative of acetylating the dehydrolinalool and then performing the final hydrogenation. Linalool is used to make synthetic nerolidol. See below under Sesquiterpenes.

Acid-catalyzed rearrangement of linalool to geraniol and nerol, and to α-terpineol, is general, but in no case is the yield good enough to use linalool for the economic preparation of the primary alcohols.

Linalool can be oxidized to a mixture of *cis*- and *trans*-citrals by the chromic acid method, but except in special circumstances linalool is too expensive and the yield too poor to make this of interest.

Uses. Linalool and its esters are used in perfumes and flavors. Some linalool is hydrogenated to tetrahydrolinalool, which is a perfume chemical. See under Sesquiterpenes for use in manufacture of nerolidol.

Geraniol (*trans*) **and Nerol** (*cis*). *Source and Manufacture.* Natural geraniol is produced chiefly by the rectification of citronella oil. This oil contains citronellal as the other major component, along with appreciable citronellol and many minor compounds. See Oils, essential.

Synthetic geraniol is now manufactured in large quantities from myrcene, and serves as an intermediate to a number of related materials, as well as having its own use as an odorant. Technical myrcene, prepared by the pyrolysis of β-pinene, is hydrochlorinated under conditions to give chiefly the primary chlorides, geranyl chloride and neryl chloride. See above under Myrcene. The crude mixture, freed of copper if a copper catalyst was used in preparing the chlorides, is heated with sodium acetate to give a mixture of geranyl and neryl acetates. The reaction is facilitated by use of nitrogen bases (32), phosphorus analogs (33), special solvents (34), and in proprietary

$$\text{(structure)} + HCl \longrightarrow \text{(structure)}-Cl \xrightarrow{AcONa} \text{(structure)}-OAc$$

ways. The crude primary acetates are then saponified and the alcohols recovered by distillation. Care must be taken to ensure complete removal of chlorides. Geraniol and nerol are obtained in good yield and in a ratio of about 60% geraniol to 40% nerol. A high grade of synthetic geraniol is manufactured by careful rectification. In many cases the refined mixture of geraniol and nerol can be used for perfumery purposes, and this is the usual product sold as synthetic geraniol. The isomers can be separated by high-efficiency fractionation, but there is only a small demand for isolated nerol.

Natural geraniols are available in several grades. Their physical properties are described in manufacturers' literature. The compositions of both natural and synthetic geraniols are most commonly determined by GC. Odor quality is a major factor in determining the value of perfume grades.

U.S. production of perfume-grades geraniol in 1966 was reported as 1.1 million lb. Average value was $1.31/lb.

Reactions. Geraniol and nerol can be rearranged to citronellal by heating with a copper catalyst. The citronellal can be reduced to citronellol by chemical (35) or catalytic means, or hydrated to hydroxycitronellal. Geraniol and nerol themselves can be hydrogenated to citronellol (36). Geraniol and nerol can be dehydrogenated to citral by passage over a copper catalyst in the vapor phase under vacuum (37). If heated with metal alcoholates, geraniol and nerol isomerize to isogeraniols. Older literature confused the isogeraniols with nerol.

$$\text{(structure)}-OH$$

isogeraniol

Uses. Geraniol and nerol are used as odorants in perfumery. Technical grades serve as raw material for the manufacture of citronellol, citronellal, citral, hydroxycitronellal, the ionones, and ultimately vitamin A.

Citral. *Source and Manufacture.* Natural citral is obtained by rectification of lemongrass oil, of which it comprises 70–80%. The best grades are purified through the bisulfite compound. Synthetic citral is made by dehydrogenation of synthetic geraniol/nerol made from myrcene. The reaction is carried out over a copper-containing catalyst in the vapor phase under vacuum (37). A mixture of *cis-* and *trans-*citrals (neral and geranial) is obtained.

$$\text{(structure)}-OH \xrightarrow{Cu} \text{(structure)}=O + H_2$$

The Essential Oil Association of the U.S.A. specifies the properties of citral as sp gr, 25/25°C, 0.885–0.891; n_D^{20}, 1.4860–1.4900; aldehyde content, 96% min; bisulfite solubility, 98% minimum at 25°C; optically inactive. Specifications for lower grades are given in manufacturers' literature. Odor quality is, of course, the most important characteristic for the perfume and flavor grades.

U.S. production of citral in 1966 was given as 316,000 lb.

Reactions. Citral has an extensive chemistry, but the only reaction of commercial importance is condensation with acetone or methyl ethyl ketone to produce the ionones and methylionones, respectively. The immediate products are the acyclic pseudo-ionones, which are cyclized by treatment with acidic reagents to the ionones.

Uses. Pure citral is used as an odorant in perfumes and flavors. Large quantities of technical grade material are used in the manufacture of the ionones, methylionones, and vitamin A.

Citronellal. *Source and Manufacture.* Natural *d*-citronellal is obtained by rectification of citronella oil. Synthetic *dl*-citronellal is obtained by rearrangement of synthetic geraniol/nerol over a copper catalyst (38).

Properties of commercial grades of citronellal are given in manufacturers' literature. One producer offers material with sp gr, 25/25°C, 0.852–0.860; n_D^{20}, 1.4460–1.4520; purity by oximation, 85% minimum.

Reactions. The major reactions of citronellal are reduction to citronellol, cyclization to isopulegol, and hydration to hydroxycitronellal. The reduction is carried out by using the Meerwein-Ponndorf method or active metals (35). Citronellal is also catalytically hydrogenated to citronellol. Cyclization to isopulegol for the manufacture of *l*-menthol is carried out with acidic catalysts. In the hydration to hydroxycitronellal, the aldehyde group is first protected by conversion to the sodium bisulfite derivative, the hydration carried out with aqueous mineral acid, and the bisulfite adduct then split to recover the hydrated aldehyde (39). The bisulfite derivative may also be used as a means of purification of citronellal.

Uses. *d*-Citronellal is used for the manufacture of synthetic *l*-menthol. Optically active or racemic citronellal is used for reduction to citronellol or hydration to hydroxycitronellal. Citronellal is also used directly as an odorant.

Citronellol. *Source and Manufacture.* Citronellol is made by reduction of citronellal or of natural or synthetic geraniol. Catalytic hydrogenation (40) and chemical reduction are employed (35). In catalytic hydrogenation it is difficult to avoid formation of some dimethyloctanol, the fully saturated product, which is usually considered to have a less desirable odor. Commercial citronellols often contain some geraniol, the amount depending on method of manufacture, and for some purposes this content is desirable. Optically active citronellol can be made from pinane (28), but this process does not seem to have been commercialized. See above under Menthol.

The Essential Oil Association of the U.S.A. gives the following properties for commercial citronellol from natural sources: sp gr, 25/25°C, 0.850–0.860; n_D^{20}, 1.4540–1.4620; 90% minimum alcohols, calculated as citronellol. Properties of other grades are given in manufacturers' literature.

U.S. production of citronellol in 1966 was given as 653,000 lb. Average value was $1.51/lb.

Reactions. Citronellol can be readily dehydrogenated to citronellal, or hydrated to hydroxycitronellol. The only important reaction of citronellol is esterification.

Uses. Citronellol and its esters are used as odorants.

Hydroxycitronellal. *Source and Manufacture.* Hydroxycitronellal is made by hydration of citronellal (39). The citronellal is first converted to the bisulfite adduct to cover the aldehyde group and to protect against cyclization. The double bond is then hydrated by treatment with aqueous mineral acid; the hydrated aldehyde is regenerated from its bisulfite adduct, and purified by rectification. In recent years processes have been proposed for manufacture of hydroxycitronellal by rearrangement of 1,2-epoxy-3,7-dimethyloctan-8-ol (41), by rearrangement of 3,7-dimethyl-2-octene-1,7-diol (geraniol hydrate) (42), and by dehydrogenation of 3,7-dimethyloctane-1,7-diol (hydroxycitronellol) (43). Hydration of citronellal is the preferred process.

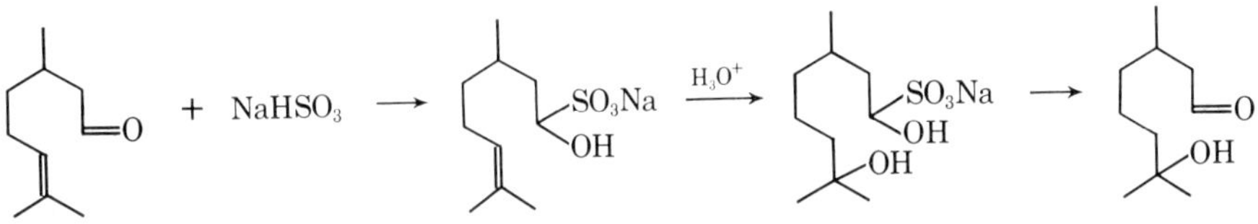

Physical properties of commercial materials are sp gr, 25/25°C, 0.917–0.921; n_D^{20}, 1.4470–1.4500. These materials analyze 98% pure or better by GC. Odor quality largely determines the value.

U.S. production of hydroxycitronellal for 1966 was given as 513,000 lb. Average value was $3.84/lb.

Reactions. A small amount of hydroxycitronellal is converted to the dimethyl acetal. No other reaction of hydroxycitronellal is of technical importance.

Uses. Hydroxycitronellal is used in perfumery.

Ionones and Methylionones. *Source and Manufacture.* The ionones and methylionones are made by cyclization of the corresponding pseudoionones with acidic catalysts. The pseudoionones are made by condensing citral with acetone or methyl ethyl ketone using a base catalyst (44):

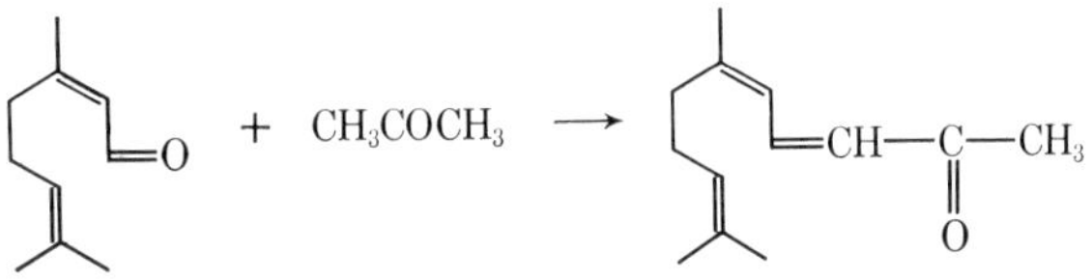

When methyl ethyl ketone is used, the citral can condense on the methyl or on the methylene group. The "methylionones" are derived from condensation on the methyl group of methyl ethyl ketone, and the "isomethylionones" from condensation on the methylene group. Some selectivity is obtained by varying reaction parameters. Both the citrals and the pseudoionones are mixtures of cis and trans isomers. This is of little importance because equilibration occurs under the reaction conditions (45), and both geometric isomers ultimately give the same ionones. Cyclization is accomplished via a carbonium ion reaction, for which H_3PO_4, H_2SO_4, and BF_3 are catalysts:

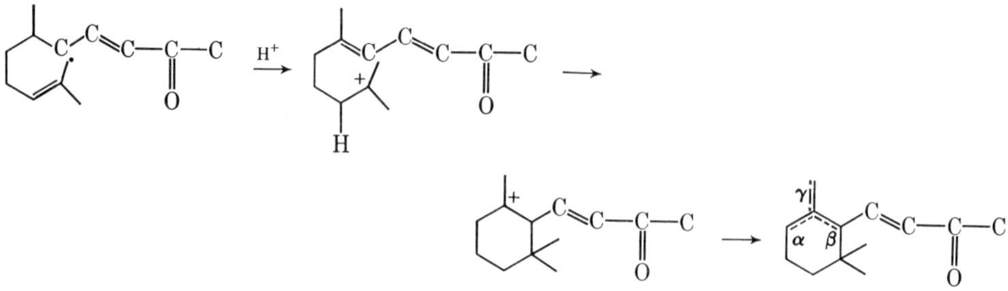

By careful control of reagent and reaction conditions, either the α- or β-isomer can be favored, the β being thermodynamically more stable and therefore obtained with the stronger acids and more vigorous conditions. The α-isomer is the kinetic product.

Another commercial preparation of ionone is a step in the commercial total synthesis of vitamin A. Dehydrolinalool (see above under Linalool) is converted to its acetoacetic ester and this rearranged (Carroll reaction) to give initially the allenic isomer of pseudoionone and then pseudoionone itself (46). The pseudoionone is cyclized in the usual way.

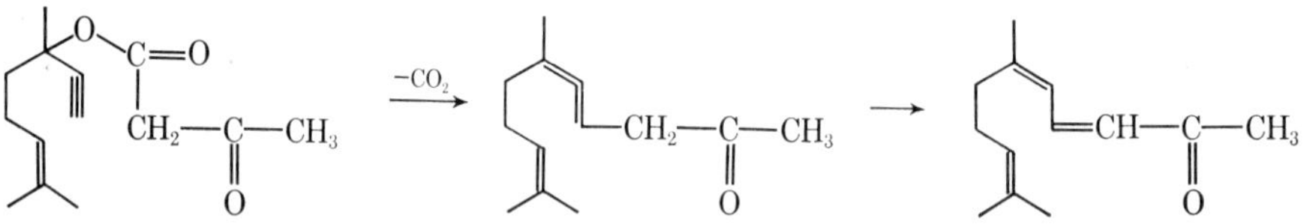

Many grades of ionones and methylionones are offered on the market. Standards for some of the higher perfume grades are given by the Essential Oil Association of the U.S.A. Properties of other grades are given in manufacturers' literature. Odor quality is an important factor in the perfume grades.

U.S. production of perfumery-type ionones and methylionones in 1966 was given as 860,000 lb. Average value was $4.18/lb.

Reactions. The only important reaction of the ionones is the use of β-ionone in the manufacture of vitamin A.

Uses. The ionones and methylionones are used in perfumery and flavors. β-Ionone is an intermediate in the manufacture of vitamin A.

Isobornyl Acetate and Isoborneol. *Source and Manufacture.* Isobornyl acetate is prepared by the acid-catalyzed addition of acetic acid to commercial camphene (47).

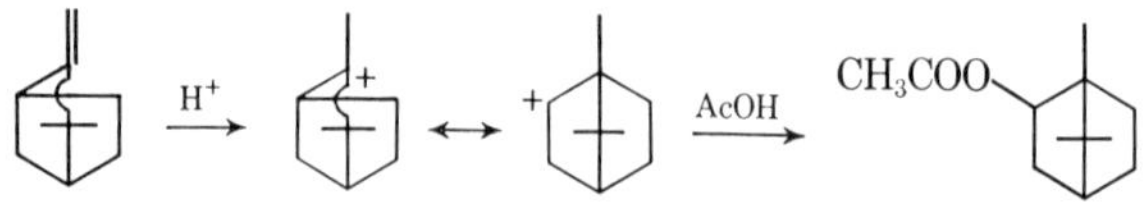

The equilibrium reaction is reached slowly at room temperature in the presence of a mineral acid catalyst and more rapidly at 100°C. The degree of dissociation increases as the temperature is raised. An industrial grade of camphene (actually a mixture of camphene and tricyclene) with minimum melting point of 46°C and clean odor is used for perfumery-grade isobornyl acetate. The tricyclene present equilibrates with camphene in the presence of the catalyst. When the ester content approaches equilibrium, the mineral acid is separated or neutralized. The product, isobornyl acetate, is separated from unreacted camphene and acetic acid by distillation. Overall yields are very high. An isomer, exoisocamphane-6-exo-yl acetate (pseudobornyl acetate), is formed as a by-product in small amounts (10).

pseudobornyl acetate
exoisocamphane-6-exo-yl acetate
5,5,6-trimethyl-2-norbornanol acetate (CA)

Physical properties of commercial isobornyl acetate are given in the standards of the Essential Oils Association of U.S.A. as follows: sp gr, $25/25°C$, 0.980–0.984; n_D^{20}, 1.460–1.4650; purity, not less than 97% isobornyl acetate by saponification. Odor quality is an important factor.

U.S. production of perfumery-grade isobornyl acetate in 1966 was about 1 million lb; the average value was 38¢/lb.

Reactions. Isobornyl acetate (exo) is much less stable than its geometric isomer bornyl acetate (endo). Distillation at atmospheric pressure causes cleavage to camphene and acetic acid. Saponification of isobornyl acetate yields isoborneol, which may be dehydrogenated to camphor.

Uses. Isobornyl acetate is used as an odorant where a low cost pine-needle scent is desired. Isoborneol is used in the manufacture of synthetic camphor.

Camphor (qv). *Source and Manufacture.* Some years ago camphor was an important industrial chemical because of its use as a plasticizer for celluloid. A large domestic production was provided by E. I. du Pont de Nemours & Co., Inc. The process underwent changes from an early stage in which camphene was made by dehydrochlorination of bornyl chloride (from pinene and HCl) to the present catalytic methods of producing camphene. The camphene was converted via isoborneol to camphor.

U.S. requirements of camphor today are supplied chiefly by imports of natural and synthetic camphor. Natural (dextro) camphor is isolated by rectification and freezing from camphor oil (see Oils, essential), of which it is the main component. Synthetic (racemic) camphor is produced chiefly by dehydrogenation of isoborneol over a copper catalyst.

Both natural dextro and synthetic racemic camphor are acceptable to the *U.S. Pharmacopeia*, which gives specifications for the pharmaceutical grade. Technical grades of lower purity are also available.

U.S. imports of camphor in 1967 were reported to be 1.9 million lb. Average value 50¢/lb.

Reactions. Camphor has an extensive chemistry, but only a few reactions used to produce minor medicinal chemicals are of commercial importance (eg, bromocamphor, camphorsulfonic acid).

Uses. Camphor is used as an odorant/flavorant in pharmaceutical, household, and industrial products.

Cineoles. *Source and Manufacture.* 1,8-Cineole (eucalyptol) makes up the major portion of commercial eucalyptus oils. USP-grade eucalyptol is obtained from the oils by rectification and crystallization. This grade must have a congealing point no lower than 0°C. Other specifications are given in the *U.S. Pharmacopeia*.

Mixed 1,4- and 1,8-cineoles, along with some hydrocarbons, are obtained as by-products from the manufacture of perfume-grade terpineol and synthetic pine oil. The mixture is known in the trade as "terpinolene." A typical GC analysis (in %) is:

eluting before 1,4-cineole	5	1,8-cineole	25
1,4-cineole	40	after 1,8-cineole	5
dipentene	25		

Reactions. The cineoles have no reactions of technical importance.

Uses. USP-grade eucalyptol is used in medicines. Mixed cineoles are used as odorants.

Carvone. *Source and Manufacture.* Natural *l*-carvone is obtained from spearmint oil, of which it is the major component. Natural *d*-carvone is obtained from caraway oil. Isolation is usually by rectification, but it can be accomplished via the bisulfite derivative.

Synthetic *l*-carvone is made through the reaction of nitrosyl chloride with citrus *d*-limonene (**17**):

d-limonene   *l*-carvone

The elements of hydrogen chloride are readily split out from the nitrosochloride with a weak base, even in the absence of an added base (the oxime evidently serves as a base), to give *l*-carvoxime, which is then hydrolyzed to *l*-carvone and hydroxylamine. The hydrolysis is carried out under carefully controlled conditions of acidity and contact to avoid further isomerization of the carvone to carvacrol. This synthesis can of course be applied to *l*-limonene to obtain *d*-carvone and to *dl*-limonene (dipentene). Only *d*-limonene from citrus is readily available, however.

Carvone can be made from α-pinene via α-pinene oxide, sobrerol, and 8-hydroxycarvotanacetone (**48**). The carvone has the same sign as the starting pinene.

As sobrerol is readily racemized by acids, it is necessary to use a nonacid oxidizing system when converting sobrerol to 8-hydroxycarvotanacetone. Optical activity is retained in the dehydration procedure shown.

Suppliers should be consulted for grades of carvone currently available.

Reactions. Carvone can be reduced to carveols and dihydrocarvone, which are useful in making synthetic spearmint oil and for other odorant purposes. Carvone is easily rearranged to carvacrol by strong acids.

Uses. Carvone is used as an odorant and flavorant.

The Sesquiterpenes

Source and Manufacture. Most sesquiterpenes are obtained as essential oils and isolates therefrom, such as cedrol (**64**) and α- and β-cedrene, (**62**), and (**63**) from cedarwood oil, vetiverol from vetiver oil, guaiol (**65**) from guaiac wood oil, α- and β-santalol (**66, 67**) from sandalwood oil, etc. See Oils, essential. Separation of the isolates is by rectification and, where applicable, crystallization. Except where isolation is made by crystallization, the commercial products are mixtures.

Small amounts of sesquiterpenes, particularly α- and β-caryophyllene, (**59**) and (**60**), and longifolene (**61**) are found in crude sulfate turpentines, and have been recovered therefrom on an experimental basis. Caryophyllenes were at one time available in fair quantities as a by-product when vanillin was made from clove oil.

Synthetic nerolidol is manufactured as an outgrowth of the total synthesis route to vitamin A. Synthetic linalool is converted to geranyl acetone by the Carroll reaction, and this in turn to dehydronerolidol by reaction with sodium acetylide. Partial hydrogenation of the acetylenic bond gives *dl*-nerolidol, a mixture of cis and trans isomers:

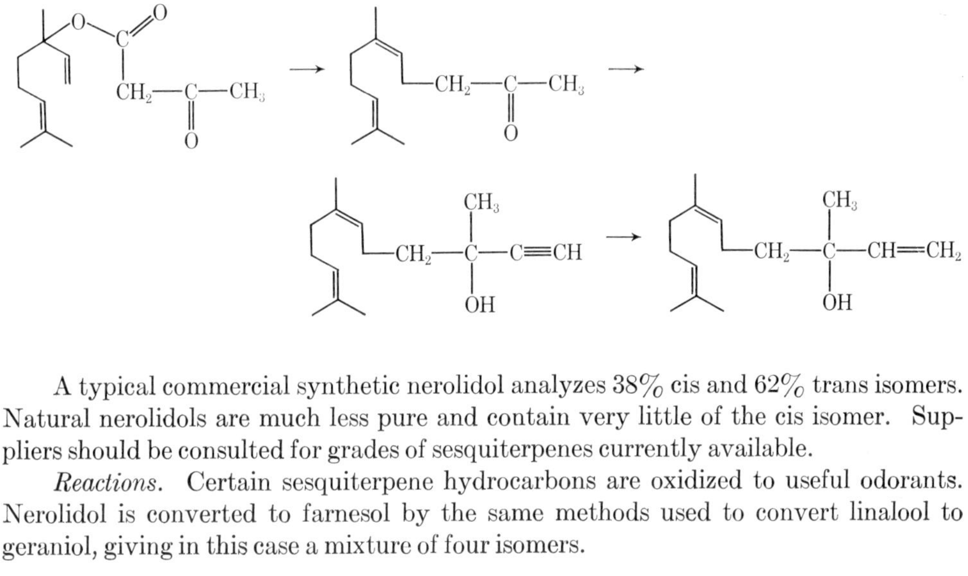

A typical commercial synthetic nerolidol analyzes 38% cis and 62% trans isomers. Natural nerolidols are much less pure and contain very little of the cis isomer. Suppliers should be consulted for grades of sesquiterpenes currently available.

Reactions. Certain sesquiterpene hydrocarbons are oxidized to useful odorants. Nerolidol is converted to farnesol by the same methods used to convert linalool to geraniol, giving in this case a mixture of four isomers.

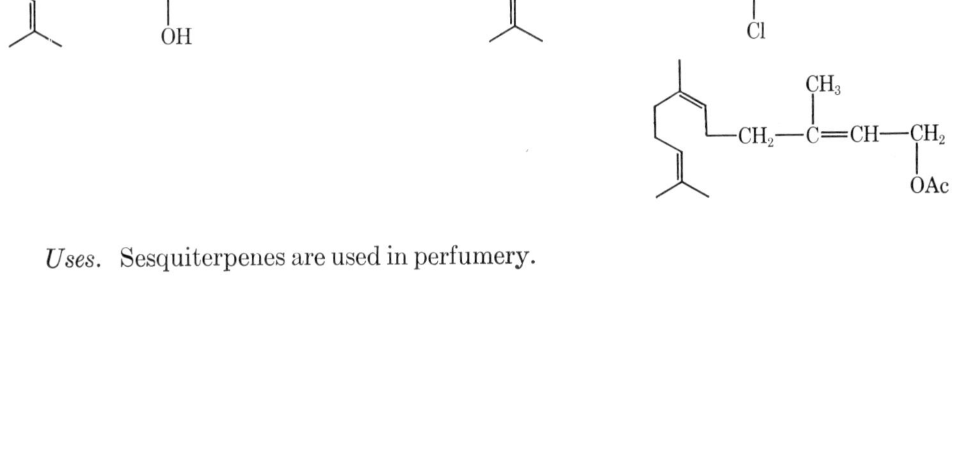

Uses. Sesquiterpenes are used in perfumery.

Terpene Resins

Terpene resins are pale-amber, thermoplastic, hydrocarbon resins manufactured by polymerization of terpene hydrocarbons. Only a few terpene hydrocarbons polymerize to useful resins. The resins are low-molecular-weight polymers completely unlike long-chain polymers of the vinyl type.

Source and Manufacture. All terpene resins are made by polymerization of terpene hydrocarbons in a solvent with aluminum chloride catalyst. The usual terpenes used are β-pinene, α- and β-pinene mixtures, and thermally isomerized α-pinene (essentially a dipentene–alloocimene mixture). Terpene resins range from viscous liquids to solids with ring-and-ball method softening points (see Vol. 2, p. 791) up to 135°C; the highest demand is for resins with a softening point about 115°C. Resins of the same softening point, but made from different feedstocks, show quite different molecular weights and melt viscosities, and so find different, though overlapping, uses. Major differences in chemical structure are further shown by differences in unsaturation and in infrared and ultraviolet spectra of the resins.

There is convincing evidence that the structure of β-pinene resin is composed of the repeating monocyclic C_{10} units as shown (51):

$$\text{—C—}\bigcirc\!\!\!=\!\!\!\langle\text{—C—}\bigcirc\!\!\!=\!\!\!\langle$$

The relatively low thermal stability is due to the weak bond between the allylic carbon C and the adjacent quaternary carbon. The structures of the other terpene resins are less understood, but their spectra and properties show them to be quite different from the β-pinene resin and from each other.

The terpene resins produced in largest volume are made from technical β-pinene analyzing 80% minimum by gas chromatography. Polymerization has traditionally been carried out by mixing the β-pinene with a diluent such as toluene, xylene, or naphtha, and feeding in aluminum chloride little by little. This procedure is calculated to develop the highest molecular weight, but is very hazardous because of the potential for a lag, followed by a runaway reaction. A safer procedure is to stir the catalyst in the solvent and to feed in the pinene slowly. The heat of reaction is thereby liberated in a more controlled manner. Reaction temperatures may be from 10 to 60°C or so, depending on feedstock and resin softening point desired. Higher reaction temperatures produce crude resins with lower softening points, other things being equal. When the reaction is complete, the catalyst is destroyed by careful addition of water or dilute acid, and the aluminum chloride washed out. Solvent is then distilled off, and if a higher softening point resin is being made, some of the lower-molecular-weight polymers may be topped off. Care must be taken to avoid overheating, which causes depolymerization or cracking. Even at normal processing temperatures some reduction in molecular weight occurs, without, however, significant effect on the softening point. With proper operating conditions technical β-pinene gives a 115°C softening point resin in 90–95% yield.

Essentially the same process is used to make terpene resins from α- and β-pinene mixtures. The crude resins from the mixture have lower softening points than resins from technical β-pinene, but higher softening point resins can be made from this feedstock by appropriate topping of the crude resin. The yield is correspondingly reduced. α-β-Pinene resins are more thermally stable than straight β-pinene resins, but have lower molecular weights for the same softening point.

The third type of resin starts by pyrolysis of α-pinene to give a dipentene/alloocimene mixture (3) (see pyrolysis of β-pinene, above, under Myrcene).

α-pinene → dipentene + [ocimene (unstable) → alloocimene]

From the heats of combustion (50) of the materials involved, the isomerization would be highly exothermic if it could be carried out at 25°C, but at the temperatures of 250–300°C which are actually used, very little, if any, heat is evolved.

The dipentene can be separated by distillation and polymerized to give a high softening point resin in nearly quantitative yield. Citrus limonene can be used as a source of technically pure dipentene. Straight dipentene resin has the highest thermal stability of any terpene resin, exhibiting little breakdown at 300°C. Like the α, β-pinene resin, it has a lower molecular weight than β-pinene resin for the same softening point. A better yield of resin on the starting pinene is obtained if the dipentene and alloocimene are polymerized together. The crude resin has a lower softening point than straight dipentene resin and must be topped to make high softening point resin, but even after topping there is a yield advantage because part of the alloocimene is incorporated along with the dipentene. Whereas straight alloocimene resins show serious thermal instability (49), the commercial alloocimene/dipentene resins are as good as β-pinene resins in this respect. The molecular weight of these resins is lower than that of β-pinene resins for the same softening point. Table 6 shows the relationship between feedstock and resin properties.

Reactions. Terpene resins, being hydrocarbons, are relatively inert. However, they are unsaturated to the extent of about 0.6–1.0 double bond per C_{10} unit, and so are subject to the common reactions of olefins. Oxidation, maleic anhydride addition, and hydrogenation are typical reactions and give rise to important modifications of their properties. At room temperature, the pale-amber resins are color-stable, although surface oxidation occurs. Powdered resin stored at room temperature, in contact with air,

Table 6. Terpene Resins with 115°C Ring-and-Ball Softening Point

Starting terpene	Average molecular weight	Temperature for melt viscosity of 5 P, °C
β-pinene	1000–1500	185
α- and β-pinene	600–800	174
dipentene	600–800	186
dipentene and alloocimene	600–800	186

becomes insoluble in naphtha due to oxidation. If such oxidized but undarkened resins are heated, they develop color rapidly. Holding hot terpene resins in contact with air for prolonged periods causes serious darkening. Terpene resins can be hydrogenated. In this process the original pale-amber color of the resin becomes lighter, the resin eventually becoming colorless. Stability toward oxidation increases as the unsaturation is removed. Essentially completely saturated terpene resins can be attained by carrying the hydrogenation this far. Maleic anhydride derivatives of terpene resins are made by heating the resin with the anhydride.

Uses. The largest use for terpene resins is in adhesives (see Vol. 1, pp. 381–383). Pressure-sensitive adhesives are the most important. For this use, the terpene resins are compounded with natural or synthetic rubbers, modifiers, and suitable antioxidants, so that a composition of good stability to light, heat, and air results. Hot-melt adhesives and coatings are the next most important. In this application, the terpene resins are blended with copolymers of ethylene and vinyl acetate, waxes, antioxidants, other resins, and modifiers. Terpene resins are important in imparting the desired pot life to hot-melt compositions. Resins derived from α- and β-pinene mixtures and from thermally isomerized α-pinene are usually used in hot melts. Terpene resins are also used to formulate general-purpose solvent cements.

Other uses are in chewing gum bases and in drycleaning sizes. The last use involves retreating outer wear to restore some measure of water repellency to the garment after drycleaning. Both of these uses are declining ones where the terpene resins are being supplanted by other materials.

New applications for terpene resins and their derivatives are as a modifier for polyolefin films and in paper sizes. The terpene resins (52) and the hydrogenated terpene resins (53) are incorporated in oriented polypropylene films to increase modulus and improve heat sealability. Both resins also improve clarity and brilliance of the films. The maleic anhydride adduct of terpene resins as well as the resins themselves may be substituted for a portion of the rosin in paper sizes. The adduct resin improves the emulsifiability of high solids paste sizes (54).

Bibliography

"Terpene Resins" in *ECT* 1st ed., Vol. 13, pp. 700–704, by W. J. Roberts and A. L. Ward, Pennsylvania Industrial Chemical Corporation. "Terpenes and Terpenoids" in *ECT* 1st ed., Vol. 13, pp. 705–771, by W. S. Ropp, Hercules Powder Company; J. E. Hawkins, University of Florida; E. G. Reitz, Chicago City Colleges, Wright Branch; P. de Mayo, Birkbeck College, University of London; G. C. Harris, Hercules Powder Company.

1. R. N. Moore, C. Golumbic, and G. S. Fisher, *J. Am. Chem. Soc.* **58**, 1173 (1936). U.S. Pat. 2,863,882 (Dec. 9, 1958), J. P. Bain, A. B. Booth, and E. A. Klein (to The Glidden Co.).
2. U.S. Pats. 2,792,631 and 2,792,672 (Feb. 21, 1961), J. P. Bain, H. G. Hunt, E. A. Klein, and A. B. Booth (to The Glidden Co.).
3. L. A. Goldblatt and S. Palkin, *J. Am. Chem. Soc.* **63**, 3517 (1941); R. E. Fuguitt and J. E. Hawkins, *J. Am. Chem. Soc.* **67**, 242 (1945); **69**, 319 (1947); U.S. Pat. 3,281,485 (Oct. 25, 1966), R. L. Blackmore (to A. Boake Roberts and Co., Ltd.).
4. Brit. Pat. 981,466 (Appl. Nov. 13, 1962), (to The Glidden Co.); W. Cocker, P. V. R. Shannon, and P. A. Staniland, *J. Chem. Soc.* **1966**, 41.
5. J. E. Hawkins, *J. Am. Chem. Soc.* **76**, 2669 (1954).
6. U.S. Pat. 3,278,623 (Oct. 11, 1966), J. M. Derfer (to The Glidden Co.). U.S. Pat. 3,264,362 (Aug. 3, 1966), R. L. Webb (to Union-Camp Corp.).
7. U.S. Pat. 2,863,882 (Dec. 9, 1958), J. P. Bain, A. B. Booth, and E. A. Klein (to The Glidden Co.).
8. L. A. Goldblatt and S. Palkin, *J. Am. Chem. Soc.* **63**, 3517 (1941); R. L. Burwell, Jr., *J. Am. Chem. Soc.* **73**, 4421 (1951). E. T. Theimer and B. M. Mitzner, *Can. J. Chem.* **42** (4), 959–960.
9. U.S.S.R. Pat. 64,839, V. I. Lyubomilov; *Chem. Abstr.* **40**, 5775 (1946). U.S. Pat. 2,450,119 (Sept. 28, 1948), W. F. Carson (to Hercules Powder Co.). U.S. Pat. 2,540,689 (Feb. 6, 1951), D. Porret (to Ciba Ltd.). U.S. Pat. 2,551,795 (May 8, 1951), G. Etzel, (to E. I. du Pont de Nemours & Co., Inc.). Japan. Pat. 4518 (1956), M. Kitajima and T. Nakahata (to Nippon Monopoly Co.); *Chem. Abstr.* **51**, 18000 (1957). Pol. Pat. 42,122, M. Bukala, B. Burczyk, J. Blaszkowicz, and K. Roczniakowa; *Chem. Abstr.* **55**, 6526 (1961).

10. K. Hacker, G. Keicher, and K. H. Miltenberger, *Tetrahedron Letters* (in German) **34**, 2987 (1965).

11. B. A. Arbusov, *J. Gen. Chem. U.S.S.R. (Eng. Transl.)* **6 (1936)**, 299.

12. G. Ohloff, K. H. Schulte-Elte, and W. Giersch, *Helv. Chim. Acta* **48**, (7), 1665 (1965).

13. W. Cocker, P. V. R. Shannon, and P. A. Staniland, *Chem. Commun.* **1965** (12), 254; *J. Chem. Soc.* **1966**, 41.

14. M. Matsui, H. Yashioka, Y. Yamada, H. Sakamoto, and T. Kitahara, *Agr. Biol. Chem. (Tokyo)* (in English) **29** (8), 784 (1965).

15. U.S. Pat. 2,799,717 (July 16, 1957), R. C. Palmer and A. F. Wicke (to Heyden-Newport Chemical Co.). U.S. Pat. 2,933,542 (April 19, 1960), J. P. Bain and W. Y. Gary (to The Glidden Co.).

16. H. E. Eschinazi and H. Pines, *J. Am. Chem. Soc.* **78**, 1176 (1956). U.S. Pat. 2,866,826 (Dec. 30, 1958), H. E. McLaughlin, J. H. Stump, and M. E. Cleere (to Heyden-Newport Chemical Co.). U.S. Pat. 2,933,542 (April 19, 1960), J. P. Bain and W. Y. Gary (to The Glidden Co.).

17. U.S. Pat. 2,802,874 (Aug. 13, 1957), R. H. Reitsema (to A. M. Todd Co.); *J. Org. Chem.* **23**, 2038 (1958). U.S. Pat. 3,293,301 (Dec. 20, 1966), J. M. Derfer, B. J. Kane, and D. G. Young (to The Glidden Co.).

18. U.S. Pat. 3,014,047 (Dec. 19, 1961), J. P. Bain, W. Y. Gary, and E. A. Klein (to The Glidden Co.). See also U.S. Pat. 2,863,882, reference 1.

19. U.S. Pat. 2,882,323 (April 14, 1959), R. Weiss (to Van Ameringen-Haebler, Inc.). U.S. Pat. 3,016,408 (Jan. 9, 1962), R. L. Webb (to The Glidden Co.).

20. U.S. Pat. 3,293,286 (Dec. 20, 1966), R. L. Webb (to Union-Camp Corp.).

21. U.S. Pat. 3,075,003 (Jan. 22, 1963), J. H. Blumenthal (to International Flavors and Fragrances, Inc.).

22. U.S. Pat. 2,902,515 (Sept. 1, 1959), M. Montavon and G. Saucy (to Hoffman-LaRoche, Inc.). U.S.S.R. Pat. 122,252 (Appl. June 3, 1958), S. M. Makin and V. B. Mochalin; *Chem. Abstr.* **54**, 5737 (1960).

23. U.S. Pat. 2,851,480 (Sept. 9, 1958), G. C. Kitchens (to The Givaudan Corp.). U.S. Pats. 2,902,510 (Sept. 1, 1959), and 2,919,290 (Dec. 29, 1959), R. L. Webb (to The Glidden Co.).

24. U.S. Pat. 2,898,380 (Aug. 4, 1959), R. Herrlinger and M. Garber (to American Cyanamid Co.). U.S. Pat. 2,178,349 (Oct. 31, 1940), D. H. Sheffield (to Hercules Powder Co.).

25. W. D. Burroughs and R. H. Eastman, *J. Am. Chem. Soc.* **81**, 245 (1959).

26. Brit. Pat. 1,003,355 (Appl. April 18, 1963), G. W. Gladden, F. Johnson, and G. Watson (to Cocker Chem. Co., Ltd.).

27. Ger. Pat. 1,197,081 (Appl. Oct. 31, 1963), B. T. D. Sully and P. L. Williams (to A. Boake Roberts and Co., Ltd.).

28. U.S. Pat. 2,961,542 (Nov. 22, 1960), R. A. Raphael (to The Glidden Co.). Ger. Pat. 1,118,775 (Appl. June 7, 1960), R. Rienaecker and G. Ohloff (to Karl Ziegler).

29. Y. R. Naves, *Helv. Chim. Acta* **42** (4), 1174 (1959). U.S. Pat. 2,866,826 (Dec. 30, 1958), H. E. McLaughlin, J. H. Stump, and M. E. Cleere (to Heyden-Newport Chem. Corp.).

30. Fr. Pat. 1,328,113 (Appl. July 2, 1962), (to Studiengesellschaft Kohle m.b.H.).

31. T. F. West, H. F. Strausz, and D. H. R. Barton, *Synthetic Perfumes*, 1st ed., Edward Arnold and Co., London, 1949, p. 249. U.S. Pat. 2,794,826 (Jan. 4, 1957), A. Bell, C. J. Kibler, and T. H. Strickland (to Eastman Kodak Co.). U.S. Pat. 3,076,839 (Feb. 5, 1963), R. L. Webb (to The Glidden Co.).

32. U.S. Pat. 3,031,442 (April 24, 1962), R. L. Webb (to The Glidden Co.).

33. U.S. Pat. 3,293,286 (Dec. 20, 1966), R. L. Webb (to Union-Camp Corp.).

34. I. N. Nazarov, B. P. Gusev, and V. I. Gunar, *Izvest. Akad. Nauk SSSR, Otd. Khim. Nauk* **1957**, 1267; *Chem. Abstr.* **52**, 6150 (1958). U.S. Pat. 3,280,177 (Oct. 18, 1966), R. L. Webb (to Union-Camp Corp.).

35. U.S. Pats. 1,802,468 and 1,802,472 (April 28, 1931), E. C. Kunz.

36. Peter T. Forbath, ed., *Chem. Eng.* **65** (4), 112 (1958); V. G. Cherkaev and V. M. Balashov, *Tr. Vses. Nauchn.-Issled. Inst. Sintetich. i Natural'n. Dushistykh Veshchestv.* **6 (1963)**, 5; *Chem. Abstr.* **61**, 8124 (1964).

37. L. Bouveault, *Bull. Soc. Chim. France* (4), 3 124 (1908). V. N. Kraseva and A. A. Bag, *Tr. Vses. Nauchn.-Issled. Inst. Sintetich i Natural'n Dushistykh Veshchestv.* **4 (1958)**, 55; *Chem. Abstr.* **53**, 12590 (1959).

38. W. Treibs and H. Schmidt, *Chem. Ber.* **60B**, 2335 (1927).

39. U.S. Pat. 2,235,840 (March 25, 1941), W. C. Meuly (to E. I. du Pont de Nemours & Co., Inc.).
     U.S. Pat. 2,306,332 (Dec. 22, 1943), A. C. Flisik and L. Nicholl (to Kay Fries Chemicals, Inc.).
     V. G. Cherkaev, A. A. Bag, and S. A. Prepelkina, *Tr. Vses. Nauchn.-Issled. Inst. Sintetich. i Natural'n Dushistykh Veshchestv.* **2 (1954)**, 35; *Chem. Abstr.* **53,** 18082 (1959).

40. H. Rupe and R. Rinderknecht, *Helv. Chim. Acta* **7,** 541 (1924).

41. U.S. Pat. 2,902,495 (Sept. 1, 1959), R. L. Webb (to The Glidden Co.).

42. U.S. Pat. 3,060,237 (Oct. 23, 1962), J. P. Bain (to The Glidden Co.).

43. U.S. Pat. 3,028,431 (April 3, 1962), R. L. Webb (to The Glidden Co.).

44. A. Lewinson, *Perfumery Essent. Oil Record* **14,** 259 (1923). H. Hibbert and L. T. Cannon, *J. Am. Chem. Soc.* **46,** 123 (1924).

45. Y. R. Naves and A. Odermatt, *Bull. Soc. Chim. France* **1955,** 377.

46. U.S. Pat. 2,661,368 (Dec. 1, 1953), W. Kimel and N. W. Sax (to Hoffman-LaRoche Inc.); *J. Org. Chem.* **23,** 153 (1958).

47. J. Bertram and H. Walbaum, *J. Prakt. Chem.* **49,** 2 (1894); Beilstein H VI 86. Ger. Pat. 1,196,190 (Appl. Sept. 5, 1962), H. Fernholz and H.-J. Schmidt (to Farbwerke-Hoechst A.G.).

48. U.S. Pat. 2,796,428 (June 18, 1957), A. B. Booth and E. A. Klein (to The Glidden Co.). U.S. Pat. 2,815,378 (Dec. 3, 1958), E. A. Klein (to The Glidden Co.). U.S. Pat. 2,949,489 (Aug. 16, 1960), A. J. Durbetaki and S. M. Linder (to Food Machinery and Chemical Corp.).

49. C. S. Marvel, P. E. Kiener, and E. D. Vessel, *J. Am. Chem. Soc.* **81,** 4694 (1959).

50. J. E. Hawkins and W. T. Erikson, *J. Am. Chem. Soc.* **76,** 2669 (1954).

51. W. J. Roberts and A. R. Day, *J. Am. Chem. Soc.* **72,** 1226 (1950); Hercules Incorporated, unpublished data.

52. U.S. Pat. 3,278,646 (Oct. 11, 1966), J. V. C. Lambert, Jr. (to Hercules Incorporated).

53. U.S. Pat. 3,361,849 (Jan. 2, 1968), T. A. Cramer and J. R. Lewis (to Hercules Incorporated).

54. U.S. Pats. 3,193,449 (July 6, 1965) and 3,287,206 (Nov. 22, 1966), P. H. Aldrich and H. I. Enos, Jr. (to Hercules Incorporated).

General References

Chemistry and Technology:

J. L. Simonsen et al., *The Terpenes*, Vols. 1–3, 2nd ed., Cambridge University Press, New York, 1947–1951.

E. H. Rodd, ed., *Chemistry of Carbon Compounds*, Vol. 2B, 2nd ed., American Elsevier Publishing Co., New York, 1968.

Paul Z. Bedoukian, *Perfumery and Flavoring Synthetics*, 2nd rev. ed., American Elsevier Publishing Co., New York, 1967.

E. Guenther, *The Essential Oils*, Vol. 2, D. Van Nostrand Co., Inc., Princeton, N.J., 1949.

T. F. West, H. J. Strausz, and D. H. R. Barton, *Synthetic Perfumes*, Edward Arnold and Co., London, 1949.

Infrared Spectra of Terpenes and Sesquiterpenes:

B. M. Mitzner, E. T. Theimer, and S. K. Freeman, *Appl. Spectry.* **19,** 169 (1965).

B. M. Mitzner, V. J. Mancini, S. Lemberg, and E. T. Theimer, *Appl. Spectry.* **22,** 34 (1968).

J. Pliva, M. Horak, V. Herout, and F. Sorm, *Die Terpene, Sammlung der Spektren und Physikalischen Konstanten*, Teil 1: *Sesquiterpene*, Akademie-Verlag, GmbH, 1960.

ALBERT B. BOOTH
Hercules Incorporated
J. S. AUTENRIETH AND
ALBERT B. BOOTH
(Terpene resins)
Hercules Incorporated

TERPHENYLS, $C_{18}H_{14}$.   See Diphenyl and terphenyls, Vol. 7, p. 194.

TERPIN HYDRATE, TERPINENE, TERPINEOL, TERPINOLENE.   See Terpenes and terpenoids.

TESTOSTERONE.   See Hormones (Sex).

TETRACENE.   See Explosives, Vol. 8, p. 592.

TETRACHLOROETHANES.   See Chlorocarbons and chlorohydrocarbons, Vol. 5, p. 159.